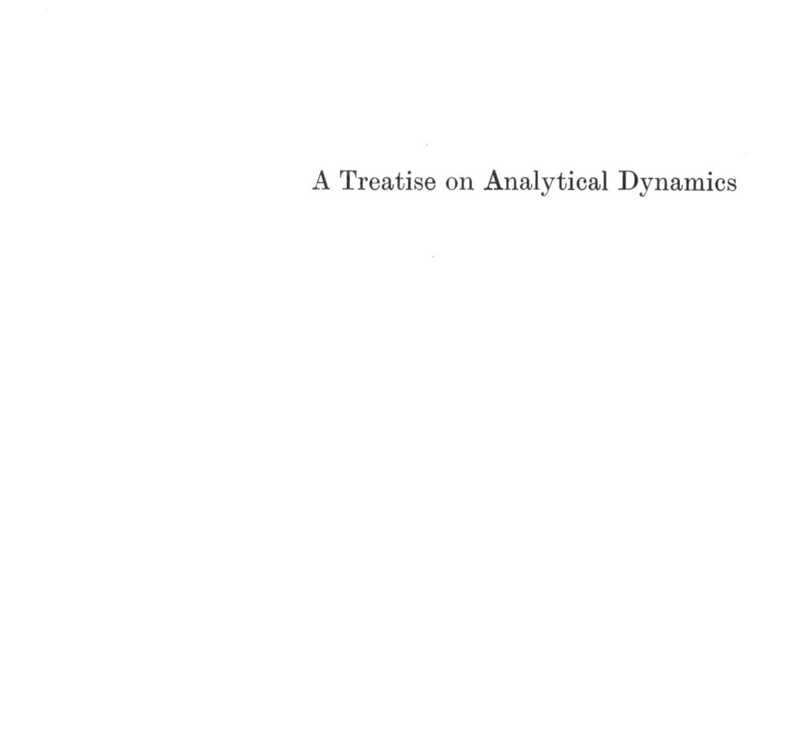

A Treatise on Analytical Dynamics

By the same author

An Introduction to the Calculus of Variations

A Treatise on

ANALYTICAL DYNAMICS

L. A. PARS

Fellow of Jesus College, Cambridge

John Wiley & Sons, Inc

New York, N.Y.

Library of Congress Catalog Card Number 64-24556

SBN 435 52690 1

First published 1965

Reprinted with corrections 1968

Published by
John Wiley & Sons, Inc
605 Third Avenue, New York, N.Y. 10016
Printed in Northern Ireland.

A. E. Ingham

arte mathematica praestanti

officiis et amicitia constanti

D.D.D.

L. A. Pars

Introduction

The subject of particle dynamics was founded by Galileo early in the seventeenth century, and developed further by Huygens after Galileo's death. The fundamental principles were clarified and crystallized by Newton, whose great work, the *Principia* (**1**)* appeared in 1687. The extension of Newton's principles to embrace the problems of rigid dynamics was made by d'Alembert in 1743 (**2**). The foundations of analytical dynamics (sometimes called rational dynamics) were laid by Euler as early as 1736 (**3**); but the outstanding event in the early history of analytical dynamics was the publication by Lagrange of the *Mécanique Analytique* in 1788 (**4**). The development of the subject since the time of Lagrange brings in many of the most famous names in the history of mathematics. Among those who have made contributions of fundamental importance in analytical dynamics are Laplace, Hamilton, Jacobi, Gauss, and Poincaré.

The object of this book is to give a compact, consistent, and reasonably complete account of the subject as it now stands. The whole of analytical dynamics is based upon, and is developed from, the theorem of Lagrange that I call *the fundamental equation.* This result is established, after some necessary preliminary discussion, in Chapter III. The presentation of the subject that seems to be both the most elegant and the most powerful involves the translation of the fundamental equation into a number of different forms. It is this presentation that I follow in this book. Each of these various forms, six in all, has its own particular merits, and each is (I think) the right starting-point for some particular domain of the theory. I have taken pains to explain clearly the conditions for the validity of each of the six forms, and the context in which it is most valuable. If I seem to have been over-careful in these matters it is because of their vital importance to the comprehension of the subject as a whole. Moreover, when once they have been understood, the subject unfolds and blossoms in a simple and natural way.

From the various forms of the fundamental equation we derive the basic equations for the various branches of the subject; and then we are faced with a formidable difficulty—the vast extent of the available material. One of the major tasks facing an author who sets out to give a conspectus of the subject as a whole is that of selection. The difficulty is aggravated by the peculiar position occupied by dynamics in the hierarchy of the physical sciences. The principles of dynamics are of prime importance to all sorts and conditions of men—not only to the scholar who is interested in the subject for its own sake, but to many others, including the engineer, the astronomer, and the physicist. To each of these the subject presents a different aspect, and demands a different distribution of emphasis among the various topics. The engineer would give more attention to rigid dynamics, to elasticity, and to problems of vibrations: the astronomer would expect more attention to specific problems of celestial mechanics: the physicist would expand those parts of the

* The numbers in bold type refer to the Bibliography on page 635.

subject where it impinges on statistical mechanics and on quantum theory. There is, I fear, no choice of material and no distribution of emphasis that will seem exactly right to all readers. Nevertheless, I hope that each of these diverse classes of readers will find an adequate presentation of the basic theory that he needs for his own particular purpose. I have aimed at developing each topic so far that the reader is not left with any sense of frustration; if he has not been permitted to explore the promised land, at least he has reached a Pisgah-height from which he can overlook it.

I have endeavoured to find suitable concrete examples to illustrate the various branches of the theory; to some readers the stark presentation of abstract theory may appear lifeless and forbidding, and the application to specific concrete problems is the best way to ensure that it has vitality and reality. In order to keep the book within reasonable limits of size I have, on the whole, resisted the temptation to explore attractive by-ways of the subject; but I have admitted a few topics, on grounds of elegance or of historical interest, that cannot claim to be components in the main line of development. (Perhaps the six energy theorems of § 14.7, perhaps indeed a large part of the theory of impulsive motion, would come into this category.) I have also resisted the temptation to stray beyond the boundaries of pure dynamics into electronics and quantum theory and practical problems of engineering, though there are many points at which the theory presented impinges closely on all these subjects. As some compensation for this abstinence I have allowed myself the luxury of giving two independent proofs of some of the most important theorems.

"On a déjà plusieurs Traités de Mécanique"—these are the opening words of the *Avertissement* to the *Mécanique Analytique*—and, needless to say, the number of treatises on mechanics is vastly greater today than it was in 1788. Many books exist that treat in detail topics discussed here only in outline, in a single Chapter or even a single section. Many examples could be mentioned. A brief account of the motion of a spinning top is given in § 8.9; but the subject, treated in detail, is extensive enough to occupy the four volumes of Klein and Sommerfeld's *Theorie des Kreisels* (**33**). The classical linear theory of vibrations is dealt with in Chapter IX, and some non-linear vibration problems are considered briefly in Chapter XIX; but in recent years the general theory of non-linear systems has received much attention, and many books and papers have appeared dealing with the theory in far greater detail than is possible here; in (**46**) the Bibliography alone, the mere list of recent contributions to the subject, occupies nearly seventy pages. (An admirable survey of the present state of the theory is given by Minorsky in (**43**).) I give a proof of the Ergodic Theorem in Chapter XXII; but the fundamental ergodic theorem of dynamics is only the starting-point for an abstract theory that is now very extensive. Over fifty papers on ergodic theory were quoted by Hopf (**47**) in 1937, and the list today is enormously greater.* No survey of dynamics would be complete without some account of the problem of three bodies, a problem which has probably exercised a more profound influence on the development of the subject than any other. Chapters XXVIII and XXIX contain a brief introduction to this problem—but only an introduction. Anything approaching an exhaustive treatment would lead us to trespass too far into the realm of the professional astronomer.

In matters of nomenclature and notation I have been on the whole conservative. For example, I often use the term *centre of gravity*; this usage is so well-established

* See for example the list of references in (**49**), pp. 731–826.

that it would be pedantic to object to it, though strictly speaking it is only defensible in the context in which it arises—a rigid body in a uniform field. I follow traditional usage in writing q for a Lagrangian coordinate, L for the Lagrangian function, H for Hamilton's function, and S for the principal function. Only in a few cases of minor importance do I depart, for particular reasons, from conventional usage.

A word about what may seem to be a trifling matter, that of footnotes. It is somewhat controversial. One school of opinion favours numerous footnotes, with the idea that all relevant references should be immediately to hand. Another school objects to footnotes, on the ground that they continually distract attention from the line of argument. Perhaps the first school is right in the main in relation to a paper of original research on a restricted topic, and the second in relation to a text-book giving a connected account of a large subject. In this book I have inclined to the second school and used footnotes sparingly. One reason for this choice is the desirability already mentioned of a continuous uninterrupted text; but there is another reason that is special to the particular subject. It is that the literature is now so extensive that a footnote giving references to a particular topic, with any sort of claim to completeness, would in many cases be quite unwieldy. It might be possible to reduce the list to two or three especially important references, but in practice even this is not always easy; it is especially difficult when claims to priority are involved.

Such claims to priority are sometimes dubious. For one thing, many results have been discovered independently, and sometimes almost contemporaneously, by two different workers; for another, although a certain reference contains the first explicit statement of a result in a particular form, yet a result that appeared earlier is so closely related that the claim to priority can reasonably be disputed. These difficulties arise especially in relation to the work done in the middle years of the nineteenth century, when the main corpus of the subject was being built up. A conspicuous example of closely related theories being propounded independently and almost simultaneously by two different workers appears in the central theorem that I (and most other English mathematicians) call the Hamilton-Jacobi theorem; the name commemorates two of the founders of the subject working contemporaneously on similar lines of thought. Another example of a fundamental theory discovered independently by two different scholars (though in this case not contemporaneously) occurs in the equations that I call the Gibbs-Appell equations. When the equations were discovered by Willard Gibbs, they seem to have made no deep impression, and it was not until they were rediscovered twenty years later by Appell that their importance was properly appreciated. And there are many other examples of two scholars arriving independently at much the same goal. I have given in an Appendix a few miscellaneous notes, and these contain some material that might perhaps have found a place in footnotes. The notes are mostly of a historical nature, but I have made no systematic attempt to provide references to the original sources for all the topics discussed in the text. The compilation of a comprehensive classified list of all the papers on classical dynamics published in the present century would be a rewarding, if somewhat laborious, task.

Theoretically the book should start with a discussion of the notions of mass and of force, and of the logical basis of Newton's Laws of Motion; these are matters of fundamental importance. But an adequate discussion would require more space than can easily be spared, and moreover such a discussion is likely to be already familiar to most readers of this book. I decided therefore, after some hesitation, to start from the severely practical standpoint in which the logical basis of the theory is taken as known.*

One or two further points as to the content of the book may be mentioned. The first is the obvious remark that the subject would be simpler and more compact if we confined our attention wholly to holonomic systems. Such a limitation would be disastrous: it would give a completely distorted view of the structure of the subject as a whole. Nevertheless, I have kept it in mind that in practice we are usually concerned with holonomic systems, and therefore I have not allowed the theory of non-holonomic systems to take too large a place. I have laid some stress on certain classical problems of rigid dynamics, a topic which, in my opinion, has been inadequately represented in some expositions of the subject. This feeling (that rigid dynamics has often been underemphasized) is one of the reasons for including an account of the theory of rotations of a rigid body (Chapter VII). It could reasonably be argued that this topic belongs to group-theory rather than to dynamics, and that its claim to inclusion in the canon is dubious. Perhaps the decision to include it was influenced as much by the intrinsic elegance of the theory as by its immediate relevance.

In making a systematic survey of a large subject it is natural that a number of new results, usually fairly obvious generalizations of familiar theory, should have come to light; and also many new, or simplified, proofs of results already known. Some of these I have published elsewhere, some have found their way into print in other contexts, and some appear for the first time in this book.

When I try to assess my indebtedness to previous authors, the two names that come first to mind are Routh and Appell. The Gallic charm and perspicuity of Appell's *Mécanique Rationelle* (**21**) was one of the factors that first attracted me to the classical dynamics; that my approach to the subject was largely influenced by him will be evident to those readers who are familiar with his book. The great text-book of Routh (**20**), first published in 1860, and followed by many later editions, has had an enormous influence on the study of dynamics, and it is astonishing how much of the basic theory finds a place in this book. But Routh (whose stature as a mathematician has often been underestimated) suffered from the handicap that much of the fundamental theory was being developed at the time at which he was writing. He was perhaps too near the new discoveries to see them in proper perspective, and many highly important results appear as inconspicuous addenda in the later editions.

As we contemplate the history of the subject through some two centuries, and observe the successive triumphs of the theory, the ever-widening scope of its applications, the great variety and versatility of its techniques, and the inevitable change of emphasis as the focus of interest moves with the growth of knowledge, we cannot fail to be impressed by this example of the perseverance and power of the human spirit. Very many seemingly intractable problems have finally given up their secrets, and in many others, which have not been completely solved, significant and substantial progress has been made. And yet, however much we are impressed by the greatness of the achievement, we must also be conscious of the magnitude and variety of the

* The reader who is interested in the axiomatic approach may consult G. Hamel, "Die Axiome der Mechanik" in (**24**), pp. 1–42.

problems that are still unsolved. We are still as children playing on the seashore, with the great ocean of truth lying all undiscovered before us.

In recent years there has been a marked decline among mathematicians of interest in the classical dynamics. A number of causes have contributed to this decline. Among them may be mentioned the increasing interest in the theory of relativity, and the consequential weakening of the prestige of Newtonian mechanics: the fundamental change in the outlook of physics from the older idea of pure determinism to the newer idea of events determined statistically: the growth of statistical mechanics: the interest aroused by the new developments in quantum theory and in atomic physics: and (in a different direction from these) the growing preference of applied mathematicians for concrete numerical results that can be checked against observed measurements, and a corresponding impatience with abstract theories. I believe that these contemporary trends, laudable in themselves, have gone too far in obscuring the importance and elegance of the classical theory, and my earnest hope is that this book may do something to revive interest in the subject of analytical dynamics *per se*.

As I finish my task, and take leave of an old and agreeable companion, I wish to record my indebtedness to the many friends and pupils, too numerous to mention individually, who have helped me at various stages of the work. In particular, if I can do so without invidiousness, I should like to express my thanks, for advice on various points of the text, to Dr. B. J. Birch, Dr. Mary Cartwright, Mr. J. C. Clegg, Prof. P. Hall, Mr. A. E. Ingham, Prof. Sir H. Jeffreys, Prof. J. E. Littlewood, Prof. G. S. S. Ludford, Dr. H. K. Moffatt, Prof. W. B. Pennington, Dr. F. Smithies, Mr. H. P. F. Swinnerton-Dyer, Dr. A. J. Ward, and Mr. F. P. White. My grateful thanks for help with the diagrams are due to Dr. M. F. Ingham, and for help with proof-reading to Canon C. D. Waddams, Dr. C. T. C. Wall, and Dr. N. C. Wickramasinghe.

Jesus College,
Cambridge
1 *June* 1964

L. A. P.

Contents

Chapter XIII. Applications of the Gibbs-Appell equations

Chapter XIV. Impulsive motion

Chapter XV. The sixth form of the fundamental equation

Chapter XVI. The Hamilton-Jacobi theorem

Chapter XIX. Systems with one degree of freedom, motion near a singular point

Chapter XX. Systems with one degree of freedom, the cyclic characteristics

Chapter XXI. Systems with n degrees of freedom, properties of the characteristics

Chapter XXII. Hamilton's equations

Chapter I

Motion of a particle

1.1 The free particle. The motion of a single free particle or point-mass under the action of a given force is determined by Newton's Second Law of Motion, which may be expressed in the traditional form

$$\mathbf{P} = m\mathbf{f}. \tag{1.1.1}$$

The base of reference is a *Newtonian* or *inertial base;* the existence of such a base is the fundamental postulate of Newtonian dynamics. In (1.1.1) **P** denotes the given force, the multiplier m denotes the mass of the particle, and **f** denotes its acceleration (relative to the chosen base). If we denote by x, y, z the coordinates of the particle at time t referred to rectangular axes fixed in the base, and by X, Y, Z the components of the given force parallel to these axes, the motion of the particle is determined by the *equations of motion*

$$m\ddot{x} = X, \quad m\ddot{y} = Y, \quad m\ddot{z} = Z, \tag{1.1.2}$$

which are equivalent to (1.1.1).

In the equations (1.1.2) the components X, Y, Z are given functions of the seven variables $x, y, z;\ \dot{x}, \dot{y}, \dot{z};\ t$. These functions are defined for some domain D of values in the seven-fold space of $(x, y, z;\ \dot{x}, \dot{y}, \dot{z};\ t)$; in the simplest case they are defined for all real values of the seven variables. But it should be remarked that problems in which X, Y, Z depend upon t are comparatively rare; in many cases they depend only on the six variables $x, y, z;\ \dot{x}, \dot{y}, \dot{z}$. A still more special case, and one that occurs frequently, is that in which each of X, Y, Z is a given function of the three variables x, y, z; in that case the particle is said to move in a *field of force.*

The rectangular trihedral of axes in (1.1.1–2) is at rest in a Newtonian base, and it will be convenient, for the sake of brevity, to speak of such axes as *fixed axes.* If we have a rigid rectangular trihedral in motion relative to the original axes, we speak of the new axes so defined as *moving axes.* Later (§ 10.7) we shall consider the effect of the motion of the axes on the motion of a dynamical system as it appears to an observer in the moving axes who takes the moving axes as his base of reference.

In the special case when the new trihedral moves uniformly and without rotation relative to the original trihedral, it defines a new Newtonian base. The equations of motion are then of the same form (1.1.1–2), though the formulae for X, Y, Z must now be expressed in terms of the new coordinates and their first derivatives and the time. (In the important special case of the problem of three bodies, where the forces on the particles depend only on their relative positions, the equations of motion have the same form whatever Newtonian base we use.)

In the above, m is a positive constant, and this assumption, that the mass of the particle remains constant during the motion, will always be made unless the contrary is stated explicitly. But later (Chapter XI) we shall consider problems in which m is a known function of the speed $\sqrt{(\dot{x}^2 + \dot{y}^2 + \dot{z}^2)}$. In these problems of *variable mass* the equations (1.1.2) must be replaced by

$$\frac{d}{dt}(m\dot{x}) = X, \quad \frac{d}{dt}(m\dot{y}) = Y, \quad \frac{d}{dt}(m\dot{z}) = Z. \tag{1.1.3}$$

The equations of motion (1.1.1–3) express the acceleration-components $\ddot{x}$, $\ddot{y}$, $\ddot{z}$ uniquely and explicitly as functions of the seven variables $x, y, z;\ \dot{x}, \dot{y}, \dot{z};\ t$. We shall find that the situation observed in this simple case reappears in the theory of the general dynamical system. It is characteristic of the classical dynamics that the equations of motion provide explicit expressions for the acceleration-components as functions of position and velocity and time.

For the motion of a single free particle, Newton's law supplies all the purely dynamical information that we need. The problem is reduced to that of the integration of a set of three simultaneous ordinary differential equations of the second order. In these equations the second derivatives occur only linearly. If X, Y, Z are of class C_1* in a domain D of $(x, y, z;\ \dot{x}, \dot{y}, \dot{z};\ t)$, the equations determine the values of x, y, z at time t, if the values $x_0, y_0, z_0, u_0, v_0, w_0$ of $x, y, z, \dot{x}, \dot{y}, \dot{z}$ at time τ are prescribed; $(x_0, y_0, z_0;\ u_0, v_0, w_0;\ \tau)$ belongs to D, and the solution is valid for some time-interval containing $t = \tau$. In the simplest cases the solution is valid for all real values of t.

If we introduce three new variables u, v, w, defined by the equations

$$u = \dot{x}, \quad v = \dot{y}, \quad w = \dot{z}, \tag{1.1.4}$$

the three second-order differential equations (1.1.2) may be replaced by the six first-order differential equations

$$\begin{cases} \dot{x} = u, & \dot{y} = v, & \dot{z} = w, \\ \dot{u} = X/m, & \dot{v} = Y/m, & \dot{w} = Z/m, \end{cases} \tag{1.1.5}$$

where X, Y, Z now denote functions of $x, y, z;\ u, v, w;\ t$. We can write the equations (1.1.5) compactly in the form

$$\dot{\mathbf{x}} = \mathbf{X}, \tag{1.1.6}$$

where $\mathbf{x}$ denotes the column matrix

$$\begin{pmatrix} x \\ y \\ z \\ u \\ v \\ w \end{pmatrix},$$

and $\mathbf{X}$ denotes the column matrix

$$\begin{pmatrix} u \\ v \\ w \\ X/m \\ Y/m \\ Z/m \end{pmatrix}.$$

* We shall say that a function, of one or of several variables, is of class C_p in a domain D of the variables if all its derivatives of order p exist and are continuous in D.

Strictly speaking we should distinguish between a vector $\mathbf{X}$ and the column matrix whose elements are its components, but in practice we shall often regard the terms vector and column matrix as synonymous, a usage that will not give rise to any confusion. For convenience we shall sometimes write the components of a vector horizontally instead of vertically, and we shall use braces instead of round brackets in those contexts where it is important to emphasize the character of the vector as a column matrix. Thus for $\mathbf{x}$ we can write $\{x, y, z, u, v, w\}$, and for $\mathbf{X}$ we can write $\{u, v, w, X/m, Y/m, Z/m\}$. An equation of the form (1.1.6) will appear frequently in the sequel. In general $\mathbf{x}$ will denote the vector $\{x_1, x_2, \ldots, x_m\}$ and $\mathbf{X}$ the vector $\{X_1, X_2, \ldots, X_m\}$, and in general the components X_r of $\mathbf{X}$ will be functions of the $m + 1$ variables $x_1, x_2, \ldots, x_m, t$; expressed compactly, $\mathbf{X} = \mathbf{X}(\mathbf{x}; t)$. But frequently (as we have remarked already in the particular case of a single free particle) the variable t does not appear in $\mathbf{X}$, $\mathbf{X} = \mathbf{X}(\mathbf{x})$; in that case the system is said to be *autonomous*.

The equations (1.1.2) define the motion of a particle in ordinary space. In a similar way, the equations (1.1.5) can be thought of as defining the motion of a *representative point* or *mobile*, whose coordinates are x, y, z, u, v, w, in a space of six dimensions. The system (1.1.5) involves six dependent variables instead of the three dependent variables of (1.1.2). But (1.1.5) has the important advantage that the position of the mobile in the six-fold at time τ determines its position at time t, at least for some interval of values of t including $t = \tau$. This technique, replacing n second-order differential equations by $2n$ first-order differential equations, will be used frequently in the sequel.

1.2 Rectilinear motion in a field. A problem that is elementary, but is nevertheless of fundamental importance, is that of a particle moving on the straight line Ox in a field of force. Here

$$X = F(x), \tag{1.2.1}$$

where $F(x)$ is a given function of the independent variable x, of class C_1 in a certain domain of values of x; in the simplest cases $F(x)$ is defined for all real values of x. We need also the *potential function* $V(x)$ defined by the equation

$$V(x) = -\int_a^x F(\xi)\, d\xi, \tag{1.2.2}$$

where a is any convenient value in the domain for which $F(x)$ is defined. Thus $V(a) = 0$, $V(x) \in C_2$, and

$$X = F(x) = -\frac{dV}{dx}. \tag{1.2.3}$$

The *kinetic energy function* T of the particle is defined by the equation

$$T = \tfrac{1}{2}m\dot{x}^2. \tag{1.2.4}$$

The equation of motion is

$$m\ddot{x} = X = F(x). \tag{1.2.5}$$

The symbol $F(x)$ on the right in (1.2.5) now means the value of $F(x)$ at the point $x(t)$ occupied by the particle at time t (in contrast to the meaning in (1.2.1), where $F(x)$ is a function of the independent variable x). Similarly if $V(x)$ means the value at the point $x(t)$ occupied by the particle at time t (in contrast to the meaning in (1.2.2), where $V(x)$ is a function of the independent variable x) we have

$$\frac{dV}{dt} = \frac{dV}{dx}\dot{x} = -F(x)\dot{x}.$$

Therefore if we multiply (1.2.5) through by $\dot{x}$ we find $\frac{d}{dt}(T + V) = 0$, whence

$$T + V = h, \tag{1.2.6}$$

where h is a constant.

The equation (1.2.6) is the famous *equation of energy* or *integral of energy*. The second-order equation (1.2.5) giving $\ddot{x}$ in terms of x is replaced by the first-order equation (1.2.6) giving $\dot{x}^2$ in terms of x. It is characteristic of the problem that two values of $\dot{x}$, equal in magnitude but opposite in sign, correspond to the same value of x. Since $T \geqslant 0$ it follows from (1.2.6) that the particle can never leave the region $V \leqslant h$.

If we use the technique mentioned in § 1.1, replacing the single second-order equation (1.2.5) by two first-order equations, we get

$$\dot{x} = u, \quad \dot{u} = F(x)/m. \tag{1.2.7}$$

We do not need this technique for our immediate purpose, but we shall find that it is of paramount importance in other contexts. The equation of energy gives the equation of the path of the mobile in the (x, u)-plane, namely

$$\tfrac{1}{2}mu^2 + V = h. \tag{1.2.8}$$

The equation of energy

$$\tfrac{1}{2}m\dot{x}^2 = h - V \tag{1.2.9}$$

dominates the whole theory of rectilinear motion in a field; moreover, an equation of similar form

$$\dot{x}^2 = \varphi(x), \tag{1.2.10}$$

where $\varphi(x) \in C_2$ in the relevant domain of x, appears in many other problems of dynamics. We must therefore consider briefly the integration of the differential equation (1.2.10); we shall find that the nature of the motion can be inferred from the graph of $\varphi(x)$.

Let us first dispose of an exceptional case. If there is a point x_0 at which $\varphi(x)$ and $\varphi'(x)$ both vanish, the graph $y = \varphi(x)$ *touches* Ox at $x = x_0$, and this point is a position of equilibrium. If $x = x_0$ (and therefore $\dot{x} = 0$) at $t = 0$, then $x = x_0$ for all time; the particle rests in equilibrium.

Apart from this exceptional case there are just four possible ways in which the function $x(t)$ can behave as t increases; they are as follows:

(i) The particle oscillates continually between two points $x = a$ and $x = b$ of the x-axis, and the motion is periodic; such a motion is called a *libration motion*:

(ii) $x \to a$ as $t \to \infty$; such a motion is called a *limitation motion*:

(iii) $x \to \infty$ (or $x \to -\infty$) as $t \to \infty$:

(iv) $x \to \infty$ (or $x \to -\infty$) as $t \to t_0$.

We now show how these four types of motion can arise from the equation (1.2.10). We do this by reference to the graph $y = \varphi(x)$; the ordinate y of this graph for any value of x gives the corresponding value of $\dot{x}^2$, and the slope dy/dx of the graph gives the corresponding value of $2\ddot{x}$. Motion can only take place on a stretch of the x-axis for which $\varphi(x) \geqslant 0$. Let us suppose in the first instance that $x = x_0$ at $t = 0$, that $\varphi(x_0) > 0$ (not $\varphi(x_0) = 0$) and that $\dot{x} > 0$ at $t = 0$, so that $\dot{x} = \sqrt{\varphi(x_0)}$. The velocity $\dot{x}$ is positive for sufficiently small values of t, and for these values of t the relation between t and x is

$$t = \int_{x_0}^{x} \frac{d\xi}{\sqrt{\varphi(\xi)}} . \tag{1.2.11}$$

(i) Suppose first that x_0 lies between two consecutive simple real zeros a, b of $\varphi(x)$, where $a < b$. The graph $y = \varphi(x)$ in this case has the form shown in Fig. 1.2a; the graph crosses the x-axis at a and at b, and $\varphi(x) > 0$ for $a < x < b$, while $d\varphi/dx > 0$ at a and $d\varphi/dx < 0$ at b. Since b is a simple zero of $\varphi(x)$ the integral on the right in (1.2.11) converges as $x \to b$, so the particle reaches b in a finite time. At b the particles comes to rest, but it only rests instantaneously (since $\ddot{x} < 0$ at b) and then it moves to the left. By a similar argument we see that the particle reaches a in a finite time, rests there instantaneously, and then moves to the right. It arrives at the starting point x_0, with the same (positive) velocity with which it started, at a time

$$\sigma = \oint \frac{d\xi}{\sqrt{\varphi(\xi)}} = 2\int_{a}^{b} \frac{d\xi}{\sqrt{\varphi(\xi)}} \tag{1.2.12}$$

after the start. (In the first integral on the right in (1.2.12) ξ increases from a to b, and then decreases from b to a; the radical is positive when ξ is increasing, negative when ξ is decreasing. In the second integral the radical is positive.) The motion in the interval from $t = \sigma$ to $t = 2\sigma$ is a repetition of the motion in the interval from $t = 0$ to $t = \sigma$; and so is the motion during the interval from $t = r\sigma$ to $t = (r + 1)\sigma$ for any positive integral value of r. The motion is periodic, with period σ.

So far we have supposed that $\varphi(x_0) > 0$, but it is clear that the same periodic motion occurs if the particle starts from rest at a or at b. Further, the same periodic motion occurs if $\varphi(x_0) > 0$ and $\dot{x} < 0$ ($\dot{x} = -\sqrt{\varphi(x_0)}$) at $t = 0$.

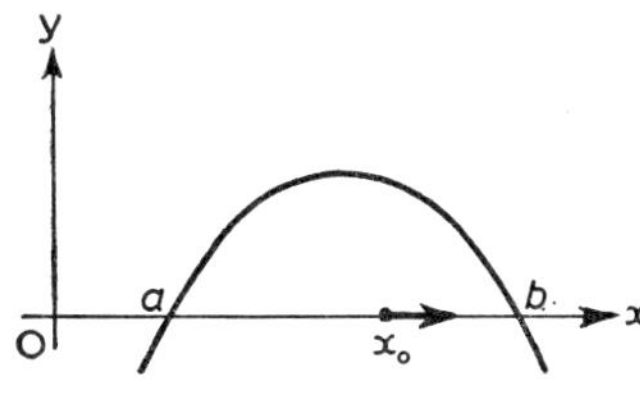

Figure 1.2a

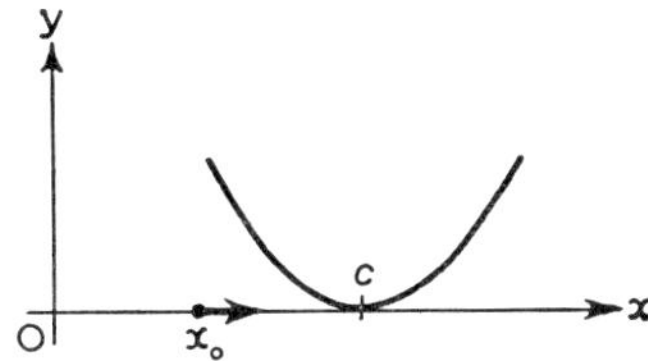

Figure 1.2b

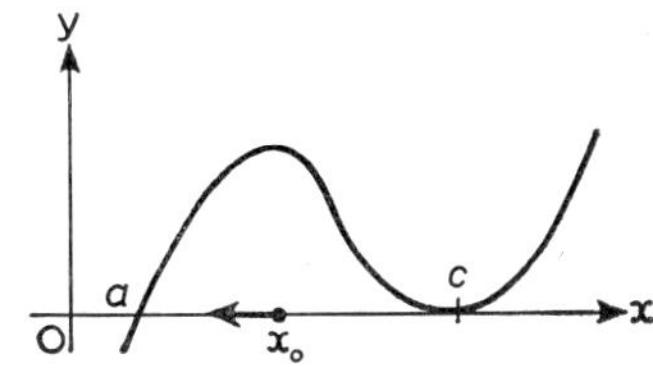

Figure 1.2c

(ii) Suppose next that as x increases from x_0 it approaches a double (or multiple) zero c of $\varphi(x)$. The graph of $\varphi(x)$ touches Ox at $x = c$ (Fig. 1.2b). This time the integral on the right in (1.2.11) diverges as $x \to c$, and $x \to c$ as $t \to \infty$.

In the case illustrated in Fig. 1.2c, x_0 lies between a simple zero of $\varphi(x)$ at a and a double zero of $\varphi(x)$ at c, $a < x_0 < c$. If $\dot{x} < 0$ at $t = 0$, $\dot{x} = -\sqrt{\varphi(x_0)}$, x initially decreases, and the particle reaches the point a in a finite time; the particle rests instantaneously at a, then moves to the right, and $x \to c$ as $t \to \infty$.

Finally if $\varphi(x) > 0$ for $x > x_0$ the particle continues to move to the right (assuming $\dot{x} > 0$ initially) and (1.2.11) holds throughout the motion. There are two possibilities. If (iii) the integral on the right in (1.2.11) diverges as $x \to \infty$ the motion is such that $x \to \infty$ with t. If (iv) the integral converges to the value t_0 as $x \to \infty$, then the motion is such that $x \to \infty$ as $t \to t_0$.

It is easy to see that no new possibilities emerge if $\dot{x} \leqslant 0$ at $t = 0$, except that x may tend to $-\infty$ instead of to $+\infty$ as $t \to \infty$ or as $t \to t_0$. The classification is complete. In any particular problem a glance at the graph of $\varphi(x)$ will tell us to which type the motion belongs. In the particular case from which we started, where $\varphi(x)$ has the form $2(h - V)$, the graph of $V(x)$ will show the type of motion that takes place for any given value of h.

We now consider some simple concrete examples of rectilinear motion in a field of force. These problems are elementary, and can be solved quite easily without reference to the general theory. Nevertheless it is advantageous to bear the theory in mind, because, when we attack the problem of expressing x as a function of t, it is helpful to know in advance to which of the four types the motion belongs.

Example 1.2A. The harmonic oscillator. The force is an attraction towards a fixed point O of the line, the magnitude of the attraction being proportional to the distance from O. We take O as origin, and write

(1.2.13) $$X = -mn^2x,$$

where n is a positive constant. The equation of motion is

(1.2.14) $$\ddot{x} + n^2x = 0,$$

and since this is a linear equation with constant coefficients we can write down the solution without recourse to the general theory, namely

(1.2.15) $$x = a \cos nt + (b/n) \sin nt,$$

where a is the value of x, and b is the value of $\dot{x}$, at $t = 0$. We can also write (1.2.15) in the form

(1.2.16) $$x = c \cos (nt - \alpha),$$

where $$c = \sqrt{\{a^2 + (b/n)^2\}},$$

and α is the angle in the range $0 \leqslant \alpha < 2\pi$ defined by

$$c \cos \alpha = a, \quad c \sin \alpha = b/n.$$

The equation (1.2.16) exhibits the motion as the projection on Ox of a point moving in a circle with uniform angular velocity n. The motion is periodic with period $2\pi/n$.

In this particular case we have solved the problem *ab initio;* let us now consider it from the point of view of the general theory. We have $V = \frac{1}{2}mn^2x^2$, taking $V = 0$ at O, and the equation of energy (1.2.9) becomes

(1.2.17) $$\dot{x}^2 + n^2x^2 = 2h/m$$

It is clear that h is non-negative. If $h = 0$ we have the trivial case of rest at O; $x = 0$ for all time. If h is positive, and we write $h = \frac{1}{2}mn^2c^2$, where $c > 0$, the graph of $y = h - V$ takes the form

(1.2.18) $$y = \tfrac{1}{2}mn^2(c^2 - x^2),$$

and the motion is clearly a libration motion between the values $\pm c$; indeed the harmonic oscillator is the prototype of all libration motions. The period is easily found from (1.2.12). To integrate the equation

$$\dot{x}^2 = n^2(c^2 - x^2) \tag{1.2.19}$$

we introduce in place of x a parameter θ defined by the formula $x = c \cos \theta$, and we may assume without loss of generality that θ increases always with t. Substituting $x = c \cos \theta$ in (1.2.19) we find $\dot{\theta}^2 = n^2$, whence $\dot{\theta} = n$, and $\theta = nt - \alpha$. We thus recover (1.2.16).

Before leaving the problem of the harmonic oscillator it may be of interest to consider briefly the theory that develops if we replace the single second-order equation (1.2.14) by two first-order equations (§ 1.1); these equations are

$$\dot{x} = u, \quad \dot{u} = -n^2 x. \tag{1.2.20}$$

The path of the mobile in the (x, u)-plane is the ellipse

$$\frac{x^2}{c^2} + \frac{u^2}{n^2c^2} = 1, \tag{1.2.21}$$

traversed clockwise. But it is even simpler in this case to use as the second variable $y = \dot{x}/n$, and then the equations become

$$\dot{x} = ny, \quad \dot{y} = -nx. \tag{1.2.22}$$

The path of the mobile in the (x, y)-plane is a circle, traversed clockwise with uniform angular velocity n; we easily deduce (1.2.16). An equivalent manoeuvre is to replace the independent variable t at the outset by τ $(= nt)$, and then the original differential equation (1.2.14) becomes

$$x'' + x = 0, \tag{1.2.23}$$

where the accent denotes differentiation with respect to τ. We can replace this by the equations

$$x' = y, \quad y' = -x, \tag{1.2.24}$$

and the mobile moves in a circle; the angular velocity is unity, and the period in τ is 2π.

We get a motion that approximates to a harmonic motion whenever a particle in a field of force is disturbed from rest at a point a at which $V(x)$, which is of class C_2, has a minimum value. For the undisturbed motion the equation of energy (1.2.9) has the form

$$\tfrac{1}{2}m\dot{x}^2 = V(a) - V(x), \tag{1.2.25}$$

and the graph of $V(a) - V(x)$ touches Ox at $x = a$. Moreover $V(a) - V(x)$ has a maximum at $x = a$, and therefore the graph lies below Ox near $x = a$. If now the energy constant h is increased from $V(a)$ to $V(a) + \delta h$, where δh is a small positive number, we get a libration between two values both near to a. Equilibrium of this type is said to be *stable*. Explicitly, the energy equation for the disturbed motion is

$$\tfrac{1}{2}m\dot{x}^2 = V(a) + \delta h - V(x), \tag{1.2.26}$$

and if we write $a + \xi$ for x, this becomes

$$\tfrac{1}{2}m\dot{\xi}^2 = \delta h - \{V(a + \xi) - V(a)\}. \tag{1.2.27}$$

Now ξ remains small throughout the motion, so we have approximately

$$\tfrac{1}{2}m\dot{\xi}^2 = \delta h - \tfrac{1}{2}V''(a)\xi^2. \tag{1.2.28}$$

Comparing (1.2.28) with (1.2.19) we see that the disturbed motion is approximately a harmonic oscillation with period $2\pi/n$, where $n^2 = V''(a)/m$, and amplitude $\sqrt{\{2\delta h/V''(a)\}}$.

Example 1.2B. The uniform field. The force is constant in magnitude and direction, say $X = mc$ where $c > 0$, and the equation of motion is

(1.2.29) $$\ddot{x} = c.$$

The solution is given by the (finite) Taylor series

(1.2.30) $$x = a + bt + \tfrac{1}{2}ct^2,$$

where a is the value of x, and b is the value of $\dot{x}$, at $t = 0$. We can write (1.2.30) in the form

(1.2.31) $$x - x_0 = \tfrac{1}{2}c(t - t_0)^2,$$

where $x_0 = a - (b^2/2c)$, $t_0 = -b/c$. Throughout the motion $x \geqslant x_0$, and $x = x_0$ at $t = t_0$. The equation of energy is

(1.2.32) $$\tfrac{1}{2}\dot{x}^2 = c(x - x_0).$$

This is an example of case (iii), where $x \to \infty$ as $t \to \infty$.

Example 1.2C. The field is a *repulsion* proportional to distance from O,

(1.2.33) $$X = mn^2x.$$

The equation of motion is

(1.2.34) $$\ddot{x} - n^2x = 0,$$

and the solution is

(1.2.35) $$x = a \cosh nt + (b/n) \sinh nt,$$

where a is the value of x, and b is the value of $\dot{x}$, at $t = 0$. The equation of energy is

(1.2.36) $$\tfrac{1}{2}(\dot{x}^2 - n^2x^2) = h.$$

If initially $x = a$, $\dot{x} = -na$, then $h = 0$, and the graph of $h - V$ is the parabola

(1.2.37) $$y = \tfrac{1}{2}n^2x^2.$$

We have a limitation motion in which $x \to 0$ as $t \to \infty$, an example of case (ii). Explicitly, the solution of (1.2.34) with the given initial conditions is

(1.2.38) $$x = ae^{-nt},$$

and $x \to 0$ as $t \to \infty$, as predicted by the theory.

If initially $x = a$, $\dot{x} = 0$, the solution is

(1.2.39) $$x = a \cosh nt,$$

and we have an example of case (iii). The particle goes to infinity much faster than it does in the uniform field. Here $x = O(e^{nt})$, whereas in the uniform field $x = O(t^2)$.

Example 1.2D. Attraction $\mu m/r^n$. For $x > 0$ the field is $X = -\mu m/x^n$, where n is an integer greater than 1. If the particle is projected from $x = a$ away from the origin with the speed that it would acquire in falling from rest at infinity (so that $h = 0$) we have

(1.2.40) $$\tfrac{1}{2}\dot{x}^2 = \frac{\mu}{(n-1)x^{n-1}}.$$

We know from the theory (by constructing the graph of the second member) that the particle moves to infinity, and in fact

(1.2.41) $$x = a(1 + \lambda t)^{\frac{2}{n+1}}$$

where $\lambda = \dfrac{n+1}{2}\sqrt{\left\{\dfrac{2\mu}{(n-1)a^{n+1}}\right\}}$. We have again an example of case (iii); the particle goes to infinity more slowly than in the uniform field, since here $x = O\left(t^{\frac{2}{n+1}}\right)$.

Example 1.2E. We consider the field

(1.2.42) $$X = m\{-n^2x + 3n^2x^2/(2a)\}, \qquad n > 0,\ a > 0,$$

and suppose that the particle starts from rest at $x = a$ at $t = 0$. The solution is

(1.2.43) $$x = a \sec^2 (\tfrac{1}{2}nt),$$

and $x \to \infty$ as $t \to \pi/n$. We have here an example of case (iv). The equation of energy is

(1.2.44) $$\tfrac{1}{2}\dot{x}^2 = \frac{1}{2a}\, n^2x^2(x - a).$$

1.3 Libration motion. Let us consider more particularly a libration motion, case (i) in the enumeration in § 1.2. In the motion defined by the equation

(1.2.10) $$\dot{x}^2 = \varphi(x),$$

x lies initially between consecutive simple real zeros a, b of $\varphi(x)$. We write

(1.3.1) $$\varphi(x) = (b - x)(x - a)\psi(x),$$

where $\psi(x) > 0$ in the closed interval $a \leqslant x \leqslant b$. The equation (1.2.10) now takes the form

(1.3.2) $$\dot{x}^2 = (b - x)(x - a)\psi(x).$$

It is clear that the ambiguity of sign for $\dot{x}$ is inherent in the problem, since during the oscillatory motion the particle is sometimes moving to the right and sometimes to the left: the ambiguity is not an awkwardness that could have been avoided. We can now fix the ambiguous sign in the equation

(1.3.3) $$dt = \pm \frac{dx}{\sqrt{\varphi(x)}}\,.$$

For as x oscillates between its limiting values a and b the sign is such that the second member of (1.3.3) is always positive. So we need the plus sign when x is increasing and the minus sign when x is decreasing. This determination of the ambiguous sign in this sort of context has been noticed already in § 1.2, and will recur frequently in the sequel.

Nevertheless, though the rule just given is simple enough, the ambiguity of sign is sometimes awkward in practice, and it may be expedient to avoid it by introducing a new variable θ, a so-called *angle variable*, which continually increases with t. We think of the libration as the projection of motion in a circle having the points $x = a$ and $x = b$ on Ox at the ends of a diameter. As Q (Fig. 1.3) moves round the circle, always in the same sense, P oscillates between the points A and B. The relation between x and θ is

(1.3.4) $$x = \alpha - \beta \cos \theta,$$

where

(1.3.5) $$\alpha - \beta = a, \quad \alpha + \beta = b,$$

and

(1.3.6) $$(b - x)(x - a) = \beta^2 \sin^2 \theta.$$

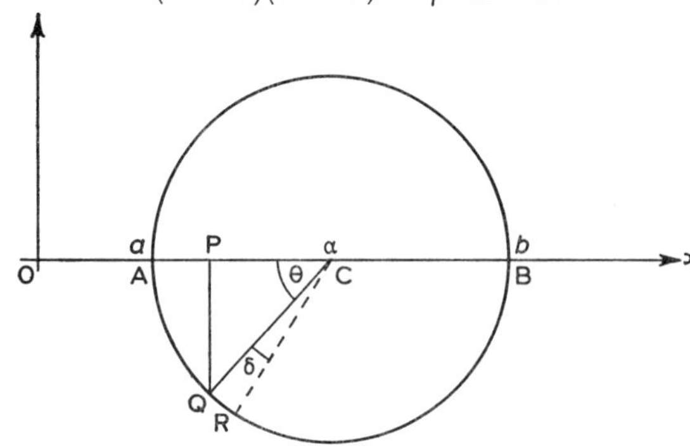

Figure 1.3

Equation (1.3.2) now becomes $\dot{\theta}^2 = \psi(\alpha - \beta \cos \theta)$, giving

(1.3.7) $$\dot{\theta} = \sqrt{\{\psi(\alpha - \beta \cos \theta)\}},$$

and there is no ambiguity of sign here, since $\dot{\theta}$ is positive. If $\psi(x)$ were constant, $\dot{\theta}$ would have a constant value; this actually happens, as we have noticed, in the special case of harmonic motion. We write

(1.3.8) $$\frac{1}{\sqrt{\{\psi(\alpha - \beta \cos \theta)\}}} = \chi(\theta),$$

and $\chi(\theta)$ is an even function of θ, always positive, and periodic with period 2π. The relation connecting t and θ is

(1.3.9) $$t - t_0 = \int_0^\theta \chi(\xi)\, d\xi,$$

where t_0 is a value of t at which $x = a$; we can put $t_0 = 0$ without loss of generality. We notice that $\theta = 0$ when $x = a$, and that $\dot{x} > 0$ during the half-period $0 < t < \frac{1}{2}\sigma$. The period σ is given by

(1.3.10) $$\sigma = \int_0^{2\pi} \chi(\xi)\, d\xi = 2\int_0^{\pi} \chi(\xi)\, d\xi,$$

and we write $\sigma = 2\pi/n$ so that n denotes the mean value of $\dot{\theta}$.*

We are now in a position to solve our problem completely, i.e. to find an explicit expression for x as a function of t. Since x is an even function of t, periodic with period $2\pi/n$, we can in general express x as a Fourier series

(1.3.11) $$x = \tfrac{1}{2}a_0 + a_1 \cos nt + a_2 \cos 2nt + \cdots,$$

* The period can also be expressed in the form $2\displaystyle\int_a^b \frac{\lambda(x)}{\sqrt{\{(b - x)(x - a)\}}}\, dx$, where $1/\{\lambda(x)\}^2$ is written for $\psi(x)$. This leads to a useful approximation to the period, namely $\pi\{\lambda(a) + \lambda(b)\}$. This formula can also be written in the form $\pi(b - a)^{1/2}\{[\varphi'(a)]^{-1/2} + [-\varphi'(b)]^{-1/2}\}$. The formula gives the period exactly if $\lambda(\alpha - \beta \cos \theta)$ is a linear function of θ.

and our object is to determine the coefficients $a_0, a_1, a_2, \ldots$. To achieve this end, we first express $\chi(\theta)$ as a Fourier series

$$\chi(\theta) = \tfrac{1}{2}c_0 + c_1 \cos\theta + c_2 \cos 2\theta + \cdots, \tag{1.3.12}$$

where
$$c_0 = \frac{2}{\pi}\int_0^\pi \chi(\theta)\,d\theta = \frac{2}{n},$$

and
$$c_r = \frac{2}{\pi}\int_0^\pi \chi(\theta)\cos r\theta\,d\theta, \qquad r \geqslant 1.$$

Then

$$t = \int_0^\theta \chi(\xi)\,d\xi = \tfrac{1}{2}c_0\theta + c_1 \sin\theta + \tfrac{1}{2}c_2 \sin 2\theta + \tfrac{1}{3}c_3 \sin 3\theta + \cdots, \tag{1.3.13}$$

whence

$$nt = \theta + \delta, \tag{1.3.14}$$

and

$$\delta = \delta(\theta) = n\sum_{r=1}^{\infty} (c_r/r)\sin r\theta. \tag{1.3.15}$$

Equation (1.3.14) gives us the explicit relation between t and θ. Let us write $\varphi = nt$, so that the point R in Fig. 1.3, where the angle $ACR = \varphi$, moves uniformly on the circle. Now $\theta = \varphi - \delta$, and δ represents geometrically the variation of the libration motion from a strictly harmonic motion; δ vanishes, and Q coincides with R, whenever R is at A or B, i.e. whenever t is an integral number of half-periods.

Finally we determine the coefficients a_r. Since

$$x = \tfrac{1}{2}a_0 + a_1 \cos\varphi + a_2 \cos 2\varphi + \cdots \tag{1.3.16}$$

we have

$$\begin{aligned} a_r &= \frac{2}{\pi}\int_0^\pi x\cos r\varphi\,d\varphi \\ &= -\frac{2}{\pi r}\int_a^b \sin r\varphi\,dx \\ &= -\frac{2\beta}{\pi r}\int_0^\pi \sin r\varphi \sin\theta\,d\theta \\ &= \frac{b-a}{2\pi r}\int_0^\pi \{\cos(r\varphi+\theta) - \cos(r\varphi-\theta)\}\,d\theta, \end{aligned} \tag{1.3.17}$$

and since $\varphi = \theta + \delta$ we obtain

$$a_r = \frac{b-a}{2\pi r}\int_0^\pi \{\cos[(r+1)\theta + r\delta] - \cos[(r-1)\theta + r\delta]\}\,d\theta, \tag{1.3.18}$$

and δ is a known function of θ defined by (1.3.15). Thus the coefficients a_r in the second member of (1.3.16) are determined, and the solution is complete.

1.4 The given force cannot be a function of acceleration. We saw in (1.1) that the given force is a function of position and velocity and time. Some authors* have attempted to construct a theory of greater generality by allowing X, Y, Z to be functions of the acceleration-components $\ddot{x}, \ddot{y}, \ddot{z}$ as well as of the seven variables $x, y, z;\ \dot{x}, \dot{y}, \dot{z};\ t$. This idea is foreign to

* See for example G. D. Birkhoff, "Dynamical Systems" (**35**), p. 15.

Newtonian mechanics, and inconsistent with one of its fundamental postulates. To prove this it will suffice to consider a problem of rectilinear motion. Suppose then that a particle of mass m moves on the line Ox, and consider two forces $m\varphi(f)$ and $m\psi(f)$, where f is the acceleration, $f = \ddot{x}$. The functions φ and ψ may also involve x, u $(= \dot{x})$ and t, but it is the dependence on f that primarily concerns us at the moment and that is emphasized in the notation. We now consider three experiments. In the first experiment the particle is acted on by the force $m\varphi$, in the second by $m\psi$, and in the third by $m(\varphi + \psi)$. The values of x, u, t are the same in all three experiments. If we denote the accelerations in the three experiments by f_1, f_2, and f_3 we have

$$f_1 = \varphi(f_1), \tag{1.4.1}$$

$$f_2 = \psi(f_2), \tag{1.4.2}$$

$$f_3 = \varphi(f_3) + \psi(f_3). \tag{1.4.3}$$

The first point that catches our attention is that an equation such as (1.4.1) does not necessarily determine f_1 uniquely, a situation in itself foreign to the Newtonian outlook. However we can afford to ignore this point, because a much more serious difficulty confronts us in a moment. We will assume therefore that f_1, f_2, and f_3 are uniquely determined.

Now it is a fundamental postulate of Newtonian mechanics that when two forces act simultaneously on a particle the effect is the same as that of a single force equal to their (vector) sum. An equivalent form of the same postulate is that each force gives rise to the acceleration that it would produce if the other force were absent. Thus we must have

$$f_3 = f_1 + f_2, \tag{1.4.4}$$

and combining this with (1.4.3) we find

$$f_1 + f_2 = \varphi(f_1 + f_2) + \psi(f_1 + f_2). \tag{1.4.5}$$

Now it is easy to see that in general the equations (1.4.1), (1.4.2), and (1.4.5) are inconsistent. For (1.4.1) involves only the value of φ at f_1 and (1.4.2) involves only the value of ψ at f_2, and neither involves any reference to or any restriction on the value of φ or the value of ψ at $f_1 + f_2$.

As a concrete example, consider the simple case in which φ and ψ are linear, say

$$\varphi(f) = Af + B,$$

$$\psi(f) = Cf + D.$$

We may assume that A is not 0 or 1, and that C is not 0 or 1, and then unique solutions for f_1 and f_2 certainly exist. But the equations (1.4.1), (1.4.2), and (1.4.5) are consistent only if

$$BC(1 - C) + DA(1 - A) = 0.$$

Thus forces depending on the acceleration are not admissible in Newtonian dynamics. This does not preclude their appearance in electrodynamics, where the postulate quoted does not hold.

1.5 The constrained particle (i). Let us suppose now that the particle is acted on by a given force (X, Y, Z) as before, but, instead of being free, it is confined to a given smooth surface. The constraint is a two-sided constraint; it is not a one-sided constraint, as, for example, when a particle moves on a table which it cannot penetrate but which it can leave. The condition expressing the constraint is an equation, not an inequality.

Let the equation of the surface be $\varphi(x, y, z) = 0$, where $\varphi \in C_2$. Then the coordinates x, y, z of the particle satisfy for all time the relation

$$\varphi(x, y, z) = 0. \tag{1.5.1}$$

We can express this relation in other ways. We can say that a homogeneous linear relation

$$\frac{\partial \varphi}{\partial x} \dot{x} + \frac{\partial \varphi}{\partial y} \dot{y} + \frac{\partial \varphi}{\partial z} \dot{z} = 0 \tag{1.5.2}$$

connects the velocity-components $\dot{x}$, $\dot{y}$, $\dot{z}$, the coefficients being given functions of (x, y, z) of class C_1. Or we can say that a homogeneous linear relation

$$\frac{\partial \varphi}{\partial x} dx + \frac{\partial \varphi}{\partial y} dy + \frac{\partial \varphi}{\partial z} dz = 0 \tag{1.5.3}$$

connects the differentials dx, dy, dz representing a possible infinitesimal displacement of the particle. It is hardly necessary to emphasize that (1.5.3) is exact. It is precisely equivalent to (1.5.2); the differentials are merely a set of ratios. We shall speak of any of the three conditions (1.5.1), (1.5.2), (1.5.3) as the *equation of constraint*. For reasons that will appear shortly, the last form (1.5.3), a Pfaffian equation, is the one that is most generally useful.

It is important to observe that the equation of constraint—let us consider for the moment the form (1.5.2)—is satisfied by all the possible velocities $(\dot{x}, \dot{y}, \dot{z})$ that the particle might have when it is at the point (x, y, z). We could project the particle from this point with any velocity that satisfies the equation of constraint. When we consider a particular problem, in which the particle passes through the point (x, y, z) at the instant t, one of these velocities is distinguished by being the actual velocity; it enjoys the special privilege of existence. But the equation of constraint is satisfied also by all the hypothetical velocities that the particle might, but in fact does not, have.

We speak of the whole class of displacements (dx, dy, dz) which the particle can suffer from the point (x, y, z) in the interval dt as the *possible displacements*. The displacement that the particle does actually suffer in the interval dt is one among the possible displacements.

The mechanism by which the actual motion is made to conform to the equation of constraint is well known. An additional force, the reaction of the surface, is called into play. This force is normal to the surface—this is what we mean by saying that the surface is smooth—but this is the only limitation imposed on it *a priori*; there is no limitation imposed on its magnitude. The surface can supply a normal reaction of any magnitude (and sign), and the magnitude adjusts itself so that the motion of the particle, under the action of both forces together, is confined to the surface.

The reaction of the surface on the particle is called a *force of constraint*. Let us consider more closely the nature of such a force. In our problem the only restriction imposed on the reaction is that it must be normal to the surface. We seek to generalize this, and we ask: "What is the general characteristic of a force of constraint of which the reaction in this problem is a particular example?" The answer is already familiar from the study of the principle of Virtual Work in statics. It is that the force of constraint does no work in any possible displacement. That this is true in the case before us is evident. For if we denote the force of constraint by (X', Y', Z') we have

$$\frac{X'}{\frac{\partial\varphi}{\partial x}} = \frac{Y'}{\frac{\partial\varphi}{\partial y}} = \frac{Z'}{\frac{\partial\varphi}{\partial z}}, \tag{1.5.4}$$

whence

$$X'\,dx + Y'\,dy + Z'\,dz = 0 \tag{1.5.5}$$

for any displacement (dx, dy, dz) satisfying (1.5.3).

We have in this simple example the first appearance of a principle that will play an important part in the theory—the principle that the forces acting all belong to one or other of the two classes, given forces and forces of constraint. We may notice by way of contrast the situation in elementary dynamics, where a quite different division into two classes is often important—namely the division into external and internal forces. There are in fact systems for which the principle enunciated—that the forces all belong either to the category of given forces or to the category of forces of constraint—does not hold. But such systems will not be considered in this book.

1.6 The constrained particle (ii). We now consider a slightly more complicated problem. We suppose that the particle is acted on by a given force as before, but that this time the particle moves, not on a fixed smooth surface, but on a variable smooth surface $\psi(x, y, z, t) = 0$, where $\psi \in C_2$. The three forms of the equation of constraint are now

$$\psi(x, y, z, t) = 0, \tag{1.6.1}$$

$$\frac{\partial\psi}{\partial x}\dot{x} + \frac{\partial\psi}{\partial y}\dot{y} + \frac{\partial\psi}{\partial z}\dot{z} + \frac{\partial\psi}{\partial t} = 0, \tag{1.6.2}$$

$$\frac{\partial\psi}{\partial x}\,dx + \frac{\partial\psi}{\partial y}\,dy + \frac{\partial\psi}{\partial z}\,dz + \frac{\partial\psi}{\partial t}\,dt = 0. \tag{1.6.3}$$

These differ in an important way from the corresponding equations in §1.5. For one thing the coefficients contain t as well as x, y, and z; but this is not the vital difference. The vital difference between (1.5.2) and (1.6.2) is that the former is a *homogeneous* linear relation connecting the velocity-components $\dot{x}$, $\dot{y}$, $\dot{z}$, whereas the latter is not homogeneous. And similarly (1.6.3) differs essentially from (1.5.3) because (1.6.3) contains a term in dt.

The force of constraint is still normal to the surface, so that

$$\frac{X'}{\frac{\partial\psi}{\partial x}} = \frac{Y'}{\frac{\partial\psi}{\partial y}} = \frac{Z'}{\frac{\partial\psi}{\partial z}}, \tag{1.6.4}$$

but *it is no longer true that the work done by the force of constraint in any possible displacement is zero.* We are thus led to consider another class of displacements $(\delta x, \delta y, \delta z)$ which satisfy the equation

$$\frac{\partial\psi}{\partial x}\,\delta x + \frac{\partial\psi}{\partial y}\,\delta y + \frac{\partial\psi}{\partial z}\,\delta z = 0. \tag{1.6.5}$$

These displacements, which differ essentially from the possible displacements, are called the *virtual displacements*. The work done by the force of constraint in any virtual displacement is zero. The corresponding velocities $(\dot{x}, \dot{y}, \dot{z})$ are called *virtual velocities*, and they satisfy the condition

$$\frac{\partial\psi}{\partial x}\dot{x} + \frac{\partial\psi}{\partial y}\dot{y} + \frac{\partial\psi}{\partial z}\dot{z} = 0. \tag{1.6.6}$$

It is easy to see what is the physical significance of the virtual displacements: they are the displacements that would be possible on the surface if it were petrified in the form that it has at the instant t. As a simple concrete example, suppose that the particle moves on the floor of a lift which is rising with speed W. Taking the axis of z vertically upwards we see that the possible displacements satisfy

$$dz - W\,dt = 0,$$

whereas the virtual displacements satisfy

$$\delta z = 0.$$

Or, expressing the same distinction in terms of velocities instead of displacements, the possible velocities satisfy

$$\dot{z} = W,$$

and the virtual velocities satisfy

$$\dot{z} = 0.$$

The two classes not only do not coincide, but actually they have no member in common: all the possible velocities have vertical component W, and all the virtual velocities have vertical component zero.

The distinction between possible displacements and virtual displacements (or between possible velocities and virtual velocities) in this example is vitally important. The distinction did not arise in §1.5, where the two classes happen to coincide. We notice that the equation (1.6.5) satisfied by the virtual displacements can be obtained very simply from the equation (1.6.3) satisfied by the possible displacements: we obtain (1.6.5) from (1.6.3) by omitting the term in dt and replacing the symbols dx, dy, dz by δx, δy, δz.

1.7 The constrained particle (iii). With the two preceding examples in mind the general idea of a constraint presents no difficulty. But we need one generalization. In the two examples considered the first member of the Pfaffian equation of constraint was a complete differential, but this is by no means essential to the idea of a constraint. The equation may involve any Pfaffian form, not necessarily one that admits an integrating factor. We shall take the equation of constraint in the general case to be

$$a\,dx + b\,dy + c\,dz + p\,dt = 0, \tag{1.7.1}$$

where a, b, c, p are given functions, of class C_1, of x, y, z, and t. The displacements satisfying (1.7.1) are the possible displacements. The virtual displacements satisfy

$$a\,\delta x + b\,\delta y + c\,\delta z = 0. \tag{1.7.2}$$

Instead of possible and virtual displacements we can work with possible and virtual velocities. The possible velocities satisfy

$$a\dot{x} + b\dot{y} + c\dot{z} + p = 0, \tag{1.7.3}$$

and the virtual velocities satisfy

$$a\dot{x} + b\dot{y} + c\dot{z} = 0. \tag{1.7.4}$$

In practice the Pfaffian equations (1.7.1) and (1.7.2) are usually more convenient than the equations (1.7.3) and (1.7.4).

The general dynamical problem is now readily comprehended. A given force (X, Y, Z) acts on the particle, and a force of constraint is called into play by the constraint. The force of constraint (X', Y', Z') is such that it does no work in any virtual displacement, and such that the motion under the two forces together is a possible motion, i.e. the actual motion satisfies (1.7.3).

Now it is easy to see that the motion is in general determinate. Since

$$X'\,\delta x + Y'\,\delta y + Z'\,\delta z = 0 \tag{1.7.5}$$

for all $(\delta x, \delta y, \delta z)$ satisfying (1.7.2) we have

$$\frac{X'}{a} = \frac{Y'}{b} = \frac{Z'}{c}. \tag{1.7.6}$$

We call the common value of these three fractions λ, so

$$X' = \lambda a, \qquad Y' = \lambda b, \qquad Z' = \lambda c. \tag{1.7.7}$$

Thus the variables x, y, z satisfy the equations

$$m\ddot{x} = X + \lambda a, \tag{1.7.8}$$

$$m\ddot{y} = Y + \lambda b, \tag{1.7.9}$$

$$m\ddot{z} = Z + \lambda c, \tag{1.7.10}$$

$$a\dot{x} + b\dot{y} + c\dot{z} + p = 0. \tag{1.7.3}$$

These four equations suffice in general to determine the four unknowns x, y, z, λ as functions of the independent variable t. Ideally we can find the solution if we know the values of x, y, z and the values of $\dot{x}$, $\dot{y}$, $\dot{z}$ (satisfying (1.7.3)) at $t = 0$.

One or two points deserve comment before we leave this topic. The geometrical interpretation of (1.7.2) is that the virtual displacements lie in a plane at right angles to the vector (a, b, c), while (1.7.6) tells us that the force of constraint is in the direction of this vector. The physical meaning of the multiplier is now clear, namely that it is proportional to the magnitude of the force of constraint. The actual magnitude of the force of constraint is $\lambda\sqrt{(a^2 + b^2 + c^2)}$.

In general the two classes of displacements, possible and virtual, have no member in common; but if $p = 0$ identically the two classes are identical. The system is then said to be *catastatic*. Notice that in a catastatic system the coefficients a, b, c may be functions of t as well as of x, y, and z. The characteristic properties of a catastatic system are (i) that the classes of possible and of virtual displacements are identical, and (ii) that $\{\dot{x}, \dot{y}, \dot{z}\} = \mathbf{0}$ is a possible velocity. A system which is not catastatic is called *acatastatic*.

1.8 Holonomic and non-holonomic systems. When the Pfaffian equation of constraint (1.7.1) is integrable (after multiplication by a suitable integrating factor) the system is said to be *holonomic*. The equation of constraint can then be written in the finite form

$$\psi(x, y, z, t) = 0. \tag{1.8.1}$$

When the equation (1.7.1) is not integrable, the system is said to be *non-holonomic*.

What is the essential difference between the character of holonomic and of non-holonomic systems? To answer this question it will suffice to consider catastatic systems, and indeed it will suffice to consider the simple case in which the coefficients a, b, c do not depend on t.

If the Pfaffian form $a\,dx + b\,dy + c\,dz$ admits an integrating factor the system is holonomic, and the equation of constraint can be written in the form

(1.8.2) $$\varphi(x, y, z) = \text{constant}.$$

It follows that from a given point (say, for definiteness, the origin) *only a two-fold infinity of positions is accessible*, namely the points on the surface

(1.8.3) $$\varphi(x, y, z) = \varphi(0, 0, 0).$$

On the other hand, if the system is non-holonomic *a three-fold infinity of positions is accessible*. Suppose, for example, that the equation of constraint is

(1.8.4) $$dy - z\,dx = 0,$$

which clearly does not admit an integrating factor. Then we can find a path satisfying (1.8.4) and leading from the origin to an arbitrary point (x_2, y_2, z_2). To prove this statement, consider the path

(1.8.5) $$y = f(x), \qquad z = f'(x),$$

where $f(x) \in C_3$. The equation of constraint (1.8.4) is clearly satisfied, and we have only to choose $f(x)$ with the properties

(1.8.6) $$f(0) = 0, \quad f'(0) = 0; \quad f(x_2) = y_2, \quad f'(x_2) = z_2.$$

That infinitely many such functions exist is evident by a simple geometrical argument; alternatively we can choose as a concrete example of such a function one of the family

(1.8.7)
$$f(x) = (3y_2 - z_2x_2)(x/x_2)^2 - (2y_2 - z_2x_2)(x/x_2)^3 + Ax^2(x_2 - x)^2 + B\sin^2(\pi x/x_2).$$

The number of coordinates less the number of constraints is called the number of *degrees of freedom* of the system, or, briefly, the number of *freedoms*. In our present problem, with three coordinates and one constraint, the number of degrees of freedom (or number of freedoms) is two. The important property that we have established is that when the system is holonomic, only a two-fold infinity of positions is accessible from a given starting-point; but when the system is non-holonomic a three-fold infinity of positions is accessible, although there are still only two degrees of freedom.

The argument given is general in spite of the fact that the constraint considered had the special form (1.8.4). The general non-integrable Pfaffian equation can be reduced to the form (1.8.4) by a suitable transformation.*

It may be mentioned in passing that non-holonomic systems containing only one particle rarely occur in practice. Perhaps the simplest example is provided by the so-called *curve of pursuit*. A point Q moves on the axis Ox, the distance OQ being a prescribed function $\xi(t)$

* This follows from Pfaff's theorem; for a proof of the theorem see for example Goursat, E., "Problème de Pfaff" (Paris, 1922) Chapter I.

of t. The particle, whose position at time t is (x, y), moves in the (x, y)-plane, and is constrained so that at each instant its velocity is directed towards Q. The equation of constraint

(1.8.8) $$y\,dx + (\xi - x)\,dy = 0$$

does not admit an integrating factor (except in the trivial case when ξ is constant) and the system is non-holonomic.

1.9 Two constraints. We now consider a particle moving in space under the action of a given force (X, Y, Z) and subject to two constraints whose equations are

(1.9.1) $$\omega \equiv a\,dx + b\,dy + c\,dz + p\,dt = 0,$$

(1.9.2) $$\omega' \equiv a'\,dx + b'\,dy + c'\,dz + p'\,dt = 0,$$

where the coefficients $a, a', \ldots,$ are given functions, of class C_1, of x, y, z and t. There are three possibilities which we now describe.

(i) The system of Pfaffian equations is *completely integrable*, i.e. it is equivalent to two equations of the form

(1.9.3) $$df = 0, \quad df' = 0.$$

The equations of constraint can be written in the form of two equations

(1.9.4) $$f = c, \quad f' = c',$$

and the system is holonomic.

(ii) There exists one and only one integrable combination of the two equations (1.9.1) and (1.9.2). In this case there exist multipliers μ, μ' such that $\mu\omega + \mu'\omega'$ is a perfect differential df, but there is no second integrable combination independent of the first. (The Pfaffian form $\varphi(f)(\mu\omega + \mu'\omega')$ is also a perfect differential, but is for our purpose equivalent to the original one.) The equations of constraint can be put in the form of one finite and one Pfaffian equation

(1.9.5) $$f = c, \quad \omega = 0.$$

The system is non-holonomic.

(iii) There exists no integrable combination, and the original form, (1.9.1) and (1.9.2), of the equations of constraint cannot be simplified. The system is non-holonomic.

The system has one degree of freedom. In case (iii) a three-fold infinity of positions is accessible from a given position, in case (ii) a two-fold infinity, and in case (i) a single infinity. Case (i) occurs for example if the particle is a bead sliding on a wire of given fixed or varying form.

The virtual displacements satisfy

(1.9.6) $$a\,\delta x + b\,\delta y + c\,\delta z = 0,$$

(1.9.7) $$a'\,\delta x + b'\,\delta y + c'\,\delta z = 0.$$

The force of constraint (X', Y', Z') does no work in any virtual displacement, so

(1.9.8) $$X'\,\delta x + Y'\,\delta y + Z'\,\delta z = 0$$

for any $(\delta x, \delta y, \delta z)$ satisfying (1.9.6) and (1.9.7). Hence there exist multipliers λ, λ' such that

(1.9.9) $$\begin{cases} X' = \lambda a + \lambda' a', \\ Y' = \lambda b + \lambda' b', \\ Z' = \lambda c + \lambda' c'. \end{cases}$$

The motion of the particle under the force $(X + X', Y + Y', Z + Z')$ conforms to (1.9.1) and (1.9.2). We easily see that the motion is in general determinate. For the system of five differential equations

$$\left\{\begin{aligned} m\ddot{x} &= X + \lambda a + \lambda' a', \\ m\ddot{y} &= Y + \lambda b + \lambda' b', \\ m\ddot{z} &= Z + \lambda c + \lambda' c', \\ a\dot{x} + b\dot{y} &+ c\dot{z} + p = 0, \\ a'\dot{x} + b'\dot{y} &+ c'\dot{z} + p' = 0, \end{aligned}\right. \tag{1.9.10}$$

suffices to determine the five variables x, y, z, λ, λ' as functions of t. It is clear that the multipliers λ, λ' are proportional to the reactions arising from the two constraints.

Finally we may notice the case of three constraints; but this problem is trivial. The three equations of constraint

$$\left\{\begin{aligned} a\dot{x} + b\dot{y} + c\dot{z} + p &= 0, \\ a'\dot{x} + b'\dot{y} + c'\dot{z} + p' &= 0, \\ a''\dot{x} + b''\dot{y} + c''\dot{z} + p'' &= 0, \end{aligned}\right. \tag{1.9.11}$$

determine $\dot{x}$, $\dot{y}$, and $\dot{z}$ as functions of (x, y, z, t). We now have equations of the first order, and the position at $t = 0$ implies the position for other values of t. The equations analogous to (1.9.10) merely serve to determine the multipliers λ, λ', λ'', which are proportional to the forces of constraint, in terms of the given force $\{X, Y, Z\}$.

Chapter II

Dynamical systems

2.1 A simple example. In the preceding chapter we considered the dynamics of a single particle. It might seem natural, following the historic order of development, to discuss next the theory of the motion of a single rigid body; this is in fact the order usually followed in a first study of rigid Dynamics. Our approach will however be somewhat different. In Analytical Dynamics we proceed directly from the single particle to the general dynamical system. The single rigid body is of course a special case of a dynamical system and indeed one that we shall frequently find useful as a specific illustration.

The fundamental principles of dynamics were developed by Newton for the case of a single particle, and expounded in his famous treatise, the *Principia* (1687). The dynamics of a rigid body was first systematically studied some half-century later,* and it was natural to conceive of a rigid body as an aggregate of particles. The idea of a rigid body in the classical dynamics is a collection of particles set in a rigid and imponderable frame. Similarly we shall think of the general dynamical system as a collection of particles acted on by given forces and controlled by various kinds of constraints.

We begin with the discussion of a simple concrete example of a dynamical system. The example is too simple to be of any great practical importance—it contains only two particles—and moreover it is somewhat artificial; but it serves the useful purpose of illustrating the fundamental ideas in a rather striking way.

We consider a system containing two particles P_1 and P_2 joined by a light rod of length a, where $a(= a(t))$ is *a prescribed function of the time*; the function $a(t) \in C_1$. It will suffice for our present purpose, and will simplify the formulae, if we suppose the system to move in the plane $z = 0$, so that we can deal with a space of two dimensions. The particles have masses m_1 and m_2, and they are acted on by given forces (X_1, Y_1) and (X_2, Y_2); in addition there is a thrust or tension in the rod. The coordinates of the particles satisfy the equation of constraint

$$(x_2 - x_1)^2 + (y_2 - y_1)^2 = a^2, \tag{2.1.1}$$

and the possible displacements satisfy the equation

$$(x_2 - x_1)(dx_2 - dx_1) + (y_2 - y_1)(dy_2 - dy_1) = a\dot{a}\, dt. \tag{2.1.2}$$

The system has three degrees of freedom.

We now consider the equations of motion

$$\begin{cases} m_1\ddot{x}_1 = X_1 + X_1', \\ m_1\ddot{y}_1 = Y_1 + Y_1', \\ m_2\ddot{x}_2 = X_2 + X_2', \\ m_2\ddot{y}_2 = Y_2 + Y_2', \end{cases} \tag{2.1.3}$$

where the forces of constraint (X_1', Y_1'), (X_2', Y_2') arise from the thrust in the rod. If this thrust is λa we have

$$\frac{X_2'}{x_2 - x_1} = \frac{Y_2'}{y_2 - y_1} = \frac{-X_1'}{x_2 - x_1} = \frac{-Y_1'}{y_2 - y_1} = \lambda, \tag{2.1.4}$$

* d'Alembert's "Traité de dynamique" (**2**) was published in 1743.

and the system of forces of constraint does no work in any displacement $(\delta x_1, \delta y_1, \delta x_2, \delta y_2)$ satisfying

$$(x_2 - x_1)(\delta x_2 - \delta x_1) + (y_2 - y_1)(\delta y_2 - \delta y_1) = 0. \tag{2.1.5}$$

The displacements satisfying (2.1.5) are called virtual displacements (cf. § 1.6). The physical meaning of the virtual displacements is that they are displacements with the length of the rod unvaried.

It is clear that the problem is in general determinate. The system of five differential equations

$$\begin{cases} m_1\ddot{x}_1 = X_1 - \lambda(x_2 - x_1), \\ m_1\ddot{y}_1 = Y_1 - \lambda(y_2 - y_1), \\ m_2\ddot{x}_2 = X_2 + \lambda(x_2 - x_1), \\ m_2\ddot{y}_2 = Y_2 + \lambda(y_2 - y_1), \\ (x_2 - x_1)^2 + (y_2 - y_1)^2 = a^2, \end{cases} \tag{2.1.6}$$

suffices to determine the five variables $x_1, y_1, x_2, y_2, \lambda$ as functions of t.

It is now clear that the situation is similar to that encountered in § 1.6. Forces of constraint are called into play; the characteristic properties of the forces of constraint are that they do no work, as a whole, in an arbitrary virtual displacement, and that the motion of the system under the action of the two sets of forces together (given forces and forces of constraint) conforms to the equations of constraint.

A problem that should be strongly contrasted with the one just discussed is that of two particles moving freely in a plane under various forces including a mutual attraction. Here there is no constraint, and all the forces, including the mutual attraction, belong to the category of given forces. The system has four freedoms.

The two systems just considered are holonomic. Now let us return to the first problem, the particles being joined by a rod; it will suffice now to consider the case where the rod is rigid, the length a being constant. This is the simplest possible example of a rigid body—a rigid body containing only two particles. Let us suppose that the system is constrained in such a way that the velocity of P_1 is always directed along the rod, the force of constraint on P_1 being at right angles to the rod. (This constraint is approximately realized in the hatchet planimeter, where a wheel with a sharp edge can roll on a sheet of paper but cannot side-slip.) There are now two equations of constraint

$$(x_2 - x_1)^2 + (y_2 - y_1)^2 = a^2, \tag{2.1.7}$$

$$(y_2 - y_1)\, dx_1 - (x_2 - x_1)\, dy_1 = 0. \tag{2.1.8}$$

The Pfaffian equation (2.1.8) is not integrable, and the system is non-holonomic.

The system has two degrees of freedom, but nevertheless a three-fold infinity of configurations is accessible from a given configuration; in fact any configuration is accessible from any other. This is easily proved by a simple geometrical argument. Alternatively we may think of the configuration as described by the three variables x_1, y_1, z, where

$$z = \frac{y_2 - y_1}{x_2 - x_1}; \tag{2.1.9}$$

z is the tangent of the angle between Ox and the rod P_1P_2. The Pfaffian equation of constraint takes the form

$$dy_1 - z\, dx_1 = 0, \tag{2.1.10}$$

which we have already considered in § 1.8, and, as we saw, any configuration is accessible from any other configuration.

2.2 The dynamical system. We have now considered a number of simple concrete examples of dynamical systems, and we have taken the opportunity to illustrate some of the fundamental notions of dynamical theory. We now turn to a generalization based on examples such as these, the theory of the general dynamical system.

We consider then a finite number ν of particles. We assume that each particle maintains a separate distinguishable identity throughout the motion, so that we can make a statement about a particular particle such as: "This particle, which was *there* at $t = 0$, is now *here*." Thus we can enumerate the particles and attach to them, once for all, the labels $1, 2, 3, \ldots, \nu$. Usually we shall assume that each particle has constant mass (though this assumption is not an essential part of the idea of a dynamical system, and later, in Chapter XI, we shall discuss how the more familiar theory is modified if the mass of each particle is a given function of its speed). We denote the coordinates of the particles, referred to fixed rectangular axes, by $x_1, x_2, \ldots, x_N$, where $N = 3\nu$. The x-, y-, and z-coordinates of the rth particle are x_{3r-2}, x_{3r-1}, x_{3r}. The mass of this particle is denoted indifferently by m_{3r-2}, m_{3r-1}, or m_{3r}. At first sight it may appear to be a defect of the notation that three different symbols should all represent the same quantity; but in practice the notation is convenient and concise.

Occasionally it is desirable to concentrate our attention on the ν particles rather than on the N coordinates. In that case we use x, y, z to denote the coordinates of a typical particle of mass m, and we use a special symbol S to denote a summation over the ν particles. Thus the two formulae

$$Sm(\ddot{x}\,\delta x + \ddot{y}\,\delta y + \ddot{z}\,\delta z), \tag{2.2.1}$$

$$\sum_{r=1}^{N} m_r \ddot{x}_r\,\delta x_r, \tag{2.2.2}$$

mean the same thing. The latter will sometimes be shortened by omitting the suffixes and writing

$$\sum m\ddot{x}\,\delta x; \tag{2.2.3}$$

we speak of this notation (with the suffixes omitted) as the *abridged notation*. It will only be used when it is clear, with no danger of ambiguity, that a summation over the N coordinates is implied.

Given forces $X_1, X_2, \ldots, X_N$ act on the particles; the components of the force acting on the rth particle are X_{3r-2}, X_{3r-1}, X_{3r}. To say that these forces are given means that they are known functions of the x's, the $\dot{x}$'s, and t.

It is sometimes convenient to picture the coordinates $x_1, x_2, \ldots, x_N$ as the coordinates of a *representative point* or *mobile* in an N-dimensional space. In that context we denote the point or vector $\{x_1, x_2, \ldots, x_N\}$ by $\mathbf{x}$. Similarly we denote the force $\{X_1, X_2, \ldots, X_N\}$ by $\mathbf{X}$, the velocity $\{\dot{x}_1, \dot{x}_2, \ldots, \dot{x}_n\}$ by $\dot{\mathbf{x}}$ or $\mathbf{u}$, and so on.

The possible displacements of the particles are not arbitrary (except in the *problem of ν bodies*, where we are concerned with a swarm of ν free particles) but are subject to L equations of constraint,

$$\sum_{s=1}^{N} A_{rs}\,dx_s + A_r\,dt = 0, \qquad r = 1, 2, \ldots, L < N. \tag{2.2.4}$$

The coefficients A_{rs}, A_r are given functions, of class C_1, in some domain of $(x_1, x_2, \ldots, x_N;\ t)$. These equations are assumed to be independent; they have been reduced to the least possible number. This implies that the matrix of the coefficients has rank L (though in practice the rank may be less than L for isolated values of $\mathbf{x}$, t). In the equations

$$\sum_{s=1}^{N} A_{rs}\dot{x}_s + A_r = 0, \qquad r = 1, 2, \ldots, L, \tag{2.2.5}$$

we can prescribe the values of $N - L$ of the $\dot{x}$'s, and we can solve for the remaining L of the $\dot{x}$'s. The number

$$k = N - L \tag{2.2.6}$$

is the number of *degrees of freedom* of the system; it is the number of velocity-components that can be given arbitrary values.

In the simplest and commonest cases the system of Pfaffian equations (2.2.4) is *completely integrable*, i.e. it is equivalent to L equations of the form

$$df_r = 0, \qquad r = 1, 2, \ldots, L, \tag{2.2.7}$$

where

$$f_r = f_r(x_1, x_2, \ldots, x_N;\ t).$$

When this happens the system is said to be *holonomic*. In this case the equations of constraint can be written in the form

$$f_r = c_r, \qquad r = 1, 2, \ldots, L. \tag{2.2.8}$$

In practice the equations of constraint are frequently given in the form (2.2.8) instead of in the form (2.2.4), and the constants c_r have prescribed values.

Whatever given forces are acting, the motion of the system conforms to the equations of constraint (2.2.5). The mechanism by which this is achieved has already been illustrated by particular examples. Forces of constraint X_1', X_2', $\ldots$, X_N' (or, briefly, a force of constraint $\mathbf{X}'$) are called into play, and they are subject to the condition that they do no work in an arbitrary virtual displacement. A virtual displacement is defined to be any displacement $\delta x_1, \delta x_2, \ldots, \delta x_N$ which satisfies the equations

$$\sum_{s=1}^{N} A_{rs}\, \delta x_s = 0, \qquad r = 1, 2, \ldots, L. \tag{2.2.9}$$

Thus

$$\sum_{s=1}^{N} X_s'\, \delta x_s = 0 \tag{2.2.10}$$

for any $(\delta x_1, \delta x_2, \ldots, \delta x_N)$ satisfying (2.2.9). The forces of constraint so adjust themselves that the motion under the action of the two sets of forces together satisfies (2.2.5).

In general the motion is determined by the preceding theory. From (2.2.10) and (2.2.9) we see that X_1', X_2', $\ldots$, X_N' can be expressed in terms of L multipliers λ_r by the formulae

$$X_s' = \sum_{r=1}^{L} \lambda_r A_{rs}, \qquad s = 1, 2, \ldots, N, \tag{2.2.11}$$

and the N equations of motion

(2.2.12) $$m_s\ddot{x}_s = X_s + X_s', \qquad s = 1, 2, \ldots, N,$$

become

(2.2.13) $$m_s\ddot{x}_s = X_s + \sum_{r=1}^{L} \lambda_r A_{rs}, \qquad s = 1, 2, \ldots, N.$$

To these we must adjoin the L equations of constraint

(2.2.5) $$\sum_{s=1}^{N} A_{rs}\dot{x}_s + A_r = 0, \qquad r = 1, 2, \ldots, L,$$

and *the* $N + L$ *equations* (2.2.13) *and* (2.2.5) *together determine the* $N + L$ *variables* $x_1, x_2, \ldots, x_N$; $\lambda_1, \lambda_2, \ldots, \lambda_L$ *as functions of* t. Theoretically we can determine the motion for some interval containing $t = 0$ if the values of x's and $\dot{x}$'s at $t = 0$ are prescribed.

The theorem just enunciated expresses the equations of motion for the general dynamical system in a conspicuously simple and comprehensive form. Nevertheless it is not the form that turns out to be the most useful. In practice we are not as a rule interested in the λ's (which are related to the magnitudes of the forces of constraint) and (in the next Chapter) we shall transform the equations into a different form in which the λ's do not appear.

2.3 The catastatic system. When the coefficients A_r in the equations of constraint, (2.2.4) or (2.2.5), are all identically zero, the system is said to be *catastatic*. The notion has already been mentioned, for the case of a single particle, in § 1.7. The characteristic properties of the catastatic system are (i) that the class of virtual displacements is identical with the class of possible displacements (or, in other words, the class of virtual velocities is identical with the class of possible velocities), and (ii) that the class of virtual or possible velocities includes the system

(2.3.1) $$\dot{x}_r = 0, \qquad r = 1, 2, \ldots, N.$$

The system is capable of rest.

A system that is not catastatic is called *acatastatic*; this nomenclature has been introduced already, for the case of a single particle, in § 1.7.

2.4 The forces of constraint. When we apply the theory given in the preceding paragraph to concrete problems, it is necessary to be able to recognize which forces belong to the category of forces of constraint. In practice this usually presents no difficulty, since these forces are already familiar from the study of the Principle of Virtual Work in statics. Nevertheless it may be useful at this stage to enumerate the types of forces of constraint which most frequently appear in the classical problems. The enumeration may serve to give concreteness and reality to the abstract theory.

A force exerted on a particle of the system by an agent outside the system is a force of constraint only if it does no work in an arbitrary virtual displacement, i.e. only if, in every virtual displacement, the particle moves at right angles to the force. This is illustrated in the types (i)–(iv) below. On the other hand the mutual actions between two points belonging to the system belong to the category of forces of constraint whenever the action and reaction together do no work in an arbitrary virtual displacement. This is illustrated in the types (v)–(viii).

(i) A particle belonging to the system is constrained to move on a smooth surface which is fixed or which has an inexorable motion imposed from outside the system. The action of the surface on the particle is a force of constraint. For in a virtual displacement the particle moves on the petrified surface, i.e. it moves in a direction at right angles to the force.

(ii) A particle of the system has an inexorable motion imposed from outside the system. The force exerted on the particle by the external agent is a force of constraint. The classical example is that in which the system is a single rigid body, one point of which is held and moved in a given way.

(iii) The surface of a rigid body belonging to the system slides on a smooth surface which is fixed or which has an inexorable motion. The action of the smooth surface on the body is a force of constraint.

(iv) The surface of a rigid body belonging to the system rolls without sliding on a surface which is fixed or which has an inexorable motion. In such cases we conventionally speak of *perfectly rough* surfaces. The action of the rough surface on the body is a force of constraint.

(v) The thrust or tension in a rod joining two particles of the system, when the length of the rod is *a prescribed function of the time*, provides a pair of forces which belong to the category of forces of constraint. The action and reaction on the two particles are equal and opposite, and in any virtual displacement the components of displacement of the two particles in the direction of the rod are equal.

The simplest and most familiar case, of course, is that in which the distance between the two particles is invariable. This includes the important case of the internal reactions on the particles of a rigid body, for the system of internal reactions can be built up of equal and opposite reactions between pairs of particles.

In a virtual displacement the rigid body remains rigid. There is no reason why we should not, in some other context, contemplate a displacement in which the rigid body is distorted. But we must remember that in such a displacement it is no longer true that the internal reactions as a whole do no work.

Another example to be mentioned at this point is the action and reaction at a point when two rigid bodies of the system are hinged together. The action and reaction (i.e. the two forces considered together, not each one separately) belong to the category of forces of constraint.

(vi) A particle belonging to the system slides on the smooth surface of a rigid body belonging to the system. The action and reaction between the particle and the body belong to the class of forces of constraint.

(vii) The action and reaction between the smooth surfaces in contact of two rigid bodies belonging to the system are forces of constraint.

(viii) The action and reaction between the perfectly rough surfaces in contact of two rigid bodies belonging to the system are forces of constraint.

(ix) The list just given is not exhaustive; it merely enumerates the cases that most commonly occur. Any forces called into play by less familiar types of constraint belong to the category of forces of constraint provided they satisfy the crucial condition that, as a whole, they do no work in an arbitrary virtual displacement of the system.

2.5 The idea of a dynamical system. The definition of a dynamical system that we have given is a generalization based on particular concrete cases. It should be noticed however that there is some latitude of choice in this generalization—it is not something exactly and inevitably determined by the nature of things in the physical world. The choice we have made is on the whole the most useful, giving rise to a theory just powerful enough to deal with the types of problem in which we are interested. But it may be of interest to see how the definition of a dynamical system could have been varied to give either a wider or a narrower scope.

The scope of the definition could have been made wider in various ways.

(i) We have assumed that all the forces acting on the particles of the system are either given forces or forces of constraint. We could have adopted a wider definition to include systems for which this is not true. A conspicuous example is provided by a particle sliding on an imperfectly rough surface. The reaction of the surface on the particle is determined by the rule that the tangential component is in a direction directly opposite to the direction of motion, and its magnitude is μ times the normal component, where μ is a physical constant depending on the nature of the surface at the point. (In most practical problems it is assumed that the multiplier μ has the same value at all points of the surface.) The reaction of the surface on the particle is neither a given force nor a force of constraint, and this problem is therefore excluded from the theory expounded in this book. (But that does not mean that such problems cannot be solved!)

(ii) The constraints to which the system is subject have been defined by equations, but we might also have included constraints defined by inequalities. Such constraints are called *unilateral.* A simple example of a unilateral constraint is provided by a particle sliding on a smooth horizontal table, where we allow the possibility of the particle leaving the table (but exclude the possibility of penetrating the table). If we take the axis of z vertically upwards we have a constraint defined by the inequality $\dot{z} \geqslant 0$. The definition we have adopted excludes unilateral constraints, and systems involving such constraints cannot be handled immediately by the methods expounded in this book. (But we may be able to devise a modification suitable for the purpose.)

(iii) We have assumed that the equations of constraint are of the form

(2.5.1) $$f(x_1, x_2, \dots, x_N;\ \dot{x}_1, \dot{x}_2, \dots, \dot{x}_N;\ t) = 0,$$

where the functions f are linear in $\dot{x}_1, \dot{x}_2, \dots, \dot{x}_N$ (see 2.2.5), and that the equations for the virtual displacements are derived from the equations for the possible displacements (see 2.2.9). We could abandon the restriction to linear functions, allowing the functions f in (2.5.1) to have a more general form. In that case we should need independent equations, not immediately derivable from the equations of constraint, to define the class of virtual displacements; these equations would have the form (2.2.9).

(iv) We could replace the assumption that the forces of constraint do no work in an arbitrary virtual displacement by a wider assumption, e.g. that the work done by these forces in an arbitrary virtual displacement is measured by the scalar product of the displacement with an additional given force intrinsic to the system. The equation

(2.2.10) $$\sum_{s=1}^{N} X_s' \,\delta x_s = 0$$

would be replaced by an equation of the form

(2.5.2) $$\sum_{s=1}^{N} X_s' \,\delta x_s = \sum_{s=1}^{N} X_s'' \,\delta x_s,$$

where the components X_s'' are given functions of the x's, the $\dot{x}$'s, and t.

The scope of the definition of a dynamical system could have been made narrower in (at least) two ways.

(i) We could restrict the discussion to systems which are *catastatic* (§ 2.3) and for which the coefficients A_{rs} are not functions of t. Our equations of constraint (2.2.4) would then be replaced by the system

(2.5.3) $$\sum_{s=1}^{N} A_{rs} \,dx_s = 0, \qquad r = 1, 2, \dots, L,$$

where the coefficients A_{rs} are functions of $(x_1, x_2, \dots, x_N)$.

(ii) We could restrict the discussion to *holonomic* systems. The equations of constraint would be L equations

$$f_r(x_1, x_2, \ldots, x_N; t) = c_r. \tag{2.2.8}$$

This restriction would simplify the theory, but would exclude many important and interesting problems.

In this book we shall take as our definition of a dynamical system the definition given in § 2.2. It is easy to see how the theory would be modified if we accepted the restrictions just mentioned, not quite so easy to see what would be the effect of allowing the larger liberty described at the beginning of this section.

Chapter III

The first form of the fundamental equation

3.1 The fundamental equation. We consider the general dynamical system defined in § 2.2. We have the N equations of motion

$$(2.2.12) \qquad m_r \ddot{x}_r = X_r + X_r', \qquad r = 1, 2, \ldots, N,$$

and the forces of constraint X_r' satisfy the condition

$$(2.2.10) \qquad \sum_{r=1}^{N} X_r' \, \delta x_r = 0$$

for an arbitrary virtual displacement $\delta x_1, \delta x_2, \ldots, \delta x_N$. We derive immediately *the fundamental equation* for a dynamical system

$$(3.1.1) \qquad \sum_{r=1}^{N} (m_r \ddot{x}_r - X_r) \, \delta x_r = 0,$$

valid for an arbitrary virtual displacement. It is a generalization both of the principle of Virtual Work in statics, and of d'Alembert's principle for a single rigid body. The importance of the equation lies in the fact that it does not contain the forces of constraint. The significance of this was first realized by Lagrange, who discovered the equation in or about 1760.

The equation is the basis of the succeeding theory. We shall need to express the equation in a number of different forms, and we shall therefore refer to (3.1.1) as *the first form of the fundamental equation.*

The fundamental equation can also be derived very simply from the equations of motion (2.2.13) established in § 2.2. If we multiply the rth equation

$$(2.2.13) \qquad m_r \ddot{x}_r = X_r + \sum_{m=1}^{L} \lambda_m A_{mr}, \qquad r = 1, 2, \ldots, N,$$

by δx_r, and sum for $r = 1$ to $r = N$, we obtain

$$(3.1.2) \qquad \sum_{r=1}^{N} (m_r \ddot{x}_r - X_r) \, \delta x_r = \sum_{m=1}^{L} \lambda_m \left(\sum_{r=1}^{N} A_{mr} \, \delta x_r \right).$$

If $\delta x_1, \delta x_2, \ldots, \delta x_N$ is a virtual displacement the second member vanishes in virtue of (2.2.9), and we recover (3.1.1).

In accordance with the notation introduced in § 2.2 we can also write the fundamental equation (3.1.1) in the form

$$(3.1.3) \qquad S\{(m\ddot{x} - X) \, \delta x + (m\ddot{y} - Y) \, \delta y + (m\ddot{z} - Z) \, \delta z\} = 0,$$

or, using the abridged notation, in the form

$$(3.1.4) \qquad \sum (m\ddot{x} - X) \, \delta x = 0.$$

We repeat the warning that the abridged notation should only be used when it is clear that a summation over the N coordinates is implied.

We devote the present Chapter to the immediate applications of (3.1.1).

3.2 The conservation of momentum. It may happen that among the virtual displacements is included a displacement in which the whole system is shifted, as if rigid, and without rotation, parallel to the axis of x. Then in (3.1.3) we can write, for each particle,

(3.2.1) $$\delta x = a, \qquad \delta y = 0, \qquad \delta z = 0,$$

where a is an arbitrary real number, and (3.1.3) leads to

(3.2.2) $$Sm\ddot{x} = SX.$$

But this result can be simplified. We can omit from the second member all internal forces, since these consist of equal and opposite pairs, and we find

(3.2.3) $$Sm\ddot{x} = S'X,$$

where S' denotes a summation over those of the given forces that are external forces.

The reader is no doubt already familiar with the closely related theorem in which the second member of (3.2.3) is replaced by a summation over *all* the external forces. In (3.2.3) the external forces which are forces of constraint do not appear, and their omission is justified by the fact that the class of virtual displacements for the system includes (3.2.1).

The simplest case of (3.2.3) is that in which $S'X = 0$, and then (3.2.3) becomes

(3.2.4) $$Sm\ddot{x} = 0.$$

If this holds, not merely at a particular instant but for all time, we deduce

(3.2.5) $$Sm\dot{x} = \text{constant}.$$

This is the theorem of *the conservation of momentum.* Since

(3.2.6) $$Smx = (Sm)\xi,$$

where ξ, η, ζ are the coordinates of the centre of gravity (centre of mass) G of the system, we can write (3.2.5) in the equivalent form

(3.2.7) $$\dot{\xi} = \text{constant}.$$

An important special case is that in which the system is a single rigid body moving in space; if the sum of the x-components of the given forces is zero the x-component of the velocity of G is constant. Another important special case occurs in the problem of ν bodies; here all the given forces are internal, and the centre of gravity has uniform rectilinear motion. We can in fact use a Newtonian base in which the centre of gravity is at rest.

Similarly it may happen that the class of virtual displacements includes an infinitesimal rotation of the whole system, as if rigid, about the axis Oz. We can then write in (3.1.3) for each particle

(3.2.8) $$\delta x = -y\,\delta\theta, \qquad \delta y = x\,\delta\theta, \qquad \delta z = 0,$$

and we obtain

(3.2.9) $$Sm(x\ddot{y} - y\ddot{x}) = S(xY - yX).$$

Again we can omit all internal forces from the second member, and write

(3.2.10) $$Sm(x\ddot{y} - y\ddot{x}) = S'(xY - yX).$$

In particular if the sum of the moments of the external given forces about Oz is zero we have

(3.2.11) $$Sm(x\ddot{y} - y\ddot{x}) = 0,$$

and if this holds for all time

(3.2.12) $$Sm(x\dot{y} - y\dot{x}) = \text{constant}.$$

The equation (3.2.12) is the theorem of *the conservation of angular momentum*. The simplest example is that of a particle moving in the plane $z = 0$ under a central force through O. The conditions required are clearly fulfilled, and we have

(3.2.13) $$x\dot{y} - y\dot{x} = \text{constant}.$$

Geometrically this result implies that the rate of sweeping out of area by the radius vector is constant, which is the *theorem of areas*. Another example in which (3.2.13) holds is that of a particle sliding under gravity on a smooth surface of revolution which has a vertical axis Oz; the most familiar case is the problem of the *spherical pendulum* where the surface is a sphere with its centre on Oz.

3.3 The catastatic system and the first form of the equation of energy. When the system is catastatic—i.e. when the coefficients A_r in (2.2.4) are all identically zero—the class of virtual velocities coincides with the class of possible velocities. In particular the actual velocity of the system is a virtual velocity, and we can write $\dot{x}_r$ for δx_r in the fundamental equation (3.1.1). We obtain the equation

(3.3.1) $$\sum_{r=1}^{N} m_r\dot{x}_r\ddot{x}_r = \sum_{r=1}^{N} X_r\dot{x}_r,$$

or

(3.3.2) $$\frac{dT}{dt} = \sum_{r=1}^{N} X_r\dot{x}_r,$$

where

(3.3.3) $$T = \frac{1}{2}\sum_{r=1}^{N} m_r\dot{x}_r^2.$$

T is called the *kinetic energy function* of the system. We can also write the formula for T in the forms

(3.3.4) $$T = \tfrac{1}{2}Sm(\dot{x}^2 + \dot{y}^2 + \dot{z}^2),$$

(3.3.5) $$T = \tfrac{1}{2}\sum m\dot{x}^2,$$

which are equivalent to (3.3.3). The kinetic energy is formed by multiplying the mass of each particle by the square of its speed, summing over the particles, and taking one-half of the result.

The equation (3.3.2) is the first, or primitive, form of the equation of energy. It expresses the fact that the rate of increase of the kinetic energy is equal to the rate of working of the given forces. The equation holds for any catastatic system, even for systems for which the coefficients A_{rs} in the equations of constraint depend upon t.

3.4 Conservative forces and the second form of the equation of energy. Hitherto we have thought of the x's as the actual coordinates at time t in some particular motion of the system. The x's were functions of t that we wished to determine. Let us now consider instead the whole field of values of the x's, not merely a sequence of values chosen by the motion of the system. The x's now take on, for the moment, the role of independent variables.

Suppose now that the given forces $X_1, X_2, \ldots, X_N$ depend only on the x's, not on the $\dot{x}$'s nor on t. We shall find that in many problems the Pfaffian form $\sum_{r=1}^{N} X_r\, dx_r$ (which appears in the fundamental equation (3.1.1)) is the complete differential of a uniform (one-valued) function $-V$ of $x_1, x_2, \ldots, x_N$,

$$\sum_{r=1}^{N} X_r\, dx_r = -dV. \tag{3.4.1}$$

In this case we say that the given forces are *conservative* (or that the dynamical system is conservative) and we call the function V the *potential energy function* of the given forces (or of the system). If the given forces are conservative, and we consider an arbitrary closed curve in the N-fold space of $\mathbf{x}$, we have

$$\oint \sum_{r=1}^{N} X_r\, dx_r = 0. \tag{3.4.2}$$

The result (3.4.2) follows immediately from (3.4.1). It is easy to see that, conversely, the existence of a function V satisfying (3.4.1) is implied by (3.4.2); in fact the value of V at the point P of the space is the value of the integral $-\int \sum_{r=1}^{N} X_r\, dx_r$ along an arbitrary path from a fixed origin O to P.

When the system is conservative, the fundamental equation (3.1.1) can be written

$$\sum_{r=1}^{N} m_r \ddot{x}_r\, \delta x_r + \delta V = 0. \tag{3.4.3}$$

A simple example of a conservative system, containing only one particle, has been encountered already in § 1.2. Another simple example is that of a particle moving in space in the field $-\nabla V$. If the field is a uniform field $-mg$ in the direction Oz the potential energy is

$$V = mgz,$$

and if the field is an attraction $\varphi(r)$ to the origin O, where $r = \sqrt{(x^2 + y^2 + z^2)}$, we have

$$V = \int^r \varphi(\xi)\, d\xi.$$

Particular cases are (i) the isotropic oscillator, where $\varphi(r) = mn^2 r$, $V = \frac{1}{2}mn^2r^2$, and (ii) the Newtonian attraction, where $\varphi(r) = \mu m/r^2$, $V = -\mu m/r$. In all these cases there is a constant of integration which can be given any convenient value; in practice we are only interested in the change in V when the system moves from one configuration to another. For systems containing many particles a familiar example of conservative force is the attraction between two particles when this attraction is a function of r, the distance between the particles. Explicitly, if the attraction is $\varphi(r)$, the contribution to V of these forces of attraction is $\int^r \varphi(\xi)\, d\xi$. In particular, if $\varphi(r) = k(r - a)$, the contribution to V is $\frac{1}{2}k(r - a)^2$; and if $\varphi(r)$ is of the Newtonian type $\gamma Mm/r^2$, the contribution to V is $-\gamma Mm/r$. For three particles under their mutual gravitational attractions, we have

$$V = -\gamma\left(\frac{m_2 m_3}{r_{23}} + \frac{m_3 m_1}{r_{31}} + \frac{m_1 m_2}{r_{12}}\right),$$

where m_1, m_2, m_3 are the masses of the particles, and r_{ij} is the distance between m_i and m_j. The extension to the problem of ν bodies is immediate.

Let us now return to the catastatic dynamical system, and let us suppose that the given forces are conservative, the potential energy function being V. Let us substitute in V the values of $x_1, x_2, \ldots, x_N$ at time t in a particular motion of the system. The symbol V now represents, not the value at a general point, but the value at the particular point occupied at time t, the potential energy of the system at time t. Then

$$\frac{dV}{dt} = \sum_{r=1}^{N} \frac{\partial V}{\partial x_r}\dot{x}_r = -\sum_{r=1} X_r \dot{x}_r,$$

and (3.3.2) leads to

$$\frac{d}{dt}(T + V) = 0, \tag{3.4.4}$$

whence

$$T + V = h, \tag{3.4.5}$$

where h is a constant. *Equation (3.4.5) is the second, or classical, form of the equation of energy, or integral of energy.* For a catastatic system under the action of conservative given forces the sum of the kinetic and potential energies of the system remains constant during any motion of the system; the value of h for a particular motion is determined by the initial conditions.

The manifold $V = h$ in the N-fold space of $x_1, x_2, \ldots, x_N$, is called the *energy level* for the motion under discussion. Since $T \geqslant 0$ the mobile is confined throughout the motion to the region $V \leqslant h$.

It may seem surprising at first sight that the classical form of the energy equation is still valid for a system in which the coefficients A_{rs} in the equations of constraint involve t; and though these coefficients do not contain t in most cases of practical interest, a simple concrete illustration of a system in which they do contain t may be of interest. Let us consider the problem of a particle of mass m moving in a plane under the action of a uniform field $(0, mg)$, the particle being subject to the constraint $t\,dx - dy = 0$. Let us suppose that the particle is projected from the origin at $t = 0$ with velocity $(u, 0)$. The equations of motion are

$$m\ddot{x} = X', \quad m\ddot{y} = mg + Y', \tag{3.4.6}$$

and we have also the relations

$$X' + tY' = 0, \quad \dot{y} = t\dot{x}. \tag{3.4.7}$$

The integration is elementary, and leads to the formulae

$$x = g \sinh\theta + (u - g)\theta, \quad y = \tfrac{1}{2}g\sinh^2\theta + (u - g)(\cosh\theta - 1), \tag{3.4.8}$$

where $\sinh\theta = t$. The verification of the energy equation

$$\tfrac{1}{2}m(\dot{x}^2 + \dot{y}^2) - mgy = \tfrac{1}{2}mu^2 \tag{3.4.9}$$

is simple.

Before leaving the classical form of the equation of energy it may be noticed that we have in fact assumed more about the functions X_r $(= X_r(\mathbf{x}))$ than is strictly necessary. We have assumed that $\sum_{r=1}^{N} X_r\, dx_r$ is a perfect differential for an arbitrary variation $dx_1, dx_2, \ldots, dx_N$, whereas it will suffice if we assume this to be true for an arbitrary displacement of the system. (Fundamentally we are concerned with an arbitrary *virtual* displacement, but here we can omit the adjective "virtual" since we are dealing with a catastatic system in which virtual and possible displacements coincide.) A simple illustration may serve to clarify this point. Suppose that we have a particle moving in space in a field of force X, Y, Z. We can, in virtue of Pfaff's theorem, express the Pfaffian form $X\,dx + Y\,dy + Z\,dz$ in the form $-dV + \theta\, d\varphi$, where V, θ and φ are functions of (x, y, z). There is not in general an equation of energy of the classical form (3.4.5). But if the system is subject to the constraint

$$d\varphi = 0 \tag{3.4.10}$$

then for an arbitrary (virtual) displacement we have

$$X\,dx + Y\,dy + Z\,dz = -dV, \tag{3.4.11}$$

and the classical integral of energy (3.4.5) still stands.

Finally we may notice that we shall occasionally meet with systems in which the given forces $X_1, X_2, \ldots, X_N$ depend on t as well as on $\mathbf{x}$, and for which

$$\sum_{r=1}^{N} X_r\, dx_r = -d_s V, \tag{3.4.12}$$

where $V = V(x_1, x_2, \ldots, x_N, t)$, and the symbol $d_s V$ represents the space-differential $\sum_{r=1}^{N} \frac{\partial V}{\partial x_r}\, dx_r$ with t unvaried. (A simple example is provided by a magnetic particle moving in a uniform magnetic field whose intensity varies with the time.) There is no integral of energy of the classical form; but we shall find that the property expressed by (3.4.12) leads to a simplification of the equations of motion (§ 6.5).

3.5 The third form of the equation of energy. It may happen that the given forces as a whole do not constitute a conservative system, but that the system can be built up as the sum of two systems, one of which *is* conservative. In this case we can write

$$X_r = X_{r1} + X_{r2}, \tag{3.5.1}$$

where the component X_{r1} is a function of $x_1, x_2, \ldots, x_N$, and the system composed of the terms X_{r1} is conservative, so that

$$\sum_{r=1}^{N} X_{r1}\, dx_r = -dV. \tag{3.5.2}$$

In this case the equation (3.3.2) for the catastatic system becomes

$$\begin{aligned} \frac{dT}{dt} &= \sum_{r=1}^{N} X_{r1}\dot{x}_r + \sum_{r=1}^{N} X_{r2}\dot{x}_r \\ &= -\frac{dV}{dt} + \sum_{r=1}^{N} X_{r2}\dot{x}_r, \end{aligned}$$

whence

$$\frac{d}{dt}(T + V) = \sum_{r=1}^{N} X_{r2}\dot{x}_r. \tag{3.5.3}$$

This is the third form of the equation of energy. It clearly implies each of the other two forms as particular cases. It expresses the fact that the rate of change of the total energy, kinetic and potential, of the system is equal to the rate of working of the remaining forces, i.e. of the forces not accounted for in the potential energy V. We have here a hint of a new outlook on the problem, in which the dynamical system and the conservative forces are thought of as constituting a single physical entity to which the remaining forces are extraneous.

3.6 The conservation of energy. The result expressed by the classical integral of energy (3.4.5) is a famous and far-reaching one which will play an important part in our subject. Its implications extend beyond the classical dynamics into the whole realm of physics. For example, we think of the work done in stretching a string as energy stored up in the string. If one end of the string is fixed, and the other attached to a particle, this store of energy is drawn upon, and converted into kinetic energy of the particle, when the string is allowed to relax. The generalization of the *conservation of energy* occupies so central a position in our thought about the physical world that when we encounter a dynamical problem in which the energy is not conserved we prefer to say, not that energy has been destroyed, but that it has been converted into a form (such as heat) other than the kinetic energy and the potential energy of the dynamical system. Nevertheless, in spite of the overwhelming importance of the principle in physics as a whole, we must be careful not to attribute to the equation (3.4.5) a deeper import than it merits. It is just one first integral, of a strikingly simple form, of the equations of motion.

3.7 Hamilton's principle. We can derive at once from the fundamental equation the beautiful theorem known as Hamilton's principle. We consider the motion of the dynamical system in the interval of time from t_0 to t_1. Consider now at each instant a virtual displacement $(\delta x_1, \delta x_2, \ldots, \delta x_N)$ from the position $(x_1, x_2, \ldots, x_N)$ occupied in the actual motion. The virtual displacement is arbitrary, save that its components $\delta x_1, \delta x_2, \ldots, \delta x_N$ are functions of t of class C_2 which vanish at t_0 and at t_1. We may speak of the sequence of configurations $\mathbf{x} + \delta\mathbf{x}$ as the varied path; but we must be careful not to assume that this is a possible path, i.e. that it satisfies the equations of constraint. In fact in general the varied path is not possible if the system is not a holonomic system (§ 3.8).

We denote by δT the change in T from its value in the actual motion at the instant t to its value at the same instant in the varied path. Thus, using the abridged notation (§ 2.2),

$$\delta T = \tfrac{1}{2}\sum m\{(\dot{x} + \delta\dot{x})^2 - \dot{x}^2\}$$

$$= \sum m\dot{x}\,\delta\dot{x} + \tfrac{1}{2}\sum m\,\delta\dot{x}^2,$$

where the summation is over the N coordinates. Let us now suppose that δx and $\delta\dot{x}$ are small, of order ε, and that terms of order ε^2 may be neglected. To the requisite order of approximation

$$\delta T = \sum m\dot{x}\,\delta\dot{x}, \tag{3.7.1}$$

and, since the variations are contemporaneous,

$$\delta\dot{x} = \frac{d}{dt}\,\delta x. \tag{3.7.2}$$

Hence

$$\int_{t_0}^{t_1} \delta T\, dt = \int_{t_0}^{t_1} \sum m\dot{x}\, \delta\dot{x}\, dt$$

$$= \int_{t_0}^{t_1} \sum m\dot{x} \frac{d}{dt}(\delta x)\, dt$$

$$= \sum m\dot{x}\, \delta x \Big|_{t_0}^{t_1} - \int_{t_0}^{t_1} \sum m\ddot{x}\, \delta x\, dt.$$

The first term on the right vanishes, since δx vanishes at t_0 and at t_1, and thus

(3.7.3) $$\int_{t_0}^{t_1} (\delta T + \sum X\, \delta x)\, dt = -\int_{t_0}^{t_1} \{\sum (m\ddot{x} - X)\, \delta x\}\, dt.$$

The integrand in the second member vanishes at each instant in virtue of the fundamental equation (3.1.1), since $\delta \mathbf{x}$ is a virtual displacement, and we arrive at the conclusion

(3.7.4) $$\int_{t_0}^{t_1} (\delta T + \sum X\, \delta x)\, dt = 0.$$

This is Hamilton's principle. If the given forces are conservative we can write (3.7.4) in the form

(3.7.5) $$\int_{t_0}^{t_1} \delta(T - V)\, dt = 0.$$

In applying the principle we must remember that the terminal points are fixed, and so are the instants of departure and arrival.

We have proved that if we start with the actual motion, and vary the path in the way described, then (3.7.4) is true, i.e. it is a *necessary* condition for the motion. In fact the condition is also *sufficient*. If $\mathbf{x}(t)$ is a geometrically possible motion of the system, i.e. a path in the N-fold satisfying (2.2.5), and if (3.7.4) holds for an arbitrary variation of the type prescribed, then the original motion is the actual (*dynamically* possible) motion of the system. To prove this we notice that (3.7.4) implies the vanishing of the second member of (3.7.3) for all variations $\delta \mathbf{x}$ of the prescribed type. Now, since the rank of the matrix (A_{rs}) in (2.2.9) is L, the most general virtual displacement $\delta \mathbf{x}$ at time t is a linear combination of k independent displacements $\delta \mathbf{x}^{(1)}, \delta \mathbf{x}^{(2)}, \ldots, \delta \mathbf{x}^{(k)}$, so that the rth component δx_r of $\delta \mathbf{x}$ can be written

(3.7.6) $$\delta x_r = \sum_{s=1}^{k} \lambda_s\, \delta x_r^{(s)}.$$

Thus

(3.7.7) $$\int_{t_0}^{t_1} \left\{ \sum_{s=1}^{k} \lambda_s \left[\sum_{r=1}^{N} (m_r \ddot{x}_r - X_r)\, \delta x_r^{(s)} \right] \right\} dt = 0.$$

Now the multipliers λ are arbitrary functions of t, save for the conditions of being continuous in $[t_0, t_1]$ and vanishing at t_0 and t_1, so the coefficient of each λ in the integrand must vanish. This implies that, at each instant, the fundamental equation (3.1.1) is satisfied, and therefore the original motion is a dynamically possible motion.

If the system is holonomic we may write, instead of (3.7.5),

(3.7.8) $$\delta \int_{t_0}^{t_1} (T - V)\, dt = 0.$$

In this case the value of the integral $\int_{t_0}^{t_1} (T - V)\, dt$ for the actual motion is stationary in comparison with its value for neighbouring motions with the same termini and the same times of departure and arrival. But if the system is not holonomic the shift from (3.7.5) to (3.7.8) cannot be made, unless indeed (3.7.8) is interpreted, somewhat artificially, as being equivalent to (3.7.5). If the system is not holonomic, and we interpret (3.7.8) in the more natural way, as meaning that the integral $\int_{t_0}^{t_1} (T - V)\, dt$ is stationary in comparison with neighbouring geometrically possible paths with the same termini and the same times of departure and arrival, then the statement (3.7.8) is not true. We shall return to this point in Chapter XXVI.

Hamilton's principle is of great theoretical interest, but it is not of great practical value for dealing with concrete problems. It is, in essence, merely an integrated form of the fundamental equation. The results that are sometimes found by application of the principle to particular systems, and quoted as illustrations of its power, can usually be found more expeditiously by direct application of the fundamental equation itself. The two problems considered later in § 3.9, both concerned with continuous systems, illustrate this remark. The results deduced in § 3.9 from the fundamental equation can also be deduced from Hamilton's principle, but, as the reader will easily verify, the deduction from the fundamental equation is more concise.

3.8 The varied path. The varied path produced in Hamilton's principle is not in general a possible path if the system is not holonomic; that is to say, the system cannot travel along the varied path without violating the constraints. To prove this statement it will suffice to consider a simple concrete example.

Suppose we have a particle moving in space, and subject to the constraint

$$\omega \equiv a\, dx + b\, dy + c\, dz = 0, \tag{3.8.1}$$

where a, b, and c are functions of (x, y, z) of class C_1, and the Pfaffian form ω does not admit an integrating factor. The original orbit surely satisfies the condition (3.8.1), and so by hypothesis do the variations from it, so we have

$$a\dot{x} + b\dot{y} + c\dot{z} = 0, \tag{3.8.2}$$

$$a\, \delta x + b\, \delta y + c\, \delta z = 0, \tag{3.8.3}$$

and the question is: Does the varied path also satisfy the condition? Let us assume provisionally that it does, i.e. we assume that

$$\delta(a\dot{x} + b\dot{y} + c\dot{z}) = 0. \tag{3.8.4}$$

Now (3.8.3) is satisfied at each instant, so

$$\frac{d}{dt}(a\, \delta x + b\, \delta y + c\, \delta z) = 0. \tag{3.8.5}$$

Subtracting (3.8.4) from (3.8.5) we find, in virtue of (3.7.2),

$$\left(\frac{da}{dt}\, \delta x - \dot{x}\, \delta a\right) + \left(\frac{db}{dt}\, \delta y - \dot{y}\, \delta b\right) + \left(\frac{dc}{dt}\, \delta z - \dot{z}\, \delta c\right) = 0. \tag{3.8.6}$$

If we write (3.8.6) *in extenso* we obtain

(3.8.7)

$$\left(\frac{\partial c}{\partial y} - \frac{\partial b}{\partial z}\right)(\dot{y}\, \delta z - \dot{z}\, \delta y) + \left(\frac{\partial a}{\partial z} - \frac{\partial c}{\partial x}\right)(\dot{z}\, \delta x - \dot{x}\, \delta z) + \left(\frac{\partial b}{\partial x} - \frac{\partial a}{\partial y}\right)(\dot{x}\, \delta y - \dot{y}\, \delta x) = 0.$$

But, from (3.8.2) and (3.8.3),

$$\frac{\dot{y}\, \delta z - \dot{z}\, \delta y}{a} = \frac{\dot{z}\, \delta x - \dot{x}\, \delta z}{b} = \frac{\dot{x}\, \delta y - \dot{y}\, \delta x}{c},$$

so (setting aside the trivial case in which $\delta x/\dot{x} = \delta y/\dot{y} = \delta z/\dot{z}$, and the displacement is along the orbit itself) we find, from (3.8.6) and (3.8.7),

$$a\left(\frac{\partial c}{\partial y} - \frac{\partial b}{\partial z}\right) + b\left(\frac{\partial a}{\partial z} - \frac{\partial c}{\partial x}\right) + c\left(\frac{\partial b}{\partial x} - \frac{\partial a}{\partial y}\right) = 0. \tag{3.8.8}$$

But (3.8.8) is false, since (3.8.1) is not integrable. The assumption that the varied path is geometrically possible leads to a contradiction.

If the system is holonomic the difficulty does not arise, and the varied path is always possible.

3.9 Continuous systems. In the classical dynamics we are concerned with systems having a finite number of degrees of freedom, and it is with such systems that we shall be mainly concerned in this book. Nevertheless it is natural to suppose, on physical grounds, that the fundamental equation will also hold for continuous systems, where the number of degrees of freedom is infinite—for example systems involving fluids in motion and vibrating strings. In such problems the summation occurring in the fundamental equation will be replaced by an integration. The present brief digression is concerned with problems of this type.

(i) Consider then a problem of classical hydrodynamics. We have a mass of perfect (inviscid) incompressible liquid, acted on by given forces, and confined by inner and outer boundaries which are fixed or which have an inexorable motion. The motion of the boundaries must be such as to leave unvaried the volume enclosed, a condition which is automatically satisfied if the boundaries are rigid surfaces.

But now a puzzle confronts us. The motion of the liquid is completely determined by the motion of the boundaries, whatever given forces act on the liquid. What then can the fundamental equation tell us about the motion that we do not know independently?

The answer is that it establishes the existence of a pressure function by which the internal stress in the liquid is completely described.

The fundamental equation, adapted to a form that is suitable for a continuous system, is

$$\int \rho\{(f - X)u + (g - Y)v + (h - Z)w\}\, d\tau = 0, \tag{3.9.1}$$

where ρ is the density of the liquid (not necessarily uniform), f, g, h are components of acceleration, X, Y, Z are components of the given force per unit mass of the liquid, u, v, w are components of an arbitrary virtual velocity, and the integration extends through the space occupied by the liquid. The equation (3.9.1) can be written compactly, in vector notation, in the form

$$\int (\mathbf{P} \,.\, \mathbf{U})\, d\tau = 0, \tag{3.9.2}$$

where $\mathbf{P}$ is the vector $\{\rho(f - X), \rho(g - Y), \rho(h - Z)\}$, and the virtual velocity $\mathbf{U}$ is such that div $\mathbf{U} = 0$, and the normal component U_n vanishes on the boundary surface S. If we put

$$\mathbf{U} = \text{curl}\, \mathbf{A}, \tag{3.9.3}$$

the equation of continuity is satisfied, and if we put

$$\mathbf{A} = \theta\, \nabla\varphi, \tag{3.9.4}$$

where θ and φ are scalar functions of class C_2, we have

(3.9.5) $$\mathbf{U} = \operatorname{curl} \mathbf{A} = \nabla\theta \times \nabla\varphi.$$

The stream-lines in the virtual velocity (in which the boundary surfaces are fixed) are the intersections of the surfaces θ = constant and φ = constant, so we can be sure that U_n vanishes on S if we choose for θ a function that vanishes on S.

The fundamental equation (3.9.2) now takes the form

(3.9.6) $$\int (\mathbf{P} \,.\, \operatorname{curl} \mathbf{A})\, d\tau = 0.$$

Now in virtue of the relation

(3.9.7) $$\operatorname{div} (\mathbf{P} \times \mathbf{A}) = \mathbf{A} \,.\, \operatorname{curl} \mathbf{P} - \mathbf{P} \,.\, \operatorname{curl} \mathbf{A},$$

the equation (3.9.6) leads to

(3.9.8) $$\int (\mathbf{A} \,.\, \operatorname{curl} \mathbf{P})\, d\tau = \int \operatorname{div} (\mathbf{P} \times \mathbf{A})\, d\tau,$$

and the integral on the right vanishes, since it is equal to the integral of the normal component of $\mathbf{P} \times \mathbf{A}$ over the boundary S, and this is zero since $\mathbf{A}$ vanishes on S. Thus

(3.9.9) $$\int \theta(\nabla\varphi \,.\, \operatorname{curl} \mathbf{P})\, d\tau = 0,$$

and this equation holds for all functions θ which are of class C_2 and which vanish on S. Hence

(3.9.10) $$\nabla\varphi \,.\, \operatorname{curl} \mathbf{P} = 0$$

at each point of the liquid. It follows easily that

(3.9.11) $$\operatorname{curl} \mathbf{P} = 0$$

throughout the liquid. (For example, we can take $\varphi = x$, and then (3.9.10) shows that the x-component of curl $\mathbf{P}$ vanishes.)

Now since (3.9.11) is satisfied at each point of the space occupied by the liquid, there exists a scalar function p such that

(3.9.12) $$\mathbf{P} = -\operatorname{grad} p,$$

and hence

(3.9.13) $$\begin{cases} f = X - \dfrac{1}{\rho}\dfrac{\partial p}{\partial x}, \\[2ex] g = Y - \dfrac{1}{\rho}\dfrac{\partial p}{\partial y}, \\[2ex] h = Z - \dfrac{1}{\rho}\dfrac{\partial p}{\partial z}. \end{cases}$$

These are the equations of motion for the liquid, and p is the pressure function.

(ii) Consider as a second example of a continuous system the problem of a vibrating string. We take the problem of a uniform and slightly elastic string, stretched at a large tension P between its two ends, which are held fixed at $x = 0$ and $x = l$ on the axis Ox. The string is assumed to be perfectly flexible, and to execute small transverse oscillations in the plane $z = 0$. The tension is sensibly constant throughout the motion.

Making the appropriate modification of the equation (3.4.3) for the continuous system we have

$$\rho \int_0^l \ddot{y}\, \delta y\, dx + \delta V = 0, \tag{3.9.14}$$

where ρ is the (constant) mass per unit length, and $y(x, t)$ is the transverse displacement of the string. The equation (3.9.14) holds at any instant $t = t_1$, and the virtual displacement $\delta y(x)$ is of class C_2 in $0 \leqslant x \leqslant l$, and δy vanishes at $x = 0$ and at $x = l$. Now

$$\delta V = P\, \delta\lambda, \tag{3.9.15}$$

where λ is the length of the string in its displaced form at the instant t_1, and

$$\lambda = \int_0^l \sqrt{(1 + y'^2)}\, dx, \tag{3.9.16}$$

where y' stands for $\partial y/\partial x$. Thus (3.9.14) becomes

$$\rho \int_0^l \ddot{y}\, \delta y\, dx + P \int_0^l y'\, \delta y'\, dx = 0. \tag{3.9.17}$$

Now $\delta y' = \dfrac{\partial}{\partial x} \delta y$, so integrating by parts, and remembering that $\delta y = 0$ at $x = 0$ and at $x = l$, we have

$$\int_0^l (\ddot{y} - c^2 y'')\, \delta y\, dx = 0, \tag{3.9.18}$$

where $c^2 = P/\rho$, and y'' stands for $\partial^2 y/\partial x^2$. This holds, at every instant t_1, for an arbitrary choice of δy of the prescribed form, so $y(x, t)$ must satisfy the differential equation

$$\frac{\partial^2 y}{\partial t^2} = c^2 \frac{\partial^2 y}{\partial x^2}. \tag{3.9.19}$$

This is the *wave equation*, and the whole theory of the transverse vibrations follows from it.

We have derived the equation for a string of finite length l, but the equation holds also for an infinite or semi-infinite string. The name, the wave equation, comes from the fact that it is satisfied by $f(x - ct)$, where $f(x)$ is any function of class C_2: the solution

$$y = f(x - ct) \tag{3.9.20}$$

represents a wave travelling along the string in the direction of increasing x. The solution

$$y = f(x + ct) \tag{3.9.21}$$

represents a wave travelling in the opposite direction.

Chapter IV

The second and third forms of the fundamental equation

4.1 The second form of the fundamental equation. In any possible motion of the system the equations of constraint

(2.2.5) $$\sum_{s=1}^{N} A_{rs}\dot{x}_s + A_r = 0, \qquad r = 1, 2, \ldots, L,$$

are satisfied. Consider another possible velocity

$$\dot{x}_1 + \Delta\dot{x}_1, \quad \dot{x}_2 + \Delta\dot{x}_2, \ldots, \dot{x}_n + \Delta\dot{x}_n,$$

from the same configuration at the same instant. We have also

(4.1.1) $$\sum_{s=1}^{N} A_{rs}(\dot{x}_s + \Delta\dot{x}_s) + A_r = 0, \qquad r = 1, 2, \ldots, L.$$

From the two equations we derive immediately

(4.1.2) $$\sum_{s=1}^{N} A_{rs}\,\Delta\dot{x}_s = 0, \qquad r = 1, 2, \ldots, L.$$

The (finite) velocity-variations $\Delta\dot{x}_1, \Delta\dot{x}_2, \ldots, \Delta\dot{x}_N$ satisfy the equations (2.2.9) for the virtual displacements, and we may write $\Delta\dot{x}_r$ in place of δx_r in the fundamental equation (3.1.1). We thus obtain the equation

(4.1.3) $$\sum_{r=1}^{N} (m_r\ddot{x}_r - X_r)\,\Delta\dot{x}_r = 0,$$

and this is *the second form of the fundamental equation.* We can also write the result in the form

(4.1.4) $$S\{(m\ddot{x} - X)\,\Delta\dot{x} + (m\ddot{y} - Y)\,\Delta\dot{y} + (m\ddot{z} - Z)\,\Delta\dot{z}\} = 0.$$

In the second form of the fundamental equation we suppose configuration and time to be given, and consider the difference—finite, not infinitesimal—between any two velocity-systems which are possible with the given configuration at the given instant. The simplest case is that in which $\Delta\dot{\mathbf{x}}$ is an *infinitesimal* variation from the actual velocity to a neighbouring possible velocity.* But it is important to observe that the theorem holds in the more general case when $\Delta\dot{\mathbf{x}}$ is the *finite* difference between any two possible velocity-systems.

As a simple and immediate application of (4.1.3) we can derive again the equation of energy for the catastatic system. For we can substitute the actual velocity $\dot{\mathbf{x}}$ for $\Delta\dot{\mathbf{x}}$ in (4.1.3), and (3.3.2) follows immediately.

The most important application of the second form of the fundamental equation occurs in the theory of impulsive motion, which will be considered in Chapter XIV.

* This case of the result was given by P. E. B. Jourdain in 1908.

4.2 The third form of the fundamental equation. In any possible motion of the system the equations of constraint

$$(2.2.5)\qquad \sum_{s=1}^{N} A_{rs}\dot{x}_s + A_r = 0, \qquad r = 1, 2, \ldots, L,$$

are valid at each instant. If we differentiate with respect to t we obtain

$$(4.2.1)\qquad \sum_{s=1}^{N}\left(A_{rs}\ddot{x}_s + \frac{dA_{rs}}{dt}\dot{x}_s\right) + \frac{dA_r}{dt} = 0, \qquad r = 1, 2, \ldots, L,$$

where the operator $\frac{d}{dt}$ stands for

$$(4.2.2)\qquad \frac{\partial}{\partial t} + \sum_{i=1}^{N}\dot{x}_i\frac{\partial}{\partial x_i}.$$

If then we consider two possible motions with the same configuration at the instant t *and the same velocity*, but with different accelerations, $\ddot{\mathbf{x}}$ in the one case and $\ddot{\mathbf{x}} + \Delta\ddot{\mathbf{x}}$ in the other, we have in addition to (4.2.1)

$$(4.2.3)\qquad \sum_{s=1}^{N}\left\{A_{rs}(\ddot{x}_s + \Delta\ddot{x}_s) + \frac{dA_{rs}}{dt}\dot{x}_s\right\} + \frac{dA_r}{dt} = 0, \qquad r = 1, 2, \ldots, L.$$

It follows from (4.2.1) and (4.2.3) that

$$\sum_{s=1}^{N} A_{rs}\,\Delta\ddot{x}_s = 0, \qquad r = 1, 2, \ldots, L.$$

Thus the (finite) acceleration-variations $\Delta\ddot{x}_1, \Delta\ddot{x}_2, \ldots, \Delta\ddot{x}_N$ satisfy the equations (2.2.9) for the virtual displacements, and we may write $\Delta\ddot{x}_r$ for δx_r in the fundamental equation (3.1.1). We thus obtain the equation

$$(4.2.4)\qquad \sum_{r=1}^{N}(m_r\ddot{x}_r - X_r)\,\Delta\ddot{x}_r = 0,$$

and this is *the third form of the fundamental equation.* We can also write the result in the form

$$(4.2.5)\qquad S\{(m\ddot{x} - X)\,\Delta\ddot{x} + (m\ddot{y} - Y)\,\Delta\ddot{y} + (m\ddot{z} - Z)\,\Delta\ddot{z}\} = 0.$$

In the third form of the fundamental equation we suppose configuration and velocity and time to be given, and consider the difference—finite, not infinitesimal—between any two acceleration-systems which are possible with the given configuration and velocity at the given instant. The simplest case is that in which $\Delta\ddot{\mathbf{x}}$ is an *infinitesimal* variation from the actual acceleration to a neighbouring possible acceleration.* But it is important to observe that the theorem holds in the more general case when $\Delta\ddot{\mathbf{x}}$ is the *finite* difference between any two possible acceleration-systems.

It may be helpful at this point to review the conditions contemplated in the three forms we have found of the fundamental equation. In the first form we consider an infinitesimal virtual displacement from a given configuration. In the second form the configuration is not varied, and we use the difference, not necessarily small, between any two possible velocities. In the third form both coordinates and velocities are unvaried, and we use the difference, not necessarily small, between any two possible accelerations.

* In this form the principle was used by Gauss and by Gibbs.

4.3 Gauss's principle of Least Constraint. We suppose the configuration and velocity of the system at time t to be prescribed, and we consider

$$C = \frac{1}{2}\sum_{r=1}^{N} m_r\left(\ddot{x}_r - \frac{X_r}{m_r}\right)^2 \tag{4.3.1}$$

regarded as a function of $\ddot{x}_1, \ddot{x}_2, \ldots, \ddot{x}_N$; the values of $\ddot{\mathbf{x}}$ considered are those that are possible to the system with the given configuration and the given velocity. Gauss's principle is that, in this class of values of $\ddot{\mathbf{x}}$, *C is a minimum for the actual acceleration.* In other words, the value of C is less for the actual acceleration than for any other possible acceleration.

This beautiful and powerful theorem was discovered by Gauss in 1829. The proof is simple. If $\ddot{\mathbf{x}}$ represents the actual acceleration, and $\ddot{\mathbf{x}} + \Delta\ddot{\mathbf{x}}$ represents any other possible acceleration, we have, using the abridged notation,

$$\begin{aligned} \Delta C &= \tfrac{1}{2}\sum m\left\{\left(\ddot{x} + \Delta\ddot{x} - \frac{X}{m}\right)^2 - \left(\ddot{x} - \frac{X}{m}\right)^2\right\} \\ &= \tfrac{1}{2}\sum m(\Delta\ddot{x})^2 + \sum (m\ddot{x} - X)\,\Delta\ddot{x}, \end{aligned} \tag{4.3.2}$$

and the last term vanishes in virtue of (4.2.4). Thus

$$\Delta C > 0 \tag{4.3.3}$$

unless $\Delta\ddot{\mathbf{x}}$ is zero.

To find the equations of motion for a given system we need only the less powerful result that C is *stationary* for the actual motion. The first-order condition

$$\delta C = 0 \tag{4.3.4}$$

will suffice to establish the equations of motion.

Notice that in Gauss's principle we are concerned with the simple algebraic problem of minimizing a quadratic form. The procedure enables us to find the differential equations that determine the motion.

4.4 Applications of Gauss's principle. Gauss's principle is closely related to the Gibbs-Appell equations of motion, which we shall consider in Chapters XII and XIII, and the solution of more complicated problems is best considered in that context. For the present therefore we content ourselves with some very simple concrete illustrations.

Example 4.4*A*. *Atwood's machine.* Two particles, whose masses are M and m, are joined by a light inextensible string passing over a smooth peg; the particles move in the vertical line through the peg. To find the motion.

If f is the acceleration of M downwards and of m upwards we have

$$C = \tfrac{1}{2}\{M(f - g)^2 + m(-f - g)^2\}, \tag{4.4.1}$$

whence

$$(M + m)C = \tfrac{1}{2}\{(M + m)f - (M - m)g\}^2 + 2Mmg^2. \tag{4.4.2}$$

We get the minimum value for C when

$$f = \frac{M - m}{M + m}g, \tag{4.4.3}$$

so the acceleration has this constant value. We can get the result even more simply from the equation

$$\frac{\partial C}{\partial f} = 0,$$

which is the first-order condition for a stationary value of C.

Example 4.4*B*. *Monkey and counterpoise.* The mass m fixed to the string in Atwood's machine is replaced by a monkey of mass m who climbs the string, his displacement relative to the string at time t being a given function $\varphi(t)$ of class C_2. We suppose that the system is initially at rest, and that $\varphi(0) = \dot{\varphi}(0) = 0$.

If z is the height of the monkey m (regarded as a particle) and ζ the height of the counterpoise M at time t, we have

$$C = \tfrac{1}{2}\{m(\ddot{z} + g)^2 + M(\ddot{\zeta} + g)^2\}, \tag{4.4.4}$$

and since (taking $z = \zeta = 0$ at $t = 0$) $z + \zeta = \varphi$ we have

$$C = \tfrac{1}{2}m(\ddot{z} + g)^2 + \tfrac{1}{2}M(\ddot{\varphi} - \ddot{z} + g)^2. \tag{4.4.5}$$

We have to find $\ddot{z}$ to minimize C, and the required value is

$$(M + m)\ddot{z} = M\ddot{\varphi} + (M - m)g. \tag{4.4.6}$$

So far we have simply found $\ddot{z}$ to minimize (4.4.5). The equation (4.4.6) obtained by this method is a differential equation for z, and the solution is

$$(M + m)z = M\varphi + \tfrac{1}{2}(M - m)gt^2. \tag{4.4.7}$$

In the particular case $M = m$ we have $z = \zeta = \tfrac{1}{2}\varphi$; the monkey is always at the same level as the counterpoise.

Example 4.4*C*. *Particle on wedge.* A wedge, of mass M, slides on a table, and a particle of mass m slides on the face of the wedge. The face is inclined at an angle α to the table. All the surfaces are smooth, and motion takes place in a vertical plane through a line of greatest slope. To determine the motion.

If f is the acceleration of the wedge at time t, f' the acceleration of the particle relative to the wedge at the same instant, we have

$$C = \tfrac{1}{2}Mf^2 + \tfrac{1}{2}m\{(f' \cos\alpha - f)^2 + (f' \sin\alpha - g)^2\}. \tag{4.4.8}$$

The equations $\partial C/\partial f = 0$, $\partial C/\partial f' = 0$ lead to the values

$$\frac{f}{m\cos\alpha} = \frac{f'}{M + m} = \frac{g\sin\alpha}{M + m\sin^2\alpha}, \tag{4.4.9}$$

and both f and f' are constant, independent of t.

4.5 The physical significance of Gauss's principle. Consider the system at time t with a given configuration $(x_1, x_2, \ldots, x_N)$ and a given velocity $(\dot{x}_1, \dot{x}_2, \ldots, \dot{x}_N)$. The problem is to find the acceleration-components $\ddot{x}_1, \ddot{x}_2, \ldots, \ddot{x}_N$.

Let a be the position of a typical particle at time t, and c its position at time $t + dt$, in the actual motion. Let b be the position that the particle would occupy at time $t + dt$ if there were no constraints, i.e. if only the given forces acted. (Of course the configuration of the positions b is not possible in general.) Then the x-component of ac is approximately

$$\dot{x}\,dt + \tfrac{1}{2}\ddot{x}\,dt^2, \tag{4.5.1}$$

and the x-component of ab is approximately

$$\dot{x}\,dt + \frac{1}{2}\frac{X}{m}\,dt^2. \tag{4.5.2}$$

Thus

$$2Sm(bc)^2 = dt^4C, \tag{4.5.3}$$

and the physical meaning of Gauss's principle is that the actual acceleration minimizes $2Sm(bc)^2$: it has a value smaller than it would have if the acceleration had any other value. If, following Gauss, we take the sum $2Sm(bc)^2$ as a measure of the departure of the system from the motion that it would have if there were no constraints, we can say that the motion keeps as near as it can to the unconstrained motion.

Chapter V

Lagrangian coordinates

5.1 The idea of Lagrangian coordinates. So far we have worked always with the Cartesian coordinates of the particles of the system. We must now, in order to make further progress, free ourselves from this restriction, and introduce coordinates of a more general type. It is worth while to notice at the outset that the introduction of such coordinates may itself give rise to difficulties—difficulties of an algebraic nature connected with the choice of coordinates rather than with the dynamics. We must take care to distinguish between phenomena of nature and mere properties of the coordinate system that we choose to employ.

The idea of Lagrangian coordinates is as follows. We choose n parameters $q_1, q_2, \ldots, q_n$ whose values at time t determine the configuration of the system at that instant. The Cartesian coordinates $x_1, x_2, \ldots, x_N$ of the individual particles are certain functions of the q's and of t. (In most cases the x's will be functions of the q's only, not of t.) The coordinates $q_1, q_2, \ldots, q_n$ are to be so chosen that the values of the q's represent all possible configurations of the system, not merely a sequence from among the possible configurations.

We shall find that if the system is holonomic we can choose n equal to k, the number of freedoms. If the system is not holonomic this is no longer possible. For a non-holonomic system the smallest value for n is $k + l$, where l is an invariant of the system implicit in the equations of constraint.

We shall consider later (§ 5.7 and § 5.8) the formal theory of the transition from the Cartesian to the Lagrangian coordinates. But in the meanwhile we may notice that in practice a suitable choice of Lagrangian coordinates usually suggests itself naturally. We can use Lagrangian coordinates for particular problems without any appeal to the formal theory for the general dynamical system.

As concrete examples of Lagrangian coordinates we may consider the following systems.

(i) *The simple pendulum.* A heavy particle moves without friction on a circle in a vertical plane. To realize the constraint, we may think of a bead sliding on a smooth wire bent into the form of a circle of radius a; or we may think of a particle attached to one end of a light rod of length a, the other end of the rod being fixed at O, and the rod being free to swing about O in a vertical plane. We specify the position of the particle on the circle by its angular distance θ from the lowest point of the circle. The Cartesian coordinates (x, y) of the particle are expressed in terms of the Lagrangian coordinate θ by the equations

$$x = a \sin \theta, \quad y = a \cos \theta, \tag{5.1.1}$$

where Ox is horizontal, and Oy is vertically downwards.

(ii) *Central orbit.* A particle moves in a plane under the action of a force directed always to the origin O. We use as Lagrangian coordinates the polar coordinates r, θ.

The Cartesian coordinates (x, y) are given as functions of the Lagrangian coordinates by the formulae

$$x = r\cos\theta, \quad y = r\sin\theta. \tag{5.1.2}$$

(iii) *Spherical pendulum.* A heavy particle P slides, under the action of gravity, on the smooth surface of a sphere of radius a with its centre at O. We use as Lagrangian coordinates the polar angles θ, φ, where θ is the angular distance of OP from the upward vertical Oz, and φ is the azimuthal angle between the plane POz and the coordinate plane xOz. Here

$$x = a\sin\theta\cos\varphi, \quad y = a\sin\theta\sin\varphi, \quad z = a\cos\theta. \tag{5.1.3}$$

(iv) *A rigid lamina* moves in a plane. We take as Lagrangian coordinates the coordinates ξ, η of the centre of gravity (centre of mass) G of the lamina referred to axes fixed in the plane, and the angle θ that a line Gx' fixed in the lamina makes with the axis Ox fixed in the plane. If the coordinates of a particle of the lamina with respect to axes Gx', Gy' fixed in the lamina are a, b, we have

$$\begin{cases} x = \xi + a\cos\theta - b\sin\theta, \\ y = \eta + a\sin\theta + b\cos\theta. \end{cases} \tag{5.1.4}$$

(v) *A rigid body* moves in space. The system is a holonomic system with six freedoms, and we can choose as Lagrangian coordinates the coordinates ξ, η, ζ of the centre of gravity G, referred to fixed rectangular axes $Oxyz$, and three angles θ_1, θ_2, θ_3 defining the orientation of the body. We take a rectangular trihedral $G123$ fixed in the body (usually $G1$, $G2$, $G3$ will be principal axes of inertia at G) and we introduce the matrix of direction cosines $\mathbf{l}$,

$$\mathbf{l} = \begin{pmatrix} l_1 & m_1 & n_1 \\ l_2 & m_2 & n_2 \\ l_3 & m_3 & n_3 \end{pmatrix}, \tag{5.1.5}$$

in which the elements of the first row are direction cosines of $G1$ with repect to $Oxyz$, the elements of the second row are direction cosines of $G2$, and the elements of the third row are direction cosines of $G3$. The elements of $\mathbf{l}$ are known functions of $(\theta_1, \theta_2, \theta_3)$; the explicit values for two ways of choosing θ_1, θ_2, θ_3 will be found later (§ 7.11). For a particle of the body whose coordinates in the trihedral $G123$ are a, b, c we have

$$\begin{cases} x = \xi + l_1 a + l_2 b + l_3 c, \\ y = \eta + m_1 a + m_2 b + m_3 c, \\ z = \zeta + n_1 a + n_2 b + n_3 c. \end{cases} \tag{5.1.6}$$

We can write (5.1.6) in the matrix form

$$\mathbf{x} = \boldsymbol{\xi} + \mathbf{l}'\mathbf{a}, \tag{5.1.7}$$

where $\mathbf{x}$ is the vector $\{x, y, z\}$, $\boldsymbol{\xi}$ is the vector $\{\xi, \eta, \zeta\}$, $\mathbf{a}$ is the vector $\{a, b, c\}$ and $\mathbf{l}'$ is the transpose of $\mathbf{l}$.

Sometimes we shall find it convenient to use a different notation, writing $GABC$ for the trihedral fixed in the body (instead of $G123$); and sometimes it will be convenient to use a different notation for the elements of $\mathbf{l}$ as follows:

$$\mathbf{l} = \begin{pmatrix} l_{11} & l_{12} & l_{13} \\ l_{21} & l_{22} & l_{23} \\ l_{31} & l_{32} & l_{33} \end{pmatrix}. \tag{5.1.8}$$

(vi) So far, in the examples (i)–(v), we have been concerned entirely with holonomic systems, and in each case we have chosen the number n of Lagrangian coordinates equal to k, the number of freedoms of the dynamical system. We conclude this section with a simple example of a non-holonomic system.

A rod P_1P_2 moves in a plane, the motion being constrained by a smooth constraint in such a way that the motion of P_1 is in the direction P_1P_2 (cf. § 2.1). We choose as Lagrangian coordinates the coordinates x_1, y_1 of P_1 (referred to rectangular axes Oxy fixed in the plane) and the inclination θ of P_1P_2 to Ox. The possible displacements satisfy the equation (cf. (2.1.10))

$$\cos\theta\, dy_1 - \sin\theta\, dx_1 = 0. \tag{5.1.9}$$

This equation does not admit an integrating factor. The system has two degrees of freedom ($k = 2$, $l = 1$) but we need three Lagrangian coordinates ($n = k + l = 3$). The Cartesian coordinates of a particle of the rod at distance a from P_1 are

$$x = x_1 + a\cos\theta, \qquad y = y_1 + a\sin\theta. \tag{5.1.10}$$

We remind the reader that although the system has only two degrees of freedom a threefold infinity of configurations is accessible from a given configuration—in fact, any configuration is accessible from any other. This we have proved already (§ 2.1).

5.2 Some classical problems. Later (§ 6.2) we shall establish Lagrange's equations of motion for a dynamical system described by Lagrangian coordinates. But already, even without Lagrange's equations, we have in our hands tools sufficient to deal with a number of famous and important problems. We choose five of these as illustrations. The first four (*Examples* 5.2*A*, 5.2*B*, 5.2*C*, and § 5.3) are such that we only need to appeal to the principles of the conservation of energy (3.4.5) and the conservation of angular momentum (3.2.12). For the fifth problem (§§ 5.4, 5.5, 5.6) we use also the equations of motion for Cartesian axes.

Example 5.2*A*. *The simple pendulum.* The particle moves without friction on a circle of radius a in a vertical plane. The system is a holonomic system with one freedom, and we choose as Lagrangian coordinate the angular displacement θ from the lowest point of the circle. The given force is the weight of the particle, the force of constraint is the normal reaction of the wire (if we think of the particle as a bead sliding on a smooth wire) or the tension in the rod (if the particle is attached to one end of a light rod whose other end is fixed). The potential energy is mgz, where z is the height of the particle above the centre of the circle. The equation of energy is

$$\tfrac{1}{2}ma^2\dot{\theta}^2 - mga\cos\theta = h. \tag{5.2.1}$$

We write $h = mga\eta$, so that η is dimensionless, and $a\eta$ is the height of the energy level λ above the centre of the circle (Fig. 5.2*a*). Then (5.2.1) takes the form

$$\tfrac{1}{2}\dot{\theta}^2 = n^2(\eta + \cos\theta), \qquad n^2 = g/a, \tag{5.2.2}$$

which is an equation of the type (1.2.10) whose solution we have already studied. No motion is possible if $\eta < -1$, so there are four cases, as we see by considering the graph of the second member of (5.2.2) in Fig. 5.2*b*, as follows:

(i) $\eta = -1$, the particle rests in stable equilibrium at $\theta = 0$;
(ii) $-1 < \eta < 1$, there is a libration motion between $-\alpha$ and α, the typical pendulum to-and-fro motion;
(iii) $\eta = 1$, the particle rests in unstable equilibrium at $\theta = \pi$, or there is a limitation motion in which $\theta \to \pi$ (or $-\pi$) as $t \to \infty$;
(iv) $\eta > 1$, θ increases continually with t (assuming $\dot{\theta} > 0$ initially).

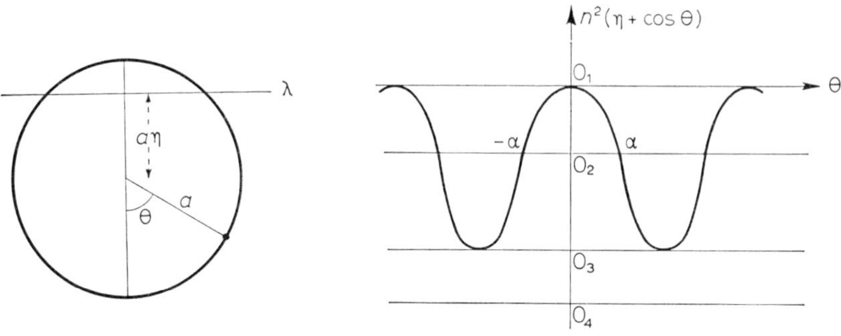

Figure 5.2*a* Figure 5.2*b*

We now consider the various cases in greater detail.

(i) If we increase η from -1 to $-1 + \delta\eta$ there is a small oscillation about $\theta = 0$ with period $2\pi/n$ and amplitude $\sqrt{(2\,\delta\eta)}$ (cf. *Example* 1.2*A*).

(ii) $\eta = -\cos\alpha$, $\quad \frac{1}{2}\dot{\theta}^2 = n^2(\cos\theta - \cos\alpha) = 2n^2(\sin^2\frac{1}{2}\alpha - \sin^2\frac{1}{2}\theta)$.

If we put

$$\sin\tfrac{1}{2}\theta = \sin\tfrac{1}{2}\alpha \sin\varphi$$

we find

$$\dot{\varphi}^2 = n^2(1 - k^2\sin^2\varphi), \qquad k = \sin\tfrac{1}{2}\alpha, \tag{5.2.3}$$

and, taking $\theta = \varphi = 0$ at $t = 0$, the solution is

$$\sin\varphi = \text{sn}\, nt. \tag{5.2.4}$$

Thus finally

$$\sin\tfrac{1}{2}\theta = \sin\tfrac{1}{2}\alpha\, \text{sn}\, nt = k\, \text{sn}\, nt, \tag{5.2.5}$$

where $k^2 = \frac{1}{2}(1 + \eta) = (\omega/2n)^2$, and ω is the angular velocity when $\theta = 0$. The period σ is $4K/n$. We notice that σ increases steadily from $2\pi/n$ to ∞ as α increases from 0 to π.

(iii) $\eta = 1$. Let us consider the limitation motion, taking $\theta = 0$, $\dot{\theta} > 0$, at $t = 0$. We have

$$\dot{\theta}^2 = 2n^2(1 + \cos\theta) = 4n^2\cos^2\tfrac{1}{2}\theta,$$

whence

$$\frac{d}{dt}(\tfrac{1}{2}\theta) = n\cos\tfrac{1}{2}\theta,$$

and

$$nt = \log(\sec\tfrac{1}{2}\theta + \tan\tfrac{1}{2}\theta). \tag{5.2.6}$$

We can put this into more convenient forms. Since

$$\sec\tfrac{1}{2}\theta + \tan\tfrac{1}{2}\theta = e^{nt},$$

we have

$$\sec\tfrac{1}{2}\theta - \tan\tfrac{1}{2}\theta = e^{-nt},$$

whence

$$\sec\tfrac{1}{2}\theta = \cosh nt, \qquad \tan\tfrac{1}{2}\theta = \sinh nt,$$

and finally

$$\sin\tfrac{1}{2}\theta = \tanh nt. \tag{5.2.7}$$

The last form (5.2.7) is probably the most convenient. We observe that (as we know already from the general theory) $\theta \to \pi$ as $t \to \infty$.

If we put $\theta = \pi - \theta'$, $\tan\frac{1}{2}\theta' = 1/(\sinh nt)$, and approximately $\theta' = 4e^{-nt}$.

(iv) $\eta > 1$. Here $\quad \frac{1}{2}\dot{\theta}^2 = n^2(\eta + 1 - 2\sin^2\frac{1}{2}\theta) = 2\dfrac{n^2}{k^2}(1 - k^2\sin^2\frac{1}{2}\theta)$,

where $k^2 = \dfrac{2}{1+\eta} = \left(\dfrac{2n}{\omega}\right)^2$, and finally

$$\sin\tfrac{1}{2}\theta = \operatorname{sn}\frac{1}{k}(nt), \tag{5.2.8}$$

again taking $\theta = 0$ at $t = 0$.

The motion is periodic. It is true that θ increases always, but θ is a *cyclic coordinate*; the values θ, $\theta + 2\pi$, $\theta + 4\pi, \ldots$ are equivalent, since they all represent the same configuration of the system. The period is $2kK/n$.

We can summarize the three cases (ii), (iii), (iv) as follows:

$$\begin{cases} \text{(ii)} & -1 < \eta < 1, & \sin\frac{1}{2}\theta = k \operatorname{sn} nt, & k^2 = \dfrac{1+\eta}{2} = \dfrac{\omega}{2n}, \\ \text{(iii)} & \eta = 1, & \sin\frac{1}{2}\theta = \tanh nt, & \\ \text{(iv)} & \eta > 1, & \sin\frac{1}{2}\theta = \operatorname{sn}\dfrac{1}{k}(nt), & k^2 = \dfrac{2}{1+\eta} = \dfrac{2n}{\omega}. \end{cases} \tag{5.2.9}$$

In conclusion we notice the second order differential equation controlling the motion

$$\ddot{\theta} + n^2\sin\theta = 0, \tag{5.2.10}$$

which we can deduce from (5.2.1) or establish directly by elementary methods. Conversely we readily deduce (5.2.1) from (5.2.10). If we consider a small oscillation about the position of stable equilibrium, $\theta = 0$, the equation approximates to the equation of harmonic motion

$$\ddot{\theta} + n^2\theta = 0, \tag{5.2.11}$$

and the period is approximately $2\pi/n$, as we have noticed already.

For the motion defined by (5.2.10) the variation of θ with t for different positive values of ω is illustrated in Fig. 5.2*c*. For values of ω greater than the critical value $2n$, θ increases always with t. In these cases we can substitute for a value of θ in the interval $[(2n - 1)\pi, (2n + 1)\pi]$ the congruent value in the interval $(-\pi, \pi)$, which represents the same point on the circle, and in the diagram this substitution has been used.

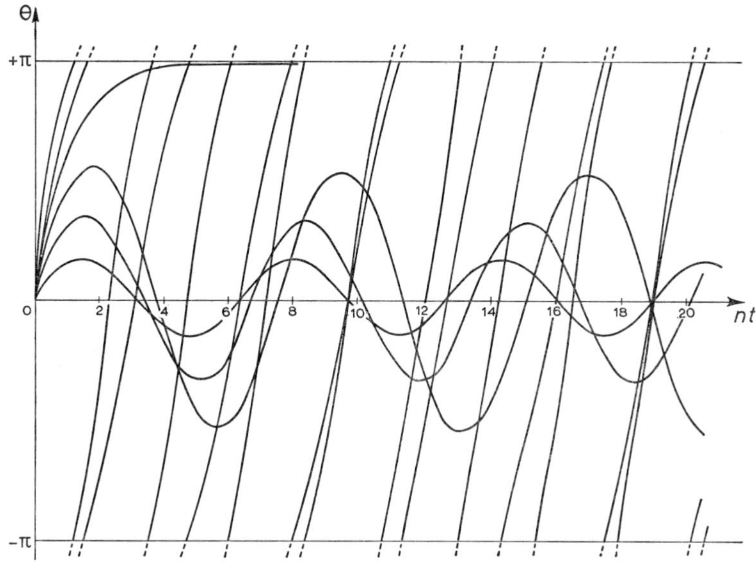

Figure 5.2c

Approximation to the period. In case (ii), where the pendulum swings to-and-fro with amplitude α, the period is $4K/n$, with $k = \sin \frac{1}{2}\alpha$. This is exact; but there are various ways of approximating to the period without using elliptic functions.

The first point to notice is that the period for small oscillations, $2\pi/n$, is a good approximation to the period if α is reasonably small. If the amplitude is an acute angle α

(5.2.12) $$\tfrac{1}{2}\dot{\theta}^2 = n^2(\cos\theta - \cos\alpha) = n^2\int_\theta^\alpha \sin x\, dx = n^2\int_\theta^\alpha \frac{\sin x}{x}\, x\, dx.$$

Consider a quarter-period in which θ and $\dot{\theta}$ are positive. As x increases from 0 to α, $\sin x/x$ decreases steadily from 1 to $\sin\alpha/\alpha$, so for a given θ

(5.2.13) $$\tfrac{1}{2}\dot{\theta}^2 < n^2\int_\theta^\alpha x\, dx = \tfrac{1}{2}n^2(\alpha^2 - \theta^2),$$

and

(5.2.14) $$\tfrac{1}{2}\dot{\theta}^2 > n^2\frac{\sin\alpha}{\alpha}\int_\theta^\alpha x\, dx = \frac{\sin\alpha}{\alpha}\,\tfrac{1}{2}n^2(\alpha^2 - \theta^2).$$

Thus the quarter-period

(5.2.15) $$\tfrac{1}{4}\sigma = \int_0^\alpha \frac{d\theta}{\dot{\theta}}$$

lies between

(5.2.16) $$\frac{1}{n}\int_0^\alpha \frac{d\theta}{\sqrt{(\alpha^2 - \theta^2)}} \quad \text{and} \quad \sqrt{\left(\frac{\alpha}{\sin\alpha}\right)}\frac{1}{n}\int_0^\alpha \frac{d\theta}{\sqrt{(\alpha^2 - \theta^2)}},$$

and therefore σ lies between

(5.2.17) $$\frac{2\pi}{n} \quad \text{and} \quad \frac{2\pi}{n}\sqrt{\left(\frac{\alpha}{\sin\alpha}\right)}.$$

If the amplitude is 5°, $\sqrt{\left(\dfrac{\alpha}{\sin\alpha}\right)}$ is approximately 1.0007, and the classical value $2\pi/n$ differs from the true period by less than one part in 1000.

A more accurate estimate is obtained from an interesting theorem concerning arithmetic and geometric means. Two infinite sequences $\{a_r\}$ and $\{b_r\}$ are defined in terms of two given numbers a and b, where $a > b > 0$, as follows: $a_0 = a$, $b_0 = b$, and, for $r \geqslant 1$, a_r is the arithmetic mean of a_{r-1} and b_{r-1}, and b_r is the geometric mean of a_{r-1} and b_{r-1}. Then $\{a_r\}$ is a monotone decreasing sequence, and $\{b_r\}$ is a monotone increasing sequence, and both sequences tend to the same limit μ as $r \to \infty$. For each value of r, $a_r > \mu > b_r$, and a_{r+1} is an approximation to μ with an error less than $\frac{1}{2}(a_r - b_r)$.

Let us now consider the integral

(5.2.18) $$J(a, b) = \int_0^{\pi/2} \frac{d\theta}{\sqrt{(a^2\cos^2\theta + b^2\sin^2\theta)}}.$$

By means of the substitution

(5.2.19) $$\sin\theta = \frac{2a\sin\varphi}{(a+b) + (a-b)\sin^2\varphi}$$

we prove that

(5.2.20) $$J(a, b) = J(a_1, b_1),$$

and proceeding similarly step by step we see that

(5.2.21) $$J(a, b) = J(a_r, b_r)$$

for all values of r. Now $J(a_r, b_r)$ lies between $\dfrac{\pi}{2a_r}$ and $\dfrac{\pi}{2b_r}$, and each of these tends to the limit $\dfrac{\pi}{2\mu}$, so

(5.2.22) $$J(a, b) = \frac{\pi}{2\mu}.$$

To estimate the rate of convergence we use the properties

(5.2.23) $$8a_{r+1}(a_r - b_r) = (a_{r-1} - b_{r-1})^2,$$

which is easily proved since each member is equal to $4(a_r^2 - b_r^2)$; and

(5.2.24) $$2(a_r \pm b_r) = (\sqrt{a_{r-1}} \pm \sqrt{b_{r-1}})^2.$$

Let us apply these results to find an approximation to the period σ_α for amplitude α $(0 < \alpha < \pi)$. If σ_0 is the period for small oscillations we have, from (5.2.3),

(5.2.25) $$\frac{\sigma_\alpha}{\sigma_0} = \frac{2}{\pi}\int_0^{\pi/2} \frac{d\theta}{\sqrt{(1 - k^2\sin^2\theta)}},$$

where $k = \sin\frac{1}{2}\alpha$, and therefore

(5.2.26) $$\frac{\sigma_\alpha}{\sigma_0} = \frac{2}{\pi}J(a, b) = \frac{1}{\mu},$$

with $a = 1$ and $b = k' = \cos\frac{1}{2}\alpha$. The first few terms of the sequences $\{a_r\}$ and $\{b_r\}$ are as follows:

$$(5.2.27)\quad \begin{cases} a_0 = 1 & b_0 = \cos\frac{1}{2}\alpha \\ a_1 = \frac{1}{2}(1 + \cos\frac{1}{2}\alpha) = \cos^2\frac{1}{4}\alpha & b_1 = (\cos\frac{1}{2}\alpha)^{1/2} \\ a_2 = \frac{1}{4}\{1 + (\cos\frac{1}{2}\alpha)^{1/2}\}^2 = \frac{1}{2}\{\cos^2\frac{1}{4}\alpha + (\cos\frac{1}{2}\alpha)^{1/2}\} & b_2 = \cos\frac{1}{4}\alpha(\cos\frac{1}{2}\alpha)^{1/4} \\ a_3 = \frac{1}{4}\{\cos\frac{1}{4}\alpha + (\cos\frac{1}{2}\alpha)^{1/4}\}^2 & \end{cases}$$

We can use $\dfrac{1}{a_r}$ or $\dfrac{1}{b_r}$ as an approximation to $\dfrac{1}{\mu}$. To estimate the relative error we define δ_r and ε_r by the equations

$$(5.2.28)\qquad \frac{1}{\mu} = \frac{1}{a_r}(1 + \delta_r) = \frac{1}{b_r}(1 - \varepsilon_r).$$

Then

$$(5.2.29)\qquad 0 < \delta_r = \frac{a_r - \mu}{\mu} < \frac{a_r - b_{r+1}}{\mu} = \frac{a_r(a_r - b_r)}{\mu(a_r + b_{r+1})} < \frac{a_r(a_r - b_r)}{2\mu a_{r+1}},$$

since $a_r^2 - b_{r+1}^2 = a_r(a_r - b_r)$, and $a_r + b_{r+1} > a_r + b_r = 2a_{r+1}$.

Taking $r = 2$, and using (5.2.23), we have

$$(5.2.30)\quad 0 < \delta_2 < \frac{a_2}{2\mu a_3}\frac{(a_1 - b_1)^2}{8a_3} = \frac{a_2}{2\mu a_3}\frac{(a_0 - b_0)^4}{8a_3(8a_2)^2} = \frac{\{\frac{1}{2}(a_0 - b_0)\}^4}{2^6\mu a_3{}^2 a_2} < \frac{N}{D},$$

where

$$(5.2.31)\quad N = \{\tfrac{1}{2}(1 - \cos\tfrac{1}{2}\alpha)\}^4 = (\sin\tfrac{1}{4}\alpha)^8,\quad D = 2^6 b_2{}^4 = 2^6(\cos\tfrac{1}{4}\alpha)^4\cos\tfrac{1}{2}\alpha.$$

Also

$$(5.2.32)\qquad 0 < \frac{\varepsilon_r}{\delta_r} = \frac{\mu - b_r}{a_r - \mu} < 1,$$

and therefore

$$(5.2.33)\qquad 0 < \varepsilon_2 < \delta_2 < \frac{1}{2^6\cos\frac{1}{2}\alpha}(\sin\tfrac{1}{4}\alpha\tan\tfrac{1}{4}\alpha)^4.$$

Let us denote the last expression in (5.2.33) by η. Now (5.2.33) holds for $0 < \alpha < \pi$, but it is useless if α is too near π. However if $0 < \alpha \leqslant \frac{1}{2}\pi$, which is the case of most interest, the last expression in (5.2.33) is greatest when $\alpha = \frac{1}{2}\pi$; in that case

$$(5.2.34)\qquad \frac{\cos^2\frac{1}{4}\alpha}{\sqrt{2}+1} = \frac{\sin^2\frac{1}{4}\alpha}{\sqrt{2}-1} = \frac{1}{2\sqrt{2}},$$

and

$$(5.2.35)\qquad \eta = \frac{\sqrt{2}}{2^9}\frac{1}{(\sqrt{2}+1)^6} = \frac{\sqrt{2}}{2^9(99 + 70\sqrt{2})} < \frac{1}{2^{10}.70},$$

since $(99)^2 - (70\sqrt{2})^2 = 1 > 0$. Thus finally

$$(5.2.36)\qquad \frac{\sigma_\alpha}{\sigma_0} = \left\{\frac{2}{1 + (\cos\frac{1}{2}\alpha)^{1/2}}\right\}(1 + \delta_2) = \frac{1}{\cos\frac{1}{4}\alpha(\cos\frac{1}{2}\alpha)^{1/4}}(1 - \varepsilon_2),$$

where

$$(5.2.37)\qquad 0 < \varepsilon_2 < \delta_2 < \eta < \tfrac{1}{70000}.$$

This is as accurate as we need for most purposes, but if desired $\dfrac{1}{a_3}$ will give a still closer approximation, with $\delta_3 < \dfrac{1}{2 \times 10^{10}}$.

Example 5.2B. Central orbit. We take the centre of attraction as origin, and choose as Lagrangian coordinates the polar coordinates r, θ of the particle. The lines of force are radial, and (since the equipotential curves are the orthogonal trajectories of the lines of force) the equipotentials are the circles $r =$ constant. The potential function is therefore a function of r, and we denote it by $m\mathfrak{V}(r)$, so that $\mathfrak{V}$ is here the potential per unit mass. The attraction $md\mathfrak{V}/dr$ is also a function of r. For a field that is everywhere an *attraction* towards O, $\mathfrak{V}(r)$ is a monotonic increasing function of r.

We have the integrals of energy and of angular momentum

(5.2.38)
$$\begin{cases} \frac{1}{2}(\dot{r}^2 + r^2\dot{\theta}^2) + \mathfrak{V} = h, \\ r^2\dot{\theta} = \alpha. \end{cases}$$

We will suppose for definiteness that α is positive, so that θ increases with t. For a field of attraction the orbit lies inside the circle $\mathfrak{V} = h$ if such a circle exists.

Eliminating $\dot{\theta}$ we find

(5.2.39)
$$\dot{r}^2 = 2h - 2\mathfrak{V} - \frac{\alpha^2}{r^2}.$$

This is an equation of the type (1.2.10), and we have already studied the solution. In the simple cases r lies initially between consecutive simple real zeros r_1, r_2 of $f(r)$, where $f(r)$ denotes the second member of (5.2.39), and $0 < r_1 < r_2$. There is a libration in r between the values r_1 and r_2, which are called the *apsidal distances*, and the orbit touches alternately the circles $r = r_1$ and $r = r_2$. The points of contact with these circles, where r attains its minimum and maximum values, are called *apses*. An apse at which $r = r_1$ is called a *perihelion*, an apse at which $r = r_2$ is called an *aphelion*. The angular velocity $\dot{\theta}$ varies between the greatest value α/r_1^2 (at perihelion) and the least value α/r_2^2 (at aphelion). The angle through which the radius vector turns between any two consecutive apses is called the *apsidal angle*.

We can write the relation between t and r in the form

(5.2.40)
$$dt = \pm \frac{dr}{\sqrt{f(r)}},$$

where the ambiguous sign is fixed by the rule given in § 1.3. Thus, if the particle is at perihelion at $t = t_0$,

(5.2.41)
$$t - t_0 = \int_{r_1}^{r} \frac{d\xi}{\sqrt{f(\xi)}},$$

where the sign of the radical in the second member, omitted here for convenience, is fixed by the rule just mentioned.

The relation between r and θ can be written in the form

(5.2.42)
$$d\theta = \frac{\alpha}{r^2}\,dt = \frac{\alpha}{r^2}\frac{dr}{\sqrt{f(r)}},$$

where the sign of the radical is again determined by the same rule. The equation of the orbit, taking $\theta = \theta_0$ at perihelion, is

(5.2.43)
$$\theta - \theta_0 = \int_{r_1}^{r} \frac{(\alpha/\xi^2)}{\sqrt{f(\xi)}}\,d\xi.$$

The apsidal angle is

(5.2.44)
$$\psi = \int_{r_1}^{r_2} \frac{(\alpha/r^2)\,dr}{\sqrt{f(r)}}.$$

The orbit is a simple closed orbit, with one perihelion and one aphelion, if $\psi = \pi$. It is periodic if ψ/π is rational, say if

$$\frac{\psi}{\pi} = \frac{p}{q}, \tag{5.2.45}$$

where p and q are integers with no common factor. The period is

$$\sigma = 2q\int_{r_1}^{r_2} \frac{dr}{\sqrt{f(r)}}. \tag{5.2.46}$$

Two special cases are of particular interest. In the isotropic oscillator the attraction is proportional to the distance from O, $\mathfrak{V} = \frac{1}{2}n^2r^2$, and the orbit is an ellipse with its centre at O. The apsidal angle is $\frac{1}{2}\pi$. For a Newtonian centre of attraction, the attraction varies inversely as the square of the distance from O, and $\mathfrak{V} = -\mu/r$. The orbit is a conic with O in one focus. It is an ellipse if the velocity of projection is less than $\sqrt{(2\mu/r_0)}$, where r_0 is the distance of the point of projection from O. The apsidal angle is π. We notice a peculiarity of both these problems, the isotropic oscillator and the Newtonian elliptic orbit; the orbit is always periodic, whatever the circumstances of projection.

We recall very briefly the details of the calculations in the two cases mentioned.

(i) *The isotropic oscillator.* Here

$$\dot{r}^2 = 2h - n^2r^2 - \frac{\alpha^2}{r^2} = \frac{n^2}{r^2}(a^2 - r^2)(r^2 - b^2), \tag{5.2.47}$$

where we write a for the aphelion distance r_2 and b for the perihelion distance r_1, $a > b > 0$. For the differential equation of the orbit we have

$$\left(\frac{dr}{d\theta}\right)^2 = \frac{\dot{r}^2}{\dot{\theta}^2} = \frac{n^2r^2}{\alpha^2}(a^2 - r^2)(r^2 - b^2). \tag{5.2.48}$$

If we put $v = \dfrac{1}{r^2}$ the differential equation of the orbit (5.2.48) becomes

$$\left(\frac{dv}{d\theta}\right)^2 = 4(v_2 - v)(v - v_1), \tag{5.2.49}$$

where $v_1 = \dfrac{1}{a^2}$ and $v_2 = \dfrac{1}{b^2}$. If we substitute

$$v = \frac{v_2 + v_1}{2} - \frac{v_2 - v_1}{2}\cos\varphi, \tag{5.2.50}$$

we find $\varphi = \pm 2(\theta - \theta_0)$, and the equation of the orbit is

$$\frac{1}{r^2} = v_2 \sin^2(\theta - \theta_0) + v_1 \cos^2(\theta - \theta_0). \tag{5.2.51}$$

If we now turn the axes through an angle θ_0 the equation of the orbit is

$$\frac{x^2}{a^2} + \frac{y^2}{b^2} = 1, \tag{5.2.52}$$

representing an ellipse with its centre at O.

The relation between position on the orbit and the time is

$$r^2\dot{r}^2 = n^2(a^2 - r^2)(r^2 - b^2), \tag{5.2.53}$$

giving

$$r^2 = a^2 \cos^2 n(t - t_0) + b^2 \sin^2 n(t - t_0). \tag{5.2.54}$$

The eccentric angle of the point on the ellipse occupied by the particle increases uniformly with the time.

For this particular problem the calculations are somewhat easier if we use Cartesian coordinates rather than polar coordinates.

(ii) *The Newtonian orbit.* Here

$$\dot{r}^2 = (2hr^2 + 2\mu r - \alpha^2)/r^2, \tag{5.2.55}$$

and in the case mentioned $h < 0$, and there is a libration in r between r_1 and r_2 $(0 < r_1 < r_2)$, where r_1 and r_2 are the zeros of $2hr^2 + 2\mu r - \alpha^2$. The differential equation of the orbit (using $dr/d\theta = \dot{r}/\dot{\theta}$) is

$$\left(\frac{1}{r^2}\frac{dr}{d\theta}\right)^2 = \left(\frac{1}{r_1} - \frac{1}{r}\right)\left(\frac{1}{r} - \frac{1}{r_2}\right). \tag{5.2.56}$$

To effect the integration we introduce a parameter ψ defined by the equation

$$\frac{1}{r} = \frac{1}{2}\left(\frac{1}{r_1} + \frac{1}{r_2}\right) + \frac{1}{2}\left(\frac{1}{r_1} - \frac{1}{r_2}\right) \cos \psi, \tag{5.2.57}$$

and we find $\left(\dfrac{d\psi}{d\theta}\right)^2 = 1$, $\psi = \pm(\theta - \theta_0)$. Thus the orbit is the curve

$$\frac{1}{r} = \frac{1}{2}\left(\frac{1}{r_1} + \frac{1}{r_2}\right) + \frac{1}{2}\left(\frac{1}{r_1} - \frac{1}{r_2}\right) \cos \theta, \tag{5.2.58}$$

when we measure θ from the perihelion. If we write, as usual,

$$r_1 = a(1 - e), \quad r_2 = a(1 + e), \tag{5.2.59}$$

the equation becomes

$$\frac{p}{r} = 1 + e \cos \theta, \tag{5.2.60}$$

where $p = a(1 - e^2)$. This represents an ellipse whose eccentricity is e and semi-latus rectum p. Since $r_1 + r_2 = -\mu/h$, the energy constant h has the value

$$h = -\mu/(2a). \tag{5.2.61}$$

The relation between position and time is

$$\dot{r}^2 = \mu(r_2 - r)(r - r_1)/(ar^2). \tag{5.2.62}$$

We introduce a parameter w defined by the equation

$$r = \tfrac{1}{2}(r_2 + r_1) - \tfrac{1}{2}(r_2 - r_1) \cos w = a(1 - e \cos w), \tag{5.2.63}$$

so that w is in fact the eccentric angle measured from the perihelion. The relation is

$$\sqrt{\left(\frac{\mu}{a}\right)}\, dt = r\, dw = a(1 - e \cos w)\, dw, \tag{5.2.64}$$

giving

$$n(t - t_0) = w - e \sin w, \tag{5.2.65}$$

where n, the *mean motion*, stands for $\sqrt{(\mu/a^3)}$. The relation (5.2.65), known as *Kepler's equation*, is the fundamental relation connecting the position on the elliptic orbit and the time.

Example 5.2C. Newton's theorem on revolving orbits. As a corollary to *Example 5.2B* we establish Newton's theorem on the effect of superposing on a given central attraction an additional attraction $m\nu/r^3$. To solve the new problem we must replace $\mathfrak{V}$ by $\mathfrak{V}_1$, where

$$\mathfrak{V}_1 = \mathfrak{V} - \frac{\nu}{2r^2}, \tag{5.2.66}$$

and $f(r)$ by $f_1(r)$, where

$$f_1(r) = 2h_1 - 2\mathfrak{V} + \frac{\nu}{r^2} - \frac{{\alpha_1}^2}{r^2}, \tag{5.2.67}$$

where h_1, α_1 are the constants of energy and of angular momentum in the new motion. Now $f_1(r)$ becomes identical with $f(r)$ if we choose h_1, α_1 to satisfy

$$h_1 = h, \quad {\alpha_1}^2 = \alpha^2 + \nu. \tag{5.2.68}$$

To see that a motion with these values of h_1 and α_1 is possible, consider an apse of the original orbit at which $r = c$ and the speed is u. If we project from the same point, at right angles to the radius vector, with speed u_1, where

$${u_1}^2 = u^2 + \nu/c^2, \tag{5.2.69}$$

then

$$\left\{\begin{aligned} h_1 &= \tfrac{1}{2}{u_1}^2 + \mathfrak{V}(c) - \frac{\nu}{2c^2} = \tfrac{1}{2}u^2 + \mathfrak{V}(c) = h,\\ {\alpha_1}^2 &= c^2{u_1}^2 = c^2u^2 + \nu = \alpha^2 + \nu,\end{aligned}\right. \tag{5.2.70}$$

and the conditions (5.2.68) are fulfilled.

If we take $t = 0$, $\theta = 0$ at the apse in both problems, the relation between t and r is the same in both. If the orbit in the original problem is given by

$$r = \varphi(\theta), \tag{5.2.71}$$

the orbit in the new problem is given by

$$r = \varphi\left(\frac{\alpha}{\alpha_1}\theta\right) = \varphi(k\theta), \tag{5.2.72}$$

where $k^2 = \dfrac{\alpha^2}{\alpha^2 + \nu} < 1$. To reach the value of r corresponding to $\theta = \theta_0$ in the first orbit the radius vector must turn through a larger angle θ_0/k in the second. The effect of the additional attraction can therefore be described as a rotation of the original orbit.

5.3 The spherical pendulum. A particle moves under the action of gravity on a smooth sphere of radius a. We take as Lagrangian coordinates the polar angles θ, φ of the radius to the particle, θ being measured from the upward vertical. The equations of energy and of angular momentum are

$$\tfrac{1}{2}ma^2(\dot{\theta}^2 + \sin^2\theta\dot{\varphi}^2) + mga\cos\theta = \text{constant} = mgah, \tag{5.3.1}$$

$$\sin^2\theta\dot{\varphi} = \text{constant} = \sqrt{(2g\alpha/a)}, \tag{5.3.2}$$

where the parameters chosen, h and α, are dimensionless; they are not the actual values of the conserved energy and angular momentum. We will suppose $\dot{\varphi} \geqslant 0$. The height of the energy level above the centre of the sphere is ah. Motion is impossible if $h < -1$, and we need $\alpha \geqslant 0$.

The procedure is very similar to that followed in *Example 5.2B*. Eliminating $\dot{\varphi}$ from (5.3.1) and (5.3.2) we find

$$\dot{\theta}^2 = \frac{2g}{a}\left(h - \cos\theta - \frac{\alpha}{\sin^2\theta}\right), \tag{5.3.3}$$

and, writing z for $\cos\theta$, this becomes

$$\frac{a}{2g}\dot{z}^2 = f(z), \tag{5.3.4}$$

where

$$f(z) = (h - z)(1 - z^2) - \alpha. \tag{5.3.5}$$

The equation (5.3.4) is the equation connecting z and t; it is of the now-familiar type (1.2.10).

To find the path on the sphere we need the relation connecting φ and z, which is

$$d\varphi = \frac{dt}{1 - z^2}\sqrt{\left(\frac{2g\alpha}{a}\right)} = \frac{\sqrt{\alpha}}{1 - z^2}\frac{dz}{\sqrt{f(z)}}. \tag{5.3.6}$$

We can sum up these results compactly in the form

$$\sqrt{\left(\frac{2g}{a}\right)}dt = \frac{dz}{\sqrt{f(z)}} = \frac{(1 - z^2)\,d\varphi}{\sqrt{\alpha}}. \tag{5.3.7}$$

We now consider the motion represented by given values of h and α. We must have $h \geqslant -1$, $\alpha \geqslant 0$. If $h = -1$ the only possible value for α is zero; in that case the particle rests at the lowest point of the sphere.

Consider now the graph of the cubic polynomial $f(z)$ (Fig. 5.3a). There is a maximum at $z = z_0$, where

$$z_0 = \tfrac{1}{3}\{h - \sqrt{(h^2 + 3)}\}. \tag{5.3.8}$$

As h increases from -1 to ∞, z_0 increases from -1 to 0. The height of the graph at z_0 is

$$f(z_0) = \psi(h) - \alpha, \tag{5.3.9}$$

where
$$\psi(h) = \frac{2}{27}\{(h^2 + 3)^{3/2} + 9h - h^3\}.$$

No motion is possible unless $f(z_0) \geqslant 0$, so we need

$$0 \leqslant \alpha \leqslant \psi(h). \tag{5.3.10}$$

A very convenient method of classifying the various possible motions is given by reference to a subsidiary diagram (Fig. 5.3b) in which (h, α) are coordinates. The curve shown is the curve $\alpha = \psi(h)$, and the permissible values of (h, α) are given by points satisfying (5.3.10), i.e. by points lying in the unshaded area and on its boundaries. As an aid to drawing the figure, we notice that

$$\psi(h) = h + \frac{1}{4h} + O\left(\frac{1}{h^3}\right) \tag{5.3.11}$$

as $h \to \infty$.

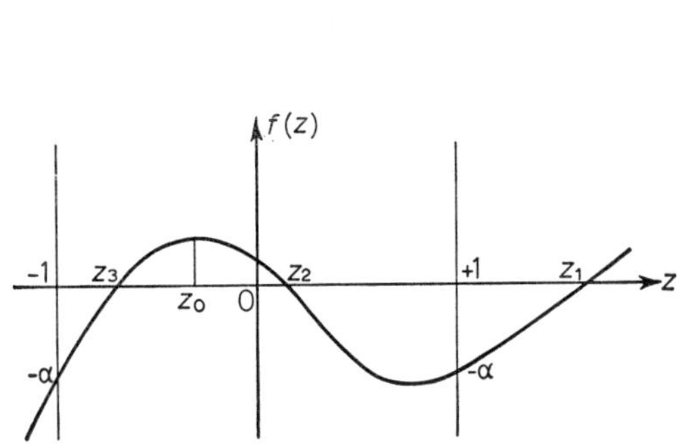

Figure 5.3a

Figure 5.3b

The classification of the orbits is now simple; there are three types corresponding to the conditions following:

$$\text{(i) } \alpha = 0, \qquad \text{(ii) } 0 < \alpha < \psi(h), \qquad \text{(iii) } \alpha = \psi(h).$$

We consider these in turn.

(i) $\alpha = 0$. This is the problem of the simple pendulum already discussed in *Example* 5.2A.

(ii) $0 < \alpha < \psi(h)$. The cubic has three real zeros (Fig. 5.3a), and

(5.3.12)
$$-1 < z_3 < z_0 < z_2 < 1 < z_1.$$

z_3 is negative, $-1 < z_3 < z_0 < 0$, z_2 may be positive or negative. The z-motion is a libration between z_3 and z_2. The path of the particle on the sphere lies in the zone between two horizontal circles, which it touches alternately. The motion is periodic if ρ is rational, where

(5.3.13)
$$\rho = \frac{1}{\pi}\int_{z_3}^{z_2} \frac{\sqrt{\alpha}\, dz}{(1 - z^2)\sqrt{f(z)}}.$$

If $\rho = p/q$, where p and q are positive integers with no common factor, the period is

(5.3.14)
$$q\sqrt{\left(\frac{2a}{g}\right)}\int_{z_3}^{z_2} \frac{dz}{\sqrt{f(z)}}.$$

For the increment in φ when z goes from z_3 to z_2 and back again to z_3 is

$$2\int_{z_3}^{z_2} \frac{\sqrt{\alpha}\, dz}{(1 - z^2)\sqrt{f(z)}},$$

and the orbit is periodic if this is a rational multiple of 2π, say $(p/q)2\pi$; the period is the time required for q oscillations from z_3 to z_2 and back to z_3.

Let us now find the explicit relation between t and z. We have

(5.3.15)
$$z'^2 = 4(z - z_1)(z_1 - z_2)(z - z_3),$$

where z' is written for $dz/d\tau$, and τ is a new dimensionless time-variable, $\tau = \sqrt{\left(\frac{g}{2a}\right)}t$.

We write (5.3.15) in the form

(5.3.16)
$$\left\{\frac{d}{d\tau}\left(z - \frac{h}{3}\right)\right\}^2$$
$$= 4\left\{\left(z - \frac{h}{3}\right) - \left(z_1 - \frac{h}{3}\right)\right\}\left\{\left(z - \frac{h}{3}\right) - \left(z_2 - \frac{h}{3}\right)\right\}\left\{\left(z - \frac{h}{3}\right) - \left(z_3 - \frac{h}{3}\right)\right\},$$

and we need the function $\wp(z)$, with

$$e_1 = z_1 - \frac{h}{3}, \qquad e_2 = z_2 - \frac{h}{3}, \qquad e_3 = z_3 - \frac{h}{3},$$

i.e. with

$$g_2 = \frac{4}{3}(h^2 + 3), \quad g_3 = 4\left\{\alpha - \frac{2}{27}(9h - h^3)\right\}.$$

If we choose the zero of the time-scale so that $z = z_3$ (i.e. $z - \frac{h}{3} = e_3$) at $t = \tau = 0$, we have

(5.3.17)
$$z - \frac{h}{3} = \wp(\tau + \omega_3),$$

(5.3.18)
$$z = \frac{h}{3} + \wp\left[\sqrt{\left(\frac{g}{2a}\right)}t + \omega_3\right].$$

The value of φ at time t is found from the relation

(5.3.19)
$$d\varphi = \frac{2\sqrt{\alpha}}{(1 - z^2)}\, d\tau,$$

where, in the second member, z is given by (5.3.17).

(iii) $\alpha = \psi(h)$. This is the problem of the conical pendulum. The particle moves on the horizontal circle $z = z_0$. The period σ is $2\pi\sqrt{(-az_0/g)}$, i.e. $2\pi\sqrt{(b/g)}$, where b is the depth of the plane of motion below the centre of the sphere. The motion is stable in the sense that a small disturbance will result in a motion of type (ii) confined to a narrow belt on the sphere in the neighbourhood of the original circular path.

Finally we may notice that the anomalous point $h = -1$, $\alpha = 0$, can be regarded as a limiting case of each of the three classes. The particle rests in stable equilibrium at the lowest point of the sphere.

5.4 The problem of two bodies. Two particles, P_1 and P_2, move in space under their mutual gravitation. We denote the masses of the particles by m_1 and m_2, and the length P_1P_2 by r. The force on P_1 at any instant is $\gamma m_1 m_2/r^2$ in the direction P_1P_2, where γ is the constant of gravitation. The force on P_2 is $\gamma m_1 m_2/r^2$ in the direction P_2P_1. Thus the acceleration of P_2 *relative to* P_1 at any instant is $\gamma(m_1 + m_2)/r^2$ in the direction P_2P_1. The relative motion is the same as the motion of a particle P_2 moving in space, its acceleration at each instant being directed towards a *fixed* point P_1 and of magnitude $\gamma(m_1 + m_2)/r^2$. It is clear that the (relative) orbit is plane, and that the plane in which it lies is the plane defined by the initial direction of P_1P_2 and the initial direction of the (relative) velocity of P_2 (unless this velocity is itself in the line P_1P_2, in which case the motion is rectilinear).

If we know the motion of P_2 relative to P_1 we can at once deduce the motion of P_2 relative to the centre of mass G, since

$$GP_2 = \frac{m_1}{m_1 + m_2} P_1P_2.$$

Now in the problem of two bodies (where we consider a universe containing only two particles) the centre of mass G moves uniformly in a straight line. If we know the motion of G, and the motion of P_2 relative to G, we can deduce the motion of P_2 in space; and of course we can find similarly the motion of P_1 in space. Since the motion of G is uniform we can, and often do, use a Newtonian base in which G is at rest.

Let us then consider the problem of the motion of P_2 relative to P_1; a particle moves in such a way that its acceleration is directed towards a fixed point, and is of magnitude μ/r^2, where $\mu = \gamma(m_1 + m_2)$. We take the fixed centre of attraction as origin, and the plane of motion as the plane $z = 0$. We have already considered this problem, rather summarily, as an illustration of the general theory of central orbits in § 5.2; we now exhibit a simpler way of solving the problem, and we then discuss the solution in rather more detail. The equations of motion are

$$\ddot{x} = -\frac{\mu}{r^2}\cos\theta, \quad \ddot{y} = -\frac{\mu}{r^2}\sin\theta, \tag{5.4.1}$$

where (x, y) are Cartesian coordinates, and (r, θ) are polar coordinates, as usual. Now, from the conservation of angular momentum,

$$r^2\dot{\theta} = \text{constant} = \alpha, \tag{5.4.2}$$

and we will suppose for definiteness that $\alpha > 0$. (We set aside the case $\alpha = 0$ in which the motion is rectilinear.) In virtue of (5.4.2) the equations (5.4.1) lead to

$$\ddot{x} = -\frac{\mu}{\alpha}\dot{\theta}\cos\theta, \quad \ddot{y} = -\frac{\mu}{\alpha}\dot{\theta}\sin\theta, \tag{5.4.3}$$

and integration of (5.4.3) leads to

$$\dot{x} = \frac{\mu}{\alpha}(-\sin\theta + A), \quad \dot{y} = \frac{\mu}{\alpha}(\cos\theta + B), \tag{5.4.4}$$

where A and B are constants. The values of A and B are determined by the initial conditions. Now

$$x\dot{y} - y\dot{x} = \alpha, \tag{5.4.5}$$

and substituting for $\dot{x}$ and $\dot{y}$ from (5.4.4) we have

$$\frac{\mu}{\alpha}x(\cos\theta + B) - \frac{\mu}{\alpha}y(-\sin\theta + A) = \alpha. \tag{5.4.6}$$

Since $x\cos\theta + y\sin\theta = r$, the equation (5.4.6) can be written

$$r = -Bx + Ay + (\alpha^2/\mu). \tag{5.4.7}$$

Thus the orbit is the locus of a point which moves so that its distance from O is proportional to its distance from the line

$$-Bx + Ay + (\alpha^2/\mu) = 0, \tag{5.4.8}$$

i.e., the orbit is a conic with O as focus and the line (5.4.8) as directrix. The eccentricity e has the value $\sqrt{(A^2 + B^2)}$.

The length of the chord of (5.4.7) parallel to the directrix is $2\alpha^2/\mu$, so if we denote the length of the *latus rectum* of the conic by $2p$ we have

$$\alpha^2 = \mu p. \tag{5.4.9}$$

Further, using (5.4.4), we have

$$\begin{aligned} e^2 = A^2 + B^2 &= \left(\frac{\alpha}{\mu}\dot{x} + \sin\theta\right)^2 + \left(\frac{\alpha}{\mu}\dot{y} - \cos\theta\right)^2 \\ &= 1 + \frac{\alpha^2}{\mu^2}(\dot{x}^2 + \dot{y}^2) - \frac{2\alpha}{\mu r}(x\dot{y} - y\dot{x}) \\ &= 1 + \frac{2\alpha^2}{\mu^2}\left\{\tfrac{1}{2}(\dot{x}^2 + \dot{y}^2) - \frac{\mu}{r}\right\} \\ &= 1 + \frac{2\alpha^2}{\mu^2}h, \end{aligned} \tag{5.4.10}$$

where h is the (conserved) total energy,

$$h = \tfrac{1}{2}(\dot{x}^2 + \dot{y}^2) - \frac{\mu}{r}. \tag{5.4.11}$$

Thus

$$e \lesseqgtr 1 \text{ according as } h \lesseqgtr 0. \tag{5.4.12}$$

Finally, substituting $\alpha^2 = \mu p$ in (5.4.10), we have

$$h = \frac{\mu}{2p}(e^2 - 1). \tag{5.4.13}$$

For the elliptic orbit, $e < 1$, $p = a(1 - e^2)$, and therefore

$$h = -\frac{\mu}{2a}, \tag{5.4.14}$$

where $2a$ is the length of the major axis of the ellipse. For the parabolic orbit, $e = 1$, and

$$h = 0. \tag{5.4.15}$$

For the hyperbolic orbit, $e > 1$, $p = a(e^2 - 1)$, and

$$h = \frac{\mu}{2a}. \tag{5.4.16}$$

The formulae (5.4.9) and (5.4.14) (or (5.4.16)) are the classical formulae expressing the shape and size of the orbit in terms of the constant of energy h and the constant of angular momentum α.

5.5 Kepler's equation. The principle of the conservation of angular momentum implies that the rate of sweeping out of area by the radius vector is constant; explicitly the area covered per second is $\frac{1}{2}\alpha$. Thus in a central orbit the area swept out by the radius vector is proportional to the time, and this gives us a way of finding the relation between the position on the orbit and the time.

Let us consider specifically the elliptic orbit. The period σ is $2\Delta/\alpha$, where Δ is the area of the ellipse, so

(5.5.1) $$\sigma = \frac{2\pi ab}{\alpha} = \frac{2\pi a^2\sqrt{(1-e^2)}}{\sqrt{(\mu p)}} = \frac{2\pi}{n},$$

where n, the *mean motion*, denotes $\sqrt{(\mu/a^3)}$.

To find the time t from the perihelion A to a point P of the ellipse we have

(5.5.2) $$\frac{t}{\sigma} = \frac{\delta}{\Delta},$$

where δ is the area of the sector ASP of the ellipse. Now we can regard the ellipse as the orthogonal projection of its auxiliary circle (Fig. 5.5), and the ratio of areas is unaltered by orthogonal projection. Thus, if Q is the point on the auxiliary circle of which P is the projection,

(5.5.3) $$\frac{t}{\sigma} = \frac{\delta}{\Delta} = \frac{\delta'}{\Delta'},$$

where δ' is the area of the sector ASQ of the auxiliary circle, Δ' the area of the circle. Now the sector ASQ is the sector ACQ minus the triangle CSQ, so

(5.5.4) $$\delta' = \tfrac{1}{2}a^2 w - \tfrac{1}{2}a^2 e \sin w,$$

where w is the eccentric angle of P, i.e. the angle QCA. Thus we have

(5.5.5) $$\frac{t}{\sigma} = \frac{\delta'}{\Delta'} = \frac{w - e\sin w}{2\pi},$$

giving, in virtue of (5.5.1),

(5.5.6) $$nt = w - e\sin w.$$

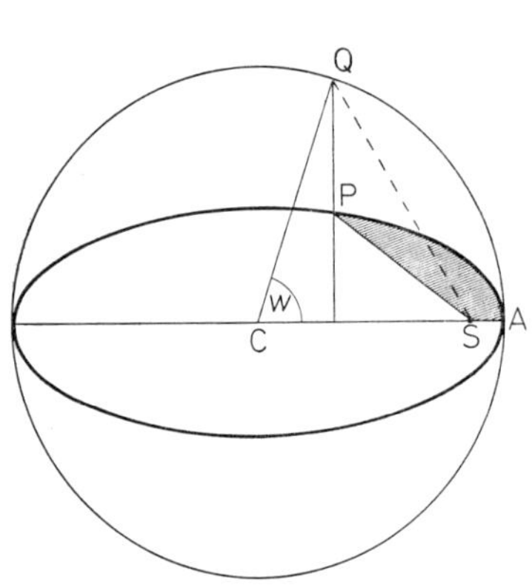

Figure 5.5

The relation (5.5.6), known as *Kepler's equation*, has already been found by another method in § 5.2. It is the fundamental relation connecting the position on the elliptic orbit and the time.

This method is perhaps the most straightforward method of establishing Kepler's equation in the first instance, since the eccentric angle occurs naturally. But it is easy to establish the equation without reference to the geometry of the ellipse. One method has already been noticed in § 5.2. An even simpler method is the following. The coordinates of a point on the ellipse, taking the axes of the ellipse as axes of coordinates, are $(a\cos w, b\sin w)$. If then we take axes (still parallel to the axes of the ellipse) with S as origin, we have

(5.5.7) $$x = a(\cos w - e), \quad y = b\sin w,$$

and

(5.5.8) $$abn = \alpha = x\dot{y} - y\dot{x} = ab(1 - e\cos w)\dot{w}.$$

Therefore

$$n = (1 - e \cos w)\dot{w}, \tag{5.5.9}$$

which leads again to (5.5.6).

The polar coordinates (r, θ), taking SA as initial line, are easily expressed in terms of w,

$$r = a(1 - e \cos w), \tag{5.5.10}$$

$$\tan \tfrac{1}{2}\theta = k \tan \tfrac{1}{2}w, \tag{5.5.11}$$

where $k = \sqrt{\left(\dfrac{1+e}{1-e}\right)}$. To find the explicit relation between r and t, for example, we must eliminate w between (5.5.6) and (5.5.10); we postpone this calculation until § 18.14.

5.6 Collision. We now return to the problem of two bodies. We consider the case where $\alpha = 0$; the particle (in the relative motion) moves in a straight line through O. Without loss of generality we can take this line as the axis Ox. We have the energy equation (for $x > 0$)

$$\tfrac{1}{2}\dot{x}^2 - \frac{\mu}{x} = h, \tag{5.6.1}$$

and we consider more particularly the case $h < 0$, say (by analogy with the elliptic motion considered above) $h = -\mu/(2a)$, where $a > 0$. It is clear that $2a$ is the greatest distance from O that is reached by the particle, if both x and $\dot{x}$ are positive initially. To investigate the relation connecting position and time we introduce an auxiliary variable θ defined by the equation

$$x = a(1 + \cos\theta). \tag{5.6.2}$$

Thus $\theta = 0$ when $x = 2a$, and we may suppose θ to increase steadily with t until the collision with the particle at O, when $\theta = \pi$. Substituting for x from (5.6.2) in

$$\tfrac{1}{2}\dot{x}^2 = \mu\left(\frac{1}{x} - \frac{1}{2a}\right) \tag{5.6.3}$$

we find

$$(1 + \cos\theta)^2\dot{\theta}^2 = n^2, \tag{5.6.4}$$

whence, since $\dot{\theta} > 0$,

$$(1 + \cos\theta)\dot{\theta} = n, \tag{5.6.5}$$

and therefore

$$\theta + \sin\theta = nt, \tag{5.6.6}$$

if we take $t = 0$ when $\theta = 0$ and $x = 2a$.

Now in the first instance (5.6.6) only holds for $-\pi < \theta < \pi$, because $\dot{x} \to -\infty$ as $x \to 0$. But we shall sometimes wish to suppose the motion continued after the collision, and in that case we shall assume that (5.6.6) also holds *after* the collision. This seems the natural assumption to make. If α were not actually zero, but had a small positive value, the orbit would be a very thin ellipse, and we should have a periodic motion with a near-collision once in each period. Our assumption is that the effect is similar even in the limiting case of rectilinear motion.

If we put $\theta = \pi + \varphi$, $t = (\pi/n) + \tau$, the relations become

$$x/a = 1 - \cos\varphi, \tag{5.6.7}$$

$$n\tau = \varphi - \sin\varphi, \tag{5.6.8}$$

and the collision occurs at $x = \tau = \varphi = 0$. If we think in terms of complex variables the second members of (5.6.7) and (5.6.8) are integral functions, and the elimination of φ gives x as an analytic function of τ. Explicitly, expanding about $\tau = 0$, we have

$$\frac{x}{a} = \frac{1}{2}(6n\tau)^{2/3} - \frac{1}{40}(6n\tau)^{4/3} + \cdots = \sum_{n=1}^{\infty} c_n\tau^{2n/3}.$$

The function $x(\tau)$ has an algebraic branch point at $\tau = 0$ at which three sheets of the appropriate Riemann surface are united. We notice that $x(\tau)$ is real on only one of the three sheets, and there is one real analytic continuation over the singularity at $\tau = 0$. This is the function we have chosen to represent the motion after the instant of collision. We notice that the chosen branch of $x(\tau)$ is an even function of τ.

These ideas are important in the problem of three bodies. It may happen that the initial conditions are such that, at a certain instant $t = t_0$, two of the bodies collide. We wish to make a plausible assumption about how the motion will continue afterwards, and the assumption we make is that just described. It is clear that, in a short time-interval about the instant of collision, the influence of the third body is negligible, and we can deal with the collision as a problem of two bodies.

5.7 Lagrangian coordinates for a holonomic system. We now turn to the formal theory, postponed from § 5.1, of the transition from Cartesian to Lagrangian coordinates. We suppose in the first instance that the equations of constraint (2.2.4) are completely integrable, i.e. they are equivalent to L equations of the form

$$df_r = 0, \qquad r = 1, 2, \ldots, L, \tag{5.7.1}$$

where

$$f_r = f_r(x_1, x_2, \ldots, x_N;\ t), \tag{5.7.2}$$

and $f_r \in C_2$. In this case the system is said to be holonomic.

Consider now the transformation

$$q_r = f_r, \qquad r = 1, 2, \ldots, N, \tag{5.7.3}$$

where the first L of the f's are the functions (5.7.2) arising from the equations of constraint, and the remaining $k(=N - L)$ of the f's are suitably chosen functions, of class C_2, of $(x_1, x_2, \ldots, x_N;\ t)$. If we consider a sufficiently small domain D of $(x_1, x_2, \ldots, x_N;\ t)$ in which the Jacobian

$$\frac{\partial(f_1, f_2, \ldots, f_N)}{\partial(x_1, x_2, \ldots, x_N)} \tag{5.7.4}$$

does not vanish, the equations (5.7.3) define a $1 - 1$ correlation between the domain D of $(\mathbf{x};\ t)$ and a domain Δ of $(\mathbf{q}, t)$. We can solve the equations (5.7.3) for $x_1, x_2, \ldots, x_N$ as functions of the q's and t; these functions are of class C_2 in Δ. In most practical cases the x's are functions of the q's only, not of t.

Now the equations of constraint, in terms of the new variables, take the simple form

(5.7.5) $$q_r = \alpha_r, \qquad r = 1, 2, \ldots, L.$$

(Indeed in most cases the equations of constraint are expressible at the outset in this form, the α's being absolute constants, not dependent on the initial conditions.) The values of the constants α_r in (5.7.5) being settled, once for all, the values of the last k of the q's determine the configuration of the system. The x's are expressed as explicit function of k coordinates $q_{L+1}, q_{L+2}, \ldots, q_N$ and the time, and this is the fundamental property of Lagrangian coordinates. There are now no equations of constraint, a displacement represented by arbitrary differentials $dq_{L+1}, dq_{L+2}, \ldots, dq_N, dt$ is possible, and

(5.7.6) $$dx_r = \sum_{s=L+1}^{N} \frac{\partial x_r}{\partial q_s} dq_s + \frac{\partial x_r}{\partial t} dt, \qquad r = 1, 2, \ldots, N.$$

Next, we must consider the virtual displacements. Now the virtual displacements $(\delta x_1, \delta x_2, \ldots, \delta x_N)$ are displacements satisfying the equations

(5.7.7) $$\sum_{s=1}^{N} \frac{\partial f_r}{\partial x_s} \delta x_s = 0, \qquad r = 1, 2, \ldots, L.$$

These equations (5.7.7) are satisfied by

(5.7.8) $$\delta x_s = \sum_{m=L+1}^{N} \frac{\partial x_s}{\partial q_m} \delta q_m, \qquad s = 1, 2, \ldots, N,$$

for arbitrary values of $\delta q_{L+1}, \delta q_{L+2}, \ldots, \delta q_N$, since

(5.7.9) $$\sum_{s=1}^{N} \frac{\partial f_r}{\partial x_s} \frac{\partial x_s}{\partial q_m} = 0$$

if $r \leqslant L$ and $m > L$. Moreover this is the most general virtual displacement. The virtual displacements are defined by taking arbitrary increments $\delta q_{L+1}, \delta q_{L+2}, \ldots, \delta q_N$, without varying t.

The process just described achieves the formal transition from the Cartesian to the Lagrangian coordinates, but the method used in practice is essentially simpler. As we have noticed already (§ 5.1) in most cases a convenient choice of Lagrangian coordinates suggests itself immediately.

5.8 Lagrangian coordinates for a non-holonomic system. Suppose now that the equations of constraint (2.2.4) are not completely integrable. Let the number of independent linear combinations which admit an integrating factor be $L - l$, so that the equations of constraint can be written

(5.8.1) $$df_r = 0, \qquad r = 1, 2, \ldots, L - l,$$

(5.8.2) $$\omega_r = 0, \qquad r = 1, 2, \ldots, l,$$

where the ω's are Pfaffian forms in $dx_1, dx_2, \ldots, dx_N, dt$. The number l is an invariant of the system, and there exists no integrable combination of the equations of constraint independent of (5.8.1).

Consider now the transformation

(5.8.3) $$q_r = f_r, \qquad r = 1, 2, \ldots, N,$$

where $f_1, f_2, \ldots, f_{L-l}$ are the functions appearing in the first members of (5.8.1), and the last $l + k$ of the f's are any convenient functions of $x_1, x_2, \ldots, x_N, t$. The functions $f_1, f_2, \ldots, f_N$ are N independent functions, of class C_2, of $x_1, x_2, \ldots, x_N$ and t. We assume as before that the transformation is reversible, so that for the appropriate domain of $q_1, q_2, \ldots, q_N, t$ the x's are one-valued functions of the q's and of t.

In terms of the new variables the first $L - l$ equations of constraint take the simple form

(5.8.4) $$q_r = \alpha_r, \qquad r = 1, 2, \ldots, L - l,$$

and then, the values of these constants α_r being fixed once for all, the values of the last $k + l$ of the q's determine the configuration of the system. But now there survive the l equations of constraint (5.8.2) which admit no integrable combination. In terms of the new variables these take the form

(5.8.5) $$\sum_{s=1}^{N} B_{rs}\, dq_s + B_r\, dt = 0, \qquad r = 1, 2, \ldots, l,$$

and these l Pfaffian equations admit no integrable combination. Since $q_1, q_2, \ldots, q_{L-l}$ are constant, (5.8.5) is equivalent to

(5.8.6) $$\sum_{s=L-l+1}^{N} B_{rs}\, dq_s + B_r\, dt = 0, \qquad r = 1, 2, \ldots, l,$$

a Pfaffian equation with $k + l + 1$ terms. The coefficients B_{rs}, B_r are known functions, of class C_1, of the last $k + l$ of the q's and of t.

Thus, for a non-holonomic system, it is no longer possible to choose Lagrangian coordinates equal in number to the degrees of freedom. The least possible number of Lagrangian coordinates exceeds the number of freedoms by the number of equations of constraint which admit no integrable combination.

The possible displacements of the system are given by

(5.8.7) $$dx_r = \sum_{s=L-l+1}^{N} \frac{\partial x_r}{\partial q_s}\, dq_s + \frac{\partial x_r}{\partial t}\, dt,$$

where the $k + l + 1$ differentials

$$dq_{L-l+1}, dq_{L-l+2}, \ldots, dq_N, dt,$$

are subject only to the relations (5.8.6). The virtual displacements of the system are given by

(5.8.8) $$\delta x_r = \sum_{s=L-l+1}^{N} \frac{\partial x_r}{\partial q_s}\, \delta q_s,$$

where the $k + l$ differentials

$$\delta q_{L-l+1}, \delta q_{L-l+2}, \ldots, \delta q_N$$

are subject only to the relations

(5.8.9) $$\sum_{s=L-l+1}^{N} B_{rs}\, \delta q_s = 0, \qquad r = 1, 2, \ldots, l.$$

To verify that the virtual displacements are defined by (5.8.8) and (5.8.9) we have to prove that the equations

(5.8.10) $$\sum_{r=1}^{N} \frac{\partial f_m}{\partial x_r}\, \delta x_r = 0, \qquad m = 1, 2, \ldots, L - l,$$

and the equations (cf. (2.2.9))

$$\sum_{r=1}^{N} A_{mr}\,\delta x_r = 0, \qquad m = 1, 2, \ldots, l, \tag{5.8.11}$$

are satisfied by (5.8.8) if the δq's obey (5.8.9). Of these (5.8.10) is evident, and (5.8.11) is true because

$$B_{rs} = \sum_{m=1}^{N} A_{rm}\frac{\partial x_m}{\partial q_s}, \qquad s = L - l + 1, L - l + 2, \ldots, N.$$

We remark again that, as for a holonomic system, the method of introducing the Lagrangian coordinates in practice is simpler than the formal method just described, because for a concrete problem suitable Lagrangian coordinates usually suggest themselves in a fairly obvious way.

5.9 Rolling bodies. Two simple, but somewhat artificial, examples of non-holonomic systems have already been mentioned, the curve of pursuit in § 1.8, and the hatchet planimeter in § 2.1. In practice, by far the commonest type of non-holonomic system that occurs involves the rolling of one body on another. Consider a rigid body whose position and orientation are defined by the six coordinates ξ, η, ζ, θ_1, θ_2, θ_3 as in § 5.1(v). For a given particle of the body

$$x = \xi + al_1 + bl_2 + cl_3, \tag{5.9.1}$$

and for an arbitrary displacement $(d\xi, d\eta, d\zeta, d\theta_1, d\theta_2, d\theta_3)$ we get

$$dx = d\xi + a\,dl_1 + b\,dl_2 + c\,dl_3, \tag{5.9.2}$$

with two similar relations. In (5.9.2) the coordinates a, b, and c are constants. If the particle is at rest

$$d\xi + a\,dl_1 + b\,dl_2 + c\,dl_3 = 0. \tag{5.9.3}$$

Now, if (5.9.3) refers always to the same particle of the body, the equation is integrable,

$$\xi + al_1 + bl_2 + cl_3 = \text{constant}, \tag{5.9.4}$$

and there are two similar relations. In this case the body has one point fixed, and we have a holonomic system with three freedoms; the only thing we have to discuss is the orientation of the body as it rotates about the fixed point. But if (5.9.3) refers to different particles (a, b, c) at different instants—e.g. if the particle is at the point of contact of the body with a fixed surface on which the body rolls—the system comprising (5.9.3) and the two similar relations is not completely integrable, and the system is not holonomic.

Similar remarks hold if the particle (a, b, c), instead of being at rest, has a prescribed velocity (U, V, W), where U, V, W are prescribed functions of t. The equation (5.9.3) is replaced by

$$d\xi + a\,dl_1 + b\,dl_2 + c\,dl_3 = U\,dt, \tag{5.9.5}$$

and again, if (a, b, c) represents the same particle throughout, the system is holonomic. We now have the problem of a rigid body one point of which has an inexorable motion. But it may be that (a, b, c) is the point of contact of the body with a moving surface on which the body rolls. In that case a, b and c have different values at different instants, and the system is not holonomic.

As a concrete illustration let us consider the classical example of a sphere of radius ρ rolling on a perfectly rough horizontal plane. Suppose that the plane rotates about a point O of itself with prescribed angular velocity Ω $(=\Omega(t))$. We take fixed axes with O as origin and Oz vertically upwards. We describe the configuration at time t by the coordinates ξ, η of the point of contact (so that the centre of the sphere has coordinates ξ, η, ρ) and the Eulerian angles θ, φ, ψ to describe the orientation (anticipating for a moment the theory of these angles, which is developed formally in § 7.11; for our immediate purpose we need only the definition and the matrix (7.11.1)). The first rolling condition (5.9.5) becomes

$$d\xi + a\,dl_1 + b\,dl_2 + c\,dl_3 = -\eta\Omega\,dt, \tag{5.9.6}$$

and, since (a, b, c) is the point of the sphere in contact with the table

$$(a, b, c) = -\rho(n_1, n_2, n_3), \tag{5.9.7}$$

where ρ is the radius of the sphere. Thus (5.9.6) becomes

$$d\xi - \rho(n_1\,dl_1 + n_2\,dl_2 + n_3\,dl_3) = -\eta\Omega\,dt. \tag{5.9.8}$$

Notice particularly that in finding (5.9.6) the coordinates a, b, c are *constants*, since we need the motion of a particle which is fixed in the sphere; but it is a different particle with which we are concerned at different instants, and to find the equation (5.9.8), valid at all times, the coordinates a, b, c are replaced by the variables defined by (5.9.7). There is no serious difficulty in transforming (5.9.8) by direct substitution of the values of $l_1, m_1, \ldots, n_3$ in terms of θ, φ, ψ. However, we can shorten the calculation by means of the following observation. The direction cosines of Ox with respect to the moving axes $G123$ are l_1, l_2, l_3. Thus the vector $\mathbf{L}(\mathbf{L} = \{l_1, l_2, l_3\})$ is a fixed vector, and therefore

$$\dot{\mathbf{L}} + \boldsymbol{\omega} \times \mathbf{L} = 0, \tag{5.9.9}$$

where $\boldsymbol{\omega}$ is the angular velocity of the body, and therefore also of the moving axes, referred to $G123$. Now, referring to the expression $n_1\,dl_1 + n_2\,dl_2 + n_3\,dl_3$ in (5.9.8), we have

$$n_1\dot{l}_1 + n_2\dot{l}_2 + n_3\dot{l}_3 = \mathbf{N}\,.\,\dot{\mathbf{L}} = \mathbf{N}\,.\,(\mathbf{L} \times \boldsymbol{\omega}) = \boldsymbol{\omega}\,.\,(\mathbf{N} \times \mathbf{L}) = \boldsymbol{\omega}\,.\,\mathbf{M}, \tag{5.9.10}$$

where $\mathbf{N}$ is the vector $\{n_1, n_2, n_3\}$ and $\mathbf{M}$ is the vector $\{m_1, m_2, m_3\}$. Now $\boldsymbol{\omega}\,.\,\mathbf{M}$ is the component ω_y of angular velocity in the direction Oy, and (5.9.8) takes the form

$$d\xi - \rho\omega_y\,dt = -\eta\Omega\,dt. \tag{5.9.11}$$

Now

$$\omega_y = \cos\varphi\,\dot{\theta} + \sin\theta\sin\varphi\,\dot{\psi}, \tag{5.9.12}$$

so (5.9.8) leads finally to

$$d\xi - \rho\cos\varphi\,d\theta - \rho\sin\theta\sin\varphi\,d\psi = -\eta\Omega\,dt. \tag{5.9.13}$$

This is the first of the two equations of constraint for the non-holonomic system.

It should be noticed that (5.9.11) can be obtained by using axes through G in fixed directions parallel to Ox, Oy, Oz; the first rolling condition is

$$\dot{\xi} - \rho\omega_y = -\eta\Omega, \tag{5.9.14}$$

which is equivalent to (5.9.11). This method is actually a little shorter than the preceding, but we have preferred to illustrate the method described in the text.

We find similarly the second rolling condition

$$d\eta - \rho \sin \varphi \, d\theta + \rho \sin \theta \cos \varphi \, d\psi = \xi\Omega \, dt. \tag{5.9.15}$$

The third condition is merely $\zeta = \rho$.

It is easy to see that there is no integrable combination of the Pfaffian equations (5.9.13) and (5.9.15). The system is a non-holonomic system with three freedoms, but the least number of Lagrangian coordinates required to describe the configuration is 5; we can take these to be ξ, η, θ, φ, ψ. Here $n = 5$, $k = 3$, $l = 2$.

5.10 Accessibility. Consider now the case in which the sphere rolls on a *fixed* table, so that the equations of constraint are

$$d\xi - \rho \cos \varphi \, d\theta - \rho \sin \theta \sin \varphi \, d\psi = 0, \tag{5.10.1}$$

$$d\eta - \rho \sin \varphi \, d\theta + \rho \sin \theta \cos \varphi \, d\psi = 0. \tag{5.10.2}$$

We have a non-holonomic system with three degrees of freedom. But the space of configurations accessible from a given configuration has five dimensions; in fact any configuration described by arbitrary values of ξ, η, θ, φ, ψ is accessible from any other. This phenomenon we have noticed already in simpler examples of non-holonomic systems in § 1.8 and in § 2.1. In this case to prove that any configuration of the system is accessible from any other, we proceed as follows. Suppose that in the initial configuration P_1 a point A on the surface of the sphere is in contact with a point A' of the plane, and that in the final configuration P_2 a point B of the sphere is in contact with a point B' of the plane. Consider a great-circle arc AB, denote its length by $\rho\alpha$, and let the length of the line $A'B'$ be $\rho(2n\pi + \beta)$, where n is an integer and $0 \leqslant \beta < 2\pi$. On the sphere let the arc AB be produced (if necessary) to C, where AC is of length $\rho\beta$, and let D be the midpoint of the arc BC. To reach P_2 from P_1 we first rotate the sphere about the diameter through A' until AB lies in the vertical plane through $A'B'$. We next roll the sphere towards B' through an angle $2n\pi + \frac{1}{2}(\alpha + \beta)$, so that D comes into contact with a point D' of the plane. We next rotate the sphere through an angle π about the diameter through D', and then roll through a further angle $\frac{1}{2}(\beta - \alpha)$ until B comes into contact with B'. Finally, we rotate the sphere about the diameter through B' until we reach the desired configuration P_2. The five operations can of course be carried out in a finite time, the coordinates during the motion having continuous second derivatives with respect to t. (A line can be turned through an angle γ in the finite time-interval from $t = 0$ to $t = \tau$ by taking its angular velocity at time t to be $30\gamma t^2(\tau - t)^2/\tau^5$, and the angular velocity and acceleration vanish both at $t = 0$ and at $t = \tau$.)

5.11 The varied path in Hamilton's principle. In Hamilton's principle (§ 3.7) the varied path is obtained from the actual path by taking at each instant a virtual displacement. If the system is not holonomic, however, the varied path is not in general possible. We have proved this statement already for one simple non-holonomic system (§ 3.8). We now prove it for two other cases, (i) the planimeter rod (§ 5.1(vi)), and (ii) the rolling sphere (§ 5.10).

(i) The actual motion satisfies the equation

$$\dot{y}_1 - \tan\theta\,\dot{x}_1 = 0, \tag{5.11.1}$$

and the displacement is a virtual displacement, so

$$\delta y_1 - \tan\theta\,\delta x_1 = 0. \tag{5.11.2}$$

The varied path is possible if and only if

$$\delta(\dot{y}_1 - \tan\theta\,\dot{x}_1) = 0. \tag{5.11.3}$$

Since (5.11.2) is true at each instant, (5.11.3) is equivalent to

$$\delta(\dot{y}_1 - \tan\theta\,\dot{x}_1) - \frac{d}{dt}(\delta y_1 - \tan\theta\,\delta x_1) = 0, \tag{5.11.4}$$

which is the same as

$$\sec^2\theta(\dot{\theta}\,\delta x_1 - \dot{x}_1\,\delta\theta) = 0. \tag{5.11.5}$$

The varied path is possible if and only if

$$\frac{\delta\theta}{\dot{\theta}} = \frac{\delta x_1}{\dot{x}_1}, \tag{5.11.6}$$

which is not true in general.

(ii) For the sphere the equations of constraint are the rolling conditions (5.10.1) and (5.10.2). Consider the simple case in which the original motion is one of rolling along Ox with no spin about the vertical. If we consider a displacement in which at each instant the centre is displaced through an infinitesimal distance $\rho\alpha$ at right angles to the plane $y = 0$ the new path *is* possible! For the points of contact on the sphere lie on a circle of circumference $2\pi\rho\cos\alpha$, which is equal to $2\pi\rho$ to the first order in α. But in general the varied path is not possible without skidding. In the original motion

$$\theta = \varphi = \tfrac{1}{2}\pi, \quad \eta = 0, \quad \dot{\xi} = \rho\dot{\psi}, \tag{5.11.7}$$

and the variation is such that

$$\delta\xi - \rho\,\delta\psi = 0, \quad \delta\eta - \rho\,\delta\theta = 0. \tag{5.11.8}$$

The equations of constraint (5.10.1) and (5.10.2) are satisfied in the varied path if and only if

$$\delta(\dot{\xi} - \rho\cos\varphi\,\dot{\theta} - \rho\sin\theta\sin\varphi\,\dot{\psi}) = 0, \tag{5.11.9}$$

$$\delta(\dot{\eta} - \rho\sin\varphi\,\dot{\theta} + \rho\sin\theta\cos\varphi\,\dot{\psi}) = 0, \tag{5.11.10}$$

which are equivalent (when we remember the values in the original motion) to

$$\frac{d}{dt}(\delta\xi - \rho\,\delta\psi) = 0, \quad \frac{d}{dt}(\delta\eta - \rho\,\delta\theta) - \rho\dot{\psi}\,\delta\varphi = 0.$$

These are not satisfied except in the special case, already noticed, when $\delta\varphi = 0$.

Thus we find, as in the simpler case discussed in § 3.8, that the varied path is not possible without violating the constraints. It is hardly necessary to remind the reader that this fact does not invalidate Hamilton's principle in any way.

5.12 Summary. We sum up briefly our conclusions about Lagrangian coordinates. Making an obvious change of notation, the Lagrangian coordinates $q_1, q_2, \ldots, q_n$ are such that the x's can be expressed as explicit uniform functions of the q's and t,

$$x_r = x_r(q_1, q_2, \ldots, q_n; t), \qquad r = 1, 2, \ldots, N, \tag{5.12.1}$$

and all possible configurations of the system are comprehended by giving appropriate values to $q_1, q_2, \ldots, q_n, t$ in a certain domain D of the $(\mathbf{q}, t)$-space. In a sufficiently small region of this space (though not always throughout the whole domain D) the relation connecting $\mathbf{q}$ and $\mathbf{x}$ is a $1 - 1$ relation.

In the applications which follow we shall assume that the functions $x_r(q_1, q_2, \ldots, q_n; t) \in C_2$ in D. In most cases of practical interest the x's are functions of the q's only, not of t.

If the system is holonomic, the least possible value for n is k, the number of degrees of freedom. If the system is not holonomic, the least possible value for n is $k + l$, and there are l equations of constraint

$$\sum_{s=1}^{n} B_{rs}\, dq_s + B_r\, dt = 0, \qquad r = 1, 2, \ldots, l, \tag{5.12.2}$$

and these admit no integrable combination. The coefficients in (5.12.2) are of class C_1. The possible displacements are given by

$$dx_r = \sum_{s=1}^{n} \frac{\partial x_r}{\partial q_s}\, dq_s + \frac{\partial x_r}{\partial t}\, dt, \qquad r = 1, 2, \ldots, N, \tag{5.12.3}$$

where the differentials $dq_1, dq_2, \ldots, dq_n, dt$ satisfy (5.12.2). The virtual displacements are given by

$$\delta x_r = \sum_{s=1}^{n} \frac{\partial x_r}{\partial q_s}\, \delta q_s, \qquad r = 1, 2, \ldots, N, \tag{5.12.4}$$

where the differentials $\delta q_1, \delta q_2, \ldots, \delta q_n$ satisfy

$$\sum_{s=1}^{n} B_{rs}\, \delta q_s = 0, \qquad r = 1, 2, \ldots, l. \tag{5.12.5}$$

The formulae (5.12.3) and (5.12.4) are of course valid also for holonomic systems, but in that case the differentials δq_s are unrestricted.

In either case we can, if we wish, employ more than the minimum number of Lagrangian coordinates, say p more than the minimum number. In this case, in addition to the Pfaffian equations of constraint (if any) there will be p further relations. These relations will be expressed by finite equations of the form

$$F_r(q_1, q_2, \ldots, q_n; t) = 0, \qquad r = 1, 2, \ldots, p, \tag{5.12.6}$$

not by Pfaffian equations. We shall assume that the functions F_r have continuous first derivatives in the appropriate domain of $(q_1, q_2, \ldots, q_n; t)$. When we use more than the minimum number of Lagrangian coordinates we speak of *redundant coordinates*. The kind of problem in which they appear conspicuously is one concerned with a new system formed by imposing constraints on a given system; it may be convenient to adhere to the coordinates used to describe the original system, even though their number is not the least possible number for the new system.

We shall often find it convenient to think of $q_1, q_2, \ldots, q_n$ as defining the position of a representative point or mobile in a space of n dimensions. The motion of the mobile in this space gives a picture of the motion of the dynamical system, the path (i.e. the sequence of configurations) of the system being correlated with the path of the mobile in the n-fold space. It will sometimes be convenient to write $\mathbf{q}$ in place of $\{q_1, q_2, \ldots, q_n\}$, and $\dot{\mathbf{q}}$ in place of $\{\dot{q}_1, \dot{q}_2, \ldots, \dot{q}_n\}$.

Chapter VI

Lagrange's equations

6.1 The fourth form of the fundamental equation, Lagrangian coordinates. Our next step is the expression of the fundamental equation in terms of Lagrangian coordinates: we translate the first form of the fundamental equation (3.1.1) from the language of x into the language of q. The characteristic property of the Lagrangian coordinates is that the x's can be expressed as explicit functions of $q_1, q_2, \ldots, q_n, t$. We shall assume always that these functions are of class C_2 in a suitable domain D of $q_1, q_2, \ldots, q_n, t$.

Since

(6.1.1) $$x_r = x_r(q_1, q_2, \ldots, q_n;\ t), \qquad r = 1, 2, \ldots, N,$$

we have

(6.1.2) $$\dot{x}_r = \sum_{s=1}^{n} \frac{\partial x_r}{\partial q_s} \dot{q}_s + \frac{\partial x_r}{\partial t}, \qquad r = 1, 2, \ldots, N,$$

which expresses $\dot{x}_r$ as a linear function of the $\dot{q}$'s with coefficients which are functions of $(q_1, q_2, \ldots, q_n, t)$. Two simple properties of the functions occurring on the right in (6.1.2) are contained in the two lemmas following:

Lemma 1.

(6.1.3) $$\frac{\partial \dot{x}_r}{\partial \dot{q}_s} = \frac{\partial x_r}{\partial q_s},$$

Lemma 2.

(6.1.4) $$\frac{\partial \dot{x}_r}{\partial q_s} = \frac{d}{dt}\left(\frac{\partial x_r}{\partial q_s}\right).$$

The first result is obvious, and to prove the second we have

$$\begin{aligned}\frac{\partial \dot{x}_r}{\partial q_s} &= \sum_{m=1}^{n} \frac{\partial^2 x_r}{\partial q_s\, \partial q_m} \dot{q}_m + \frac{\partial^2 x_r}{\partial q_s\, \partial t} \\ &= \sum_{m=1}^{n} \frac{\partial^2 x_r}{\partial q_m\, \partial q_s} \dot{q}_m + \frac{\partial^2 x_r}{\partial t\, \partial q_s} \\ &= \frac{d}{dt}\left(\frac{\partial x_r}{\partial q_s}\right),\end{aligned}$$

where the inversion of the order of differentiation is justified because $x_r(q_1, q_2, \ldots, q_n;\ t) \in C_2$ in D.

If we substitute from (6.1.2) for $\dot{x}_r$ in the formula for the kinetic energy

(3.3.3) $$T = \tfrac{1}{2} \sum_{r=1}^{N} m_r \dot{x}_r^2$$

we obtain a polynomial $\mathfrak{T}$ of the second degree in $\dot{q}_1, \dot{q}_2, \ldots, \dot{q}_n$, with coefficients which are functions of $q_1, q_2, \ldots, q_n, t$. We notice that $\mathfrak{T}$ has the form

(6.1.5) $$\mathfrak{T} = T_2 + T_1 + T_0,$$

where T_2 is a homogeneous quadratic function of the $\dot{q}$'s,

(6.1.6) $$T_2 = \tfrac{1}{2} \sum_{r=1}^{n} \sum_{s=1}^{n} a_{rs}\dot{q}_r\dot{q}_s,$$

T_1 is a homogeneous linear function of the $\dot{q}$'s,

(6.1.7) $$T_1 = \sum_{r=1}^{n} a_r\dot{q}_r,$$

and T_0 is a function of $q_1, q_2, \ldots, q_n, t$. We notice that T_2 is the formula we should obtain from T if we omitted the term $\dfrac{\partial x_r}{\partial t}$ in the second member of (6.1.2), and therefore T_2 is a positive definite quadratic form in the $\dot{q}$'s for all values of $q_1, q_2, \ldots, q_n, t$; and that $T_0\left(= \sum_{r=1}^{N} m_r\left(\dfrac{\partial x_r}{\partial t}\right)^2\right)$ is non-negative for all values of $q_1, q_2, \ldots, q_n, t$.

We now turn to the fundamental equation (3.1.1). For a virtual displacement we have

(5.12.4) $$\delta x_r = \sum_{s=1}^{n} \frac{\partial x_r}{\partial q_s}\,\delta q_s, \qquad r = 1, 2, \ldots, N,$$

and (3.1.1) becomes

(6.1.8) $$\sum_{s=1}^{n}\left\{\sum_{r=1}^{N} (m_r\ddot{x}_r - X_r)\frac{\partial x_r}{\partial q_s}\right\}\delta q_s = 0.$$

If we consider a single term $\ddot{x}_r \dfrac{\partial x_r}{\partial q_s}$ we have

$$\begin{aligned}\ddot{x}_r\frac{\partial x_r}{\partial q_s} &= \frac{d}{dt}\left(\dot{x}_r\frac{\partial x_r}{\partial q_s}\right) - \dot{x}_r\frac{d}{dt}\left(\frac{\partial x_r}{\partial q_s}\right)\\ &= \frac{d}{dt}\left(\dot{x}_r\frac{\partial \dot{x}_r}{\partial \dot{q}_s}\right) - \dot{x}_r\frac{\partial \dot{x}_r}{\partial q_s},\end{aligned}$$

where we have used the lemmas (6.1.3) and (6.1.4). Thus the coefficient of δq_s in (6.1.8) becomes

(6.1.9) $$\sum_{r=1}^{N} m_r\left\{\frac{d}{dt}\left(\dot{x}_r\frac{\partial \dot{x}_r}{\partial \dot{q}_s}\right) - \dot{x}_r\frac{\partial \dot{x}_r}{\partial q_s}\right\} - Q_s,$$

where

(6.1.10) $$Q_s = \sum_{r=1}^{N} X_r\frac{\partial x_r}{\partial q_s}.$$

Now (6.1.9) is

(6.1.11) $$\frac{d}{dt}\left(\frac{\partial \mathfrak{T}}{\partial \dot{q}_s}\right) - \frac{\partial \mathfrak{T}}{\partial q_s} - Q_s,$$

and thus, finally, we obtain

(6.1.12) $$\sum_{s=1}^{n}\left\{\frac{d}{dt}\left(\frac{\partial \mathfrak{T}}{\partial \dot{q}_s}\right) - \frac{\partial \mathfrak{T}}{\partial q_s} - Q_s\right\}\delta q_s = 0,$$

and this is *the fourth form of the fundamental equation.*

It is important to notice the physical significance of the Q's: the form

$$Q_1\,\delta q_1 + Q_2\,\delta q_2 + \cdots + Q_n\,\delta q_n$$

is the work done by the given forces in the virtual displacement $\delta q_1, \delta q_2, \ldots, \delta q_n$. The Q's are called *generalized force-components*, or briefly *generalized forces.*

6.2 Lagrange's equations. The equation (6.1.12) is valid for an arbitrary virtual displacement $\delta q_1, \delta q_2, \ldots, \delta q_n$. Let us suppose first that the system is holonomic, and that we have used the minimum number of Lagrangian coordinates, so that $n = k$. Then (6.1.12) holds for arbitrary values of $\delta q_1, \delta q_2, \ldots, \delta q_n$, and we obtain *Lagrange's equations of motion*

$$\frac{d}{dt}\left(\frac{\partial \mathfrak{T}}{\partial \dot{q}_r}\right) - \frac{\partial \mathfrak{T}}{\partial q_r} = Q_r, \qquad r = 1, 2, \ldots, n. \tag{6.2.1}$$

Suppose next that the system is not holonomic, and that we have used the minimum number of Lagrangian coordinates, so that $n = k + l$. There are l equations of constraint

$$\sum_{s=1}^{n} B_{rs}\,dq_s + B_r\,dt = 0, \qquad r = 1, 2, \ldots, l, \tag{5.12.2}$$

and (6.1.12) holds, not for arbitrary $\delta\mathbf{q}$, but for $\delta\mathbf{q}$ satisfying the conditions

$$\sum_{s=1}^{n} B_{rs}\,\delta q_s = 0, \qquad r = 1, 2, \ldots, l. \tag{5.12.5}$$

This time the equations of motion take the form

$$\frac{d}{dt}\left(\frac{\partial \mathfrak{T}}{\partial \dot{q}_r}\right) - \frac{\partial \mathfrak{T}}{\partial q_r} = Q_r + \sum_{m=1}^{l} \lambda_m B_{mr}, \qquad r = 1, 2, \ldots, n, \tag{6.2.2}$$

involving l multipliers $\lambda_1, \lambda_2, \ldots, \lambda_l$. With the equations (6.2.2) we must associate the equations of constraint

$$\sum_{s=1}^{n} B_{rs}\dot{q}_s + B_r = 0, \qquad r = 1, 2, \ldots, l, \tag{6.2.3}$$

and the system of $n + l$ equations (6.2.2) and (6.2.3) suffices to determine the $n + l$ unknowns, q's and λ's, as functions of t. The multipliers λ are related linearly to the reactions called into play by the constraints; for example in the problem of the rolling sphere they are related to the reactions on the sphere at its point of contact with the table.

For the sake of completeness we may notice how the equations are modified if there are redundant coordinates, say p more than the minimum number, with p relations

$$F_r(q_1, q_2, \ldots, q_n;\ t) = 0, \qquad r = 1, 2, \ldots, p, \tag{5.12.6}$$

connecting them. In this case we must add in the second member of (6.2.1) or of (6.2.2) the terms

$$\sum_{i=1}^{p} \mu_i \frac{\partial F_i}{\partial q_r}, \qquad r = 1, 2, \ldots, n. \tag{6.2.4}$$

There are p additional unknowns, namely the multipliers $\mu_1, \mu_2, \ldots, \mu_p$, and p additional equations, namely the equations (5.12.6).

The beautiful and powerful theorem contained in the equations (6.2.1) and (6.2.2) was established by Lagrange in 1760. It provides a simple and expeditious method of forming the equations of motion for any dynamical system. To apply the method we have first to choose appropriate Lagrangian coordinates q_r for the system, then to construct the function $\mathfrak{T}$, which is the kinetic energy expressed as a polynomial in the $\dot{q}$'s (with coefficients which are functions of the q's, and possibly also of t), and then to express the work done by the given forces in an arbitrary virtual displacement as a linear differential form $\Sigma\, Q_r\, \delta q_r$. The equations have a central place in Lagrange's great work, the "Mécanique Analytique" (**4**) published in 1788, one of the epoch-making books in the history of mathematics. Lagrange insisted that his method effected the reduction of the dynamical problem to a problem of pure analysis; there is no need to appeal to geometrical arguments constructed *ad hoc* for the particular problem under discussion—"On ne trouvera point de Figures dans cet Ouvrage". The Mécanique Analytique is the primary source of the subject of analytical dynamics, and it is rightly regarded as one of the outstanding intellectual achievements of mankind.

6.3 Lagrange's equations deduced from Hamilton's principle. In § 3.7 we established Hamilton's principle in the form

(3.7.4) $$\int_{t_0}^{t_1}\left(\delta T + \sum_{r=1}^{N} X_r\, \delta x_r\right) dt = 0.$$

Here δ refers to a displacement from a point of the actual path to the *contemporaneous* point on the varied path, so that

(6.3.1) $$\delta \dot{x}_r = \frac{d}{dt}\, \delta x_r.$$

The variation $\delta\mathbf{x}$ is a virtual displacement, arbitrary save for the conditions that each component δx_r is a function of t of class C_2 which vanishes at t_0 and at t_1. Now the principle expresses a property of the dynamical system which is independent of the coordinates in terms of which the configuration of the system is described. Let us express it in terms of Lagrangian coordinates q_r.

We consider the path of the mobile in the q-space. We wish to express Hamilton's principle in the language of q instead of the language of x. Let us build up a varied path by taking at each instant a virtual displacement $\delta\mathbf{q}$ to the contemporaneous point on the varied path; the virtual displacement is arbitrary, save that each δq_r is a function of t of class C_2 vanishing at t_0 and at t_1. Since the variation is contemporaneous,

(6.3.2) $$\delta \dot{q}_r = \frac{d}{dt}\, \delta q_r, \qquad r = 1, 2, \ldots, n.$$

Now the relations (6.3.1) and (6.3.2) are equivalent. This is almost evident if the relations between q's and x's do not involve t, but it is true also in the general case when $x_r = x_r(q_1, q_2, \ldots, q_n;\ t)$, where these functions have the properties mentioned in § 6.1. We can prove this very simply by using the lemmas (6.1.3) and (6.1.4). We have

(5.12.4) $$\delta x_r = \sum_{s=1}^{n} \frac{\partial x_r}{\partial q_s}\, \delta q_s, \qquad r = 1, 2, \ldots, N,$$

(6.1.2) $$\dot{x}_r = \sum_{s=1}^{n} \frac{\partial x_r}{\partial q_s}\, \dot{q}_s + \frac{\partial x_r}{\partial t}, \qquad r = 1, 2, \ldots, N.$$

If therefore we consider a displacement $\delta \mathbf{q}$ satisfying (6.3.2) we have

$$\frac{d}{dt}\,\delta x_r = \sum_{s=1}^{n}\left\{\frac{d}{dt}\left(\frac{\partial x_r}{\partial q_s}\right)\delta q_s + \frac{\partial x_r}{\partial q_s}\frac{d}{dt}\,\delta q_s\right\} \tag{6.3.3}$$

$$= \sum_{s=1}^{n}\left(\frac{\partial \dot{x}_r}{\partial q_s}\,\delta q_s + \frac{\partial \dot{x}_r}{\partial \dot{q}_s}\,\delta \dot{q}_s\right) = \delta \dot{x}_r,$$

where we have used (6.1.3), (6.1.4), and (6.3.2). Thus the displacement $\delta \mathbf{q}$ satisfying (6.3.2) does indeed satisfy (6.3.1), and conversely (the relation between q's and x's being a 1–1 relation) a displacement $\delta \mathbf{x}$ satisfying (6.3.1) also satisfies (6.3.2).

In Hamilton's principle we compare the actual motion of the system with a varied motion in which the terminal configurations are unchanged, and so are the times of departure and of arrival. Thus when we express the principle in terms of Lagrangian coordinates $q_1, q_2, \ldots, q_n$, the terminal points are still fixed (even though the relations between q's and x's involve t) and so are the instants of departure and of arrival. Hamilton's principle therefore takes the form

$$\int_{t_0}^{t_1}\left(\delta \mathfrak{T} + \sum_{r=1}^{n} Q_r\,\delta q_r\right)dt = 0\,. \tag{6.3.4}$$

We shall see that (6.3.4) leads easily to Lagrange's equations. In fact, as we have remarked already, Hamilton's principle is, in essence, only an integrated form of the fundamental equation. The deduction of Lagrange's equations from Hamilton's principle is essentially the same process as that used in the deduction from the fundamental equation itself.

Transforming the first member of (6.3.4) we have

$$\int_{t_0}^{t_1}\left(\delta \mathfrak{T} + \sum_{r=1}^{n} Q_r\,\delta q_r\right)dt = \int_{t_0}^{t_1}\sum_{r=1}^{n}\left(\frac{\partial \mathfrak{T}}{\partial q_r}\,\delta q_r + \frac{\partial \mathfrak{T}}{\partial \dot{q}_r}\,\delta \dot{q}_r + Q_r\,\delta q_r\right)dt \tag{6.3.5}$$

$$= \int_{t_0}^{t_1}\sum_{r=1}^{n}\left(\frac{\partial \mathfrak{T}}{\partial q_r}\,\delta q_r + \frac{\partial \mathfrak{T}}{\partial \dot{q}_r}\frac{d}{dt}\,\delta q_r + Q_r\,\delta q_r\right)dt$$

$$= \sum_{r=1}^{n}\frac{\partial \mathfrak{T}}{\partial \dot{q}_r}\,\delta q_r\Bigg|_{t_0}^{t_1} - \int_{t_0}^{t_1}\sum_{r=1}^{n}\left\{\frac{d}{dt}\left(\frac{\partial \mathfrak{T}}{\partial \dot{q}_r}\right) - \frac{\partial \mathfrak{T}}{\partial q_r} - Q_r\right\}\delta q_r\,dt,$$

where we have used (6.3.2). Since each δq_r vanishes at t_0 and at t_1, (6.3.4) and (6.3.5) lead to

$$\int_{t_0}^{t_1}\sum_{r=1}^{n}\left\{\frac{d}{dt}\left(\frac{\partial \mathfrak{T}}{\partial \dot{q}_r}\right) - \frac{\partial \mathfrak{T}}{\partial q_r} - Q_r\right\}\delta q_r\,dt = 0. \tag{6.3.6}$$

If the system is holonomic, with $n = k$, the equation (6.3.6) holds for values of $\delta q_1, \delta q_2, \ldots, \delta q_n$ which are arbitrary (save for the restriction that $\delta q_r \in C_2$). It follows from a Lemma familiar in the Calculus of Variations that the coefficient of each δq_r in the integrand vanishes identically, and we deduce Lagrange's equations

$$\frac{d}{dt}\left(\frac{\partial \mathfrak{T}}{\partial \dot{q}_r}\right) - \frac{\partial \mathfrak{T}}{\partial q_r} = Q_r, \qquad r = 1, 2, \ldots, n. \tag{6.2.1}$$

If the system is non-holonomic, with $n = k + l$, the equation (6.3.6) holds for values of $\delta q_1, \delta q_2, \ldots, \delta q_n$ satisfying the equations

$$\sum_{s=1}^{n} B_{rs}\,\delta q_s = 0, \qquad r = 1, 2, \ldots, l, \tag{5.12.5}$$

and therefore

$$\frac{d}{dt}\left(\frac{\partial \mathfrak{T}}{\partial \dot{q}_r}\right) - \frac{\partial \mathfrak{T}}{\partial q_r} = Q_r + \sum_{m=1}^{l} \lambda_m B_{mr}, \qquad r = 1, 2, \ldots, n. \tag{6.2.2}$$

In this case we have also the l equations of constraint

$$\sum_{s=1}^{n} B_{rs}\dot{q}_s + B_r = 0, \qquad r = 1, 2, \ldots, l. \tag{6.2.3}$$

As we have noticed (§ 3.8 and § 5.11) the varied path does not in general satisfy the equations of constraint if the system is not holonomic.

6.4 The form of the equations. The rth Lagrangian equation (6.2.1) for a holonomic system has the form

$$a_{r1}\ddot{q}_1 + a_{r2}\ddot{q}_2 + \cdots + a_{rn}\ddot{q}_n = \varphi_r, \tag{6.4.1}$$

where φ_r depends only on the q's, the $\dot{q}$'s, and t: the Lagrangian equations are linear in the $\ddot{q}$'s. Moreover the coefficients a_{rs} are the coefficients in the positive definite quadratic form T_2, and the determinant $\|a_{rs}\|$ does not vanish for any values of the q's and t, so the equations (6.4.1) can be solved for the $\ddot{q}$'s in the form

$$\ddot{q}_r = \psi_r(q_1, q_2, \ldots, q_n;\ \dot{q}_1, \dot{q}_2, \ldots, \dot{q}_n;\ t), \qquad r = 1, 2, \ldots, n; \tag{6.4.2}$$

the functions ψ_r on the right in (6.4.2) depend only on the q's and $\dot{q}$'s and t. It is characteristic of the classical dynamics that the equations of motion determine the acceleration *explicitly* in terms of position and velocity and time. We have noticed this fact already in the simple case of a single free particle (§ 1.1).

If we write $\dot{q}_r = \omega_r$ we can replace the n second-order equations (6.4.2) by the $2n$ first-order equations

$$\dot{q}_r = \omega_r, \qquad \dot{\omega}_r = \psi_r(q_1, q_2, \ldots, q_n;\ \omega_1, \omega_2, \ldots, \omega_n;\ t), \qquad r = 1, 2, \ldots, n. \tag{6.4.3}$$

The equations have been reduced to the form

$$\dot{\mathbf{x}} = \mathbf{X}, \tag{6.4.4}$$

where $\mathbf{x}$ and $\mathbf{X}$ are column matrices, or vectors, with $2n$ components, and $\mathbf{X}$ is a function of $\mathbf{x}$ and t. The form (6.4.4) is of fundamental importance, and will appear frequently in the sequel; we have already noticed it in connexion with the problem of a single particle in § 1.1. We can think of the equations (6.4.3) or (6.4.4) as defining the motion of a representative point or mobile in a space of $2n$ dimensions. We notice that, in the present reduction to the form (6.4.4), the first n equations are purely geometrical: they merely define the variables ω_r, and involve no appeal to the principles of dynamics. These n equations would not be altered if a different set of given forces acted on the same material system. The last n equations, on the other hand, do depend on the laws of motion and on the given forces. But in the applications the two sets are united into a single system of the form (6.4.4), and the original difference of status for the two sets loses its importance.

A far more convenient and more important reduction of the equations of motion to the form (6.4.4) is given by Hamilton's equations, which we shall consider in § 10.13 and in later Chapters.

Returning to the second-order Lagrangian equations, we notice for future reference the explicit form of the contribution to the equations of motion of the components T_2 and T_1 of $\mathfrak{T}$. If we write, as in (6.1.6),

$$T_2 = \tfrac{1}{2}\sum_{r=1}^{n}\sum_{s=1}^{n} a_{rs}\dot{q}_r\dot{q}_s,$$

we have

$$\frac{d}{dt}\left(\frac{\partial T_2}{\partial \dot{q}_r}\right) - \frac{\partial T_2}{\partial q_r} = \sum_{s=1}^{n} a_{rs}\ddot{q}_s + \sum_{s=1}^{n}\frac{\partial a_{rs}}{\partial t}\dot{q}_s + \frac{1}{2}\sum_{u=1}^{n}\sum_{v=1}^{n}\left(\frac{\partial a_{ru}}{\partial q_v} + \frac{\partial a_{rv}}{\partial q_u} - \frac{\partial a_{uv}}{\partial q_r}\right)\dot{q}_u\dot{q}_v. \tag{6.4.5}$$

Further if we write, as in (6.1.7),

$$T_1 = \sum_{r=1}^{n} a_r\dot{q}_r,$$

we have

$$\frac{d}{dt}\left(\frac{\partial T_1}{\partial \dot{q}_r}\right) - \frac{\partial T_1}{\partial q_r} = \frac{\partial a_r}{\partial t} + \sum_{s=1}^{n}\gamma_{rs}\dot{q}_s, \tag{6.4.6}$$

where

$$\gamma_{rs} = \frac{\partial a_r}{\partial q_s} - \frac{\partial a_s}{\partial q_r}. \tag{6.4.7}$$

6.5 Conservative systems and other systems with a potential function. Let us suppose that the given forces X_r are functions of the x's only (not of the $\dot{x}$'s, nor of t) and that for an arbitrary virtual displacement δx the Pfaffian form $\sum_{r=1}^{N} X_r\,\delta x_r$ is a perfect differential $-\delta V$, where V is a uniform function of $x_1, x_2, \ldots, x_N$ of class C_1. The given forces are then said to be *conservative* (cf. § 3.4) and V is the *potential energy function*. Let us suppose further that the relations between q's and x's do not contain t. Then

$$\sum_{r=1}^{N} X_r\,\delta x_r = \sum_{s=1}^{n}\left(\sum_{r=1}^{N} X_r\frac{\partial x_r}{\partial q_s}\right)\delta q_s = \sum_{s=1}^{n} Q_s\,\delta q_s, \tag{6.5.1}$$

and

$$\sum_{s=1}^{n} Q_s\,\delta q_s = -\delta\mathfrak{V}, \tag{6.5.2}$$

where

$$V(x_1, x_2, \ldots, x_N) = \mathfrak{V}(q_1, q_2, \ldots, q_n). \tag{6.5.3}$$

Thus the fourth form of the fundamental equation (6.1.12) becomes

$$\sum_{r=1}^{n}\left\{\frac{d}{dt}\left(\frac{\partial\mathfrak{T}}{\partial\dot{q}_r}\right) - \frac{\partial\mathfrak{T}}{\partial q_r} + \frac{\partial\mathfrak{V}}{\partial q_r}\right\}\delta q_r = 0. \tag{6.5.4}$$

In this case the Lagrangian equations (6.2.1) and (6.2.2), for holonomic and for non-holonomic systems respectively, take the forms

(6.5.5) $$\frac{d}{dt}\left(\frac{\partial \mathfrak{T}}{\partial \dot{q}_r}\right) - \frac{\partial \mathfrak{T}}{\partial q_r} = -\frac{\partial \mathfrak{V}}{\partial q_r}, \qquad r = 1, 2, \ldots, n,$$

(6.5.6) $$\frac{d}{dt}\left(\frac{\partial \mathfrak{T}}{\partial \dot{q}_r}\right) - \frac{\partial \mathfrak{T}}{\partial q_r} = -\frac{\partial \mathfrak{V}}{\partial q_r} + \sum_{m=1}^{l} \lambda_m B_{mr}, \qquad r = 1, 2, \ldots, n.$$

In some cases the given forces contain other forces, say $\bar{X}_r$, in addition to the conservative forces. These may be, for example, non-conservative forces depending on position, or forces depending on velocity. If, as in (6.1.10),

(6.5.7) $$\bar{Q}_s = \sum_{r=1}^{N} \bar{X}_r \frac{\partial x_r}{\partial q_s},$$

so that the work done by the additional forces in a virtual displacement is $\sum_{s=1}^{n} \bar{Q}_s\, \delta q_s$, the equation (6.5.4) must be replaced by

(6.5.8) $$\sum_{r=1}^{n}\left\{\frac{d}{dt}\left(\frac{\partial \mathfrak{T}}{\partial \dot{q}_r}\right) - \frac{\partial \mathfrak{T}}{\partial q_r} + \frac{\partial \mathfrak{V}}{\partial q_r} - \bar{Q}_r\right\}\delta q_r = 0,$$

which comprises both (6.1.12) and (6.5.4). The Lagrangian equations, for the two cases of holonomic and non-holonomic systems, now become

(6.5.9) $$\frac{d}{dt}\left(\frac{\partial \mathfrak{T}}{\partial \dot{q}_r}\right) - \frac{\partial \mathfrak{T}}{\partial q_r} = -\frac{\partial \mathfrak{V}}{\partial q_r} + \bar{Q}_r, \qquad r = 1, 2, \ldots, n,$$

(6.5.10) $$\frac{d}{dt}\left(\frac{\partial \mathfrak{T}}{\partial \dot{q}_r}\right) - \frac{\partial \mathfrak{T}}{\partial q_r} = -\frac{\partial \mathfrak{V}}{\partial q_r} + \bar{Q}_r + \sum_{m=1} \lambda_m B_{mr}, \qquad r = 1, 2, \ldots, n.$$

The form (6.5.4) is valid also in other cases. Suppose more generally, that the given forces X_r depend upon t as well as upon the x's, and suppose also that the relations between q's and x's do involve t,

(6.5.11) $$x_r = x_r(q_1, q_2, \ldots, q_n;\ t),$$

It may happen (cf. § 3.4) that for an arbitrary virtual displacement δx

(6.5.12) $$\sum_{r=1}^{N} X_r\, \delta x_r = -\delta_s V,$$

where the differential in the second member is a space-differential with t unvaried,

(6.5.13) $$\delta_s V = \sum_{r=1}^{N} \frac{\partial V}{\partial x_r}\, \delta x_r.$$

If now

(6.5.14) $$V(x_1, x_2, \ldots, x_N;\ t) = \mathfrak{V}(q_1, q_2, \ldots, q_n;\ t),$$

we have

(6.5.15) $$\sum_{r=1}^{N} \frac{\partial V}{\partial x_r}\, \delta x_r = \sum_{s=1}^{n}\left(\sum_{r=1}^{N} \frac{\partial V}{\partial x_r}\frac{\partial x_r}{\delta q_s}\right)\delta q_s = \sum_{s=1}^{n} \frac{\partial \mathfrak{V}}{\delta q_s}\, \delta q_s,$$

so

(6.5.16) $$\sum_{s=1}^{n} Q_s\, \delta q_s = -\delta_s \mathfrak{V},$$

where $\delta_s \mathfrak{V}$ denotes a space-differential $\sum_{s=1}^{n} \frac{\partial \mathfrak{V}}{\partial q_s}\, \delta q_s$ with t unvaried. In this case also (6.5.4) is still valid.

The simplest, and also the commonest, case is that in which (i) the relations between q's and x's do not involve t, (ii) the given forces are conservative, and (iii) the system is holonomic, and we choose Lagrangian coordinates such that $n = k$. In this case

$$\mathfrak{T} = T_2 = \tfrac{1}{2} \sum_{r=1}^{n} \sum_{s=1}^{n} a_{rs}\dot{q}_r\dot{q}_s, \tag{6.5.17}$$

and the coefficients a_{rs} are functions of the q's only; $\mathfrak{V}$ also is a function of the q's only, and (6.5.4) holds for arbitrary values of $\delta q_1, \delta q_2, \ldots, \delta q_n$. Such a system is called a *natural system*.

6.6 The Lagrangian function. At this point it is convenient to make a change of notation. Hitherto, when describing the configuration and motion of the system by x's and $\dot{x}$'s, we have denoted the kinetic and potential energy functions by T and V. In establishing the fourth form of the fundamental equation and Lagrange's equations we have, to avoid any possibility of confusion, denoted the corresponding functions, expressed in terms of q's and $\dot{q}$'s, by $\mathfrak{T}$ and $\mathfrak{V}$. We can now safely drop the last symbols and denote the kinetic and potential energy functions, expressed in terms of q's and $\dot{q}$'s (and possibly also of t), by T and V. Thus, for the cases discussed in § 6.5, the fourth form of the fundamental equation is

$$\sum_{r=1}^{n}\left\{\frac{d}{dt}\left(\frac{\partial T}{\partial \dot{q}_r}\right) - \frac{\partial T}{\partial q_r} + \frac{\partial V}{\partial q_r}\right\}\delta q_r = 0. \tag{6.6.1}$$

If we write L for $T - V$ the equation (6.6.1) can be written (since V does not involve the $\dot{q}$'s)

$$\sum_{r=1}^{n}\left\{\frac{d}{dt}\left(\frac{\partial L}{\partial \dot{q}_r}\right) - \frac{\partial L}{\partial q_r}\right\}\delta q_r = 0. \tag{6.6.2}$$

If the system is holonomic, with $n = k$, the equations of motion are

$$\frac{d}{dt}\left(\frac{\partial L}{\partial \dot{q}_r}\right) = \frac{\partial L}{\partial q_r}, \qquad r = 1, 2, \ldots, n. \tag{6.6.3}$$

If the system is non-holonomic, with $n = k + l$, the equations of motion are

$$\frac{d}{dt}\left(\frac{\partial L}{\partial \dot{q}_r}\right) = \frac{\partial L}{\partial q_r} + \sum_{m=1}^{l} \lambda_m B_{mr}, \qquad r = 1, 2, \ldots, n. \tag{6.6.4}$$

With these n equations we must associate the l equations of constraint

$$\sum_{s=1}^{n} B_{rs}\dot{q}_s + B_r = 0, \qquad r = 1, 2, \ldots, l. \tag{6.2.3}$$

The Lagrangian function L is called a *descriptive function* for the dynamical system. From the function we can construct the equations of motion for the system, so the single function contains in itself a complete description of the motions that are possible for the dynamical system. We shall meet other descriptive functions in the sequel.

We can extend the results (6.6.3) and (6.6.4) to include certain cases in which the given forces depend on the velocities. If the work done by the given forces in an arbitrary virtual displacement can be expressed in the form

$$\sum_{r=1}^{n}\left\{\frac{d}{dt}\left(\frac{\partial V}{\partial \dot{q}_r}\right) - \frac{\partial V}{\partial q_r}\right\}\delta q_r, \tag{6.6.5}$$

where V is now a function of q's and $\dot{q}$'s (and possibly also of t) the equation (6.6.2), with $L = T - V$, still holds. The equations (6.6.3) and (6.6.4) still follow as before.

But now a word of caution is necessary. The function V can only involve the $\dot{q}$'s *linearly*, i.e. it must have the form

$$-a_1\dot{q}_1 - a_2\dot{q}_2 - \cdots - a_n\dot{q}_n + V_0, \tag{6.6.6}$$

where the a's and V_0 depend only on the q's (and possibly on t). Otherwise the given forces would be functions of the acceleration-components, which, as we have seen (§ 1.4), is inadmissible in Newtonian dynamics.

For a natural system, L is of the form $T - V$, where T is a homogeneous quadratic function of the $\dot{q}$'s. In other cases T may contain terms linear in the $\dot{q}$'s, and now we see another context in which terms linear in the $\dot{q}$'s may appear in L. The effect in the equations of motion of terms in L which are linear in the $\dot{q}$'s will be discussed later (§ 10.6).

6.7 Jacobi's integral. Let us suppose that the system described by the Lagrangian function L satisfies the following two conditions:

(i) L does not contain t explicitly,

(ii) the velocity $\dot{\mathbf{q}}$ in the actual motion is a virtual velocity. Then we may write $\dot{q}_r$ for δq_r in (6.6.2), and we have

$$\sum_{r=1}^{n}\left\{\frac{d}{dt}\left(\frac{\partial L}{\partial \dot{q}_r}\right) - \frac{\partial L}{\partial q_r}\right\}\dot{q}_r = 0. \tag{6.7.1}$$

We can write the first member of this equation in the form

$$\frac{d}{dt}\left(\sum_{r=1}^{n}\dot{q}_r\frac{\partial L}{\partial \dot{q}_r}\right) - \sum_{r=1}^{n}\left(\frac{\partial L}{\partial q_r}\dot{q}_r + \frac{\partial L}{\partial \dot{q}_r}\ddot{q}_r\right) = \frac{d}{dt}\left(\sum_{r=1}^{n}\dot{q}_r\frac{\partial L}{\partial \dot{q}_r} - L\right),$$

and (6.7.1) leads to

$$\sum_{r=1}^{n}\dot{q}_r\frac{\partial L}{\partial \dot{q}_r} - L = h, \tag{6.7.2}$$

where h is a constant. This is *Jacobi's integral*. It is also called the integral of energy, or the equation of energy, because in the particular case of a natural system

$$\sum_{r=1}^{n}\dot{q}_r\frac{\partial L}{\partial \dot{q}_r} = 2T, \tag{6.7.3}$$

and (6.7.2) is therefore equivalent to the equation

$$T + V = h. \tag{6.7.4}$$

Let us consider in what circumstances the conditions for the existence of an integral of the form (6.7.2) are fulfilled. The condition (i) will certainly be satisfied if neither T nor V involves t. Now T will not involve t explicitly if the relations between x's and q's do not contain the time. But this is not the only possibility, and sometimes T does not involve t explicitly even though the x's are functions of the q's and of t. A conspicuous example occurs when we use axes rotating uniformly. Suppose for example that the trihedral $Ox'y'z'$ revolves *steadily* about the axis Oz'

which coincides with the axis Oz in the original fixed trihedral $Oxyz$. Then, for a particular particle of the system,

$$\left\{\begin{aligned} x &= x' \cos \omega t - y' \sin \omega t, \\ y &= x' \sin \omega t + y' \cos \omega t, \\ z &= z', \end{aligned}\right. \tag{6.7.5}$$

where ω is the (constant) angular velocity. Thus,

$$\dot{x}^2 + \dot{y}^2 + \dot{z}^2 = (\dot{x}' - y'\omega)^2 + (\dot{y}' + x'\omega)^2 + \dot{z}'^2, \tag{6.7.6}$$

and therefore

$$\begin{aligned} T &= \tfrac{1}{2}Sm\{(\dot{x}' - y'\omega)^2 + (\dot{y}' + x'\omega)^2 + \dot{z}'^2\} \\ &= \tfrac{1}{2}Sm(\dot{x}'^2 + \dot{y}'^2 + \dot{z}'^2) + \omega Sm(x'\dot{y}' - y'\dot{x}') + \tfrac{1}{2}\omega^2 Sm(x'^2 + y'^2). \end{aligned} \tag{6.7.7}$$

Suppose now that we choose Lagrangian coordinates so that the Cartesian coordinates *relative to the rotating axes* are functions of the q's not involving the time. Then

$$\left\{\begin{aligned} \tfrac{1}{2}Sm(\dot{x}'^2 + \dot{y}'^2 + \dot{z}'^2) &= T_2, \\ \omega Sm(x'\dot{y}' - y'\dot{x}') &= T_1, \\ \tfrac{1}{2}\omega^2 Sm(x'^2 + y'^2) &= T_0, \end{aligned}\right. \tag{6.7.8}$$

where T_2 is a quadratic form in the $\dot{q}$'s with coefficients which are functions of the q's, T_1 is a linear form in the $\dot{q}$'s with coefficients which are functions of the q's, and T_0 is a function of the q's. Thus the function T,

$$T = T_2 + T_1 + T_0, \tag{6.7.9}$$

does not involve t, though the relations between q's and x's do involve t.

Again, the work done by the given forces in a virtual displacement is

$$S(X\,\delta x + Y\,\delta y + Z\,\delta z) = S(X'\,\delta x' + Y'\,\delta y' + Z'\,\delta z'), \tag{6.7.10}$$

and this will be of the form $-\delta V$, where $V = V(q_1, q_2, \ldots, q_n)$, if the given forces, when measured in the rotating axes, constitute a conservative system. An important case is that of symmetry about the axis of rotation Oz. A trivial example is provided by a laboratory experiment in which the axis of rotation is vertical and the given forces are the weights.

The condition (ii) is certainly satisfied if the system is holonomic and $n = k$. It holds also for a non-holonomic system, provided that the coefficients B_r in the equations of constraint (6.2.3) are all zero. This is clearly true if the system is catastatic (§ 2.3) and the relations connecting x's and q's do not involve t. An example is provided by a sphere rolling under gravity on a fixed perfectly rough surface.

6.8 The explicit form of Jacobi's integral. Let us suppose that the conditions for the existence of Jacobi's integral are fulfilled, i.e. L does not contain t explicitly, and the actual velocity is a virtual velocity. Then

$$\sum_{r=1}^{n} \dot{q}_r \frac{\partial L}{\partial \dot{q}_r} - L = h, \tag{6.7.2}$$

where

$$L = T_2 + T_1 + T_0 - V. \tag{6.8.1}$$

Now by Euler's theorem on homogeneous functions

$$\sum_{r=1}^{n} \dot{q}_r \frac{\partial L}{\partial \dot{q}_r} = 2T_2 + T_1, \tag{6.8.2}$$

so (6.7.2) becomes

$$T_2 + V - T_0 = h. \tag{6.8.3}$$

This is the explicit form of Jacobi's integral.

The terms T_0 and $-V$ have equal status in the Lagrangian function, and the effects of these two terms in the equations of motion are indistinguishable—a fact not without significance in the history of the theory of magnetic energy. We are not surprised therefore at the appearance of the expression $V - T_0$, in which the two terms are associated, in the first member of (6.8.3). It is important to notice that the term T_1 in L has no part in Jacobi's integral. An important application occurs in the rotating axes problem considered above in § 6.7. The integral of energy is the same as we should get if the axes were not rotating and the centrifugal forces were added to the given forces; in other words, if the terms

$$-\tfrac{1}{2}Sm\omega^2(x'^2 + y'^2) \tag{6.8.4}$$

were added to V.

The terms T_1 do not appear in (6.8.3). In certain cases we can go further and assert that they do not affect the motion at all, and then they can be discarded from L. This is true whenever T_1 has the form

$$\frac{d}{dt} f(q_1, q_2, \ldots, q_n) = \sum_{r=1}^{n} \frac{\partial f}{\partial q_r} \dot{q}_r. \tag{6.8.5}$$

In this case, each of the expressions

$$\frac{d}{dt}\left(\frac{\partial T_1}{\partial \dot{q}_r}\right) - \frac{\partial T_1}{\partial q_r}$$

vanishes identically (as we see from the second lemma (6.1.4) of § 6.1). If T_1 has the form (6.8.5) it is annihilated by the Lagrangian operator

$$\frac{d}{dt}\frac{\partial}{\partial \dot{q}_r} - \frac{\partial}{\partial q_r}.$$

The result has an important application to the problem of the motion of a system relative to rotating axes. We notice that if $T_1 (= \omega Sm(x'\dot{y}' - y'\dot{x}'))$ has the form (6.8.5) the effect of the rotation (on the motion relative to the moving axes) is completely accounted for by the centrifugal field. This is true, in particular, for any system with only one freedom. This fact is evident otherwise, because in the case of one freedom Jacobi's integral suffices for the solution of the problem, and this integral is independent of T_1.

As a concrete example we may consider a bead sliding on a smooth rigid wire (not necessarily a plane curve) which rotates inexorably, with constant angular velocity ω, about a vertical axis. To study the motion of the bead relative to the wire we may forget the rotation and add a centrifugal force $mr\omega^2$, where r is the distance from the axis of rotation; this is equivalent to adding a term $-\tfrac{1}{2}mr^2\omega^2$ in V. An important special case is considered in *Example* 6.8 below.

Before leaving this topic another result of this type, but somewhat more general, should be noticed. The addition of an expression

$$\frac{d}{dt} f(q_1, q_2, \ldots, q_r; t) \tag{6.8.6}$$

to the Lagrangian function L has no effect in the equations of motion. This follows again from the lemma (6.1.4). Terms in L of the form (6.8.6) are nugatory, and can simply be omitted. The result is evident also as a consequence of Hamilton's principle.

Example 6.8. *Simple pendulum in rotating axes.* A bead slides on a smooth wire, in the form of a circle of radius a, which rotates inexorably about a vertical diameter with constant angular velocity ω; to study the motion of the bead relative to the wire.

We denote the angular displacement of the bead from the lowest point of the wire by θ (as in *Example* 5.2*A*). Jacobi's integral is

$$\tfrac{1}{2}ma^2\dot{\theta}^2 - mga\cos\theta - \tfrac{1}{2}ma^2\omega^2\sin^2\theta = mga\eta,$$

which can be written in the form

$$\tfrac{1}{2}\dot{\theta}^2 = n^2(\eta + \cos\theta) + \tfrac{1}{2}\omega^2\sin^2\theta, \tag{6.8.7}$$

where $n^2 = g/a$. This is an equation of the type (1.2.10), and, as we have seen, the nature of the motion for different values of η can be seen from the graph of the second member. If $\omega = 0$ we return to the problem of the simple pendulum, and (6.8.7) reduces to (5.2.2). For small values of ω the graph is not very different from Fig. 5.2*b*, and the possible types of motion are roughly similar to those for the simple pendulum. The critical value of ω is n, and for $\omega > n$ the possible types of motion differ fundamentally from those for the simple pendulum. The condition $\omega > n$ means, of course, that the period of rotation is less than the period for small oscillations of the pendulum. Let us therefore consider this case $\omega > n$, and write $\omega^2 = n^2\sec\alpha$, where α is an acute angle. The second member of (6.8.7) is now

$$\begin{aligned} f(\theta) &= n^2(\eta + \cos\theta + \tfrac{1}{2}\sec\alpha\sin^2\theta) \\ &= \tfrac{1}{2}n^2\sec\alpha\,\{2\eta\cos\alpha + 1 + \cos^2\alpha - (\cos\theta - \cos\alpha)^2\}, \end{aligned} \tag{6.8.8}$$

and its graph is shown in Fig. 6.8.* There are maxima at $\theta = \pm\alpha$, and a minimum at $\theta = 0$. Six types of motion are possible, according to the value of η, as indicated in the figure. (Instead of raising the graph to indicate an increase in the value of η, we draw the graph once for all, and lower the x-axis when η is increased.)

(i) $\eta = -1 - \lambda$, where $\lambda = (1 - \cos\alpha)^2/(2\cos\alpha) = (\omega^2 - n^2)^2/(2n^2\omega^2)$. This is the least possible value for η. The bead rests (relative to the wire) in stable equilibrium at $\theta = \alpha$ or at $\theta = -\alpha$. The period of a small oscillation (relative to the wire) if the equilibrium is disturbed is $2\pi/(\omega\sin\alpha)$.

(ii) $-1 - \lambda < \eta < -1$. There is a libration motion between θ_1 and θ_2 (see figure). or between $-\theta_1$ and $-\theta_2$, where $0 < \theta_1 < \alpha < \theta_2 < \tfrac{1}{2}\pi$.

(iii) $\eta = -1$. The bead rests in unstable equilibrium at $\theta = 0$, or there is a limitation motion in which θ, perhaps after first increasing to a value θ_3, decreases steadily and tends to zero as $t \to \infty$.

* The graph is drawn for the case $\omega^2 = 2n^2$; in this case, $\theta_3 = \tfrac{1}{2}\pi$.

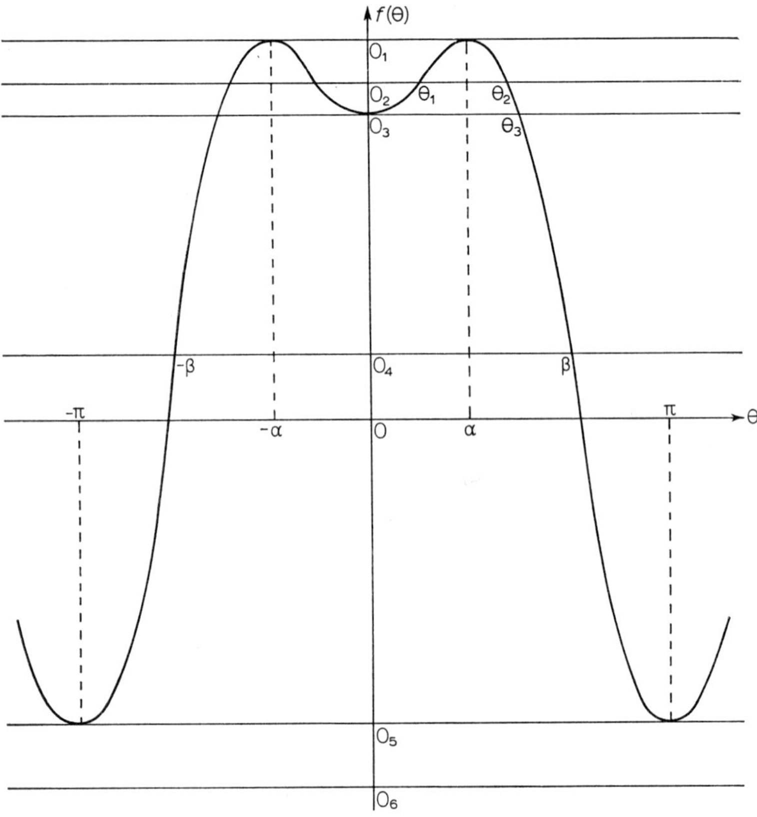

Figure 6.8

(iv) $-1 < \eta < 1$. There is a libration motion between $-\beta$ and β (see figure) roughly similar to the libration motion of the ordinary simple pendulum.

(v) $\eta = 1$. The bead rests in unstable equilibrium at $\theta = \pi$ (or, what is the same thing, at $\theta = -\pi$), or there is a limitation motion in which $\theta \to \pi$, or $\theta \to -\pi$, as $t \to \infty$.

(vi) $\eta > 1$. If $\dot{\theta} > 0$ initially, θ increases always with t.

This completes our survey of the problem. The type of motion depends on the particular range of values in which η lies, and in each case the explicit relation connecting θ with the time can be derived from (6.8.7).

6.9 An insidious fallacy. An error that has appeared many times in the history of dynamics* is the deduction of Lagrange's equations from Jacobi's integral. We have, from (6.7.2),

(6.9.1) $$\frac{d}{dt}\left(\sum_{r=1}^{n} \dot{q}_r \frac{\partial L}{\partial \dot{q}_r} - L\right) = 0,$$

and we can write this in the form

(6.9.2) $$\sum_{r=1}^{n}\left\{\frac{d}{dt}\left(\frac{\partial L}{\partial \dot{q}_r}\right) - \frac{\partial L}{\partial q_r}\right\}\dot{q}_r = 0.$$

* See for example G. D. Birkhoff, "Dynamical Systems" (**35**) p. 17.

This merely amounts to reversing the steps of the argument by which we deduced Jacobi's integral from Lagrange's equations.

We cannot deduce Lagrange's equations from (6.9.2). To do so we should need to know that

$$\sum_{r=1}^{n}\left\{\frac{d}{dt}\left(\frac{\partial L}{\partial \dot{q}_r}\right)-\frac{\partial L}{\partial q_r}\right\}\lambda_r = 0. \tag{6.9.3}$$

is true for *arbitrary* values of $\lambda_1, \lambda_2, \ldots, \lambda_n$, whereas (6.9.2) only tells us that (6.9.3) holds when each λ_r is equal to the value of the corresponding $\dot{q}_r$ in the actual motion.

6.10 The generalized momentum-components. The quantities $\partial L/\partial \dot{q}_r$ which appear in Lagrange's equations are called *generalized momentum-components,* or simply *momenta,* and they are usually denoted by the symbols p_r,

$$p_r = \frac{\partial L}{\partial \dot{q}_r}. \tag{6.10.1}$$

We observe that the momenta are linear functions of the velocity-components $\dot{q}_1, \dot{q}_2, \ldots, \dot{q}_n$; for a natural system they are homogeneous linear functions of the velocity-components, with coefficients which are functions of the q's.

We shall find in the sequel that it is sometimes more convenient to describe the state of the system at a given instant by giving the values of q's and p's (coordinates and momenta) rather than the values of q's and $\dot{q}$'s (coordinates and velocities).

The provenance of the name *momentum* is clear from elementary examples.

(i) If a particle moves in space in a conservative field whose potential function is V we have

$$L = \tfrac{1}{2}m(\dot{x}^2+\dot{y}^2+\dot{z}^2) - V, \tag{6.10.2}$$

where (x, y, z) are ordinary Cartesian coordinates. The generalized momentum-component corresponding to the coordinate x is

$$\frac{\partial L}{\partial \dot{x}} = m\dot{x}, \tag{6.10.3}$$

and this is the component of linear momentum in the direction Ox. In a problem such as this in which the Lagrangian coordinates are not numbered we shall sometimes denote the generalized momentum-component corresponding to a Lagrangian coordinate q by p_q; for example in the problem before us we write

$$p_x = \frac{\partial L}{\partial \dot{x}} = m\dot{x}. \tag{6.10.4}$$

(ii) If a particle moves in a plane under a central attraction $\varphi(r)$ towards O, the Lagrangian function (using polar coordinates as in *Example* 5.2B) is

$$L = \tfrac{1}{2}m(\dot{r}^2 + r^2\dot{\theta}^2) - V, \tag{6.10.5}$$

where

$$V = V(r) = \int_{r_0}^{r}\varphi(\xi)\,d\xi. \tag{6.10.6}$$

In this case

$$p_\theta = \frac{\partial L}{\partial \dot{\theta}} = mr^2\dot{\theta}, \tag{6.10.7}$$

and this is the angular momentum about O.

6.11 Ignorable coordinates. In § 6.7 we found, for systems of a certain type, a first integral of the equations of motion. Another first integral can be found immediately if the system is described by coordinates one of which is *ignorable*; a coordinate q_1 is said to be ignorable if q_1 does not appear in L (though of course $\dot{q}_1$ must appear). In this case the corresponding Lagrangian equation is

$$\frac{d}{dt}\left(\frac{\partial T}{\partial \dot{q}_1}\right) = 0, \tag{6.11.1}$$

whence

$$\frac{\partial T}{\partial \dot{q}_1} = \text{constant.} \tag{6.11.2}$$

This is a first integral of the equations of motion; it expresses the constancy of the momentum-component p_1 corresponding to the ignorable coordinate q_1,

$$p_1 = \text{constant} = \beta_1, \tag{6.11.3}$$

and it is called an *integral of momentum.*

Let us consider again the elementary examples cited in § 6.10. In (i) if V is independent of x, then x is an ignorable coordinate. In this case the force acting on the particle is always perpendicular to Ox. The corresponding momentum integral is

$$p_x = m\dot{x} = \beta,$$

exhibiting the conservation of linear momentum in the direction Ox. In (ii) the coordinate θ is ignorable, and the corresponding momentum integral is

$$p_\theta = mr^2\dot{\theta} = \beta,$$

exhibiting the conservation of angular momentum about O.

6.12 The invariance of Lagrange's equations. The fact that the Lagrangian equations of motion for a holonomic system have the same form whatever Lagrangian coordinates are chosen to describe the system is evident, whether we derive the equations from the fundamental equation (§ 6.2) or from Hamilton's principle (§ 6.3). Nevertheless a direct proof of the invariance may be of interest.

Consider a one-one transformation from the Lagrangian coordinates $q_1, q_2, \ldots, q_n$ to new coordinates $q_1', q_2', \ldots, q_n'$, where

$$q_r = f_r(q_1', q_2', \ldots, q_n'; t), \qquad r = 1, 2, \ldots, n, \tag{6.12.1}$$

and $f_r \in C_2$. We shall need two lemmas similar to (6.1.3) and (6.1.4), namely

$$\frac{\partial \dot{q}_r}{\partial \dot{q}_s'} = \frac{\partial q_r}{\partial q_s'}, \quad \frac{\partial \dot{q}_r}{\partial q_s'} = \frac{d}{dt}\left(\frac{\partial q_r}{\partial q_s'}\right). \tag{6.12.2}$$

If

$$L(q, \dot{q}, t) = L'(q', \dot{q}', t), \tag{6.12.3}$$

we have

$$\begin{aligned}\frac{\partial L'}{\partial q_r'} &= \sum_{s=1}^{n} \frac{\partial L}{\partial q_s}\frac{\partial q_s}{\partial q_r'} + \sum_{s=1}^{n} \frac{\partial L}{\partial \dot{q}_s}\frac{\partial \dot{q}_s}{\partial q_r'} \\ &= \sum_{s=1}^{n} \frac{\partial L}{\partial q_s}\frac{\partial q_s}{\partial q_r'} + \sum_{s=1}^{n} \frac{\partial L}{\partial \dot{q}_s}\frac{d}{dt}\left(\frac{\partial q_s}{\partial q_r'}\right)\end{aligned} \tag{6.12.4}$$

and

(6.12.5)
$$\frac{\partial L'}{\partial \dot{q}_r'} = \sum_{s=1}^{n} \frac{\partial L}{\partial \dot{q}_s}\frac{\partial \dot{q}_s}{\partial \dot{q}_r'} = \sum_{s=1}^{n} \frac{\partial L}{\partial \dot{q}_s}\frac{\partial q_s}{\partial q_r'}.$$

Hence

(6.12.6)
$$\frac{d}{dt}\left(\frac{\partial L'}{\partial \dot{q}_r'}\right) - \frac{\partial L'}{\partial q_r'} = \frac{d}{dt}\left(\sum_{s=1}^{n} \frac{\partial L}{\partial \dot{q}_s}\frac{\partial q_s}{\partial q_r'}\right) - \sum_{s=1}^{n} \frac{\partial L}{\partial q_s}\frac{\partial q_s}{\partial q_r'} - \sum_{s=1}^{n} \frac{\partial L}{\partial \dot{q}_s}\frac{d}{dt}\left(\frac{\partial q_s}{\partial q_r'}\right)$$
$$= \sum_{s=1}^{n}\left\{\frac{d}{dt}\left(\frac{\partial L}{\partial \dot{q}_s}\right) - \frac{\partial L}{\partial q_s}\right\}\frac{\partial q_s}{\partial q_r'}.$$

Now the determinant $\left\| \frac{\partial q_s}{\partial q_r'} \right\|$ is non-vanishing, and the invariance of the equations follows.

Chapter VII

The theory of rotations

7.1 Motion of a rigid body. When we use Lagrange's equations to study the motion of a single rigid body, we need to express the kinetic energy of the body in terms of the Lagrangian coordinates chosen to describe its position and orientation. The same formulae will be needed when we discuss the motion of a dynamical system involving a number of rigid bodies. We are therefore led to a discussion of the theory of the motion of a rigid body.

Our discussion, however, will have a far wider scope than that suggested by the objective just mentioned, that of constructing a Lagrangian function. We shall consider in this Chapter a number of theorems, of great interest and importance, which are concerned with the displacement and the motion of a rigid body. The use of some of these results in Lagrange's equations is only one among many applications.

We consider the dynamical system consisting of a single rigid body. The configuration of the system is defined by the position of a particular particle of the rigid body (i.e. of a point fixed in the body), say the centre of gravity G, and by the orientation of the body. This dichotomy reappears in the theorem of König, which enables us to express the kinetic energy of the body as the sum of two parts, one determined by the motion of G, the other by the motion relative to G, i.e. by the change of orientation with G thought of as fixed. Explicitly

(7.1.1)
$$\begin{aligned} T &= \tfrac{1}{2}Sm(\dot{x}^2 + \dot{y}^2 + \dot{z}^2) \\ &= \tfrac{1}{2}Sm\{(\dot{\xi} + \dot{\alpha})^2 + (\dot{\eta} + \dot{\beta})^2 + (\dot{\zeta} + \dot{\gamma})^2\}, \end{aligned}$$

where (α, β, γ) defines the position of the typical particle relative to the centre of gravity (ξ, η, ζ). Since $Sm\dot{\alpha} = Sm\dot{\beta} = Sm\dot{\gamma} = 0$ we have *König's theorem*,

(7.1.2)
$$T = \tfrac{1}{2}M(\dot{\xi}^2 + \dot{\eta}^2 + \dot{\zeta}) + \tfrac{1}{2}Sm(\dot{\alpha}^2 + \dot{\beta}^2 + \dot{\gamma}^2),$$

where $M(= Sm)$ is the mass of the body. The kinetic energy is expressed as the sum of two parts. The first is the formula we should get if all the mass were concentrated at G, the second is the formula we should get if G were fixed and the body rotated about G.

To define a change of configuration of the body we need to specify first the displacement of G, and second the change of orientation. We shall find it convenient to isolate the second of these, and in the first instance to study changes of orientation alone. To begin with, therefore, we shall deal with a body of which one point, say O, is fixed.

7.2 Euler's theorem. The theorem (discovered by Euler in 1776) asserts, of a body with one point O fixed, that *any displacement is a rotation*. In other words, any change of orientation of the body can be achieved by a rotation about some axis through O.

The orientation of the body is defined by the directions of two lines OA, OB, fixed in the body. It will be convenient to take OA and OB of unit length, so that A and B are fixed points of the body at unit distance from O. We can think of two spheres, with O as centre, a sphere of radius 1 fixed in space, and a thin shell, of inner radius 1, fixed in the body and moving with it. The motion of the shell as it slides over the fixed sphere defines the motion of the body.

Suppose that in a certain displacement of the body the point A of the shell moves to B, and the point of the shell which was originally at B moves to C. (We have taken OA arbitrarily, but have chosen a special OB suited to our particular purpose.) The plane ABC cuts the fixed sphere in a circle (Fig. 7.2a). If L is either pole of this circle the isosceles triangles LAB, LBC are congruent; the arcs AB, BC are equal because they represent two positions of the same arc of the moving shell. Thus AB can be brought into the position BC by a rotation about OL through an angle ALB.

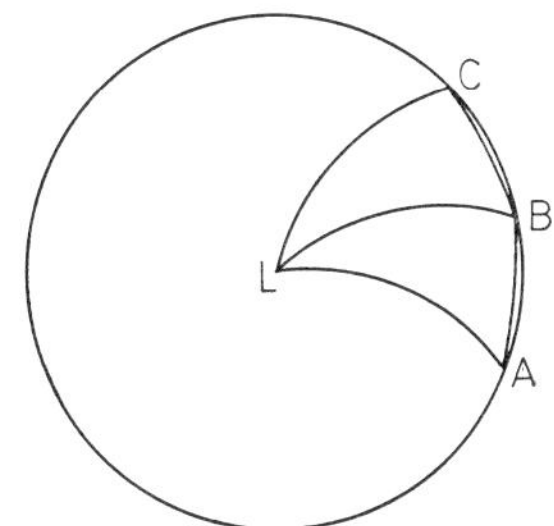

Figure 7.2a

Some exceptional cases should be noticed. If B coincides with A, the truth of the theorem is evident, and the displacement is a rotation about OA. If B does not coincide with A, but C does coincide with A, there are two possibilities. (i) If A,O,B are not collinear, there is a unique great circle through A and B, and the displacement is a *half-turn* (i.e. a rotation through an angle π) about OM, where M is the mid-point of either of the great-circle arcs AB. (ii) If A,O,B are collinear, the argument fails. The points A and B are at opposite ends of a diameter of the shell, and this is the exceptional case in which the directions OA and OB do not suffice to define the orientation of the body. There is no longer a unique great circle through A and B. To meet this difficulty, we proceed as follows. We take another starting-point A' on the shell; A' is arbitrary, except that it must not coincide with, nor be diametrically opposite to, A, and then the directions OA and OA' define the orientation of the body precisely. We then construct the points B' and C', which are derived from A' in the same way that B and C are derived from A. Then C' coincides with A' (for otherwise C would not coincide with A). If A',O,B' are not collinear, we complete the proof as before. If A',O,B' are collinear, the displacement is a half-turn about OL, where L is either pole of the great circle $ABA'B'$. It is apparent that the troublesome case is that in which the rotation is a half-turn, and this difficulty connected with half-turns will reappear later.

Euler's theorem is equivalent to the statement that in any two orientations of the body there is one line OL fixed in the body whose direction (and sense) remains invariant. If we consider any line parallel to OL and fixed in the body, its direction after the displacement is parallel to its initial direction; and if we consider a section of the body by a plane perpendicular to OL, the section can reach its final position by moving in its own plane.

We give another proof of Euler's theorem, now looked at from this new point of view. We can bring OA into its new position OA' by a half-turn about OM, where M is the mid-point of the great circle arc AA'. We can then bring the body into its final position by a rotation through an angle φ (say) about OA'. We can suppose $AA' \leqslant \pi$

and $|\varphi| \leqslant \pi$. But a half-turn about OM, followed by a rotation φ about OA', leaves one line of the body fixed. To prove this we construct the spherical triangles $A'ML$, $A'ML'$ as shown in Fig. 7.2b; $L'ML$ is the perpendicular bisector of AA', and each of the angles $LA'M$, $MA'L'$ is equal to $\frac{1}{2}\varphi$. The figure is drawn for the case where the rotation about OA' through an angle less than π is positive. The half-turn about M brings the point P of the moving shell which is originally at L to L', and the rotation about A' brings P to L. Thus the line OP of the rigid body remains fixed, and the combined operation is equivalent to a rotation about this line.

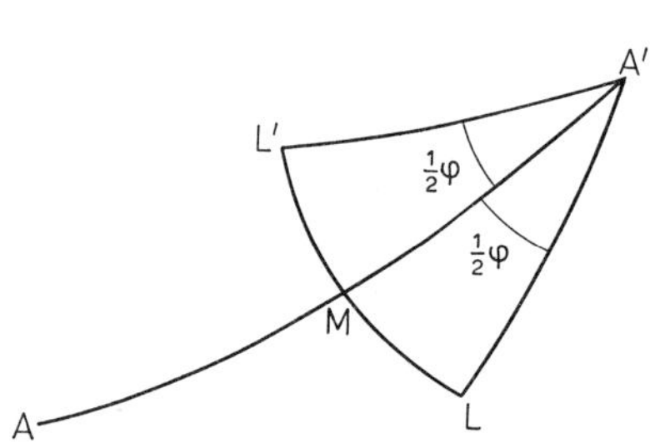

Figure 7.2b

7.3 The matrix l and the vector T. We now consider the displacement of the body, and the theorem that one line of the body remains fixed, from another point of view. We take a rectangular trihedral OY_1, OY_2, OY_3 fixed in the body, and consider the matrix of direction cosines of OY_1, OY_2, OY_3 referred to a rectangular trihedral OX_1, OX_2, OX_3 fixed in space. Both trihedrals are right-handed. (We shall sometimes find it convenient to use a different notation, denoting the arms of the moving trihedral by OA, OB, OC, and the arms of the fixed trihedral by Ox, Oy, Oz.) We write

$$\mathbf{l} = \begin{pmatrix} l_{11} & l_{12} & l_{13} \\ l_{21} & l_{22} & l_{23} \\ l_{31} & l_{32} & l_{33} \end{pmatrix}. \tag{7.3.1}$$

The elements in the rth row (l_{r1}, l_{r2}, l_{r3}) are direction cosines of OY_r with respect to $OX_1X_2X_3$. We notice that the first *column* of the matrix gives the direction cosines of OX_1 with respect to $OY_1Y_2Y_3$; and generally that l_{rs} is the cosine of the angle between OY_r and OX_s.

If the coordinates of a point are (x_1, x_2, x_3) in the axes $OX_1X_2X_3$, and (y_1, y_2, y_3) in the axes $OY_1Y_2Y_3$, we have

$$\mathbf{y} = \mathbf{l}\mathbf{x}, \tag{7.3.2}$$

where $\mathbf{x}$ is the column matrix $\{x_1, x_2, x_3\}$ and $\mathbf{y}$ is the column matrix $\{y_1, y_2, y_3\}$.

If we think of the body as having moved from an original position in which $OY_1Y_2Y_3$ coincides with $OX_1X_2X_3$, a particle of the body (or a point fixed in the body) originally at $\mathbf{y}$ has moved to $\mathbf{x}$; in this statement the base of reference is of course the fixed trihedral $OX_1X_2X_3$.

Now the matrix $\mathbf{l}$ is a proper orthogonal 3×3 matrix,

$$|\mathbf{l}| = +1, \quad \mathbf{l}\mathbf{l}' = \mathbf{l}'\mathbf{l} = \mathbf{I}, \tag{7.3.3}$$

where $\mathbf{l}'$ is the transpose of $\mathbf{l}$; and one of the eigenvalues for such a matrix is $+1$. Thus there exists a non-zero vector $\mathbf{x}$ such that

$$\mathbf{y} = \mathbf{x}. \tag{7.3.4}$$

This proves again that there is one line fixed in the body which remains unmoved by the displacement.

To prove that there is an eigenvalue $+1$, let us consider

$$f(\lambda) = |\mathbf{l} - \lambda\mathbf{I}| = |\mathbf{l}' - \lambda\mathbf{I}|.$$

Now
$$\mathbf{l}(\mathbf{l}' - \mathbf{I}) = \mathbf{I} - \mathbf{l},$$
whence
$$|\mathbf{l}|\,|\mathbf{l}' - \mathbf{I}| = |\mathbf{I} - \mathbf{l}|.$$
Therefore
$$f(1) = (-)^3 f(1), \quad f(1) = 0.$$

But we can go further and find, in terms of the matrix $\mathbf{l}$, explicit formulae for the angle of rotation and for the direction cosines of the axis of rotation. (In this statement we mean direction cosines with the respect to the fixed trihedral $OX_1X_2X_3$; though in fact they are the same with respect to $OY_1Y_2Y_3$!) We can think of the equation

$$\mathbf{y} = \mathbf{l}\mathbf{x} \tag{7.3.2}$$

as expressing the shift in position, from R to S, of a particle fixed in the body; the coordinates of R (relative to the fixed axes $OX_1X_2X_3$) are (y_1, y_2, y_3), and the coordinates of S are (x_1, x_2, x_3). Now we can write (7.3.2) in the form

$$\mathbf{x} - \mathbf{y} = \mathbf{K}(\mathbf{x} + \mathbf{y}), \tag{7.3.5}$$

where $\mathbf{K}$ is the matrix $(\mathbf{I} - \mathbf{l})(\mathbf{I} + \mathbf{l})^{-1} = (\mathbf{I} + \mathbf{l})^{-1}(\mathbf{I} - \mathbf{l})$. The matrix $\mathbf{K}$ surely exists, provided that -1 is not an eigenvalue of $\mathbf{l}$.*

Now $\mathbf{K}$ is skew-symmetric. To prove this we have

$$\mathbf{K}(\mathbf{I} + \mathbf{l}) = (\mathbf{I} - \mathbf{l}). \tag{7.3.6}$$

If we multiply on the right by $\mathbf{l}'$, we find

$$\mathbf{K}(\mathbf{l}' + \mathbf{I}) = (\mathbf{l}' - \mathbf{I}), \tag{7.3.7}$$

whence, taking the transpose on each side,

$$(\mathbf{l} + \mathbf{I})\mathbf{K}' = \mathbf{l} - \mathbf{I}. \tag{7.3.8}$$

Hence

$$\mathbf{K}' = (\mathbf{l} + \mathbf{I})^{-1}(\mathbf{l} - \mathbf{I}) = -\mathbf{K}, \tag{7.3.9}$$

and $\mathbf{K}$ is skew-symmetric, say

$$\mathbf{K} = \begin{pmatrix} 0 & -T_3 & T_2 \\ T_3 & 0 & -T_1 \\ -T_2 & T_1 & 0 \end{pmatrix}. \tag{7.3.10}$$

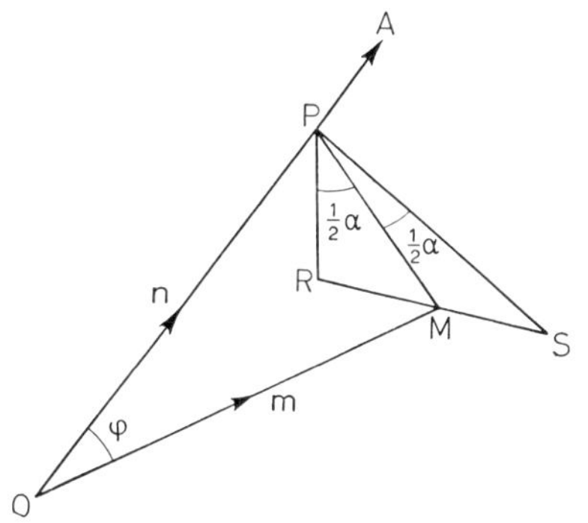

Figure 7.3

Now $\mathbf{Km}$ (where $\mathbf{m} = \frac{1}{2}(\mathbf{x} + \mathbf{y})$) is the vector product $\mathbf{T} \times \mathbf{m}$ expressed as a column matrix, where $\mathbf{T}$ is the vector $\{T_1, T_2, T_3\}$. In Fig. 7.3 the line OA is in the direction of the vector $\mathbf{T}$, M is the mid-point of RS, RS is perpendicular to the plane of $\mathbf{T}$ and $\mathbf{m}$ (since $\frac{1}{2}\overrightarrow{RS} = \mathbf{T} \times \mathbf{m}$), and P is the point where the plane through R perpendicular to OA meets OA. Now since

$$\overrightarrow{MS} = \tfrac{1}{2}(\mathbf{x} - \mathbf{y}) = \mathbf{T} \times \mathbf{m}, \tag{7.3.11}$$

$$|MS| = |\mathbf{T}|\,|\mathbf{m}| \sin\varphi = |\mathbf{T}|\,|PM|, \tag{7.3.12}$$

and therefore

$$|\mathbf{T}| = \tan\tfrac{1}{2}\alpha, \tag{7.3.13}$$

* If the rotation is a half-turn, the eigenvalues are $1, -1, -1$.

where α is the angle RPS, and we may assume $0 < \alpha < \pi$. The shift from R to S has been achieved by a rotation through an angle α about OA.

Thus, from the matrix $\mathbf{l}$ we have determined the vector $\mathbf{T}$,

$$\mathbf{T} = (\tan \tfrac{1}{2}\alpha)\mathbf{n}, \tag{7.3.14}$$

where $\mathbf{n}$ is a unit vector in the axis of rotation and α is the angle of rotation; the axis of rotation and the angle of rotation have been determined from the matrix $\mathbf{l}$. The *rotation vector* $\mathbf{T}$ will play an important part in the sequel.

If now we denote the position vector of a particle of the body (relative to the fixed axes) before the displacement by $\mathbf{r}$, and the position vector of the same particle of the body after the displacement by $\mathbf{s}$, we can write (7.3.11) in the useful form

$$\mathbf{s} - \mathbf{r} = \mathbf{T} \times (\mathbf{s} + \mathbf{r}), \tag{7.3.15}$$

where $\mathbf{T}$ is the rotation vector. The formula fails if α is an odd multiple of π, in particular for a half-turn. In the other cases we can usually suppose (as already mentioned) that $0 < \alpha < \pi$. For any value of α (other than an odd multiple of π) can be written in the form $2k\pi + \theta$, where k is an integer and $|\theta| < \pi$. If $\theta > 0$ the rotation $2k\pi + \theta$ has the same ultimate effect as a rotation θ. If $\theta < 0$, the rotation $2k\pi + \theta$ about OA has the same ultimate effect as a rotation $-\theta$ about AO. The vector $\mathbf{T}$ is unaltered (as of course it must be if it is to define the displacement) if α is replaced by $2\pi - \alpha$ and $\mathbf{n}$ is replaced by $-\mathbf{n}$.

Example 7.3. As a trivial illustration, let us find the axis of rotation and the angle of rotation if, in the displaced position, OY_1 coincides with OX_2, OY_2 with OX_3, and OY_3 with OX_1. In this case

$$\mathbf{l} = \begin{pmatrix} 0 & 1 & 0 \\ 0 & 0 & 1 \\ 1 & 0 & 0 \end{pmatrix}, \quad \mathbf{K} = \begin{pmatrix} 0 & -1 & 1 \\ 1 & 0 & -1 \\ -1 & 1 & 0 \end{pmatrix},$$

so $\mathbf{T}$ is the vector $\{1, 1, 1\}$. The axis of rotation is equally inclined to the three axes OX_1, OX_2, OX_3, and $\tan \frac{1}{2}\alpha = \sqrt{3}$, $\alpha = \frac{2}{3}\pi$. Of course in this simple case the result is evident without the calculation. Alternatively we can find the axis of rotation from the fact that this axis is the eigenvector corresponding to the eigenvalue $+1$; and the *magnitude* of the rotation can be found from the fact that the other eigenvalues are $e^{i\alpha}$ and $e^{-i\alpha}$. (The matrix $\mathbf{l}$ has the same eigenvalues as the matrix $\mathbf{R}_1$ defined in (7.6.6) below.)

7.4 Generalization of Euler's theorem. The theorem that one line fixed in the body remains invariant implies that the mapping of the unit sphere onto itself, obtained by any displacement of the shell sliding on it (§ 7.2), has a fixed point. Now a fixed point exists for *any* continuous mapping of the sphere onto itself, provided that the mapping can be continuously deformed into the identity mapping; Euler's theorem appears, in the light of this remark, as a special case of a highly general result. In fact we can go further and assert an analogous result even if the body is not rigid, provided that the distortion of the body permitted is a continuous distortion in which the straight lines through O remain straight. In any displacement of the body, accompanied by any distortion of this type, there exists one line through O which is unmoved.

7.5 Chasles's theorem. Let us relinquish for the moment the condition that the rigid body has a fixed point, and consider a quite general displacement. We shall prove the theorem, discovered by Chasles in 1830, that this general displacement can be effected *by a translation along a certain line and a rotation about that line.* Such a description of the displacement is called a *screw*; the general displacement of the body can be obtained by attaching the body to a nut moving on a screw of suitable pitch.

The general displacement can be produced by a displacement without rotation, say a displacement in which a certain particle of the body moves from O to O', followed by a rotation about an axis through O'. Now the direction of this axis is invariant, independent of the particle chosen to define the first displacement. The theorem of Chasles can be deduced from (7.3.15), but a straightforward geometrical argument is simpler and more illuminating. There is a set of planes fixed in the body which remain, after the general displacement, parallel to their original positions. These are the planes perpendicular to the axis of rotation. Let PQR be a triangle in one of these planes, say ϖ, and let it be moved in the displacement to the position $P'Q'R'$ in the plane ϖ', which is parallel to ϖ. Now by a pure translation parallel to the axis of rotation we can bring ϖ into coincidence with ϖ', and this manoeuvre brings PQR into the position $P''Q''R''$ in ϖ'. Then $P''Q''R''$ can be brought into coincidence with $P'Q'R'$ by a pure rotation about an axis λ parallel to the axis of rotation. Thus the most general displacement can be produced by a translation along λ and a rotation about λ.

7.6 The rotation formula. We now return to the problem in which the body has one point O fixed, and we consider a displacement of the body. The displacement can be described, as we have seen, as a rotation through an angle α about an axis OA. A particle fixed in the body is carried by this operation from its original position R to its final position S. Our object is as follows; given OA and α, to find a formula to determine S when R is given.

Let us denote the vector OR by $\mathbf{r}$ and the vector OS by $\mathbf{s}$; the vectors $\mathbf{r}$ and $\mathbf{s}$ play the same parts as the column matrices $\mathbf{y}$ and $\mathbf{x}$ of § 7.3. We denote a unit vector in the axis of rotation OA by $\mathbf{n}$. We shall establish *the rotation formula*

$$\mathbf{s} = \gamma\mathbf{r} + (1 - \gamma)(\mathbf{n} \cdot \mathbf{r})\mathbf{n} + \sigma\mathbf{n} \times \mathbf{r}, \tag{7.6.1}$$

where $\gamma = \cos\alpha$, $\sigma = \sin\alpha$. Expressed in terms of the rotation vector $\mathbf{T}\,[= (\tan\frac{1}{2}\alpha)\mathbf{n}]$ already introduced in § 7.3, the rotation formula can be written

$$\mathbf{s} + \mathbf{r} = \frac{2}{1 + t^2}\{\mathbf{r} + (\mathbf{T} \cdot \mathbf{r})\mathbf{T} + \mathbf{T} \times \mathbf{r}\}, \tag{7.6.2}$$

where $t = \tan\frac{1}{2}\alpha = |\mathbf{T}|$.

There are many ways of establishing the rotation formula. We give three proofs illustrating various lines of approach.

(i) We start from the equation (7.3.15),

$$\mathbf{s} - \mathbf{r} = \mathbf{T} \times (\mathbf{s} + \mathbf{r}).$$

We wish to solve this equation for $\mathbf{s}$. To achieve this end we proceed as follows. If we form the vector product of each member by premultiplication by $\mathbf{T}$ we find

$$\begin{aligned} \mathbf{T} \times (\mathbf{s} - \mathbf{r}) &= \mathbf{T} \times \{\mathbf{T} \times (\mathbf{s} + \mathbf{r})\} \\ &= \{\mathbf{T} \cdot (\mathbf{s} + \mathbf{r})\}\mathbf{T} - t^2(\mathbf{s} + \mathbf{r}) \\ &= 2(\mathbf{T} \cdot \mathbf{r})\mathbf{T} - t^2(\mathbf{s} + \mathbf{r}), \end{aligned} \tag{7.6.3}$$

where we have used the property

$$\mathbf{T} \cdot (\mathbf{s} + \mathbf{r}) = 2(\mathbf{T} \cdot \mathbf{r}). \tag{7.6.4}$$

Adding (7.3.15) and (7.6.3) we have

$$(1 + t^2)\mathbf{s} = (1 - t^2)\mathbf{r} + 2(\mathbf{T} \cdot \mathbf{r})\mathbf{T} + 2(\mathbf{T} \times \mathbf{r}),$$

which is equivalent to (7.6.2).

(ii) We establish the rotation formula by a straightforward geometrical argument. Let P be the foot of the perpendicular from R on to OA, and let N be the foot of the perpendicular from S on to PR (Fig. 7.6). Then NS is normal to the plane POR, and

$$\mathbf{n} \times \mathbf{r} = r \sin \psi \, \mathbf{w} = p\mathbf{w},$$

where $r = |\mathbf{r}|$, $p = PR$, and $\mathbf{w}$ is a unit vector in NS.

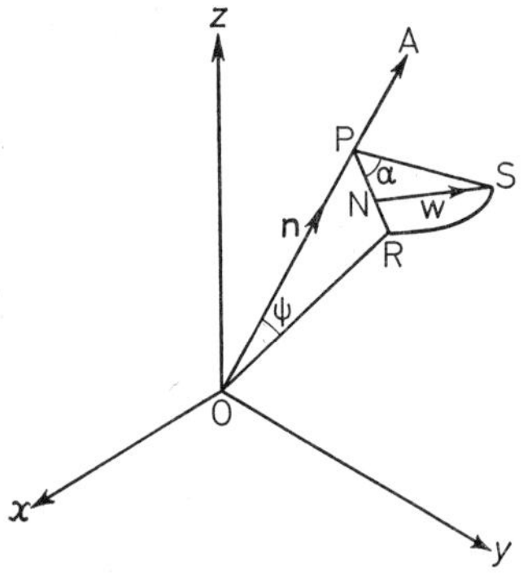

Hence

$$\sin \alpha \, (\mathbf{n} \times \mathbf{r}) = p \sin \alpha \, \mathbf{w} = \overrightarrow{NS}.$$

Finally

$$\begin{aligned} \mathbf{s} &= \mathbf{r} + \overrightarrow{RN} + \overrightarrow{NS} \\ &= \mathbf{r} - (1 - \cos \alpha)\{\mathbf{r} - (\mathbf{n} \cdot \mathbf{r})\mathbf{n}\} + \sin \alpha(\mathbf{n} \times \mathbf{r}) \\ &= \gamma \mathbf{r} + (1 - \gamma)(\mathbf{n} \cdot \mathbf{r})\mathbf{n} + \sigma \mathbf{n} \times \mathbf{r}, \end{aligned}$$

which is (7.6.1).

Figure 7.6

(iii) We establish the rotation formula by introducing new axes $Oy_1y_2y_3$ in such a way that Oy_1 is the axis of rotation. We begin by establishing a *Lemma* which will be needed frequently in the sequel.

Lemma. If the trihedral $OY_1Y_2Y_3$ is rotated through an angle α about OY_1 the matrix of direction cosines for the new position, which we will call $\mathbf{l}_1$, is given by

$$\mathbf{l}_1 = \mathbf{R}_1\mathbf{l}, \tag{7.6.5}$$

where $\mathbf{R}_1$ is the orthogonal matrix

$$\mathbf{R}_1 = \begin{pmatrix} 1 & 0 & 0 \\ 0 & \cos \alpha & \sin \alpha \\ 0 & -\sin \alpha & \cos \alpha \end{pmatrix}. \tag{7.6.6}$$

To prove the lemma, we notice that the direction cosines of a line are the coordinates of a point on it at unit distance from O. From $\mathbf{y} = \mathbf{lx}$ it follows that $\mathbf{x} = \mathbf{l}'\mathbf{y}$, and therefore

$$\mathbf{l}_1' = \mathbf{l}' \begin{pmatrix} 1 & 0 & 0 \\ 0 & \cos \alpha & -\sin \alpha \\ 0 & \sin \alpha & \cos \alpha \end{pmatrix} = \mathbf{l}'\mathbf{R}_1', \tag{7.6.7}$$

and (7.6.5) follows from (7.6.7) by taking the transpose of each member.

We now deduce the rotation formula from the lemma. Using the column matrix $\mathbf{x}$ in place of the vector $\mathbf{r}$, and the column matrix $\mathbf{x}_1$ in place of the vector $\mathbf{s}$, we have

$$\mathbf{y} = \mathbf{l}\mathbf{x} = \mathbf{l}_1\mathbf{x}_1, \tag{7.6.8}$$

whence

$$\mathbf{x}_1 = \mathbf{l}_1'\mathbf{l}\mathbf{x} = \mathbf{l}'\mathbf{R}_1'\mathbf{l}\mathbf{x} = \mathbf{W}\mathbf{x}, \tag{7.6.9}$$

where

$$\mathbf{W} = \mathbf{l}'\mathbf{R}_1'\mathbf{l} = \gamma\mathbf{I} + (1-\gamma)\begin{pmatrix} l_{11}{}^2 & l_{11}l_{12} & l_{11}l_{13} \\ l_{12}l_{11} & l_{12}{}^2 & l_{12}l_{13} \\ l_{13}l_{11} & l_{13}l_{12} & l_{13}{}^2 \end{pmatrix} + \sigma\begin{pmatrix} 0 & -l_{13} & l_{12} \\ l_{13} & 0 & -l_{11} \\ -l_{12} & l_{11} & 0 \end{pmatrix}. \tag{7.6.10}$$

Now the axis of rotation, defining the unit vector $\mathbf{n}$, has direction cosines (l_{11}, l_{12}, l_{13}), so interpreting the result (7.6.9) in terms of vectors we have

$$\mathbf{s} = \gamma\mathbf{r} + (1-\gamma)(\mathbf{n} \cdot \mathbf{r})\mathbf{n} + \sigma\mathbf{n} \times \mathbf{r},$$

which is (7.6.1).

7.7 Half-turns and reflexions. The effect of a rotation can be achieved in other ways, for example by two *half-turns* (i.e. rotations through an angle π) about two intersecting lines. Let OA, OB be two lines through O inclined at an angle $\frac{1}{2}\alpha$. A half-turn about OA followed by a half-turn about OB is equivalent to a rotation α, in the sense from OA to OB, about the line OL perpendicular both to OA and to OB. The proof is immediate. By Euler's theorem (§ 7.2) the double operation is equivalent to a rotation, and OL must be the axis of this rotation, since particles on OL are not displaced by the double operation. A particle originally on OA is not displaced by the first operation, and is moved through an angle α on to the line OA' (Fig. 7.7a) by the second. This completes the proof.

If $\mathbf{u}$, $\mathbf{v}$ are unit vectors in OA, OB, and if as before $\mathbf{n}$ denotes a unit vector, and $\mathbf{T}$ a vector of magnitude $\tan \frac{1}{2}\alpha$, in the axis of rotation OL, then

$$\mathbf{u} \times \mathbf{v} = \sin \tfrac{1}{2}\alpha\, \mathbf{n} = \cos \tfrac{1}{2}\alpha\, \mathbf{T}. \tag{7.7.1}$$

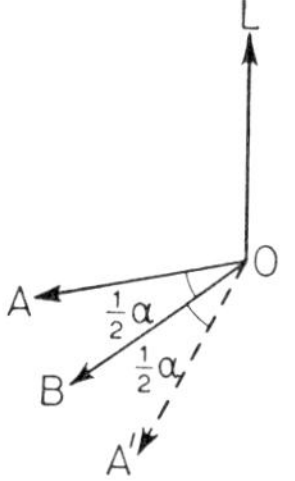

Figure 7.7a

A half-turn about an axis a, followed by a half-turn about a parallel axis b, is equivalent to a translation without rotation. The direction of the translation is that of a line meeting both a and b at right angles, and in the direction from a to b; the magnitude of the displacement is twice the distance between a and b. These statements are almost evident; it is clear that ultimately there is no change in the orientation of the body, and the direction and magnitude of the displacement are obvious if we consider a particle of the rigid body lying originally on a.

Consider now the effect of successive half-turns about two skew axes a and b. Let AB be the common normal (A lying on a and B on b) and let a' be the axis through B parallel to a (Fig. 7.7b). We can interpose two half-turns about a' without altering the final result. Now a half-turn about a, followed by a half-turn about a', results in a translation of the body in the direction AB through a distance $2AB$. Then a half-turn about a' followed by a half-turn about b gives a rotation about AB through an angle α, where $\frac{1}{2}\alpha$ is the angle between a and b. Thus the resultant is a screw motion with axis AB. Any displacement of a rigid body can be produced by successive half-turns about two axes suitably chosen.

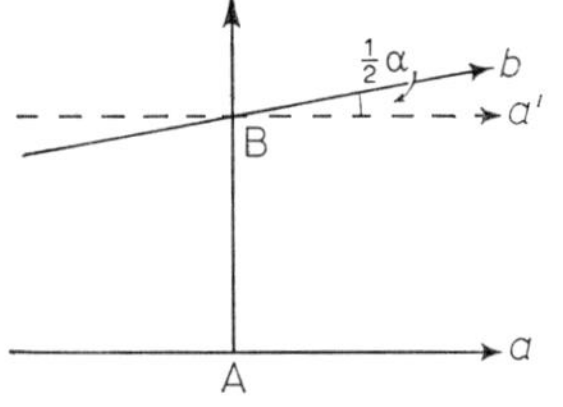

Figure 7.7b

Another way of obtaining the effect of a rotation is by successive *reflexions* in two planes. A single reflexion has no physical significance, since it alters the aspect of the body (e.g. it changes a body shaped like a right hand into a body shaped like a left hand). But a second reflexion restores the original aspect, and the two reflexions together represent a possible displacement. The displacement is a rotation about OL, the line of intersection of the planes, and the angle of rotation is twice the angle between the planes.

Still further proofs of the rotation formula can be constructed from either of the ideas just mentioned, regarding the rotation as the resultant of two half-turns, or as the resultant of two reflexions. The reader may find it interesting to construct the proofs.

7.8 Quaternion form of the rotation formula. We can think of a quaternion

(7.8.1) $$q = a + Xi + Yj + Zk$$

as built up of a scalar a and a vector $\mathbf{A}$ whose components are X, Y, Z. It is convenient sometimes to use the same symbol $\mathbf{A}$ both for the vector (X, Y, Z) and for the associated quaternion

$$0 + Xi + Yj + Zk,$$

so that

(7.8.2) $$q = a + \mathbf{A},$$

and this usage will not give rise to any ambiguity. If we form the product

$$qq' = (a + \mathbf{A})(a' + \mathbf{A}')$$

we find

(7.8.3) $$qq' = (aa' - \mathbf{A} \,.\, \mathbf{A}') + a'\mathbf{A} + a\mathbf{A}' + \mathbf{A} \times \mathbf{A}',$$

where, in the second member, each vector is to be interpreted as the associated quaternion.

For the study of rotations we need the quaternion

(7.8.4) $$q = c + \xi i + \eta j + \zeta k = c(1 + \mathbf{T}),$$

where $c = \cos\frac{1}{2}\alpha$, and ξ, η, ζ are components of a vector of magnitude $\sin\frac{1}{2}\alpha$ in the axis of rotation. The parameters c, ξ, η, ζ appearing in q were first used by Euler about 1776. We notice that q is a unit quaternion, and that

(7.8.5) $$q^{-1} = c(1 - \mathbf{T}).$$

If the rotation carries $\mathbf{r}$ *into* $\mathbf{s}$ *then*

(7.8.6) $$\mathbf{s} = q\mathbf{r}q^{-1},$$

where $\mathbf{r}$ *now denotes the quaternion* $xi + yj + zk$. To establish the fundamental result (7.8.6) we have to prove that

$$(7.8.7) \qquad \mathrm{s}(1 + \mathbf{T}) = (1 + \mathbf{T})\mathbf{r},$$

which we can write, in virtue of (7.8.3), as

$$-(\mathrm{s} \,.\, \mathbf{T}) + \mathrm{s} + \mathrm{s} \times \mathbf{T} = -(\mathbf{T} \,.\, \mathbf{r}) + \mathbf{r} + \mathbf{T} \times \mathbf{r}.$$

The scalars on the two sides are equal, since $\mathbf{T} \,.\, \mathbf{r} = \mathbf{T} \,.\, \mathrm{s}$, and the vectors are equal in virtue of (7.3.15).

7.9 Composition of rotations. We consider the effect of a rotation α about OA followed by a rotation β about OB. The effect of the double operation is a rotation γ about an axis OC, and the problem is to find γ and OC.

(i) We begin with a simple geometrical solution of the problem. We suppose OA and OB to be of unit length, so that A and B lie on the unit sphere about O. We construct the spherical triangle ABC on the unit sphere as shown in Fig. 7.9, with the angle $A = \frac{1}{2}\alpha$ and $B = \frac{1}{2}\beta$. Then OC is the axis of the resultant rotation. For the first operation carries the particle of the rigid body originally at C to C', and the second operation restores it to C. Notice that the triangle ABC is drawn clockwise; the twist about OA is not in the sense from AB to AC, but in the opposite sense, from AC to AB.

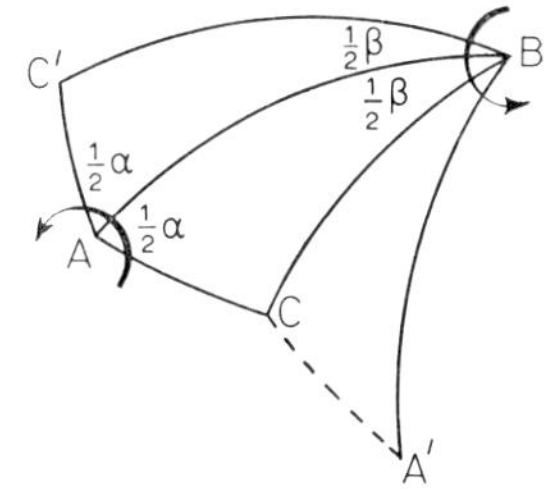

Figure 7.9

To find γ we construct the triangle $A'BC$ which is the image of ABC in BC. The first rotation leaves unmoved the particle of the body originally at A, the second moves it to A', and therefore γ is the angle ACA'. Thus $\gamma = 2(\pi - C)$, or effectively $\gamma = -2C$, since a rotation 2π leaves the body where it was originally.

We can express the result in a more picturesque form. If ABC is a spherical triangle (drawn clockwise when viewed from outside the sphere) *a rotation* $2A$ *about* OA, *followed by a rotation* $2B$ *about* OB, *followed by a rotation* $2C$ *about* OC, *will restore the body to its original position.* This theorem was discovered by Hamilton in 1844.

Now in a spherical triangle, with the usual notation,

$$\cos C = -\cos A \cos B + \sin A \sin B \cos c,$$

whence

$$(7.9.1) \qquad \cos \tfrac{1}{2}\gamma = \cos \tfrac{1}{2}\alpha \cos \tfrac{1}{2}\beta - \sin \tfrac{1}{2}\alpha \sin \tfrac{1}{2}\beta \cos \lambda,$$

where λ is the angle between the two axes of rotation.

Notice particularly that the two operations are not commutative. If we perform them in the reverse order the axis of rotation for the combined operation is OC'.

(ii) *The composite rotation formula.* We describe the first rotation by the rotation vector $\mathbf{T}_1$, a vector of magnitude $\tan \frac{1}{2}\alpha$ in the direction OA, and the second rotation by the rotation vector $\mathbf{T}_2$, of magnitude $\tan \frac{1}{2}\beta$ in the direction OB. The composite rotation γ about the axis OC can be described by the rotation vector $\mathbf{T}_3$, a vector of magnitude $\tan \frac{1}{2}\gamma$ in the direction OC. The effect of the double operation is determined unambiguously by *the composite rotation formula*

$$\mathbf{T}_3 = (\mathbf{T}_1 + \mathbf{T}_2 - \mathbf{T}_1 \times \mathbf{T}_2)/(1 - \mathbf{T}_1 \cdot \mathbf{T}_2). \tag{7.9.2}$$

The formula fails if $\mathbf{T}_1 \cdot \mathbf{T}_2 = 1$, and then γ is an integral multiple of π.

In the particular case when the axes of the two rotations are at right angles $\mathbf{T}_1 \cdot \mathbf{T}_2 = 0$, and the formula takes the simpler form

$$\mathbf{T}_3 = \mathbf{T}_1 + \mathbf{T}_2 - \mathbf{T}_1 \times \mathbf{T}_2. \tag{7.9.3}$$

We notice, in (7.9.2), that $\mathbf{T}_3$ is not coplanar with $\mathbf{T}_1$ and $\mathbf{T}_2$, and that, as we have noticed already, the resultant is different if we reverse the order in which the two operations are performed. It is clear therefore that we cannot replace the magnitude $\tan \frac{1}{2}\theta$ (where θ is the angle of rotation) in the typical rotation vector by some other function of θ in such a way that the resultant, or physical sum, of two rotations is given by the vector sum of the two vectors. Rotations can be represented in various ways by directed quantities in the axes of rotation, but in no case are these directed quantities vectors in the strict sense, since they do not conform to the vector law of addition. To this extent therefore the term *rotation vector* is a misnomer.

First proof, using half-turns. As we have seen (§ 7.7) a half-turn about a unit vector $\mathbf{u}$, followed by a half-turn about a unit vector $\mathbf{v}$, is equivalent to a rotation θ about $\mathbf{u} \times \mathbf{v}$, where $\frac{1}{2}\theta$ is the angle between $\mathbf{u}$ and $\mathbf{v}$; in fact the rotation vector $\mathbf{T}$ is given by the formula

$$\mathbf{u} \times \mathbf{v} = c\mathbf{T}, \tag{7.9.4}$$

where $c = \cos \frac{1}{2}\theta$. Thus, if $\mathbf{v}$ is any unit vector perpendicular to $\mathbf{T}_1$, we can find a unit vector $\mathbf{u}$ such that the first rotation is equivalent to a half-turn about $\mathbf{u}$ followed by a half-turn about $\mathbf{v}$. Explicitly

$$\mathbf{u} = c_1(\mathbf{v} - \mathbf{T}_1 \times \mathbf{v}), \tag{7.9.5}$$

where $c_1 = \cos \frac{1}{2}\alpha$. Similarly, if $\mathbf{v}$ is a unit vector perpendicular to $\mathbf{T}_2$, we can represent the second rotation by a half-turn about $\mathbf{v}$ followed by a half-turn about $\mathbf{w}$, where

$$\mathbf{w} = c_2(\mathbf{v} + \mathbf{T}_2 \times \mathbf{v}). \tag{7.9.6}$$

Let us then choose for $\mathbf{v}$ a unit vector perpendicular both to $\mathbf{T}_1$ and to $\mathbf{T}_2$. The resultant displacement is achieved by a half-turn about $\mathbf{u}$, followed by a half-turn about $\mathbf{v}$, followed by another half-turn about $\mathbf{v}$, followed by a half-turn about $\mathbf{w}$. The two successive half-turns about $\mathbf{v}$ give rise to no resultant displacement, and can be ignored. Thus the total effect is that of a half-turn about $\mathbf{u}$ followed by a half-turn about $\mathbf{w}$, whence

$$\begin{aligned} c_3\mathbf{T}_3 &= \mathbf{u} \times \mathbf{w} \\ &= c_1c_2\{(\mathbf{v} - \mathbf{T}_1 \times \mathbf{v}) \times (\mathbf{v} + \mathbf{T}_2 \times \mathbf{v})\} \\ &= c_1c_2\{\mathbf{v} \times (\mathbf{T}_2 \times \mathbf{v}) - (\mathbf{T}_1 \times \mathbf{v}) \times \mathbf{v} - (\mathbf{T}_1 \times \mathbf{v}) \times (\mathbf{T}_2 \times \mathbf{v})\} \\ &= c_1c_2(\mathbf{T}_1 + \mathbf{T}_2 - \mathbf{T}_1 \times \mathbf{T}_2), \end{aligned} \tag{7.9.7}$$

since

$$(\mathbf{T}_1 \times \mathbf{v}) \times (\mathbf{T}_2 \times \mathbf{v}) = \mathbf{T}_1 \times \mathbf{T}_2. \tag{7.9.8}$$

Now from (7.9.1)

$$c_3/c_1c_2 = 1 - \tan \tfrac{1}{2} \tan \tfrac{1}{2}\beta \cos \lambda = 1 - \mathbf{T}_1 \cdot \mathbf{T}_2, \tag{7.9.9}$$

giving the result already stated,

(7.9.2) $$\mathbf{T}_3 = (\mathbf{T}_1 + \mathbf{T}_2 - \mathbf{T}_1 \times \mathbf{T}_2)/(1 - \mathbf{T}_1 \cdot \mathbf{T}_2).$$

Second proof, using quaternions. We use the quaternion

(7.9.10) $$q_1 = c_1(1 + \mathbf{T}_1)$$

for the first rotation, as in § 7.8, and

(7.9.11) $$q_2 = c_2(1 + \mathbf{T}_2)$$

for the second. A particle of the body originally at $\mathbf{r}$ is moved to $\bar{\mathbf{r}}$ by the first rotation, and to $\mathbf{s}$ by the second, where

(7.9.12) $$\bar{\mathbf{r}} = q_1\mathbf{r}q_1^{-1},$$

and

(7.9.13) $$\mathbf{s} = q_2\bar{\mathbf{r}}q_2^{-1} = q_2q_1\mathbf{r}q_1^{-1}q_2^{-1} = q_3\mathbf{r}q_3^{-1},$$

where

(7.9.14) $$\begin{aligned} q_3 &= q_2q_1 \\ &= c_2(1 + \mathbf{T}_2)c_1(1 + \mathbf{T}_1) \\ &= c_1c_2(1 - \mathbf{T}_1 \cdot \mathbf{T}_2 + \mathbf{T}_1 + \mathbf{T}_2 - \mathbf{T}_1 \times \mathbf{T}_2). \end{aligned}$$

But q_3, the quaternion defining the composite rotation, is

(7.9.15) $$q_3 = c_3(1 + \mathbf{T}_3),$$

so, comparing (7.9.14) and (7.9.15), we have

(7.9.16) $$c_3 = c_1c_2(1 - \mathbf{T}_1 \cdot \mathbf{T}_2)$$

and

(7.9.17) $$c_3\mathbf{T}_3 = c_1c_2(\mathbf{T}_1 + \mathbf{T}_2 - \mathbf{T}_1 \times \mathbf{T}_2).$$

From (7.9.16) and (7.9.17) we again deduce (7.9.2).

If we reverse the order of the operations the effect is to change the sign preceding the vector product in the second member of (7.9.2). The difference between the two results for $\mathbf{T}_3$ is in the direction of $\mathbf{T}_1 \times \mathbf{T}_2$, as we have noticed already.

Example 7.9A. To find the resultant of a rotation ψ about Oz, followed by a rotation θ about Oy, followed by a rotation φ about Oz.

We write $t_1 = \tan \frac{1}{2}\theta$, $t_2 = \tan \frac{1}{2}\varphi$, $t_3 = \tan \frac{1}{2}\psi$. The resultant of the operations defined by $\mathbf{T}_1(= (0, 0, t_3))$ and $\mathbf{T}_2(= (0, t_1, 0))$ is

(7.9.18) $$\mathbf{T}' = (t_1t_3, t_1, t_3).$$

The resultant of the operations defined by $\mathbf{T}'$ and $\mathbf{T}_3(= (0, 0, t_2))$ is

(7.9.19) $$\mathbf{T} = \{-t_1(t_2 - t_3), t_1(1 + t_2t_3), t_2 + t_3\}/(1 - t_2t_3).$$

Alternatively we can find the result equally simply by quaternions. We have

(7.9.20) $$\begin{aligned} q = q_3q_2q_1 &= (c_2 + s_2k)(c_1 + s_1j)(c_3 + s_3k) \\ &= (c_1c_2c_3 - c_1s_2s_3) + (s_1c_2s_3 - s_1s_2c_3)i + (s_1s_2s_3 + s_1c_2c_3)j \\ &\quad + (c_1c_2s_3 + c_1s_2c_3)k \\ &= c_1c_2c_3\{(1 - t_2t_3) + t_1(t_3 - t_2)i + t_1(1 + t_2t_3)j + (t_2 + t_3)k\} \end{aligned}$$

where $c_1 = \cos\frac{1}{2}\theta$, $s_1 = \sin\frac{1}{2}\theta$; $c_2 = \cos\frac{1}{2}\varphi$, $s_2 = \sin\frac{1}{2}\varphi$; $c_3 = \cos\frac{1}{2}\psi$, $s_3 = \sin\frac{1}{2}\psi$. The formula we have found is also equal to

(7.9.21) $$\cos\tfrac{1}{2}\gamma + \sin\tfrac{1}{2}\gamma(li + mj + nk),$$

where l, m, n are direction cosines of the axis of the resultant rotation, and γ is the angle of the resultant rotation. The vector $\mathbf{T}$ is $\tan\frac{1}{2}\gamma(l, m, n)$, and comparing (7.9.20) and (7.9.21) we recover (7.9.19).

We notice that

(7.9.22) $$1 + |\mathbf{T}|^2 = (1 + t_1^2)(1 + t_2^2)(1 + t_3^2)/(1 - t_2t_3)^2,$$

and the rotation formula for the operation defined by $\mathbf{T}$ is, as in (7.6.2),

(7.9.23) $$\mathbf{s} + \mathbf{r} = \frac{2(1 - t_2t_3)^2}{(1 + t_1^2)(1 + t_2^2)(1 + t_3^2)}\{\mathbf{r} + (\mathbf{T}\,.\,\mathbf{r})\mathbf{T} + (\mathbf{T}\times\mathbf{r})\}.$$

Example 7.9B. To find the resultant of a rotation φ_3 about Oz, followed by a rotation φ_2 about Oy, followed by a rotation φ_1 about Ox.

Proceeding as in the previous example we find

(7.9.24) $$\mathbf{T} = (t_1 + t_2t_3,\ t_2 - t_1t_3,\ t_3 + t_1t_2)/(1 - t_1t_2t_3),$$

where $t_r = \tan\frac{1}{2}\varphi_r$. The rotation formula is

(7.9.25) $$\mathbf{s} + \mathbf{r} = \frac{2(1 - t_1t_2t_3)^2}{(1 + t_1^2)(1 + t_2^2)(1 + t_3^2)}\{\mathbf{r} + (\mathbf{T}\,.\,\mathbf{r})\mathbf{T} + (\mathbf{T}\times\mathbf{r})\}.$$

7.10 Angular velocity. If in the composite rotation formula (7.9.2) the angles α and β are small, and we neglect squares and products of α and β, the formula takes the simple form

(7.10.1) $$\mathbf{T}_3 = \mathbf{T}_1 + \mathbf{T}_2.$$

In this case the two operations are commutative.

We readily deduce from (7.10.1) the famous theorem of the vectorial character of angular velocity. If we represent an angular velocity by a vector $\boldsymbol{\omega}$, whose direction is the axis of rotation and whose magnitude is the angular velocity ω, the resultant of two simultaneous angular velocities is found by the vector law of addition,

(7.10.2) $$\boldsymbol{\omega}_3 = \boldsymbol{\omega}_1 + \boldsymbol{\omega}_2.$$

The result (7.10.2) can of course be established by elementary reasoning, without first finding the composite rotation formula. One method is based on the geometrical argument of § 7.9(i). Let us write

$$\alpha = \omega_1\,\delta t, \qquad \beta = \omega_2\,\delta t, \qquad \gamma = \omega_3\,\delta t,$$

and consider what happens when $\delta t \to 0$. Referring to Fig. 7.9 we have

(7.10.3) $$\frac{\sin AC}{\sin CB} = \frac{\sin\frac{1}{2}\beta}{\sin\frac{1}{2}\alpha} \to \frac{\omega_2}{\omega_1},$$

and, as $\delta t \to 0$, the point C tends to the point C_0 on AB such that

(7.10.4) $$\frac{\sin AC_0}{\sin C_0B} = \frac{\omega_2}{\omega_1}.$$

Further, as $\delta t \to 0$, (7.9.1) leads to

(7.10.5) $$\omega_3^2 = \omega_1^2 + \omega_2^2 + 2\omega_1\omega_2\cos\lambda,$$

and (7.10.4) and (7.10.5) are together equivalent to (7.10.2).

7.11 The orientation of a rigid body, Euler's angles. We now consider how to define the orientation of a moving trihedral $OABC$ relative to a fixed trihedral $Oxyz$. In what follows the lines OA, OB, OC are fixed in the rigid body and moving with it, and the lines OA, OB, OC form a right-handed rectangular trihedral. The most familiar, and on the whole the simplest way of defining the orientation of $OABC$ relative to $Oxyz$ is by means of Euler's angles θ, φ, ψ; θ, φ are the polar angles of OC, ψ is the angle between the plane zOC and the plane COA, measured so that $\psi = 0$ when A lies on the great circle zC produced (Fig. 7.11).

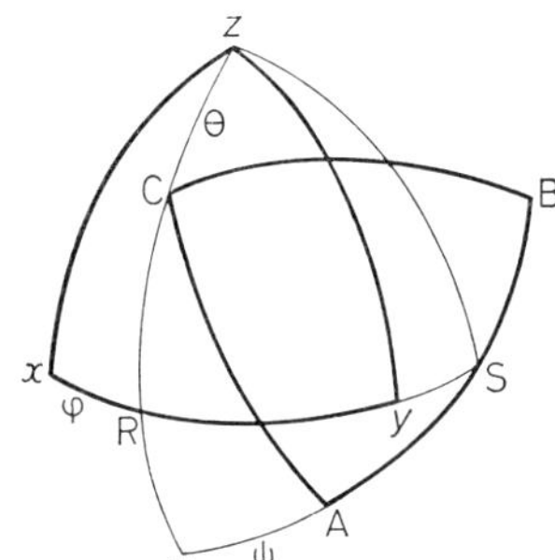

Figure 7.11

The matrix of direction cosines is

(7.11.1) $$\mathbf{l} = \begin{pmatrix} \cos\theta\cos\varphi\cos\psi - \sin\varphi\sin\psi & \cos\theta\sin\varphi\cos\psi + \cos\varphi\sin\psi & -\sin\theta\cos\psi \\ -\cos\theta\cos\varphi\sin\psi - \sin\varphi\cos\psi & -\cos\theta\sin\varphi\sin\psi + \cos\varphi\cos\psi & \sin\theta\sin\psi \\ \sin\theta\cos\varphi & \sin\theta\sin\varphi & \cos\theta \end{pmatrix}.$$

A simple way to prove this is to notice that the elements in the first row are components in the directions Ox, Oy, Oz of a unit force in OA. The second row is obtained from the first by replacing ψ by $\psi + \frac{1}{2}\pi$. We can write the result more compactly in the form

(7.11.2) $$\mathbf{l} = \begin{pmatrix} c_1c_2c_3 - s_2s_3 & c_1s_2c_3 + c_2s_3 & -s_1c_3 \\ -c_1c_2s_3 - s_2c_3 & -c_1s_2s_3 + c_2c_3 & s_1s_3 \\ s_1c_2 & s_1s_2 & c_1 \end{pmatrix},$$

where the suffixes 1, 2, 3 refer to θ, φ, ψ respectively; c_1 means $\cos\theta$, s_1 means $\sin\theta$, and so on.

If we regard the standard position of $OABC$ as that in which it coincides with $Oxyz$ we can get from the standard position to the final position in either of two ways:–

(*a*) We begin with (i) a rotation φ about $OC(\equiv Oz)$; after this operation $OABC$ coincides with $ORSz$ (Fig. 7.11). Then (ii) we make a rotation θ about the carried position of OB, i.e. about OS; after this operation C has reached its final position, and $OABC$ coincides with $OTSC$. Finally (iii) we make a rotation ψ about the carried position of OC, and this brings the trihedral $OABC$ into its final position.

(*b*) A rotation ψ about Oz, followed by a rotation θ about Oy, followed by a rotation φ about Oz.

Of course either sequence of operations is equivalent to a single rotation, and the rotation vector $\mathbf{T}$ defining this rotation has already been found in (7.9.19).

7.12 The orientation of a rigid body, the angles φ_1, φ_2, φ_3. Another, and more symmetrical, method of defining the orientation of the trihedral $OABC$ is as follows. Suppose we start with $OABC$ in its standard position, coincident with the fixed trihedral $Oxyz$, and that we arrive at its final position by the following sequence of operations: a rotation φ_1 about $OA(\equiv Ox)$, followed by a rotation φ_2 about the carried position of OB, followed by a rotation φ_3 about the carried position of OC (Fig. 7.12). Our first object is to find the matrix $\mathbf{l}$ for the position $OABC$ arrived at in this way.

The matrix of direction cosines is

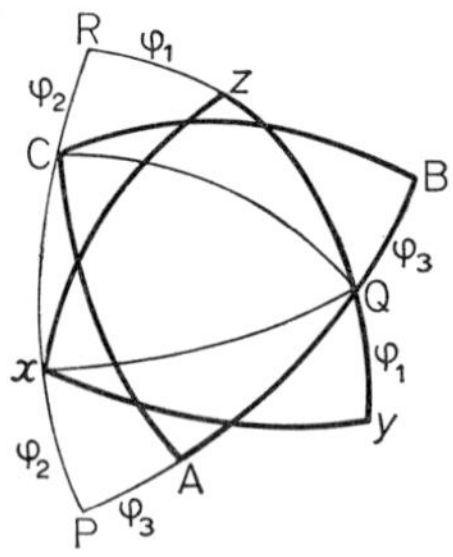

$$(7.12.1)\qquad \mathbf{l} = \begin{pmatrix} c_2c_3 & c_1s_3 + s_1s_2c_3 & s_1s_3 - c_1s_2c_3 \\ -c_2s_3 & c_1c_3 - s_1s_2s_3 & s_1c_3 + c_1s_2s_3 \\ s_2 & -s_1c_2 & c_1c_2 \end{pmatrix},$$

Figure 7.12

where c_r means $\cos\varphi_r$ and s_r means $\sin\varphi_r$. We prove this easily by the same method as before, regarding the elements in the first row as the components in the directions Ox, Oy, Oz of a unit force in OA. The second row is obtained from the first by replacing φ_3 by $\varphi_3 + \frac{1}{2}\pi$.

7.13 Rotations about the moving axes. We now consider another method of finding the matrix (7.12.1). As we have seen (§ 7.6), a rotation θ about OA has the effect of replacing the matrix $\mathbf{l}$ by $\mathbf{R}_1\mathbf{l}$, where $\mathbf{R}_1(=\mathbf{R}_1(\theta))$ is the orthogonal matrix

$$(7.13.1)\qquad \mathbf{R}_1(\theta) = \begin{pmatrix} 1 & 0 & 0 \\ 0 & \cos\theta & \sin\theta \\ 0 & -\sin\theta & \cos\theta \end{pmatrix}.$$

Similarly a rotation θ about OB replaces $\mathbf{l}$ by $\mathbf{R}_2\mathbf{l}$, where $\mathbf{R}_2$ is the orthogonal matrix

$$(7.13.2)\qquad \mathbf{R}_2(\theta) = \begin{pmatrix} \cos\theta & 0 & -\sin\theta \\ 0 & 1 & 0 \\ \sin\theta & 0 & \cos\theta \end{pmatrix},$$

and a rotation θ about OC replaces $\mathbf{l}$ by $\mathbf{R}_3\mathbf{l}$, where $\mathbf{R}_3$ is the orthogonal matrix

$$(7.13.3)\qquad \mathbf{R}_3(\theta) = \begin{pmatrix} \cos\theta & \sin\theta & 0 \\ -\sin\theta & \cos\theta & 0 \\ 0 & 0 & 1 \end{pmatrix}.$$

If initially $OABC$ coincides with the fixed trihedral $Oxyz$ the initial value of $\mathbf{l}$ is $\mathbf{I}$. If therefore we arrive at the final position of $OABC$ by the rotations φ_1, φ_2, φ_3 described in § 7.12, the final value of $\mathbf{l}$ is

$$(7.13.4)\qquad \mathbf{R}_3(\varphi_3)\mathbf{R}_2(\varphi_2)\mathbf{R}_1(\varphi_1),$$

which is equal to (7.12.1).

We can, of course, use the same method for finding the matrix of direction cosines in terms of Euler's angles. The required matrix is

$$(7.13.5)\qquad \mathbf{R}_3(\psi)\mathbf{R}_2(\theta)\mathbf{R}_3(\varphi),$$

which leads again to (7.11.2).

7.14 Rotations about the fixed axes. If the body suffers a rotation θ about the fixed axis Ox the trihedral $OABC$ (fixed in the body) moves to a new position, and the matrix of direction cosines $\mathbf{l}$ is replaced by a new matrix which is easily seen to be $\mathbf{l}\mathbf{R}_1(\theta)$; the determination of the new matrix involves postmultiplication by $\mathbf{R}_1$. There are similar results for rotations about Oy and about Oz.

Thus a rotation φ_3 about Oz, followed by a rotation φ_2 about Oy, followed by a rotation φ_1 about Ox, gives for the final matrix of direction cosines (since $\mathbf{l} = \mathbf{I}$ initially)

$$\mathbf{R}_3(\varphi_3)\mathbf{R}_2(\varphi_2)\mathbf{R}_1(\varphi_1), \tag{7.14.1}$$

and this is precisely the same as (7.13.4). Thus, if the moving trihedral $OABC$ coincides initially with the fixed trihedral $Oxyz$, *the effect of rotations in order about OA, OB, OC is the same as the effect of the same rotations about Ox, Oy, Oz performed in the reverse order.*

The remarkable theorem just proved permits us to think in terms of rotations about the fixed axes instead of in terms of rotations about the instantaneous positions of the moving axes. A special case of the theorem has already been noticed at the end of § 7.11.

In virtue of the theorem just proved, the examples 7.9A and 7.9B determine the rotation vector $\mathbf{T}$ for the displacement of the trihedral $OABC$, from its initial to its final position, in terms of Euler's angles and in terms of φ_1, φ_2, φ_3. The associated rotation formulae give us another method of finding $\mathbf{l}$ in terms of Euler's angles or in terms of φ_1, φ_2, φ_3, though the method is less convenient in practice than those given previously. Thus, for example, if in (7.9.25) we take for $\mathbf{r}$ the vector (1, 0, 0) we find

$$\mathbf{s} = (c_2c_3,\ c_1s_3 + s_1s_2c_3,\ s_1s_3 - c_1s_2c_3), \tag{7.14.2}$$

giving the elements of the first row of (7.12.1).

7.15 Angular velocity found from $\mathbf{l}$ and $\dot{\mathbf{l}}$. Suppose we start from a given orientation of the body and arrive at a new orientation by the following sequence of operations: a rotation φ_1 about OA, followed by a rotation φ_2 about the carried position of OB, followed by a rotation φ_3 about the carried position of OC. As we have seen (§ 7.13) the matrix of direction cosines for the final position of the trihedral is

$$\mathbf{R}_3(\varphi_3)\mathbf{R}_2(\varphi_2)\mathbf{R}_1(\varphi_1)\mathbf{l}. \tag{7.15.1}$$

The order of the operations is not commutative in general.

If however the rotations are infinitesimal, say $\delta\varphi_1$, $\delta\varphi_2$, $\delta\varphi_3$, and we neglect squares and products of these numbers, then the order is irrelevant, and

$$\mathbf{l} + \delta\mathbf{l} = \begin{pmatrix} 1 & \delta\varphi_3 & 0 \\ -\delta\varphi_3 & 1 & 0 \\ 0 & 0 & 1 \end{pmatrix}\begin{pmatrix} 1 & 0 & -\delta\varphi_2 \\ 0 & 1 & 0 \\ \delta\varphi_2 & 0 & 1 \end{pmatrix}\begin{pmatrix} 1 & 0 & 0 \\ 0 & 1 & \delta\varphi_1 \\ 0 & -\delta\varphi_1 & 1 \end{pmatrix}\mathbf{l} \tag{7.15.2}$$

$$= \begin{pmatrix} 1 & \delta\varphi_3 & -\delta\varphi_2 \\ -\delta\varphi_3 & 1 & \delta\varphi_1 \\ \delta\varphi_2 & -\delta\varphi_1 & 1 \end{pmatrix}\mathbf{l},$$

whence

$$\delta\mathbf{l} = \begin{pmatrix} 0 & \delta\varphi_3 & -\delta\varphi_2 \\ -\delta\varphi_3 & 0 & \delta\varphi_1 \\ \delta\varphi_2 & -\delta\varphi_1 & 0 \end{pmatrix}\mathbf{l}. \tag{7.15.3}$$

Thus

$$\frac{d\mathbf{l}}{dt} + \mathbf{\Omega l} = \mathbf{0}, \tag{7.15.4}$$

where $\frac{d\mathbf{l}}{dt}$ (or $\dot{\mathbf{l}}$) is the matrix obtained by differentiating the individual elements of $\mathbf{l}$. and $\mathbf{\Omega}$ is the skew-symmetric matrix

$$\mathbf{\Omega} = \begin{pmatrix} 0 & -\omega_3 & \omega_2 \\ \omega_3 & 0 & -\omega_1 \\ -\omega_2 & \omega_1 & 0 \end{pmatrix}, \tag{7.15.5}$$

where $\omega_1, \omega_2, \omega_3$ are components of angular velocity in the directions OA, OB, OC.

The geometric meaning of (7.15.4) is clear. If we take (say) the first column of $\mathbf{l}$ its elements are components, measured in $OABC$, of a unit vector in the fixed direction Ox The vanishing of the first column on the left in (7.15.4) is equivalent to the familiar result

$$\dot{\mathbf{u}} + \boldsymbol{\omega} \times \mathbf{u} = 0, \tag{7.15.6}$$

where $\mathbf{u}$ is a unit vector in Ox, and $\boldsymbol{\omega}$ is the angular velocity measured in $OABC$.

Since $\mathbf{l}$ is orthogonal, (7.15.4) leads to

$$\mathbf{\Omega} = -\dot{\mathbf{l}}\mathbf{l}', \tag{7.15.7}$$

and this equation determines the angular velocity in terms of $\mathbf{l}$ and $\dot{\mathbf{l}}$. It is easy to see independently that the matrix $\dot{\mathbf{l}}\mathbf{l}'$ is skew-symmetric.

7.16 Components of angular velocity. We now determine the components of angular velocity of the rigid body in the directions OA, OB, OC. We suppose that the orientation of the body is described either in terms of Euler's angles, or in terms of $\varphi_1, \varphi_2, \varphi_3$.

(i) *Euler's angles.* The angular velocity is the vector sum of $\dot{\varphi}$ about Oz, $\dot{\theta}$ about OS, and $\dot{\psi}$ about OC (Fig. 7.11). Hence if the components of angular velocity in the directions OA, OB, OC are $\omega_1, \omega_2, \omega_3$, we have

$$\begin{cases} \omega_1 = \dot{\theta}\sin\psi - \dot{\varphi}\sin\theta\cos\psi, \\ \omega_2 = \dot{\theta}\cos\psi + \dot{\varphi}\sin\theta\sin\psi, \\ \omega_3 = \dot{\varphi}\cos\theta + \dot{\psi}. \end{cases} \tag{7.16.1}$$

A curious antimony, arising from the unsymmetrical way in which Euler's angles are measured, emerges at this point. If at a certain instant $OABC$ coincides with $Oxyz$, so that at this instant $\theta = \varphi = \psi = 0$, the formulae (7.16.1) give

$$\omega_1 = 0, \qquad \omega_2 = \dot{\theta}, \qquad \omega_3 = \dot{\varphi} + \dot{\psi}.$$

The component ω_1 vanishes whatever finite values we give to $\dot{\theta}$, $\dot{\varphi}$, and $\dot{\psi}$. Euler's angles are therefore not well suited to a problem in which, at some instant, $OABC$ coincides with $Oxyz$, unless indeed at this instant the angular velocity vector lies in the plane Oyz. More generally, whenever $\theta = 0$ the formulae (7.16.1) would imply $\omega_1 = \omega_2 \tan\psi$, which is not true in general.

(ii) *The angles* $\varphi_1, \varphi_2, \varphi_3$. The angular velocity is the vector sum of $\dot{\varphi}_1$ about Ox, $\dot{\varphi}_2$ about OQ, and $\dot{\varphi}_3$ about OC (Fig. 7.12). Hence, if the components of angular velocity in the directions OA, OB, OC, are $\omega_1, \omega_2, \omega_3$, we have

$$\text{(7.16.2)} \qquad \begin{cases} \omega_1 = \quad c_2 c_3 \dot{\varphi}_1 + s_3 \dot{\varphi}_2, \\ \omega_2 = -c_2 s_3 \dot{\varphi}_1 + c_3 \dot{\varphi}_2, \\ \omega_3 = \quad s_2 \dot{\varphi}_1 \qquad\qquad + \dot{\varphi}_3, \end{cases}$$

where $c_r = \cos\varphi_r$, $s_r = \sin\varphi_r$. Again, anomalies arise in certain circumstances, for example when $c_2 = 0$.

These reduce, as they must, to $\dot{\varphi}_1, \dot{\varphi}_2, \dot{\varphi}_3$ when $\varphi_1 = \varphi_2 = \varphi_3 = 0$.

(iii) The results can also be deduced from the formula for $\mathbf{\Omega}$ given in (7.15.7). Taking for definiteness the angles $\varphi_1, \varphi_2, \varphi_3$, we have

$$\text{(7.13.4)} \qquad \mathbf{l} = \mathbf{R}_3(\varphi_3)\mathbf{R}_2(\varphi_2)\mathbf{R}_1(\varphi_1),$$

and

$$\text{(7.15.7)} \qquad \mathbf{\Omega} = -\dot{\mathbf{l}}\mathbf{l}'.$$

Hence

$$\text{(7.16.3)} \qquad \mathbf{\Omega} = -\left(\dot{\varphi}_1 \mathbf{R}_3 \mathbf{R}_2 \frac{d\mathbf{R}_1}{d\varphi_1} + \dot{\varphi}_2 \mathbf{R}_3 \frac{d\mathbf{R}_2}{d\varphi_2} \mathbf{R}_1 + \dot{\varphi}_3 \frac{d\mathbf{R}_3}{d\varphi_3} \mathbf{R}_2 \mathbf{R}_1\right) \mathbf{R}_1' \mathbf{R}_2' \mathbf{R}_3',$$

$$= -\dot{\varphi}_1 \mathbf{R}_3 \mathbf{R}_2 \frac{d\mathbf{R}_1}{d\varphi_1} \mathbf{R}_1' \mathbf{R}_2' \mathbf{R}_3' - \dot{\varphi}_2 \mathbf{R}_3 \frac{d\mathbf{R}_2}{d\varphi_2} \mathbf{R}_2' \mathbf{R}_3' - \dot{\varphi}_3 \frac{d\mathbf{R}_3}{d\varphi_3} \mathbf{R}_3',$$

where it is understood that the argument in $\mathbf{R}_i$ and in $\mathbf{R}_i'$ is φ_i. Now the matrix $\mathbf{R}_1(\theta)$ has the property

$$\text{(7.16.4)} \qquad \frac{d\mathbf{R}_1}{d\theta} \mathbf{R}_1' = \begin{pmatrix} 0 & 0 & 0 \\ 0 & 0 & 1 \\ 0 & -1 & 0 \end{pmatrix},$$

and similarly

$$\text{(7.16.5)} \qquad \frac{d\mathbf{R}_2}{d\theta} \mathbf{R}_2' = \begin{pmatrix} 0 & 0 & -1 \\ 0 & 0 & 0 \\ 1 & 0 & 0 \end{pmatrix},$$

and

$$\text{(7.16.6)} \qquad \frac{d\mathbf{R}_3}{d\theta} \mathbf{R}_3' = \begin{pmatrix} 0 & 1 & 0 \\ -1 & 0 & 0 \\ 0 & 0 & 0 \end{pmatrix}.$$

Using these results in (7.16.3) we find

$$\text{(7.16.7)} \qquad \mathbf{\Omega} = \begin{pmatrix} 0 & -(s_2\dot{\varphi}_1 + \dot{\varphi}_3) & -c_2 s_3 \dot{\varphi}_1 + c_3 \dot{\varphi}_2 \\ s_2 \dot{\varphi}_1 + \dot{\varphi}_3 & 0 & -(c_2 c_3 \dot{\varphi}_1 + s_3 \dot{\varphi}_2) \\ -(-c_2 s_3 \dot{\varphi}_1 + c_3 \dot{\varphi}_2) & c_2 c_3 \dot{\varphi}_1 + s_3 \dot{\varphi}_2 & 0 \end{pmatrix},$$

and we thus recover (7.16.2). But the method given in (ii) above is simpler.

Chapter VIII

First applications of Lagrange's equations

8.1 The differential equations. We now turn to the application of Lagrange's equations of motion to some concrete dynamical systems. To begin with, let us consider a conservative holonomic system with k freedoms. We choose Lagrangian coordinates $q_1, q_2, \ldots, q_n$ to describe the configuration of the system at time t, and the smallest possible value of n is k. We will suppose for the present that this choice has been made, $n = k$. We construct the Lagrangian function L (§ 6.6), $L = T - V$, and the equations of motion are

$$\frac{d}{dt}\left(\frac{\partial L}{\partial \dot{q}_r}\right) = \frac{\partial L}{\partial q_r}, \qquad r = 1, 2, \ldots, n. \tag{6.6.3}$$

We are then faced with a set of n simultaneous ordinary differential equations of the second order to determine the n unknown functions $q_1(t), q_2(t), \ldots, q_n(t)$. Theoretically the system (6.6.3) suffices to determine the q's as functions of t, at any rate in some interval about $t = 0$, if the values of the q's and $\dot{q}$'s at $t = 0$ are prescribed.

What do we mean by *solving* a dynamical problem? We mean, if we interpret the question in the most exacting sense, determining the q's as functions of t for all real values of t, or at least for some range of values of t, in terms of the arbitrarily prescribed values q_{r0} of q_r and ω_{r0} of $\dot{q}_r$ at $t = 0$. In this complete sense only a few specially simple problems of classical dynamics are soluble. One conspicuous example in which the problem is soluble in this complete sense occurs in the theory of small oscillations (Chapter IX).

Usually, however, we have to be content with something less than a complete solution in this sense. Even if we cannot find explicit formulae giving the q's as functions of the $2n + 1$ parameters $q_{10}, q_{20}, \ldots, q_{n0}, \omega_{10}, \omega_{20}, \ldots, \omega_{n0}, t$, we may still be able to determine the general nature of the motion, and we may be able to discover important and significant properties of it. Moreover, we can use numerical methods of integration, or expansions in power-series (§ 21.4), to find approximations that are valid for sufficiently small values of t.

Similar remarks apply to non-holonomic systems, though here the set-up is more complex. We recall briefly the procedure. The least possible value for n is $k + l$, and there are l equations of constraint

$$\sum_{s=1}^{n} B_{rs}\dot{q}_s + B_r = 0, \qquad r = 1, 2, \ldots, l. \tag{6.2.3}$$

The equations of motion are

$$\frac{d}{dt}\left(\frac{\partial L}{\partial \dot{q}_r}\right) = \frac{\partial L}{\partial q_r} + \sum_{m=1}^{l} \lambda_m B_{mr}, \qquad r = 1, 2, \ldots, n. \tag{6.6.4}$$

This time we have $n + l$ equations, and $n + l$ unknown functions of t to determine, namely $q_1, q_2, \ldots, q_n, \lambda_1, \lambda_2, \ldots, \lambda_l$.

Finally, if there are p redundant coordinates, and p relations

$$F_r(q_1, q_2, \ldots, q_n;\ t) = 0, \qquad r = 1, 2, \ldots, p, \tag{5.12.6}$$

we must add in the second member of (6.6.3) or (6.6.4) the terms

$$\sum_{i=1}^{p} \mu_i \frac{\partial F_i}{\partial q_r}, \qquad r = 1, 2, \ldots, n. \tag{6.2.4}$$

There are p additional unknowns, namely the multipliers $\mu_1, \mu_2, \ldots, \mu_p$, and p additional equations, namely the equations (5.12.6).

We now consider the application of Lagrange's equations to some particular systems.

8.2 Formulae for acceleration in general orthogonal coordinates. A particle moves in space, its position being defined by orthogonal curvilinear coordinates α, β, γ for which the line-element ds is given by

$$ds^2 = A^2\, d\alpha^2 + B^2\, d\beta^2 + C^2\, d\gamma^2. \tag{8.2.1}$$

The coefficients A, B, C are functions of (α, β, γ) of class C_1. At each point of space three principal directions are defined, and they are mutually orthogonal. At $(\alpha_0, \beta_0, \gamma_0)$ the first principal direction, for example, is along the tangent to the curve $\beta = \beta_0$, $\gamma = \gamma_0$, in the direction of increasing α. We sometimes speak of this as the α-direction.

For a particle of unit mass,

$$T = \tfrac{1}{2}(A^2\dot{\alpha}^2 + B^2\dot{\beta}^2 + C^2\dot{\gamma}^2). \tag{8.2.2}$$

If the particle is acted on by a force whose components in the principal directions are X, Y, Z, the work done in a virtual displacement is

$$XA\, d\alpha + YB\, d\beta + ZC\, d\gamma. \tag{8.2.3}$$

The first Lagrangian equation is

$$\frac{d}{dt}(A^2\dot{\alpha}) - \left(A\frac{\partial A}{\partial \alpha}\dot{\alpha}^2 + B\frac{\partial B}{\partial \alpha}\dot{\beta}^2 + C\frac{\partial C}{\partial \alpha}\dot{\gamma}^2\right) = XA. \tag{8.2.4}$$

The component of acceleration in the α-direction is

$$X = \frac{1}{A}\left\{\frac{d}{dt}(A^2\dot{\alpha}) - \left(A\frac{\partial A}{\partial \alpha}\dot{\alpha}^2 + B\frac{\partial B}{\partial \alpha}\dot{\beta}^2 + C\frac{\partial C}{\partial \alpha}\dot{\gamma}^2\right)\right\}. \tag{8.2.5}$$

Written *in extenso* this formula becomes

$$A\ddot{\alpha} + 2\dot{\alpha}\left(\frac{\partial A}{\partial \alpha}\dot{\alpha} + \frac{\partial A}{\partial \beta}\dot{\beta} + \frac{\partial A}{\partial \gamma}\dot{\gamma}\right) - \frac{1}{A}\left(A\frac{\partial A}{\partial \alpha}\dot{\alpha}^2 + B\frac{\partial B}{\partial \alpha}\dot{\beta}^2 + C\frac{\partial C}{\partial \alpha}\dot{\gamma}^2\right). \tag{8.2.6}$$

The components of acceleration in the β-direction and in the γ-direction are given by the corresponding formulae.

Here are two important special cases:

(i) For cylindrical polar coordinates r, θ, z we have

$$ds^2 = dr^2 + r^2\, d\theta^2 + dz^2, \tag{8.2.7}$$

and the components of acceleration are

$$\ddot{r} - r\dot{\theta}^2, \quad r\ddot{\theta} + 2\dot{r}\dot{\theta}, \quad \ddot{z}. \tag{8.2.8}$$

(ii) For spherical polar coordinates r, θ, φ we have

$$ds^2 = dr^2 + r^2\,d\theta^2 + r^2\sin^2\theta\,d\varphi^2, \tag{8.2.9}$$

and the components of acceleration are

$$\ddot{r} - r(\dot{\theta}^2 + \sin^2\theta\,\dot{\varphi}^2), \quad r\ddot{\theta} + 2\dot{r}\dot{\theta} - r\cos\theta\sin\theta\,\dot{\varphi}^2, \tag{8.2.10}$$
$$r\sin\theta\,\ddot{\varphi} + 2(\dot{r}\sin\theta + r\cos\theta\,\dot{\theta})\dot{\varphi}.$$

8.3 Monkey and counterpoise. We consider again a problem already discussed in another context (*Example* 4.4*B*). A light flexible inextensible rope passes over a smooth peg, and carries at one end a mass M; a monkey, of mass m, climbs the rope on the other side, his displacement relative to the rope being a prescribed function of t, $\varphi(t)$. We suppose as before that $\varphi \in C_2$, that $\varphi(0) = \dot{\varphi}(0) = 0$, and that the system is initially at rest.

This is an example of the type discussed in § 6.5, where the work done by the given forces in a virtual displacement is $-\delta_s V$, where V contains t explicitly, but the symbol δ_s refers to a displacement with t unvaried. If z is the height through which the monkey has risen at time t, the height of the counterpoise is $c + \varphi - z$, and

$$T = \tfrac{1}{2}\{m\dot{z}^2 + M(\dot{\varphi} - \dot{z})^2\}, \tag{8.3.1}$$

$$V = mgz + Mg(\varphi - z). \tag{8.3.2}$$

The Lagrangian equation of motion is

$$\frac{d}{dt}\{(m + M)\dot{z} - M\dot{\varphi}\} = -(m - M)g, \tag{8.3.3}$$

and we recover the formula (4.4.7),

$$(m + M)z = M\varphi + \tfrac{1}{2}(M - m)gt^2,$$

since φ, $\dot{\varphi}$, z, $\dot{z}$ all vanish at $t = 0$.

8.4 Kinetic energy of a rigid body. Suppose first that the body has one point O fixed. If OA, OB, OC are principal axes of inertia at O, and the components of angular velocity in the directions OA, OB, OC are ω_1, ω_2, ω_3, we have

$$T = \tfrac{1}{2}Sm\{(\omega_2 c - \omega_3 b)^2 + (\omega_3 a - \omega_1 c)^2 + (\omega_1 b - \omega_2 a)^2\}, \tag{8.4.1}$$

where a, b, c are coordinates of a particle of the body referred to the axes OA, OB, OC. Since the axes OA, OB, OC are fixed in the body, the coordinates a, b, c are constants. Now

$$Smbc = Smca = Smab = 0, \tag{8.4.2}$$

so (8.4.1) becomes

$$\begin{aligned} T &= \tfrac{1}{2}Sm\{(b^2 + c^2)\omega_1{}^2 + (c^2 + a^2)\omega_2{}^2 + (a^2 + b^2)\omega_3{}^2\} \\ &= \tfrac{1}{2}(A\omega_1{}^2 + B\omega_2{}^2 + C\omega_3{}^2), \end{aligned} \tag{8.4.3}$$

where A, B, C are the moments of inertia about OA, OB, OC, i.e. they are the principal moments of inertia at O.

Suppose next that the body moves in space. Let the coordinates of the centre of gravity G (referred to fixed axes $Oxyz$) be ξ, η, ζ, and let the principal axes of inertia at G be GA, GB, GC. If ω_1, ω_2, ω_3 are components of angular velocity in the directions GA, GB, GC we have, in virtue of König's theorem (§ 7.1),

$$T = \tfrac{1}{2}M(\dot{\xi}^2 + \dot{\eta}^2 + \dot{\zeta}^2) + \tfrac{1}{2}(A\omega_1{}^2 + B\omega_2{}^2 + C\omega_3{}^2). \tag{8.4.4}$$

Before we can use this formula in Lagrange's equations we must express ω_1, ω_2, ω_3 in terms of three Lagrangian coordinates, for example Euler's angles, or the angles $(\varphi_1, \varphi_2, \varphi_3)$ (§ 7.16).

The method of constructing T just given is simple and expeditious, but it may appear at first sight somewhat remote from the original definition of T,

$$T = \tfrac{1}{2}\, Sm\, (\dot{x}^2 + \dot{y}^2 + \dot{z}^2) \tag{8.4.5}$$

given in § 3.3. It should be emphasized, however, that the direct derivation from (8.4.5) is quite practicable. For

$$x = \xi + al_1 + bl_2 + cl_3, \tag{8.4.6}$$

where, for the moment, the direction cosines of GA are written (l_1, m_1, n_1), and so on, so that (cf. § 7.3)

$$\mathbf{l} = \begin{pmatrix} l_1 & m_1 & n_1 \\ l_2 & m_2 & n_2 \\ l_3 & m_3 & n_3 \end{pmatrix}. \tag{8.4.7}$$

The direction cosines are certain simple functions of the Lagrangian coordinates (§ 7.11 and § 7.12). Thus

$$\dot{x} = \dot{\xi} + a\dot{l}_1 + b\dot{l}_2 + c\dot{l}_3, \tag{8.4.8}$$

with similar formulae for $\dot{y}$ and $\dot{z}$. Since

$$Sm\, a = Sm\, b = Sm\, c = 0, \quad Sm\, bc = Sm\, ca = Sm\, ab = 0, \tag{8.4.9}$$

our formula (8.4.5) for T reduces to

$$\begin{aligned} T = \tfrac{1}{2}M(\dot{\xi}^2 + \dot{\eta}^2 + \dot{\zeta}^2) &+ \tfrac{1}{2}\, Sm\, a^2(\dot{l}_1{}^2 + \dot{m}_1{}^2 + \dot{n}_1{}^2) \\ &+ \tfrac{1}{2}\, Sm\, b^2(\dot{l}_2{}^2 + \dot{m}_2{}^2 + \dot{n}_2{}^2) + \tfrac{1}{2}\, Sm\, c^2(\dot{l}_3{}^2 + \dot{m}_3{}^2 + \dot{n}_3{}^2). \end{aligned} \tag{8.4.10}$$

Our next step is therefore the expression of $\dot{l}_1$, for example, in terms of $\dot{\theta}$, $\dot{\varphi}$, $\dot{\psi}$, or in terms of $\dot{\varphi}_1$, $\dot{\varphi}_2$, $\dot{\varphi}_3$. The calculation is not particularly formidable, but it can be shortened by the simple observation that (l_1, l_2, l_3) is a unit vector in a fixed direction, so that

$$\dot{l}_1 = l_2\omega_3 - l_3\omega_2. \tag{8.4.11}$$

Thus

$$\begin{aligned} T &= \tfrac{1}{2}M(\dot{\xi}^2 + \dot{\eta}^2 + \dot{\zeta}^2) + \tfrac{1}{2}\, Sm\, a^2\{(l_2\omega_3 - l_3\omega_2)^2 + (m_2\omega_3 - m_3\omega_2)^2 \\ &\quad + (n_2\omega_3 - n_3\omega_2)^2\} + \ldots + \ldots \\ &= \tfrac{1}{2}M(\dot{\xi}^2 + \dot{\eta}^2 + \dot{\zeta}^2) + \tfrac{1}{2}\, Sm\, a^2(\omega_2{}^2 + \omega_3{}^2) + \tfrac{1}{2}\, Sm\, b^2(\omega_3{}^2 + \omega_1{}^2) \\ &\quad + \tfrac{1}{2}\, Sm\, c^2(\omega_1{}^2 + \omega_2{}^2), \end{aligned} \tag{8.4.12}$$

which leads at once to (8.4.4).

8.5 A problem of motion in two dimensions. As a typical example of two-dimensional motion we consider the following. A uniform thin right cylindrical shell, of mass M and radius b, rolls on a horizontal plane, and a second uniform thin right cylindrical shell, of mass m and radius a, rolls inside the first. All the surfaces are perfectly rough, so the motion involves only pure rolling without skidding.

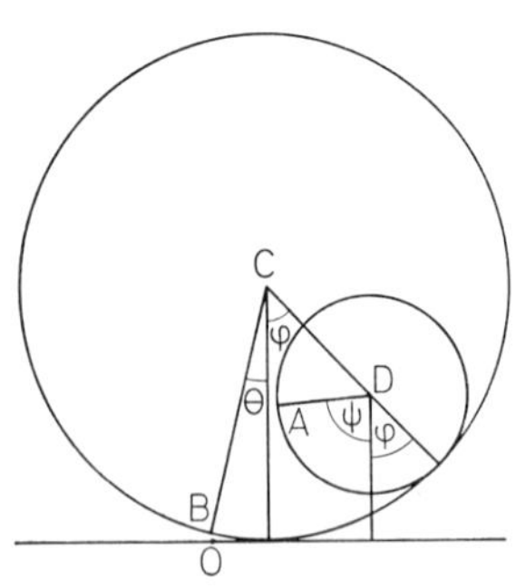

Figure 8.5

The system is a holonomic system with two freedoms. In Fig. 8.5, representing a section at right angles to the axes of the cylinders, C is the centre of the first cylinder, D of the second. The point B is a fixed point of the first cylinder, and A is a fixed point of the second; in a standard position, B coincides with a point O of the plane, and A coincides with B. We take as Lagrangian coordinates the inclination θ of CB to the downward vertical through C, and the inclination φ of CD to the downward vertical through C, θ and φ being measured in opposite senses as shown. The condition of pure rolling is

$$a(\varphi + \psi) = b(\theta + \varphi),$$

$$a\psi = b\theta + c\varphi, \tag{8.5.1}$$

where $c = b - a$. In practice we must be alive to the possibility that the surfaces may separate. But we will avoid this complication by considering a motion in which separation does not occur; or alternatively we can suppose that an imponderable mechanism is supplied which prevents separation. As a concrete problem let us consider the motion that ensues when the system starts from rest with $\varphi = \alpha$, where $0 < \alpha < \frac{1}{2}\pi$. We may suppose, without loss of generality, that initially $\theta = 0$.

We have

$$\begin{aligned} T &= \tfrac{1}{2}Mb^2\dot{\theta}^2 + \tfrac{1}{2}Mb^2\dot{\theta}^2 + \tfrac{1}{2}m(b^2\dot{\theta}^2 + c^2\dot{\varphi}^2 + 2bc\dot{\theta}\dot{\varphi}\cos\varphi) + \tfrac{1}{2}ma^2\dot{\psi}^2 \\ &= Mb^2\dot{\theta}^2 + \tfrac{1}{2}m(b^2\dot{\theta}^2 + c^2\dot{\varphi}^2 + 2bc\dot{\theta}\dot{\varphi}\cos\varphi) + \tfrac{1}{2}m(b\dot{\theta} + c\dot{\varphi})^2 \\ &= (M + m)b^2\dot{\theta}^2 + mc^2\dot{\varphi}^2 + mbc\dot{\theta}\dot{\varphi}(1 + \cos\varphi), \end{aligned} \tag{8.5.2}$$

$$V = -mgc\cos\varphi. \tag{8.5.3}$$

The momentum integral corresponding to the ignorable coordinate θ is

$$2(M + m)b\dot{\theta} + mc\dot{\varphi}(1 + \cos\varphi) = 0, \tag{8.5.4}$$

and we deduce immediately

$$2(M + m)b\theta + mc(\varphi + \sin\varphi) = mc(\alpha + \sin\alpha). \tag{8.5.5}$$

The equation (8.5.5) determines θ explicitly if φ is known, and it will suffice therefore to concentrate our attention on the determination of φ.

The energy equation is

$$(M + m)b^2\dot{\theta}^2 + mc^2\dot{\varphi}^2 + mbc\dot{\theta}\dot{\varphi}(1 + \cos\varphi) = mgc(\cos\varphi - \cos\alpha), \tag{8.5.6}$$

and eliminating $\dot{\theta}$ between (8.5.4) and (8.5.6) (either by using the trivial identity

$$ax^2 + 2hxy + by^2 = \{(ax + hy)^2 + (ab - h^2)y^2\}/a,$$

or otherwise) we find

$$\dot{\varphi}^2\{1 - \beta^2(1 + \cos\varphi)^2\} = n^2(\cos\varphi - \cos\alpha), \tag{8.5.7}$$

where

$$\beta^2 = \frac{m}{4(M + m)} < \frac{1}{4}, \quad n^2 = \frac{g}{c}. \tag{8.5.8}$$

The equation (8.5.7) determines the relation between φ and t. It is evident that the motion is periodic, φ oscillating between α and $-\alpha$. The period is

$$\frac{4}{n}\int_0^\alpha \sqrt{\left\{\frac{1-\beta^2(1+\cos\varphi)^2}{\cos\varphi-\cos\alpha}\right\}}\,d\varphi. \tag{8.5.9}$$

8.6 The spinning top, the fundamental equations. A top is a rigid body with axial symmetry; one point O on the axis, called the *peg*, is fixed, and the body, which is free to move about O, moves under the action of gravity. If we take a trihedral $OABC$ fixed in the top, with OC along the axis, then OA, OB, OC are principal axes of inertia at O, and the moments of inertia about OA and OB are equal. The centre of gravity G lies on OC. We denote the principal moments of inertia at the peg by A, A, C, the mass by M, and the length OG by l. If $C = 0$ we recover the problem of the spherical pendulum, already discussed in § 5.3.

From the point of view of pure dynamics the condition that the body is axially symmetric is more than we actually need. The equations we shall establish are valid for any body which is such that the ellipsoid of inertia at G is a spheroid, if O is taken on the axis of this spheroid.

Using Euler's angles to define the orientation of the trihedral $OABC$, and taking Oz vertically upwards, we have

(8.6.1)

$$\begin{aligned}T &= \tfrac{1}{2}A(\dot\theta\sin\psi-\dot\varphi\sin\theta\cos\psi)^2+\tfrac{1}{2}A(\dot\theta\cos\psi+\dot\varphi\sin\theta\sin\psi)^2+\tfrac{1}{2}C(\dot\psi+\dot\varphi\cos\theta)^2\\ &= \tfrac{1}{2}A(\dot\theta^2+\dot\varphi^2\sin^2\theta)+\tfrac{1}{2}C(\dot\psi+\dot\varphi\cos\theta)^2,\end{aligned}$$

$$V = Mgl\cos\theta. \tag{8.6.2}$$

The Lagrangian equation for θ is

$$A(\ddot\theta-\dot\varphi^2\sin\theta\cos\theta)+C(\dot\psi+\dot\varphi\cos\theta)\dot\varphi\sin\theta = Mgl\sin\theta, \tag{8.6.3}$$

and the momentum integrals for the ignorable coordinates φ and ψ are

$$A\sin^2\theta\dot\varphi+C\cos\theta(\dot\psi+\dot\varphi\cos\theta) = \text{constant} = 2A\lambda, \tag{8.6.4}$$

$$\dot\psi+\dot\varphi\cos\theta = \text{constant} = n. \tag{8.6.5}$$

Equation (8.6.4) expresses the fact that the angular momentum about Oz has a constant value (called $2A\lambda$), and equation (8.6.5) expresses the fact that the *spin* (i.e. the component of angular velocity about the axis of the top) has a constant value (called n). We shall suppose $n > 0$, and we recall that, in most cases of practical interest, n is large.

We derive at once the equations defining θ and φ as functions of t, i.e. the equations controlling the motion of the axis,

$$\ddot\theta-\sin\theta(\cos\theta\dot\varphi^2-2p\dot\varphi+q) = 0, \tag{8.6.6}$$

$$\sin^2\theta\dot\varphi+2p\cos\theta = 2\lambda, \tag{8.6.7}$$

where $2p = Cn/A$, $q = Mgl/A$; the parameters p and q are both positive.

We next establish the integral of energy. We can derive this from the equations of motion, as in § 6.7, or we can quote the general theorem of § 6.7. The integral of energy can be written in the form

$$\dot\theta^2+\sin^2\theta\dot\varphi^2+2q\cos\theta = 2\mu. \tag{8.6.8}$$

In the scheme of equations, (8.6.6) and (8.6.8) may be regarded as alternatives, and for some purposes (8.6.8) is more useful than (8.6.6). The elimination of $\dot{\varphi}$ from (8.6.7) and (8.6.8) leads to the equation

$$\tfrac{1}{2}\dot{z}^2 = (\mu - qz)(1 - z^2) - 2(\lambda - pz)^2, \tag{8.6.9}$$

where $z = \cos\theta$. We denote the cubic polynomial on the right in (8.6.9) by $f(z)$. The dependence of z upon t can be expressed in terms of a $\wp$-function, as in the special case of the spherical pendulum (to which the present problem is equivalent if $p = 0$). Further,

$$\dot{\varphi} = \frac{2(\lambda - pz)}{1 - z^2}. \tag{8.6.10}$$

We have a three-fold infinity of motions (ignoring for the moment the *phase constants* which depend on the choice of the zero of measurement for t, φ, ψ) corresponding to the three parameters p, λ, μ.

8.7 The spinning top, another method. It is interesting to recover the results found in § 8.6 by another method. We will assume the theorem that the spin retains the constant value n. Then, if $\mathbf{u}$ is a unit vector in the axis OC, the angular momentum vector, with O as origin, is

$$Cn\mathbf{u} + A\mathbf{u} \times \dot{\mathbf{u}}, \tag{8.7.1}$$

and the equation of motion is

$$Cn\dot{\mathbf{u}} + A\mathbf{u} \times \ddot{\mathbf{u}} = Mgl\mathbf{u} \times \mathbf{v}, \tag{8.7.2}$$

where $\mathbf{v}$ is a unit vector in the direction of gravity.

If then we write x, y, z for the components of $\mathbf{u}$, and take Oz vertically upwards, so that $\mathbf{v} = \{0, 0, -1\}$, we have

$$A(y\ddot{z} - z\ddot{y}) + Cn\dot{x} = -Mgly, \tag{8.7.3}$$

$$A(z\ddot{x} - x\ddot{z}) + Cn\dot{y} = Mglx, \tag{8.7.4}$$

$$A(x\ddot{y} - y\ddot{x}) + Cn\dot{z} = 0. \tag{8.7.5}$$

From (8.7.5) we deduce immediately

$$A(x\dot{y} - y\dot{x}) + Cnz = \text{constant}, \tag{8.7.6}$$

which is equivalent to (8.6.7). If we multiply the equations (8.7.3–5) by $(\dot{y} - \dot{z})$, $(\dot{z} - \dot{x})$, $(\dot{x} - \dot{y})$ respectively, and add, we find

$$A\{(x\dot{x} + y\dot{y} + z\dot{z})(\ddot{x} + \ddot{y} + \ddot{z}) - (x + y + z)(\dot{x}\ddot{x} + \dot{y}\ddot{y} + \dot{z}\ddot{z})\} \\ = Mgl\{(x + y + z)\dot{z} - (x\dot{x} + y\dot{y} + z\dot{z})\}. \tag{8.7.7}$$

Since $x\dot{x} + y\dot{y} + z\dot{z} = 0$, (8.7.7) reduces to

$$A(\dot{x}\ddot{x} + \dot{y}\ddot{y} + \dot{z}\ddot{z}) + Mgl\dot{z} = 0, \tag{8.7.8}$$

whence

$$\tfrac{1}{2}A(\dot{x}^2 + \dot{y}^2 + \dot{z}^2) + Mglz = \text{constant}, \tag{8.7.9}$$

which is equivalent to (8.6.8).

8.8 Gyroscopic forces. We consider a moving top, the only force on it (other than the constraint at O) being a force $\mathbf{F}$ through G. Then, with the notation of § 8.7, we have

$$Cn\dot{\mathbf{u}} + A\mathbf{u} \times \ddot{\mathbf{u}} = l\mathbf{u} \times \mathbf{F}. \tag{8.8.1}$$

If we form the vector product of $\mathbf{u}$ with each member, and write $l\mathbf{u} = \mathbf{r}$ (so that $\mathbf{r}$ is the vector $\overrightarrow{OG}$) we find

$$\frac{A}{l^2}\{\ddot{\mathbf{r}} - (\mathbf{u} \cdot \ddot{\mathbf{r}})\mathbf{u}\} = \{\mathbf{F} - (\mathbf{u} \cdot \mathbf{F})\mathbf{u}\} + \frac{Cn}{l^2}(\mathbf{u} \times \dot{\mathbf{r}}). \tag{8.8.2}$$

Now the expression $\{\ddot{\mathbf{r}} - (\mathbf{u} \cdot \ddot{\mathbf{r}})\mathbf{u}\}$ in the first member is the component of the acceleration of G perpendicular to OG, i.e. the component in the tangent plane to the sphere on which G moves. Similarly $\{\mathbf{F} - (\mathbf{u} \cdot \mathbf{F})\mathbf{u}\}$ in the second member is the component of $\mathbf{F}$ in the tangent plane. But the acceleration-component is not in the direction of the force-component, unless indeed G is instantaneously at rest. If $\dot{\mathbf{r}} \neq 0$, and if n is large, the dominating term in the second member of (8.8.2) is the last, and this is in the direction perpendicular both to OG and to the velocity of G.

We can picture the motion of G as that of a particle of mass A/l^2 sliding on a smooth sphere. But the motion is not that due simply to the force $\mathbf{F}$; the particle appears to be acted on also by a force at right angles to the direction of motion and proportional to the speed. Apparent forces of this type appear conspicuously in problems with tops and gyroscopes, and are called *gyroscopic forces*.

8.9 The spinning top, study of the motion. We return to the problem of § 8.6, the motion of a top. The inclination of the axis to the vertical at time t, and the value of $\dot{\varphi}$ at time t, are given by (8.6.9) and (8.6.10),

$$\begin{cases} \frac{1}{2}\dot{z}^2 = f(z) = (\mu - qz)(1 - z^2) - 2(\lambda - pz)^2, \\ \dot{\varphi} = \dfrac{2(\lambda - pz)}{1 - z^2}, \end{cases} \tag{8.9.1}$$

where $z = \cos\theta$. Let us consider the cubic polynomial $f(z)$. We have

$$f(-1) = -2(\lambda + p)^2 < 0, \quad f(1) = -2(\lambda - p)^2 \leqslant 0. \tag{8.9.2}$$

If also $\dot{z}^2 > 0$ at some value of z in $(-1, 1)$, then $f(z)$ has three real zeros z_1, z_2, z_3 such that

$$-1 < z_3 < z_2 \leqslant 1 < z_1, \tag{8.9.3}$$

as shown in Fig. 8.9a. If we consider the point P on the axis of the top at unit distance from the peg O, its motion takes place in the zone of the unit sphere bounded by the circles $z = z_3$ and $z = z_2$.

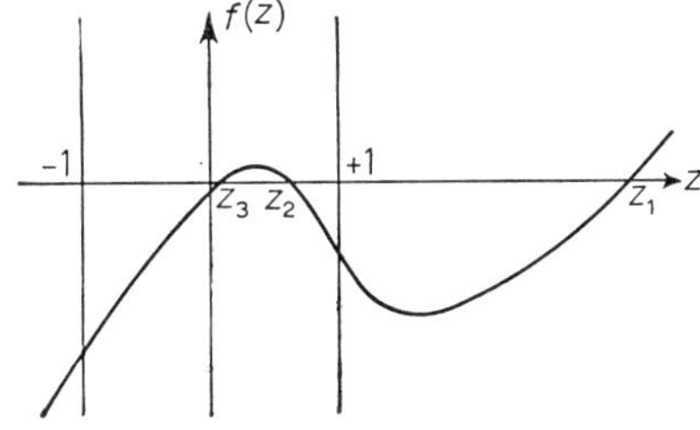

Figure 8.9a

If z_2 and z_3 coincide, we have a steady motion; P moves on the circle $z = z_3$ on the unit sphere. Consider an acute angle α, and let us ask what steady motions are possible on $\theta = \alpha$. If the value of $\dot{\varphi}$ in the steady motion is Ω, we see from (8.6.6) that Ω must be a root of the quadratic equation

$$F(\Omega) \equiv \cos\alpha\,\Omega^2 - 2p\Omega + q = 0. \tag{8.9.4}$$

This equation has two real positive roots Ω_1 and Ω_2 (where $0 < \Omega_1 < \Omega_2$) if $p^2 > q \cos \alpha$. We shall in fact assume $p^2 > q$, so the condition $p^2 > q \cos \alpha$ is satisfied for all values of α. The condition $p^2 > q$ is amply satisfied in the cases of practical interest, since in these cases p is large. (If q/p^2 is small, an approximation to the small root is $q/2p$, and an approximation to the large root is $2p/\cos \alpha$. These approximations lie outside the range bounded by the actual values; $q/2p$ is smaller than Ω_1, and $2p/\cos \alpha$ is larger than Ω_2.)

It would take us too far afield to discuss all the possibilities exhaustively, but we can exhibit the general character of the zone-motion (assuming always that $p^2 > q$) as follows. Let us suppose that initially P moves horizontally, tangentially to the circle $z = \cos \alpha$, where $0 < \alpha < \frac{1}{2}\pi$. Then initially $\dot{\theta} = 0$, $\dot{\varphi} = \Omega$ (say), and therefore

(8.9.5) $$2\lambda = 2p \cos \alpha + \Omega \sin^2 \alpha,$$

(8.9.6) $$2\mu = 2q \cos \alpha + \Omega^2 \sin^2 \alpha.$$

Now

(8.9.7) $$\ddot{z} = \frac{d}{dz}(\tfrac{1}{2}\dot{z}^2) = -q(1 - z^2) - 2z(\mu - qz) + 4p(\lambda - pz),$$

and therefore the initial value of $\ddot{z}$ is

(8.9.8) $$\begin{aligned} &-q \sin^2 \alpha - \cos \alpha\, (\Omega^2 \sin^2 \alpha) + 2p(\Omega \sin^2 \alpha) \\ &= -\sin^2 \alpha(\cos \alpha\, \Omega^2 - 2p\Omega + q) \\ &= -\sin^2 \alpha\, F(\Omega). \end{aligned}$$

It follows that $\ddot{z} > 0$ initially if Ω lies between Ω_1 and Ω_2, which are the values of $\dot{\varphi}$ in the steady motions with $\theta = \alpha$. If Ω lies between Ω_1 and Ω_2, $z = \cos \alpha$ is the lower of the two bounding circles, and $z_3 = \cos \alpha$. We notice that λ and μ are both positive.

Let us consider how the motion changes as Ω increases from Ω_1 to Ω_2; we are considering a sequence of motions in which the lower circle $z = z_3 = \cos \alpha$ is fixed throughout, and we assume also that α is acute, $z_3 > 0$. The crucial question is: Does $\dot{\varphi}$ vanish and change sign during the motion? Now, in virtue of (8.6.10), $\dot{\varphi}$ has the same sign as $\lambda - pz$. Thus $\dot{\varphi}$ cannot vanish if $\lambda > p$; but $\dot{\varphi}$ does vanish during the motion if (i) $\lambda < p$, and (ii) λ/p lies between z_2 and z_3. Now

(8.9.9) $$\begin{aligned} 2(p - \lambda) &= 2p(1 - \cos \alpha) - \Omega \sin^2 \alpha \\ &= (1 - \cos \alpha)\{2p - \Omega(1 + \cos \alpha)\}, \end{aligned}$$

so the condition (i) is equivalent to

(8.9.10) $$\Omega < \frac{2p}{1 + \cos \alpha}.$$

The condition (ii) is satisfied if $f(\lambda/p) > 0$, i.e. if $p\mu > q\lambda$; since λ and μ are given by (8.9.5–6), this condition is equivalent to

(8.9.11) $$\Omega > q/p.$$

Let us then mark in Fig. 8.9b the points on the Ω-axis represented by these values; at B, $\Omega = q/p$, and at C, $\Omega = 2p/(1 + \cos\alpha)$. Each of these values lies between Ω_1 and Ω_2, and the second is the greater; for (as we verify immediately) $F\left(\frac{q}{p}\right)$ and $F\left(\frac{2p}{1+\cos\alpha}\right)$ are negative, and

$$\frac{2p}{1+\cos\alpha} - \frac{q}{p} = \frac{2p^2 - q(1+\cos\alpha)}{p(1+\cos\alpha)} > 0.$$

Thus if the graph cuts the axis at A (where $\Omega = \Omega_1$) and at D (where $\Omega = \Omega_2$) the points A, B, C, D lie in this order.

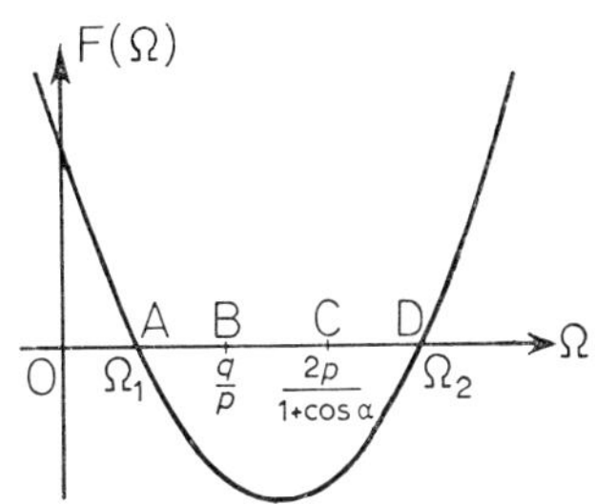

Figure 8.9b

Let us now represent the value of Ω for the motion under discussion by a representative point W which takes all positions on the segment AD. When W is at A or at D (i.e. when Ω has the value Ω_1 or the value Ω_2) z_2 coincides with z_3, and P moves on a horizontal circle. When W is at B we have

$$\Omega = \frac{q}{p}, \quad 2\lambda = 2p\cos\alpha + \frac{q}{p}\sin^2\alpha, \quad 2\mu = 2q\cos\alpha + \frac{q^2}{p^2}\sin^2\alpha, \tag{8.9.12}$$

and

$$\frac{\lambda}{p} = \frac{\mu}{q} = \cos\alpha + \frac{q}{2p^2}\sin^2\alpha = z_2 = \cos\beta, \text{ say.} \tag{8.9.13}$$

This is a critical case, and $\dot\varphi$ vanishes on $z = z_2$. The cubic polynomial $f(z)$ is

$$f(z) = q(z - \cos\alpha)(\cos\beta - z)\left(\left(\frac{2p^2}{q} - \cos\alpha\right) - z\right). \tag{8.9.14}$$

The path of P has cusps on the upper circle. This is almost evident, since P is at rest when $z = z_2$; if we release the top from a state in which its axis is at rest, with $\theta = \beta$, the axis will start to move directly away from the vertical. Formally, if the path of P cuts the meridian at an angle χ,

$$\tan\chi = \sin\theta\,\frac{d\varphi}{d\theta} = -\sin^2\theta\,\frac{d\varphi}{dz} = -(1-z^2)\,\frac{\dot\varphi}{\dot z} = -\frac{2(\lambda - pz)}{\sqrt{\{2f(z)\}}}. \tag{8.9.15}$$

In general, $\chi = \frac{1}{2}\pi$ at a zero of $f(z)$. But if (as in this case) the zero is λ/p, then $\chi = 0$ at λ/p, and the path of P has cusps on $z = z_2$.

When W is at C,

$$\Omega = \frac{2p}{1+\cos\alpha}, \quad \lambda = p, \quad \mu = q\cos\alpha + 2p^2\,\frac{1-\cos\alpha}{1+\cos\alpha}, \tag{8.9.16}$$

and

$$\tfrac{1}{2}\dot z^2 = f(z) = q(z - \cos\alpha)(1-z)\left\{\left(\frac{4p^2}{q(1+\cos\alpha)} - 1\right) - z\right\}. \tag{8.9.17}$$

In this case $z_2 = 1$, and P passes during the motion through the highest point of the unit sphere. We notice that $\dot\varphi$ does not vanish during the motion; in fact

$$\dot\varphi = \frac{2p}{1+z}. \tag{8.9.18}$$

We can now discern how the motion of the axis, or equivalently the motion of P on the unit sphere, varies as Ω increases from Ω_1 to Ω_2. As W moves from A to C (Fig. 8.9*b*) z_2 rises from z_3 to 1, passing through the critical value $\cos\beta$ when W is at B; and as W moves further, from C to D, z_2 decreases from 1 to z_3. For values of Ω in the range BC, $\dot{\varphi}$ changes sign during the motion, and the path of P is looped. The Figs. 8.9*c*–*f* exhibit the progressive change in the character of the motion as Ω increases from Ω_1 to Ω_2. In Fig. 8.9*c*, W lies between A and B, and the path of P lies between two circles on the unit sphere, touching each in turn. In Fig. 8.9*d*, W

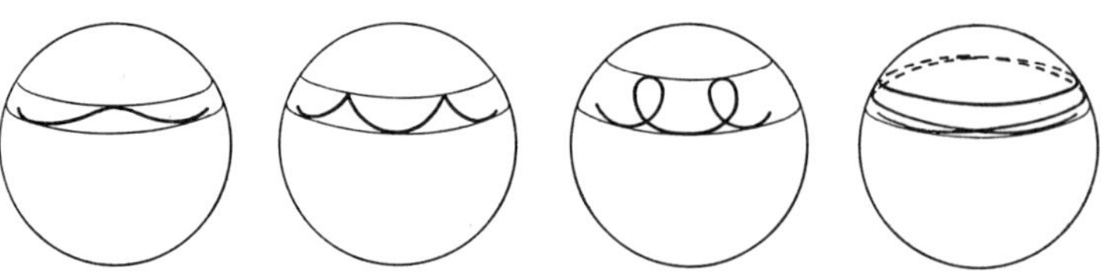

Figure 8.9*c* Figure 8.9*d* Figure 8.9*e* Figure 8.9*f*

is at B, and the path is a festoon with cusps; this is the motion that ensues if the axis of the top is released from rest on $\theta = \beta$. In Fig. 8.9*e*, W lies between B and C, and the motion is a zone-motion with loops. When W is at C, P moves through the highest point of the unit sphere; and when W lies between C and D we have again a zone-motion in which $\dot{\varphi}$ remains positive (Fig. 8.9*f*).

8.10 Numerical example. Let us consider, as a concrete illustration of the preceding theory, a problem in which $p^2 = \frac{3}{2}q$, and in which $z_3 = \frac{1}{2}$, $\alpha = \frac{1}{3}\pi = 60°$. In this case the equation (8.9.4) takes the form

$$3\Omega^2 - 12p\Omega + 4p^2 = 0, \tag{8.10.1}$$

giving the approximate values

$$\Omega_1 = \cdot 367p, \qquad \Omega_2 = 3\cdot 633p. \tag{8.10.2}$$

When W is at B, $\Omega = \frac{2}{3}p$; and $\cos\beta = \frac{3}{4}$, $\beta = 41°24'$. When W is at C, $\Omega = \frac{4}{3}p$.

Consider first the motion for W at B. Here

$$z_2 = \tfrac{3}{4}, \qquad \lambda = \tfrac{3}{4}p, \qquad \mu = \tfrac{3}{4}q, \tag{8.10.3}$$

and

$$f(z) = q(\tfrac{3}{4} - z)(z - \tfrac{1}{2})(\tfrac{5}{2} - z). \tag{8.10.4}$$

Further

$$\dot{\varphi} = \frac{2p(\frac{3}{4} - z)}{1 - z^2}, \tag{8.10.5}$$

so $\dot{\varphi} \geqslant 0$ throughout, and $\dot{\varphi} = 0$ on $z = z_2 = \frac{3}{4}$.

To get a clearer picture of the motion we should like to know what is the increment in φ between two successive cusps. Now

$$\frac{d\varphi}{dz} = \frac{\dot{\varphi}}{\dot{z}} = \frac{1}{(1 - z^2)}\sqrt{\left\{\frac{3(\frac{3}{4} - z)}{(z - \frac{1}{2})(\frac{5}{2} - z)}\right\}}, \tag{8.10.6}$$

so, if we denote the change in φ between two successive cusps by 2γ, we have

$$\gamma = \int_{1/2}^{3/4} \frac{1}{(1 - z^2)} \sqrt{\left\{\frac{3(\frac{3}{4} - z)}{(z - \frac{1}{2})(\frac{5}{2} - z)}\right\}}\, dz. \tag{8.10.7}$$

We can obtain a rough approximation to the value of γ as follows. We notice first that, if $0 < a < b$,

$$\int_a^b \sqrt{\left(\frac{b - z}{z - a}\right)}\, dz = \tfrac{1}{2}(b - a)\pi, \tag{8.10.8}$$

and next that the other factor in the integrand is monotonic. Thus 2γ lies between $(\sqrt{6}/6)\pi$ and $(8\sqrt{21}/49)\pi$, and *a fortiori* 2γ lies between $\frac{2}{5}\pi$ and $\frac{3}{4}\pi$. In this example the actual value of 2γ is $83°45'$.

Now consider the motion for the case in which W is at C. Here

$$z_2 = 1, \qquad \lambda = p, \qquad \mu = \tfrac{3}{2}q, \tag{8.10.9}$$

$$f(z) = q(1 - z)(z - \tfrac{1}{2})(3 - z), \tag{8.10.10}$$

$$\dot{\varphi} = 2p/(1 + z), \tag{8.10.11}$$

(8.10.12)

$$\frac{d\varphi}{dz} = \frac{2p}{(1 + z)\sqrt{\{2q(1 - z)(z - \frac{1}{2})(3 - z)\}}} = \frac{\sqrt{3}}{(1 + z)\sqrt{\{(1 - z)(z - \frac{1}{2})(3 - z)\}}}.$$

The increment in φ when z increases from $\frac{1}{2}$ to 1 is

$$\gamma = \int_{1/2}^{1} \frac{\sqrt{3}\, dz}{(1 + z)\sqrt{\{(1 - z)(z - \frac{1}{2})(3 - z)\}}} = \int_0^\pi \frac{\sqrt{3}\, d\theta}{(1 + z)\sqrt{(3 - z)}}, \tag{8.10.13}$$

where, in the last formula on the right, $z = \frac{3}{4} - \frac{1}{4}\cos\theta$. The factor $(1 + z)\sqrt{(3 - z)}$ is monotonic in $(\frac{1}{2}, 1)$, so γ lies between $\pi\sqrt{6}/4$ and $2\pi\sqrt{30}/15$; *a fortiori* γ lies between $\frac{3}{5}\pi$ and $\frac{3}{4}\pi$. The actual value of γ is $119°48'$.

8.11 Rod in a rotating plane. A rod is constrained to move in a smooth plane which rotates about a horizontal line, fixed in the plane, with constant angular velocity ω. Let $O\xi$, $O\eta$ be axes fixed in the plane, $O\xi$ being the fixed horizontal line about which the axis rotates, and $O\eta$ being inclined at the angle ωt below the horizontal. If at time t the inclination of the rod to $O\xi$ is θ, we have

$$L = \tfrac{1}{2}(\dot{\xi}^2 + \dot{\eta}^2 + \omega^2\eta^2) + \tfrac{1}{2}k^2(\dot{\theta}^2 + \omega^2 \sin^2\theta) + g\eta \sin \omega t, \tag{8.11.1}$$

where (ξ, η) is the centre of gravity G of the rod, and Mk^2 its moment of inertia about an axis through G at right angles to the rod.

The interest of this problem lies in the fact that L is the sum of three separate Lagrangian functions, each containing only one of the coordinates, and therefore the motion in each coordinate is independent of the others. The system is *completely separable*; it can be treated as three independent systems. The phenomenon of complete separability appears conspicuously in the theory of small oscillations which we shall consider in the next chapter. Later (Chapters XVII and XVIII) we shall consider systems which are *separable* but not completely separable; in these systems the variation of one coordinate is not entirely self-contained, but is (in a way which will become clear in the sequel) to some extent independent of the other coordinates. (It should be noticed, however, that the system we are now considering is not a separable system in the usual sense, since the theory of separable systems expounded in Chapters XVII and XVIII refers only to systems for which the Lagrangian function L does not contain t; in this case t does appear explicitly in L.)

The equations of motion are

$$\ddot{\xi} = 0, \quad \ddot{\eta} - \omega^2\eta = g \sin \omega t, \quad \ddot{\theta} = \omega^2 \cos \theta \sin \theta. \tag{8.11.2}$$

The value of $\dot{\xi}$ remains constant (as is evident otherwise) and the value of η at time t is

$$\eta = \alpha \cosh \omega t + \frac{\beta}{\omega} \sinh \omega t + \frac{g}{2\omega^2}(\sinh \omega t - \sin \omega t), \tag{8.11.3}$$

where α is the value of η, and β is the value of $\dot{\eta}$, at $t = 0$. The θ-equation can be written in the form

$$\ddot{\varphi} + \omega^2 \sin \varphi = 0, \tag{8.11.4}$$

where $\varphi = \pi - 2\theta$, and this is the equation (5.2.10) for the motion of a simple pendulum.

8.12 The rolling penny. So far our applications of Lagrange's equations have all been to holonomic systems. We now consider the application to a non-holonomic system, a uniform disc, or a uniform circular hoop, rolling on a rough horizontal plane. There are three degrees of freedom, but to define the configuration of the system we need five Lagrangian coordinates. The differentials of these five coordinates which represent a virtual displacement must satisfy two Pfaffian equations of constraint, and the Lagrangian equations of motion will involve two multipliers (§ 6.2).

We take fixed axes $Oxyz$ with Oz vertically upwards, and O in the plane on which the disc rolls. We use Euler's angles θ, φ, ψ to define the orientation of the disc, the axis GC (of the trihedral $GABC$ fixed in the disc) being along the axis of symmetry. The coordinates of the centre G are ξ, η, $a \sin \theta$, where a is the radius of the disc, and

$$L = \tfrac{1}{2}M(\dot{\xi}^2 + \dot{\eta}^2 + a^2 \cos^2 \theta\dot{\theta}^2) + \tfrac{1}{2}A(\dot{\theta}^2 + \dot{\varphi}^2 \sin^2 \theta) + \tfrac{1}{2}C(\dot{\psi} + \dot{\varphi} \cos \theta)^2 - Mga \sin \theta, \tag{8.12.1}$$

where M is the mass of the disc, and A, A, C are its moments of inertia at G; actually $C = 2A$.

In a virtual displacement the differentials $d\xi$, $d\eta$, $d\theta$, $d\varphi$, $d\psi$ are connected by two relations, the rolling conditions, as follows:

$$d\xi \cos \varphi + d\eta \sin \varphi - a\, d\theta \sin \theta = 0, \tag{8.12.2}$$

$$-d\xi \sin \varphi + d\eta \cos \varphi + a\, d\psi + a\, d\varphi \cos \theta = 0. \tag{8.12.3}$$

Of course, in this problem, the virtual displacements are the same as the possible displacements. The equations (8.12.2) and (8.12.3) can be established in many ways, for example by either of the methods used for the rolling sphere in § 5.9. But perhaps the simplest way is to use the moving axes $O123$ (not fixed in the disc) shown in Fig. 8.12, and to notice that, since the particle of the disc at K is at rest, the velocity of G is $(0, -a\omega_3, a\omega_2) = (0, -a(\dot{\psi} + \dot{\varphi} \cos \theta), a\dot{\theta})$. Hence the components of the velocity of G in the directions OP, $O2$ are $(a\dot{\theta} \sin \theta, -a(\dot{\psi} + \dot{\varphi} \cos \theta))$, and equating these to $(\dot{\xi} \cos \varphi + \dot{\eta} \sin \varphi, -\dot{\xi} \sin \varphi + \dot{\eta} \cos \varphi)$ we arrive at (8.12.2–3).

With the Lagrangian function (8.12.1) and the equations of constraint (8.12.2–3) we form the equations of motion

$$M\ddot{\xi} = \lambda \cos \varphi - \mu \sin \varphi, \tag{8.12.4}$$

$$M\ddot{\eta} = \lambda \sin \varphi + \mu \cos \varphi, \tag{8.12.5}$$

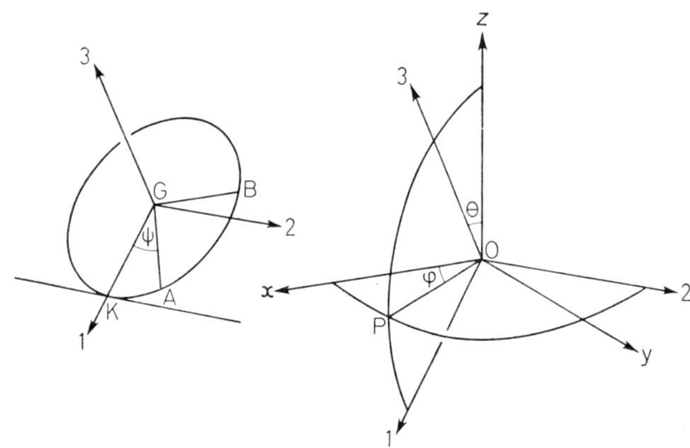

Figure 8.12

(8.12.6) $$\frac{d}{dt}(Ma^2 \cos^2 \theta\dot{\theta} + A\dot{\theta}) = -Ma^2 \cos\theta \sin\theta\dot{\theta}^2 + A \cos\theta \sin\theta\dot{\varphi}^2 - C\omega_3\dot{\varphi} \sin\theta - Mga \cos\theta - \lambda a \sin\theta,$$

(8.12.7) $$\frac{d}{dt}(A \sin^2 \theta\dot{\varphi} + C \cos\theta\omega_3) = \mu a \cos\theta,$$

(8.12.8) $$\frac{d}{dt}(C\omega_3) = \mu a,$$

where we have written ω_3, for the sake of brevity, for $\dot{\psi} + \dot{\varphi} \cos\theta$. We have, in all, seven equations, the five equations (8.12.4–8) and the rolling conditions

(8.12.9) $$\dot{\xi} \cos\varphi + \dot{\eta} \sin\varphi = a \sin\theta\dot{\theta},$$

(8.12.10) $$-\dot{\xi} \sin\varphi + \dot{\eta} \cos\varphi = -a\omega_3.$$

These seven equations determine the seven variables ξ, η, θ, φ, ψ, λ, μ.

The physical meaning of λ and μ is evident, for from (8.12.4–5) we have

(8.12.11) $$M(\ddot{\xi} \cos\varphi + \ddot{\eta} \sin\varphi) = \lambda,$$

(8.12.12) $$M(-\ddot{\xi} \sin\varphi + \ddot{\eta} \cos\varphi) = \mu,$$

and we identify λ and μ as components, in the directions OP and $O2$, of the force of constraint on the disc at the point of contact K.

Next, we easily express λ and μ in terms of θ, φ, ψ and their derivatives, for from (8.12.9–10) we have

(8.12.13) $$\ddot{\xi} \cos\varphi + \ddot{\eta} \sin\varphi + (-\dot{\xi} \sin\varphi + \dot{\eta} \cos\varphi)\dot{\varphi} = a(\sin\theta\ddot{\theta} + \cos\theta\dot{\theta}^2),$$

(8.12.14) $$-\ddot{\xi} \sin\varphi + \ddot{\eta} \cos\varphi - (\dot{\xi} \cos\varphi + \dot{\eta} \sin\varphi)\dot{\varphi} = -a\dot{\omega}_3,$$

so, using (8.12.9–12) we have

(8.12.15) $$\lambda = Ma(\sin\theta\,\ddot{\theta} + \cos\theta\,\dot{\theta}^2 + \omega_3\dot{\varphi}),$$

(8.12.16) $$\mu = Ma(\sin\theta\,\dot{\theta}\dot{\varphi} - \dot{\omega}_3).$$

If now we substitute these formulae for λ and μ in (8.12.6) and (8.12.8), and if we eliminate μ from (8.12.7) and (8.12.8), we find

$$(8.12.17)\quad (A + Ma^2)\ddot{\theta} = A\dot{\varphi}^2 \cos\theta \sin\theta - (C + Ma^2)\omega_3\dot{\varphi}\sin\theta - Mga\cos\theta,$$

$$(8.12.18)\quad (C + Ma^2)\dot{\omega}_3 = Ma^2\dot{\theta}\dot{\varphi}\sin\theta\,,$$

$$(8.12.19)\quad \frac{d}{dt}(A\dot{\varphi}\sin^2\theta) = C\omega_3\dot{\theta}\sin\theta.$$

These three equations involve only the three variables θ, φ, ω_3.

We can now find equations giving ω_3 and $\dot{\varphi}$ as functions of θ. If we write p for $\cos\theta$ the equations (8.12.18) and (8.12.19) take the form

$$(8.12.20)\quad (2k + 1)\frac{d\omega_3}{dp} = -\dot{\varphi},$$

$$(8.12.21)\quad \frac{d}{dp}\{(1 - p^2)\dot{\varphi}\} = -2\omega_3,$$

where $A = kMa^2$ and $C = 2kMa^2$. Eliminating $\dot{\varphi}$ we find

$$(8.12.22)\quad \frac{d}{dp}\left\{(1 - p^2)\frac{d\omega_3}{dp}\right\} - \frac{2}{2k + 1}\omega_3 = 0,$$

which is a differential equation of Legendre's type to determine ω_3 as a function of p. The value of the coefficient $\dfrac{2}{2k+1}$ is 1 for a hoop and $\frac{4}{3}$ for a disc. If we eliminate ω_3 from (8.12.20) and (8.12.21) we find

$$(8.12.23)\quad (1 - p^2)\frac{d^2\zeta}{dp^2} = \frac{2}{2k + 1}\zeta,$$

where ζ is written for $(1 - p^2)\dot{\varphi}$, and (8.12.23) is a differential equation which determines ζ, and hence $\dot{\varphi}$, as a function of p.

From the equation (8.12.17) we can derive the condition for a steady motion in which the disc makes an angle α with the plane, and its centre travels in a circle of radius b with speed $b\omega$. The value of $\dot{\varphi}$ in the steady motion is ω, and (using $-a\omega_3 = b\omega$) the value of ω is given by the equation

$$(8.12.24)\quad \{(2k + 1)b + ka\cos\alpha\}\omega^2 = g\cot\alpha.$$

The problem just considered exemplifies the application of Lagrange's method to a system which is not holonomic, and, as we have seen, the process is quite practicable. But before leaving the subject it should be remarked that Lagrange's method is not in general particularly well suited to problems of this type. A different method, that of the Gibbs-Appell equations, which we shall consider in Chapters XII and XIII, is usually more convenient and more powerful when the system with which we are dealing is a non-holonomic system.

Chapter IX

The theory of vibrations

9.1 Oscillations about equilibrium. One class of problem to which Lagrange applied his method with conspicuous success is concerned with the theory of the small oscillations of a dynamical system about a position of stable equilibrium. It is true that the equations of motion with which we deal in this theory represent only an approximation to the actual motion. On the other hand, these equations are of particular interest, because, as we have noticed already (§ 8.1), they are of a type that we can solve completely; given the values of q's and $\dot{q}$'s at $t = 0$, we can find explicit formulae giving the solutions of the equations for all subsequent values of t.

We consider a natural system (§ 6.5) with kinetic energy function T,

$$T = \tfrac{1}{2}\sum\sum a_{rs}\dot{q}_r\dot{q}_s, \tag{9.1.1}$$

and potential energy function V,

$$V = V(q_1, q_2, \ldots, q_n). \tag{9.1.2}$$

At a point $q_1, q_2, \ldots, q_n$ at which V is a minimum, the system can rest in stable equilibrium. It will be convenient to measure from the equilibrium position, so that the equilibrium position is the point O, $q_1 = q_2 = \cdots = q_n = 0$; and we may suppose, without loss of generality, that $V = 0$ at O. At all points in a neighbourhood of O, except at O itself, $V > 0$. For sufficiently small values of C the equation $V = C$ represents a closed $(n - 1)$-dimensional manifold $S(C)$, whose interior $I(C)$ is the region $V < C$, which is a small neighbourhood of O. If we expand V in a Taylor series about the origin, the leading terms in the development,

$$\tfrac{1}{2}\sum\sum b_{rs}q_rq_s, \tag{9.1.3}$$

constitute a positive definite form. For sufficiently small values of C, $S(C)$ approximates to an ellipsoid-like manifold with O as centre.

We have the integral of energy

$$T + V = C, \tag{9.1.4}$$

and, if the system starts from a point near O with a small velocity, C is small. In this case *the q's and $\dot{q}$'s remain small throughout the motion*, and the equilibrium at O is stable. For, since $T \geqslant 0$, the motion takes place in the region

$$V \leqslant C. \tag{9.1.5}$$

The representative point lies in the region $I(C)$, or exceptionally (if during the motion the representative point comes to rest) on the surface $S(C)$. Thus $q_1, q_2, \ldots, q_n$ remain small during the motion. Further, since $V \geqslant 0$ throughout the motion,

$$T \leqslant C, \tag{9.1.6}$$

and therefore $\dot{q}_1, \dot{q}_2, \ldots, \dot{q}_n$ also remain small. Thus we shall get a good approximation to the motion, at least for a time-range not too extended, if we retain in the equations of motion only terms of the first order in the q's and $\dot{q}$'s and $\ddot{q}$'s. This is the so-called *linear approximation.* The motion determined by the linear approximation is the better approximation to the actual motion the smaller the value of C.

The rth Lagrangian equation can be written (as in (6.4.5)) in the form

$$\sum_{s=1}^{n} a_{rs}\ddot{q}_s + \frac{1}{2}\sum_{u=1}^{n}\sum_{v=1}^{n}\left(\frac{\partial a_{ru}}{\partial q_v} + \frac{\partial a_{rv}}{\partial q_u} - \frac{\partial a_{uv}}{\partial q_r}\right)\dot{q}_u\dot{q}_v = -\frac{\partial V}{\partial q_r}, \tag{9.1.7}$$

and we require the approximation in which only terms of the first order in q's and $\dot{q}$'s and $\ddot{\mathbf{q}}$'s are retained. This means that in the first member of (9.1.7) only the terms

$$a_{r1}\ddot{q}_1 + a_{r2}\ddot{q}_2 + \cdots + a_{rn}\ddot{q}_n \tag{9.1.8}$$

survive, and moreover that in this expression the coefficients a_{rs} may be given the constant values that they have in the position of equilibrium; and that in the second member of (9.1.7) we need only an expansion to the first order in $q_1, q_2, \ldots, q_n$.

The upshot is that, to obtain the linear approximation, we can form the Lagrangian equations from expressions for T and V each of which is *a quadratic form with constant coefficients.* We can give the coefficients in T the values that they have in the equilibrium position; in other words, it suffices for our present purpose to find a formula for T at an instant when the system is moving through the position of equilibrium. We can replace V by the second-order terms in the expansion about O, i.e. we can use for V the quadratic form (9.1.3). The theory of vibrations is thus the theory arising from Lagrange's equations when both T and V are quadratic forms with constant coefficients, and both are positive definite forms. We shall use the same notation as before,

$$T = \tfrac{1}{2}\sum\sum a_{rs}\dot{q}_r\dot{q}_s, \tag{9.1.9}$$

remembering that now the coefficients a_{rs} are constants. For V we need the approximation (9.1.3),

$$V = \tfrac{1}{2}\sum\sum b_{rs}q_rq_s, \tag{9.1.10}$$

where the coefficients b_{rs} are constants. The resulting equations are linear equations with constant coefficients

$$\sum_{s=1}^{n} a_{rs}\ddot{q}_s + \sum_{s=1}^{n} b_{rs}q_s = 0, \qquad r = 1, 2, \ldots, n. \tag{9.1.11}$$

If $\mathbf{A}$ denotes the matrix (a_{rs}) and $\mathbf{B}$ the matrix (b_{rs}), and if $\mathbf{q}$ is the vector (column matrix) $\{q_1, q_2, \ldots, q_n\}$, the equations (9.1.11) can be written in the matrix form

$$\mathbf{A}\ddot{\mathbf{q}} + \mathbf{B}\mathbf{q} = 0. \tag{9.1.12}$$

Now by a real non-singular linear transformation the two quadratic forms (9.1.9) and (9.1.10) can be reduced simultaneously to sums of squares with positive coefficients. The simultaneous reduction of two quadratic forms to sums of squares is always possible if at least one of the forms is positive definite. (The fact that in this case one form contains q's and one contains $\dot{q}$'s does not invalidate the theory, since a linear transformation of q's implies the same transformation of $\dot{q}$'s.) We can find new coordinates $\xi_1, \xi_2, \ldots, \xi_n$, which are linear functions of the q's, such that

$$\begin{cases} T = \tfrac{1}{2}(\lambda_1\dot{\xi}_1^{\,2} + \lambda_2\dot{\xi}_2^{\,2} + \cdots + \lambda_n\dot{\xi}_n^{\,2}), \\ V = \tfrac{1}{2}(\lambda_1 p_1^{\,2}\xi_1^{\,2} + \lambda_2 p_2^{\,2}\xi_2^{\,2} + \cdots + \lambda_n p_n^{\,2}\xi_n^{\,2}), \end{cases} \tag{9.1.13}$$

where the λ's and the p's are real positive constants. If we wish, we can go a step further, and reduce T to a sum of squares with all the coefficients unity; but this final step is not essential for the dynamical problem.

The rth equation of motion with the coordinates ξ is

$$\ddot{\xi}_r + p_r^2\xi_r = 0. \tag{9.1.14}$$

This equation involves only the one coordinate ξ_r; the system has been separated into n completely independent systems. The value of ξ_r at time t is determined when we know the value α_r of ξ_r, and the value β_r of $\dot{\xi}_r$, at $t = 0$,

$$\xi_r = \alpha_r \cos p_r t + (\beta_r/p_r) \sin p_r t, \tag{9.1.15}$$

and this result is self-contained, independent of the other ξ's.

The coordinates $\xi_1, \xi_2, \ldots, \xi_n$ are called *normal coordinates* for the vibrating system, and a vibration in which only one normal coordinate varies, the others remaining zero throughout, is called a *normal mode* of oscillation. In a normal oscillation we say that the corresponding normal coordinate is *excited*, and that the others are *quiescent*. We have seen, in (9.1.14) that in the rth normal mode ξ_r varies harmonically with period $2\pi/p_r$. There are n such periods, not necessarily all different called the *natural periods* or *free periods* for the system. The free periods are invariants of the system, independent of the Lagrangian coordinates originally chosen to describe the system. The normal mode of longest period and smallest frequency, i.e. the mode with smallest p_r, is called the *fundamental* mode. Since the q's are linear functions of the ξ's, any oscillation can be built up of superposed normal oscillations.

The motion of the system in general, as contrasted with motion in a normal mode, is not usually periodic; but there is one case in which the motion is always periodic, whatever the initial conditions. This phenomenon appears if the ratio of every pair of p's is rational. If there exist integers $m_1, m_2, \ldots, m_n$ (with no common factor) such that

$$\frac{p_1}{m_1} = \frac{p_2}{m_2} = \cdots = \frac{p_n}{m_n} = \varpi, \tag{9.1.16}$$

then any oscillation is periodic, with period $2\pi/\varpi$. If the ratio of one pair of p's, say p_i and p_j, is irrational, any motion in which both the ith and jth normal modes are excited cannot be periodic. We can, however, always find integers $m_1, m_2, \ldots, m_n$ such that (9.1.16) is satisfied *approximately*, and, in a broad sense, every motion is approximately periodic; in fact, each q_r is an almost periodic function of t. But to get a good approximation to a periodic motion, the approximative period $2\pi/\varpi$ may need to be very large.

In a normal oscillation, say for definiteness an oscillation in the first normal mode, the coordinates $\xi_2, \xi_3, \ldots, \xi_n$ are permanently zero, and this implies that the ratios $q_1 : q_2 : \cdots : q_n$ are constant. In fact, if the relation between q's and ξ's is defined by the equations

$$\begin{cases} q_1 = m_{11}\xi_1 + m_{12}\xi_2 + \cdots + m_{1n}\xi_n, \\ q_2 = m_{21}\xi_1 + m_{22}\xi_2 + \cdots + m_{2n}\xi_n, \\ \quad \cdots\cdots \\ q_n = m_{n1}\xi_1 + m_{n2}\xi_2 + \cdots + m_{nn}\xi_n, \end{cases} \tag{9.1.17}$$

then in the first normal mode

$$\frac{q_1}{m_{11}} = \frac{q_2}{m_{21}} = \cdots = \frac{q_n}{m_{n1}}, \tag{9.1.18}$$

and each q_r varies harmonically with period $2\pi/p_1$,

$$\frac{\ddot{q}_1}{q_1} = \frac{\ddot{q}_2}{q_2} = \cdots = \frac{\ddot{q}_n}{q_n} = -p_1^2. \tag{9.1.19}$$

In a normal oscillation the visible *shape* of the system, as determined by the ratios $q_1:q_2:\cdots:q_n$, remains constant, and its *size* varies harmonically, the period of this variation being the period of the particular normal mode.

We can write the transformation (9.1.17) in the form

$$\mathbf{q} = \mathbf{S}\boldsymbol{\xi}, \tag{9.1.20}$$

where $\mathbf{q}$ is the vector (column matrix) $\{q_1, q_2, \ldots, q_n\}$, $\boldsymbol{\xi}$ is the vector $\{\xi_1, \xi_2, \ldots, \xi_n\}$, and $\mathbf{S}$ is the square matrix (m_{rs}).

With these observations in mind the solution of a concrete problem presents no difficulty, at least if the periods of the normal modes are all different. One attack, illustrated in the *Example* 9.1*A* below, is as follows. We first determine the periods of the normal modes, and then the ratios $q_1:q_2:\cdots:q_n$ in each mode. We thus find the elements of the matrix S, and the transformation (9.1.17) will reduce the equations of motion to the form (9.1.14). The solution, in terms of $\xi_1, \xi_2, \ldots, \xi_n$, can be written down when the initial values of the ξ's and $\dot{\xi}$'s are known; and these can be determined when the initial values of the q's and $\dot{q}$'s are prescribed. Hence we can find the values of the q's, which are linear functions of the ξ's, at any time if the initial value of q's and $\dot{q}$'s are prescribed. The problem is thus completely solved with quite arbitrary initial conditions.

In the process just described the values of the coefficients λ in (9.1.13) are not precisely defined, since we have only found the *ratios* of the elements in each column of S. There is a corresponding indeterminacy in the ξ's. This deficiency is, however, not important for the practical work. If we make a further transformation

$$\xi_r = \mu_r \eta_r, \qquad r = 1, 2, \ldots, n, \tag{9.1.21}$$

where the μ's are constants, the η's are normal coordinates, and we can choose the μ's so as to obtain for T and V the forms

$$T = \tfrac{1}{2}\sum_{r=1}^{n} \dot{\eta}_r^2, \qquad V = \tfrac{1}{2}\sum_{r=1}^{n} p_r^2\eta_r^2. \tag{9.1.22}$$

This form we shall often use in theoretical work, but the last step, from (9.1.13) to (9.1.22), can be dispensed with for practical work. The normal coordinates η appearing in (9.1.22) are uniquely defined (save for sign) if the p's are all different.

One final warning should be noticed. The form (9.1.10) must be a positive definite form; the theory outlined above fails if V is only semi-definite. For example, if one ξ, say ξ_1, is absent from V the corresponding equations of motion is $\ddot{\xi}_1 = 0$. This leads to $\xi_1 = \alpha_1 + \beta_1 t$, and ξ_1 does not in general remain small throughout the motion.

We now illustrate the theory by application to concrete examples. In the first of these the method is general; in the second there are only two degrees of freedom, and for this case the technique is much simpler.

Example 9.1*A*. A light string, of length $4a$, is tightly stretched at tension P between its end-points, which are fixed. Particles of masses m, $\frac{4}{3}m$, m are attached to the string at the points of quadrisection. The system executes small transverse oscillations in a plane. To discuss the motion.

We can think of the motion as taking place on a smooth table. The tension P is large, and, to the required order of approximation, variations of tension can be neglected.

We denote the displacements of the particles at time t by x, y, z. The equations of motion, correct to the first order in x, y, z, are

$$\begin{cases} m\ddot{x} = P\left(\dfrac{y-x}{a} - \dfrac{x}{a}\right), \\ \dfrac{4}{3}m\ddot{y} = P\left(\dfrac{x-y}{a} + \dfrac{z-y}{a}\right), \\ m\ddot{z} = P\left(\dfrac{y-z}{a} - \dfrac{z}{a}\right). \end{cases}$$

We can write these equations in the form

$$\begin{cases} \ddot{x} + 2n^2(2x - y) = 0, \\ \frac{4}{3}\ddot{y} + 2n^2(-x + 2y - z) = 0, \\ \ddot{z} + 2n^2(2z - y) = 0, \end{cases} \tag{9.1.23}$$

where $n^2 = P/2ma$.

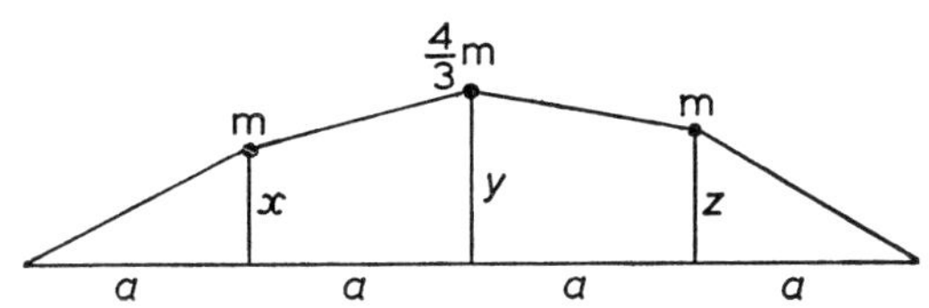

Figure 9.1*a*

We can, of course, also obtain the equations by Lagrange's method. The stretch of the first quarter of the string, correct to the second order in x, is $x^2/2a$, and, supplying the similar formulae for the other segments, we have

$$V = \frac{P}{2a}\{x^2 + (x-y)^2 + (y-z)^2 + z^2\} = 2mn^2(x^2 + y^2 + z^2 - xy - yz).$$

Further

$$T = \tfrac{1}{2}m(\dot{x}^2 + \tfrac{4}{3}\dot{y}^2 + \dot{z}^2),$$

and Lagrange's equations derived from these forms of T and V are the same equations of motion (9.1.23).

In a normal mode, of period $2\pi/p$, we have

$$\frac{\ddot{x}}{x} = \frac{\ddot{y}}{y} = \frac{\ddot{z}}{z} = -p^2, \tag{9.1.24}$$

and, substituting for $\ddot{x}$, $\ddot{y}$, $\ddot{z}$ in the equations of motion, we find

$$(9.1.25)\qquad \begin{cases} (p^2 - 4n^2)x + 2n^2y = 0, \\ 2n^2x + (\tfrac{4}{3}p^2 - 4n^2)y + 2n^2z = 0, \\ 2n^2y + (p^2 - 4n^2)z = 0. \end{cases}$$

These are consistent if

$$(9.1.26)\qquad \begin{vmatrix} p^2 - 4n^2 & 2n^2 & 0 \\ 2n^2 & \tfrac{4}{3}p^2 - 4n^2 & 2n^2 \\ 0 & 2n^2 & p^2 - 4n^2 \end{vmatrix} = 0,$$

which gives, as we expect, three positive values of p^2,

$$(9.1.27)\qquad p_1{}^2 = n^2, \qquad p_2{}^2 = 4n^2, \qquad p_3{}^2 = 6n^2.$$

In the first, or fundamental, normal mode, $p^2 = n^2$, and the equations (9.1.25) for $x:y:z$ are the (consistent) set

$$(9.1.28)\qquad \begin{cases} -3x + 2y = 0, \\ 3x - 4y + 3z = 0, \\ 2y - 3z = 0, \end{cases}$$

so that, in the first normal mode,

$$\frac{x}{2} = \frac{y}{3} = \frac{z}{2}.$$

Similarly in the second normal mode, $p^2 = 4n^2$, we find $\dfrac{x}{1} = \dfrac{y}{0} = \dfrac{z}{-1}$; and in the third normal mode, $p^2 = 6n^2$, and $\dfrac{x}{1} = \dfrac{y}{-1} = \dfrac{z}{1}$. The shapes in the three modes (somewhat reminiscent of the first three modes for a uniform continuous string) are illustrated in Fig. 9.1*b*. We notice that in any motion in which the third normal mode is quiescent, the motion is periodic, with period $2\pi/n$.

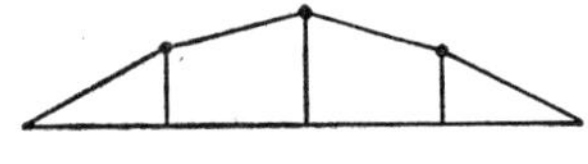
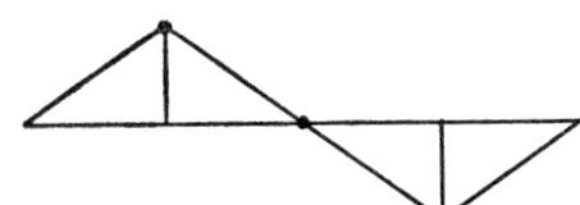
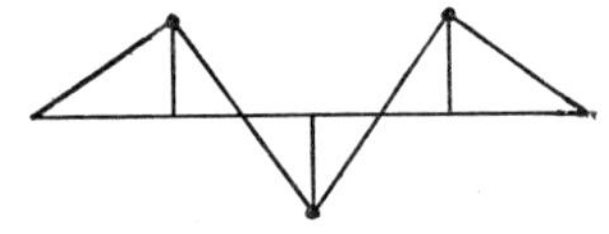

Figure 9.1*b*

The transformation to normal coordinates ξ, η, ζ is

$$(9.1.29)\qquad \begin{cases} x = 2\xi + \eta + \zeta, \\ y = 3\xi - \zeta, \\ z = 2\xi - \eta + \zeta, \end{cases}$$

giving

$$(9.1.30)\qquad \begin{cases} \xi = \tfrac{1}{10}(x + 2y + z), \\ \eta = \tfrac{1}{2}(x - z), \\ \zeta = \tfrac{1}{10}(3x - 4y + 3z). \end{cases}$$

We easily verify that T and V, when expressed in terms of ξ, η, ζ, are sums of squares; explicitly

$$\begin{cases} T = \frac{1}{2}m(20\dot{\xi}^2 + 2\dot{\eta}^2 + \frac{10}{3}\dot{\zeta}^2), \\ V = \frac{1}{2}mn^2(20\xi^2 + 8\eta^2 + 20\zeta^2). \end{cases} \tag{9.1.31}$$

We can now solve completely the problem represented by the linear approximation with any given initial values. The value of ξ at time t, for example, is given by the formula

$$\xi = \alpha \cos p_1 t + \frac{\beta}{p_1} \sin p_1 t,$$

where α is the value of ξ, and β is the value of $\dot{\xi}$, at $t = 0$.

As a concrete example, suppose that the system is initially at rest in the position of equilibrium, and that the motion is set up by a small transverse impulse mu on the first particle. Initially we have

$$\begin{cases} x = y = z = 0; \quad \dot{x} = u,\ \dot{y} = \dot{z} = 0; \\ \xi = \eta = \zeta = 0; \quad \dot{\xi} = \frac{1}{10}u,\ \dot{\eta} = \frac{1}{2}u,\ \dot{\zeta} = \frac{3}{10}u. \end{cases} \tag{9.1.32}$$

Hence, at any subsequent time,

$$\xi = \frac{u}{10p_1} \sin p_1 t, \quad \eta = \frac{5u}{10p_2} \sin p_2 t, \quad \zeta = \frac{3u}{10p_3} \sin p_3 t, \tag{9.1.33}$$

and the final solution is therefore

$$\begin{cases} x = \dfrac{u}{10}\left(\dfrac{2}{p_1}\sin p_1 t + \dfrac{5}{p_2}\sin p_2 t + \dfrac{3}{p_3}\sin p_3 t\right), \\ y = \dfrac{3u}{10}\left(\dfrac{1}{p_1}\sin p_1 t - \dfrac{1}{p_3}\sin p_3 t\right), \\ z = \dfrac{u}{10}\left(\dfrac{2}{p_1}\sin p_1 t - \dfrac{5}{p_2}\sin p_2 t + \dfrac{3}{p_3}\sin p_3 t\right), \end{cases} \tag{9.1.34}$$

where

$$\frac{{p_1}^2}{1} = \frac{{p_2}^2}{4} = \frac{{p_3}^2}{6} = n^2 = \frac{P}{2ma}. \tag{9.1.35}$$

Example 9.1*B*. A light string AD of length $4a$ is stretched at a large tension P between two fixed points. A particle of mass m is attached to the string at its mid-point B, and a particle of mass $2m$ is attached to the string at the point C mid-way between B and D. The system executes small transverse oscillations in a plane through A and D. Prove that the motion is periodic, with period $2\pi/n$, where $n^2 = P/(2ma)$.

If each particle is pulled aside through a small distance b from the line AD, and the system is let go from rest in this position at the instant $t = 0$, find the configuration at any subsequent time.

We denote the displacement of B by x and of C by y. The equations of motion are

$$m\ddot{x} = P\left(\frac{y - x}{a} - \frac{x}{2a}\right), \quad 2m\ddot{y} = P\left(\frac{x - y}{a} - \frac{y}{a}\right).$$

As in the previous example, these can be found equally simply from Lagrange's equations; to the requisite order of approximation

$$T = \tfrac{1}{2}m\dot{x}^2 + m\dot{y}^2, \quad V = P\left(\frac{x^2}{4a} + \frac{(x-y)^2}{2a} + \frac{y^2}{2a}\right) = mn^2(\tfrac{3}{2}x^2 - 2xy + 2y^2),$$

where $n^2 = P/2am$. The equations can be written in the form

$$\ddot{x} + n^2(3x - 2y) = 0, \quad \ddot{y} + n^2(2y - x) = 0. \tag{9.1.36}$$

The system has only two degrees of freedom, and in this case the discussion is simpler than in the general case. We exhibit two methods of solving the problem.

(i) As in the previous example, we observe that, in a normal mode, $\ddot{x} = -p^2x$ and $\ddot{y} = -p^2y$, and substituting these values of $\ddot{x}$ and $\ddot{y}$ in the equations of motion we find

$$(p^2 - 3n^2)x + 2n^2y = 0, \quad n^2x + (p^2 - 2n^2)y = 0. \tag{9.1.37}$$

There is a non-zero vector $\{x, y\}$ satisfying these equations if

$$(p^2 - 2n^2)(p^2 - 3n^2) - 2n^4 = 0, \tag{9.1.38}$$

so the values of p^2 in the two normal modes are

$$p_1{}^2 = n^2, \quad p_2{}^2 = 4n^2. \tag{9.1.39}$$

In the first normal mode, $-x + y = 0$, and in the second, $x + 2y = 0$. We can, of course, now find the transformation to normal coordinates by the technique used in the previous example; but this is unnecessary, because this time, with only two degrees of freedom, the result is evident. For when the system vibrates in the first normal mode, the second normal coordinate has the value zero, and when it vibrates in the second normal mode, the first normal coordinate has the value zero. Thus the first and second normal coordinates ξ and η can be taken to be

$$\xi = x + 2y, \quad \eta = x - y, \tag{9.1.40}$$

giving

$$x = \tfrac{1}{3}(\xi + 2\eta), \quad y = \tfrac{1}{3}(\xi - \eta). \tag{9.1.41}$$

We easily verify that, in terms of these coordinates, T and V are sums of squares,

$$T = \tfrac{1}{6}m(\dot{\xi}^2 + 2\dot{\eta}^2), \quad V = \tfrac{1}{6}mn^2(\xi^2 + 8\eta^2). \tag{9.1.42}$$

(ii) If we multiply the second equation of motion by λ, and add to the first, we find

$$\ddot{x} + \lambda\ddot{y} + n^2\{(3 - \lambda)x + (-2 + 2\lambda)y\} = 0, \tag{9.1.43}$$

which is of the form $\ddot{\theta} + p^2\theta = 0$ if

$$\frac{1}{\lambda} = \frac{3 - \lambda}{-2 + 2\lambda}, \tag{9.1.44}$$

giving $\lambda = 2$ or $\lambda = -1$. If $\lambda = 2$ the equation is

$$\ddot{x} + 2\ddot{y} + n^2(x + 2y) = 0, \tag{9.1.45}$$

and if $\lambda = -1$ the equation is

$$(\ddot{x} - \ddot{y}) + 4n^2(x - y) = 0, \tag{9.1.46}$$

and we find by this method both the normal coordinates and the corresponding periods. The normal coordinates are $\xi = x + 2y$ and $\eta = x - y$, and

$$\ddot{\xi} + n^2\xi = 0, \quad \ddot{\eta} + 4n^2\eta = 0. \tag{9.1.47}$$

The periods of the normal modes are $2\pi/n$ and $2\pi/(2n)$, and since the first is twice the second any motion of the system is periodic with period $2\pi/n$.

In the rider, the conditions at $t = 0$ are

$$x = y = b; \quad \dot{x} = \dot{y} = 0; \tag{9.1.48}$$

so that, at $t = 0$,

$$\xi = 3b, \eta = 0; \quad \dot{\xi} = \dot{\eta} = 0. \tag{9.1.49}$$

Therefore, at any subsequent time,

$$\xi = 3b \cos nt, \quad \eta = 0, \tag{9.1.50}$$

and throughout the motion

$$x = y = b \cos nt. \tag{9.1.51}$$

Example 9.1*C*. *Transference of vibrations.* If two pendulum clocks hang on the same wall, and the first pendulum is set swinging with amplitude α, it may happen that, after a certain period of time, the amplitude of the first pendulum is reduced almost to zero, and the second is swinging with amplitude α; and after a further period, the second pendulum comes to rest, and the first swings with amplitude α as at the start. The vibration is transferred alternately from one to the other. The genesis of this phenomenon is illustrated in the following problem.

A heavy rod AB, of mass M, hangs in a horizontal position from two supports, to which it is attached by vertical light strings, each of length a, attached to A and B. A particle C, of mass m, hangs from A by a light string of length a, and a similar particle D hangs from B by a similar string. The equilibrium is slightly disturbed, and the system oscillates in a vertical plane.

If at time t the supporting strings make an angle θ with the vertical, and the pendulums make angles φ and ψ with the vertical, we have, to the requisite order of approximation,

$$\begin{cases} T = \frac{1}{2}Ma^2\dot{\theta}^2 + \frac{1}{2}ma^2(\dot{\theta} + \dot{\varphi})^2 + \frac{1}{2}ma^2(\dot{\theta} + \dot{\psi})^2, \\ V = \frac{1}{2}Mga\theta^2 + \frac{1}{2}mga(\theta^2 + \varphi^2) + \frac{1}{2}mga(\theta^2 + \psi^2). \end{cases} \tag{9.1.52}$$

The equations of motion are

$$\begin{cases} 2k^2\ddot{\theta} + \ddot{\varphi} + \ddot{\psi} + 2k^2n^2\theta = 0, \\ \ddot{\theta} + \ddot{\varphi} + n^2\varphi = 0, \\ \ddot{\theta} + \ddot{\psi} + n^2\psi = 0, \end{cases} \tag{9.1.53}$$

where $k^2 = \dfrac{M}{2m} + 1$ and $n^2 = \dfrac{g}{a}$. Hence

$$\ddot{\varphi} - \ddot{\psi} + n^2(\varphi - \psi) = 0, \tag{9.1.54}$$

and one normal coordinate is $(\varphi - \psi)$. If we take the sum of the second and third equations multiplied by k, and add or subtract the first equation, we get

$$(9.1.55)\qquad \begin{cases} (k+1)(2k\ddot{\theta}+\ddot{\varphi}+\ddot{\psi})+kn^2(2k\theta+\varphi+\psi)=0,\\ (k-1)(2k\ddot{\theta}-\ddot{\varphi}-\ddot{\psi})+kn^2(2k\theta-\varphi-\psi)=0, \end{cases}$$

exhibiting the other two normal coordinates. Thus we may take as normal coordinates

$$(9.1.56)\qquad \begin{cases} \xi = 2k\theta+\varphi+\psi,\\ \eta = \varphi-\psi,\\ \zeta = 2k\theta-\varphi-\psi, \end{cases}$$

and $p_1{}^2 = \dfrac{k}{k+1}n^2$, $p_2{}^2 = n^2$, $p_3{}^2 = \dfrac{k}{k-1}n^2$. The case in which we are interested is that in which M/m is large (and therefore k is large), and in this case the three periods are nearly equal, as we should expect. Solving for θ, φ, ψ we have

$$(9.1.57)\qquad \begin{cases} 4k\theta = \xi + \zeta,\\ 4\varphi = \xi+2\eta-\zeta,\\ 4\psi = \xi-2\eta-\zeta. \end{cases}$$

Consider now a motion with the initial values

$$(9.1.58)\qquad \theta=\alpha/2k,\quad \varphi=\alpha,\quad \psi=0;\quad \dot{\theta}=\dot{\varphi}=\dot{\psi}=0.$$

Then in the subsequent motion

$$(9.1.59)\qquad \xi = 2\alpha\cos p_1t,\quad \eta=\alpha\cos p_2t,\quad \zeta=0,$$

and therefore

$$(9.1.60)\qquad \varphi=\tfrac{1}{2}\alpha(\cos p_1t+\cos p_2t),\quad \psi=\tfrac{1}{2}\alpha(\cos p_1t-\cos p_2t).$$

Suppose now that M/m is large. Then $p_2 = n$, and p_1 is slightly smaller than n, say $p_1 = n - 2\nu$, where ν is small. We can now express φ and ψ in the forms

$$(9.1.61)\qquad \varphi=\alpha\cos\nu t\cos(n-\nu)t,\quad \psi=\alpha\sin\nu t\sin(n-\nu)t.$$

We can think of the φ-motion as a harmonic motion of period $2\pi/(n-\nu)$ (which is very nearly the same as the free period $2\pi/n$ of one of the pendulums when the rod AB is held fixed) with a slowly-varying amplitude of long period $2\pi/\nu$. The ψ-motion is of the same type. But the φ-amplitude is a maximum (at $t = 0, \pi/\nu, 2\pi/\nu, \ldots$) when the ψ-amplitude is a minimum, and *vice versa*. The oscillation is slowly transferred from the first pendulum to the second, and back again from the second to the first, and so on.

9.2 Theory of the transformation to normal coordinates. So far we have assumed the existence of the transformation to normal coordinates; we now turn to the proof.

We recall that the matrices **A** and **B** are real symmetric matrices associated with positive definite forms. The equation for p^2,

$$(9.2.1)\qquad |p^2\mathbf{A}-\mathbf{B}|=0,$$

is called the *period equation*. Its roots are all real and positive. For if $p_r{}^2$ is a root there exists a non-zero vector (column matrix) $\mathbf{u}_r$ such that

(9.2.2) $$(p_r^2\mathbf{A} - \mathbf{B})\mathbf{u}_r = \mathbf{0}.$$

Hence

(9.2.3) $$p_r^2(\bar{\mathbf{u}}_r'\mathbf{A}\mathbf{u}_r) = \bar{\mathbf{u}}_r'\mathbf{B}\mathbf{u}_r,$$

(where the vector $\bar{\mathbf{u}}_r$ is obtained from $\mathbf{u}_r$ by replacing each component by the conjugate complex number) and this proves that p_r^2 is real and positive. The roots $p_1^2, p_2^2, \ldots, p_n^2$ of the period equation are the *eigenvalues*, and a vector $\mathbf{u}_r$ satisfying (9.2.2) is an *eigenvector* corresponding to the eigenvalue p_r^2. Since p_r^2 is real we can take $\mathbf{u}_r$ real, and this we shall always do. We use the symbol p_r to denote the positive square root of the eigenvalue p_r^2.

The crux of the theory is the theorem that there exists a real non-singular transformation which reduces both T and V to sums of squares. We prove this by induction, assuming the theorem to hold for $(n - 1)$ variables and deducing the theorem for n variables, as follows.

Choose any eigenvalue p_1^2, not necessarily a simple root of the period equation, and let u_1 be any associated real non-zero eigenvector, so that

(9.2.4) $$(p_1^2\mathbf{A} - \mathbf{B})\mathbf{u}_1 = \mathbf{0}.$$

Then the single homogeneous equation

(9.2.5) $$\mathbf{u}_1'\mathbf{A}\mathbf{u} = 0$$

has $(n - 1)$ linearly independent solutions, say $\mathbf{u} = \mathbf{v}_2, \mathbf{v}_3, \ldots, \mathbf{v}_n$. Let $\mathbf{T}$ be the matrix whose first column is $\mathbf{u}_1$, and whose remaining columns are $\mathbf{v}_2, \mathbf{v}_3, \ldots, \mathbf{v}_n$,

(9.2.6) $$\mathbf{T} = (\mathbf{u}_1, \mathbf{v}_2, \mathbf{v}_3, \ldots, \mathbf{v}_n).$$

Then $\mathbf{T}$ is non-singular, and the matrix $\mathbf{T}'\mathbf{A}\mathbf{T}$ has the form

(9.2.7) $$\mathbf{T}'\mathbf{A}\mathbf{T} = \begin{pmatrix} \lambda_1 & 0 \quad 0 \quad \cdots \quad 0 \\ 0 & \\ 0 & \\ \cdot & \mathbf{A}_1 \\ \cdot & \\ \cdot & \\ 0 & \end{pmatrix},$$

because the rth member of the first row, for $r > 1$, is $\mathbf{u}_1'\mathbf{A}\mathbf{v}_r$, and the rth member of the first column, for $r > 1$, is $\mathbf{v}_r'\mathbf{A}\mathbf{u}_1$, and both of these vanish.

A similar statement holds for $\mathbf{B}$, because

(9.2.8) $$p_1^2\mathbf{A}\mathbf{u}_1 = \mathbf{B}\mathbf{u}_1,$$

so that

(9.2.9) $$\mathbf{v}_r'\mathbf{B}\mathbf{u}_1 = \mathbf{u}_1'\mathbf{B}\mathbf{v}_r = 0, \qquad r = 2, 3, \ldots, n.$$

Thus

(9.2.10) $$\mathbf{T}'\mathbf{B}\mathbf{T} = \begin{pmatrix} p_1^2\lambda_1 & 0 \quad 0 \quad \cdots \quad 0 \\ 0 & \\ 0 & \\ \cdot & \mathbf{B}_1 \\ \cdot & \\ \cdot & \\ 0 & \end{pmatrix}.$$

Now $\mathbf{A}_1$ and $\mathbf{B}_1$ are matrices of positive definite forms (viz., the forms got from those with the matrices $\mathbf{T}'\mathbf{A}\mathbf{T}$, $\mathbf{T}'\mathbf{B}\mathbf{T}$ by giving the first variable the value zero). By the induction hypothesis there exists a non-singular matrix $\mathbf{U}_1$ such that $\mathbf{U}_1'\mathbf{A}_1\mathbf{U}_1$ and $\mathbf{U}_1'\mathbf{B}_1\mathbf{U}_1$ are diagonal. If

(9.2.11) $$\mathbf{S} = \mathbf{T}\mathbf{U},$$

where $\mathbf{U}$ is the matrix

(9.2.12) $$\mathbf{U} = \begin{pmatrix} 1 & 0 & 0 & \cdots & 0 \\ 0 & & & & \\ 0 & & & & \\ \cdot & & \mathbf{U}_1 & & \\ \cdot & & & & \\ \cdot & & & & \\ 0 & & & & \end{pmatrix},$$

the transformation

(9.2.13) $$\mathbf{q} = \mathbf{S}\boldsymbol{\xi}$$

achieves the reduction of T and V to sums of squares.
For

(9.2.14) $$\mathbf{q}'\mathbf{A}\mathbf{q} = \boldsymbol{\xi}'\mathbf{S}'\mathbf{A}\mathbf{S}\boldsymbol{\xi},$$

and

(9.2.15) $$\mathbf{S}'\mathbf{A}\mathbf{S} = \mathbf{U}'\mathbf{T}'\mathbf{A}\mathbf{T}\mathbf{U} = \begin{pmatrix} \lambda_1 & 0 & 0 & \cdots & 0 \\ 0 & & & & \\ 0 & & & & \\ \cdot & & \mathbf{U}_1'\mathbf{A}_1\mathbf{U}_1 & & \\ \cdot & & & & \\ \cdot & & & & \\ 0 & & & & \end{pmatrix},$$

which is a diagonal matrix $\boldsymbol{\Lambda}$,

(9.2.16) $$\boldsymbol{\Lambda} = \begin{pmatrix} \lambda_1 & & & & \\ & \lambda_2 & & & \\ & & \cdot & & \\ & & & \cdot & \\ & & & & \cdot \\ & & & & & \lambda_n \end{pmatrix}.$$

Similarly

(9.2.17) $$\mathbf{S}'\mathbf{B}\mathbf{S} = \boldsymbol{\Lambda}\mathbf{P},$$

where $\mathbf{P}$ denotes the diagonal matrix

(9.2.18) $$\mathbf{P} = \begin{pmatrix} p_1^2 & & & & \\ & p_2^2 & & & \\ & & \cdot & & \\ & & & \cdot & \\ & & & & \cdot \\ & & & & & p_n^2 \end{pmatrix},$$

and

$$\mathbf{\Lambda P} = \begin{pmatrix} \lambda_1 p_1{}^2 & & & & \\ & \lambda_2 p_2{}^2 & & & \\ & & \cdot & & \\ & & & \cdot & \\ & & & & \cdot \\ & & & & & \lambda_n p_n{}^2 \end{pmatrix}. \tag{9.2.19}$$

Thus T and V are reduced to the forms

$$\begin{cases} T = \frac{1}{2}(\lambda_1 \dot{\xi}_1{}^2 + \lambda_2 \dot{\xi}_2{}^2 + \cdots + \lambda_n \dot{\xi}_n{}^2), \\ V = \frac{1}{2}(\lambda_1 p_1{}^2 \xi_1{}^2 + \lambda_2 p_2{}^2 \xi_2{}^2 + \cdots + \lambda_n p_n{}^2 \xi_n{}^2), \end{cases} \tag{9.2.20}$$

and the ξ's are normal coordinates.

A number of important corollaries follow from the main theorem:

(i) As we have noticed already, the equations of motion can be written in the form

$$\ddot{\xi}_r + p_r{}^2 \xi_r = 0, \qquad r = 1, 2, \ldots, n. \tag{9.2.21}$$

These are simply the Lagrangian equations of motion for the reduced forms (9.2.20) of T and V.

It may be of interest to establish (9.2.21) also in a different way. The equations of motion can be written compactly, as in (9.1.12), in the form

$$\mathbf{A}\ddot{\mathbf{q}} + \mathbf{B}\mathbf{q} = \mathbf{0}, \tag{9.2.22}$$

where $\mathbf{q}$ is the vector, or column matrix, $\{q_1, q_2, \ldots, q_n\}$. The transformation (9.2.13) leads to

$$\mathbf{A}\mathbf{S}\ddot{\boldsymbol{\xi}} + \mathbf{B}\mathbf{S}\boldsymbol{\xi} = \mathbf{0}, \tag{9.2.23}$$

and since

$$\mathbf{S}'\mathbf{A}\mathbf{S} = \mathbf{\Lambda}, \quad \mathbf{S}'\mathbf{B}\mathbf{S} = \mathbf{\Lambda P}, \tag{9.2.24}$$

we derive from (9.2.23)

$$\mathbf{\Lambda}(\ddot{\boldsymbol{\xi}} + \mathbf{P}\boldsymbol{\xi}) = \mathbf{0}. \tag{9.2.25}$$

Since $\mathbf{\Lambda}$ is non-singular, this is equivalent to

$$\ddot{\boldsymbol{\xi}} + \mathbf{P}\boldsymbol{\xi} = \mathbf{0}, \tag{9.2.26}$$

and this is equivalent to the n equations (9.2.21).

(ii) There exist n linearly independent eigenvectors, k of these corresponding to any k-fold root of the period equation (9.2.1). If we denote by $\mathbf{u}_r$ the rth column of $\mathbf{S}$, we see from (9.2.24) that

$$\begin{cases} \mathbf{u}_r'\mathbf{A}\mathbf{u}_s = 0 \quad \text{if } r \neq s, \qquad \mathbf{u}_r'\mathbf{A}\mathbf{u}_r = \lambda_r, \\ \mathbf{u}_r'\mathbf{B}\mathbf{u}_s = 0 \quad \text{if } r \neq s, \qquad \mathbf{u}_r'\mathbf{B}\mathbf{u}_r = \lambda_r p_r{}^2. \end{cases} \tag{9.2.27}$$

Hence the vector $\mathbf{y}_r$, defined by

$$(p_r{}^2\mathbf{A} - \mathbf{B})\mathbf{u}_r = \mathbf{y}_r \tag{9.2.28}$$

satisfies the equation

$$\mathbf{u}_s'\mathbf{y}_r = 0 \tag{9.2.29}$$

for all s. Since $\mathbf{u}_1, \mathbf{u}_2, \ldots, \mathbf{u}_n$ are linearly independent (being columns of the non-singular matrix $\mathbf{S}$) the equation (9.2.29) implies

(9.2.30) $$\mathbf{x}'\mathbf{y}_r = 0$$

for all $\mathbf{x}$. In particular

(9.2.31) $$\mathbf{y}_r'\mathbf{y}_r = 0,$$

and it follows, since $\mathbf{y}_r$ is real, that $\mathbf{y}_r = \mathbf{0}$. Thus

(9.2.2) $$(p_r^2\mathbf{A} - \mathbf{B})\mathbf{u}_r = \mathbf{0},$$

and the columns of $\mathbf{S}$ are n linearly independent eigenvectors.

The roots of the equation (9.2.1) are the same as the roots of the equation

(9.2.32) $$|p^2\mathbf{\Lambda} - \mathbf{\Lambda P}| = 0,$$

and these are precisely the diagonal elements of $\mathbf{P}$, viz. $p_1^2, p_2^2, \ldots, p_n^2$. Thus if, for example, $p_1^2 = p_2^2 = \cdots = p_k^2$ is a k-fold root, the corresponding k columns of $\mathbf{S}$ give a set of k linearly independent eigenvectors corresponding to the k-fold eigenvalue.

We notice, in virtue of (9.2.24), that if we *normalize* the eigenvectors $\mathbf{u}_r$ to make

(9.2.33) $$\mathbf{u}_r'\mathbf{A}\mathbf{u}_r = 1, \qquad r = 1, 2, \ldots, n,$$

then each λ_r has the value 1, and T and V are reduced to the forms (9.1.22).

(iii) The n linearly independent eigenvectors $\mathbf{u}_r$ found in the way just described satisfy the *orthogonality conditions*

(9.2.34) $$\mathbf{u}_r'\mathbf{A}\mathbf{u}_s = 0, \qquad r \neq s,$$

(9.2.35) $$\mathbf{u}_r'\mathbf{B}\mathbf{u}_s = 0. \qquad r \neq s,$$

It will be useful to observe here, for future reference, the essential difference between a problem in which the roots of the period equation are simple, and a problem in which there are multiple roots. Let us now approach the problem from another direction, namely from the equations of motion instead of from the algebra of quadratic forms. If the roots of the period equation are all simple roots, the eigenvalues defined by (9.2.2) are unique, save for a scalar multiplier, and automatically satisfy the orthogonality conditions (9.2.34–35). For from (9.2.2)

(9.2.36) $$p_r^2(\mathbf{u}_s'\mathbf{A}\mathbf{u}_r) = \mathbf{u}_s'\mathbf{B}\mathbf{u}_r,$$

and similarly

(9.2.37) $$p_s^2(\mathbf{u}_r'\mathbf{A}\mathbf{u}_s) = \mathbf{u}_r'\mathbf{B}\mathbf{u}_s.$$

Since $\mathbf{A}$ and $\mathbf{B}$ are symmetric

(9.2.38) $$\mathbf{u}_s'\mathbf{A}\mathbf{u}_r = \mathbf{u}_r'\mathbf{A}\mathbf{u}_s, \quad \mathbf{u}_s'\mathbf{B}\mathbf{u}_r = \mathbf{u}_r'\mathbf{B}\mathbf{u}_s,$$

so, from (9.2.36–37)

(9.2.39) $$(p_r^2 - p_s^2)\mathbf{u}_r'\mathbf{A}\mathbf{u}_s = 0.$$

The condition (9.2.34) follows from (9.2.39), since $p_r^2 - p_s^2 \neq 0$, and (9.2.35) then follows from (9.2.37). The same argument shows that in any case, whether the roots of the period equation are simple or not, two eigenvectors corresponding to *different* eigenvalues always satisfy (9.2.34–35).

Consider now a problem in which the period equation has multiple roots. If $p_1{}^2$ is a k-fold root, and we start from the equation

$$(p_1{}^2\mathbf{A} - \mathbf{B})\mathbf{u} = \mathbf{0}, \tag{9.2.40}$$

a set of k linearly independent eigenvectors $\mathbf{u}_1, \mathbf{u}_2, \ldots, \mathbf{u}_n$, constructed from solutions of this equation, do not necessarily satisfy (9.2.34–35). However from the given set $\mathbf{u}_1, \mathbf{u}_2, \ldots, \mathbf{u}_k$ we can construct, by a familiar process,* an orthogonal set $\mathbf{w}_1, \mathbf{w}_2, \ldots, \mathbf{w}_k$. To achieve this end we take

$$\mathbf{w}_1 = \mathbf{u}_1, \quad \mathbf{w}_{r+1} = \mathbf{u}_{r+1} - \sum_{s=1}^{r} \alpha_s \mathbf{u}_s, \tag{9.2.41}$$

where

$$\alpha_s = \mathbf{w}_s{}'\mathbf{A}\mathbf{u}_{r+1}/\mathbf{w}_s{}'\mathbf{A}\mathbf{w}_s, \tag{9.2.42}$$

and the set $\mathbf{w}_1, \mathbf{w}_2, \ldots, \mathbf{w}_k$ satisfies the orthogonality conditions. In practice we find the vectors one by one in turn; if $\mathbf{w}_1, \mathbf{w}_2, \ldots, \mathbf{w}_r$, where $r < k$, have been found, we take for $\mathbf{w}_{r+1}$ any solution of (9.2.40) which also satisfies

$$\mathbf{w}_s{}'\mathbf{A}\mathbf{u} = 0, \qquad s = 1, 2, \ldots, r. \tag{9.2.43}$$

(iv) If the period equation has only simple roots the normal coordinates η appearing in (9.1.22) are unique, save for sign. This is no longer true if the period equation has multiple roots. For example, if $p_1{}^2 = p_2{}^2$, the forms T and V can be reduced to

$$\begin{cases} T = \frac{1}{2}(\dot{\eta}_1{}^2 + \dot{\eta}_2{}^2 + \cdots + \dot{\eta}_n{}^2), \\ V = \frac{1}{2}p_1{}^2(\eta_1{}^2 + \eta_2{}^2) + \frac{1}{2}p_3{}^2\eta_3{}^2 + \cdots + \frac{1}{2}p_n{}^2\eta_n{}^2, \end{cases} \tag{9.2.44}$$

and we still have normal coordinates if we use ζ_1 and ζ_2 in place of η_1 and η_2, where $\eta_1 = \zeta_1 \cos\alpha + \zeta_2 \sin\alpha$, $\eta_2 = \zeta_1 \sin\alpha - \zeta_2 \cos\alpha$.

9.3 Application of the theory. The theory of the transformation to normal coordinates developed in § 9.2 suggests another method of attacking a concrete problem. Of course the new method is not in principle essentially distinct from the method of § 9.1; the new attack is in general less expeditious than the old, but it has the advantage of being immediately applicable to a problem whose period equation has multiple roots.

We begin as before by solving the period equation

$$|p^2\mathbf{A} - \mathbf{B}| = 0. \tag{9.3.1}$$

Let the roots be $p_1{}^2, p_2{}^2, \ldots, p_n{}^2$. Conventionally we write these in ascending order of magnitude

$$p_1{}^2 \leqslant p_2{}^2 \leqslant \cdots \leqslant p_n{}^2. \tag{9.3.2}$$

We then determine a real eigenvector $\mathbf{u}_r$ corresponding to each eigenvalue $p_r{}^2$. If the eigenvalues are simple there is no difficulty; the eigenvectors are unique (save for a scalar multiplier) and any pair satisfies the orthogonality conditions (9.2.34–35). If the period equation has multiple roots the matter is less simple. The k eigenvectors corresponding to a k-fold root must be so chosen that they form an independent set in which each pair satisfies the orthogonality conditions (cf. § 9.2, (iii)). In practice

* The Gram-Schmidt orthogonalization process.

it is sufficient to satisfy the first condition (9.2.34), since the second condition (9.2.35) is then implied.

Now let $\mathbf{S}$ be the matrix whose rth column is the real non-zero eigenvector $\mathbf{u}_r$,

$$\mathbf{S} = (\mathbf{u}_1, \mathbf{u}_2, \ldots, \mathbf{u}_n). \tag{9.3.3}$$

Then the transformation

$$\mathbf{q} = \mathbf{S}\boldsymbol{\xi} \tag{9.3.4}$$

achieves the transformation to normal coordinates. The complete solution of the problem now follows as before.

All of this is implied by the theory developed in § 9.2, but a direct verification is not without interest. We observe first that the vectors $\mathbf{u}_1, \mathbf{u}_2, \ldots, \mathbf{u}_n$ that we have determined are independent. For a relation

$$\mathbf{u}_{r+1} = \alpha_1\mathbf{u}_1 + \alpha_2\mathbf{u}_2 + \cdots + u_r\mathbf{u}_r \tag{9.3.5}$$

would imply

$$\mathbf{u}'_{r+1}\mathbf{A}\mathbf{u}_{r+1} = \sum_{s=1}^{n} \alpha_s(\mathbf{u}'_{r+1}\mathbf{A}\mathbf{u}_s), \tag{9.3.6}$$

which is clearly false, since the first member is positive and the second is zero. Thus the columns of $\mathbf{S}$ are independent, and $\mathbf{S}$ is non-singular.

The equations of motion can be written in the form

$$\mathbf{A}\ddot{\mathbf{q}} + \mathbf{B}\mathbf{q} = 0. \tag{9.3.7}$$

Now

$$\begin{aligned} \mathbf{BS} &= \mathbf{B}(\mathbf{u}_1, \mathbf{u}_2, \ldots, \mathbf{u}_n) \\ &= (\mathbf{Bu}_1, \mathbf{Bu}_2, \ldots, \mathbf{Bu}_n) \\ &= (p_1{}^2\mathbf{Au}_1, p_2{}^2\mathbf{Au}_2, \ldots, p_n{}^2\mathbf{Au}_n) \\ &= (\mathbf{Au}_1, \mathbf{Au}_2, \ldots, \mathbf{Au}_n)\mathbf{P} \\ &= \mathbf{A}(\mathbf{u}_1, \mathbf{u}_2, \ldots, \mathbf{u}_n)\mathbf{P} \\ &= \mathbf{ASP}, \end{aligned} \tag{9.3.8}$$

where, as before, $\mathbf{P}$ denotes the diagonal matrix

$$\mathbf{P} = \begin{pmatrix} p_1{}^2 & & & & \\ & p_2{}^2 & & & \\ & & \cdot & & \\ & & & \cdot & \\ & & & & \cdot \\ & & & & & p_n{}^2 \end{pmatrix}. \tag{9.3.9}$$

We now express the equation of motion (9.3.7) in terms of $\boldsymbol{\xi}$ by means of (9.3.4), and we obtain

$$\mathbf{AS}\ddot{\boldsymbol{\xi}} + \mathbf{BS}\boldsymbol{\xi} = \mathbf{0}, \tag{9.3.10}$$

which, in virtue of (9.3.8), is equivalent to

$$\mathbf{AS}(\ddot{\boldsymbol{\xi}} + \mathbf{P}\boldsymbol{\xi}) = \mathbf{0}. \tag{9.3.11}$$

But **AS** is non-singular (since **S** is non-singular) so (9.3.11) leads to

(9.3.12) $$\boldsymbol{\xi} + \mathbf{P}\boldsymbol{\xi} = \mathbf{0},$$

which is equivalent to the n equations

(9.3.13) $$\ddot{\xi}_r + p_r{}^2\xi_r = 0, \qquad r = 1, 2, \ldots, n,$$

so the ξ's are normal coordinates, and this is what we set out to prove.

As we know from the theory developed in § 9.2, the transformation (9.3.4) reduces T and V to sums of squares. This fact also is easily verified directly, because

(9.3.14) $$2T = \dot{\mathbf{q}}'\mathbf{A}\dot{\mathbf{q}} = \ddot{\boldsymbol{\xi}}'\mathbf{S}'\mathbf{AS}\ddot{\boldsymbol{\xi}},$$

and $\mathbf{S}'\mathbf{AS}$ is diagonal; for if we put

(9.3.15) $$\mathbf{S}'\mathbf{AS} = (c_{rs})$$

we have

(9.3.16) $$c_{rs} = \mathbf{u}_r{}'\mathbf{A}\mathbf{u}_s,$$

and $c_{rs} = 0$ if $r \neq s$ in virtue of the orthogonality conditions. The matrix $\mathbf{S}'\mathbf{AS}$ is the diagonal matrix $\boldsymbol{\Lambda}$,

(9.3.17) $$\boldsymbol{\Lambda} = \begin{pmatrix} \lambda_1 & & & & \\ & \lambda_2 & & & \\ & & \cdot & & \\ & & & \cdot & \\ & & & & \cdot \\ & & & & & \lambda_n \end{pmatrix},$$

where

(9.3.18) $$\lambda_r = \mathbf{u}_r{}'\mathbf{A}\mathbf{u}_r,$$

which is real and positive. Thus

(9.3.19) $$2T = \dot{\boldsymbol{\xi}}'\boldsymbol{\Lambda}\dot{\boldsymbol{\xi}} = \sum_{r=1}^{n} \lambda_r\dot{\xi}_r{}^2.$$

Similarly

(9.3.20) $$2V = \mathbf{q}_r\mathbf{Bq} = \boldsymbol{\xi}'\mathbf{S}'\mathbf{BS}\boldsymbol{\xi},$$

and since, from (9.3.8),

(9.3.21) $$\mathbf{S}'\mathbf{BS} = \mathbf{S}'\mathbf{ASP},$$

we see that $\mathbf{S}'\mathbf{BS}$ is the diagonal matrix

(9.3.22) $$\boldsymbol{\Lambda}\mathbf{P} = \begin{pmatrix} \lambda_1 p_1{}^2 & & & & \\ & \lambda_2 p_2{}^2 & & & \\ & & \cdot & & \\ & & & \cdot & \\ & & & & \cdot \\ & & & & & \lambda_n p_n{}^2 \end{pmatrix},$$

and

(9.3.23) $$2V = \sum_{r=1}^{n} \lambda_r p_r{}^2\xi_r{}^2.$$

As we have noticed, if we *normalize* the eigenvectors $\mathbf{u}_r$ to make

(9.3.24) $$\mathbf{u}_r{}'\mathbf{A}\mathbf{u}_r = 1, \qquad r = 1, 2, \ldots, n,$$

then each λ_r has the value 1, and T and V are reduced to the forms (9.1.22).

Example 9.3. To find the transformation to normal coordinates if

$$(9.3.25)\qquad \begin{cases} 2T = 3\dot{q}_1^{\,2} + 2\dot{q}_2^{\,2} + \dot{q}_3^{\,2} + 2\dot{q}_2\dot{q}_3 + 2\dot{q}_3\dot{q}_1 + 4\dot{q}_1\dot{q}_2, \\ 2V = n^2(6q_1^{\,2} + 5q_2^{\,2} + 4q_3^{\,2} + 8q_2q_3 + 8q_3q_1 + 10q_1q_2). \end{cases}$$

Here

$$(9.3.26)\qquad \mathbf{A} = \begin{pmatrix} 3 & 2 & 1 \\ 2 & 2 & 1 \\ 1 & 1 & 1 \end{pmatrix}, \qquad \mathbf{B} = n^2\begin{pmatrix} 6 & 5 & 4 \\ 5 & 5 & 4 \\ 4 & 4 & 4 \end{pmatrix},$$

and the period equation is

$$(9.3.27)\qquad (p^2 - n^2)^2(p^2 - 4n^2) = 0,$$

whence

$$(9.3.28)\qquad p_1^{\,2} = p_2^{\,2} = n^2, \quad p_3^{\,2} = 4n^2.$$

For $p^2 = p_1^{\,2}$ the eigenvectors satisfy the single equation

$$(9.3.29)\qquad q_1 + q_2 + q_3 = 0,$$

and two solutions, satisfying the orthogonality condition, are $(1, -1, 0)$ and $(0, 1, -1)$.

For $p^2 = p_3^{\,2}$ the equations for the eigenvectors are

$$(9.3.30)\qquad 6q_1 + 3q_2 = 0, \quad 3q_1 + 3q_2 = 0.$$

so we can take for the eigenvector $(0, 0, 1)$.

Thus the transformation to normal coordinates is

$$(9.3.31)\qquad \mathbf{q} = \begin{pmatrix} 1 & 0 & 0 \\ -1 & 1 & 0 \\ 0 & -1 & 1 \end{pmatrix}\boldsymbol{\xi}.$$

Actually the eigenvectors are normalized, and

$$(9.3.32)\qquad \begin{cases} 2T = \dot{\xi}_1^{\,2} + \dot{\xi}_2^{\,2} + \dot{\xi}_3^{\,2}, \\ 2V = n^2(\xi_1^{\,2} + \xi_2^{\,2}) + 4n^2\xi_3^{\,2}. \end{cases}$$

9.4 Imposition of a constraint. If we impose a single constraint on a vibrating system with n freedoms we obtain a new vibrating system with $(n - 1)$ freedoms. The constrained system has the following property: *the* $(n - 1)$ *free periods for the constrained system lie in the intervals between successive free periods of the original system.* In particular, the frequency of the fundamental mode is raised.

To prove the result, let us use normal coordinates for the original system, so that

$$(9.4.1)\qquad T = \tfrac{1}{2}(\dot{q}_1^{\,2} + \dot{q}_2^{\,2} + \cdots + \dot{q}_n^{\,2}), \quad V = \tfrac{1}{2}(p_1^{\,2}q_1^{\,2} + p_2^{\,2}q_2^{\,2} + \cdots + p_n^{\,2}q_n^{\,2}),$$

where we assume in the first instance that all the periods are distinct, and $p_1^{\,2} < p_2^{\,2} < \cdots < p_{n-1}^2 < p_n^{\,2}$. We take as the equation of constraint

$$(9.4.2)\qquad A_1q_1 + A_2q_2 + \cdots + A_nq_n = 0.$$

It will be convenient to use the same coordinates for the constrained system, so we have a problem of a holonomic system in which we use redundant coordinates (§ 5.8). The equations of motion for the constrained system are

$$(9.4.3)\qquad \ddot{q}_r + p_r^{\,2}q_r = \lambda A_r, \qquad r = 1, 2, \ldots, n,$$

where λ is an undetermined multiplier, and there is now an equation of constraint (9.4.2). Now in a normal oscillation of the constrained system, of period $2\pi/p$, we have

$$\frac{\ddot{q}_1}{q_1} = \frac{\ddot{q}_2}{q_2} = \cdots = \frac{\ddot{q}_n}{q_n} = -p^2, \tag{9.4.4}$$

so (from (9.4.3) and (9.4.4)) in the normal oscillation

$$(-p^2 + p_r^2)q_r = \lambda A_r. \tag{9.4.5}$$

Therefore, in virtue of (9.4.2), the period equation is

$$\frac{A_1^2}{p^2 - p_1^2} + \frac{A_2^2}{p^2 - p_2^2} + \cdots + \frac{A_n^2}{p^2 - p_n^2} = 0. \tag{9.4.6}$$

If no coefficient A_r vanishes, and no two periods of the original system are equal, one root for p^2 lies between p_1^2 and p_2^2, one between p_2^2 and p_3^2, and so on.

If one A_r is zero, the corresponding coordinate is still a normal coordinate, and the period of that particular normal mode is unchanged. If two periods of the original system are equal, their common value is also a period of the constrained system.

9.5 Rayleigh's principle. If we impose $(n - 1)$ constraints on a vibrating system with n degrees of freedom, we obtain a system with only one degree of freedom. Interpreted physically, we impose a prescribed *shape* on the system, and allow it to oscillate only in that shape. What is the period of the oscillation of the system so constrained?

We again choose normal coordinates for the original system, so that

$$T = \tfrac{1}{2}(\dot{q}_1^2 + \dot{q}_2^2 + \cdots + \dot{q}_n^2), \quad V = \tfrac{1}{2}(p_1^2q_1^2 + p_2^2q_2^2 + \cdots + p_n^2q_n^2), \tag{9.5.1}$$

and we suppose the constraints to be represented by the equations

$$\frac{q_1}{\alpha_1} = \frac{q_2}{\alpha_2} = \cdots = \frac{q_n}{\alpha_n}. \tag{9.5.2}$$

If we put each term in (9.5.2) equal to θ, we can use θ as the single Lagrangian coordinate for the constrained system, and for this system

$$T = \tfrac{1}{2}(\alpha_1^2 + \alpha_2^2 + \cdots + \alpha_n^2)\dot{\theta}^2, \quad V = \tfrac{1}{2}(p_1^2\alpha_1^2 + p_2^2\alpha_2^2 + \cdots + p_n^2\alpha_n^2)\theta^2. \tag{9.5.3}$$

The single period of oscillation for the constrained system is therefore $2\pi/p$, where

$$p^2 = \frac{\alpha_1^2p_1^2 + \alpha_2^2p_2^2 + \cdots + \alpha_n^2p_n^2}{\alpha_1^2 + \alpha_2^2 + \cdots + \alpha_n^2}. \tag{9.5.4}$$

Now the second member of (9.5.4), *qua* function of $\alpha_1, \alpha_2, \ldots, \alpha_n$, is stationary when all but one of the α's vanish. We thus arrive at the following theorem: *the period of oscillation of the constrained system, considered as a function of the constraint, has a stationary value when the original system is constrained to vibrate in one of its normal modes.* This is Rayleigh's principle.

In some problems we can guess the general character of the normal modes on grounds of symmetry, and then Rayleigh's principle enables us to find the periods, and, hence to complete the solution of the problem (*Example* 9.5*A*). In other cases we may be able to make a reasonably good guess at the shape of a particular mode;

usually the gravest, or fundamental, mode. The stationary property of the normal modes implies that a reasonably good estimate of the shape of a normal mode will in general give rise to a close approximation to the period of that mode. (If α_2/α_1, $\alpha_3/\alpha_1, \ldots, \alpha_n/\alpha_1$ are $O(\varepsilon)$, the value of $p^2 - p_1{}^2$ derived from (9.5.4) is $O(\varepsilon^2)$.) This property is illustrated in *Example* 9.5*B*.

Example 9.5*A*. Consider again the *Example* 9.1*A*, in which

(9.5.5) $$T = \tfrac{1}{2}m(\dot{x}^2 + \tfrac{4}{3}\dot{y}^2 + \dot{z}^2), \quad V = 2mn^2(x^2 + y^2 + z^2 - xy - yz).$$

If we constrain the system to vibrate in the shape

(9.5.6) $$\frac{x}{\alpha} = \frac{y}{\beta} = \frac{z}{\gamma},$$

the period is $2\pi/p$, where

(9.5.7) $$p^2 = \frac{4n^2(\alpha^2 + \beta^2 + \gamma^2 - \alpha\beta - \beta\gamma)}{\alpha^2 + \tfrac{4}{3}\beta^2 + \gamma^2}.$$

It is evident that there is a normal mode in which $x + z = y = 0$, and putting $\beta = 0$, $\alpha = -\gamma$, we find

(9.5.8) $$p^2 = p_2{}^2 = 4n^2.$$

Further, we expect a normal mode in which $x = z$, and putting $\alpha = \gamma$ we have

(9.5.9) $$\frac{p^2}{6n^2} = \frac{2\alpha^2 - 2\alpha\beta + \beta^2}{3\alpha^2 + 2\beta^2} = \frac{(3\alpha - 2\beta)^2 + (\alpha + \beta)^2}{(3\alpha - 2\beta)^2 + 6(\alpha + \beta)^2},$$

which is stationary if $\dfrac{\alpha}{\beta} = \dfrac{2}{3}$ and if $\dfrac{\alpha}{\beta} = -1$. These give the values $p_1{}^2 = n^2$ and $p_3{}^2 = 6n^2$.

We thus recover the values of $p_1{}^2$, $p_2{}^2$, $p_3{}^2$ previously found by direct calculation, and we can now complete the solution of the problem as before. It will be observed that Rayleigh's principle affords a quite practicable method of attacking a concrete problem if the shapes of the normal modes are known, or if their general form can be foreseen on physical grounds.

Example 9.5*B*. As a simple example of finding an approximation to the period of a normal mode when we know an approximation to its shape, consider a uniform flexible string stretched at a large tension, with its ends attached to two fixed points, and vibrating transversely. Let the length be l, the line-density ρ, the tension P, and the transverse displacement $y = y(x, t)$. We have here a continuous system (cf. § 3.9), and strictly speaking the analysis we have given, which is concerned with a system with a finite number of freedoms, is not applicable; but we may assume the extension to continuous systems on general physical grounds. To the requisite order of approximation

(9.5.10) $$T = \tfrac{1}{2}\rho\int_0^l \dot{y}^2\,dx, \quad V = \tfrac{1}{2}\rho c^2\int_0^l \left(\frac{\partial y}{\partial x}\right)^2 dx, \qquad c^2 = P/\rho.$$

In the fundamental mode of vibration we observe a simple arc symmetrical about the mid-point $x = \tfrac{1}{2}l$. So let us constrain the string to vibrate in the form of a parabolic arc symmetrical about $x = \tfrac{1}{2}l$. Thus

(9.5.11) $$y = Ax(l - x)\theta,$$

where $\theta = \theta(t)$; for this form of the string

(9.5.12) $$T = \tfrac{1}{60}\rho l^5 A^2\dot{\theta}^2, \quad V = \tfrac{1}{6}\rho c^2 l^3 A^2\theta^2,$$

giving $p^2 = 10c^2/l^2$. The correct form is

(9.5.13) $$y = A\theta \sin (\pi x/l),$$

giving $p^2 = \pi^2c^2/l^2$, and the approximation to p^2 found from our fairly crude application of Rayleigh's principle is wrong by only about 1·3%.

9.6 Stability of steady motion. The idea of *stability*, associated so far only with small displacements from a position of equilibrium, can be extended to displacements from a given motion.

An equilibrium position is stable if, after a sufficiently small disturbance, the system remains near to the equilibrium position and the velocity remains small. To express this formally it will be convenient to introduce the symbol r $(= r(t))$ defined by the equation

$$r = \sqrt{\left\{\sum_{s=1}^{n} (q_s - \alpha_s)^2 + \sum_{s=1}^{n} \dot{q}_s{}^2\right\}},$$

where $(\alpha_1, \alpha_2, \ldots, \alpha_n)$ is the equilibrium position. The position $\boldsymbol{\alpha}$ is stable if, given a positive number ε, however small, there exists a positive number κ $(= \kappa(\varepsilon))$ such that if $r(0) < \kappa$ then $r(t) < \varepsilon$ for $t > 0$.*

When we turn to problems of motion, instead of problems of equilibrium, a similar definition of stability suggests itself; the motion is stable if, after a small disturbance, the motion remains, in some sense, *near* to the undisturbed motion. But the idea of a stable motion is more complex than the idea of stable equilibrium, and the general theory must be postponed (to Chapter XXIII). There is, however, one class of problem for which the theory is simple, and for which there exists a simple test for stability analogous to the minimum-potential test for stability of equilibrium.

We consider a *gyroscopic system*, i.e. a natural system in which some of the Lagrangian coordinates are ignorable (§ 6.11). We suppose that $q_1, q_2, \ldots, q_m$ are *ignorable*, and that $q_{m+1}, q_{m+2}, \ldots, q_n$ are non-ignorable or *palpable*. We know $(m + 1)$ first integrals for the system, namely the m momentum integrals corresponding to the m ignorable coordinates

(9.6.1) $$\frac{\partial T}{\partial \dot{q}_r} = \beta_r, \qquad r = 1, 2, \ldots, m,$$

and the integral of energy

(9.6.2) $$T + V = C.$$

We define a *steady motion* to be one in which the velocities $\dot{q}_1, \dot{q}_2, \ldots, \dot{q}_m$, and the coordinates $q_{m+1}, q_{m+2}, \ldots, q_n$, have constant values. In a steady motion the palpable coordinates satisfy the equations

(9.6.3) $$\frac{\partial T_\sigma}{\partial q_r} = \frac{\partial V}{\partial q_r}, \qquad r = m + 1, m + 2, \ldots, n,$$

where T_σ is obtained from T by giving to $\dot{q}_1, \dot{q}_2, \ldots, \dot{q}_m$ the constant values appropriate to the steady motion, and to each of $\dot{q}_{m+1}, \dot{q}_{m+2}, \ldots, \dot{q}_n$ the value zero. Examples of steady motion are provided by a particle in a central field moving in a circular orbit, the conical-pendulum motion of a spherical pendulum, the steady precession of a spinning top.

* Or we can use instead of r the function $\sum_{s=1}^{n} |q_s - \alpha_s| + \sum_{s=1}^{n} |\dot{q}_s|$.

Let us then consider a steady motion in which the conserved momenta are β_1, $\beta_2, \ldots, \beta_m$, and the palpable coordinates have the values $\alpha_{m+1}, \alpha_{m+2}, \ldots, \alpha_n$. We consider a disturbed motion in which the momenta are unchanged, and in which the initial values of

$$|q_{m+1} - \alpha_{m+1}|,\ |q_{m+2} - \alpha_{m+2}|, \ldots, |q_n - \alpha_n|;\ |\dot{q}_{m+1}|,\ |\dot{q}_{m+2}|, \ldots, |\dot{q}_n|,$$

are small; if they remain small for all future time we say that the original steady motion is *stable*. More precisely, the steady motion is said to be stable if, given a positive number ε, there exists a positive number κ $(= \kappa(\varepsilon))$, such that if $r(0) < \kappa$, then $r(t) < \varepsilon$ for $t > 0$, where now

$$r(t) = \sqrt{\left\{\sum_{s=m+1}^{n} (q_s - \alpha_s)^2 + \sum_{s=m+1}^{n} \dot{q}_s^{\,2}\right\}}. \tag{9.6.4}$$

We can write the m integrals (9.6.1) in the form

(9.6.5)

$$\begin{cases} a_{11}\dot{q}_1 + a_{12}\dot{q}_2 + \cdots + a_{1m}\dot{q}_m = \beta_1 - (a_{1,m+1}\dot{q}_{m+1} + a_{1,m+2}\dot{q}_{m+2} + \cdots + a_{1,n}\dot{q}_n), \\ a_{21}\dot{q}_1 + a_{22}\dot{q}_2 + \cdots + a_{2m}\dot{q}_m = \beta_2 - (a_{2,m+1}\dot{q}_{m+1} + a_{2,m+2}\dot{q}_{m+2} + \cdots + a_{2,n}\dot{q}_n), \\ \cdots\cdots\cdots\cdots\cdots\cdots\cdots\cdots\cdots\cdots\cdots\cdots \\ a_{m1}\dot{q}_1 + a_{m2}\dot{q}_2 + \cdots + a_{mm}\dot{q}_m = \beta_m - (a_{m,m+1}\dot{q}_{m+1} + a_{m,m+2}\dot{q}_{m+2} + \cdots + a_{m,n}\dot{q}_n), \end{cases}$$

and we write the second members, for the sake of brevity,

$$\beta_1 - B_1,\ \beta_2 - B_2, \ldots, \beta_m - B_m. \tag{9.6.6}$$

The $m \times m$ matrix (a_{rs}) is non-singular, and we can solve the equations (9.6.5) for $\dot{q}_1, \dot{q}_2, \ldots, \dot{q}_m$. If (d_{rs}) is the $m \times m$ matrix inverse to the $m \times m$ matrix (a_{rs}), we have

$$\dot{q}_r = d_{r1}(\beta_1 - B_1) + d_{r2}(\beta_2 - B_2) + \cdots + d_{rm}(\beta_m - B_m), \quad r = 1, 2, \ldots, m. \tag{9.6.7}$$

We can now express T in terms of the β's instead of $\dot{q}_1, \dot{q}_2, \ldots, \dot{q}_m$, i.e. we suppress the first m velocities in T in favour of the momenta. We have

(9.6.8)

$$\begin{aligned} 2T &= \dot{q}_1\beta_1 + \dot{q}_2\beta_2 + \cdots + \dot{q}_m\beta_m + \dot{q}_{m+1}\frac{\partial T}{\partial \dot{q}_{m+1}} + \dot{q}_{m+2}\frac{\partial T}{\partial \dot{q}_{m+2}} + \cdots + \dot{q}_n\frac{\partial T}{\partial \dot{q}_n} \\ &= \dot{q}_1(\beta_1 + B_1) + \dot{q}_2(\beta_2 + B_2) + \cdots + \dot{q}_m(\beta_m + B_m) + \sum_{r=m+1}^{n}\sum_{s=m+1}^{n} a_{rs}\dot{q}_r\dot{q}_s \\ &= \sum_{r=1}^{m} (\beta_r + B_r)\{d_{r1}(\beta_1 - B_1) + d_{r2}(\beta_2 - B_2) + \cdots + d_{rm}(\beta_m - B_m)\} \\ &\quad + \sum_{r=m+1}^{n}\sum_{s=m+1}^{n} a_{rs}\dot{q}_r\dot{q}_s \\ &= \sum_{r=1}^{m}\sum_{s=1}^{m} d_{rs}\beta_r\beta_s - \sum_{r=1}^{m}\sum_{s=1}^{m} d_{rs}B_rB_s + \sum_{r=m+1}^{n}\sum_{s=m+1}^{n} a_{rs}\dot{q}_r\dot{q}_s \\ &= \sum_{r=1}^{m}\sum_{s=1}^{m} d_{rs}\beta_r\beta_s + 2\overline{T}, \end{aligned}$$

where $\bar{T}$ is a quadratic form in $\dot{q}_{m+1}, \dot{q}_{m+2}, \ldots, \dot{q}_n$; moreover, it is a positive definite form, because $T \geqslant 0$ if we give the special value zero to each of the β's. The energy equation (9.6.2) now takes the form

$$\bar{T} + W = C, \tag{9.6.9}$$

where

$$W = W(\beta_1, \beta_2, \ldots, \beta_m; q_{m+1}, q_{m+2}, \ldots, q_n) = \tfrac{1}{2}\sum_{r=1}^{m}\sum_{s=1}^{m} d_{rs}\beta_r\beta_s + V. \tag{9.6.10}$$

Thus, during the motion,

$$W \leqslant C, \tag{9.6.11}$$

and therefore, by the argument used previously in the theory of vibrations about equilibrium (§ 9.1) the steady motion is stable if W is a minimum at $(\alpha_{m+1}, \alpha_{m+2}, \ldots, \alpha_n)$.

We can see that W must be *stationary* for the steady motion, whether this motion is stable or not, because the equations

$$\frac{\partial W}{\partial q_r} = 0, \qquad r = m+1, m+2, \ldots, n, \tag{9.6.12}$$

are equivalent to (9.6.3). To prove this we notice that

$$W = \sum_{r=1}^{m} \dot{q}_r\beta_r - T_\sigma + V, \tag{9.6.13}$$

whence, considering a small displacement from the steady motion,

$$\begin{aligned} \delta W &= \sum_{r=1}^{m}\left(\dot{q}_r\,\delta\beta_r + \beta_r\,\delta\dot{q}_r - \frac{\partial T_\sigma}{\partial \dot{q}_r}\,\delta\dot{q}_r\right) + \sum_{r=m+1}^{n}\frac{\partial(V - T_\sigma)}{\partial q_r}\,\delta q_r \\ &= \sum_{r=1}^{m}\dot{q}_r\,\delta\beta_r + \sum_{r=m+1}^{n}\frac{\partial(V - T_\sigma)}{\partial q_r}\,\delta q_r. \end{aligned} \tag{9.6.14}$$

Thus

$$\frac{\partial W}{\partial q_r} = \frac{\partial(V - T_\sigma)}{\partial q_r}, \qquad r = m+1, m+2, \ldots, n, \tag{9.6.15}$$

and this proves the statement that (9.6.12) is equivalent to (9.6.3).

A procedure, both for *finding* the steady motions, and for testing their *stability*, is now clear. We suppress $\dot{q}_1, \dot{q}_2, \ldots, \dot{q}_m$ in $T + V$ in favour of $\beta_1, \beta_2, \ldots, \beta_m$, and then replace each of $\dot{q}_{m+1}, \dot{q}_{m+2}, \ldots, \dot{q}_n$ by zero. The resulting expression is W $(= W(\beta_1, \beta_2, \ldots, \beta_m; q_{m+1}, q_{m+2}, \ldots, q_n))$. *For a steady motion W, qua function of $q_{m+1}, q_{m+2}, \ldots, q_n$, is stationary; and if W is a minimum the motion is stable.*

Example 9.6*A*. *Central field.* A particle moves under the central attraction μ/r^n per unit mass. Here

$$T + V = \tfrac{1}{2}(\dot{r}^2 + r^2\dot{\theta}^2) - \frac{1}{(n-1)}\frac{\mu}{r^{n-1}}. \tag{9.6.16}$$

The coordinate θ is ignorable, and the corresponding momentum integral is

$$r^2\dot{\theta} = \beta, \tag{9.6.17}$$

whence

$$W = \frac{1}{2}\frac{\beta^2}{r^2} - \frac{1}{(n-1)}\frac{\mu}{r^{n-1}}. \tag{9.6.18}$$

For the steady motion (the circular orbit) W is stationary,

$$\frac{dW}{dr} = -\frac{\beta^2}{r^3} + \frac{\mu}{r^n} = 0, \tag{9.6.19}$$

and the motion is stable if

$$\frac{d^2W}{dr^2} = \frac{3\beta^2}{r^4} - \frac{n\mu}{r^{n+1}} > 0. \tag{9.6.20}$$

In virtue of (9.6.19) the condition (9.6.20) is equivalent to $n < 3$, and this is the condition for stability. Of course (9.6.19) is evident for elementary reasons, since in the circular orbit

$$r\dot{\theta}^2 = \mu/r^n. \tag{9.6.21}$$

Example 9.6*B*. *Conical pendulum.* For the spherical pendulum (*Example* 5.2*D*), measuring θ from the downward vertical,

$$T + V = \tfrac{1}{2}ma^2(\dot{\theta}^2 + \sin^2\theta\dot{\varphi}^2) - mga\cos\theta, \tag{9.6.22}$$

or say

$$T + V = \tfrac{1}{2}(\dot{\theta}^2 + \sin^2\theta\dot{\varphi}^2) - n^2\cos\theta, \qquad n^2 = g/a. \tag{9.6.23}$$

The coordinate φ is ignorable, and the corresponding momentum integral is

$$\sin^2\theta\dot{\varphi} = \beta, \tag{9.6.24}$$

whence

$$W = \frac{\beta^2}{2\sin^2\theta} - n^2\cos\theta, \tag{9.6.25}$$

$$\frac{dW}{d\theta} = -\frac{\beta^2\cos\theta}{\sin^3\theta} + n^2\sin\theta, \tag{9.6.26}$$

$$\frac{d^2W}{d\theta^2} = \frac{\beta^2(\sin^2\theta + 3\cos^2\theta)}{\sin^4\theta} + n^2\cos\theta, \tag{9.6.27}$$

and the steady motion is stable. Actually the stability is evident from § 5.2 without reference to the general theory. For a steady motion, the zeros z_3 and z_2 of $f(z)$ coincide, and the graph of $f(z)$ touches Oz at $z = z_3$ (cf. Fig. 5.2*c*). The effect of a small disturbance is to modify the graph so that it cuts Oz in two nearly-coincident points. The motion is confined to a narrow zone on the sphere near to the original circle.

Example 9.6*C*. *Precession of a spinning top.* For the spinning top, there are, as we saw in § 8.6, two possible steady motions with the axis inclined at any prescribed angle α to the upward vertical, provided that $p^2 > q$. By a similar argument to that just given for the spherical pendulum we can be sure that these steady motions are stable without reference to the general theory. For a steady motion the graph of $f(z)$ in Fig. 8.9a touches Oz, and after a small disturbance the graph is so modified that it cuts Oz in two nearly-coincident points. However, it is not without interest to verify the fact of stability from the general theory.

We have

$$T + V = \tfrac{1}{2}A(\dot{\theta}^2 + \sin^2\theta\dot{\varphi}^2) + \tfrac{1}{2}C(\dot{\psi} + \dot{\varphi}\cos\theta)^2 + Mgl\cos\theta, \tag{9.6.28}$$

and the momentum integrals for the ignorable coordinates φ and ψ are

$$A\sin^2\theta\dot{\varphi} + C(\dot{\psi} + \dot{\varphi}\cos\theta)\cos\theta = 2A\lambda, \tag{9.6.29}$$

$$C(\dot{\psi} + \dot{\varphi}\cos\theta) = Cn, \tag{9.6.30}$$

and these give for W

$$\frac{W}{A} = 2\frac{(\lambda - p\cos\theta)^2}{\sin^2\theta} + q\cos\theta + \frac{Cn^2}{2A}, \tag{9.6.31}$$

where, as before, we write $2p$ for Cn/A and q for Mgl/A. Writing z for $\cos\theta$ we have, effectively,

$$W = \frac{2(\lambda - pz)^2}{1 - z^2} + qz \tag{9.6.32}$$

$$= \frac{(\lambda - p)^2}{1 - z} + \frac{(\lambda + p)^2}{1 + z} + qz - 2p^2,$$

$$\frac{dW}{dz} = \frac{(\lambda - p)^2}{(1 - z)^2} - \frac{(\lambda + p)^2}{(1 + z)^2} + q, \tag{9.6.33}$$

$$\frac{d^2W}{dz^2} = \frac{2(\lambda - p)^2}{(1 - z)^3} + \frac{2(\lambda + p)^2}{(1 + z)^3}, \tag{9.6.34}$$

and the steady motion is stable. The vanishing of dW/dz in the steady motion is equivalent to the condition (8.9.4).

9.7 Oscillations about steady motion. If we know that the steady motion is stable, so that the divergence from the steady motion resulting from a small disturbance remains small, we can find an approximation to the new motion by writing

$$\dot{q}_r = \omega_r + \eta_r, \qquad r = 1, 2, \ldots, m, \tag{9.7.1}$$

$$q_r = \alpha_r + \xi_r, \qquad r = m + 1, m + 2, \ldots, n, \tag{9.7.2}$$

in the equations of motion (where ω_r denotes the constant value of $\dot{q}_r$, for $r = 1, 2, \ldots, m$, in the steady motion) and retaining only terms of the first order in ξ's and η's.

As illustrations we find a first approximation to the disturbed motion in the three classical problems considered in § 9.6. We recall that the theory refers explicitly to a disturbance in which the momentum constants β_r have the same values that they have in the original steady motion. In practice this limitation is unimportant, because if we do allow small changes in the momentum constants we are merely transferring our attention to oscillations about a neighbouring state of steady motion.

Example 9.7A. *Central field* μ/r^n, *disturbed circular orbit.* A particle moves in the circle $r = a$ under the central attraction μ/r^n, where $n < 3$. To find the motion resulting when the particle receives a small outward radial velocity λu at the instant $t = 0$, where u is the velocity in the circular orbit.

We have

$$\left\{\begin{aligned} \ddot{r} - r\dot{\theta}^2 &= -\frac{\mu}{r^n}, \\ r^2\dot{\theta} &= \sqrt{(\mu a^{3-n})}, \end{aligned}\right. \tag{9.7.3}$$

whence, eliminating $\dot{\theta}$,

$$\ddot{r} - \frac{\mu a^{3-n}}{r^3} = -\frac{\mu}{r^n}. \tag{9.7.4}$$

If we write $r = a + \xi$, and expand to the first order in ξ, we have

$$\ddot{\xi} + p^2\xi = 0, \tag{9.7.5}$$

where

$$p^2 = (3 - n)\mu/a^{n+1}. \tag{9.7.6}$$

Hence

$$\xi = \frac{\lambda u}{p}\sin pt = \frac{\lambda a}{\sqrt{(3 - n)}}\sin pt, \tag{9.7.7}$$

and the value of r at time t is

$$r = a\left(1 + \frac{\lambda}{\sqrt{(3 - n)}}\sin pt\right). \tag{9.7.8}$$

Further, again neglecting terms of order λ^2,

$$\dot{\theta} = \frac{\sqrt{(\mu a^{3-n})}}{r^2} = \omega\left(1 - \frac{2\lambda}{\sqrt{(3 - n)}}\sin pt\right), \tag{9.7.9}$$

$$\theta = \omega t - \frac{2\lambda}{3 - n}(1 - \cos pt), \tag{9.7.10}$$

where $\omega(= \sqrt{(\mu/a^{n+1})})$ is the angular velocity in the steady motion, and we suppose $\theta = 0$ when $t = 0$. The approximate equation of the disturbed orbit is

$$r = a\left(1 + \frac{\lambda}{\sqrt{(3 - n)}}\sin\sqrt{(3 - n)}\theta\right). \tag{9.7.11}$$

The apsidal distances are $a\left(1 \pm \frac{\lambda}{\sqrt{(3 - n)}}\right)$, and the apsidal angle is $\pi/\sqrt{(3 - n)}$. In two familiar cases, $n = -1$ and $n = 2$, this formula for the apsidal angle is exactly, not merely approximately, correct.

Example 9.7*B*. *The spherical pendulum, oscillations about conical motion.* Measuring θ from the downward vertical, the functions T and V for the spherical pendulum are

$$T = \tfrac{1}{2}(\dot{\theta}^2 + \sin^2\theta\dot{\varphi}^2), \quad V = -n^2\cos\theta, \tag{9.7.12}$$

where $n^2 = g/a$. Originally the bob moves in a horizontal circle $\theta = \alpha$, where $0 < \alpha < \frac{1}{2}\pi$, and $\dot{\varphi} = n\sqrt{(\sec\alpha)}$. We suppose that, at $t = 0$, the bob receives a small outward impulse in the meridian plane, so that initially $\dot{\theta}$ has the small value λ.

From Lagrange's equations

$$\begin{cases} \ddot{\theta} = \cos\theta \sin\theta\dot{\varphi}^2 - n^2 \sin\theta, \\ \sin^2\theta\dot{\varphi} = n \sin^2\alpha\sqrt{(\sec\alpha)}, \end{cases} \tag{9.7.13}$$

and eliminating $\dot{\varphi}$ we find

$$\ddot{\theta} + n^2 \sin\alpha\left(\frac{\sin\theta}{\sin\alpha} - \frac{\cos\theta \sin^3\alpha}{\cos\alpha \sin^3\theta}\right) = 0. \tag{9.7.14}$$

Writing $\theta = \alpha + \xi$, and expanding to the first order in ξ, we find

$$\ddot{\xi} + p^2\xi = 0, \tag{9.7.15}$$

where

$$p^2 = n^2(\sec\alpha + 3\cos\alpha). \tag{9.7.16}$$

The value of ξ at time t is $(\lambda/p)\sin pt$, and the extreme values of θ are $\alpha \pm (\lambda/p)$ The value of φ at time t, taking $\varphi = 0$ when $t = 0$, is

$$\varphi = n\sqrt{(\sec\alpha)}\left\{t - \frac{2\lambda\cot\alpha}{p^2}(1 - \cos pt)\right\}, \tag{9.7.17}$$

and the path of the bob on the sphere is given by

$$\theta = \alpha + \frac{\lambda}{p}\sin k\varphi, \tag{9.7.18}$$

where $k^2 = 1 + 3\cos^2\alpha$.

Example 9.7*C*. *Nutation of a spinning top*. As in § 8.6, the equations determining the motion of the axis of the top are

$$\ddot{\theta} - \sin\theta(\cos\theta\dot{\varphi}^2 - 2p\dot{\varphi} + q) = 0, \tag{9.7.19}$$

$$\sin^2\theta\dot{\varphi} + 2p\cos\theta = 2\lambda. \tag{9.7.20}$$

We assume that $p^2 > q$. Originally the top is precessing steadily, with $\theta = \alpha$, $\dot{\varphi} = \Omega$, where $0 < \alpha < \frac{1}{2}\pi$, and Ω is one of the roots of the quadratic equation

$$\cos\alpha\,\Omega^2 - 2p\Omega + q = 0. \tag{9.7.21}$$

We consider a disturbance in which p and λ are unchanged; the conditions at $t = 0$ are $\theta = \alpha$, $\dot{\varphi} = \Omega$, $\dot{\theta} = \zeta$, where ζ is small. Writing $\theta = \alpha + \xi$, $\dot{\varphi} = \Omega + \eta$ the equation (9.7.20), correct to the first order in ξ and η, becomes

$$\eta = \frac{2(p - \Omega\cos\alpha)}{\sin\alpha}\xi, \tag{9.7.22}$$

so η/ξ remains constant throughout the motion. In finding the linear approximation to (9.7.19) we notice that the expression in the bracket is a first-order quantity (because of (9.7.21)) so we can replace the multiplier $\sin\theta$ outside the bracket by $\sin\alpha$, and then we easily find the required approximation

$$\ddot{\xi} + \Omega^2\sin^2\alpha\xi + 2\sin\alpha(p - \Omega\cos\alpha)\eta = 0. \tag{9.7.23}$$

Substituting for η (as a multiple of ξ) from (9.7.22), the equation (9.7.23) becomes

$$\ddot{\xi} + \kappa^2\xi = 0, \tag{9.7.24}$$

where

$$\kappa^2 = \Omega^2\sin^2\alpha + 4(p - \Omega\cos\alpha)^2 = \Omega^2\sin^2\alpha + 4p^2 - 4q\cos\alpha. \tag{9.7.25}$$

When the spin of the top is very large, κ is of the order of $2p$ $(= Cn/A)$. To the order of approximation considered, the period of the nutation (i.e. the oscillation about the steady precession) is $2\pi/\kappa$. The value of θ at time t is

$$\alpha + \frac{\zeta}{\kappa}\sin \kappa t, \tag{9.7.26}$$

and the inclination θ of the axis to the upward vertical varies between the values $\alpha \pm (\zeta/\kappa)$.

9.8 Foucault's gyroscope. We consider a spinning top hanging down from the peg, with its centre of gravity G vertically below the peg O, and spinning about its axis. If the top is slightly disturbed, the axis OG will remain in the neighbourhood of the downward vertical, and this is true whatever the value of the spin. This is evident from the energy equation, which we may write in a form analogous to (8.6.8),

$$\dot{\theta}^2 + \sin^2\theta\dot{\varphi}^2 - 2q\cos\theta = 2\mu. \tag{9.8.1}$$

The value of 2μ when the axis is stationary is $-2q$, and if we consider a small increase, to $-2q\cos\alpha$, where α is small, we have in the disturbed motion

$$\dot{\theta}^2 + \sin^2\theta\dot{\varphi}^2 - 2q\cos\theta = -2q\cos\alpha, \tag{9.8.2}$$

and $\theta \leqslant \alpha$ throughout the motion.

To study the disturbed motion in the neighbourhood of the downward vertical, it will be convenient to take the axis Ox vertically downwards, in order to avoid the awkwardness of having φ indeterminate in the position of rest, which would happen if we took Oz vertical. Then

$$L = \tfrac{1}{2}A(\dot{\theta}^2 + \sin^2\theta\dot{\varphi}^2) + \tfrac{1}{2}C(\dot{\psi} + \dot{\varphi}\cos\theta)^2 + Mgl\sin\theta\cos\varphi. \tag{9.8.3}$$

As usual

$$\dot{\psi} + \dot{\varphi}\cos\theta = n, \tag{9.8.4}$$

and, using this result in the Lagrangian equations for θ and φ, we obtain

$$\begin{cases} A(\ddot{\theta} - \dot{\varphi}^2\cos\theta\sin\theta) + Cn\dot{\varphi}\sin\theta - Mgl\cos\theta\cos\varphi = 0, \\ A(\ddot{\varphi}\sin\theta + 2\dot{\theta}\dot{\varphi}\cos\theta) - Cn\dot{\theta} + Mgl\sin\varphi = 0, \end{cases} \tag{9.8.5}$$

where we have removed from the second equation a factor $\sin\theta$, which is non-zero since $\sin\theta$ is nearly equal to 1.

To study the disturbed motion in the neighbourhood of the downward vertical we write $\theta = \frac{1}{2}\pi - z$, $\varphi = y$, and then, correct to the first order in y and z, the direction cosines of the axis are $(1, y, z)$. The motion, correct to the first order in y and z, is given by the linear approximation

$$\begin{cases} A\ddot{y} + Cn\dot{z} + Mgly = 0, \\ A\ddot{z} - Cn\dot{y} + Mglz = 0. \end{cases} \tag{9.8.6}$$

These are the same as the equations of motion for a particle moving in the (y, z)-plane under the action of a harmonic attraction and a gyroscopic force (§ 8.8). Writing $w = y + iz$, and introducing the symbols p $(= Cn/2A)$ and q $(= Mgl/A)$ as before, we see that w satisfies the differential equation

$$\ddot{w} - 2ip\dot{w} + qw = 0. \tag{9.8.7}$$

The solution is

$$w = Ae^{i(s+p)t} + Be^{-i(s-p)t}, \tag{9.8.8}$$

where

$$s = \sqrt{(p^2 + q)}, \tag{9.8.9}$$

and the coefficients A, B may be complex. In a small disturbance in which $|w|$ and $|\dot{w}|$ are small initially, $|w|$ remains small for all time, and the linear approximation gives a good approximation to the actual motion, at least for a not too extended range of values of t.

We can also find the equations (9.8.6) very simply by the method of § 8.7. We have

$$Cn\dot{\mathbf{u}} + A\mathbf{u} \times \mathbf{u} = Mgl\mathbf{u} \times \mathbf{v}, \tag{8.7.2}$$

and since $\mathbf{v}$ is now the vector $\{1, 0, 0\}$ the three component equations of (8.7.2) are

$$\begin{cases} A(y\ddot{z} - z\ddot{y}) + Cn\dot{x} = 0, \\ A(z\ddot{x} - x\ddot{z}) + Cn\dot{y} = Mglz, \\ A(x\ddot{y} - y\ddot{x}) + Cn\dot{z} = -Mgly, \end{cases} \tag{9.8.10}$$

where $\mathbf{u}$ is the vector (x, y, z). In our present problem y and z are small, and x is effectively 1, and these approximations lead again to (9.8.6).

We consider the solution of (9.8.7) in two particular cases; we denote the initial values of w and $\dot{w}$ by w_0 and v_0.

(i) $w_0 = 0$, v_0 is real and positive (and of course small); the axis of the top is passing through the downward vertical at $t = 0$. The solution is

$$w = ae^{ipt} \sin st, \qquad (a = v_0/s), \tag{9.8.11}$$

the rosette orbit whose polar equation is

$$r = a \sin \lambda\theta, \tag{9.8.12}$$

where $\lambda = s/p > 1$. The path is shown in Fig. 9.8a; this figure is drawn for the case in which the spin is fairly small, so λ is fairly large. If the spin is large, λ is only a little greater than 1, and the path approximates to a circle

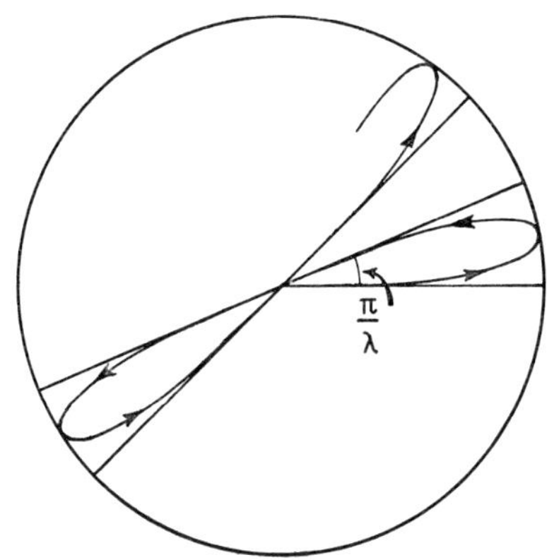

Figure 9.8a

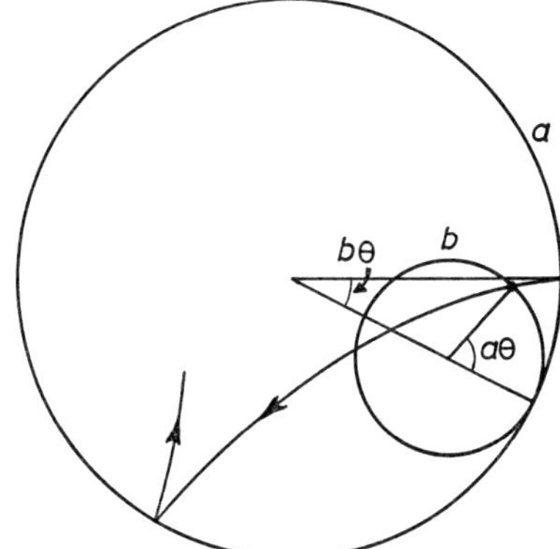

Figure 9.8b

(ii) $v_0 = 0$, $\omega_0 = a$, which is real and positive; the axis is released from rest near the downward vertical. The solution is

$$w = \frac{a}{2s}\{(s-p)e^{i(s+p)t} + (s+p)e^{-i(s-p)t}\}, \tag{9.8.13}$$

which represents a hypocycloid. We can exhibit it as the path of a point on a circle of radius b, where $b < \frac{1}{2}a$, rolling on the inside of a circle of radius a, as in Fig. 9.8b. With the notation indicated in the figure,

$$w = (a-b)e^{-ib\theta} + be^{i(a-b)\theta}. \tag{9.8.14}$$

The formulae (9.8.13) and (9.8.14) are reconciled by taking

$$b = \frac{s-p}{2s}a, \qquad \theta = \frac{2s}{a}t. \tag{9.8.15}$$

9.9 The sleeping top. If a top rests with its axis vertical, and the centre of gravity above the peg, the equilibrium is unstable if the top is not spinning. But the vertical position becomes stable if the top is given a sufficiently large spin, as every schoolboy knows. Explicitly, a sufficient condition for stability is $p^2 > q$. If this condition is fulfilled, and if the displacement and the angular velocity of the axis are small initially, they will remain small for all time. In this case (when $p^2 > q$) the linear approximation will give a good approximation to the actual motion in the neighbourhood of the equilibrium position.

In the problem of the sleeping top we have empirical evidence that the vertical position is stable when the spin is large. To construct a formal proof of stability we use a method similar to that provided by the energy integral in the theory of small oscillations (§ 9.1). If x, y, z are direction cosines of the axis, Ox being vertically upwards, we have the integrals of energy and of angular momentum about Ox (cf. § 8.7),

$$\tfrac{1}{2}(\dot{x}^2 + \dot{y}^2 + \dot{z}^2) + qx = \text{constant}, \tag{9.9.1}$$

$$y\dot{z} - z\dot{y} + 2px = \text{constant}, \tag{9.9.2}$$

and we remember that

$$x^2 + y^2 + z^2 = 1. \tag{9.9.3}$$

We write $x = 1 + \xi$, measuring from the equilibrium position, so that ξ, y, z are small in the neighbourhood of the equilibrium position. The integrals now become

$$\tfrac{1}{2}(\dot{\xi}^2 + \dot{y}^2 + \dot{z}^2) + q\xi = \text{constant}, \tag{9.9.4}$$

$$y\dot{z} - z\dot{y} + 2p\xi = \text{constant}, \tag{9.9.5}$$

while

$$\xi^2 + y^2 + z^2 + 2\xi = 0. \tag{9.9.6}$$

We now construct an integral which is a positive definite quadratic form in (ξ, y, z, $\dot{\xi}$, $\dot{y}$, $\dot{z}$). From (9.9.4) and (9.9.5) we form the integral

$$\tfrac{1}{2}(\dot{\xi}^2 + \dot{y}^2 + \dot{z}^2) + q\xi - p(y\dot{z} - z\dot{y} + 2p\xi) = C, \tag{9.9.7}$$

and this is equivalent, in virtue of (9.9.6), to

$$\tfrac{1}{2}\dot{\xi}^2 + \tfrac{1}{2}(\dot{y} + pz)^2 + \tfrac{1}{2}(\dot{z} - py)^2 + \tfrac{1}{2}(2p^2 - q)\xi^2 + \tfrac{1}{2}(p^2 - q)(y^2 + z^2) = C. \tag{9.9.8}$$

If ξ, y, z, $\dot{\xi}$, $\dot{y}$, $\dot{z}$ are small initially, C is small; and if $p^2 > q$ the first member of (9.9.8) is a positive definite quadratic form. It follows, as in § 9.1, that ξ, y, z, $\dot{\xi}$, $\dot{y}$, $\dot{z}$ remain small for all time. Moreover, we can find explicit bounds for the variables; for example throughout the motion $\frac{1}{2}(2p^2 - q)\xi^2 < C$, and $\frac{1}{2}(p^2 - q)(y^2 + z^2) < C$.

Thus we have prior assurance of stability, and therefore the linear approximation will give a good approximation to the motion (at least for a period of time not too extended) if the initial disturbance is small.

A different approach to the problem should be noticed at this point, since it is typical of a situation that occurs frequently, and one that has played a prominent part in the history of dynamics. We have a position of equilibrium of a dynamical system, and we choose Lagrangian coordinates q_r which vanish in this position. (Or the q's may denote (as here) the palpable coordinates in a gyroscopic system; there is a position of apparent equilibrium, and the q's are chosen to vanish in this position.) We wish to determine if the equilibrium at $\mathbf{q} = \mathbf{0}$ is stable; if the q's and $\dot{q}$'s are small at $t = 0$, do they remain small for all time? The traditional approach to this problem is to write the linear approximation to the equations of motion. If we have independent evidence that the disturbance does remain small, as we have, for example, in the present problem and in the problem of small oscillations about a position of minimum potential energy, the linear approximation gives a good approximation to the disturbed motion. But if we have no such independent evidence we must proceed with caution. If the linear approximation indicates stability (i.e. if smallness in the initial values of q's and $\dot{q}$'s indicates smallness for all time) the equilibrium position is said to have *first-order stability*. The difficulty is that first-order stability does not invariably ensure that there will be stability when we turn from the linear approximation to the exact equations.

In the discussion of the stability of a position of equilibrium we may use n Lagrangian coordinates $q_1, q_2, \ldots, q_n$, representing the displacement from the equilibrium position (as in § 9.1). There are n second-order differential equations, and the motion of stability requires smallness both of q's and of $\dot{q}$'s. Or we may use $2n$ first-order equations (the variables being, for example q's and $\dot{q}$'s, or q's and p's) and then the notion of stability requires only smallness of the displacement from the position of equilibrium; for this implies, for the dynamical system, smallness of velocity as well as of displacement. If we replace the n equations of the second order by m $(= 2n)$ equations of the first order, the equations take the form (6.4.4),

$$\dot{x}_r = X_r(x_1, x_2, \ldots, x_m), \qquad r = 1, 2, \ldots, m.$$

The positions of equilibrium are the singular points in the field $\mathbf{X}$, i.e. the points at which all the X's vanish. If we wish to examine the stability of a particular singular point, we change the coordinates so as to bring the singular point to the origin. Since the equations are first-order equations, the subsequent motion is determined by the position of the representative point $(x_1, x_2, \ldots, x_m)$ at $t = 0$. We write

$$r(t) = \sqrt{(x_1{}^2 + x_2{}^2 + \cdots + x_m{}^2)},$$

and the question is, if $r(0)$ is small, does this imply that $r(t)$ is small for $t > 0$? We may assume that X_r can be expanded in a multiple power-series in $x_1, x_2, \ldots, x_m$. There is no constant term in the expansion, since the origin is a singular point, and if we retain only the terms of the first degree in $x_1, x_2, \ldots, x_m$ we obtain the linear approximation. If the motion defined by the linear approximation is stable, the position of equilibrium has first-order stability.

If the position of equilibrium has first-order stability we have a plausible reason for expecting stability, but this expectation is not invariably fulfilled; indeed it is not difficult to construct examples in which it is falsified in a quite startling way. Consider for example the problem in which the motion of the representative point in the (x, y)-plane is defined by the first-order equations

$$\dot{x} = -y + rx, \qquad \dot{y} = x + ry, \tag{9.9.9}$$

where $r = \sqrt{(x^2 + y^2)}$. The linear approximation

$$\dot{x} = -y, \qquad \dot{y} = x, \tag{9.9.10}$$

has the familiar solution (expressed in terms of polar coordinates)

$$r = r_0, \qquad \theta = \theta_0 + t, \tag{9.9.11}$$

and so far as the linear approximation is concerned the origin is surely a point of stable equilibrium. If r is small initially, it remains small for all time. But if we include the second-order terms we have

$$r\dot{r} = x\dot{x} + y\dot{y} = r^3, \qquad \dot{r} = r^2, \tag{9.9.12}$$

giving

$$r = 1/(\alpha - t), \tag{9.9.13}$$

where $\alpha = 1/r_0$. Thus, $r \to \infty$ as $t \to \alpha$. However small r_0 (> 0) may be, r continually increases, and tends to infinity in a finite time.

On the other hand, if the linear approximation implies *instability*, the equilibrium is indeed unstable. At first sight it might appear possible that replacing the linear approximation by the exact equations might convert instability into stability, but in fact this can only happen in exceptional circumstances.*

There is a third possibility, which may be mentioned here for the sake of completeness. In some problems of motion near a position of equilibrium, the motion given by the linear approximation is such that each q and each $\dot{q}$ tends to zero as t tends to infinity. When this happens we speak of first-order *complete stability*, and complete stability also persists when we turn from the linear approximation to the exact equations; if the q's and $\dot{q}$'s are small initially, they tend to zero as t tends to infinity.

To sum up, if the linear approximation implies instability or complete stability, we can in general infer that the same holds for the exact equations; but ordinary stability cannot be inferred with certainty from the linear approximation. We shall return to this topic, and give proofs of the results just mentioned, in Chapter XIX and in Chapter XXI.

Let us now return to the problem of the sleeping top. We take the axis Ox vertically upwards (cf. § 9.8, where the axis Ox was vertically downwards) to avoid the awkwardness of having φ indeterminate in the position of apparent equilibrium. If the

* An illustration of the exceptional case appears in *Example* 19.11c.

direction cosines of the axis are $(1, y, z)$, the linear approximation to the equations of motion, obtained by either of the methods used in § 9.8, is

$$\ddot{w} - 2ip\dot{w} - qw = 0, \tag{9.9.14}$$

where $w = y + iz$; this is the same as the equation (9.8.7) except for the change of sign in the last term on the left. If $p^2 < q$, the solution does not remain small, but if $p^2 > q$ the solution is

$$w = Ae^{i(p+s)t} + Be^{i(p-s)t}, \tag{9.9.15}$$

where $s = \sqrt{(p^2 - q)}$, and the coefficients A, B may be complex. If $p^2 > q$, and if $|w|$ and $|\dot{w}|$ are small initially, $|w|$ and $|\dot{w}|$ remain small for all time, as our foreknowledge of the stability leads us to expect.

To illustrate the motion defined by the equation (9.9.14), let us consider again the problem discussed in § 8.9; initially the point P on the axis of the top moves horizontally, so we can take $w = a$ and $\dot{w} = ika$ at $t = 0$, where a and k are real and positive. Let us consider in particular (as in § 8.9) the range of values of k for which the axis *rises* from the initial position; the path lies *inside* the circle $r = a$. In the former discussion of this problem, in § 8.9, the equations were exact, the solution given was mainly descriptive; here the equations are approximations, valid only for small values of $|w|$, but the solution is exact.

The solution of (9.9.14) with the given initial conditions is

$$w = \frac{a}{2s}\{(p + s - k)e^{i(p-s)t} + (k - p + s)e^{i(p+s)t}\}. \tag{9.9.16}$$

The path is an epitrochoid. If a disc of radius β rolls on the outside of a fixed circle of radius α, and P is a point fixed to the rolling disc at distance γ from its centre, the path of P can be written with the notation shown in Fig. 9.9a,

$$w = (\alpha + \beta)e^{i\beta\varphi} + \gamma e^{i(\alpha+\beta)\varphi}. \tag{9.9.17}$$

The formulae (9.9.16) and (9.9.17) are reconciled if

$$\alpha = \frac{p + s - k}{p + s}\,a, \qquad \beta = \frac{p - s}{2s}\,\alpha, \qquad \gamma = \frac{k - p + s}{2s}\,a; \tag{9.9.18}$$

the relation connecting t and φ is

$$\frac{\varphi}{t} = \frac{2s(p + s)}{p + s - k}\frac{1}{a}. \tag{9.9.19}$$

We follow the same line of thought as in § 8.9, considering how the motion changes as k increases from $(p - s)$ to $(p + s)$. The four critical cases, which we denote (as in § 9.8) by A, B, C, D, are as follows:

$$A, k = (p - s); \quad B, k = p - (s^2/p); \quad C, k = p; \quad D, k = (p + s).$$

For the case A, the motion is a slow precession on the circle $r = a$. Between A and B there is a libration between the circles $r = a$ and $r = \{(p - k)/s\}a$, as in Fig. 9.9b. At B the path is an epicycloid, with cusps on the circle $r = (s/p)a$, as in Fig. 9.9c. Between B and C the path is a looped curve between the circles $r = a$ and $r = \{(p - k)/s\}a$, as in Fig. 9.9d, and at C the path is the curve $r = a \cos (s/p)\theta$, passing through O, as in Fig. 9.9e. Between C and D we again have a libration between two circles (Fig. 9.9f), and at D the motion is a fast precession on the circle $r = a$.

12

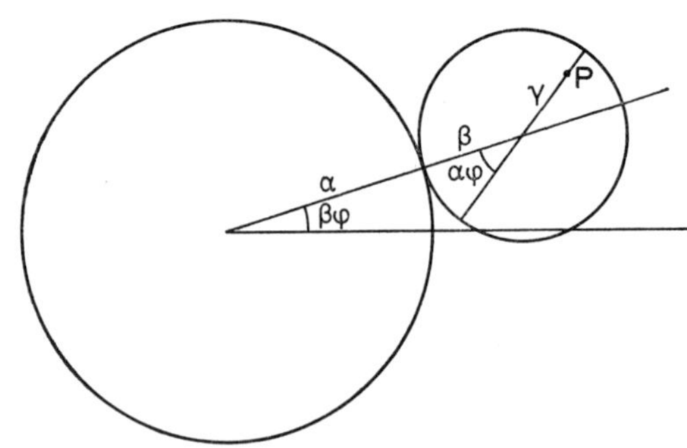

Figure 9.9a

The two particular problems that we discussed in connexion with Foucault's gyroscope, (i) when the axis passes through the vertical, and (ii) when the axis is released from rest in an inclined position, are comprehended in the discussion just given; (i) occurs in the case C, and (ii) occurs in the case B. The reader may find it of interest to find the solutions independently as in the discussion of Foucault's gyroscope in § 9.8.

9.10 Forced oscillations. In §§ 9.1–9.3 we considered the theory of *free oscillations* about a position of stable equilibrium. We now turn to the *forced oscillations* that are set up when additional forces, varying periodically with the time, act on the system. The subject is a large one, and we must be content here with a brief introduction to it.

The simplest problem is that of the harmonic oscillator when the additional force is proportional to sin pt, and the equation of motion is

$$\ddot{x} + n^2 x = c \sin pt. \tag{9.10.1}$$

If $p \neq n$, the solution is

$$x = \frac{c}{n^2 - p^2} \sin pt + a \cos nt + \frac{1}{n}\left(u - \frac{pc}{n^2 - p^2}\right) \sin nt, \tag{9.10.2}$$

where a is the value of x, and u is the value of $\dot{x}$, at $t = 0$. The first term in this solution represents the *forced oscillation* (with period $2\pi/p$), and the remaining terms represent the *free oscillation* (with period $2\pi/n$).

The amplitude $\dfrac{c}{n^2 - p^2}$ of the forced oscillation is large if p is nearly equal to n. This phenomenon, the production of a forced oscillation whose amplitude is large in comparison with the amplitude c of the additional force, is called *resonance*; though this term is sometimes restricted to the case when p is exactly, not merely approximately, equal to n. In the particular case when $p = n$ the solution is

$$x = -\frac{c}{2n} t \cos nt + a \cos nt + \frac{1}{n}\left(u + \frac{c}{2n}\right) \sin nt, \tag{9.10.3}$$

and the forced oscillation $-\dfrac{c}{2n} t \cos nt$ may be regarded as a sinusoidal oscillation of period $2\pi/n$ with an amplitude which increases continually with t.

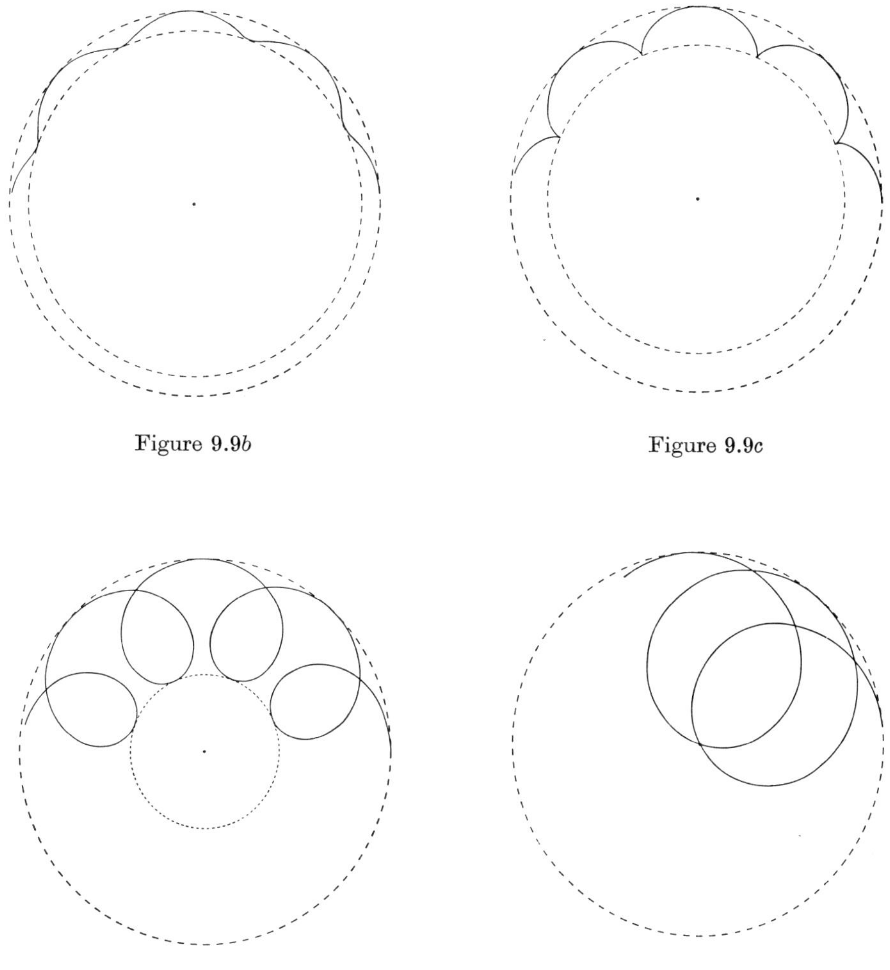

Figure 9.9*b*

Figure 9.9*c*

Figure 9.9*d*

Figure 9.9*e*

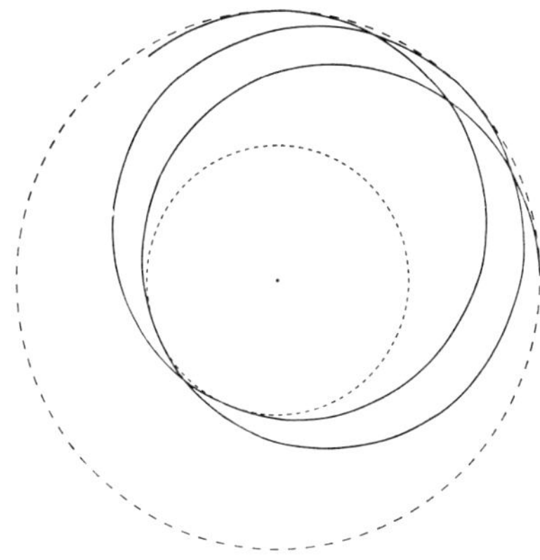

Figure 9.9*f*

In practice however the equation of motion (9.10.1) is usually an approximation which is only valid for small values of x, and the solution we have found is not reliable in the case of resonance, when the amplitude of the forced oscillation is large. This warning is especially pertinent when we have resonance in the strict sense, $p = n$, for in that case the amplitude increases without limit.

In practice also the system is never completely frictionless. The effect of friction is that the free oscillation is ultimately damped out, and only the forced oscillation survives. The prototype of this phenomenon is the harmonic oscillator subject to a frictional force proportional to speed as well as the additional periodic force. The equation of motion is

$$\ddot{x} + 2k\dot{x} + n^2x = c \sin pt, \tag{9.10.4}$$

where we assume $0 < k < n$. The free oscillation is represented by terms of the form $e^{-kt} \cos \mu t$ and $e^{-kt} \sin \mu t$, where $\mu = \sqrt{(n^2 - k^2)}$. We can regard this as a sinusoidal oscillation of period $2\pi/\mu$ with an amplitude proportional to e^{-kt}, which tends rapidly to zero. The free oscillation soon becomes insensible—it is said to be "damped out"—and we are left with the forced oscillation, of period $2\pi/p$, given by

$$x = \frac{c}{R} \sin (pt - \alpha), \tag{9.10.5}$$

where $R \cos \alpha = n^2 - p^2$, $R \sin \alpha = 2pk$. Even when, in problems of oscillatory motion, the friction is not explicitly represented in the equations of motion, it is important to seek and to study periodic solutions having the period of the additional force. The idea underlying this procedure is that, even if the friction is very slight, the free oscillation ultimately becomes negligible.

When we leave the simple case of the linear equation, and consider the forced oscillations of a system for which the equation of motion is not linear, the problem is more difficult. A concrete example of this type of problem will be considered in § 23.10.

Chapter X

Further applications of Lagrange's equations

10.1 The ignoration of coordinates. The system with which we start is a holonomic system with n degrees of freedom, which is described by the n Lagrangian coordinates $q_1, q_2, \ldots, q_n$, and for which the Lagrangian function L does not involve t. We consider now more particularly the case in which some of the coordinates are ignorable (§ 6.11).

We suppose that the coordinates $q_1, q_2, \ldots, q_m$ are ignorable, where $0 < m < n$. Since the first m coordinates do not appear in L, the first m Lagrangian equations lead to the momentum integrals

$$\frac{\partial L}{\partial \dot{q}_r} = \beta_r, \qquad r = 1, 2, \ldots, m, \tag{10.1.1}$$

where the β's are constants whose values are determined by the initial conditions. From the equations (10.1.1), which are linear in $\dot{q}_1, \dot{q}_2, \ldots, \dot{q}_n$, we can express $\dot{q}_1, \dot{q}_2, \ldots, \dot{q}_m$ as linear functions of $\beta_1, \beta_2, \ldots, \beta_m, \dot{q}_{m+1}, \dot{q}_{m+2}, \ldots, \dot{q}_n$,

$$\dot{q}_r = \psi_r(\beta_1, \beta_2, \ldots, \beta_m, \dot{q}_{m+1}, \dot{q}_{m+2}, \ldots, \dot{q}_n, q_{m+1}, q_{m+2}, \ldots, q_n), \qquad r = 1, 2, \ldots, m. \tag{10.1.2}$$

We substitute for $\dot{q}_1, \dot{q}_2, \ldots, \dot{q}_m$ from (10.1.2) in the function

$$L - \sum_{r=1}^{m} \dot{q}_r \frac{\partial L}{\partial \dot{q}_r} = L - \sum_{r=1}^{m} \beta_r \dot{q}_r, \tag{10.1.3}$$

and so obtain a function R,

$$R = R(q_{m+1}, q_{m+2}, \ldots, q_n;\ \dot{q}_{m+1}, \dot{q}_{m+2}, \ldots, \dot{q}_n;\ \beta_1, \beta_2, \ldots, \beta_m). \tag{10.1.4}$$

The function R, the *Routhian function*, is thus the function obtained from (10.1.3) by suppressing the first m of the $\dot{q}$'s in favour of the β's.

If the original system is a natural system, in which

$$T = T_2 = \tfrac{1}{2} \sum_{r=1}^{n} \sum_{s=1}^{n} a_{rs} \dot{q}_r \dot{q}_s,$$

the equations (10.1.2) take the form

$$\dot{q}_r = \sum_{s=1}^{m} d_{rs} \beta_s - \sum_{s=m+1}^{n} d_{rs} \dot{q}_s, \qquad r = 1, 2, \ldots, m, \tag{10.1.5}$$

where, for $s \leqslant m$, d_{rs} has the same meaning as in (9.6.7), and for $s > m$,

$$d_{rs} = \sum_{i=1}^{m} d_{ri} a_{is}.$$

The Routhian function has the form

$$R = T' - V = T_2' + T_1' + T_0' - V, \tag{10.1.6}$$

where T_s' is a homogeneous form of degree s in $\dot{q}_{m+1}, \dot{q}_{m+2}, \ldots, \dot{q}_n$, with coefficients of degree $(2 - s)$ in $\beta_1, \beta_2, \ldots, \beta_m$. The quadratic form T_2' is not, of course, the original kinetic energy function; but it is still a positive definite form, because it is the value of the kinetic energy when each β has the value zero.

We shall prove that R *plays the part of a Lagrangian function for a dynamical system with the coordinates* $q_{m+1}, q_{m+2}, \ldots, q_n$, the so-called *palpable coordinates*. We have therefore reduced the original problem to a problem of a system with $(n - m)$ degrees of freedom; this process is spoken of as *the ignoration of coordinates*. Ignorable coordinates appear conspicuously in systems containing gyroscopes, and systems involving ignorable coordinates are sometimes called *gyroscopic systems* (§ 9.6).

It should be noticed that there is no obligation to suppress *all* the ignorable coordinates. It is of course essential that the coordinates $q_1, q_2, \ldots, q_m$ should be ignorable, but some of the remaining coordinates $q_{m+1}, q_{m+2}, \ldots, q_n$ may be ignorable as well. For example, in the well-known problem of the spinning top, we can conveniently study the motion of the axis by applying the process of ignoration of coordinates to the coordinate ψ alone, obtaining a Lagrangian function with the coordinates θ and φ. This procedure is sometimes useful, although if Oz is vertical the coordinate φ is also an ignorable coordinate.

We now prove the statement made above, that R may be used as a Lagrangian function with the coordinates $q_{m+1}, q_{m+2}, \ldots, q_n$. For a completely general variation (including even a variation in the conserved momenta $\beta_1, \beta_2, \ldots, \beta_m$, but with t unvaried) we have

$$\delta R = \sum_{r=m+1}^{n} \frac{\partial L}{\partial q_r}\,\delta q_r + \sum_{r=1}^{n} \frac{\partial L}{\partial \dot{q}_r}\,\delta \dot{q}_r - \sum_{r=1}^{m} \frac{\partial L}{\partial \dot{q}_r}\,\delta \dot{q}_r - \sum_{r=1}^{m} \dot{q}_r\,\delta\beta_r \tag{10.1.7}$$

$$= \sum_{r=m+1}^{n} \left(\frac{\partial L}{\partial q_r}\,\delta q_r + \frac{\partial L}{\partial \dot{q}_r}\,\delta \dot{q}_r\right) - \sum_{r=1}^{m} \dot{q}_r\,\delta\beta_r.$$

Hence

$$\frac{\partial R}{\partial q_r} = \frac{\partial L}{\partial q_r}, \quad \frac{\partial R}{\partial \dot{q}_r} = \frac{\partial L}{\partial \dot{q}_r}, \qquad r = m+1, m+2, \ldots, n, \tag{10.1.8}$$

and

$$\dot{q}_r = -\frac{\partial R}{\partial \beta_r}, \qquad r = 1, 2, \ldots, m. \tag{10.1.9}$$

We deduce from (10.1.8), in virtue of the Lagrangian equations of motion for $q_{m+1}, q_{m+2}, \ldots, q_n$,

$$\frac{d}{dt}\left(\frac{\partial R}{\partial \dot{q}_r}\right) = \frac{\partial R}{\partial q_r}, \qquad r = m+1, m+2, \ldots, n, \tag{10.1.10}$$

and this is the required result.

Usually we are not much interested in the values of the ignored coordinates $q_1, q_2, \ldots, q_m$ at time t; but if the problem presented by (10.1.10) has been solved, then the values of $q_1, q_2, \ldots, q_m$ at time t can be found from (10.1.9).

10.2 Ignoration of a single coordinate. We consider a natural system, for which

$$T = \tfrac{1}{2} \sum_{r=1}^{n} \sum_{s=1}^{n} a_{rs}\dot{q}_r\dot{q}_s, \tag{10.2.1}$$

and in which the coordinate q_1 is ignorable. What is the form of the Routhian function R that results from the ignoration of q_1?

We can simplify the procedure by noticing that

$$p_1 = \sum_{s=1}^{n} a_{1s}\dot{q}_s, \tag{10.2.2}$$

and therefore

$$2a_{11}T - p_1^2 = 2a_{11}S, \tag{10.2.3}$$

where S is a homogeneous quadratic form in the $(n - 1)$ variables $\dot{q}_2, \dot{q}_3, \ldots, \dot{q}_n$,

$$S = \tfrac{1}{2}\sum_{r=2}^{n}\sum_{s=2}^{n} b_{rs}\dot{q}_r\dot{q}_s, \tag{10.2.4}$$

and

$$b_{rs} = a_{rs} - \frac{a_{1r}a_{1s}}{a_{11}}. \tag{10.2.5}$$

We have the integral of momentum

$$p_1 = \beta, \tag{10.2.6}$$

and the Routhian function R is formed from

$$T - \beta\dot{q}_1 - V = S + \frac{1}{2a_{11}}\beta^2 - \frac{\beta}{a_{11}}(\beta - a_{12}\dot{q}_2 - a_{13}\dot{q}_3 \cdots - a_{1n}\dot{q}_n) - V, \tag{10.2.7}$$

whence

$$R = S + \frac{\beta}{a_{11}}(a_{12}\dot{q}_2 + a_{13}\dot{q}_3 + \cdots + a_{1n}\dot{q}_n) - \left(V + \frac{\beta^2}{2a_{11}}\right). \tag{10.2.8}$$

This is the required function. As we have observed already (§ 10.1), S is a positive definite form.

The original system was a natural system with n freedoms. The system derived by the process of ignoration has $(n - 1)$ freedoms, and it is a non-natural system containing the linear terms

$$T_1' = \frac{\beta}{a_{11}}(a_{12}\dot{q}_2 + a_{13}\dot{q}_3 + \cdots + a_{1n}\dot{q}_n).$$

A case of particular interest, which frequently occurs in practice, is that in which a_{11} is constant; it must of course be a positive constant. In this case the Routhian function (10.2.8) for the study of the motion in the palpable coordinates $q_2, q_3, \ldots, q_n$ is effectively

$$R = S + \omega(a_{12}\dot{q}_2 + a_{13}\dot{q}_3 + \cdots + a_{1n}\dot{q}_n) - V, \tag{10.2.9}$$

where we have written $a_{11}\omega$ for β. Suppose now that the constant a_{11} is large in comparison with the other (variable) coefficients a_{rs}. Then the velocity $\dot{q}_1$ is nearly constant and equal to ω, and the coefficients b_{rs} are nearly equal to the corresponding coefficients a_{rs}, in virtue of (10.2.5). Thus in the case when a_{11} is a large positive constant, the Routhian function (10.2.9) is very nearly the same (save for the omission of constant terms) as the original Lagrangian function with $\dot{q}_1$ replaced by the constant value ω.

The linear terms can arise in either of two ways, by forming the Routhian function, or by imposing on the system the inexorable motion which gives to $\dot{q}_1$ the constant value ω. What we have found is that, in the case under discussion (where a_{11} has a large constant value) the two seemingly unrelated processes lead to the same result; they both produce the same Lagrangian function for the study of the motion in the palpable coordinates.

Consider for example a system attached to a massive body which is free to rotate about an axis. We take axes $Ox'y'z'$ fixed in the rotator, with Oz' along the axis of rotation. Then, proceeding as we did in finding (6.7.7)—though there the angular velocity was uniform, whereas here it is variable—we have

$$L = \mathfrak{T} + \dot{\theta}\eta + \tfrac{1}{2}I\dot{\theta}^2 + \tfrac{1}{2}C\dot{\theta}^2 - V, \tag{10.2.10}$$

where $\mathfrak{T}$ is the kinetic energy of the motion relative to the rotator, η $(= Sm(x'\dot{y}' - y'\dot{x}'))$ is the *apparent angular momentum* about Oz' of the motion relative to the rotator, I is the (variable) moment of inertia of the system about Oz', and C is the moment of inertia of the rotator about Oz'. There are n freedoms, the n coordinates being θ and $(n - 1)$ Lagrangian coordinates $q_2, q_3, \ldots, q_n$ describing the configuration of the system relative to the rotator. If the relations between x''s and q's do not involve t, $\mathfrak{T}$ is a homogeneous quadratic form in $\dot{q}_2, \dot{q}_3, \ldots, \dot{q}_n$, and η is a linear form in $\dot{q}_2, \dot{q}_3, \ldots, \dot{q}_n$.

Now θ is ignorable,

$$\frac{\partial L}{\partial \dot{\theta}} = \eta + (I + C)\dot{\theta}, \tag{10.2.11}$$

and $\partial L/\partial\dot{\theta}$ has a constant value, say $C\omega$. The Routhian function is

$$\begin{aligned} R &= L - C\omega\dot{\theta} \\ &= \mathfrak{T} - \tfrac{1}{2}(I + C)\dot{\theta}^2 - V \\ &= \mathfrak{T} - \frac{1}{2(C + I)}(C\omega - \eta)^2 - V. \end{aligned} \tag{10.2.12}$$

This is exact so far. If now we suppose C to be very large, and expand in powers of $1/C$, omitting all terms of order $1/C$, we obtain

$$R = \mathfrak{T} + \omega\eta + \tfrac{1}{2}I\omega^2 - \tfrac{1}{2}C\omega^2 - V, \tag{10.2.13}$$

and this differs only by a constant from the Lagrangian function (10.2.10) with $\dot{\theta}$ replaced by ω.

The energy equation (6.8.3) obtained from the Routhian function (10.2.13) is

$$\mathfrak{T} + V - \tfrac{1}{2}I\omega^2 = \text{constant}, \tag{10.2.14}$$

and this again can be obtained as a limiting case from the energy equation for the original system. For this equation, from (10.2.10), is

$$\mathfrak{T} + \dot{\theta}\eta + \tfrac{1}{2}(C + I)\dot{\theta}^2 + V = \text{constant}. \tag{10.2.15}$$

If we substitute for $\dot{\theta}$ from (10.2.11),

$$\dot{\theta} = \frac{C\omega - \eta}{C + I}, \tag{10.2.16}$$

and expand as before, neglecting terms of order $1/C$, we recover (10.2.14).

10.3 Gyroscopic stability. We have already considered one example of gyroscopic stability in the problem of the sleeping top, § 9.9; we now consider very briefly the general theory of which this is a particular example.

We consider again, as in § 10.2, a system which contains one ignorable coordinate q_1, and for which a_{11} is a constant. The motion of the system with $(n - 1)$ freedoms described by the palpable coordinates is determined from the Routhian function

$$R = S + \frac{\beta}{a_{11}}(a_{12}\dot{q}_2 + a_{13}\dot{q}_3 + \cdots + a_{1n}\dot{q}_n) - V. \tag{10.2.8}$$

Now a point $(q_2, q_3, \ldots, q_n)$ at which the derivatives $\partial V/\partial q_1, \partial V/\partial q_3, \ldots, \partial V/\partial q_n$ all vanish is a position of apparent equilibrium; it is a position of equilibrium in the palpable coordinates for all values of β. Our purpose is to study the stability (in the sense of first-order stability) of this apparent equilibrium.

Now at a point $P_0(q_{20}, q_{30}, \ldots, q_{n0})$ at which V is a *minimum* the equilibrium is certainly stable. We may suppose without loss of generality that $V = 0$ at P_0. The energy equation (6.8.3) leads to

$$S + V = C, \tag{10.3.1}$$

and, since S is positive definite, this implies

$$V \leqslant C \tag{10.3.2}$$

for all t. For sufficiently small values of C this implies that the motion takes place in a small neighbourhood of P_0, and the equilibrium at P_0 is stable.

At a point P_0 at which V is a *maximum*, or which is a *saddle point*, the equilibrium is unstable if $\beta = 0$. But in some cases we can achieve stability, or at least first-order stability, by giving a sufficiently large value to β. We then speak of *gyroscopic stability*; the sleeping top is a conspicuous example of this situation. To establish the result let us measure, as in the theory of small oscillations, from the position of equilibrium. To discuss the first-order stability conditions it will suffice to use a formula for R correct to the second order in q's and $\dot{q}$'s.

To fix the ideas, let us be content to consider the simple case of a system with only two palpable coordinates. We transform to coordinates for which S and V are sums of squares; these are normal coordinates if $\beta = 0$, and the transformation surely exists since S is a positive definite form. Then, denoting these new coordinates by x and y, we have

$$R = \tfrac{1}{2}(\dot{x}^2 + \dot{y}^2) + \beta(\xi\dot{x} + \eta\dot{y}) - \tfrac{1}{2}(\lambda x^2 + \mu y^2), \tag{10.3.3}$$

where we need ξ and η correct to the first order in x and y. The linear approximations to the equations of motion in the palpable coordinates is therefore

$$\begin{cases} \ddot{x} - \kappa\dot{y} + \lambda x = 0, \\ \ddot{y} + \kappa\dot{x} + \mu y = 0, \end{cases} \tag{10.3.4}$$

where

$$\kappa = \beta\left(\frac{\partial \eta}{\partial x} - \frac{\partial \xi}{\partial y}\right), \tag{10.3.5}$$

a certain *constant* multiple of the momentum-constant β. The solutions of (10.3.4) involve multiples of $e^{\pm p_1 t}$, $e^{\pm p_2 t}$, where $p_1{}^2$ and $p_2{}^2$ are the roots of the quadratic equation

$$\begin{vmatrix} p^2 + \lambda & -\kappa p \\ \kappa p & p^2 + \mu \end{vmatrix} = 0, \tag{10.3.6}$$

which is equivalent to

$$p^4 + (\lambda + \mu + \kappa^2)p^2 + \lambda\mu = 0. \tag{10.3.7}$$

The condition for first-order stability is that this quadratic equation for p^2 should have real negative roots, which requires

$$\lambda\mu > 0, \tag{10.3.8}$$

$$\lambda + \mu + \kappa^2 > 2\sqrt{(\lambda\mu)}. \tag{10.3.9}$$

To satisfy (10.3.8), λ and μ must both be positive or both negative. This means that both freedoms, considered separately, are stable, or both unstable, when $\beta = 0$. The potential energy must be a minimum at 0, or a maximum, but not a saddle point. The condition (10.3.9) is clearly satisfied if λ and μ are both positive. In this case V is a minimum at O, and we have noticed already that in this case the apparent equilibrium is stable for all values of β. The condition (10.3.9) can also be satisfied when λ and μ are both negatives, namely if

$$\kappa > \sqrt{(-\lambda)} + \sqrt{(-\mu)}.$$

This means that if both freedoms are unstable when $\beta = 0$ we can convert the unstable position into a stable one (in the sense of first-order stability) by giving a sufficiently large value to the momentum constant β. The unstable position becomes stable if we give the gyroscope a sufficiently large spin.

10.4 Explicit expression for R in the general case. We have already found, in § 10.2, an explicit expression for the Routhian function R in the simple case in which only one coordinate is ignorable. We now exhibit a method of finding an explicit expression for R in the general case of a natural system in which the first m coordinates are ignorable. The method is somewhat laborious in the concrete applications, and is of theoretical rather than of practical interest.

We write, as in § 6.10,

$$p_r = \frac{\partial T}{\partial \dot{q}_r} = \sum_{s=1}^{n} a_{rs}\dot{q}_s, \qquad r = 1, 2, \ldots, n, \tag{10.4.1}$$

whence

$$\dot{q}_r = \sum_{s=1}^{n} c_{rs}p_s, \qquad r = 1, 2, \ldots, n, \tag{10.4.2}$$

where (c_{rs}) is the matrix inverse to (a_{rs}). The matrix (c_{rs}) is symmetric. Now

$$R = T - \sum_{r=1}^{m} \dot{q}_r p_r - V, \tag{10.4.3}$$

whence

$$2(R + V) = -\dot{q}_1p_1 - \dot{q}_2p_2 - \cdots - \dot{q}_mp_m + \dot{q}_{m+1}p_{m+1} + \dot{q}_{m+2}p_{m+2} + \cdots + \dot{q}_np_n, \tag{10.4.4}$$

where, in the second member, $\dot{q}_1, \dot{q}_2, \ldots, \dot{q}_m$ are to be suppressed in favour of $\beta_1, \beta_2, \ldots, \beta_m$. Let us consider the determinant, with $(n + 1)$ rows and columns,

$$\begin{vmatrix} a_{11} & a_{12} & a_{1m} & -a_{1,m+1} & -a_{1,m+2} & -a_{1,n} & p_1 \\ a_{21} & a_{22} & a_{2m} & -a_{2,m+1} & -a_{2,m+2} & -a_{2,n} & p_2 \\ a_{m1} & a_{m2} & a_{mm} & -a_{m,m+1} & -a_{m,m+2} & -a_{m,n} & p_m \\ 0 & 0 & 0 & -1 & 0 & 0 & \dot{q}_{m+1} \\ 0 & 0 & 0 & 0 & -1 & 0 & \dot{q}_{m+2} \\ 0 & 0 & 0 & 0 & 0 & -1 & \dot{q}_n \\ p_1 & p_2 & p_m & p_{m+1} & p_{m+2} & p_n & -2(R+V) \end{vmatrix} \tag{10.4.5}$$

which evidently vanishes. If we replace the rth column, for $r = m + 1, m + 2, \ldots, n$, by $\sum_{s=1}^{n} (c_{rs} \times s$th column) we obtain a determinant of which the last row is

$$p_1 p_2 \cdots p_m \dot{q}_{m+1} \dot{q}_{m+2} \cdots \dot{q}_n - 2(R + V).$$

If we equate this determinant to zero, and expand (substituting β_r for p_r) we find the explicit expression for $R + V$. It is, as we have noticed already, a homogeneous quadratic form in $\beta_1, \beta_2, \ldots, \beta_m, \dot{q}_{m+1}, \dot{q}_{m+2}, \ldots, \dot{q}_n$.

10.5 The spinning top. Using Euler's angles to define the orientation of a trihedral fixed in the top, as in § 8.6, we have

(10.5.1) $$L = \tfrac{1}{2}A(\dot{\theta}^2 + \sin^2\theta\,\dot{\varphi}^2) + \tfrac{1}{2}C(\dot{\psi} + \dot{\varphi}\cos\theta)^2 - V.$$

If (i) we take Oz vertically upwards

(10.5.2) $$V = Mgl\cos\theta,$$

and both φ and ψ are ignorable. If (ii) we take Ox vertically upwards

(10.5.3) $$V = Mgl\sin\theta\cos\varphi,$$

and only ψ is ignorable.

In case (i) we can suppress both φ and ψ, and form a Lagrangian function with the single coordinate θ. We have

(10.5.4) $$p_\varphi = A\sin^2\theta\,\dot{\varphi} + C\cos\theta(\dot{\psi} + \dot{\varphi}\cos\theta) = \beta_1,$$

(10.5.5) $$p_\psi = C(\dot{\psi} + \dot{\varphi}\cos\theta) = \beta_2,$$

and

(10.5.6) $$\begin{aligned} 2(R + V) &= \dot{\theta}p_\theta - \dot{\varphi}p_\varphi - \dot{\psi}p_\psi \\ &= A\dot{\theta}^2 - \dot{\varphi}\{A\sin^2\theta\,\dot{\varphi} + C\cos\theta(\dot{\psi} + \dot{\varphi}\cos\theta)\} - C\dot{\psi}(\dot{\psi} + \dot{\varphi}\cos\theta) \\ &= A\dot{\theta}^2 - A\sin^2\theta\,\dot{\varphi}^2 - C(\dot{\psi} + \dot{\varphi}\cos\theta)^2 \\ &= A\dot{\theta}^2 - \frac{1}{A\sin^2\theta}(p_\varphi - p_\psi\cos\theta)^2 - \frac{1}{C}p_\psi^{\,2}. \end{aligned}$$

If we use the notation of § 8.6,

(10.5.7) $$p_\varphi = \beta_1 = 2A\lambda, \qquad p_\psi = \beta_2 = 2Ap, \qquad Mgl = Aq,$$

we find (omitting a constant term and removing a positive constant multiplier)

(10.5.8) $$R = \tfrac{1}{2}\dot{\theta}^2 - \frac{2}{\sin^2\theta}(\lambda - p\cos\theta)^2 - q\cos\theta.$$

The energy integral (§ 6.7), which determines the relation between t and θ during the motion, is

(10.5.9) $$\tfrac{1}{2}\dot{\theta}^2 + \frac{2}{\sin^2\theta}(\lambda - p\cos\theta)^2 + q\cos\theta = \mu,$$

which is equivalent to (8.6.9).

In case (ii) (and indeed in case (i) also) we can suppress ψ and form a Routhian function with the two coordinates θ and φ,

(10.5.10) $$R = L - p_\psi \dot{\psi},$$

where

(10.5.11) $$p_\psi = C(\dot{\psi} + \dot{\varphi} \cos \theta) = \beta.$$

Here

(10.5.12) $$R = \tfrac{1}{2}A(\dot{\theta}^2 + \sin^2 \theta \, \dot{\varphi}^2) + \beta \dot{\varphi} \cos \theta - V,$$

where a constant term has been omitted. We can use this Lagrangian function for the study of the motion of the axis; if $V = Mgl \cos \theta$ we recover the results of § 8.6, and if $V = Mgl \sin \theta \cos \varphi$ we recover the results of § 9.9.

10.6 Linear terms in *L*. For a natural system (§ 6.5) T is a homogeneous quadratic function of the $\dot{q}$'s. The Lagrangian function constructed by Routh's method, however, contains terms linear in the $\dot{q}$'s, say

(10.6.1) $$T_1 = a_1 \dot{q}_1 + a_2 \dot{q}_2 + \cdots + a_n \dot{q}_n,$$

where n now denotes the number of palpable coordinates, i.e. the effective number of freedoms of the system whose Lagrangian function is R. We have already noticed (§ 6.1 and § 6.6) that such linear terms appear also in other cases, for example in certain problems involving forces depending on velocity; and other cases in which linear terms appear in L will occur in the sequel.

The contribution of T_1 to the first member of the rth Lagrangian equation,

$$\frac{d}{dt}\left(\frac{\partial T_1}{\partial \dot{q}_r}\right) - \frac{\partial T_1}{\partial q_r},$$

is

(10.6.2) $$\frac{\partial a_r}{\partial t} + \sum_{s=1}^{n} \gamma_{rs} \dot{q}_s,$$

where

(10.6.3) $$\gamma_{rs} = \frac{\partial a_r}{\partial q_s} - \frac{\partial a_s}{\partial q_r} = -\gamma_{sr}.$$

If the a's are functions of the q's only, not of t (which is certainly the case if, for example, we have a Routhian function derived by ignoration from a natural system) the linear form T_1 gives rise to anti-symmetric linear terms, called *gyroscopic terms*, in the equations of motion. The vector whose rth component is Q_r, where

(10.6.4) $$Q_r = -\sum_{s=1}^{n} \gamma_{rs} \dot{q}_s,$$

does no work during the motion, since $\sum_{r=1}^{n} Q_r \dot{q}_r = 0$. It follows that the linear terms in the Lagrangian function do not appear in the equation of energy, a fact that we have already observed independently (§ 6.8).

We have seen how linear terms of the form (10.6.1) arise in the Lagrangian function (for the palpable coordinates) which is constructed by the process of ignoration. Let us now consider linear terms in the Lagrangian function arising from given forces depending on velocity. Consider for example the problem of a single particle moving in space, using fixed rectangular axes. Suppose that L contains the linear terms

$$T_1 = P\dot{x} + Q\dot{y} + R\dot{z}, \tag{10.6.5}$$

or say

$$T_1 = \mathbf{F} \cdot \mathbf{v}, \tag{10.6.6}$$

where $\mathbf{F}$ is the vector $\{P, Q, R\}$, $\mathbf{v}$ is the vector $\{\dot{x}, \dot{y}, \dot{z}\}$, and P, Q, R are functions of $(x, y, z;\ t)$ of class C_1. The complete Lagrangian function is

$$L = \tfrac{1}{2}m(\dot{x}^2 + \dot{y}^2 + \dot{z}^2) + (P\dot{x} + Q\dot{y} + R\dot{z}) - V, \tag{10.6.7}$$

where $V = V(x, y, z;\ t)$. The equations of motion are

$$m\ddot{x} = -\frac{\partial V}{\partial x} - \frac{\partial P}{\partial t} + (\dot{y}\zeta - \dot{z}\eta), \tag{10.6.8}$$

and two similar equations, where $\{\xi, \eta, \zeta\} = \operatorname{curl} \mathbf{F}$,

$$\xi = \frac{\partial R}{\partial y} - \frac{\partial Q}{\partial z}, \qquad \eta = \frac{\partial P}{\partial z} - \frac{\partial R}{\partial x}, \qquad \zeta = \frac{\partial Q}{\partial x} - \frac{\partial P}{\partial y}. \tag{10.6.9}$$

We can write the equations compactly in the form

$$m\ddot{\mathbf{r}} = -\operatorname{grad} V - \frac{\partial \mathbf{F}}{\partial t} + \mathbf{v} \times \operatorname{curl} \mathbf{F}. \tag{10.6.10}$$

Thus the Lagrangian function has the form (10.6.7) if the forces acting on the particle are a force derived from the potential function V and a force $-\dfrac{\partial \mathbf{F}}{\partial t} + \mathbf{v} \times \operatorname{curl} \mathbf{F}$.

We consider some important special cases:

(i) The particle is subject to an attraction to O, or a repulsion from O, of magnitude proportional to r,

$$V = \tfrac{1}{2}mkr^2 = \tfrac{1}{2}mk(x^2 + y^2 + z^2), \tag{10.6.11}$$

where $k > 0$ for attraction and $k < 0$ for repulsion; suppose that in addition there is a gyroscopic force $\mathbf{G} \times \mathbf{v}$, where $\mathbf{G}$ is constant (in magnitude and direction). In this case $\mathbf{F}$ is independent of t, and $\mathbf{G}(= -\operatorname{curl} \mathbf{F})$ is constant, and this happens if the components of $\mathbf{F}$ are linear functions of (x, y, z) with constant coefficients. In particular, if we make the simple choice

$$F = \{mpy, -mpx, 0\}, \tag{10.6.12}$$

then

$$G = -\operatorname{curl} F = \{0, 0, 2mp\}, \tag{10.6.13}$$

and the equations of motion are

$$\begin{cases} \ddot{x} + 2p\dot{y} + kx = 0, \\ \ddot{y} - 2p\dot{x} + ky = 0, \\ \ddot{z} \qquad\qquad + kz = 0. \end{cases} \tag{10.6.14}$$

The third equation is self-contained; we will assume that initially the particle moves in the plane $z = 0$, so that $z = \dot{z} = 0$ at $t = 0$, and then $z = 0$ always. The first two equations can be combined into a single equation in the complex variable $w = x + iy$,

$$\ddot{w} - 2ip\dot{w} + kw = 0. \tag{10.6.15}$$

This equation has already appeared twice, for $k > 0$ in (9.8.7), and for $k < 0$ in (9.9.14). The sign of k is important—there is an essential difference between the problems of attraction and of repulsion—but the sign of p is comparatively unimportant, since we get the same equation if we replace p by $-p$ and t by $-t$. The positive semi-characteristic (the path for positive values of t) in one problem is the same as the negative semi-characteristic (the path for negative values of t) for the problem with the sign of p reversed. To fix the ideas we suppose that $p > 0$.

The interesting case is that in which $p^2 + k > 0$. This is surely true for the case of attraction ($k > 0$), and it is true for the case of repulsion ($k < 0$) if $p^2 > |k|$; this is the condition for stability already noticed in § 9.9. We assume the condition is satisfied, and we write $p^2 + k = s^2$, $s > 0$. Then $s > p$ for $k > 0$, and $s < p$ for $k < 0$. The solution is

$$w = \frac{1}{2s}\{[(s - p)w_0 - iv_0]e^{i(s+p)t} + [(s + p)w_0 + iv_0]e^{-i(s-p)t}\}, \tag{10.6.16}$$

where w_0 is the value of w, and v_0 is the value of $\dot{w}$, at $t = 0$. Some examples of the motion represented by (10.6.16) have already been discussed and illustrated, for $k > 0$ in § 9.8 and for $k < 0$ in § 9.9.

(ii) We consider the motion of a charged particle in an electromagnetic field. The force on the particle arising from the action of the field is, using Gaussian units,

$$-e \operatorname{grad} \Omega - \frac{e}{c}\{\dot{\mathbf{A}} - v \times \operatorname{curl} \mathbf{A}\}, \tag{10.6.17}$$

where e is the charge carried by the particle, Ω is the scalar potential, and $\mathbf{A}$ the vector potential of the field. Now, as we have seen (equation (10.6.10)), a term $\mathbf{F} \cdot \mathbf{v}$ in L gives a force

$$-\dot{\mathbf{F}} + \mathbf{v} \times \operatorname{curl} \mathbf{F}$$

acting on the particle. We can therefore take account of the electromagnetic field by adding the terms

$$-e\Omega + \frac{e}{c}(\mathbf{A} \cdot \mathbf{v}) \tag{10.6.18}$$

in L.

Example 10.6*A*. *Larmor's theorem.* We consider a massive charged particle moving in a mechanical field and an electrostatic field each of which has axial symmetry about Oz. How is the motion modified if we superpose a weak uniform magnetic field γ in the direction Oz? Here

$$\mathbf{A} = \tfrac{1}{2}\gamma\{-y, x, 0\}, \tag{10.6.19}$$

and

$$L = \tfrac{1}{2}m(\dot{x}^2 + \dot{y}^2 + \dot{z}^2) + \tfrac{1}{2}\frac{e\gamma}{c}(x\dot{y} - y\dot{x}) - V - e\Omega, \tag{10.6.20}$$

where V and Ω are functions of $x^2 + y^2$ and z. Let us compare (10.6.20) with the Lagrangian function (§ 6.7) with the same mechanical and electrostatic fields, but without the magnetic field, for motion relative to axes rotating about Oz with angular velocity ω. We have

(10.6.21) $L = \frac{1}{2}m(\dot{x}^2 + \dot{y}^2 + \dot{z}^2) + m\omega(x\dot{y} - y\dot{x}) - V - e\Omega + \frac{1}{2}m(x^2 + y^2)\omega^2.$

If we take

$$\omega = e\gamma/2mc$$

and if ω is so small that the ω^2-term in (10.6.21) may be neglected, the two forms (10.6.20) and (10.6.21) are the same. The motion in space with the field γ is the same as the motion relative to the rotating frame without the field γ. *The effect of the superposition of a weak uniform magnetic field along Oz on the given mechanical and electrostatic fields is to impose a rotation $-\omega$ on the original motion.* This theorem is due to Larmor. If e is negative we get a right-handed rotation about the axis of symmetry.

Example 10.6*B*. *Crossed fields.* A charged particle moves under the action of static uniform electric and magnetic fields at right angles to one another. To find the path, assuming that the particle starts from rest.

Let the charge be $-\varepsilon$ (so that ε is positive if the charged particle is an electron), the electric field $\{-E, 0, 0\}$, the magnetic field $\{0, 0, \gamma\}$. Then

(10.6.22) $$L = \frac{1}{2}m(\dot{x}^2 + \dot{y}^2 + \dot{z}^2) - \frac{1}{2}\frac{\varepsilon\gamma}{c}(x\dot{y} - y\dot{x}) + \varepsilon Ex,$$

or say

(10.6.23) $$L = \frac{1}{2}(\dot{x}^2 + \dot{y}^2 + \dot{z}^2) - \frac{1}{2}k(x\dot{y} - y\dot{x}) + gx,$$

where $k = \varepsilon\gamma/mc$, $g = \varepsilon E/m$. The equations of motion are

(10.6.24) $$\ddot{x} = g - k\dot{y}, \qquad \ddot{y} = k\dot{x}, \qquad \ddot{z} = 0.$$

If the particle starts from rest at the origin at $t = 0$, $z = 0$ always, and the motion in the plane $z = 0$ satisfies the equation

(10.6.25) $$\ddot{w} = g + ik\dot{w},$$

where $w = x + iy$. The solution with $w = \dot{w} = 0$ at $t = 0$, is

(10.6.26) $$w = \frac{g}{k^2}(1 - e^{ikt}) + i\frac{g}{k^2}(kt).$$

The path is the cycloid

(10.6.27) $$x = \lambda(1 - \cos\theta), \qquad y = \lambda(\theta - \sin\theta),$$

where

$$\lambda = \frac{g}{k^2} = \frac{mEc^2}{\varepsilon\gamma^2},$$

and $\theta = kt = (\varepsilon\gamma/mc)t$. The cycloid has a line of cusps on Oy, and the greatest distance from Oy during the motion is

(10.6.28) $$2\lambda = 2mEc^2/\varepsilon\gamma^2.$$

10.7 Motion relative to a moving base. For a natural system the relations between x's and q's do not involve t (where as usual the x's are coordinates of the particles referred to a fixed rectangular trihedral, i.e. a trihedral fixed in a Newtonian base). We now consider more particularly some problems in which the relations between x's and q's involve t. This will happen, with a simple and natural choice of Lagrangian coordinates, if the system contains a part with inexorable motion, or if we use moving axes, and if the q's are so chosen that the coordinates x' of the particles relative to the moving axes are functions of the q's alone. A conspicuous example occurs when the moving axes are fixed in a rigid body which has prescribed motion.

Consider then the motion of a system relative to a frame of reference F' whose motion relative to the "fixed" frame F (i.e. F is a Newtonian base) is prescribed. The frame F' is defined by a trihedral attached to a rigid body whose motion in F is inexorable. We have already considered one simple case in § 6.7.

Let $\{u, v, w\}$ denote the velocity of the origin O' of the moving trihedral, $\{\theta_1, \theta_2, \theta_3\}$ the angular velocity of the trihedral relative to F, each resolved along the instantaneous directions of the moving axes. Then

(10.7.1) $$2T = Sm\{(u + \dot{x} - y\theta_3 + z\theta_2)^2 + \cdots + \cdots\},$$

where now we use x, y, z (instead of x', y', z') as coordinates relative to the moving axes. Thus

(10.7.2)
$$\begin{aligned}2T &= Sm(\dot{x}^2 + \dot{y}^2 + \dot{z}^2) + Sm(u^2 + v^2 + w^2) + Sm\{(y\theta_3 - z\theta_2)^2 + \cdots + \cdots\} \\ &\quad + 2Sm\{u(\dot{x} - y\theta_3 + z\theta_2) + \cdots + \cdots\} + 2Sm\{\dot{x}(-y\theta_3 + z\theta_2) + \cdots + \cdots\},\end{aligned}$$

and we recall that in this formula $u, v, w, \theta_1, \theta_2, \theta_3$ are known functions of t. The reduction of (10.7.2) to a manageable form is less formidable than appears at first sight; we consider the various terms separately as follows.

The term

(10.7.3) $$Sm(\dot{x}^2 + \dot{y}^2 + \dot{z}^2),$$

which we denote by $2\mathfrak{T}$ is twice the *apparent kinetic energy* of the motion relative to F', i.e. $\mathfrak{T}$ is the kinetic energy as estimated by an observer in the base F' who thinks of F' as fixed.

The term

(10.7.4) $$Sm(u^2 + v^2 + w^2) = M(u^2 + v^2 + w^2) = MU^2,$$

where $M(= Sm)$ is the mass of the whole system, and $U(= |\mathbf{U}|)$ is the speed of O'.

The term

(10.7.5) $$Sm\{(y\theta_3 - z\theta_2)^2 + (z\theta_1 - x\theta_3)^2 + (x\theta_2 - y\theta_1)^2\}$$

is equal to $I\omega^2$, where $\boldsymbol{\omega}$ is the angular velocity $(\theta_1, \theta_2, \theta_3)$ of F', $\omega = |\boldsymbol{\omega}|$, and I is the moment of inertia at the instant considered of the whole system about a line through O' in the direction of $\boldsymbol{\omega}$.

The term

(10.7.6)
$$\begin{aligned}Sm\{u(\dot{x} - y\theta_3 + z\theta_2) + \cdots + \cdots\} &= [uSm\dot{x} + (v\theta_3 - w\theta_2)Smx] + \cdots + \cdots \\ &= M[u\dot{\xi} + (v\theta_3 - w\theta_2)\xi] + \cdots + \cdots \\ &= M\frac{d}{dt}(u\xi + v\eta + w\zeta) - M\{\xi(\dot{u} - v\theta_3 + w\theta_2) + \eta(\dot{v} - w\theta_1 + u\theta_3) \\ &\quad + \zeta(\dot{w} - u\theta_2 + v\theta_1)\} \\ &= M\frac{d}{dt}(\mathbf{R}\,.\,\mathbf{U}) - M(\mathbf{R}\,.\,\mathbf{f}),\end{aligned}$$

where ξ, η, ζ are coordinates of the centre of mass G of the system, $\mathbf{R}$ is the vector $\{\xi, \eta, \zeta\}$, $\mathbf{U}$ is the velocity of O' (i.e. the vector $\{u, v, w\}$), and $\mathbf{f}$ is the acceleration of O'. All these vectors $\mathbf{R}$, $\mathbf{U}$, $\mathbf{f}$ are measured relative to a fixed trihedral coincident with the instantaneous position of the moving trihedral.

The term

$$(10.7.7) \qquad Sm\{\dot{x}(-y\theta_3 + z\theta_2) + \cdots + \cdots\} = \theta_1 Sm(y\dot{z} - z\dot{y}) + \cdots + \cdots$$
$$= \theta_1\eta_1' + \theta_2\eta_2' + \theta_3\eta_3' = (\boldsymbol{\omega} \cdot \boldsymbol{\eta}'),$$

where η_1' η_2', η_3' are the components of $\boldsymbol{\eta}'$, the *apparent angular momentum*, i.e. $\boldsymbol{\eta}'$ is the angular momentum as estimated by an observer in the base F' who thinks of F' as fixed.

Collecting the terms we find

$$(10.7.8) \qquad T = \mathfrak{T} + \tfrac{1}{2}MU^2 + \tfrac{1}{2}I\omega^2 + M\frac{d}{dt}(\mathbf{R} \cdot \mathbf{U}) - M(\mathbf{R} \cdot \mathbf{f}) + (\boldsymbol{\omega} \cdot \boldsymbol{\eta}').$$

When we form the Lagrangian function the term $\frac{1}{2}MU^2$ may be omitted, and so may the term $M\dfrac{d}{dt}(\mathbf{R} \cdot \mathbf{U})$, which is of the form (6.8.6), so finally

$$(10.7.9) \qquad L = \mathfrak{T} + (\boldsymbol{\omega} \cdot \boldsymbol{\eta}') - V',$$

and

$$(10.7.10) \qquad V' = V + M(\mathbf{R} \cdot \mathbf{f}) - \tfrac{1}{2}I\omega^2,$$

where V is the potential energy function. The case in which we are primarily interested is that in which V is a function of the configuration of the system relative to F'.

We now introduce Lagrangian coordinates $q_1, q_2, \ldots, q_n$, where n is the number of degrees of freedom of the holonomic system for motion relative to F'; the q's are such that the relations between x's and q's do not involve t. Then $\mathfrak{T}$ becomes a positive definite quadratic form in the $\dot{q}$'s, and $(\boldsymbol{\omega} \cdot \boldsymbol{\eta}')$ becomes a homogeneous linear form in the $\dot{q}$'s; the coefficients in this linear form will, in the general case, involve t as well as the q's.

We can now see what is the effect of the motion of the frame of reference on the motion of the system as it appears to an observer who thinks of the frame of reference as fixed. The effect is threefold:

(a) a force $-M\mathbf{f}$ through G,

(b) centrifugal forces arising from the apparent potential function $-\frac{1}{2}I\omega^2$ added to V,

(c) forces arising from the term $(\boldsymbol{\omega} \cdot \boldsymbol{\eta}')$ in L; if t does not appear in $(\boldsymbol{\omega} \cdot \boldsymbol{\eta}')$ these are gyroscopic forces.

Some special cases are worthy of notice:

(i) If $\boldsymbol{\omega} = 0$ and $\mathbf{f} = 0$ the motion of the frame has no effect on the equations of motion. This phenomenon is familiar. A base moving uniformly and without rotation relative to a Newtonian base is itself a Newtonian base. This principle is sometimes referred to as *the Newtonian principle of relativity*.

(ii) If $\boldsymbol{\omega} = 0$ the only effect of the motion of the frame is a uniform field $-\mathbf{f}$, which is equivalent to a force $-M\mathbf{f}$ through G. In particular we have a well-known theorem concerning the motion of a rigid body. *If one point of a rigid body is seized and moved inexorably, the motion of the body relative to the seized point is the same as if this point were fixed and a force* $-M\mathbf{f}$ *acted at G in addition to the given forces.*

(iii) If $\mathbf{f} = 0$ we have the centrifugal and gyroscopic forces. The special case when $\boldsymbol{\omega}$ is constant has been considered already (§ 6.7). The gyroscopic forces do not appear if $(\boldsymbol{\omega} \cdot \boldsymbol{\eta}')$ is a perfect differential $\dfrac{d}{dt}f(\mathbf{q};\ t)$; this will always be the case if there is only one degree of freedom. The gyroscopic forces are absent also if $\boldsymbol{\eta}'$ is throughout the motion perpendicular to $\boldsymbol{\omega}$. In these cases the effect of the rotation is represented completely by the centrifugal forces.

(iv) *The theorem of Coriolis.* If the system contains only one particle, which we will suppose for convenience to have unit mass, we have effectively

$$(10.7.11)\quad T = \tfrac{1}{2}(\dot{x}^2 + \dot{y}^2 + \dot{z}^2) + \{\theta_1(y\dot{z} - z\dot{y}) + \theta_2(z\dot{x} - x\dot{z}) + \theta_3(x\dot{y} - y\dot{x})\}$$
$$- (\alpha x + \beta y + \gamma z) + \tfrac{1}{2}\{(y\theta_3 - z\theta_2)^2 + (z\theta_1 - x\theta_3)^2 + (x\theta_2 - y\theta_1)^2\},$$

where α, β, γ are the components of $\mathbf{f}$. The x-component of acceleration is

$$(10.7.12)\qquad \frac{d}{dt}\left(\frac{\partial T}{\partial \dot{x}}\right) - \frac{\partial T}{\partial x} = \ddot{x} - 2(\dot{y}\theta_3 - \dot{z}\theta_2) + \varphi_1,$$

where

$$(10.7.13)\qquad \varphi_1 = \alpha - y\dot{\theta}_3 + z\dot{\theta}_2 - x\omega^2 + \theta_1(\mathbf{r} \cdot \boldsymbol{\omega}).$$

Now φ_1 is the x-component of acceleration of a point fixed relative to the moving axes, so we have the following result. The acceleration of the moving particle is the vector sum of three terms, (1) the acceleration of a point (at the place occupied by the particle) fixed relative to the moving axes, (2) the acceleration $\ddot{\mathbf{r}}$ relative to the moving axes, (3) the *gyroscopic term* $-2\dot{\mathbf{r}} \times \boldsymbol{\omega}$.

This is the *theorem of Coriolis.* The crucial point is the gyroscopic term; there is no analogue of this term in the corresponding theorem for the velocity of the moving particle. We have deduced the theorem as an illustration of the general theory of motion relative to a moving base, but it can of course be proved easily from the moving axes formulae without first establishing the general theory.

10.8 Motion of a particle near a given point on the Earth's surface. We observe first that the motion of the particle relative to the Earth is not affected by an external uniform field, i.e. by forces, acting both on the Earth and on the particle, which are parallel at each instant (though the direction may vary with the time) and proportional to the masses. We can therefore, to a high degree of accuracy, ignore the gravitational effect of distant masses. We shall ignore the small deviation of the Earth's shape from that of a sphere, and we shall suppose also that the density-distribution has spherical symmetry, so that the external field is the same as the field of a single particle at the centre. In the study of the relative motion we may, if we wish, think of the Earth's centre C as being at rest.

We denote the latitude of the given point O on the Earth's surface by λ. We might take axes with Oz along the Earth's radius, Ox (say) to the south, and Oy to the east. But it will be convenient to tilt the axes a little about Oy, so that Oz is (upwards) along the plumb line, in the line of apparent gravity. Then Oz lies in the meridian plane, and makes with the normal to the Earth's axis an angle $\theta = \lambda + \beta$, where β

is the small deviation of the plumb-line from the true vertical. For London, with $\lambda = 51^\circ\ 30'$, the value of β is about $6'$. The plane $z = 0$ is not quite the horizontal plane (i.e. the tangent plane to the sphere) but the deviation is slight for points near to O (Fig 10.8).

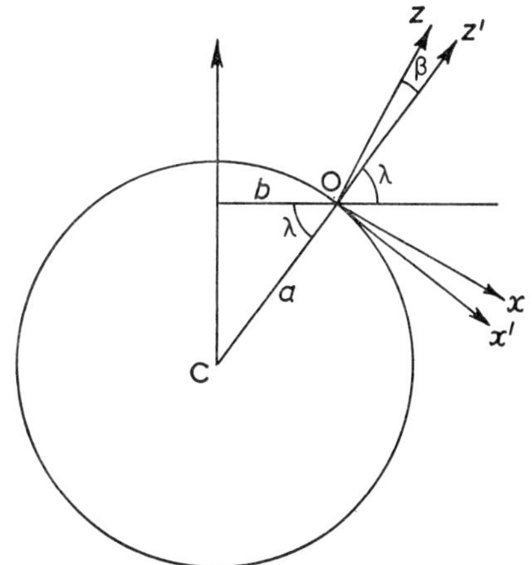

Figure 10.8

If the Earth's angular velocity is $\boldsymbol{\omega}$, assumed uniform, we have

$$L = \mathfrak{T} + (\boldsymbol{\omega}\,.\,\boldsymbol{\eta}') - V', \tag{10.8.1}$$

and, taking the mass of the particle to be unity, this is equivalent to

$$L = \tfrac{1}{2}(\dot{x}^2 + \dot{y}^2 + \dot{z}^2) - \omega\cos\theta(y\dot{z} - z\dot{y}) + \omega\sin\theta(x\dot{y} - y\dot{x}) - V',$$

where $\omega = |\boldsymbol{\omega}|$, and

$$V' = V + M(\mathbf{R}\,.\,\mathbf{f}) - \tfrac{1}{2}I\omega^2,$$

and $\mathbf{R}$ is the vector $\{x, y, z\}$. Now V' is the potential function of apparent gravity. To a first approximation $V' = gz$, and g is the acceleration due to gravity as measured by an observer in the base F'. The approximation $V' = gz$ is adequate in the problem of Foucault's pendulum (for example) where the scale of the motion is small, and the vertical motion is still smaller. We recall that ω is small (about 7.27×10^{-5} sec^{-1}.).

10.9 Foucault's pendulum. The experiment exhibits the rotation of the Earth by a study of the turning, relative to the Earth, of the plane of swing of a simple pendulum. A particle is attached to a fixed point of the laboratory by a light string of length l. Taking the equilibrium position of the particle as origin we have, to a good approximation,

$$V' = gz = \frac{g}{2l}(x^2 + y^2), \tag{10.9.1}$$

and neglecting the small terms $\dot{z}^2$, ωz, $\omega\dot{z}$ in L we find the approximation

$$L = \tfrac{1}{2}(\dot{x}^2 + \dot{y}^2) + p(x\dot{y} - y\dot{x}) - \tfrac{1}{2}n^2(x^2 + y^2), \tag{10.9.2}$$

where $p = \omega\sin\theta$, $n^2 = g/l$. We notice that there is now no obligation to adhere to the original axes for x and y; we may twist the axes about Oz into any convenient position without altering the form of L.

The equations of motion are

$$\begin{cases} \ddot{x} - 2p\dot{y} + n^2x = 0, \\ \ddot{y} + 2p\dot{x} + n^2y = 0, \end{cases} \tag{10.9.3}$$

which we can write in the form

$$\ddot{w} + 2ip\dot{w} + n^2w = 0, \tag{10.9.4}$$

where $w = x + iy$. The equation (10.9.4) is similar to the equation for the motion of the axis of Foucault's gyroscope (§ 9.8), though the sign of the coefficient of $\dot{w}$ is opposite to that in (9.8.7). And a similar equation has appeared in § 10.6. Let us consider the motion that ensues if the pendulum is released from rest, so that $w = a$ and $\dot{w} = 0$ at $t = 0$, where a is real and positive. The solution is

(10.9.5) $$w = \frac{a}{2s}\{(s + p)e^{i(s-p)t} + (s - p)e^{-i(s+p)t}\},$$

where

(10.9.6) $$s^2 = n^2 + p^2.$$

The path (Fig. 10.9) is the hypocycloid

(10.9.7) $$w = (a - b)e^{ib\theta} + be^{-i(a-b)\theta},$$

where

(10.9.8) $$b = \frac{s - p}{2s}a, \qquad \theta = \frac{2s}{a}t.$$

Since p is small, b is only slightly less than $\frac{1}{2}a$, and the successive arcs of the hypocycloid are nearly straight.

The time for a complete to-and-fro swing is $2\pi/s$, slightly smaller than the value $2\pi/n$ obtained when there is no rotation. The value of w at this time $2\pi/s$ is (from (10.9.5)) $ae^{-i(2\pi p/s)}$, so the plane of swing has turned in the negative sense through an angle $2\pi p/s$. Thus the plane of swing rotates clockwise with average angular velocity p.

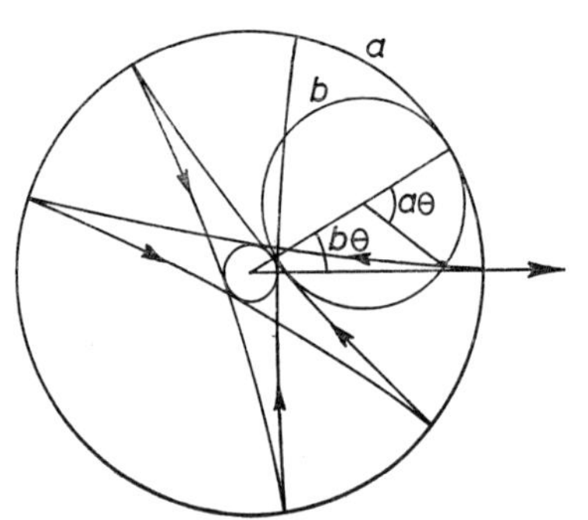

Figure 10.9

We can write (10.9.5) in the form

(10.9.9) $$w = e^{-ipt}\zeta,$$

where

(10.9.10) $$\zeta = a\cos st + i\frac{p}{s}a\sin st,$$

and the path of ζ is an elongated ellipse, with major semi-axis a, and minor semi-axis $(p/s)a$, which is small in comparison with a. The path of w can therefore be described as a revolving ellipse; but this description "hardly conveys a very clear idea of a hypocycloid."

10.10 Projectiles. In the discussion of Foucault's pendulum we had no hesitation in writing gz for V', since the variation in z in that problem is small. The same formula, $V' = gz$, will also provide an approximation in problems where the scale of motion is larger, for example in the theory of projectiles. But here the validity of the approximation is more doubtful, and it will be of interest to consider also a closer approximation. Let us consider the magnitude of the various terms that have been neglected in the first approximation, and see which are the important ones when we need a higher degree of accuracy. We suppose, as before, that the Earth is a sphere rotating with uniform angular velocity ω, and we may suppose that its centre is at rest; as we have noticed already, ω is small (about $7{\cdot}27 \times 10^{-5}\,\text{sec}^{-1}$). We have (§ 10.7)

(10.10.1) $$L = \mathfrak{T} + (\boldsymbol{\omega} \,.\, \boldsymbol{\eta}') - V',$$

where

(10.10.2) $$V' = V + (\mathbf{R} \,.\, \mathbf{f}) - \tfrac{1}{2}I\omega^2,$$

and we will suppose for convenience that the projectile has unit mass. We use the notation of Fig. 10.8, with Oz' along the Earth's radius, and we denote by r the distance of the particle from the Earth's centre C, and by ρ $(= |\mathbf{R}|)$ its distance from O. Then

$$V = -\frac{\mu}{r} = -\frac{\mu}{a}\left(1 + \frac{2z'}{a} + \frac{\rho^2}{a^2}\right)^{-1/2} \tag{10.10.3}$$

$$= -\frac{\mu}{a}\left\{1 - \frac{z'}{a} + \frac{1}{2a^2}(3z'^2 - \rho^2) - \frac{1}{2a^3}(5z'^3 - 3\rho^2 z') + O\left(\frac{\rho^4}{a^4}\right)\right\}.$$

The terms $-V - (\mathbf{R} \,.\, \mathbf{f})$ therefore contribute to L

$$b\omega^2(x' \sin\lambda + z'\cos\lambda) - G\left\{z' - \frac{1}{2a}(3z'^2 - \rho^2) + \frac{1}{2a^2}(5z'^3 - 3\rho^2 z')\right\} \tag{10.10.4}$$

$$= \{-(G - b\omega^2\cos\lambda)z' + b\omega^2 \sin\lambda\, x'\}$$

$$+ \frac{G}{2a}(3z'^2 - \rho^2) - \frac{G}{2a^2}(5z'^3 - 3\rho^2 z'),$$

where $b = a\cos\lambda$, $G = \mu/a^2$, and terms of order $G\rho^4/a^3$ have been neglected.

The linear terms in (10.10.4) are of course equal to $-gz$, where Oz is taken along the plumb-line as before, and

$$\tan\beta = \frac{b\omega^2 \sin\lambda}{G - b\omega^2\cos\lambda}, \tag{10.10.5}$$

$$G = g\cos\beta + b\omega^2\cos\lambda = g(1 + \varepsilon), \text{ say}, \tag{10.10.6}$$

where

$$\varepsilon = (a\omega^2/g)\cos^2\lambda - (1 - \cos\beta) \tag{10.10.7}$$

$$= \cot\lambda \sin\beta - 1 + \cos\beta,$$

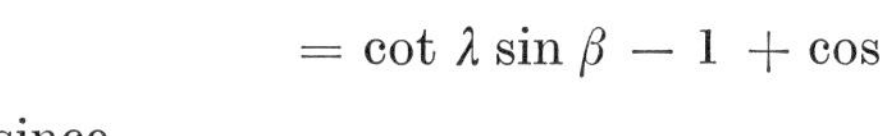

since

$$\sin\beta = (a\omega^2/g)\cos\lambda \sin\lambda. \tag{10.10.8}$$

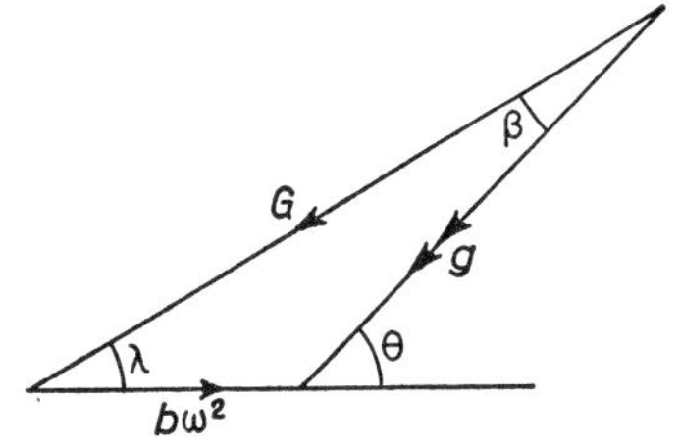

Figure 10.10

Thus a good approximation to the value of ε, correct to order β, is

$$\varepsilon = \beta\cot\lambda, \tag{10.10.9}$$

so that β and ε, *qua* functions of ω, are of the same order of smallness. The relation between the small quantities $b\omega^2$ and β is illustrated in Fig. 10.10.

The quadratic terms in (10.10.4), changing now to the axes $Oxyz$, are

$$\frac{G}{2a}(3z'^2 - \rho^2) = \frac{G}{2a}\{3(z\cos\beta + x\sin\beta)^2 - x^2 - y^2 - z^2\} \tag{10.10.10}$$

$$= \frac{G}{2a}\left\{\frac{3}{1 + \zeta^2}(z + \zeta x)^2 - x^2 - y^2 - z^2\right\},$$

where $\zeta = \tan\beta$, and this can be written in the form

$$\frac{g}{2a}(1 + \varepsilon)\left\{2z^2 - x^2 - y^2 + \frac{3}{1 + \zeta^2}[2\zeta zx + \zeta^2(x^2 - z^2)]\right\}. \tag{10.10.11}$$

We now neglect second-order terms in ε, ζ and obtain

$$\frac{g}{2a}(2z^2 - x^2 - y^2) + \frac{g}{2a}\{\varepsilon(2z^2 - x^2 - y^2) + 6\zeta zx\}. \tag{10.10.12}$$

The third-order terms are unchanged, to a sufficient degree of accuracy, by the change of axes, giving

$$-\frac{g}{2a^2}(2z^3 - 3x^2z - 3y^2z). \tag{10.10.13}$$

Thus finally, collecting the terms, we have

$$\begin{aligned} L = {} & \tfrac{1}{2}(\dot{x}^2 + \dot{y}^2 + \dot{z}^2) - \omega\cos\theta(y\dot{z} - z\dot{y}) + \omega\sin\theta(x\dot{y} - y\dot{x}) \\ & - gz + \frac{g}{2a}(2z^2 - x^2 - y^2) + \tfrac{1}{2}\omega^2y^2 + \tfrac{1}{2}\omega^2(z\cos\theta + x\sin\theta)^2 \\ & + \frac{g}{2a}\{\varepsilon(2z^2 - x^2 - y^2) + 6\zeta zx\} - \frac{g}{2a^2}(2z^3 - 3x^2z - 3y^2z). \end{aligned} \tag{10.10.14}$$

The equations of motion derived from (10.10.14) are

$$\left\{\begin{aligned} \ddot{x} - 2\omega\sin\theta\,\dot{y} &= -\frac{g}{a}x + \omega^2\sin\theta(x\sin\theta + z\cos\theta) - \frac{g}{a}\varepsilon x \\ &\qquad + \frac{3g}{a}\zeta z + \frac{3g}{a^2}zx, \\ \ddot{y} + 2\omega\sin\theta\,\dot{x} + 2\omega\cos\theta\,\dot{z} &= -\frac{g}{a}y + \omega^2 y - \frac{g}{a}\varepsilon y + \frac{3g}{a^2}yz, \\ \ddot{z} - 2\omega\cos\theta\,\dot{y} &= -g + \frac{2g}{a}z + \omega^2\cos\theta(x\sin\theta + z\cos\theta) \\ &\qquad + \frac{g}{a}(2\varepsilon z + 3\zeta x) - \frac{3g}{2a^2}(2z^2 - x^2 - y^2). \end{aligned}\right. \tag{10.10.15}$$

The equations are of theoretical rather than of practical interest, since they refer to motion in a vacuum; for motion in air the effect of air-resistance far outweighs the effects of the small terms here introduced.

(i) A first approximation, ignoring both the rotation of the Earth and the deviation of the gravitational field from a uniform field, gives the elementary theory of projectiles. The equations are

$$\ddot{x} = \ddot{y} = 0, \quad \ddot{z} = -g, \tag{10.10.16}$$

and the solution, if the particle is projected from the origin with velocity (u_0, v_0, w_0) at $t = 0$, is

$$x = u_0t, \quad y = v_0t, \quad z = w_0t - \tfrac{1}{2}gt^2. \tag{10.10.17}$$

(ii) A second approximation includes terms of order ω, and neglects the other small terms, giving

$$\ddot{x} - 2\omega\sin\theta\,\dot{y} = 0, \tag{10.10.18}$$

$$\ddot{y} + 2\omega\sin\theta\,\dot{x} + 2\omega\cos\theta\,\dot{z} = 0, \tag{10.10.19}$$

$$\ddot{z} - 2\omega\cos\theta\,\dot{y} = -g. \tag{10.10.20}$$

This is the classical approximation for motion relative to the rotating Earth. The integration of the equations (10.10.18–20) is simple; but we must remember that the equations themselves are only approximately true, and the solution will only provide a representation of the motion correct to order ω.

Another point may be noticed before we attack the problem of integration. The form of the equations suggests the use of τ $(= \omega t)$ as the independent variable, instead of t. If we do so, the symbol ω disappears from the equations, except in the expression g/ω^2. The solution will express each of x, y, z as a function of τ $(= \omega t)$, and the formulae will contain as linear multipliers the parameters U_0, V_0, W_0, Γ $(= u_0/\omega,\ v_0/\omega,\ w_0/\omega,\ g/\omega^2)$. The variable ωt is dimensionless, and each of the parameters U_0, V_0, W_0, Γ has the dimensions of a length.

We now turn to the solution of the equations (10.10.18–20). From (10.10.18) and (10.10.20) we have

(10.10.21) $$\dot{x} = u_0 + 2\omega y \sin\theta, \quad \dot{z} = w_0 - gt + 2\omega y \cos\theta.$$

We substitute these values of $\dot{x}$ and $\dot{z}$ in (10.10.19), and so obtain the differential equation for y,

(10.10.22) $$\ddot{y} + 4\omega^2 y = -2\omega(u_0 \sin\theta + w_0 \cos\theta) + (2g\omega\cos\theta)t,$$

whence

(10.10.23) $$y = \frac{v_0}{2\omega}\sin 2\omega t - \frac{1}{2}\left(\frac{u_0}{\omega}\sin\theta + \frac{w_0}{\omega}\cos\theta\right)(1 - \cos 2\omega t) + \frac{g}{4\omega^2}\cos\theta(2\omega t - \sin 2\omega t).$$

We now substitute this value for y in (10.10.21), and integrate. The complete solution, written in terms of ωt, is

(10.10.24) $$\begin{cases} x = \dfrac{u_0}{\omega}(\omega t) + \sin\theta\left\{\dfrac{1}{2}\dfrac{v_0}{\omega}P - \dfrac{1}{2}\left(\dfrac{u_0}{\omega}\sin\theta + \dfrac{w_0}{\omega}\cos\theta\right)Q - \dfrac{1}{4}\dfrac{g}{\omega^2}\cos\theta R\right\}, \\ y = \dfrac{1}{2}\dfrac{v_0}{\omega}\sin 2\omega t - \dfrac{1}{2}\left(\dfrac{u_0}{\omega}\sin\theta + \dfrac{w_0}{\omega}\cos\theta\right)P + \dfrac{1}{4}\dfrac{g}{\omega^2}\cos\theta\, Q, \\ z = \dfrac{w_0}{\omega}(\omega t) - \dfrac{1}{2}\dfrac{g}{\omega^2}(\omega t)^2 + \cos\theta\left\{\dfrac{1}{2}\dfrac{v_0}{\omega}P - \dfrac{1}{2}\left(\dfrac{u_0}{\omega}\sin\theta + \dfrac{w_0}{\omega}\cos\theta\right)Q \right. \\ \qquad\qquad \left. - \dfrac{1}{4}\dfrac{g}{\omega^2}\cos\theta R\right\}, \end{cases}$$

where

(10.10.25) $$P = 1 - \cos 2\omega t, \quad Q = 2\omega t - \sin 2\omega t, \quad R = 1 - \cos 2\omega t - \tfrac{1}{2}(2\omega t)^2.$$

The leading terms in P, Q, R are $2(\omega t)^2$, $\frac{4}{3}(\omega t)^3$, $-\frac{2}{3}(\omega t)^4$ respectively.

If u_0, v_0, w_0 are not all zero, we obtain a solution more accurate than (10.10.17) by including terms of order ω, and neglecting terms of higher order,

(10.10.26) $$\begin{cases} x = u_0 t + (v_0 \sin\theta)\omega t^2, \\ y = v_0 t - (u_0 \sin\theta + w_0 \cos\theta)\omega t^2 + \frac{1}{3}(g\cos\theta)\omega t^3, \\ z = w_0 t - \frac{1}{2}gt^2 + (v_0\cos\theta)\omega t^2. \end{cases}$$

This gives an approximation sufficiently accurate for most purposes for reasonably small values of t. We can also write the solution in terms of τ, in the form

(10.10.27) $$\begin{cases} x = U_0\tau + V_0\tau^2\sin\theta, \\ y = V_0\tau - (U_0\sin\theta + W_0\cos\theta)\tau^2 + \frac{1}{3}\Gamma\tau^3\cos\theta, \\ z = W_0\tau + (V_0\cos\theta - \frac{1}{2}\Gamma)\tau^2. \end{cases}$$

Another method of finding the solution (10.10.26), which is correct to order ω, may be of interest. The equation of motion, expressed in vector notation, has the form

(10.10.28) $$\ddot{\mathbf{r}} + 2\boldsymbol{\omega} \times \dot{\mathbf{r}} + \boldsymbol{\omega} \times (\boldsymbol{\omega} \times \mathbf{r}) = \mathbf{g}.$$

To find an approximation to the solution, correct to order ω, we proceed as follows. First, neglecting terms of order ω^2 in (10.10.28), we have

(10.10.29) $$\ddot{\mathbf{r}} + 2\boldsymbol{\omega} \times \dot{\mathbf{r}} = \mathbf{g},$$

and if $\mathbf{r} = \mathbf{0}$ and $\dot{\mathbf{r}} = \mathbf{u}$ when $t = 0$, this leads to

(10.10.30) $$\dot{\mathbf{r}} + 2\boldsymbol{\omega} \times \mathbf{r} = \mathbf{u} + \mathbf{g}t.$$

Now if we omit terms of order ω in (10.10.30) we find the first approximation

(10.10.31) $$\mathbf{r} = \mathbf{u}t + \tfrac{1}{2}\mathbf{g}t^2,$$

and to obtain the second approximation (which is the approximation that we require) we substitute this value for $\mathbf{r}$ in the small term in (10.10.30). Thus, correct to order ω, we have

(10.10.32) $$\dot{\mathbf{r}} = \mathbf{u} + \mathbf{g}t - 2\boldsymbol{\omega} \times (\mathbf{u}t + \tfrac{1}{2}\mathbf{g}t^2),$$

giving finally

(10.10.33) $$\mathbf{r} = \mathbf{u}t + \tfrac{1}{2}\mathbf{g}t^2 - (\boldsymbol{\omega} \times \mathbf{u})t^2 - (\boldsymbol{\omega} \times \mathbf{g})t^3/3.$$

Putting $\mathbf{u} = \{u_0, v_0, w_0\}$, $\mathbf{g} = \{0, 0, -g\}$, $\boldsymbol{\omega} = \{-\omega \cos\theta, 0, \omega \sin\theta\}$, (10.10.33) is equivalent to (10.10.26).

(iii) Next, if we include also the terms of order ω^2 in the equations (10.10.15), but neglect the terms arising from the variation of gravity, we have

(10.10.34) $$\begin{cases} \ddot{x} - 2\omega \sin\theta \dot{y} = \omega^2 \sin\theta(x \sin\theta + z \cos\theta), \\ \ddot{y} + 2\omega \sin\theta \dot{x} + 2\omega \cos\theta \dot{z} = \omega^2 y, \\ \ddot{z} - 2\omega \cos\theta \dot{y} = -g + \omega^2 \cos\theta(x \sin\theta + z \cos\theta). \end{cases}$$

To find the exact solution of these equations, with the given initial conditions, we proceed as follows. From the first and third equations we have

(10.10.35) $$\ddot{x} \cos\theta - \ddot{z} \sin\theta = g \sin\theta,$$

whence

(10.10.36) $$z = \cot\theta x - \tfrac{1}{2}gt^2 + At,$$

where A is written for $(w_0 - u_0 \cot\theta)$.

If we substitute for z and $\dot{z}$ from (10.10.36) in the first two equations of (10.10.34) we find

(10.10.37) $$\begin{cases} \ddot{x} - 2\omega \sin\theta \dot{y} - \omega^2 x = \omega^2 \cos\theta \sin\theta(-\tfrac{1}{2}gt^2 + At), \\ \sin\theta \ddot{y} + 2\omega \dot{x} - \omega^2 y \sin\theta = 2\omega \cos\theta \sin\theta(gt - A). \end{cases}$$

Hence, writing ξ for $x + i \sin\theta y$, we have

(10.10.38) $$\ddot{\xi} + 2i\omega\dot{\xi} = \omega^2\xi - \omega \cos\theta \sin\theta\{-\tfrac{1}{2}\omega g t^2 + A\omega t + 2i(gt - A)\}.$$

The solution, remembering that $\xi = 0$ and $\dot{\xi} = u_0 + i \sin\theta v_0$ at $t = 0$, is

(10.10.39) $$\xi = -\frac{g}{\omega^2} \cos\theta \sin\theta e^{-i\omega t} + \sin\theta\left\{(u_0 \sin\theta + w_0 \cos\theta) + i\left(v_0 - \frac{g}{\omega} \cos\theta\right)\right\}te^{-i\omega t} + \cos\theta \sin\theta\left\{\frac{g}{\omega^2} - (w_0 - u_0 \cot\theta)t + \tfrac{1}{2}gt^2\right\}.$$

We find the values of x and y at time t by taking real and imaginary parts, and then the value of z at time t follows from (10.10.36),

(10.10.40)

$$\begin{cases} x = \dfrac{g}{\omega^2}\cos\theta\sin\theta\,(1-\cos\omega t) + t\cos\theta\,(u_0\cos\theta - w_0\sin\theta) \\ \qquad + t\sin\theta\left\{(u_0\sin\theta + w_0\cos\theta)\cos\omega t + \left(v_0 - \dfrac{g}{\omega}\cos\theta\right)\sin\omega t\right\} + \tfrac{1}{2}(\cos\theta\sin\theta)gt^2, \\ y = \dfrac{g}{\omega^2}\cos\theta\sin\omega t + t\left\{-(u_0\sin\theta + w_0\cos\theta)\sin\omega t + \left(v_0 - \dfrac{g}{\omega^2}\cos\theta\right)\cos\omega t\right\}, \\ z = \dfrac{g}{\omega^2}\cos^2\theta(1-\cos\omega t) - t\sin\theta(u_0\cos\theta - w_0\sin\theta) \\ \qquad + t\cos\theta\left\{(u_0\sin\theta + w_0\cos\theta)\cos\omega t + \left(v_0 - \dfrac{g}{\omega}\cos\theta\right)\sin\omega t\right\} - \tfrac{1}{2}(\sin^2\theta)gt^2. \end{cases}$$

The formulae (10.10.40) provide the exact solution of the equations (10.10.34) with the given initial conditions. If we expand in powers of ω, and neglect terms of order ω^2, we recover the formulae (10.10.26); if we include terms of order ω^2, the terms additional to those in (10.10.26) are

for x, $\quad -\tfrac{1}{2}\sin\theta(u_0\sin\theta + w_0\cos\theta)\omega^2t^3 + \tfrac{1}{8}(g\cos\theta\sin\theta)\omega^2t^4,$

for y, $\quad -\tfrac{1}{2}v_0\omega^2t^3,$

for z, $\quad -\tfrac{1}{2}\cos\theta(u_0\sin\theta + w_0\cos\theta)\omega^2t^3 + \tfrac{1}{8}(g\cos^2\theta)\omega^2t^4.$

A case of particular interest is that in which the particle is released from rest (supposing now that the origin is *above* the Earth's surface) so that u_0, v_0, w_0 are all zero. The solution, correct to order ω^2, is

$$\begin{cases} x = \tfrac{1}{8}(g\cos\theta\sin\theta)\omega^2t^4 = \tfrac{1}{8}\Gamma\tau^4\cos\theta\sin\dot{\theta}, \\ y = \tfrac{1}{3}(g\cos\theta)\omega t^3 = \tfrac{1}{3}\Gamma\tau^3\cos\theta, \\ z = -\tfrac{1}{2}gt^2 + \tfrac{1}{8}(g\cos^2\theta)\omega^2t^4 = -\tfrac{1}{2}\Gamma\tau^2 + \tfrac{1}{8}\Gamma\tau^4\cos^2\theta. \end{cases} \tag{10.10.41}$$

As we expect, the most important deviation from the vertical is to the east; for since

$$\frac{x}{y} = \tfrac{3}{8}\omega t\sin\theta \tag{10.10.42}$$

the southerly deviation, up to the time when the particle strikes the ground, is comparatively small.

(iv) But in fact these results are of academic rather than of practical interest, because the terms arising from the variation of gravity (which we have neglected) are of more importance than the terms in ω^2 (which we have retained). Let us return to the equations (10.10.15) and consider the magnitude of the various terms that were omitted in (ii); which of these terms are the most significant for a closer approximation?

To answer this question, we must calculate the numerical values of the various coefficients. Considering more particularly the first equation and taking $\lambda = 51^\circ\,30'$

as before (so that $\beta = 6'$ approximately) we have

$$2\omega \sin \theta = 1{\cdot}14 \times 10^{-4}, \qquad \frac{g}{a} = 1{\cdot}54 \times 10^{-6},$$

$$\omega^2 \sin^2 \theta = 3{\cdot}25 \times 10^{-9}, \quad \omega^2 \cos \theta \sin \theta = 2{\cdot}57 \times 10^{-9},$$

$$\varepsilon \frac{g}{a} = 2{\cdot}05 \times 10^{-9}, \quad 3\zeta \frac{g}{a} = 7{\cdot}73 \times 10^{-9}.$$

As to the last term on the right (in the first equation of (10.10.15)) the coefficient of x is $\dfrac{3g}{a^2} z$, and even if z is as large as one mile, so that $\dfrac{z}{a} = \dfrac{1}{3955}$, the value of this coefficient is only about $1{\cdot}17 \times 10^{-9}$.

The upshot is that by far the most important term for a closer approximation is the first term in the second member, $-(g/a)x$; this term is more important than terms in ω^2, or terms containing ε or ζ, or terms of order $g(\rho/a)^2$. Similar remarks apply to the second and third of the equations (10.10.15). The equations for the third approximation to the projectile problem are therefore

(10.10.43)
$$\begin{cases} \ddot{x} - 2\omega \sin \theta \, \dot{y} = -n^2 x, \\ \ddot{y} + 2\omega \sin \theta \, \dot{x} + 2\omega \cos \theta \, \dot{z} = -n^2 y, \\ \ddot{z} - 2\omega \cos \theta \, \dot{y} = -g + 2n^2 z, \end{cases}$$

where $n^2 = g/a$.

10.11 Rayleigh's dissipation function. If there are given forces which are functions of velocity they may contribute to the terms Q_r in Lagrange's equations (6.2.1), or in certain cases where the forces are gyroscopic (e.g. a charged particle in a magnetic field, § 10.6) they may be taken into account by adding linear terms in L. We now turn to another class of problem involving forces depending on velocity; the forces are *resisting* or *dissipative* forces, i.e. the force on each particle is in the direction opposite to its velocity, and the theory is limited to the simple case in which the resistance is proportional to the speed. The typical equation of motion (2.2.12) is now modified to the form

(10.11.1)
$$m_r \ddot{x}_r = X_r + X_r' - k_r \dot{x}_r, \qquad r = 1, 2, \ldots, N,$$

where the coefficients k_r, like the coefficients m_r, have the same value for the three terms belonging to one particle, $k_{3r-2} = k_{3r-1} = k_{3r}$. The k's, like the m's, are positive, but the k's, unlike the m's, may depend on the x's as well as on r. Since in an arbitrary virtual displacement

(2.2.10)
$$\sum_{r=1}^{N} X_r' \, \delta x_r = 0,$$

the fundamental equation (3.1.1) now takes the form

(10.11.2)
$$\sum_{r=1}^{N} (m_r \ddot{x}_r - X_r) \, \delta x_r + \sum_{r=1}^{N} k_r \dot{x}_r \, \delta x_r = 0.$$

We suppose the system to be a holonomic system with n freedoms, and we introduce Lagrangian coordinates $q_1, q_2, \ldots, q_n$. We shall be content to consider only the simple case in which the x's are functions of the q's only, not of t, and in which the forces X_r (i.e. the given forces other than the dissipative forces) are conservative. The expression of the first term in (10.11.2) in terms of the Lagrangian coordinates is familiar (§ 6.1), and we have only to consider the second term $\sum^N_{=1} k_r\dot{x}_r\,\delta x_r$. Now

$$\delta x_r = \sum_{s=1}^n \frac{\partial x_r}{\partial q_s}\,\delta q_s = \sum_{s=1}^n \frac{\partial \dot{x}_r}{\partial \dot{q}_s}\,\delta q_s, \tag{10.11.3}$$

where we have quoted *Lemma 1* of § 6.1, so

$$\sum_{r=1}^N k_r\dot{x}_r\,\delta x_r = \sum_{s=1}^n \left(\sum_{r=1}^N k_r\dot{x}_r\frac{\partial \dot{x}_r}{\partial \dot{q}_s}\right)\delta q_s. \tag{10.11.4}$$

We are led therefore to introduce the function F, the *dissipation function* of Rayleigh, which is $\frac{1}{2}\sum_{r=1}^N k_r\dot{x}_r^2$ expressed in terms of q's and $\dot{q}$'s. The function F has some similarity to the kinetic energy function T: it is a homogeneous quadratic form in the $\dot{q}$'s with coefficients which are functions of the q's, and it is a positive definite form for all values of the q's. The equation (10.11.4) can be written

$$\sum_{r=1}^N k_r\dot{x}_r\,\delta x_r = \sum_{s=1}^n \frac{\partial F}{\partial \dot{q}_s}\,\delta q_s, \tag{10.11.5}$$

and the fundamental equation (10.11.2), transforming the first term as in § 6.1, becomes

$$\sum_{r=1}^n\left\{\frac{d}{dt}\left(\frac{\partial T}{\partial \dot{q}_r}\right) - \frac{\partial T}{\partial q_r} + \frac{\partial V}{\partial q_r} + \frac{\partial F}{\partial \dot{q}_r}\right\}\delta q_r = 0. \tag{10.11.6}$$

This holds for arbitrary values of the δq's, so we deduce the n equations of motion

$$\frac{d}{dt}\left(\frac{\partial T}{\partial \dot{q}_r}\right) - \frac{\partial T}{\partial q_r} = -\frac{\partial V}{\partial q_r} - \frac{\partial F}{\partial \dot{q}_r}, \qquad r = 1, 2, \ldots, n. \tag{10.11.7}$$

A physical interpretation of F is clear from the definition; the numerical value of F at any instant represents one-half the rate of loss of energy by friction. This interpretation is clear again from (10.11.7); if we multiply the rth equation by $\dot{q}_r$ and sum from $r = 1$ to $r = n$, we find (cf. § 6.7)

$$\frac{d}{dt}(T + V) = -\sum_{r=1}^n \dot{q}_r\frac{\partial F}{\partial \dot{q}_r} = -2F. \tag{10.11.8}$$

As an illustration, let us consider the effect on the small oscillations of a system about a position of stable equilibrium when dissipative forces of the type under discussion are introduced. The stability is enhanced by the dissipation, as is almost evident. We take the value of V to be zero at O as usual, so (since V has a minimum value at O) $V > 0$ near O except at O itself. If at $t = 0$ the energy $T + V$ has the value C, then, in virtue of (10.11.8), when $t > 0$, $T + V < C$; *a fortiori* $V < C$ when $t > 0$, and the equilibrium is stable.

But this is not the complete picture. In general the displacement tends to zero as $t \to \infty$, and the oscillation is damped out. When the displacement tends to zero we speak of *complete stability*, in contrast to ordinary *stability* where the displacement merely remains small (cf. § 9.9).

To prove that the introduction of dissipative forces converts stability into complete stability, consider for simplicity a system with two degrees of freedom. Let the normal coordinates for the undamped system be x, y, so that

$$T = \tfrac{1}{2}(\dot{x}^2 + \dot{y}^2), \quad V = \tfrac{1}{2}(p^2x^2 + q^2y^2). \tag{10.11.9}$$

Let us now introduce the dissipative forces derived from the dissipation function

$$F = \tfrac{1}{2}(A\dot{x}^2 + 2H\dot{x}\dot{y} + B\dot{y}^2), \tag{10.11.10}$$

where, to a sufficient order of approximation, A, H, B have their equilibrium values. The equations of motion are

$$\begin{cases} \ddot{x} + A\dot{x} + p^2x + H\dot{y} = 0, \\ \ddot{y} + B\dot{y} + q^2y + H\dot{x} = 0. \end{cases} \tag{10.11.11}$$

We notice that, if F is only semi-definite, the motion may not be completely stable; for example if $A = H = 0$ the x-motion persists as a harmonic oscillation. However, if F is positive definite, both x and y tend to zero as $t \to \infty$. For the solutions x and y of (10.11.11) are built up of multiples of $e^{\lambda_1 t}$, $e^{\lambda_2 t}$, $e^{\lambda_3 t}$, and $e^{\lambda_4 t}$, where λ_1, λ_2, λ_3, λ_4 are the roots of the quartic equation

$$(\lambda^2 + A\lambda + p^2)(\lambda^2 + B\lambda + q^2) - H^2\lambda^2 = 0, \tag{10.11.12}$$

and all the four roots of this equation have negative real parts. To prove this we observe that $f(z)$ (where $f(\lambda)$ denotes the first member of (10.11.12)) has no real and no pure-imaginary zeros, and that the variation in $am\ f(z)$ when z transverses a contour consisting of a segment of the positive real axis, an arc of a large circle in the positive quadrant, and a segment of the positive imaginary axis, is zero. Thus there is no root of the equation (10.11.12) in the positive quadrant. Now the coefficients in the equation are real, so the roots occur in conjugate pairs, and therefore there are no roots to the right of the imaginary axis. Thus all four roots lie to the left of the imaginary axis, and their real parts are all negative; and this completes the proof that both x and y tend to zero as t tends to infinity.

10.12 Gyroscopic system with dissipation. Consider a holonomic system with n degrees of freedom in which the first m Lagrangian coordinates $q_1, q_2, \ldots, q_m$ are ignorable, and suppose that there is dissipation of Rayleigh's type affecting only the palpable coordinates, so that

$$F = \sum_{r=m+1}^{n} \sum_{s=m+1}^{n} f_{rs}\dot{q}_r\dot{q}_s, \tag{10.12.1}$$

where the coefficients f_{rs} depend on $(q_{m+1}, q_{m+2}, \ldots, q_n)$. The first m Lagrangian equations yield

$$\frac{\partial L}{\partial \dot{q}_r} = \beta_r, \qquad r = 1, 2, \ldots, m, \tag{10.12.2}$$

as before, and we form the Routhian function, which is $L - \sum_{r=1}^{m} \beta_r\dot{q}_r$ expressed in terms of the arguments

$$q_{m+1}, q_{m+2}, \ldots q_n;\ \dot{q}_{m+1}, \dot{q}_{m+2}, \ldots, \dot{q}_n;\ \beta_1, \beta_2, \ldots, \beta_m,$$

as in § 10.1. In virtue of (10.11.7) the equations of motion in the palpable coordinates are

$$\frac{d}{dt}\left(\frac{\partial R}{\partial \dot{q}_r}\right) - \frac{\partial R}{\partial q_r} = -\frac{\partial F}{\partial \dot{q}_r}, \qquad r = m+1, m+2, \ldots, n. \tag{10.12.3}$$

An example of the situation envisaged here is provided by a system containing a gyroscope whose bearings are frictionless, though the motion of the frame in which the gyroscope is mounted is subject to frictional forces of Rayleigh's type.

Consider now a problem of gyroscopic stability; what is the effect of dissipation in the palpable coordinates? If V is a *minimum*, *qua* function of the palpable coordinates, in the position of apparent equilibrium, the stability is enhanced by the dissipation, as we should expect. Indeed in general there is complete stability so far as the motion in the palpable coordinates is concerned. But if V is a *maximum* the case is different. Even when, in the absence of dissipation, there is stability for sufficiently large values of β (§ 10.3) the introduction of dissipation induces instability.

To illustrate this theory, let us consider again the problem of the sleeping top (§ 9.9), and suppose now that there is a frictional couple $k\omega$ opposing the motion of the axis, and proportional to the angular velocity ω of the axis. We suppose that k is a constant, independent of position. We have a dissipation function F

(10.12.4) $$F = \tfrac{1}{2}k\omega^2 = \tfrac{1}{2}k(\dot{\theta}^2 + \sin^2\theta\dot{\varphi}^2),$$

or, to a sufficient order of approximation,

(10.12.5) $$F = \tfrac{1}{2}k(\dot{y}^2 + \dot{z}^2),$$

where we take the direction cosines of the axis to be $(1, y, z)$ as in § 9.9. We assume provisionally that y and z remain small, an assumption that will turn out in fact to be false. The equations of motion are (cf. (9.9.1))

(10.12.6) $$\begin{cases} \ddot{y} + 2p\dot{z} - qy = -2s\dot{y}, \\ \ddot{z} - 2p\dot{y} - qz = -2s\dot{z}, \end{cases}$$

where $2s = k/A > 0$. Writing $w = y + iz$ as before, we have

(10.12.7) $$\ddot{w} - 2i(p + is)\dot{w} - qw = 0.$$

Even if we assume rather more than before, namely $p^2 > q + s^2$ (instead of merely $p^2 > q$) the vertical position is unstable. The solution contains terms

(10.12.8) $$\exp i\{(p + is) \pm (\alpha + i\beta)\}t = \exp\{(-s \mp \beta) + i(p \pm \alpha)\}t,$$

where $\alpha > \beta > s > 0$, and one term contains the factor $e^{(\beta - s)t}$. The assumption, made provisionally, that the top remains near the upward vertical is falsified, and the vertical position is unstable. (As we have noticed, the linear approximation suffices to give definite evidence of instability, though in the opposite case, where $|w|$ remains small, the proof of stability derived from the linear approximation is incomplete.) The actual values of α and β are given by

(10.12.9) $$\begin{cases} 2\alpha^2 = \sqrt{\{(p^2 - q - s^2)^2 + 4p^2s^2\}} + (p^2 - q - s^2), \\ 2\beta^2 = \sqrt{\{(p^2 - q - s^2)^2 + 4p^2s^2\}} - (p^2 - q - s^2), \end{cases}$$

and

(10.12.10) $$2(\beta^2 - s^2) = \sqrt{\{(p^2 - q + s^2)^2 + 4qs^2\}} - (p^2 - q + s^2) > 0.$$

10.13 Hamilton's equations. We have noticed already (§ 6.4) that the n Lagrangian equations of the second order for a holonomic system can be replaced by $2n$ equations of the first order. These first-order equations have the form

(6.4.4) $$\dot{\mathrm{x}} = \mathbf{X},$$

where x and $\mathbf{X}$ are vectors (column matrices). The obvious way of achieving this end is to take as variables the n coordinates q_r and the n velocities ω_r $(= \dot{q}_r)$. But a far more convenient, and more important, form of first-order equations is obtained by taking as the variables the n coordinates q_r and the n momenta p_r (§ 6.10).

Let us suppose in the first instance that the system is a holonomic conservative system with n degrees of freedom. We write

$$p_r = \frac{\partial L}{\partial \dot{q}_r}, \qquad r = 1, 2, \ldots, n, \tag{10.13.1}$$

and from these equations we express the $\dot{q}$'s in terms of the p's. The $\dot{q}$'s are linear functions of the p's, with coefficients which are functions of the q's (and sometimes also of t). We substitute these formulae for the $\dot{q}$'s in the expression

$$\sum_{r=1}^{n} \dot{q}_r \frac{\partial L}{\partial \dot{q}_r} - L = \sum_{r=1}^{n} p_r \dot{q}_r - L, \tag{10.13.2}$$

and thus obtain a function of p's, q's and t. This is the Hamiltonian function H. It is the function (10.13.2) with the $\dot{q}$'s suppressed in favour of the p's, and it is a quadratic form in the p's with coefficients which are functions of the q's and of t. The Hamiltonian function

$$H = H(q_1, q_2, \ldots, q_n; p_1, p_2, \ldots, p_n; t) \tag{10.13.3}$$

is a *descriptive function* for the dynamical system, containing q's and p's instead of the q's and $\dot{q}$'s in the Lagrangian descriptive function (§ 6.6). We frequently write (10.13.3), for the sake of brevity, in the form

$$H = H(q; p; t). \tag{10.13.4}$$

Consider now an arbitrary variation of q's and $\dot{q}$'s (or, equivalently, an arbitrary variation of q's and p's), keeping t unvaried, and we have

$$\begin{aligned} \delta H &= \sum_{r=1}^{n} \left(p_r\, \delta\dot{q}_r + \dot{q}_r\, \delta p_r - \frac{\partial L}{\partial q_r}\, \delta q_r - \frac{\partial L}{\partial \dot{q}_r}\, \delta\dot{q}_r \right) \\ &= \sum_{r=1}^{n} \left(\dot{q}_r\, \delta p_r - \frac{\partial L}{\partial q_r}\, \delta q_r \right), \end{aligned} \tag{10.13.5}$$

whence

$$\dot{q}_r = \frac{\partial H}{\partial p_r}, \quad \frac{\partial L}{\partial q_r} = -\frac{\partial H}{\partial q_r}. \tag{10.13.6}$$

So far we have used only the definition of H, not the dynamics. We now bring in the equations of motion

$$\dot{p}_r = \frac{d}{dt}\left(\frac{\partial L}{\partial \dot{q}_r}\right) = \frac{\partial L}{\partial q_r}, \tag{10.13.7}$$

and we see that *the equations of motion are equivalent to the* $2n$ *equations*

$$\dot{q}_r = \frac{\partial H}{\partial p_r}, \quad \dot{p}_r = -\frac{\partial H}{\partial q_r}, \qquad r = 1, 2, \ldots, n. \tag{10.13.8}$$

These are Hamilton's equations of motion. They were introduced by Hamilton in 1834. We shall find that they are of paramount importance in analytical dynamics. They are of the form (6.4.4), but of a particular type, in which the $2n$ variables are grouped in n associated pairs (q_r, p_r), and in which the second members have the particular form shown in (10.13.8).

The two sets of equations (10.13.8) are not, to begin with, of equal status. The n equations

$$\dot{q}_r = \frac{\partial H}{\partial p_r} \tag{10.13.9}$$

are derived from the mere definition of H, and involve no appeal to the laws of dynamics. They are equivalent to the n equations defining the p's,

$$p_r = \frac{\partial L}{\partial \dot{q}_r}. \tag{10.13.10}$$

In fact the equations (10.13.9) express the $\dot{q}$'s as linear functions of the p's, and the equations (10.13.10) express the p's as linear functions of the $\dot{q}$'s. If we solve (10.13.9) for the p's we obtain (10.13.10), and if we solve (10.13.10) for the $\dot{q}$'s we obtain (10.13.9). It is only the second set of n equations in (10.13.8),

$$\dot{p}_r = -\frac{\partial H}{\partial q_r}, \tag{10.13.11}$$

that involve any appeal to dynamical principles. However, the fact that the two sets have not initially the same status is not usually significant in the applications, and we can safely treat the set (10.13.8) as $2n$ equations of equal status.

The justification for speaking of the Hamiltonian function as a descriptive function is now clear; from the function we can construct the equations of motion, so the function contains in itself a complete description of the motions that are possible for the dynamical system.

The Hamiltonian equations (10.13.8) were established for a holonomic conservative system, but it is easy to see how the equations must be modified for other types of dynamical systems.

(i) If the system is not holonomic the equations are, with the notation of § 6.2,

$$\dot{q}_r = \frac{\partial H}{\partial p_r}, \quad \dot{p}_r = -\frac{\partial H}{\partial q_r} + \sum_{m=1}^{l} \lambda_m B_{mr}, \qquad r = 1, 2, \ldots, n, \tag{10.13.12}$$

and there are l additional equations of constraint

$$\sum_{s=1}^{n} B_{rs}\dot{q}_s + B_r = 0, \qquad r = 1, 2, \ldots, l. \tag{10.13.13}$$

(ii) If the system is a holonomic system with n freedoms, and there are given forces in addition to those represented in the potential function V, the equations are, with the notation of § 6.5,

$$\dot{q}_r = \frac{\partial H}{\partial p_r}, \quad \dot{p}_r = -\frac{\partial H}{\partial q_r} + \bar{Q}_r, \qquad r = 1, 2, \ldots, n. \tag{10.13.14}$$

It is assumed that $\bar{Q}_r$ is a function of q's only, not of $\dot{q}$'s. (In general the equations are not of the form $\dot{\mathbf{x}} = \mathbf{X}$ if the $\bar{Q}$'s involve $\dot{q}$'s. They can be brought to the form $\dot{\mathbf{x}} = \mathbf{X}$ if each $\bar{Q}_r$ is a linear form in the $\dot{q}$'s with coefficients which are functions of the q's.)

(iii) If the system is a holonomic system with n freedoms, and there are resisting forces of Rayleigh type (§ 10.11) the equations of motion are

$$\dot{q}_r = \frac{\partial H}{\partial p_r}, \quad \dot{p}_r = -\frac{\partial H}{\partial q_r} - \frac{\partial F}{\partial \dot{q}_r}, \qquad r = 1, 2, \ldots, n. \tag{10.13.15}$$

These can be brought into the form $\dot{\mathbf{x}} = \mathbf{X}$, because F is a homogeneous quadratic form in the $\dot{q}$'s.

(iv) The cases (ii) and (iii) are easily modified to meet the case of a non-holonomic system. The terms $\sum_{m=1}^{l} \lambda_m B_{mr}$ must be added to the second member of the equation for $\dot{p}_r$, and the l equations of constraint (10.13.13) must be adjoined to the Hamiltonian equations so modified.

We have derived the Hamiltonian function H from the Lagrangian function L; we can equally simply derive L from H. For L is the function $\sum_{r=1}^{n} p_r\dot{q}_r - H$ with the p's suppressed in favour of the $\dot{q}$'s, and we can express the p's in terms of the $\dot{q}$'s by means of the equations $\dot{q}_r = \partial H/\partial p_r$.

10.14 The equation of energy and the explicit form of H. For a holonomic conservative system H is, in the most general case, a function of the q's and p's and of t; though in most concrete examples, t is absent. If we substitute in H the values of the q's and p's at time t during the motion, we have

$$\frac{dH}{dt} = \frac{\partial H}{\partial t} + \sum_{r=1}^{n} \frac{\partial H}{\partial q_r}\dot{q}_r + \sum_{r=1}^{n} \frac{\partial H}{\partial p_r}\dot{p}_r, \tag{10.14.1}$$

which reduces to

$$\frac{dH}{dt} = \frac{\partial H}{\partial t} \tag{10.14.2}$$

in virtue of Hamilton's equations. Thus, *if H does not contain t explicitly, H retains the same constant value throughout the motion,*

$$H = h. \tag{10.14.3}$$

This is, of course, merely a restatement of Jacobi's integral (§ 6.7). (We recall that if L does not contain t explicitly, H does not contain t explicitly, and *vice versa.*)

Let us now determine H explicitly. If the system is natural

$$T = T_2 = \tfrac{1}{2}\sum_{r=1}^{n}\sum_{s=n}^{n} a_{rs}\dot{q}_r\dot{q}_s, \tag{10.14.4}$$

and

$$\sum_{r=1}^{n} p_r\dot{q}_r - L = 2T - (T - V) = T + V, \tag{10.14.5}$$

so *H is the energy function $T + V$, with T expressed in terms of p's instead of $\dot{q}$'s.* Now since

$$p_r = \sum_{s=1}^{n} a_{rs}\dot{q}_s, \qquad r = 1, 2, \ldots, n, \tag{10.14.6}$$

$$\dot{q}_r = \sum_{s=1}^{n} c_{rs}p_s, \qquad r = 1, 2, \ldots, n, \tag{10.14.7}$$

where, as in § 10.4, (c_{rs}) is the matrix inverse to (a_{rs}). Thus, since $2T = \sum_{r=1}^{n} p_r\dot{q}_r$, the explicit form of H is

$$H = \tfrac{1}{2}\sum_{r=1}^{n}\sum_{s=1}^{n} c_{rs}p_r p_s + V. \tag{10.14.8}$$

The expression of T in terms of p's instead of q's involves the same technique as the expression of the equation of a conic (in homogeneous coordinates) in terms of line coordinates instead of point coordinates. Another way of expressing T in terms of the p's comes from the equation

$$\begin{vmatrix} a_{11} & a_{12} & a_{1n} & p_1 \\ a_{21} & a_{22} & a_{2n} & p_2 \\ & & & \\ a_{n1} & a_{n2} & a_{nn} & p_n \\ p_1 & p_2 & p_n & 2T \end{vmatrix} = 0; \tag{10.14.9}$$

the determinant, with $(n + 1)$ rows and $(n + 1)$ columns, vanishes, because if we multiply the rth column by $\dot{q}_r$, and sum from $r = 1$ to $r = n$, we obtain the last column. Expanding the determinant, we find the explicit expression of T as a quadratic form in the p's.

There is one simple special case of particular interest, namely that in which the system is referred to *orthogonal coordinates*; the matrix (a_{rs}) is a diagonal matrix, all the non-diagonal elements being zero. If

$$L = \tfrac{1}{2} \sum_{r=1}^{n} \alpha_r^2 \dot{q}_r^2 - V, \tag{10.14.10}$$

then

$$p_r = \alpha_r^2 \dot{q}_r, \tag{10.14.11}$$

and

$$H = \tfrac{1}{2} \sum_{r=1}^{n} \frac{1}{\alpha_r^2} p_r^2 + V. \tag{10.14.12}$$

In this case the form for H can be written down immediately.

Let us now consider the more general case of a non-natural system,

$$L = T_2 + T_1 + T_0 - V. \tag{10.14.13}$$

In this case, as in § 6.8,

$$\sum_{r=1}^{n} p_r \dot{q}_r - L = (2T_2 + T_1) - (T_2 + T_1 + T_0 - V) = T_2 + V - T_0, \tag{10.14.14}$$

and H *is* $T_2 + V - T_0$ *expressed in terms of* p*'s instead of* $\dot{q}$*'s*. If, as in (6.1.6) and (6.1.7),

$$T_2 = \tfrac{1}{2} \sum_{r=1}^{n} \sum_{s=1}^{n} a_{rs} \dot{q}_r \dot{q}_s, \quad T_1 = \sum_{r=1}^{n} a_r \dot{q}_r,$$

then

$$p_r = \sum_{s=1}^{n} a_{rs} \dot{q}_s + a_r, \qquad r = 1, 2, \ldots, n, \tag{10.14.15}$$

and

$$\dot{q}_r = \sum_{s=1}^{n} c_{rs}(p_s - a_s). \tag{10.14.16}$$

Therefore

$$2T_2 = \sum_{r=1}^{n} \dot{q}_r(p_r - a_r) = \sum_{r=1}^{n} \sum_{s=1}^{n} c_{rs}(p_r - a_r)(p_s - a_s), \tag{10.14.17}$$

and finally the explicit form of H is

$$H = \tfrac{1}{2} \sum_{r=1}^{n} \sum_{s=1}^{n} c_{rs}(p_r - a_r)(p_s - a_s) + V - T_0. \tag{10.14.18}$$

We notice that H has the form $H_2 + H_1 + H_0$, where H_r is of degree r in the p's. If for the moment we adopt the summation convention for repeated suffixes, we have

$$H_2 = \tfrac{1}{2} c_{rs} p_r p_s, \quad H_1 = -c_{rs} a_r p_s, \quad H_0 = \tfrac{1}{2} c_{rs} a_r a_s + V - T_0.$$

As a concrete example, consider a charged particle moving in a mechanical and an electromagnetic field, so that, as in (10.6.18),

$$L = \tfrac{1}{2} m(\dot{x}^2 + \dot{y}^2 + \dot{z}^2) + \frac{e}{c}(A_x \dot{x} + A_y \dot{y} + A_z \dot{z}) - V - e\Omega, \tag{10.14.19}$$

where Ω is the scalar potential, and $\{A_x, A_y, A_z\}$ the vector potential of the electromagnetic field. Here, using the notation of (6.10.4),

$$p_x = m\dot{x} + \frac{e}{c} A_x, \tag{10.14.20}$$

with two similar equations, and

$$\begin{aligned} H &= \tfrac{1}{2}m(\dot{x}^2 + \dot{y}^2 + \dot{z}^2) + V + e\Omega \\ &= \frac{1}{2m}(p_x{}^2 + p_y{}^2 + p_z{}^2) - \frac{e}{mc}(A_x p_x + A_y p_y + A_z p_z) \\ &\qquad + \frac{e^2}{2mc^2}(A_x{}^2 + A_y{}^2 + A_z{}^2) + V + e\Omega. \end{aligned} \tag{10.14.21}$$

10.15 The principal solid. We consider again the motion of a dynamical system relative to a moving base F' (§ 10.7); the matter now to be considered was omitted from § 10.7, since its introduction at that point would have occasioned an interruption of the line of argument there presented. We use the notation of § 10.7. We denote by $\mathbf{p}'$ the *apparent linear momentum*,

$$p_1' = Sm\dot{x}, \quad p_2' = Sm\dot{y}, \quad p_3' = Sm\dot{z}, \tag{10.15.1}$$

and by $\mathbf{h}'$ the *apparent angular momentum*,

$$h_1' = Sm(y\dot{z} - z\dot{y}), \quad h_2' = Sm(z\dot{x} - x\dot{z}), \quad h_3' = Sm(x\dot{y} - y\dot{x}). \tag{10.15.2}$$

Then $\mathbf{p}'$ and $\mathbf{h}'$ represent the linear and angular momentum of the system as estimated by an observer in the base F' who thinks of F' as fixed.

We can choose the base F' in such a way that $\mathbf{p}' = \mathbf{h}' = \mathbf{0}$. We observe that if $\mathbf{p}' = \mathbf{h}' = \mathbf{0}$ for the chosen trihedral F', the same is true for any other trihedral which is fixed relative to F'.

To prove that the moving trihedral can be chosen to make $\mathbf{p}' = \mathbf{h}' = \mathbf{0}$, we observe first that to make $\mathbf{p}' = \mathbf{0}$ we have only to choose a base in which G is at rest. It will clearly be simplest to take G as the origin for the moving trihedral. Then the component h_1 of the actual angular momentum $\mathbf{h}$ (as contrasted with the apparent angular momentum $\mathbf{h}'$) is given by

$$\begin{aligned} h_1 &= Sm\{y(w + \dot{z} - x\theta_2 + y\theta_1) - z(v + \dot{y} - z\theta_1 + x\theta_3)\} \\ &= h_1' + A\theta_1 - H\theta_2 - G\theta_3, \end{aligned} \tag{10.15.3}$$

where A, B, C, F, G, H are moments and products of inertia of the system at the instant considered. Thus $\mathbf{h}' = \mathbf{0}$ if

$$\left\{ \begin{aligned} A\theta_1 - H\theta_2 - G\theta_3 &= h_1, \\ -H\theta_1 + B\theta_2 - F\theta_3 &= h_2, \\ -G\theta_1 - F\theta_2 + C\theta_3 &= h_3, \end{aligned} \right. \tag{10.15.4}$$

and there is a unique solution for $\theta_1, \theta_2, \theta_3$, since the determinant of the coefficients is non-zero: the coefficients on the left in (10.15.3) are the coefficients in the equation of a genuine ellipsoid, the ellipsoid of inertia for the whole system.

Thus however the particles of the system move relative to the "fixed" base F, we can find a moving base F' in which $\mathbf{p}'$ and $\mathbf{h}'$ always vanish. This base is called *the principal solid.*

If F' is the principal solid, and the origin of the moving trihedral is G, the formula (10.7.8) becomes

$$T = \mathfrak{T} + \tfrac{1}{2}MU^2 + \tfrac{1}{2}I\omega^2, \tag{10.15.5}$$

a generalization of the theorem of König. We notice that $\mathfrak{T} < T$, and a slight adaptation of the argument, starting with F as an arbitrary base, not necessarily a Newtonian base, shows that $\mathfrak{T}$ is less for the principal solid than for any other base. *The principal solid is the base for which the apparent kinetic energy has the least possible value.*

We pursue the argument a little further along a more speculative line. Newton's cosmology involved the assumption of an absolute space, Euclidian in structure, of an absolute time, and of a base at rest in space. If we adhere to the notion of absolute space and time, we can replace the notion of a base at rest by the notion of the principal solid for the whole material universe. If we imagine a universe consisting of (i) a number of massive distant stars in a fixed configuration, and (ii) a number of solar systems and comets, the configuration of stars will be almost at rest in the principal solid, because the principal solid gives the least possible value to the measure of the kinetic energy. The stars will assume the status of *fixed* stars.

It is tempting at this stage to abandon the notion of a Newtonian base as an independent hypothesis, and to identify the Newtonian base with the principal solid for the whole material universe. If we do so, Newton's third law of motion is a consequence of the second law, not an independent hypothesis. For if we consider any system of particles moving in any way, and refer the motion to a trihedral fixed in the principal solid, the conditions $\mathbf{p}' = \mathbf{h}' = \mathbf{0}$ for all time imply

$$\begin{cases} Sm\ddot{x} = 0, & Sm\ddot{y} = 0, & Sm\ddot{z} = 0, \\ Sm(y\ddot{z} - z\ddot{y}) = 0, & Sm(z\ddot{x} - x\ddot{z}) = 0, & Sm(x\ddot{y} - y\ddot{x}) = 0. \end{cases} \tag{10.15.6}$$

If now we assume the truth of Newton's second law of motion, we infer that the system of all the forces on all the particles is a nul system (a system that would be in equilibrium if the particles were particles of a rigid body). Now a system of forces on the particles composed of pairs of equal and opposite forces on the pairs of particles (the forces of each pair being in the line joining the particles) is clearly a nul system. Conversely the forces of any nul system can be resolved into components in such a way that the system is built up of such equal and opposite pairs (unless indeed all the particles are collinear, and we disregard this trivial exception). To establish this principle, we prove it first for three (non-collinear) particles, and then proceed by induction. Suppose then that we consider any system of particles moving in any way, and let us take as the base of reference the principal solid. If we assume the truth of the second law of motion, the truth of the third law (the principle of the equality of action and reaction) necessarily follows.

Chapter XI

Variable mass

11.1 Particles with variable mass, the Lagrangian function. In the special theory of relativity the mass of a particle is not constant, but is a function of its speed. A particle whose *rest-mass* is m_0 has mass m, where

(11.1.1)
$$m = \frac{m_0}{\sqrt{\left(1 - \frac{v^2}{c^2}\right)}},$$

when moving with speed v, where c is a positive constant, the speed of light. In most practical experiments v/c is small, and then the variation of m from the rest-mass m_0 may be negligible. But the variation becomes important when v/c is near to 1, and indeed $m \to \infty$ as $v \to c$.

We are led therefore to consider how the theory we have developed will be modified if the mass m of each particle is a function of its speed v, $m = \varphi(v)$. So far as the theory is concerned the function $\varphi(v)$ need not be the same function for all the particles, though in fact in the applications $\varphi(v)$ is often assumed to be of the form (11.1.1) for every particle.

When the mass is variable the traditional form of Newton's law, $\mathbf{P} = m\mathbf{f}$, is replaced by $\mathbf{P} = \frac{d}{dt}(m\mathbf{v})$; kineton is replaced by rate of change of momentum. The logical basis of this law is inherent in the theory of relativity. The first point that catches our attention is that, since

(11.1.2)
$$\mathbf{P} = m\mathbf{f} + \dot{m}\mathbf{v},$$

the acceleration is not in general in the same direction as the force. The equations of motion for a single free particle, referred to fixed rectangular axes, are

(1.1.3)
$$\frac{d}{dt}(m\dot{x}) = X, \quad \frac{d}{dt}(m\dot{y}) = Y, \quad \frac{d}{dt}(m\dot{z}) = Z.$$

Let us consider then a system of particles whose masses are variable. Using the notation of § 2.2 the equations of motion (2.2.12) are replaced by

(11.1.3)
$$\frac{d}{dt}(m_r\dot{x}_r) = X_r + X_r', \qquad r = 1, 2, \ldots, N.$$

For an arbitrary virtual displacement

(2.2.10)
$$\sum_{r=1}^{N} X_r' \,\delta x_r = 0,$$

so the fundamental equation (3.1.1) for the system is replaced by

(11.1.4)
$$\sum_{r=1}^{N}\left\{\frac{d}{dt}(m_r\dot{x}_r) - X_r\right\}\delta x_r = 0.$$

The equation (11.1.4) of course reverts to the familiar form (3.1.1) if the masses are constants.

Suppose now that the system is a holonomic conservative system with n freedoms. We introduce Lagrangian coordinates $q_1, q_2, \ldots, q_n$, and since $\delta x_r = \sum_{s=1}^{n} \dfrac{\partial x_r}{\partial q_s}\,\delta q_s$, and since (11.1.4) holds for arbitrary values of $\delta q_1, \delta q_2, \ldots, \delta q_n$, we deduce

$$\sum_{r=1}^{N} \frac{d}{dt}(m_r \dot{x}_r)\frac{\partial x_r}{\partial q_s} = -\frac{\partial V}{\partial q_s}, \qquad s = 1, 2, \ldots, n. \tag{11.1.5}$$

We transform (11.1.5) in a manner similar to that used in § 6.1, and we need the two Lemmas established there,

$$\frac{\partial \dot{x}_r}{\partial \dot{q}_s} = \frac{\partial x_r}{\partial q_s}, \tag{6.1.3}$$

$$\frac{\partial \dot{x}_r}{\partial q_s} = \frac{d}{dt}\left(\frac{\partial x_r}{\partial q_s}\right). \tag{6.1.4}$$

In virtue of these Lemmas (11.1.5) becomes

$$\frac{d}{dt}\left(\sum_{r=1}^{N} m_r \dot{x}_r \frac{\partial \dot{x}_r}{\partial \dot{q}_s}\right) - \sum_{r=1}^{N} m_r \dot{x}_r \frac{\partial \dot{x}_r}{\partial q_s} = -\frac{\partial V}{\partial q_s}, \qquad s = 1, 2, \ldots, n, \tag{11.1.6}$$

which we can also write in the form

$$\frac{d}{dt}\left(Smv\frac{\partial v}{\partial \dot{q}_s}\right) - Smv\frac{\partial v}{\partial q_s} = -\frac{\partial V}{\partial q_s}. \tag{11.1.7}$$

It is advantageous here to work with the symbol S, using summation over the ν particles rather than summation over the N Cartesian coordinates, since the mass of each particle is a function of its speed v.

We now introduce the function

$$T^* = S\int mv\,dv, \tag{11.1.8}$$

or, more precisely,

$$T^* = S\int_0^v \varphi(x)x\,dx, \tag{11.1.9}$$

and (11.1.7) becomes

$$\frac{d}{dt}\left(\frac{\partial T^*}{\partial \dot{q}_s}\right) - \frac{\partial T^*}{\partial q_s} = -\frac{\partial V}{\partial q_s}, \qquad s = 1, 2, \ldots, n. \tag{11.1.10}$$

The equations of motion can be written in Lagrangian form, with

$$L = T^* - V. \tag{11.1.11}$$

It should be noticed that T^* is not, in general, a quadratic form in the $\dot{q}$'s, as it was in the problems with constant masses previously discussed.

11.2 The kinetic energy. We shall now suppose that we have the simple case in which each x_r is a function of the q's only, not of t. We introduce a function T, the kinetic energy function, defined in such a way as to verify the first form of the equation of energy (3.3.2),

$$\frac{dT}{dt} = S(X\dot{x} + Y\dot{y} + Z\dot{z}). \tag{11.2.1}$$

Now the fundamental equation (11.1.4) is valid if we write $\dot{x}_r$ for δx_r, so (11.2.1) leads to

(11.2.2)
$$\begin{aligned}\frac{dT}{dt} &= S\left\{\dot{x}\frac{d}{dt}(m\dot{x}) + \dot{y}\frac{d}{dt}(m\dot{y}) + \dot{z}\frac{d}{dt}(m\dot{z})\right\} \\ &= S\{\dot{m}(\dot{x}^2 + \dot{y}^2 + \dot{z}^2) + m(\dot{x}\ddot{x} + \dot{y}\ddot{y} + \dot{z}\ddot{z})\} \\ &= S(\dot{m}v^2 + mv\dot{v}) \\ &= Sv\frac{d}{dt}(mv).\end{aligned}$$

Hence

(11.2.3)
$$\begin{aligned}T &= S\int v\frac{d}{dt}(mv)\,dt \\ &= S\left(mv^2 - \int mv\,dv\right) \\ &= Smv^2 - T^*.\end{aligned}$$

The function T defined by (11.2.3) is the kinetic energy function. If the forces are conservative forces derived from the potential function V, we have an equation analogous to the equation of energy,

(11.2.4)
$$T + V = C.$$

It is clear, of course, that T takes the familiar form $\frac{1}{2}Smv^2$ if all the masses are constant.

11.3 The Hamiltonian function. Let us now calculate the Hamiltonian function for the system. We have

(11.3.1)
$$p_r = \frac{\partial L}{\partial \dot{q}_r} = Smv\frac{\partial v}{\partial \dot{q}_r} = Sm\frac{\partial}{\partial \dot{q}_r}(\tfrac{1}{2}v^2),$$

and therefore

(11.3.2)
$$\begin{aligned}\sum_{r=1}^{n} p_r\dot{q}_r - L &= Sm\dot{q}_r\frac{\partial}{\partial \dot{q}_r}(\tfrac{1}{2}v^2) - S\int mv\,dv + V \\ &= Smv^2 - S\int mv\,dv + V \\ &= T + V,\end{aligned}$$

where we have used the property that v^2 is a homogeneous quadratic function of the $\dot{q}$'s. Thus

(11.3.3)
$$H = T + V,$$

where T is to be expressed in terms of q's and p's. We notice that H has not the form with which we are familiar in problems in which the masses are constant; T is not a quadratic form in the p's.

11.4 The moving electron. We consider a single electron moving in space. We have

(11.4.1)
$$m = \frac{m_0}{\sqrt{\left(1 - \dfrac{v^2}{c^2}\right)}},$$

so that

$$T^* = \int_0^v \frac{m_0}{\sqrt{\left(1 - \frac{x^2}{c^2}\right)}} x\,dx = m_0c^2\left\{1 - \sqrt{\left(1 - \frac{v^2}{c^2}\right)}\right\}, \tag{11.4.2}$$

and

$$T = mv^2 - T^* = m_0c^2\left\{\frac{1}{\sqrt{\left(1 - \frac{v^2}{c^2}\right)}} - 1\right\}. \tag{11.4.3}$$

If the electron moves in a mechanical field with potential V and an electrostatic field with potential Ω, the Lagrangian function is

$$L = m_0c^2\left\{1 - \sqrt{\left(1 - \frac{v^2}{c^2}\right)}\right\} - W, \tag{11.4.4}$$

where $W = V + e\Omega$, e being the charge on the electron. The Hamiltonian function is

$$H = m_0c^2\left\{\frac{1}{\sqrt{\left(1 - \frac{v^2}{c^2}\right)}} - 1\right\} + W \tag{11.4.5}$$

expressed in terms of q's and p's.

Suppose for example we use orthogonal curvilinear coordinates α, β, γ for which the line-element ds is given, as in § 8.2, by

$$ds^2 = A^2\,d\alpha^2 + B^2\,d\beta^2 + C^2\,d\gamma^2, \tag{11.4.6}$$

where A, B, C are positive functions of (α, β, γ). Then

$$v^2 = A^2\dot{\alpha}^2 + B^2\dot{\beta}^2 + C^2\dot{\gamma}^2, \tag{11.4.7}$$

and

$$L = m_0c^2\left\{1 - \sqrt{\left(1 - \frac{A^2\dot{\alpha}^2 + B^2\dot{\beta}^2 + C^2\dot{\gamma}^2}{c^2}\right)}\right\} - W. \tag{11.4.8}$$

To find H, we have

$$p_\alpha = \frac{\partial T^*}{\partial \dot{\alpha}} = mv\frac{\partial v}{\partial \dot{\alpha}} = mA^2\dot{\alpha} = \frac{m_0A^2\dot{\alpha}}{\sqrt{\left(1 - \frac{v^2}{c^2}\right)}}, \tag{11.4.9}$$

and therefore

$$\frac{p_\alpha^{\,2}}{A^2} + \frac{p_\beta^{\,2}}{B^2} + \frac{p_\gamma^{\,2}}{C^2} = \frac{m_0^{\,2}v^2}{1 - \frac{v^2}{c^2}}. \tag{11.4.10}$$

Thus

$$m_0^{\,2}c^2 + \frac{p_\alpha^{\,2}}{A^2} + \frac{p_\beta^{\,2}}{B^2} + \frac{p_\gamma^{\,2}}{C^2} = \frac{m_0^{\,2}c^2}{1 - \frac{v^2}{c^2}}, \tag{11.4.11}$$

and finally

$$H = c\left\{\sqrt{\left(m_0^{\,2}c^2 + \frac{p_\alpha^{\,2}}{A^2} + \frac{p_\beta^{\,2}}{B^2} + \frac{p_\gamma^{\,2}}{C^2}\right)} - m_0c\right\} + W. \tag{11.4.12}$$

As an illustration, let us consider motion in the plane $z = 0$ in a uniform electrostatic field, say a field E in the direction Oy. If e is the charge on the electron, the force has components (O, eE), and $W = -eEy$. Suppose that the electron is projected from the origin at the instant $t = 0$, with speed u_0 in the direction Ox, i.e. at right angles to the field. The equations of motion, found from $\mathbf{P} = \dfrac{d}{dt}(m\mathbf{v})$ or from Lagrange's equations, are

(11.4.13) $$\frac{d}{dt}\left(\frac{m_0}{\rho}\dot{x}\right) = 0, \quad \frac{d}{dt}\left(\frac{m_0}{\rho}\dot{y}\right) = Ee,$$

where ρ is written for $\sqrt{\left(1 - \dfrac{v^2}{c^2}\right)}$. We write g for Ee/m_0, and we suppose for definiteness that $g > 0$, so e and E must have the same sign. From (11.4.13), on integrating, we have

(11.4.14) $$\frac{\dot{x}}{\rho} = \frac{u_0}{\rho_0}, \quad \frac{\dot{y}}{\rho} = gt,$$

where $\rho_0 = \sqrt{\left(1 - \dfrac{u_0^2}{c^2}\right)}$. From (11.4.14), squaring and adding, and using the equation $v^2 = c^2(1 - \rho^2)$, we have

(11.4.15) $$\frac{c^2}{\rho^2} = \frac{c^2}{\rho_0^2} + g^2t^2 = g^2(a^2 + t^2),$$

where

(11.4.16) $$a = \frac{c}{\rho_0 g} = \frac{c^2}{g\sqrt{(c^2 - u_0^2)}}.$$

It is now easy to complete the solution. The form of (11.4.15) suggests the introduction of a new variable θ in place of the time, where

(11.4.17) $$t = a \sinh \theta, \quad \frac{c}{\rho} = ga \cosh \theta, \quad \rho\, dt = \frac{c}{g}\, d\theta.$$

The equations (11.4.14) can now be written

(11.4.18) $$\frac{dx}{d\theta} = \frac{cu_0}{g\rho_0} = u_0 a, \quad \frac{dy}{d\theta} = ca \sinh \theta,$$

whence

(11.4.19) $$x = u_0 a\theta, \quad y = ca(\cosh \theta - 1).$$

The path of the electron is the curve

(11.4.20) $$y = ca\left(\cosh \frac{x}{u_0 a} - 1\right),$$

which is the curve obtained from the catenary

(11.4.21) $$\frac{y}{u_0 a} = \cosh \frac{x}{u_0 a} - 1$$

by increasing the ordinate y in the ratio c/u_0.

11.5 Electron in an electromagnetic field. The Lagrangian function, using (10.6.18), is

(11.5.1) $$L = m_0 c^2 \left\{1 - \sqrt{\left(1 - \frac{v^2}{c^2}\right)}\right\} + \frac{e}{c}(\mathbf{A} \cdot \mathbf{v}) - W,$$

where $W = V + e\Omega$, as before; Ω is the scalar potential, and $\mathbf{A}$ is the vector potential, of the electromagnetic field.

Let us now find the Hamiltonian function, using Cartesian coordinates x, y, z. We have

(11.5.2) $$p_x = \frac{\partial L}{\partial \dot{x}} = \frac{m_0 \dot{x}}{\rho} + \frac{e}{c} A_x,$$

and two similar equations, where A_x, A_y, A_z are the components of **A**, and ρ stands for $\sqrt{\left(1 - \frac{v^2}{c^2}\right)}$ as before. Now

$$H = p_x\dot{x} + p_y\dot{y} + p_z\dot{z} - L = m_0c^2\left(\frac{1}{\rho} - 1\right) + W, \tag{11.5.3}$$

and, since

$$\frac{1}{\rho^2} = 1 + \frac{1}{m_0{}^2c^2}\sum\left(p_x - \frac{e}{c}A_x\right)^2, \tag{11.5.4}$$

we have finally

$$H = c\sqrt{\left\{m_0{}^2c^2 + \sum\left(p_x - \frac{e}{c}A_x\right)^2\right\}} - m_0c^2 + W. \tag{11.5.5}$$

As an illustration, let us consider the problem of an electron moving in crossed electrostatic and magnetic fields. Let the electrostatic field be $\{-E, 0, 0\}$, the magnetic field $\{0, 0, \gamma\}$, and the charge on the electron $-\varepsilon$. The vector potential is $\frac{1}{2}\gamma\{-y, x, 0\}$, and

$$L = m_0c^2(1 - \rho) - \frac{\varepsilon\gamma}{2c}(x\dot{y} - y\dot{x}) + \varepsilon Ex. \tag{11.5.6}$$

From Lagrange's equations, or directly, we have the equations of motion

$$\frac{d}{dt}\left(\frac{\dot{x}}{\rho}\right) = g - k\dot{y}, \tag{11.5.7}$$

$$\frac{d}{dt}\left(\frac{\dot{y}}{\rho}\right) = k\dot{x}, \tag{11.5.8}$$

$$\frac{d}{dt}\left(\frac{\dot{z}}{\rho}\right) = 0, \tag{11.5.9}$$

where $g = \varepsilon E/m_0$ and $k = \varepsilon\gamma/m_0c$, and we assume that g and k are positive. If the electron is moving in the plane $z = 0$ initially, it moves in this plane for all time.

Let us consider the classical problem in which the electron starts from rest at the origin at the instant $t = 0$. We have immediately the first integrals of (11.5.7–8)

$$\frac{\dot{x}}{\rho} = gt - ky, \quad \frac{\dot{y}}{\rho} = kx. \tag{11.5.10}$$

To complete the integration we multiply the equations (11.5.7) and (11.5.8) by $\dot{x}/\rho$ and $\dot{y}/\rho$, and add, giving

$$\frac{d}{dt}\left(\frac{1}{2}\frac{v^2}{\rho^2}\right) = \frac{g\dot{x}}{\rho}. \tag{11.5.11}$$

Since $v^2 = c^2(1 - \rho^2)$ this becomes

$$\frac{d}{dt}\left(\frac{1}{2}\frac{c^2}{\rho^2}\right) = \frac{g\dot{x}}{\rho}, \tag{11.5.12}$$

whence

$$-\frac{c^2}{\rho^2}\dot{\rho} = g\dot{x}, \tag{11.5.13}$$

and therefore

$$\frac{c^2}{\rho} = c^2 + gx. \tag{11.5.14}$$

In virtue of (11.5.14) the equations (11.5.10) become

$$\dot{x}(c^2 + gx) = c^2(gt - ky), \tag{11.5.15}$$

$$\dot{y}(c^2 + gx) = c^2kx. \tag{11.5.16}$$

If we differentiate (11.5.15) with respect to t, and substitute for $\dot{y}$ from (11.5.16), we have

$$(c^2 + gx)^2\ddot{x} + g(c^2 + gx)\dot{x}^2 = c^2g(c^2 + gx) - c^4k^2x, \tag{11.5.17}$$

a relation between t and x which is equivalent to

$$\frac{d}{dx}\{(c^2 + gx)^2\dot{x}^2\} = 2c^4g - 2c^2(c^2k^2 - g^2)x. \tag{11.5.18}$$

Hence

$$(c^2 + gx)^2\dot{x}^2 = c^2x\{2c^2g - (c^2k^2 - g^2)x\}. \tag{11.5.19}$$

We assume that $ck > g$. This is equivalent to $\gamma > E$, and this condition is amply satisfied in the practical applications.

We can now find the path of the electron. From (11.5.19) and (11.5.16) we have

$$\left(\frac{dy}{dx}\right)^2 = \frac{\dot{y}^2}{\dot{x}^2} = p^2\frac{x}{2a - x}, \tag{11.5.20}$$

where

$$p^2 = \frac{c^2k^2}{c^2k^2 - g^2} = \frac{\gamma^2}{\gamma^2 - E^2}, \tag{11.5.21}$$

and

$$a = \frac{c^2g}{c^2k^2 - g^2} = \frac{m_0Ec^2}{\varepsilon(\gamma^2 - E^2)}. \tag{11.5.22}$$

To obtain a parametric representation of the path we write

$$x = 2a\sin^2\theta = a(1 - \cos 2\theta), \tag{11.5.23}$$

and then, from (11.5.20),

$$dy = p\tan\theta\, dx = 4\, ap\sin^2\theta\, d\theta = 2ap(1 - \cos 2\theta)\, d\theta,$$

giving

$$y = pa(2\theta - \sin 2\theta). \tag{11.5.24}$$

Equations (11.5.23–24) give a parametric representation of the path. If p, which is greater than 1, had the value 1, the path would be a cycloid with a line of cusps on Oy. As we have seen (*Example* 10.6B) if the electron had constant mass the path would in fact be a cycloid of this type. If we take into account the variation of mass, the cycloidal path is modified by a magnification p in the y-direction. The greatest distance of the electron from Oy during the motion is

$$2a = \frac{2m_0Ec^2}{\varepsilon(\gamma^2 - E^2)}. \tag{11.5.25}$$

The corresponding distance for a particle of constant mass m was found (in (10.6.28)) to be

$$\frac{2mEc^2}{\varepsilon\gamma^2}. \tag{11.5.26}$$

Chapter XII

The Gibbs-Appell equations

12.1 Non-holonomic systems. We have seen how Lagrange's equations of motion can be used when the system is not holonomic, and a concrete example, the rolling penny, was discussed in § 8.12. But Lagrange's equations are not particularly well suited to the study of non-holonomic systems, and in this Chapter we consider equations of motion of a new form, which is especially valuable when the system is not holonomic (though of course the equations are valid for holonomic systems also). We begin by introducing the idea of quasi-coordinates.

The masses of the particles are now assumed to be constants.

12.2 Quasi-coordinates. The Lagrangian coordinates have the property that the x's are *explicit functions* of the q's and t. It is very convenient, especially when we are dealing with non-holonomic systems, to be able to employ coordinates of a more general type. With these new coordinates each $\dot{x}_r$ is a linear function of $\dot{q}$'s, but these linear functions are not in general complete time-derivatives. Actually $\dot{x}_r$ can be expressed as a linear function of k $\dot{q}$'s, where k denotes as usual the number of degrees of freedom of the system.

Let us consider a non-holonomic system with k degrees of freedom and l equations of constraint. We need $k + l$ Lagrangian coordinates $q_1, q_2, \ldots, q_{k+l}$, and for the possible displacements of the system we have, from § 5.7,

$$0 = \sum_{s=1}^{k+l} B_{rs}\, dq_s + B_r\, dt, \qquad r = 1, 2, \ldots, l, \tag{12.2.1}$$

where the coefficients B_{rs}, B_r are functions of $(q_1, q_2, \ldots, q_{k+l};\ t)$ with continuous first derivatives in the relevant domain D of $(q_1, q_2, \ldots, q_{k+l};\ t)$.

We introduce p new symbols $\theta_1, \theta_2, \ldots, \theta_p$, where the integer p may have any suitable value. The θ's are not defined as functions of the q's and t, but their differentials are Pfaffian forms in the q's and t,

$$d\theta_r = \sum_{s=1}^{k+l} C_{rs}\, dq_s + C_r\, dt, \qquad r = 1, 2, \ldots, p, \tag{12.2.2}$$

where the coefficients C_{rs}, C_r are functions of $(q_1, q_2, \ldots, q_{k+l};\ t)$ with continuous first derivatives in D. The forms on the right in (12.2.1) and (12.2.2) are $l + p$ independent Pfaffian forms; they are not in general complete differentials. The θ's are called *quasi-coordinates*.

Let us write $\theta_r = q_{k+l+r}$, so that we now have n parameters $q_1, q_2, \ldots, q_n$, where $n = k + l + p$, of which the first $k + l$ are Lagrangian coordinates and the remaining p are quasi-coordinates; and

$$dq_{k+l+r} = \sum_{s=1}^{k+l} C_{rs}\, dq_s + C_r\, dt, \qquad r = 1, 2, \ldots, p. \tag{12.2.3}$$

We now solve the $l + p$ equations (12.2.1) and (12.2.3) for $l + p$ of the dq's in terms of the remaining k, and these k privileged dq's, in terms of which the others are expressed, can be differentials of Lagrangian coordinates or of quasi-coordinates. If for a moment we call the privileged set of k coordinates $\varphi_1, \varphi_2, \ldots, \varphi_k$, we have, if q_r is not one of the privileged set,

$$dq_r = \sum_{s=1}^{k} D_{rs}\, d\varphi_s + D_r\, dt, \tag{12.2.4}$$

and there are $l + p$ such equations. The equations (12.2.4) are precisely equivalent to the combined sets (12.2.1) and (12.2.3). The point to be observed with particular care is that the coefficients D_{rs}, D_r depend on all the Lagrangian q's and t; they are not merely functions of $(\varphi_1, \varphi_2, \ldots, \varphi_k;\ t)$.

Now x_r is a function of $(q_1, q_2, \ldots, q_{k+l};\ t)$, whence

$$dx_r = \sum_{s=1}^{k+l} \frac{\partial x_r}{\partial q_s}\, dq_s + \frac{\partial x_r}{\partial t}\, dt, \qquad r = 1, 2, \ldots, N. \tag{12.2.5}$$

In the second member of (12.2.5) we substitute, for any unprivileged dq's that appear, in terms of $d\varphi_1, d\varphi_2, \ldots, d\varphi_k$ from (12.2.4). We thus express dx_r as a linear function of $d\varphi_1, d\varphi_2, \ldots, d\varphi_k, dt$; the coefficients in this linear form contain all the Lagrangian q's and t.

At this point it is expedient to make a change of notation. In future we call the k privileged coordinates (which may be Lagrangian coordinates or quasi-coordinates) $q_1, q_2, \ldots, q_k$, and the remaining $l + p$ coordinates we call $q_{k+1}, q_{k+2}, \ldots, q_n$. Our formula for dx_r can now be written

$$dx_r = \sum_{s=1}^{k} \alpha_{rs}\, dq_s + \alpha_r\, dt, \qquad r = 1, 2, \ldots, N, \tag{12.2.6}$$

while (12.2.4) becomes, in the new notation,

$$dq_r = \sum_{s=1}^{k} \beta_{rs}\, dq_s + \beta_r\, dt, \qquad r = k+1, k+2, \ldots, n. \tag{12.2.7}$$

The formulae (12.2.6) and (12.2.7) are fundamental in the succeeding theory. We can express $\dot{x}_r$ in terms of the k velocity-components $\dot{q}_1, \dot{q}_2, \ldots, \dot{q}_k$; and similarly we can express $\dot{q}_r$, for $r > k$, in terms of the same k velocity-components $\dot{q}_1, \dot{q}_2, \ldots, \dot{q}_k$. But in each case the coefficients $\alpha_{rs}, \alpha_r, \beta_{rs}, \beta_r$ contain q's other than the k privileged q's; in general these coefficients contain all the Lagrangian q's and t. The formulae are of a very convenient form. The velocity-components $\dot{x}_r$ (for all the N Cartesian coordinates of the particles) and $\dot{q}_r$ (for the unprivileged q's) are expressed in terms of a set of velocity-components equal in number to the number of freedoms of the system. The velocities $\dot{q}_1, \dot{q}_2, \ldots, \dot{q}_k$ can have arbitrary values, but when these values are prescribed the velocity of the whole system is determined.

The virtual displacements are defined in terms of arbitrary increments $\delta q_1, \delta q_2, \ldots, \delta q_k$ by the equations

$$\delta x_r = \sum_{s=1}^{k} \alpha_{rs}\, \delta q_s, \qquad r = 1, 2, \ldots, N, \tag{12.2.8}$$

$$\delta q_r = \sum_{s=1}^{k} \beta_{rs}\, \delta q_s, \qquad r = k+1, k+2, \ldots, n. \tag{12.2.9}$$

As simple concrete examples of quasi-coordinates, consider the following. (i) A particle moves in a plane, and we write

$$dq = x\,dy - y\,dx,$$

where x, y are Cartesian coordinates. Here q represents twice the area swept out by the radius vector since a certain instant t_0, and q is a quasi-coordinate. (ii) A case that frequently occurs in practice is that in which the quasi-coordinate is the total rotation of a rigid body, since $t = t_0$, about a given line, fixed or moving. For example in the spinning-top problem the total rotation about the axis of the top is q, where, with the usual notation (§ 8.6),

$$dq = d\psi + \cos\theta\,d\varphi.$$

The second member of this equation is clearly not a complete differential, and q is a quasi-coordinate.

12.3 The fifth form of the fundamental equation. Consider the work done by the given forces in a virtual displacement. The formula for this work that appears in the first form of the fundamental equation (3.1.1) is $\sum_{r=1}^{N} X_r\,\delta x_r$. If we substitute for δx_r from (12.2.8) we get

$$\sum_{r=1}^{N} X_r\,\delta x_r = \sum_{s=1}^{k}\left(\sum_{r=1}^{N} X_r\alpha_{rs}\right)\delta q_s = \sum_{s=1}^{k} Q_s\,\delta q_s, \tag{12.3.1}$$

where

$$Q_s = \sum_{r=1}^{N} X_r\alpha_{rs}. \tag{12.3.2}$$

Now consider the corresponding formula in the second form of the fundamental equation (4.1.3), namely $\sum_{r=1}^{N} X_r\Delta\dot{x}_r$, where we recall that $\Delta\dot{x}_r$ refers to the *finite*, not infinitesimal, difference between any two velocity-systems that are possible with the given configuration at the given instant. Now from (12.2.6), for any possible velocity-system,

$$\dot{x}_r = \sum_{s=1}^{k} \alpha_{rs}\dot{q}_s + \alpha_r, \qquad r = 1, 2, \ldots, N, \tag{12.3.3}$$

and if we consider another possible velocity-system $\dot{\mathbf{q}} + \Delta\dot{\mathbf{q}}$ with the same configuration we get

$$\dot{x}_r + \Delta\dot{x}_r = \sum_{s=1}^{k} \alpha_{rs}(\dot{q}_s + \Delta\dot{q}_s) + \alpha_r, \qquad r = 1, 2, \ldots, N, \tag{12.3.4}$$

whence

$$\Delta\dot{x}_r = \sum_{s=1}^{k} \alpha_{rs}\,\Delta\dot{q}_s, \qquad r = 1, 2, \ldots, N. \tag{12.3.5}$$

Thus

$$\sum_{r=1}^{N} X_r\,\Delta\dot{x}_r = \sum_{s=1}^{k}\left(\sum_{r=1}^{N} X_r\alpha_{rs}\right)\Delta\dot{q}_s = \sum_{s=1}^{k} Q_s\,\Delta\dot{q}_s, \tag{12.3.6}$$

where the Q's are the same coefficients (12.3.2) that appeared in the first form.

Finally, let us consider the third form of the fundamental equation (4.2.4). We have, from (12.3.3),

$$\ddot{x}_r = \sum_{s=1}^{k} \alpha_{rs}\ddot{q}_s + \sum_{s=1}^{k} \frac{d\alpha_{rs}}{dt}\dot{q}_s + \frac{d\alpha_r}{dt}, \qquad r = 1, 2, \ldots, N, \tag{12.3.7}$$

where $\frac{d}{dt}$ denotes the operator $\frac{\partial}{\partial t} + \sum_{m=1}^{n} \dot{q}_m \frac{\partial}{\partial q_m}$. If we consider another possible acceleration-system $\ddot{\mathbf{q}} + \Delta\ddot{\mathbf{q}}$ with the same configuration *and velocity*. we have

$$\ddot{x}_r + \Delta\ddot{x}_r = \sum_{s=1}^{k} \alpha_{rs}(\ddot{q}_s + \Delta\ddot{q}_s) + \sum_{s=1}^{k} \frac{d\alpha_{rs}}{dt}\dot{q}_s + \frac{d\alpha_r}{dt}, \qquad r = 1, 2, \ldots, N, \tag{12.3.8}$$

whence

$$\Delta\ddot{x}_r = \sum_{s=1}^{k} \alpha_{rs}\,\Delta\ddot{q}_s, \qquad r = 1, 2, \ldots, N. \tag{12.3.9}$$

Thus

$$\sum_{r=1}^{N} X_r\Delta\ddot{x}_r = \sum_{s=1}^{k}\left(\sum_{r=1}^{N} X_r\alpha_{rs}\right)\Delta\ddot{q}_s = \sum_{s=1}^{k} Q_s\,\Delta\ddot{q}_s, \tag{12.3.10}$$

and again the same coefficients Q_r appear.

The third form of the fundamental equation (4.2.4) now leads to

$$\sum_{r=1}^{N} m_r\ddot{x}_r\,\Delta\ddot{x}_r - \sum_{s=1}^{k} Q_s\,\Delta\ddot{q}_s = 0, \tag{12.3.11}$$

and this is *the fifth form of the fundamental equation.*

12.4 Determination of the acceleration. We introduce the Gibbs function $\mathfrak{G}$, which is

$$\tfrac{1}{2}\sum_{r=1}^{N} m_r\ddot{x}_r^{\,2} \tag{12.4.1}$$

(or, in the particle notation, $\frac{1}{2}Sm(\ddot{x}^2 + \ddot{y}^2 + \ddot{z}^2)$) expressed, by means of (12.3.7), in terms of $\ddot{q}_1, \ddot{q}_2, \ldots, \ddot{q}_k$. It is a polynomial in $\ddot{q}_1, \ddot{q}_2, \ldots, \ddot{q}_k$ of the form

$$G_2 + G_1 + G_0, \tag{12.4.2}$$

where G_2 is a homogeneous quadratic function of $\ddot{q}_1, \ddot{q}_2, \ldots, \ddot{q}_k$, G_1 is a homogeneous linear function of $\ddot{q}_1, \ddot{q}_2, \ldots, \ddot{q}_k$, and G_0 does not involve $\ddot{q}$'s. In practice the terms G_2 are usually easy to find, because they have the same coefficients as the quadratic terms in T if T is expressed in terms of $\dot{q}_1, \dot{q}_2, \ldots, \dot{q}_k$. The terms G_1 must be determined independently. We shall find that the terms G_0 are immaterial and can be omitted. The heart of the matter is therefore the determination of G_1.

The coefficients in $\mathfrak{G}$ will usually contain other q's and $\dot{q}$'s, not merely the first k. We can, if we wish, get rid of $\dot{q}_{k+1}, \dot{q}_{k+2}, \ldots, \dot{q}_n$ by means of the equations

$$\dot{q}_r = \sum_{s=1}^{k} \beta_{rs}\dot{q}_s + \beta_r, \qquad r = k+1, k+2, \ldots, n, \tag{12.4.3}$$

derived from (12.2.7), but there is no advantage to be gained from this manoeuvre. The equations (12.4.3) will appear later anyway as part of the complete scheme of equations.

Consider then the system with a prescribed configuration *and velocity* at time t. We wish to find equations to determine the acceleration, and this object is achieved by the following simple and powerful theorem. *The acceleration is such that*

$$\mathfrak{G} - \sum_{s=1}^{k} Q_s \ddot{q}_s \tag{12.4.4}$$

considered as a function of $\ddot{q}_1, \ddot{q}_2, \ldots, \ddot{q}_k$ *is a minimum.* In this theorem the coordinates *and velocity-components* are mere constants, and we are in effect dealing with a quadratic function with constant coefficients.

The proof is simple. If $\ddot{\mathbf{q}}$ refers to the actual motion, and $\ddot{\mathbf{q}} + \Delta\ddot{\mathbf{q}}$ to any other possible motion, we have

$$\begin{aligned} \Delta\left(\mathfrak{G} - \sum_{s=1}^{k} Q_s \ddot{q}_s\right) &= \tfrac{1}{2}\sum_{r=1}^{N} m_r(\ddot{x}_r + \Delta\ddot{x}_r)^2 - \tfrac{1}{2}\sum_{r=1}^{N} m_r \ddot{x}_r{}^2 - \sum_{s=1}^{k} Q_s\,\Delta\ddot{q}_s \\ &= \tfrac{1}{2}\sum_{r=1}^{N} m_r(\Delta\ddot{x}_r)^2 + \left(\sum_{r=1}^{N} m_r\ddot{x}_r\,\Delta\ddot{x}_r - \sum_{s=1}^{k} Q_s\,\Delta\ddot{q}_s\right), \end{aligned} \tag{12.4.5}$$

and the last bracket on the right is identically zero by the fifth form of the fundamental equation (12.3.11). Thus

$$\Delta\left(\mathfrak{G} - \sum_{s=1}^{k} Q_s \ddot{q}_s\right) > 0 \tag{12.4.6}$$

unless $\Delta\ddot{\mathbf{x}} = 0$, and the theorem is established.

The theorem just proved is intimately related to Gauss's principle of Least Constraint (§ 4.3). For

$$C = \tfrac{1}{2}\sum_{r=1}^{N} m_r\left(\ddot{x}_r - \frac{X_r}{m_r}\right)^2, \tag{12.4.7}$$

and this is the same as

$$\mathfrak{G} - \sum_{r=1}^{N} X_r \ddot{x}_r \tag{12.4.8}$$

if we omit terms not containing accelerations. Moreover $\sum_{r=1}^{N} X_r\ddot{x}_r$ differs from $\sum_{s=1}^{k} Q_s\ddot{q}_s$ only by terms not containing accelerations. Thus (12.4.4) only differs from C by terms not containing accelerations, and it follows that the theorem (12.4.6) can be deduced from Gauss's principle of Least Constraint.

12.5 The Gibbs-Appell equations. The theorem proved above (§ 12.4) that $\mathfrak{G} - \sum_{s=1}^{k} Q_s\ddot{q}_s$ is a minimum for the actual motion, contains more than sufficient information to establish the equations of motion. The first-order conditions for a stationary value will suffice, and these give the equations

$$\frac{\partial \mathfrak{G}}{\partial \ddot{q}_r} = Q_r, \qquad r = 1, 2, \ldots, k. \tag{12.5.1}$$

These are the Gibbs-Appell equations. They are the equations that we should have obtained from the fifth form of the fundamental equation (12.3.11) if we had worked with infinitesimal, instead of finite, variations. They were first discovered by Willard Gibbs in 1879, and studied in detail by Appell twenty years later. It is clear that, so far as the equations of motion are concerned, terms in $\mathfrak{G}$ that do not contain a $\ddot{q}_r$ can be omitted altogether. To complete the scheme of differential equations we must add the $n - k$ $(= l + p)$ geometrical equations

$$\dot{q}_r = \sum_{s=1}^{k} \beta_{rs}\dot{q}_s + \beta_r, \qquad r = k + 1, k + 2, \ldots, n, \tag{12.5.2}$$

derived from (12.2.7).

The Gibbs-Appell equations provide what is probably the simplest and most comprehensive form of the equations of motion so far discovered. They are of superlatively simple form, they apply with equal facility to holonomic and to non-holonomic systems alike, and quasi-coordinates may be used freely.

The technique required in using the equations is as follows. We begin by noticing the number k of freedoms of the system, and express the so-called "kinetic energy of the accelerations", $\frac{1}{2}\sum_{r=1}^{N} m_r\ddot{x}_r^2$, in terms of k $\ddot{q}$'s. We thus obtain the function $\mathfrak{G}$. In general q's and $\dot{q}$'s other than the k chosen ones will appear in $\mathfrak{G}$, but it is essential that only k $\ddot{q}$'s should appear. The k chosen q's may be Lagrangian coordinates or quasi-coordinates, whichever is more convenient. Then we consider the work done by the given forces in a virtual displacement, and express it in the form $\sum_{s=1}^{k} Q_s\delta q_s$. The equations of motion are given by (12.5.1), and the $(n - k)$ geometrical equations (12.5.2) complete the scheme of differential equations which determines the n variables $q_1, q_2, \ldots, q_n$ as functions of t.

Chapter XIII

Applications of the Gibbs-Appell equations

13.1 Particle moving in a plane. As a first simple application of the Gibbs-Appell equations we use the equations to study the motion of a particle in a plane, using the coordinates r, q, where

$$r^2 = x^2 + y^2, \qquad dq = x\,dy - y\,dx. \tag{13.1.1}$$

Here r is a Lagrangian coordinate, q a quasi-coordinate. We have

$$r\dot{r} = x\dot{x} + y\dot{y}, \qquad \dot{q} = x\dot{y} - y\dot{x}, \tag{13.1.2}$$

whence

$$r^2\dot{r}^2 + \dot{q}^2 = r^2(\dot{x}^2 + \dot{y}^2). \tag{13.1.3}$$

Further

$$r\ddot{r} + \dot{r}^2 = x\ddot{x} + y\ddot{y} + \dot{x}^2 + \dot{y}^2 \tag{13.1.4}$$

whence, using (13.1.3),

$$x\ddot{x} + y\ddot{y} = r\ddot{r} - \frac{\dot{q}^2}{r^2}. \tag{13.1.5}$$

But also

$$x\ddot{y} - y\ddot{x} = \ddot{q}, \tag{13.1.6}$$

so, from (13.1.5) and (13.1.6),

$$r^2(\ddot{x}^2 + \ddot{y}^2) = \ddot{q}^2 + \left(r\ddot{r} - \frac{\dot{q}^2}{r^2}\right)^2. \tag{13.1.7}$$

Thus finally

$$\mathfrak{S} = \tfrac{1}{2}m(\ddot{x}^2 + \ddot{y}^2) = \tfrac{1}{2}m\left\{\left(\ddot{r} - \frac{\dot{q}^2}{r^3}\right)^2 + \frac{\ddot{q}^2}{r^2}\right\}. \tag{13.1.8}$$

Since a term not containing acceleration-components may be omitted from $\mathfrak{S}$, we can write, instead of (13.1.8),

$$\mathfrak{S} = \tfrac{1}{2}m\left(\ddot{r}^2 - \frac{2}{r^3}\,\dot{q}^2\ddot{r} + \frac{1}{r^2}\,\ddot{q}^2\right). \tag{13.1.9}$$

The formula for $\mathfrak{S}$ can be found rather more expeditiously by noticing that the radial component of acceleration is

$$\ddot{r} - r\dot{\theta}^2 = \ddot{r} - \frac{\dot{q}^2}{r^3},$$

and the transverse component is $\ddot{q}/r$, giving the same result.

If the radial and transverse components of force are R, S, the work done in a virtual displacement is

$$R\,\delta r + \frac{S}{r}\,\delta q, \tag{13.1.10}$$

and the Gibbs-Appell equations of motion are

$$m\left(\ddot{r} - \frac{\dot{q}^2}{r^3}\right) = R, \qquad m\ddot{q} = rS, \tag{13.1.11}$$

which are of course familiar from elementary considerations.

In the central orbit problem, the field is radial, $S = 0$, and we have the well-known first integral $\dot{q} = \alpha$. The first equation now becomes

$$m\left(\ddot{r} - \frac{\alpha^2}{r^3}\right) = R, \tag{13.1.12}$$

and if $R = -m\dfrac{dV}{dr}$ we derive at once the familiar first integral (5.2.39),

$$\dot{r}^2 + 2V + \frac{\alpha^2}{r^2} = 2h.$$

13.2 Analogue of König's Theorem. There is, for any dynamical system, a theorem for accelerations analogous to König's Theorem (7.1.2) for velocities. The Gibbs function $\mathfrak{G}$ can be written as the sum of two terms, one involving only the acceleration of the centre of gravity G of the system, the other involving only the acceleration of the particles relative to the centre of gravity. Writing

$$x = \xi + \alpha, \qquad y = \eta + \beta, \qquad z = \zeta + \gamma,$$

where x, y, z are Cartesian coordinates of a typical particle, as in § 7.1, we have

$$\mathfrak{G} = \tfrac{1}{2}M(\ddot{\xi}^2 + \ddot{\eta}^2 + \ddot{\zeta}^2) + \tfrac{1}{2}Sm(\ddot{\alpha}^2 + \ddot{\beta}^2 + \ddot{\gamma}^2). \tag{13.2.1}$$

The result follows from the fundamental property of the centre of gravity, which implies

$$Sm\ddot{\alpha} = Sm\ddot{\beta} = Sm\ddot{\gamma} = 0.$$

A special case of particular interest is that in which the system consists of a single rigid body. When the system contains several rigid bodies it is usually advantageous (as with König's theorem) to apply the theorem to the separate rigid bodies rather than to the system as a whole.

13.3 Two-dimensional problems. For a rigid lamina moving in a plane

$$\mathfrak{G} = \tfrac{1}{2}Mf^2 + \tfrac{1}{2}Sm(r^2\ddot{\theta}^2 + r^2\dot{\theta}^4), \tag{13.3.1}$$

where f is the acceleration of the centre of gravity G, and r, θ are polar coordinates relative to axes in fixed directions through G. Omitting irrelevancies we have

$$\mathfrak{G} = \tfrac{1}{2}Mf^2 + \tfrac{1}{2}I\ddot{\theta}^2, \tag{13.3.2}$$

where I is the moment of inertia of the lamina about its centre of gravity.

As a concrete example consider a uniform solid cylinder of radius a rolling on the inner surface of a fixed hollow cylinder of radius b. The axes of the cylinders are horizontal, the surfaces are rough enough to prevent slipping, and the motion is one in which the surfaces remain in contact. Here $k = 1$. In Fig. 13.3 the point A' on the rolling cylinder is the point that is in contact with the lowest point A of the fixed cylinder in the equilibrium position, so that the arc $A'B$ of the rolling cylinder is equal to the arc AB of the fixed cylinder. Thus, with the notation indicated in the figure, the condition for pure rolling is

(13.3.3) $$a(\theta + \varphi) = b\theta, \qquad \text{i.e.} \qquad a\varphi = c\theta,$$

where $c = b - a$. The Gibbs function is

(13.3.4) $$\mathfrak{G} = \tfrac{1}{2}M(c^2\ddot{\theta}^2 + c^2\dot{\theta}^4) + \tfrac{1}{2}(\tfrac{1}{2}Ma^2)\ddot{\varphi}^2.$$

We must express this in terms of one acceleration-component (since $k = 1$), so (omitting an irrelevant term) we have

(13.3.5) $$\mathfrak{G} = \tfrac{3}{4}Mc^2\ddot{\theta}^2.$$

The work done by the given forces (the weight) in a virtual displacement is

(13.3.6) $$Mg\ \delta(c\cos\theta) = -Mgc\sin\theta\ \delta\theta.$$

The equation of motion is therefore

$$\tfrac{3}{2}Mc^2\ddot{\theta} = -Mgc\sin\theta,$$

giving

(13.3.7) $$\ddot{\theta} + \frac{2}{3}\frac{g}{c}\sin\theta = 0.$$

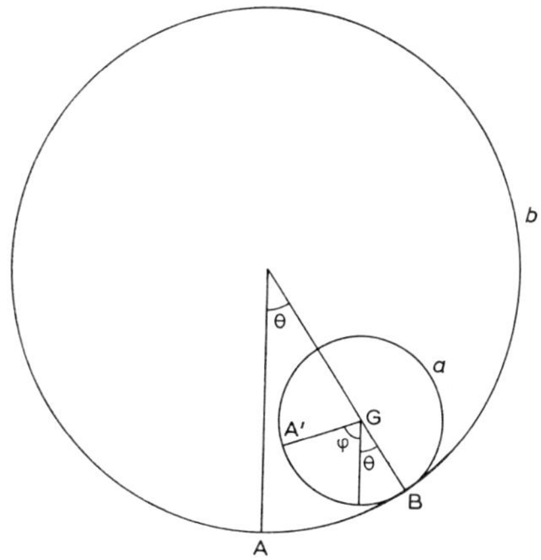

Figure 13.3

The angle θ varies as the inclination to the downward vertical of a simple pendulum of length $\tfrac{3}{2}c$.

13.4 Motion of a rigid body in space. To find the Gibbs function we use the theorem of § 13.2, so we first calculate $\mathfrak{G}$ for a rigid body having one point O fixed. We use a rectangular trihedral of moving axes with origin at O. Let $\boldsymbol{\theta}$ be the angular velocity of the trihedral, $\boldsymbol{\omega}$ the angular velocity of the body; let $\mathbf{r}$ denote the position vector of a typical particle of the body, $\mathbf{u}$ its velocity, and $\mathbf{f}$ its acceleration. All these vectors are measured relative to the moving trihedral (i.e., strictly speaking, relative to a fixed trihedral instantaneously coincident with the moving trihedral). We have

(13.4.1) $$\mathbf{u} = \dot{\mathbf{r}} + \boldsymbol{\theta} \times \mathbf{r} = \boldsymbol{\omega} \times \mathbf{r},$$

(13.4.2) $$\begin{aligned} \mathbf{f} &= \dot{\mathbf{u}} + \boldsymbol{\theta} \times \mathbf{u} \\ &= \boldsymbol{\omega} \times \dot{\mathbf{r}} + \dot{\boldsymbol{\omega}} \times \mathbf{r} + \boldsymbol{\theta} \times (\boldsymbol{\omega} \times \mathbf{r}) \\ &= \boldsymbol{\omega} \times [(\boldsymbol{\omega} - \boldsymbol{\theta}) \times \mathbf{r}] + \dot{\boldsymbol{\omega}} \times \mathbf{r} + \boldsymbol{\theta} \times (\boldsymbol{\omega} \times \mathbf{r}) \\ &= \boldsymbol{\omega} \times (\boldsymbol{\omega} \times \mathbf{r}) + \dot{\boldsymbol{\omega}} \times \mathbf{r} + [\boldsymbol{\theta} \times (\boldsymbol{\omega} \times \mathbf{r}) + \boldsymbol{\omega} \times (\mathbf{r} \times \boldsymbol{\theta})] \\ &= (\boldsymbol{\omega} \cdot \mathbf{r})\boldsymbol{\omega} - \omega^2\mathbf{r} - \mathbf{r} \times \boldsymbol{\varphi}, \end{aligned}$$

where $\boldsymbol{\varphi}$ denotes the vector

(13.4.3) $$\boldsymbol{\varphi} = \dot{\boldsymbol{\omega}} + \boldsymbol{\theta} \times \boldsymbol{\omega}.$$

The x-component of acceleration is

(13.4.4) $$\begin{aligned} (\omega_1 x + \omega_2 y + \omega_3 z)\omega_1 &- (\omega_1^2 + \omega_2^2 + \omega_3^2)x - y\varphi_3 + z\varphi_2 \\ &= -x(\omega_2^2 + \omega_3^2) + y(\omega_1\omega_2 - \varphi_3) + z(\omega_3\omega_1 + \varphi_2). \end{aligned}$$

So far the motion of the trihedral is independent of the motion of the body. To make further progress we must choose the trihedral so that its axes are principal axes of inertia for the body and the moments of inertia about these axes are constants. Then

(13.4.5) $$2\mathfrak{G} = Sm\{[z^2(\omega_2\omega_3 - \varphi_1)^2 + y^2(\omega_2\omega_3 + \varphi_1)^2] + \cdots + \cdots\},$$

where only the terms containing φ_1 have been included, irrelevant terms not containing a component of $\boldsymbol{\varphi}$ have been omitted, and we have used the properties

(13.4.6) $$Smyz = Smzx = Smxy = 0.$$

Expanding (13.4.5), and omitting terms not containing a component of $\boldsymbol{\varphi}$, we see that the terms in $2\mathfrak{G}$ containing φ_1 are

(13.4.7) $$\varphi_1{}^2Sm(y^2 + z^2) - 2\omega_2\omega_3\varphi_1Sm(z^2 - y^2).$$

Hence finally

(13.4.8) $$2\mathfrak{G} = A\varphi_1{}^2 + B\varphi_2{}^2 + C\varphi_3{}^2 - 2(B - C)\omega_2\omega_3\varphi_1 - 2(C - A)\omega_3\omega_1\varphi_2 - 2(A - B)\omega_1\omega_2\varphi_3,$$

where as usual A, B, C denote the moments of inertia about the axes of the trihedral.

In the applications (unless the body has one point fixed) we use the theorem of § 13.2, taking the origin O at the centre of gravity of the body. Consider the following cases:

(i) A uniform solid sphere, or cube, or any other body, whose ellipsoid of inertia at O is a sphere. Here $A = B = C$, and the motion of the trihedral is at our choice, and independent of the motion of the body. The Gibbs function (for the motion relative to O) is

(13.4.9) $$\mathfrak{G} = \tfrac{1}{2}A(\varphi_1{}^2 + \varphi_2{}^2 + \varphi_3{}^2).$$

(ii) A solid of revolution, such as a uniform right cylinder or a spinning top, $A = B \neq C$. Here the axis $O3$ of the trihedral must lie always along the axis of symmetry, so that $\theta_1 = \omega_1$, $\theta_2 = \omega_2$, but in general $\theta_3 \neq \omega_3$. In this case

(13.4.10) $$\varphi_1 = \dot{\omega}_1 + \omega_2(\omega_3 - \theta_3), \quad \varphi_2 = \dot{\omega}_2 - \omega_1(\omega_3 - \theta_3), \quad \varphi_3 = \dot{\omega}_3,$$

and (13.4.8) becomes

(13.4.11) $$\mathfrak{G} = \tfrac{1}{2}\{A(\dot{\omega}_1{}^2 + \dot{\omega}_2{}^2) + C\dot{\omega}_3{}^2 + 2(A\theta_3 - C\omega_3)(\omega_1\dot{\omega}_2 - \omega_2\dot{\omega}_1)\},$$

where some irrelevant terms have been omitted.

The result can be expressed in an alternative form which is sometimes useful. If we consider the point P on the axis of symmetry at unit distance from O, its velocity and acceleration are

(13.4.12) $$\mathbf{u} = \{\omega_2, \quad -\omega_1, \quad 0\},$$

(13.4.13) $$\mathbf{f} = \{\dot{\omega}_2 + \omega_1\theta_3, -\dot{\omega}_1 + \omega_2\theta_3, -(\omega_1{}^2 + \omega_2{}^2)\},$$

and we can write

(13.4.14) $$\mathfrak{G} = \tfrac{1}{2}Af^2 + \tfrac{1}{2}C\dot{\omega}_3{}^2 - C\omega_3\boldsymbol{\zeta} \cdot (\mathbf{u} \times \mathbf{f}),$$

where $f = |\mathbf{f}|$, and $\boldsymbol{\zeta}$ is the vector OP, i.e. $\{0, 0, 1\}$. We derive at once the following alternative form for $\mathfrak{G}$,

(13.4.15) $$\mathfrak{G} = \tfrac{1}{2}Af^2 + \tfrac{1}{2}C\dot{\omega}_3{}^2 - C\omega_3\mathbf{f} \cdot (\boldsymbol{\zeta} \times \mathbf{u}).$$

(iii) In the general case, where A, B, C are all different, we must use axes fixed in the body, the principal axes of inertia at the centre of gravity O. In this case $\boldsymbol{\theta} = \boldsymbol{\omega}$, $\boldsymbol{\varphi} = \{\dot\omega_1, \dot\omega_2, \dot\omega_3\}$, and therefore

$$(13.4.16) \quad \mathfrak{G} = \tfrac{1}{2}\{A\dot\omega_1{}^2 + B\dot\omega_2{}^2 + C\dot\omega_3{}^2 - 2(B - C)\omega_2\omega_3\dot\omega_1 - 2(C - A)\omega_3\omega_1\dot\omega_2 - 2(A - B)\omega_1\omega_2\dot\omega_3\}.$$

13.5 Sphere on turntable. A sphere rolls on a rough plane which turns about a fixed point O of itself with prescribed angular velocity Ω. The rotation is not necessarily uniform, Ω being a prescribed function of t of class C_1 (as in the example discussed in § 5.5). The sphere is a uniform solid sphere, or a uniform spherical shell, or any sphere whose centre of gravity G is at its centre and whose ellipsoid of inertia at G is a sphere. We use axes $Oxyz$ in fixed directions, with O as origin and Oz normal to the plane. We take the axes $G123$ in fixed directions parallel to $Oxyz$, so that in this problem $\theta_1 = \theta_2 = \theta_3 = 0$. We denote the coordinates of the centre of the rolling sphere by x, y, a, where a is the radius of the sphere. The rolling conditions are

$$(13.5.1) \quad \begin{cases} \dot x - a\omega_2 = -\Omega y, \\ \dot y + a\omega_1 = \Omega x. \end{cases}$$

The system is a non-holonomic system with three freedoms, and we use the five coordinates x, y, q_1, q_2, q_3, where

$$(13.5.2) \quad \dot q_1 = \omega_1, \qquad \dot q_2 = \omega_2, \qquad \dot q_3 = \omega_3.$$

Here $k = 3$, $l = 2$, and of the five coordinates x, y are Lagrangian coordinates, q_1, q_2, q_3 are quasi-coordinates. If in the sequel we describe the orientation of the sphere at any instant by means of Euler's angles θ, φ, ψ, then $n = 8$. The possible variations satisfy

$$(13.5.3) \quad \begin{cases} dx - a\,dq_2 + \Omega y\,dt = 0, \\ dy + a\,dq_1 - \Omega x\,dt = 0. \end{cases}$$

We now calculate the Gibbs function $\mathfrak{G}$,

$$(13.5.4) \quad 2\mathfrak{G} = M(\ddot x^2 + \ddot y^2) + A(\ddot q_1{}^2 + \ddot q_2{}^2 + \ddot q_3{}^2),$$

which we must express in terms of three acceleration-components, say $\ddot x$, $\ddot y$, $\ddot q_3$. Now

$$(13.5.5) \quad \begin{cases} a\ddot q_2 = \ddot x + \Omega\dot y + \dot\Omega y, \\ a\ddot q_1 = -\ddot y + \Omega\dot x + \dot\Omega x, \end{cases}$$

and therefore

$$(13.5.6) \quad 2\mathfrak{G} = M(\ddot x^2 + \ddot y^2) + \frac{A}{a^2}(\ddot x + \Omega\dot y + \dot\Omega y)^2 + \frac{A}{a^2}(\ddot y - \Omega\dot x - \dot\Omega x)^2 + A\ddot q_3{}^2.$$

It happens that in this simple case only the three privileged coordinates x, y, q_3 appear in $\mathfrak{G}$, though in general, as we have noticed (§ 12.4), other coordinates and velocities will appear as well.

Next we consider the work done by the given forces in a virtual displacement. Now in a virtual displacement

$$(13.5.7) \quad \delta q_1 = -\delta y/a, \qquad \delta q_2 = \delta x/a.$$

If the external force-system acting on the sphere is equivalent to a force (X, Y, Z) through the centre of the sphere and a couple (P, Q, R), the work done in a virtual displacement is

$$(13.5.8)\qquad X\,\delta x + Y\,\delta y + P\,\delta q_1 + Q\,\delta q_2 + R\,\delta q_3 = \left(X + \frac{Q}{a}\right)\delta x + \left(Y - \frac{P}{a}\right)\delta y + R\,\delta q_3.$$

It is evident of course that only the moment of the system about the point of contact is relevant, and it is just the components of this moment that appear in (13.5.8). The equations of motion are

$$(13.5.9)\qquad M\ddot{x} + \frac{A}{a^2}(\ddot{x} + \Omega\dot{y} + \dot{\Omega}y) = X + \frac{Q}{a},$$

$$(13.5.10)\qquad M\ddot{y} + \frac{A}{a^2}(\ddot{y} - \Omega\dot{x} - \dot{\Omega}x) = Y - \frac{P}{a},$$

$$(13.5.11)\qquad A\ddot{q}_3 = R.$$

Consider as a particular application the case where the rotation of the plane is uniform ($\dot{\Omega} = 0$), and where the external force-system is equivalent to a force $(M\xi, M\eta, M\zeta)$ through the centre of the sphere ($P = Q = R = 0$). From (13.5.11) $\omega_3 = \dot{q}_3 =$ constant, and the equations for the motion of the centre are

$$(13.5.12)\qquad \begin{cases} B\ddot{x} + A\Omega\dot{y} = Ma^2\xi, \\ B\ddot{y} - A\Omega\dot{x} = Ma^2\eta, \end{cases}$$

where $B(= A + Ma^2)$ is the moment of inertia about a tangent to the sphere. For a uniform solid sphere

$$(13.5.13)\qquad \frac{A}{2} = \frac{B}{7} = \frac{Ma^2}{5},$$

giving

$$(13.5.14)\qquad \begin{cases} \ddot{x} + \frac{2}{7}\Omega\dot{y} = \frac{5}{7}\xi, \\ \ddot{y} - \frac{2}{7}\Omega\dot{x} = \frac{5}{7}\eta. \end{cases}$$

These are the same as the equations for the motion of a particle of unit mass under the action of (i) a force $(\frac{5}{7}\xi, \frac{5}{7}\eta)$, and (ii) a gyroscopic force $\frac{2}{7}\,\Omega|\mathbf{v}|$ perpendicular and proportional to the velocity $\mathbf{v}$.

Take the case of a uniform field, where ξ is a positive constant and $\eta = 0$; if the sphere is heavy and the turntable is not horizontal but inclined at an angle α to the horizontal, and if we take the axis Ox down the line of greatest slope, $\xi = g \sin\alpha$. Putting $x + iy = z$ the equations (13.5.14) lead to

$$(13.5.15)\qquad \ddot{z} - i\kappa\dot{z} = \lambda,$$

where κ and λ are real constants, $\kappa = \frac{2}{7}\Omega$ and $\lambda = \frac{5}{7}\xi$. The solution is

$$(13.5.16)\qquad z - z_0 = \frac{1}{\kappa^2}(\lambda + i\kappa w_0)(1 - e^{i\kappa t}) + \frac{i\lambda}{\kappa^2}(\kappa t),$$

where $z = z_0$ and $\dot{z} = w_0$ at $t = 0$. The curve is a trochoid, generated by the rolling of a circle on a line at right angles to the field; in the problem of the inclined turntable, this line is horizontal. We observe that the value of z_0 is unimportant; the motion relative to the initial point depends only on w_0. For the particular case $w_0 = 0$ we get the cycloid

$$z - z_0 = \rho(1 - e^{i\kappa t}) + i\rho(\kappa t), \tag{13.5.17}$$

where $\rho = \lambda/\kappa^2$ (Fig. 13.5). The radius of the rolling circle is ρ, and for the problem of the inclined turntable this is $\dfrac{35}{4}\dfrac{g}{\Omega^2}\sin\alpha$.

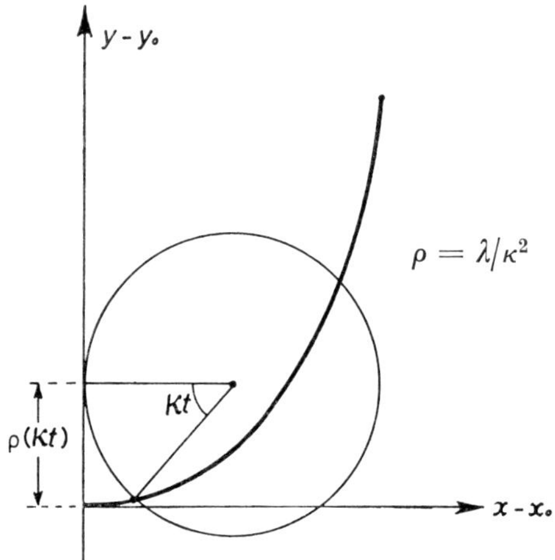

Figure 13.5

13.6 Sphere on rotating inclined plane. A plane inclined at an angle α to the horizontal rotates with uniform angular velocity Ω about a vertical axis. A uniform heavy solid sphere, of mass M and radius a, rolls on the plane. In this case $k = 3$, $l = 2$. We take the origin at O where the axis of rotation meets the plane, Oy up the line of greatest slope, Oz normal to the plane, Ox horizontal in the plane. For these axes

$$\theta_1 = 0, \quad \theta_2 = \Omega \sin\alpha, \quad \theta_3 = \Omega\cos\alpha. \tag{13.6.1}$$

If the centre G of the sphere is (x, y, z) we have for the components of acceleration

$$f_1 = \ddot{x} - 2(\dot{y}\theta_3 - \dot{z}\theta_2) - x({\theta_2}^2 + {\theta_3}^2) + \theta_1(y\theta_2 + z\theta_3), \tag{13.6.2}$$

and similar formulae for f_2 and f_3. In the case under discussion $z = a$ and $\theta_1 = 0$, and the formulae take the form

$$\begin{cases} f_1 = \ddot{x} - 2\dot{y}\theta_3 - x\Omega^2, \\ f_2 = \ddot{y} + 2\dot{x}\theta_3 - y{\theta_3}^2 + a\theta_2\theta_3, \\ f_3 = -2\dot{x}\theta_2 + y\theta_2\theta_3 - a{\theta_2}^2, \end{cases} \tag{13.6.3}$$

but the last does not contain an acceleration-component, and in this context is of no interest to us. We can now write down the part of the Gibbs function which depends on the motion of the centre of gravity of the sphere.

For the remaining part we have to calculate φ_1, φ_2, and φ_3. The rolling conditions are

$$\begin{cases} a(\omega_2 - \theta_2) = \dot{x}, \\ a\omega_1 = -\dot{y}. \end{cases} \tag{13.6.4}$$

These can be written down from the relative motion. Alternatively, if (u, v, w) is the velocity of the centre, we have, from the motion of the particle of the sphere instantaneously in contact with the plane,

$$\begin{cases} u - a\omega_2 = -y\theta_3, \\ v + a\omega_1 = x\theta_3, \\ w = -x\theta_2, \end{cases} \tag{13.6.5}$$

and from the motion of the point of contact, i.e. of the foot of the perpendicular from the centre of the sphere on to the plane, we have

$$(13.6.6)\qquad \begin{cases} u - a\theta_2 = \dot{x} - y\theta_3, \\ v = \dot{y} + x\theta_3, \\ w = -x\theta_2. \end{cases}$$

The rolling conditions (13.6.4) follow at once from (13.6.5) and (13.6.6). Thus

$$(13.6.7)\qquad \begin{cases} a\varphi_1 = a(\dot{\omega}_1 - \omega_2\theta_3 + \omega_3\theta_2) = -\ddot{y} - (\dot{x} + a\theta_2)\theta_3 + \dot{\zeta}\theta_2, \\ a\varphi_2 = a(\dot{\omega}_2 + \omega_1\theta_3) = \ddot{x} - \dot{y}\theta_3, \\ a\varphi_3 = a(\dot{\omega}_3 - \omega_1\theta_2) = \ddot{\zeta} + \dot{y}\theta_2, \end{cases}$$

where $\dot{\zeta} = a\omega_3$.

We can now write the Gibbs function in terms of the three acceleration-components $\ddot{x}$, $\ddot{y}$, $\ddot{\zeta}$, viz.

$$(13.6.8)\qquad 2\mathfrak{G}/M = (\ddot{x} - 2\dot{y}\theta_3 - x\Omega^2)^2 + (\ddot{y} + 2\dot{x}\theta_3 - y\theta_3{}^2 + a\theta_2\theta_3)^2 + \tfrac{2}{5}(\ddot{x} - \dot{y}\theta_3)^2 + \tfrac{2}{5}(\ddot{y} + \dot{x}\theta_3 - \dot{\zeta}\theta_2 + a\theta_2\theta_3)^2 + \tfrac{2}{5}(\ddot{\zeta} + \dot{y}\theta_2)^2.$$

To find the work done by the given forces in a virtual displacement we may consider the moment of the weight about the point of contact; we recall that in a virtual displacement the plane is at rest. Even more simply, the work done is $-\delta V$, where $V = Mgy \sin\alpha$, so the work done by the given forces in a virtual displacement is

$$(13.6.9)\qquad -(Mg\sin\alpha)\,\delta y.$$

We can now write the equations of motion

$$(13.6.10)\qquad \ddot{x} - 2\dot{y}\theta_3 - x\Omega^2 + \tfrac{2}{5}(\ddot{x} - \dot{y}\theta_3) = 0,$$

$$(13.6.11)\qquad \ddot{y} + 2\dot{x}\theta_3 - y\theta_3{}^2 + a\theta_2\theta_3 + \tfrac{2}{5}(\ddot{y} + \dot{x}\theta_3 - \dot{\zeta}\theta_2 + a\theta_2\theta_3) = -g\sin\alpha,$$

$$(13.6.12)\qquad \ddot{\zeta} + \dot{y}\theta_2 = 0.$$

From (13.6.12) we have

$$(13.6.13)\qquad \dot{\zeta} + y\theta_2 = \text{constant},$$

and substituting for $\dot{\zeta}$ from (13.6.13) in (13.6.11) we obtain finally the equations determining x and y as functions of t. These equations can be written in the form

$$(13.6.14)\qquad \begin{cases} 7\ddot{x} - 12\Omega\dot{y}\cos\alpha - 5\Omega^2 x = 0, \\ 7\ddot{y} + 12\Omega\dot{x}\cos\alpha - (7\cos^2\alpha - 2)\Omega^2 y + \eta = 0, \end{cases}$$

where the constant η is given by

$$(13.6.15)\qquad \eta = (5g - 2an\Omega + 7a\Omega^2\cos\alpha - 2b\Omega^2\sin\alpha)\sin\alpha,$$

b being the value of y, and n the value of ω_3, at $t = 0$. Provided that $7\cos^2\alpha \neq 2$, the equations can be made into homogeneous linear equations with constant coefficients by a change of origin.

The equations (13.6.14) are of a type that can be integrated completely if the initial values of x, y, $\dot{x}$, $\dot{y}$ are prescribed. The problem discussed in § 13.5, if $X = Y = 0$, is the special case of the present problem obtained by putting $\alpha = 0$. The answer appears there in a slightly different form, since here the axes are rotating, but the reconciliation is immediate.

13.7 Sphere rolling on a fixed surface. The surfaces are perfectly rough, or at least rough enough to prevent slipping, so there is pure rolling throughout. We take moving axes $G1$, $G2$, $G3$ with origin at G, the centre of the sphere. The sphere is a uniform solid sphere, or at least its centre of gravity is at its centre, and the ellipsoid of inertia at this point is a sphere. The axis $G3$ lies in the line from the point of contact to the centre of the sphere, so the point of contact is $(0, 0, -a)$, where a is the radius of the sphere. The rolling conditions are

$$u_1 = a\omega_2, \quad u_2 = -a\omega_1, \quad u_3 = 0, \tag{13.7.1}$$

where $\mathbf{u}$ is the velocity of G, and $\boldsymbol{\omega}$ the angular velocity of the sphere. The components of acceleration of G are

$$\begin{cases} f_1 = \dot{u}_1 - u_2\theta_3 + u_3\theta_2 = a(\dot{\omega}_2 + \omega_1\theta_3), \\ f_2 = \dot{u}_2 - u_3\theta_1 + u_1\theta_3 = -a(\dot{\omega}_1 - \omega_2\theta_3), \\ f_3 = \dot{u}_3 - u_1\theta_2 + u_2\theta_1 = -a(\omega_2\theta_2 + \omega_1\theta_1), \end{cases} \tag{13.7.2}$$

but the component f_3 is irrelevant since it does not contain an $\dot{\omega}_r$. Thus

$$\mathfrak{G} = \tfrac{1}{2}A(\varphi_1{}^2 + \varphi_2{}^2 + \varphi_3{}^2) + \tfrac{1}{2}Ma^2(\dot{\omega}_1 - \omega_2\theta_3)^2 + \tfrac{1}{2}Ma^2(\dot{\omega}_2 + \omega_1\theta_3)^2. \tag{13.7.3}$$

If $\mathbf{N}$ is the moment of the given forces about the point of contact, the work done in a virtual displacement is

$$N_1\,\delta q_1 + N_2\,\delta q_2 + N_3\,\delta q_3, \tag{13.7.4}$$

where $\dot{q}_r = \omega_r$. The system has three degrees of freedom, and we have expressed $\mathfrak{G}$ in terms of three $\ddot{q}$'s, so the equations of motion are

$$\frac{\partial \mathfrak{G}}{\partial \dot{\omega}_r} = N_r, \qquad r = 1, 2, 3, \tag{13.7.5}$$

giving

$$\begin{cases} A\varphi_1 + Ma^2(\dot{\omega}_1 - \omega_2\theta_3) = N_1, \\ A\varphi_2 + Ma^2(\dot{\omega}_2 + \omega_1\theta_3) = N_2, \\ A\varphi_3 = N_3. \end{cases} \tag{13.7.6}$$

If we write B for $A + Ma^2$, so that B is the moment of inertia of the sphere about a tangent, we can write the equations of motion (13.7.6) in the form

$$\begin{cases} B(\dot{\omega}_1 - \omega_2\theta_3) + A\omega_3\theta_2 = N_1, \\ B(\dot{\omega}_2 + \omega_1\theta_3) - A\omega_3\theta_1 = N_2, \\ A(\dot{\omega}_3 - \omega_1\theta_2 + \omega_2\theta_1) = N_3. \end{cases} \tag{13.7.7}$$

Let us consider as a concrete illustration the problem of a uniform solid sphere, of radius a, rolling on the outside of a fixed sphere of radius $c - a$. We choose the axes shown in Fig. 13.7 (the axis $G2$ is horizontal) and then

$$\omega_1 = \frac{c}{a}\,\theta_1, \quad \omega_2 = \frac{c}{a}\,\theta_2; \tag{13.7.8}$$

$$N_1 = 0, \quad N_2 = Mga \sin\theta, \quad N_3 = 0. \tag{13.7.9}$$

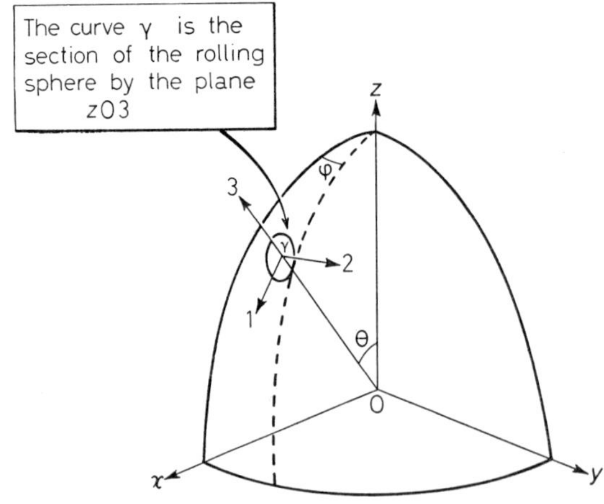

Figure 13.7

The last of the equations (13.7.7) gives ω_3 = constant, say

$$\omega_3 = n, \tag{13.7.10}$$

and the first two become

$$\begin{cases} B\dfrac{c}{a}(\dot{\theta}_1 - \theta_2\theta_3) + An\theta_2 = 0, \\[2ex] B\dfrac{c}{a}(\dot{\theta}_2 + \theta_1\theta_3) - An\theta_1 = Mga\sin\theta. \end{cases} \tag{13.7.11}$$

Now the angular velocity of the moving axes is given by

$$\theta_1 = -\dot{\varphi}\sin\theta, \quad \theta_2 = \dot{\theta}, \quad \theta_3 = \dot{\varphi}\cos\theta, \tag{13.7.12}$$

and for a uniform solid sphere

$$\frac{A}{2} = \frac{B}{7} = \frac{Ma^2}{5}. \tag{13.7.13}$$

Substituting these values in (13.7.11) we obtain

$$7c(\ddot{\varphi}\sin\theta + 2\dot{\theta}\dot{\varphi}\cos\theta) - 2an\dot{\theta} = 0, \tag{13.7.14}$$

$$7c(\ddot{\theta} - \dot{\varphi}^2\cos\theta\sin\theta) + 2an\dot{\varphi}\sin\theta = 5g\sin\theta, \tag{13.7.15}$$

and these are the equations determining the values of θ and φ at any time. If we multiply the equation (13.7.14) by $\sin\theta$, and integrate, we find

$$7c\dot{\varphi}\sin^2\theta + 2an\cos\theta = \text{constant}. \tag{13.7.16}$$

The equations (13.7.15) and (13.7.16) are identical with the equations (8.6.6) and (8.6.7) for the motion of the axis of a spinning top; to reconcile the two sets of formulae we need $p = an/7c$, $q = 5g/7c$, and the constant on the right in (13.7.16) must be $14c\lambda$. Now we know that the equations for the motion of the axis of a spinning top are the Lagrangian equations derived from the Routhian function obtained by ignoration of the coordinate ψ. The equations (13.7.15–16) are in fact the Lagrangian equation for θ, and the momentum integral for φ, derived from the Lagrangian function

(13.7.17) $$L = \tfrac{7}{2}c(\dot{\theta}^2 + \sin^2\theta\dot{\varphi}^2) + 2na\dot{\varphi}\cos\theta - 5g\cos\theta.$$

13.8 The spinning top. We turn now to problems of motion of a rigid body possessing an axis of symmetry. We begin with the familiar problem of the spinning top, already discussed by Lagrange's method in §§ 8.6–8.10. Hitherto our applications of the Gibbs-Appell equations have always been to non-holonomic systems, and indeed it must be emphasized that it is in dealing with non-holonomic systems that the power and beauty of the method are most evident. But the method is of course applicable also to holonomic systems. For the spinning top, taking the origin O at the peg, and the axis $O3$ along the axis of the top, we have, as in (13.4.11),

(13.8.1) $$\mathfrak{G} = \tfrac{1}{2}A(\dot{\omega}_1^2 + \dot{\omega}_2^2) + \tfrac{1}{2}C\dot{\omega}_3^2 + (A\theta_3 - C\omega_3)(\omega_1\dot{\omega}_2 - \omega_2\dot{\omega}_1).$$

The equations of motion, with $\dot{q}_r = \omega_r$, are

(13.8.2) $$A\dot{\omega}_1 - (A\theta_3 - C\omega_3)\omega_2 = N_1,$$

(13.8.3) $$A\dot{\omega}_2 + (A\theta_3 - C\omega_3)\omega_1 = N_2,$$

(13.8.4) $$C\dot{\omega}_3 = N_3,$$

where $N_1\,\delta q_1 + N_2\,\delta q_2 + N_3\,\delta q_3$ is the work done by the given forces in a virtual displacement.

Let us consider in particular the classical problem in which the given forces are weights. Let θ, φ denote the polar angles of the axis $O3$ of the top referred to fixed axes $Oxyz$ with Oz vertically upwards. If $O2$ is taken horizontal (Fig. 13.8) we have

(13.8.5) $$\omega_1 = -\dot{\varphi}\sin\theta, \quad \omega_2 = \dot{\theta}, \quad \theta_3 = \dot{\varphi}\cos\theta,$$

(13.8.6) $$N_1 = 0, \quad N_2 = Mgl\sin\theta, \quad N_3 = 0,$$

where l denotes the distance of the centre of gravity G from the peg O.

From (13.8.4) we have ω_3 = constant, say

(13.8.7) $$\omega_3 = n,$$

and this holds also in any other problem in which the moment of the given forces about the axis of the top is zero. The equations (13.8.2) and (13.8.3) now become

(13.8.8) $$A(\ddot{\varphi}\sin\theta + 2\dot{\theta}\dot{\varphi}\cos\theta) - Cn\dot{\theta} = 0,$$

(13.8.9) $$A\ddot{\theta} - (A\dot{\varphi}\cos\theta - Cn)\dot{\varphi}\sin\theta = Mgl\sin\theta.$$

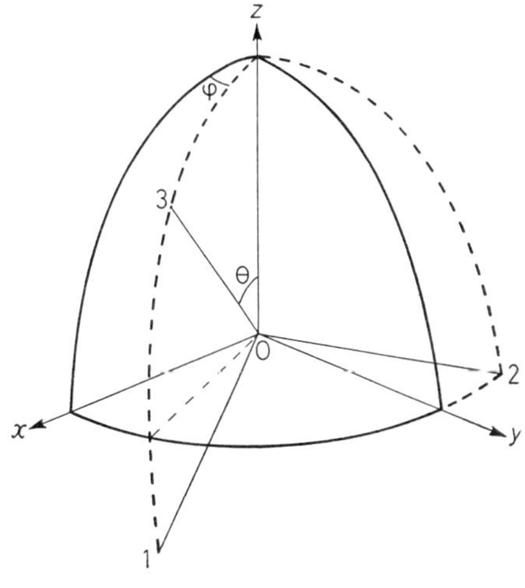

Figure 13.8

On multiplication by $\sin\theta$, the equation (13.8.8) can be integrated, giving

(13.8.10) $$A\dot{\varphi}\sin^2\theta + Cn\cos\theta = \text{constant}.$$

Now (13.8.9) and (13.8.10) are the equations (8.6.6) and (8.6.7), and the rest follows as in §§ 8.6–8.10.

If we use the other form (13.4.15) for $\mathfrak{G}$, the equations will appear in the form discussed in § 8.7. In this approach to the problem

$$\mathfrak{G} = \tfrac{1}{2}Af^2 + \tfrac{1}{2}C\dot{\omega}_3{}^2 - C\omega_3\mathbf{f}\,.\,(\boldsymbol{\zeta} \times \mathbf{u}), \tag{13.8.11}$$

and we can write this in the form

$$\mathfrak{G} = \tfrac{1}{2}A(\ddot{x}^2 + \ddot{y}^2 + \ddot{z}^2) + \tfrac{1}{2}C\dot{\omega}_3{}^2 - C\omega_3\{\ddot{x}(y\dot{z} - z\dot{y}) + \ddot{y}(z\dot{x} - x\dot{z}) + \ddot{z}(x\dot{y} - y\dot{x})\}, \tag{13.8.12}$$

where x, y, z are the direction cosines of the axis, i.e. $\boldsymbol{\zeta}$ is the vector (x, y, z). In using (13.8.12) we must remember that $\ddot{x}$, $\ddot{y}$, $\ddot{z}$ are not independent; in fact

$$x\ddot{x} + y\ddot{y} + z\ddot{z} + (\dot{x}^2 + \dot{y}^2 + \dot{z}^2) = 0. \tag{13.8.13}$$

We can use (13.8.13) to reduce (13.8.12) to a form involving only the requisite three accelerations; or, more symmetrically, we can use an undetermined multiplier. The work done by the weight in a virtual displacement is $-Mgl\ \delta z$, so the equations of motion are

$$\begin{cases} A\ddot{x} - C\omega_3(y\dot{z} - z\dot{y}) = kx, \\ A\ddot{y} - C\omega_3(z\dot{x} - x\dot{z}) = ky, \\ A\ddot{z} - C\omega_3(x\dot{y} - y\dot{x}) = kz - Mgl, \\ C\dot{\omega}_3 = 0. \end{cases} \tag{13.8.14}$$

The last gives the familiar integral $\omega_3 = n$, and the others become

$$A\ddot{x} - Cn(y\dot{z} - z\dot{y}) = kx, \tag{13.8.15}$$

$$A\ddot{y} - Cn(z\dot{x} - x\dot{z}) = ky, \tag{13.8.16}$$

$$A\ddot{z} - Cn(x\dot{y} - y\dot{x}) = kz - Mgl. \tag{13.8.17}$$

We easily recover the results previously established. From (13.8.15–17) we derive immediately the equations (8.7.3–5). For the special case of the sleeping top, x and y are small, and in forming the linear approximation we may put $z = 1$. Then, to the required order of approximation, $k = Mgl$, and (13.8.15–16) become

$$\begin{cases} A\ddot{x} + Cn\dot{y} - Mglx = 0, \\ A\ddot{y} - Cn\dot{x} - Mgly = 0, \end{cases} \tag{13.8.18}$$

and these are equivalent to (9.9.14).

13.9 The rolling penny. The system discussed in § 13.8 is a holonomic system; but, as we have noticed, it is when the system is not holonomic that the advantages of the Gibbs-Appell equations are most conspicuous. We now consider the problem of a coin or hoop rolling on a rough horizontal plane; the problem has already been attacked by Lagrange's method in § 8.12. With the notation of Fig. 8.12 we have, if $\mathbf{u}$ is the velocity and $\mathbf{f}$ the acceleration of the centre G of the solid,

$$u_1 = 0, \quad u_2 = -a\omega_3, \quad u_3 = a\omega_2, \tag{13.9.1}$$

and

$$\begin{cases} f_1 = \dot{u}_1 - u_2\theta_3 + u_3\theta_2 = a(\omega_3\theta_3 + \omega_2{}^2), \\ f_2 = \dot{u}_2 - u_3\theta_1 + u_1\theta_3 = -a(\dot{\omega}_3 + \omega_1\omega_2), \\ f_3 = \dot{u}_3 - u_1\theta_2 + u_2\theta_1 = a(\dot{\omega}_2 - \omega_3\omega_1), \end{cases} \tag{13.9.2}$$

remembering that $\theta_1 = \omega_1$ and $\theta_2 = \omega_2$. Thus

(13.9.3) $$\mathfrak{G} = \tfrac{1}{2}Ma^2(\dot\omega_2 - \omega_3\omega_1)^2 + \tfrac{1}{2}Ma^2(\dot\omega_3 + \omega_1\omega_2)^2 + \tfrac{1}{2}A(\dot\omega_1^2 + \dot\omega_2^2) + \tfrac{1}{2}C\dot\omega_3^2 + (A\theta_3 - C\omega_3)(\omega_1\dot\omega_2 - \omega_2\dot\omega_1).$$

The rate of working of the weight is $-Mga\cos\theta\omega_2$, so the equations of motion, taking $\dot q_r = \omega_r$, are

(13.9.4) $$\begin{cases} A\dot\omega_1 - A\theta_3\omega_2 + C\omega_2\omega_3 = 0, \\ (A + Ma^2)\dot\omega_2 + A\theta_3\omega_1 - (C + Ma^2)\omega_3\omega_1 = -Mga\cos\theta, \\ (C + Ma^2)\dot\omega_3 + Ma^2\omega_1\omega_2 = 0. \end{cases}$$

If now θ, φ are the polar angles of $G3$ referred to fixed rectangular axes (Fig. 8.12) we have

(13.9.5) $$\omega_1 = -\dot\varphi\sin\theta, \quad \omega_2 = \dot\theta, \quad \theta_3 = \dot\varphi\cos\theta.$$

(We recall that $\theta_3 \neq \omega_3$: in fact $\omega_3 = \theta_3 + \dot\psi = \dot\psi + \dot\varphi\cos\theta$.) On substituting these values in (13.9.4) we find

(13.9.6) $$(A + Ma^2)\ddot\theta - A\dot\varphi^2\cos\theta\sin\theta + (C + Ma^2)\omega_3\dot\varphi\sin\theta + Mga\cos\theta = 0,$$

(13.9.7) $$A(\ddot\varphi\sin\theta + 2\dot\theta\dot\varphi\cos\theta) - C\omega_3\dot\theta = 0,$$

(13.9.8) $$(C + Ma^2)\dot\omega_3 - Ma^2\dot\theta\dot\varphi\sin\theta = 0.$$

These are equivalent to the equations (8.12.17–19) previously found by Lagrange's method. We have already considered one particular application of these equations. As a second application, let us determine the condition for stability (i.e. first-order stability) when the coin or hoop rolls in a straight line. If the circle rolls along Oy with speed $a\Omega$ we have, in the steady motion, $\theta = \tfrac{1}{2}\pi$, $\varphi = 0$, $\omega_3 = -\Omega$. Let us now consider a small disturbance, and write the equations correct to the first order. From (13.9.8) see that ω_3 remains constant, and we may suppose that it retains the value $-\Omega$ of the undisturbed motion. Putting $\theta = \tfrac{1}{2}\pi + \xi$, and retaining only the first-order terms in ξ and φ, we have

(13.9.9) $$(k + 1)\ddot\xi - (2k + 1)\Omega\dot\varphi - n^2\xi = 0,$$

(13.9.10) $$\ddot\varphi + 2\Omega\dot\xi = 0,$$

where $A = \tfrac{1}{2}C = kMa^2$, and $n^2 = g/a$. From (13.9.10),

(13.9.11) $$\dot\varphi + 2\Omega\xi = \text{constant},$$

and therefore, substituting for $\dot\varphi$ from (13.9.11) in (13.9.9), we have

(13.9.12) $$(k + 1)\ddot\xi + \{2(2k + 1)\Omega^2 - n^2\}\xi = \text{constant}.$$

The condition for first-order stability is

(13.9.13) $$a^2\Omega^2 > ga/(4k + 2).$$

For a coin this gives $a^2\Omega^2 > ga/3$, for a hoop $a^2\Omega^2 > ga/4$. For a penny, with radius 19/32 inch, the critical speed is about ·73 feet per second.

13.10 Euler's equations. We now turn to some problems of the motion of a rigid body in which we use axes fixed in the body. Let us first consider the problem of a rigid body moving in space under the action of any given system of forces.

We take a trihedral $G123$, with its origin at the centre of gravity G, the axes $G1$, $G2$, $G3$ being the principal axes of inertia at G. The system is a holonomic system with six degrees of freedom, and we use as the six coordinates the coordinates ξ, η, ζ of G referred to fixed rectangular axes $Oxyz$, and q_1, q_2, q_3, where $\dot{q}_1$, $\dot{q}_2$, $\dot{q}_3$ are components in the directions $G1$, $G2$, $G3$ of the angular velocity of the body. Of these six coordinates, ξ, η, ζ are Lagrangian, q_1, q_2, q_3 are in general quasi-coordinates. The Gibbs function is, from § 13.2 and (13.4.16),

$$\mathfrak{G} = \tfrac{1}{2}M(\ddot{\xi}^2 + \ddot{\eta}^2 + \ddot{\zeta}^2) + \tfrac{1}{2}\{A\dot{\omega}_1{}^2 - 2(B - C)\omega_2\omega_3\dot{\omega}_1 + \cdots + \cdots\}. \tag{13.10.1}$$

The given forces acting on the body are equivalent to a force at G and a couple. Let the force have components X, Y, Z in the directions Ox, Oy, Oz, and let the couple have components N_1, N_2, N_3 in the directions $G1$, $G2$, $G3$. Then the equations of motion are

$$M\ddot{\xi} = X, \quad M\ddot{\eta} = Y, \quad M\ddot{\zeta} = Z; \tag{13.10.2}$$

$$\begin{cases} A\dot{\omega}_1 - (B - C)\omega_2\omega_3 = N_1, \\ B\dot{\omega}_2 - (C - A)\omega_3\omega_1 = N_2, \\ C\dot{\omega}_3 - (A - B)\omega_1\omega_2 = N_3. \end{cases} \tag{13.10.3}$$

The first thing we notice is the splitting of the equations into two groups, the first group (13.10.2) referring to the motion of G, the second group (13.10.3) referring to the variation of the orientation. This is the classical theorem of the independence of translation and rotation. The motion of the centre of gravity of the body is the same as the motion of a single particle of mass M acted on by a force which is the vector sum of the given forces; this is the result we should observe if all the mass were concentrated at one point, and all the given forces acted at that point. The equations for the rotational motion (13.10.3) are the famous equations of Euler, discovered in 1758.

Euler's equations (13.10.3) also apply to the problem of a body with one point O fixed; the body is free to rotate about O. The axes $O123$ are now the principal axes of inertia at O, and the symbols A, B, C now denote the moments of inertia about these axes.

13.11 The free body, the case of axial symmetry. One of the most famous among the classical problems of rigid dynamics is that of the *free motion* of a rigid body, i.e. motion when there are no given forces. The centre of gravity moves in a straight line with uniform speed, and the rotation satisfies the equations

$$\begin{cases} A\dot{\omega}_1 - (B - C)\omega_2\omega_3 = 0, \\ B\dot{\omega}_2 - (C - A)\omega_3\omega_1 = 0, \\ C\dot{\omega}_3 - (A - B)\omega_1\omega_2 = 0. \end{cases} \tag{13.11.1}$$

The same equations are valid also in other cases. If the body moves in space, and the given forces are equivalent to a single force through the centre of gravity, the equations (13.11.1) still hold, because in this case $\mathbf{N} = \mathbf{0}$; an important special case is that of a rigid-body projectile moving in the (uniform) gravitational field of the Earth. Again, the same equations hold in the problem of a rigid body with one point O fixed, if the given forces have zero moment about O.

We now consider the motion determined by (13.11.1) in various cases. If there is spherical symmetry, so that $A = B = C$, the matter is simple. (Remember that the axes are now fixed in the body and moving with it). We derive at once from (13.11.1) that $\boldsymbol{\omega}$ is constant, and the body continues to rotate with constant spin about a fixed line.

Next, we consider the case of axial symmetry, $A = B \neq C$. The body is for example a penny or a gyroscope or a spinning top moving freely; if it is a fixed-point problem, and we take account of gravity, the fixed point must be the centre of gravity. The third of Euler's equations gives $\omega_3 =$ constant, say

(13.11.2) $$\omega_3 = n,$$

and the first two equations become

(13.11.3) $$\dot{\omega}_1 + \lambda\omega_2 = 0,$$

(13.11.4) $$\dot{\omega}_2 - \lambda\omega_1 = 0,$$

where $\lambda = n(C - A)/A$. We will suppose for definiteness that $n > 0$. If $\omega_1 + i\omega_2 = z$ the equations (13.11.3-4) are equivalent to

(13.11.5) $$\dot{z} - i\lambda z = 0,$$

whence

(13.11.6) $$z = \rho e^{i\lambda(t-t_0)},$$

where ρ, t_0 are real constants, and $\rho > 0$. Without loss of generality we can put $t_0 = 0$, and then

(13.11.7) $$\omega_1 = \rho \cos \lambda t \quad \omega_2 = \rho \sin \lambda t, \quad \omega_3 = n.$$

From these formulae (13.11.7) we easily deduce the nature of the motion. The angular velocity vector $(\omega_1, \omega_2, \omega_3)$ and the angular momentum vector $(A\omega_1, A\omega_2, C\omega_3)$ lie in a plane through the axis of symmetry $G3$ which rotates *relative to the body* with angular velocity λ. The axis of rotation makes an angle α with $G3$, and the angular momentum vector makes an angle β with $G3$, where

(13.11.8) $$\tan \alpha = \rho/n, \quad \tan \beta = A\rho/Cn,$$

and the angular velocity $\sqrt{(\rho^2 + n^2)}$ is constant.

If $C > A$, $\lambda > 0$ and $\alpha > \beta$. The axis of rotation makes a constant angle $(\alpha - \beta)$ with the angular momentum vector, which is fixed, so the axis of rotation is a generator of a right circular cone, fixed in space, of angle $(\alpha - \beta)$. But the axis of rotation makes a constant angle α with $G3$, and traces out in the body a cone of angle α. The motion is given by the rolling of a cone of angle α, which is fixed in the body, on a cone of angle $(\alpha - \beta)$ which is fixed in space. The small cone touches the large cone internally (Fig. 13.11*a*).

If $C < A$, $\lambda < 0$, say $\lambda = -\mu$, where $\mu > 0$, and $\alpha < \beta$. A cone of angle α, fixed in the body, rolls on a fixed cone of angle $(\beta - \alpha)$ which it touches externally (Fig. 13.11*b*).

In each case the axis of the gyroscope describes a cone of angle β about the angular momentum vector, the period being $2\pi A/\sqrt{(C^2n^2 + A^2\rho^2)}$.

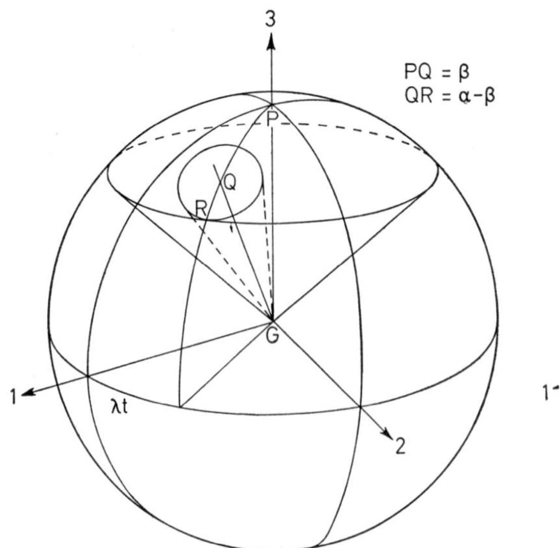

Figure 13.11a

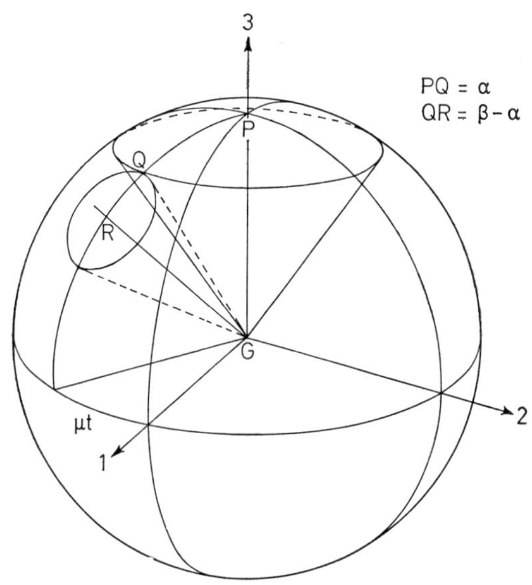

Figure 13.11b

13.12 The free body, the general case. We now consider the motion determined by (13.11.1) where no two of A, B, C are equal. We will suppose, for definiteness, $A > B > C$. If we multiply Euler's equations (13.11.1) by ω_1, ω_2, ω_3, and add, we are led to the integral

(13.12.1) $$A\omega_1{}^2 + B\omega_2{}^2 + C\omega_3{}^2 = 2T,$$

and if we multiply by $A\omega_1$, $B\omega_2$, $C\omega_3$ and add, we are led to the integral

(13.12.2) $$A^2\omega_1{}^2 + B^2\omega_2{}^2 + C^2\omega_3{}^2 = \eta^2.$$

These equations express the constancy of the kinetic energy of the rotational motion, and the constancy of the magnitude of the angular momentum. We write (13.12.1) and (13.12.2) in the forms

$$A\omega_1^2 + B\omega_2^2 + C\omega_3^2 = D\Omega^2, \tag{13.12.3}$$

$$A^2\omega_1^2 + B^2\omega_2^2 + C^2\omega_3^2 = D^2\Omega^2, \tag{13.12.4}$$

where D and Ω are positive constants, $D = \eta^2/2T$, $\Omega = 2T/\eta$. If we think of ω_1, ω_2, ω_3 as Cartesian coordinates of a representative point, the path of this point is the intersection of two ellipsoids. Since

$$D = \frac{A^2\omega_1^2 + B^2\omega_2^2 + C^2\omega_3^2}{A\omega_1^2 + B\omega_2^2 + C\omega_3^2} \tag{13.12.5}$$

we see that $A \geqslant D \geqslant C$. The extreme values are of little interest, since, for example, $A = D$ implies $\omega_2 = \omega_3 = 0$ throughout the motion; the motion is a steady rotation $\pm\Omega$ about $G1$. We therefore set aside the extreme cases and assume $A > D > C$.

We solve the equations (13.12.3–4) for ω_1^2 and ω_3^2 in terms of ω_2^2, giving

$$\omega_1^2 = \frac{B(B-C)}{A(A-C)}(\alpha^2 - \omega_2^2), \quad \omega_3^2 = \frac{B(A-B)}{C(A-C)}(\beta^2 - \omega_2^2), \tag{13.12.6}$$

where α and β are positive constants defined by

$$\alpha^2 = \frac{D(D-C)}{B(B-C)}\Omega^2, \quad \beta^2 = \frac{D(A-D)}{B(A-B)}\Omega^2. \tag{13.12.7}$$

The second of Euler's equations

$$B\dot{\omega}_2 = -(A-C)\omega_3\omega_1 \tag{13.12.8}$$

now gives

$$\dot{\omega}_2^2 = \frac{(A-B)(B-C)}{AC}(\alpha^2 - \omega_2^2)(\beta^2 - \omega_2^2). \tag{13.12.9}$$

This is an equation of a familiar type (see § 1.2) which defines the variation of ω_2 with t. We denote the quartic on the right in (13.12.9) by $f(\omega_2)$. There are two cases to consider; if $\alpha = \beta$ the quartic has double zeros, if $\alpha \neq \beta$ the quartic has simple zeros.

(i) $\alpha = \beta$. Since

$$\beta^2 - \alpha^2 = \frac{D(A-C)(B-D)}{B(A-B)(B-C)}\Omega^2, \tag{13.12.10}$$

$\alpha = \beta$ if and only if $D = B$. This implies the relation

$$\eta^2 = 2BT \tag{13.12.11}$$

connecting the angular momentum η and the kinetic energy T. When (13.12.11) is satisfied, $\alpha = \beta = \Omega$, and (13.12.9) becomes

$$\dot{\omega}_2^2 = \frac{(A-B)(B-C)}{AC}(\Omega^2 - \omega_2^2)^2. \tag{13.12.12}$$

The graph of the second member of (13.12.12) is shown in Fig. 13.12a. We know from the theory expounded in § 1.2 that there is a limitation motion in ω_2 such that $\omega_2 \to +\Omega$ or $\omega_2 \to -\Omega$ as $t \to \infty$.

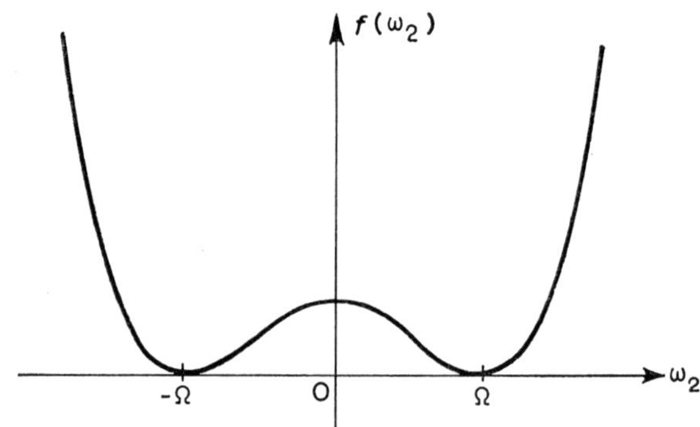

Figure 13.12a

The curve of intersection of the ellipsoids (13.12.3) and (13.12.4) lies in the planes

$$A(A - B)\omega_1{}^2 = C(B - C)\omega_3{}^2, \tag{13.12.13}$$

and consists of two ellipses. The initial value of $\boldsymbol{\omega}$ lies on one of these.

Let us suppose, for the sake of definiteness, that, at $t = 0$,

$$\omega_1 < 0, \qquad \omega_2 = 0, \qquad \omega_3 > 0. \tag{13.12.14}$$

Explicitly

$$\omega_1 = -\Omega\sqrt{\left\{\frac{B(B - C)}{A(A - C)}\right\}}, \qquad \omega_2 = 0, \quad \omega_3 = +\Omega\sqrt{\left\{\frac{B(A - B)}{C(A - C)}\right\}}. \tag{13.12.15}$$

Then ω_2 increases initially, in virtue of (13.12.8), and therefore ω_2 increases steadily always, and tends to Ω as t tends to infinity. To find the explicit value of ω_2 at time t, put

$$\omega_2 = \Omega \tanh \theta. \tag{13.12.16}$$

On substituting in (13.12.12) we find

$$\theta = nt, \tag{13.12.17}$$

where

$$n = \Omega\sqrt{\left\{\frac{(A - B)(B - C)}{AC}\right\}} \tag{13.12.18}$$

Thus

$$\omega_2 = \Omega \tanh nt, \tag{13.12.19}$$

and we deduce the values of ω_1 and ω_3 from (13.12.6), namely

$$\omega_1 = -\sqrt{\left\{\frac{B(B - C)}{A(A - C)}\right\}}\,\Omega \operatorname{sech} nt, \quad \omega_3 = \sqrt{\left\{\frac{B(A - B)}{C(A - C)}\right\}}\,\Omega \operatorname{sech} nt. \tag{13.12.20}$$

The signs are fixed by the initial values, and ω_1 remains negative, ω_3 positive, always. We see that $\omega_1 \to 0$ and $\omega_3 \to 0$ as $t \to \infty$, and the motion approaches a uniform rotation Ω about $G2$.

(ii) $\alpha \neq \beta$. This implies $D \neq B$. The quartic $f(\omega_2)$ in (13.12.9) has four simple zeros (Fig. 13.12*b*), and since $|\omega_2|$ is less than the smaller of α and β there is a libration in ω_2 between $\pm\alpha$ (if $\alpha < \beta$) or between $\pm\beta$ (if $\beta < \alpha$). To fix the ideas, let us suppose $\alpha < \beta$, which holds if $D < B$.

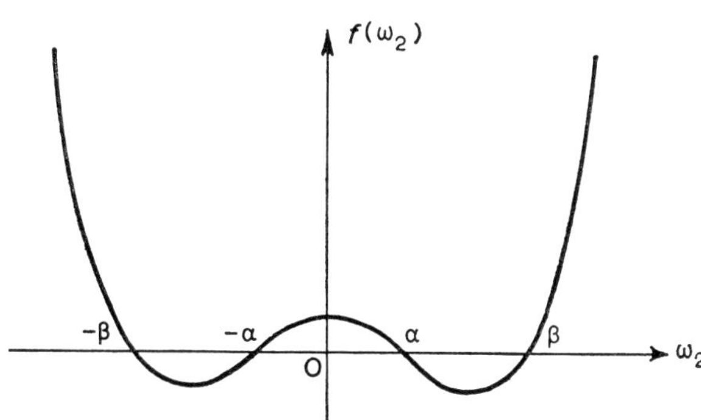

Figure 13.12*b*

We consider then the case in which

(13.12.21) $$A > B > D > C.$$

Here ω_2 oscillates between the values $\pm\alpha$, ω_1 vanishes when $\omega_2 = \pm\alpha$, but $\omega_3{}^2$ never falls below the value

(13.12.22) $$\frac{B(A - B)}{C(A - C)}(\beta^2 - \alpha^2) = \frac{D(B - D)}{C(B - C)}\Omega^2,$$

so ω_3 retains the same sign throughout; we will suppose for definiteness that $\omega_3 > 0$ at $t = 0$, and therefore $\omega_3 > 0$ always.

Now ω_2 oscillates between the values $\pm\alpha$, and we choose the origin of time so that

$$\omega_2 = 0, \qquad \dot{\omega}_2 > 0,$$

at $t = 0$. Since

$$B\dot{\omega}_2 = -(A - C)\omega_3\omega_1$$

we have $\omega_1 < 0$ at $t = 0$, and the initial conditions are like those assumed above, in (13.12.14). To integrate (13.12.9) we put

(13.12.23) $$\omega_2 = \alpha \operatorname{sn} u,$$

with

(13.12.24) $$k^2 = \frac{\alpha^2}{\beta^2} = \frac{(A - B)(D - C)}{(A - D)(B - C)},$$

and substituting in (13.12.9) we have

(13.12.25) $$\dot{u}^2 = \frac{(A - B)(B - C)}{AC}\beta^2 = \frac{(A - D)(B - C)D}{ABC}\Omega^2 = n^2, \text{ say,}$$

where $n > 0$. Thus, with the conditions prescribed at $t = 0$, we have

(13.12.26) $$u = nt,$$

and

(13.12.27) $$\omega_2 = \alpha \operatorname{sn} nt.$$

From (13.12.6)

(13.12.28) $$\omega_3 = \sqrt{\left\{\frac{D(A-D)}{C(A-C)}\right\}}\,\Omega \operatorname{dn} nt = \delta \operatorname{dn} nt, \text{ say.}$$

Finally

(13.12.29) $$\omega_1 = -\frac{B}{A-C}\frac{\dot\omega_2}{\omega_3} = -\sqrt{\left\{\frac{D(D-C)}{A(A-C)}\right\}}\,\Omega \operatorname{cn} nt = -\gamma \operatorname{cn} nt, \text{ say,}$$

where $\beta > \alpha > \gamma > 0$. Thus the complete solution for $\boldsymbol{\omega}$ is

(13.12.30) $$\omega_1 = -\gamma \operatorname{cn} nt, \qquad \omega_2 = \alpha \operatorname{sn} nt, \qquad \omega_3 = \delta \operatorname{dn} nt.$$

We notice that ω_1 varies between γ and $-\gamma$ with period $4K/n$, ω_2 varies between α and $-\alpha$ with the same period $4K/n$, and ω_3 varies between

(31.12.31) $$\Omega\sqrt{\left\{\frac{D(A-D)}{C(A-C)}\right\}} \quad \text{and} \quad \Omega\sqrt{\left\{\frac{D(B-D)}{C(B-C)}\right\}}$$

with period $2K/n$.

13.13 The free body, orientation. The free motion of a rigid body is governed by the equations (13.11.1), and from these equations we have determined the angular velocity at each instant of time, which gives a sort of *internal* description of the motion. But this is hardly a complete solution of the problem, because it does not tell us about the phenomena that we actually observe during the motion: it does not determine the actual configuration of the system at time t. To achieve this *external* description of the motion we find the Euler angles, relative to some fixed trihedral, at time t.

We suppose G to be at rest, and we simplify the calculation by taking the axis Oz of the fixed trihedral ($O \equiv G$) in the direction of the angular momentum vector which we know to be constant. With this convention the components of angular momentum along $O1$, $O2$, $O3$ are, from (7.11.1),

(13.13.1) $$A\omega_1 = D\Omega \cos z_1 = -D\Omega \sin\theta \cos\psi,$$

(13.13.2) $$B\omega_2 = D\Omega \cos z_2 = D\Omega \sin\theta \sin\psi,$$

(13.13.3) $$C\omega_3 = D\Omega \cos z_3 = D\Omega \cos\theta.$$

The equation (13.13.3), with (13.12.30), determines θ in terms of the time,

(13.13.4) $$\cos\theta = \frac{C\omega_3}{D\Omega} = \sqrt{\left\{\frac{C(A-D)}{D(A-C)}\right\}} \operatorname{dn} nt,$$

and, since

(13.13.5) $$k'^2 = \frac{(A-C)(B-D)}{(A-D)(B-C)},$$

$\cos\theta$ varies from an upper limit $\sqrt{\left\{\frac{C(A-D)}{D(A-C)}\right\}}$ to a lower limit $\sqrt{\left\{\frac{C(B-D)}{D(B-C)}\right\}}$, and back again, with a period $2K/n$.

We next find ψ as a function of t,

(13.13.6) $$\tan \psi = -\frac{B\omega_2}{A\omega_1} = \sqrt{\left\{\frac{B(A-C)}{A(B-C)}\right\}}\frac{\text{sn } nt}{\text{cn } nt},$$

and ψ always increases (as we expect); ψ increases by 2π in time $4K/n$.

We next find $\dot{\varphi}$ in terms of t. The angular velocity about OT (Fig. 7.11) is

(13.13.7) $$-\dot{\varphi}\sin\theta = \omega_1 \cos\psi - \omega_2 \sin\psi = \frac{A\omega_1{}^2 + B\omega_2{}^2}{-D\Omega \sin\theta},$$

whence

(13.13.8) $$\dot{\varphi} = \frac{A\omega_1{}^2 + B\omega_2{}^2}{D\Omega \sin^2\theta} = D\Omega\frac{A\omega_1{}^2 + B\omega_2{}^2}{A^2\omega_1{}^2 + B^2\omega_2{}^2} = D\Omega\frac{D\Omega^2 - C\omega_3{}^2}{D^2\Omega^2 - C^2\omega_3{}^2}.$$

On substituting the value of ω_3 from (13.12.28) and rearranging we get

(13.13.9) $$\dot{\varphi} = D\Omega\frac{(A-C)\,\text{sn}^2\, nt + (B-C)\,\text{cn}^2\, nt}{B(A-C)\,\text{sn}^2\, nt + A(B-C)\,\text{cn}^2\, nt},$$

which varies between $D\Omega/A$ and $D\Omega/B$, $\dot{\varphi}$ remaining positive always. The second member of (13.13.9) is periodic with period $2K/n$, so

$$\dot{\varphi}\left(t + \frac{2K}{n}\right) = \dot{\varphi}(t),$$

whence

$$\varphi\left(t + \frac{2K}{n}\right) = \varphi(t) + \varphi_0,$$

and φ increases by the constant increment φ_0 when t increases by $2K/n$. The explicit value of φ_0 can be found by integration from (13.13.9); it lies between $\dfrac{D\Omega}{A}\dfrac{2K}{n}$ and $\dfrac{D\Omega}{B}\dfrac{2K}{n}$.

When θ, φ, ψ have been determined as functions of t we can express the nine direction cosines of the moving trihedral in terms of t by (7.11.1).

13.14 The theorems of Poinsot and Sylvester. We again suppose G to be at rest. Consider the ellipsoid, fixed in the body and moving with it, whose equation with the axes $G123$ is

(13.14.1) $$Ax^2 + By^2 + Cz^2 = D\Omega^2.$$

The perpendicular from G on to the tangent plane at $P(\omega_1, \omega_2, \omega_3)$ has length Ω, and the direction cosines of the normal at $(\omega_1, \omega_2, \omega_3)$ are

(13.14.2) $$A\omega_1/D\Omega, \qquad B\omega_2/D\Omega, \qquad C\omega_3/D\Omega.$$

Thus, since the angular momentum vector is constant, *the tangent plane is a fixed plane* ϖ. Thus the free motion of the body is generated by the rolling of the ellipsoid (13.14.1), with its centre fixed, on the plane ϖ. The angular velocity is equal to the distance r from the centre G of the ellipsoid to the point of contact P with ϖ. This is Poinsot's theorem.

Sylvester observed that if the ellipsoid (13.14.1) bounds a uniform solid, and this solid, freely pivoted at G, rolls on the plane ϖ under no forces (other than the reactions at G and P), then the rolling ellipsoid will move exactly as it does in the free motion of the body to which it is attached (provided that both start with the same angular velocity). The system has only one freedom, so that we have only to show that when a solid ellipsoid, pivoted at its centre, rolls on a rough plane, then $\omega \propto r$. If M' is the mass of the ellipsoid, its semi-axes a, b, c, the kinetic energy

$$(13.14.3) \qquad T = \frac{M'}{10}\{(b^2 + c^2)\omega_1^2 + (c^2 + a^2)\omega_2^2 + (a^2 + b^2)\omega_3^2\}$$

$$= \frac{M'}{10}\frac{\omega^2}{r^2}\{(b^2 + c^2)x^2 + (c^2 + a^2)y^2 + (a^2 + b^2)z^2\}.$$

Now

$$(13.14.4) \qquad \frac{1}{a^2b^2c^2}\{(b^2 + c^2)x^2 + (c^2 + a^2)y^2 + (a^2 + b^2)z^2\}$$

$$= \left(\frac{1}{b^2} + \frac{1}{c^2}\right)\frac{x^2}{a^2} + \left(\frac{1}{c^2} + \frac{1}{a^2}\right)\frac{y^2}{b^2} + \left(\frac{1}{a^2} + \frac{1}{b^2}\right)\frac{z^2}{c^2}$$

$$= \frac{1}{a^2} + \frac{1}{b^2} + \frac{1}{c^2} - \frac{1}{p^2},$$

where p is the (constant) distance of the fixed centre of the ellipsoid from the plane. Thus, since T is constant, $\omega \propto r$, and this completes the proof.

13.15 Ellipsoid rolling on a rough horizontal plane. As a final application of the Gibbs-Appell equations we consider the problem of a uniform solid ellipsoid rolling on a rough table. We take the axes of the ellipsoid as axes, and they are principal axes of inertia at the centre G. We denote the velocity of G by (u, v, w), the direction cosines of the downward vertical by (l, m, n), the point of contact with the table by (x, y, z). The rolling conditions are

$$(13.15.1) \qquad \begin{cases} u - y\omega_3 + z\omega_2 = 0, \\ v - z\omega_1 + x\omega_3 = 0, \\ w - x\omega_2 + y\omega_1 = 0. \end{cases}$$

Our first task is to calculate the components (f_1, f_2, f_3) of the acceleration of G. Now

$$(13.15.2) \qquad f_1 = \dot{u} - v\omega_3 + w\omega_2,$$

and substituting for u, v, w from (13.15.1) we find

$$(13.15.3) \quad f_1 = y\dot{\omega}_3 - z\dot{\omega}_2 + \dot{y}\omega_3 - \dot{z}\omega_2 + x(\omega_1^2 + \omega_2^2 + \omega_3^2) - \omega_1(x\omega_1 + y\omega_2 + z\omega_3).$$

So using the coordinates q_1, q_2, q_3, where $\dot{q}_r = \omega_r$, we have

$$(13.15.4) \quad \mathfrak{G} = \tfrac{1}{2}M(f_1^2 + f_2^2 + f_3^2) + \tfrac{1}{2}\{A\dot{\omega}_1^2 - 2(B - C)\omega_2\omega_3\dot{\omega}_1\} + \cdots + \cdots,$$

where the formula (13.15.3) for f_1, and the corresponding formulae for f_2 and f_3, are supposed to be substituted in (13.15.4).

The finding of Q_1, Q_2, Q_3 is easy, for **Q** is merely the moment of the weight about the point of contact, so that

$$Q_1 = Mg(-ny + mz). \tag{13.15.5}$$

An alternative proof of (13.15.5) may be of interest. We have

$$-\delta V = -Mg\,\delta p, \tag{13.15.6}$$

where p is the height of G above the plane. Now

$$\begin{aligned} -\dot{p} &= lu + mv + nw \\ &= \sum l(y\omega_3 - z\omega_2) \\ &= \sum (-ny + mz)\omega_1. \end{aligned} \tag{13.15.7}$$

Thus

$$-\delta V = Mg \sum (-ny + mz)\,\delta q_1, \tag{13.15.8}$$

and we recover (13.15.5).

Since l, m, n is a direction fixed in space

$$\begin{cases} \dot{l} - m\omega_3 + n\omega_2 = 0, \\ \dot{m} - n\omega_1 + l\omega_3 = 0, \\ \dot{n} - l\omega_2 + m\omega_1 = 0. \end{cases} \tag{13.15.9}$$

We have also, from the elementary geometry,

$$l = \frac{px}{a^2}, \qquad m = \frac{py}{b^2}, \qquad n = \frac{pz}{c^2}, \tag{13.15.10}$$

where as usual a, b, c are the lengths of the semi-axes of the ellipsoid.

We can now write the equations of motion

$$\frac{\partial \mathfrak{G}}{\partial \dot{\omega}_r} = Q_r. \tag{13.15.11}$$

The first is

(13.15.12)

$$\begin{aligned} Mz\{z\dot{\omega}_1 - x\dot{\omega}_3 + \dot{z}\omega_1 - \dot{x}\omega_3 + y(\omega_1{}^2 + \omega_2{}^2 + \omega_3{}^2) - \omega_2(x\omega_1 + y\omega_2 + z\omega_3)\} \\ -My\{x\dot{\omega}_2 - y\dot{\omega}_1 + \dot{x}\omega_2 - \dot{y}\omega_1 + z(\omega_1{}^2 + \omega_2{}^2 + \omega_3{}^2) - \omega_3(x\omega_1 + y\omega_2 + z\omega_3)\} \\ + A\dot{\omega}_1 - (B - C)\omega_2\omega_3 = Mg(-ny + mz), \end{aligned}$$

which becomes, on rearranging the terms,

$$\begin{aligned} (Mr^2 + A)\dot{\omega}_1 - Mx(x\dot{\omega}_1 + y\dot{\omega}_2 + z\dot{\omega}_3) + Mr\dot{r}\omega_1 \\ -M(\dot{x} - y\omega_3 + z\omega_2)(x\omega_1 + y\omega_2 + z\omega_3) - (B - C)\omega_2\omega_3 = Mg(-ny + mz), \end{aligned} \tag{13.15.13}$$

where $r^2 = x^2 + y^2 + z^2$. The equation (13.15.13) and the two similar equations, are the required equations of motion.

13.16 Stability of the spinning ellipsoid. Consider as a particular application of the equations of motion (13.15.13) the ellipsoid spinning, with angular velocity ω, about its a-axis. In what circumstances is there first-order stability if this state of motion is slightly disturbed? Assuming provisionally that a permanent motion only slightly different from the original motion is possible we may assume m, n, ω_2, ω_3 to be small, of the same order, and it will suffice for our purpose to find equations of motion correct to this order. Then, neglecting terms of the second order,

$$l = 1, \qquad x = r = a, \qquad y = b^2m/a, \qquad z = c^2n/a. \tag{13.16.1}$$

The first equation of motion (13.15.13) gives $\dot{\omega}_1 = 0$, so $\omega_1 =$ constant, and we suppose that ω_1 retains the value ω of the undisturbed motion. The equations (13.15.9) now give

$$\begin{cases} \omega_2 = \dot{n} + \omega m, \\ \omega_3 = -\dot{m} + \omega n, \end{cases} \tag{13.16.2}$$

correct to the first order.

The second and third equations of motion, on using the values (13.16.2) for ω_2 and ω_3, and substituting the values $A = M(b^2 + c^2)/5$ and so on, become

$$\begin{cases} (6a^2 + c^2)\ddot{n} + (12a^2 - 5b^2)\omega\dot{m} + (c^2 - a^2)(6\omega^2 + \lambda^2)n = 0, \\ (6a^2 + b^2)\ddot{m} - (12a^2 - 5c^2)\omega\dot{n} + (b^2 - a^2)(6\omega^2 + \lambda^2)m = 0. \end{cases} \tag{13.16.3}$$

where λ^2 has been written for $5g/a$. To find the period equation we write as usual

$$\frac{\ddot{m}}{-p^2} = \frac{\dot{m}}{ip} = m, \qquad \frac{\ddot{n}}{-p^2} = \frac{\dot{n}}{ip} = n, \tag{13.16.4}$$

and eliminate m/n. The resulting equation is

$$\begin{aligned}[]
[(b^2 + 6a^2)p^2 - (b^2 - a^2)(6\omega^2 + \lambda^2)][(c^2 + 6a^2)p^2 - (c^2 - a^2)(6\omega^2 + \lambda^2)] \\ - (5b^2 - 12a^2)(5c^2 - 12a^2)\omega^2p^2 = 0.
\end{aligned} \tag{13.16.5}$$

A sufficient condition for first-order stability is that the roots of the period equation (13.16.5) for p^2 should be real and positive.

We observe first that the roots cannot both be positive unless

$$(b^2 - a^2)(c^2 - a^2) > 0, \tag{13.16.6}$$

so $(b^2 - a^2)$ and $(c^2 - a^2)$ must both be positive or both negative. There cannot be stability unless the axis about which the ellipsoid spins is either the shortest axis or the longest.

(i) If a is the shortest semi-axis, we can write (13.16.5) in the form

$$\beta^2\gamma^2p^4 - \{(\beta^2\gamma^2 + 36\theta^2\varphi^2)\omega^2 + (\beta^2\varphi^2 + \gamma^2\theta^2)\lambda^2\}p^2 + \theta^2\varphi^2(6\omega^2 + \lambda^2)^2 = 0 \tag{13.16.7}$$

where the positive numbers β, γ, θ, φ are defined as follows:

$$\beta^2 = b^2 + 6a^2, \qquad \gamma^2 = c^2 + 6a^2, \qquad \theta^2 = b^2 - a^2, \qquad \varphi^2 = c^2 - a^2. \tag{13.16.8}$$

A sufficient condition for first-order stability is that the values of p^2 given by (13.16.7) should be real and positive. The coefficient of p^2 in (13.16.7) is certainly negative, and the remaining condition is

$$(\beta^2\gamma^2 + 36\theta^2\varphi^2)\omega^2 + (\beta^2\varphi^2 + \gamma^2\theta^2)\lambda^2 > 2\beta\gamma\theta\varphi(6\omega^2 + \lambda^2), \tag{13.16.9}$$

and this can be written in the form

$$(\beta\gamma - 6\theta\varphi)^2\omega^2 + (\beta\varphi - \gamma\theta)^2\lambda^2 > 0, \tag{13.16.10}$$

which is clearly satisfied. If the ellipsoid spins about the shortest axis there is stability for all values of ω.

(ii) If a is the longest semi-axis, we can write (13.16.5) in the form

$$\beta^2\gamma^2p^4 - \{(\beta^2\gamma^2 + 36\theta^2\varphi^2)\omega^2 - (\beta^2\varphi^2 + \gamma^2\theta^2)\lambda^2\}p^2 + \theta^2\varphi^2(6\omega^2 + \lambda^2)^2 = 0, \tag{13.16.11}$$

where now

$$\beta^2 = b^2 + 6a^2, \qquad \gamma^2 = c^2 + 6a^2, \qquad \theta^2 = a^2 - b^2, \qquad \varphi^2 = a^2 - c^2. \tag{13.16.12}$$

β, γ, θ, φ being positive numbers. The values of p^2 are real and positive if the following two conditions are satisfied,

$$(\beta^2\gamma^2 + 36\theta^2\varphi^2)\omega^2 - (\beta^2\varphi^2 + \gamma^2\theta^2)\lambda^2 > 0, \tag{13.16.13}$$

$$(\beta^2\gamma^2 + 36\theta^2\varphi^2)\omega^2 - (\beta^2\varphi^2 + \gamma^2\theta^2)\lambda^2 > 2\beta\gamma\theta\varphi(6\omega^2 + \lambda^2). \tag{13.16.14}$$

The second condition implies the first, so for stability we need (13.16.14), which is equivalent to

$$(\beta\gamma - 6\theta\varphi)^2\omega^2 > (\beta\varphi + \gamma\theta)^2\lambda^2. \tag{13.16.15}$$

Now $\beta\gamma > 6\theta\varphi$, so there is stability if $|\omega| > \Omega$, where

(13.16.16)

$$\Omega = \frac{\beta\varphi + \gamma\theta}{\beta\gamma - 6\theta\varphi}\lambda = \frac{\sqrt{(6a^2 + b^2)(a^2 - c^2)} + \sqrt{(6a^2 + c^2)(a^2 - b^2)}}{\sqrt{(6a^2 + b^2)(6a^2 + c^2)} - 6\sqrt{(a^2 - b^2)(a^2 - c^2)}}\sqrt{\left(\frac{5g}{a}\right)}.$$

Thus the results can be summed up very simply. If a is the least of a, b, c there is first-order stability for all values of the spin (as we should expect). If a is the intermediate length, the motion is always unstable. If a is the greatest of a, b, c, there is stability if the spin is greater than a certain critical value Ω.

Chapter XIV

Impulsive motion

14.1 The theory of impulses. We now turn to the study of the sudden change of motion that results when a dynamical system is acted on by impulses. We shall regard an impulse as the limiting case of a large force acting for a short interval of time. For a single free particle the typical equation of motion is

(14.1.1) $$m\ddot{x} = X.$$

If X is a known function of t,

(14.1.2) $$m(u_2 - u_1) = \int_{t_1}^{t_2} X\,dt,$$

where u_r denotes the value of $\dot{x}$ at the instant $t = t_r$. The case with which we are now concerned is that in which $\tau(= t_2 - t_1)$ is small, X is large for part of the interval $(t_1, t_1 + \tau)$, and

(14.1.3) $$\int_{t_1}^{t_1+\tau} X\,dt = P$$

is finite; P is a component of *impulse*.

We spoke above of an impulse as the *limiting case* of a large force acting for a short interval of time. But it is perhaps more realistic physically not to think of a strict mathematical limit as $\tau \to 0$, but to regard τ as a very short but finite interval of time; τ is *physically small* but not *mathematically small*. But τ is to be thought of as negligibly small for all practical purposes, so that there is no sensible change in the configuration of the system in the interval from t_1 to $t_1 + \tau$, and effectively we have a discontinuity of velocity at t_1 with no change of position. In a pure impulse problem the coordinates are constants, the velocities are prescribed at $t_1 - 0$, and the problem is the determination of the velocities at $t_1 + 0$. Since the coordinate x, for example, is a constant, we usually prefer in an impulse problem to write the symbol u rather than the symbol $\dot{x}$.

The equations (14.1.2) and (14.1.3), and the corresponding equations for the y and z directions, lead to the equations

(14.1.4) $$m(u - u_0) = P, \qquad m(v - v_0) = Q, \qquad m(w - w_0) = R,$$

where $\{P, Q, R\}$ is the impulse acting on the particle at the instant t_1, $\{u_0, v_0, w_0\}$ is the velocity of the particle at $t_1 - 0$ (i.e. immediately before the impulse is applied), and $\{u, v, w\}$ is the velocity of the particle at $t_1 + 0$ (i.e. immediately after the impulse is applied). The equations (14.1.4) are the basic equations for the theory of impulsive motion.

If the particle is at rest immediately before the impulse is applied, (14.1.4) becomes

(14.1.5) $$mu = P, \qquad mv = Q, \qquad mw = R,$$

and the impulse is equal to, and is measured by, the momentum created when the particle moves from rest. We have here a close analogy with Newton's second law of motion, impulse and momentum replacing force and kineton.

Our approach to the theory of impulses, regarding the idea of force as fundamental and the idea of impulse as derivative, is the most natural in conformity with the preceding Chapters. But another approach is possible. We can construct a theory from the opposite point of view, taking the idea of impulse as fundamental and the idea of force as derivative. In this point of view a finite force acting during an interval of time is regarded as a limiting case of a large number of small impulses acting at instants distributed throughout the interval.

Consider now the impulsive motion of a rigid body. Since the given forces are large for a short interval of time, the forces of constraint required are correspondingly large. The theory involves the assumption that these large forces of constraint are forthcoming, and that the body remains rigid. This is a still further idealization of the not-quite-rigid bodies that actually exist. All bodies in fact are deformed by finite forces and *a fortiori* by impulses. The rigid bodies considered in the present theory can sustain, not only finite forces, but even impulses, without distortion.

If X' is a typical component of a force of constraint in the interval t_1 to $t_1 + \tau$, the integral $\int_{t_1}^{t_1+\tau} X'\,dt = P'$ is finite, and we are led to the notion of *impulses of constraint*, of which P' is a typical component. These impulses of constraint are analogous to the forces of constraint that appear in the problems with finite forces. Our assumption is that a rigid body can supply and sustain impulses of constraint. More generally, when we turn from the problem of the impulsive motion of a single rigid body to that of a system, we assume that the requisite impulses of constraint can be supplied.

Let us consider the general case of a dynamical system acted on by impulses. We begin with a problem with large given forces, and correspondingly large forces of constraint, during a time-interval of short duration τ. Now, since the coordinates and the time are effectively constants, the coefficients A_{rs}, A_r in the equations of constraint (2.2.4) are constants, and this property greatly simplifies the discussion.

It will be convenient in the theory of impulses to use the second form of the fundamental equation (4.1.3), which we write in the form

$$\sum_{r=1}^{N} (m_r\ddot{x}_r - X_r)\Delta u_r = 0. \tag{14.1.6}$$

Now the finite velocity-variations $\Delta\mathbf{u}$ satisfy (4.1.2)

$$\sum_{r=1}^{N} A_{rs}\,\Delta u_s = 0, \qquad r = 1, 2, \ldots, L, \tag{14.1.7}$$

and since the coefficients A_{rs} are constants we can find sets $\Delta u_1, \Delta u_2, \ldots, \Delta u_N$ satisfying (14.1.7) throughout the short interval from t_1 to $t_1 + \tau$.

The second form of the fundamental equation, not much used hitherto, now comes into its own. It is preferable, both aesthetically and logically, to deal with velocity-variations, rather than with virtual displacements, since in these problems the coordinates are constants.

We shall find that the problems involving impulses are mathematically much simpler than those involving finite forces. The equations we shall establish to determine the velocities at $t_1 + 0$ are *linear algebraic equations*, in contrast to the differential equations we arrive at in a problem with finite forces. In general the complete solution of an impulse problem is possible and easy.

14.2 Impulsive constraints. So far we have been thinking in terms of a so-called *free impulse problem*, in which the dynamical system to which the impulses are applied is of the same type as that considered in earlier Chapters—namely a system of the type defined in § 2.2. We now meet a new feature that does not occur in problems with finite forces.

In the equations of constraint (2.2.4) that have appeared so far, the coefficients A_{rs}, A_r are of class C_1; *a fortiori* they are continuous functions of position and time. The new feature is the appearance of equations of constraint

$$\sum_{s=1}^{N} E_{rs}\dot{x}_s + E_r = 0, \qquad r = 1, 2, \ldots, L', \tag{14.2.1}$$

in which the coefficients E_{rs}, E_r are discontinuous at t_1. These are *impulsive constraints*. The coefficients are continuous in an interval before t_1, and again in an interval after t_1, but discontinuous at t_1 itself. Effectively we have to take account of two sets of (constant) values of the coefficients, the values at $t_1 - 0$ and the values at $t_1 + 0$.

The cases that occur most frequently in practice, and the only ones we shall consider, are of two kinds:

(i) The *inert* constraint. A constraint defined by equations of the form

$$\sum_{s=1}^{N} E_{rs}\dot{x}_s = 0, \qquad r = 1, 2, \ldots, L',$$

is suddenly imposed at the instant t_1. The coefficients E_r in (14.2.1) are all zero throughout, the coefficients E_{rs} are all zero at $t_1 - 0$. In this case there is actually a decrease in the number of freedoms of the system after the constraint is imposed.

As a simple concrete example of an inert constraint, a particle moving in space collides with a smooth fixed inelastic plane $x = x_0$ at the instant t_1. The constraint is defined by the equation $\dot{x} = 0$ at $t_1 + 0$.

(ii) The *live* constraint. The coefficients E_{rs} are continuous (and therefore effectively constants) and the coefficients E_r all vanish at $t_1 - 0$ but do not all vanish at $t_1 + 0$. There is no change in the number of freedoms.

As a simple concrete example of a live constraint, a particle slides on a smooth plane $x = x_0$, and at the instant t_1 the plane is suddenly set in motion, in the direction Ox, with speed U. The constraint changes from $\dot{x} = 0$ at $t_1 - 0$ to $\dot{x} - U = 0$ at $t_1 + 0$.

Theoretically we can have a problem in which given impulses and impulsive constraints are applied simultaneously at the instant t_1. But in practice the problems that arise divide themselves fairly definitely into the two classes, (i) the free impulse problems, problems in which given impulses act on the system, and there are only finite, not impulsive constraints, (ii) constraint problems, problems in which there are no given impulses, but there are impulsive constraints. However, for the sake of economy, we shall suppose, when we establish the fundamental equation for the impulsive motion of a system, that given impulses and impulsive constraints are applied at the same instant; this will enable us to include both classes of problem in a comprehensive theory. (A concrete illustration of the phenomenon of given impulses and impulsive constraints appearing simultaneously occurs in the note on Carnot's and Bertrand's theorems in § 14.6.)

A word of warning about a slight awkwardness of nomenclature may be desirable at this point. The impulsive constraints described in this section must not be confused with the impulses of constraint (analogous to the forces of constraint in the finite-force problem) which appeared in § 14.1.

14.3 Impulsive motion of a system, the fundamental equation. When we established the fundamental equation for finite forces, we introduced the essential ideas by discussing first the simple case in which the system contains only one particle, and a similar procedure is possible in the impulse problem; but we omit the detailed study of the special case of a single particle, and proceed at once to the general dynamical system. We regard the impulse problem as a limiting case of the finite-force problem, and, as mentioned above, we suppose given impulses and impulsive constraints to be applied simultaneously.

Consider then the interval of time from t_1 to $t_1 + \tau$ with finite forces acting on the system. The interval is supposed so small that the coefficients in the finite equations of constraint

$$\sum_{s=1}^{N} A_{rs}u_s + A_r = 0, \qquad r = 1, 2, \ldots, L, \tag{14.3.1}$$

are sensibly constant. The impulsive constraints can be derived from the finite constraints

$$\sum_{s=1}^{N} E_{rs}u_s + \theta_r = 0, \qquad r = 1, 2, \ldots, L' \tag{14.3.2}$$

where θ_r is a function of t varying from $-\sum_{s=1}^{N} E_{rs}(u_s)_{t_1-0}$ to zero in the interval from t_1 to $t_1 + \tau$ if the constraint is inert, and from zero to $(E_r)_{t_1+0}$ if the constraint is a live constraint. The second form of the fundamental equation (4.1.3) is

$$\sum_{r=1}^{N} (m_r\ddot{x}_r - X_r)\Delta u_r = 0, \tag{14.3.3}$$

where $\Delta\mathbf{u}$ represents a (finite) velocity-variation, and the components $\Delta u_1, \Delta u_2, \ldots, \Delta u_N$ of $\Delta\mathbf{u}$ satisfy the equations

$$\sum_{s=1}^{N} A_{rs}\,\Delta u_s = 0, \qquad r = 1, 2, \ldots, L, \tag{14.3.4}$$

$$\sum_{r=1}^{N} E_{rs}\,\Delta u_s = 0, \qquad r = 1, 2, \ldots, L'. \tag{14.3.5}$$

In these linear equations the coefficients A_{rs}, E_{rs} are constants, so we can find variations $\Delta\mathbf{u}$ which are valid throughout the interval from t_1 to $t_1 + \tau$. If we take any such value of $\Delta\mathbf{u}$, and substitute the components in (14.3.3), and integrate from t_1 to $t_1 + \tau$, we find

$$\sum_{r=1}^{N} \{m_r(u_r - u_{r0}) - P_r\}\,\Delta u_r = 0, \tag{14.3.6}$$

where P_r is the given impulse-component $\int_{t_1}^{t_1+\tau} X_r\,dt$. If now τ is negligibly small, u_{r0} and u_r are the values of $\dot{x}_r$ at $t_1 - 0$ and at $t_1 + 0$, and with this interpretation (14.3.6) is *the fundamental equation for the impulsive motion of a system.*

For the free impulse problem it is possible to establish the fundamental equation using impulses throughout, instead of dealing with large finite forces during a short interval of time; the argument is exactly similar to that used in establishing the fundamental equation for finite forces in § 3.1. If P_r is a component of given impulse, P_r' a component of impulse of constraint, we have

(14.3.7) $$m_r(u_r - u_{r0}) = P_r + P_r', \qquad r = 1, 2, \ldots, N.$$

Now the impulses of constraint satisfy the condition

(14.3.8) $$\sum_{r=1}^{N} P_r' \Delta u_r = 0,$$

and (14.3.7) and (14.3.8) imply (14.3.6). But this attack is not easily adapted to deal with impulsive constraints.

14.4 The catastatic system. The crucial point in using the fundamental equation (14.3.6) is the recognition of the class of variations $\Delta \mathbf{u}$ for which the equation holds. They are the variations satisfying (14.3.4–5), and we now consider more precisely the implication of these equations in the case of a catastatic system.

(i) For a *free impulse problem*, where there are no impulsive constraints, the equations (14.3.4) satisfied by the velocity-variations are identical with the equations satisfied by the possible velocities themselves, the equations

(14.4.1) $$\sum_{s=1}^{N} A_{rs} u_s = 0, \qquad r = 1, 2, \ldots, L.$$

Looked at in another way, (14.4.1) and (14.1.7) are reconciled because zero is a possible velocity. In this case, therefore, we can write $\mathbf{U}$ for $\Delta \mathbf{u}$ in the fundamental equation, where $\mathbf{U}$ (whose components are $U_1, U_2, \ldots, U_N$) is any possible velocity-system. Thus the fundamental equation takes the new, and very useful, form

(14.4.2) $$\sum_{r=1}^{N} m_r(u_r - u_{r0})U_r = \sum P_r U_r,$$

or, using the abridged notation,

(14.4.3) $$\sum m(u - u_0)U = \sum PU.$$

(ii) Next, let us consider the imposition of an *inert constraint* on the catastatic system. The equations satisfied by $\Delta \mathbf{u}$ are precisely the equations satisfied by $\mathbf{U}$, where $\mathbf{U}$ is any velocity-system possible *for the constrained system.* Thus the fundamental equation leads to

(14.4.4) $$\sum_{r=1}^{N} m_r(u_r - u_{r0})U_r = 0,$$

where the class of values of $\mathbf{U}$ is the class of velocity-systems possible at $t_1 + 0$.

(iii) Finally, let us consider the imposition of a *live constraint*; of course in this case the system is no longer catastatic after the constraint is imposed. The coefficients E_r in (14.2.1) are all zero at $t_1 - 0$, and the equations (14.3.4–5) satisfied by $\Delta \mathbf{u}$ are precisely the equations satisfied by a velocity-system which is possible *before the constraint is imposed.* Thus the fundamental equation becomes

(14.4.5) $$\sum_{r=1}^{N} m_r(u_r - u_{r0})U_r = 0,$$

where the class of values of $\mathbf{U}$ is the class of velocity-systems possible at $t_1 - 0$.

14.5 The principle of Least Constraint for impulses. We consider a catastatic system, and suppose that given impulses, or inert constraints, or both, are applied at the instant t_1. The principle that we shall establish is that *the velocity-system* $\mathbf{u}$ *at* $t_1 + 0$ (*i.e. immediately after the impulses are applied*) *is determined by the fact that, with the abridged notation,*

$$\mathfrak{C} = \tfrac{1}{2}\sum m\left(u - u_0 - \frac{P}{m}\right)^2, \tag{14.5.1}$$

considered as a function of $\mathbf{u}$, *is a minimum in the class of velocities possible at* $t_1 + 0$. ($\mathbf{u}_0$ denotes as usual the velocity-system at $t_1 - 0$, i.e. immediately before the impulses are applied.) The theorem is analogous to Gauss's principle of Least Constraint for finite forces (§ 4.3).

The proof is simple. If $\mathbf{u}$ is the actual velocity-system at $t_1 + 0$, and $\mathbf{u} + \Delta\mathbf{u}$ is any other velocity-system possible at $t_1 + 0$, then

$$\begin{aligned}\Delta\mathfrak{C} &= \tfrac{1}{2}\sum m\left\{\left(u + \Delta u - u_0 - \frac{P}{m}\right)^2 - \left(u - u_0 - \frac{P}{m}\right)^2\right\}\\ &= \sum m\left(u - u_0 - \frac{P}{m}\right)\Delta u + \tfrac{1}{2}\sum m(\Delta u)^2,\end{aligned} \tag{14.5.2}$$

whence, in virtue of (14.3.6),

$$\Delta\mathfrak{C} = \tfrac{1}{2}\sum m(\Delta u)^2 > 0 \tag{14.5.3}$$

unless $\Delta\mathbf{u} = 0$.

The most important case is that of the imposition of an inert constraint; the theorem then asserts that

$$\mathfrak{C} = \tfrac{1}{2}\sum m(u - u_0)^2 \tag{14.5.4}$$

is a minimum for the actual value of $\mathbf{u}$ in the class of values of $\mathbf{u}$ that are possible to the constrained system.

The theorem, like the analogous theorem of § 4.3, gives us more than enough information for the solution of the given problem; the first-order conditions for a stationary value of $\mathfrak{C}$ will provide the linear equations which determine $\mathbf{u}$.

As a simple illustration of the use of the theorem we may consider the following example:

Example 14.5. Four uniform rods, each of mass M and length l, are freely jointed together at their ends to form a closed framework, and two opposite corners are joined by a light inelastic string of length $l\sqrt{2}$ (so that at an instant when the string tightens the framework is square). The system moves on a smooth table. Originally the string is slack, but at the instant t_1 it becomes taut. To find the motion immediately after the impulse.

The kinetic energy of one rod is $\frac{1}{6}M(\mathbf{u}^2 + \mathbf{u}\,.\,\mathbf{v} + \mathbf{v}^2 + 3w^2)$, where the vectors $\mathbf{u}$ and $\mathbf{v}$ are the components of velocity of the ends at right angles to the rod, and w is the velocity along the rod. In the problem proposed we denote by u, v, w, x the velocities along the rods (Fig. 14.5). The kinetic energy of the rod AB is

$$\tfrac{1}{6}M(u^2 - uw + w^2 + 3v^2), \tag{14.5.5}$$

and, using the corresponding formulae for the other rods, we have

$$(14.5.6)\quad \mathfrak{C} = \tfrac{1}{6}M\{5(u - u_0)^2 + 5(v - v_0)^2 + 5(w - w_0)^2 + 5(x - x_0)^2 - 2(u - u_0)(w - w_0) - 2(v - v_0)(x - x_0)\},$$

where u_0, v_0, w_0, x_0 are the values immediately before the string tightens.

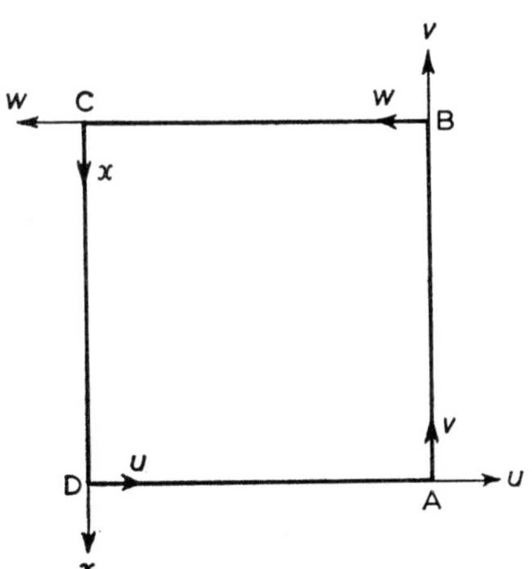

Figure 14.5

The equation of constraint is

$$(14.5.7)\qquad u - v + w - x = 0,$$

and the first-order conditions for a minimum of $\mathfrak{C}$, subject to (14.5.7), give

$$(14.5.8)\qquad \begin{cases} 5u - w - (5u_0 - w_0) = \lambda, \\ 5v - x - (5v_0 - x_0) = -\lambda, \\ 5w - u - (5w_0 - u_0) = \lambda, \\ 5x - v - (5x_0 - v_0) = -\lambda. \end{cases}$$

Hence

$$(14.5.9)\qquad \begin{cases} u - u_0 = w - w_0 = \tfrac{1}{4}\lambda, \\ v - v_0 = x - x_0 = -\tfrac{1}{4}\lambda, \end{cases}$$

where

$$(14.5.10)\qquad \lambda = -(u_0 - v_0 + w_0 - x_0).$$

14.6 The catastatic system, the superposition theorem. The configuration and velocity of the system being given, an impulse system $\mathbf{P}_1$ gives rise to a velocity-system $\mathbf{u}_1$, an impulse-system $\mathbf{P}_2$ gives rise to a velocity-system $\mathbf{u}_2$. The problem is to find the velocity-system $\mathbf{u}_3$ set-up by the application of the two impulse-systems simultaneously, i.e. by the impulse-system $\mathbf{P}_1 + \mathbf{P}_2$.

We have, from (14.4.2), with the abridged notation,

$$(14.6.1)\qquad \sum m(u_1 - u_0)U = \sum P_1U,$$

$$(14.6.2)\qquad \sum m(u_2 - u_0)U = \sum P_2U,$$

$$(14.6.3)\qquad \sum m(u_3 - u_0)U = \sum (P_1 + P_2)U,$$

and all three equations hold for the same values of $\mathbf{U}$, namely the velocities possible to the system in its configuration at t_1. Thus

$$(14.6.4)\qquad \sum m(u_1 + u_2 - u_0 - u_3)U = 0$$

for the same values of $\mathbf{U}$, whence

$$(14.6.5)\qquad u_3 = u_1 + u_2 - u_0.$$

The most important case is that in which the system is initially at rest. Then

$$(14.6.6)\qquad u_3 = u_1 + u_2$$

and *superposition of impulse-systems implies superposition of velocities.*

14.7 The catastatic system, the six energy theorems. We now establish a sequence of elegant theorems concerned with the kinetic energy of a system subjected to impulses. We use the abridged notation, so that the fundamental equations (14.4.3) and (14.4.4) take the forms

$$\sum m(u - u_0)U = \sum PU, \tag{14.7.1}$$

$$\sum m(u - u_0)U = 0. \tag{14.7.2}$$

(i) *The increment of energy in the free impulse problem.* We have

$$\sum m(u - u_0)U = \sum PU, \tag{14.7.1}$$

where $\mathbf{U}$ is any velocity-system possible at t_1. Both $\mathbf{u}_0$ and $\mathbf{u}$ belong to this category, and so does $\lambda\mathbf{u}_0 + \mu\mathbf{u}$. In particular we can take $\mathbf{U} = \frac{1}{2}(\mathbf{u} + \mathbf{u}_0)$, giving

$$\tfrac{1}{2}\sum m(u - u_0)(u + u_0) = \sum P\frac{u + u_0}{2}, \tag{14.7.3}$$

i.e.

$$T - T_0 = \tfrac{1}{2}\sum mu^2 - \tfrac{1}{2}\sum m{u_0}^2 = \sum P\frac{u + u_0}{2}. \tag{14.7.4}$$

The increase of energy is found by taking the scalar product of each impulse with the mean of the velocities, before and after, of the point of application, and summing.

In particular, if the system starts from rest the energy communicated to it is $\frac{1}{2}\Sigma\, Pu$, or, in terms of summation over the particles,

$$\tfrac{1}{2}S(Pu + Qv + Rw). \tag{14.7.5}$$

(ii) *Carnot's Theorem. Loss of energy due to the imposition of an inert constraint. When an inert constraint is imposed there is a loss of energy which is equal in value to the energy of the relative motion.* The *relative motion* is the motion in which the velocity of each particle is the vector difference of the velocities before and after the imposition of the constraint. We have

$$\sum m(u - u_0)U = 0, \tag{14.7.2}$$

and this holds (§ 14.4) for any velocity-system $\mathbf{U}$ which is possible after the constraint is imposed, i.e. at $t_1 + 0$. In particular we may put $\mathbf{U} = \mathbf{u}$, giving

$$\sum mu(u - u_0) = 0. \tag{14.7.6}$$

But

$$u(u - u_0) = \tfrac{1}{2}\{u^2 - {u_0}^2 + (u - u_0)^2\}, \tag{14.7.7}$$

so (14.7.6) is equivalent to

$$\tfrac{1}{2}\sum m{u_0}^2 - \tfrac{1}{2}\sum mu^2 = \tfrac{1}{2}\sum m(u - u_0)^2, \tag{14.7.8}$$

or say

$$T_0 - T = R_0, \tag{14.7.9}$$

where T_0 is the kinetic energy immediately before the constraint is imposed, T is the kinetic energy immediately afterwards, and R_0 is the kinetic energy of the relative motion,

$$R_0 = \tfrac{1}{2}\sum m(u - u_0)^2. \tag{14.7.10}$$

This completes the proof.

It is interesting to observe that Carnot's theorem can be derived from the two theorems that precede. Let $\mathbf{P}_0$ be an impulse-system that would set-up the motion $\mathbf{u}_0$ from rest, and $\mathbf{P}'$ the system of impulses of constraint which are called into play when the constraint is imposed. If the impulse-system $\mathbf{P}'$ is applied to the system at rest it sets up the relative motion $\mathbf{u} - \mathbf{u}_0$, and the energy of this motion is $\Sigma\, P' \dfrac{u - u_0}{2}$. Now the increase of energy when the constraint is imposed is $\Sigma\, P' \dfrac{u + u_0}{2}$, and these are equal and opposite since $\Sigma\, P'u = 0$ by (14.3.8).

A curious fallacy is worthy of notice at this point. We saw (§ 14.5) that the motion immediately after the imposition of the constraint is determined by the condition that

$$\mathfrak{C} = \tfrac{1}{2} \sum m(u - u_0)^2$$

is a minimum. Carnot's theorem tells us that the loss of energy is

$$\tfrac{1}{2} \sum m(u - u_0)^2.$$

But it does not follow that the motion at $t_1 + 0$ is such that the loss of energy is a minimum!

(iii) *Gain of energy due to the imposition of a live constraint. When a live constraint is imposed there is a gain of energy which is equal to the energy of the relative motion.* We have

$$\sum m(u - u_0)\, U = 0, \tag{14.7.2}$$

and this holds (§ 14.4) for any velocity-system $\mathbf{U}$ which is possible *before* the constraint is imposed, i.e. at $t_1 - 0$. In particular we may put $\mathbf{U} = \mathbf{u}_0$, giving

$$\sum m u_0 (u - u_0) = 0 \tag{14.7.11}$$

Hence, by an argument similar to (14.7.7),

$$T - T_0 = R. \tag{14.7.12}$$

The truth of the theorems (ii) and (iii) is immediately evident for the trivial examples of inert and live constraints mentioned in § 14.2.

(iv) *Bertrand's theorem.* The system at rest in a given configuration is set in motion by given impulses. The experiment is repeated, with the same configuration and the same given impulses, but this time the system is subject to additional (finite) constraints. The theorem states that *the energy T_1 in the second (constrained) experiment is less than the energy T in the first (free) experiment; and the difference $T - T_1$ is equal to the energy of the relative motion.*

From (14.7.1)

$$\sum muU = \sum PU, \tag{14.7.13}$$

$$\sum mu_1 U = \sum PU, \tag{14.7.14}$$

and both equations hold for $\mathbf{U} = \mathbf{u}_1$, whence

$$\sum mu_1(u - u_1) = 0. \tag{14.7.15}$$

Hence, using the argument of (14.7.7),

$$T - T_1 = R_1 > 0. \tag{14.7.16}$$

In the enunciation of this theorem we contemplate, in the second experiment, a *finite* constraint imposed before the blows are applied. But the effect is the same if an inert impulsive constraint is applied simultaneously with the blows. This leads to the observation that Bertrand's theorem may be regarded as another aspect of Carnot's theorem. We can look at the matter in this way. In Carnot's theorem the system is set in motion by given impulses, and an inert impulsive constraint is applied immediately afterwards; in Bertrand's theorem, in the second experiment, we may suppose an inert constraint to be applied simultaneously with the impulses. The effect in both cases is the same, and the content of the two theorems is the same.

The theorem is sometimes stated in terms of two experiments in which the system is less and more constrained. This is not an independent result; the less constrained system is merely "the system" as it is in the first experiment in the proof above.

(v) *Kelvin's Theorem.* The system at rest in a given configuration is set in motion by impulses applied at certain points, the *velocities* of the points struck, not the impulses, being prescribed. The theorem states that *the energy is less than that in any other motion in which the given points have the prescribed velocities.*

From (14.7.1)

$$\sum muU = \sum PU. \tag{14.7.17}$$

Let $\mathbf{u}_2$ denote any other velocity-system in which the given points have the prescribed velocities. Putting $\mathbf{U} = \mathbf{u} - \mathbf{u}_2$ we have

$$\sum mu(u - u_2) = \sum P(u - u_2) \tag{14.7.18}$$

and the second member is zero, since P is zero in any term in which $(u - u_2)$ is not zero. Hence

$$\sum mu(u - u_2) = 0, \tag{14.7.19}$$

whence, by the now familiar argument,

$$T_2 - T = R_2. \tag{14.7.20}$$

Cor. 1. The theorem is valid if the direction of the blow at each point struck is prescribed and the component of velocity in that direction is prescribed. For this ensures that the scalar products $Pu + Qv + Rw$ and $Pu_2 + Qv_2 + Rw_2$ at each point which is struck are equal, and the theorem follows as before.

Cor. 2. It is easy to formulate a generalization of the theorem for the case when the system is not initially at rest. In this case, by the same argument,

$$\sum m(u - u_0)(u - u_2) = 0, \tag{14.7.21}$$

which we can write in the form

$$\sum m(u - u_0)\{(u - u_0) - (u_2 - u_0)\} = 0. \tag{14.7.22}$$

We deduce, by the usual argument,

$$\tfrac{1}{2}\sum m(u_2 - u_0)^2 - \tfrac{1}{2}\sum m(u - u_0)^2 = \tfrac{1}{2}\sum m(u - u_2)^2 > 0. \tag{14.7.23}$$

The theorem is that the energy of the *relative* motion is a minimum for the actual motion.

Cor. 3. We can restate Kelvin's theorem in a form more nearly parallel to the statement of Bertrand's theorem. First the free system is set in motion by moving the seized points with the prescribed velocities; the energy acquired by the system is T_1. Then the experiment is repeated, but this time with the constrained system; the energy acquired is now T_2. Then $T_2 > T_1$. The imposition of the constraint *increases* the energy.

A simple illustration will bring out the relationship between the theorems of Bertrand and Kelvin. A rod AB at rest is set in motion by a blow perpendicular to the rod at B. The experiment is repeated with a point C of the rod fixed. If the *blow* at B is the same in the two experiments the energy is decreased by the constraint. If the *velocity* of B is the same in the two experiments the energy is increased by the constraint. (Indeed if C is very near to B the increase in energy, if the velocity of B is unchanged, will be very large.)

It is important to notice that the constraint contemplated in *Cor. 3* to Kelvin's theorem is not completely arbitrary, since it must be consistent with the prescribed velocities of the seized points. A simple illustration of a prohibited constraint would be the fixing of one of the seized points.

(vi) *Taylor's theorem* on the relation between Bertrand's and Kelvin's theorems. Three experiments (a), (b), (c) are performed; in each case the system starts from rest in a given configuration.

(a) Blows are applied at certain points and the kinetic energy acquired by the system is T.

(b) The system is constrained, and the same blows are applied as in (a). The energy acquired is T_1. Bertrand's theorem asserts that $T - T_1 = R_1 > 0$.

(c) The system is constrained in the same manner as in (b), and blows are applied at the same points as in (a) such that the velocities of these points are the same as in (a); in other words, the points are seized and moved with the velocities they had in (a). Kelvin's theorem asserts that $T_2 - T = R_2 > 0$.

Taylor's theorem asserts that $R_2 > R_1$; *the gain in Kelvin's theorem is greater than the loss in Bertrand's theorem.* To prove this we have only to observe that in the equations (14.7.13) and (14.7.14), which appear in the proof of Bertrand's theorem, we can put $\mathbf{U} = \mathbf{u}_2$ as well as $\mathbf{U} = \mathbf{u}_1$, and therefore

(14.7.24) $$\sum m(u - u_1)(u_2 - u_1) = 0.$$

We can write this equation in the form

(14.7.25) $$\sum m(u_1 - u)\{(u_1 - u) - (u_2 - u)\} = 0,$$

and therefore, by the argument of (14.7.7), we have

(14.7.26) $$R_1 - R_2 + R_{12} = 0,$$

where

(14.7.27) $$R_{12} = \tfrac{1}{2}\sum m(u_2 - u_1)^2.$$

Hence

(14.7.28) $$R_2 - R_1 = R_{12} > 0,$$

and this proves the result stated.

14.8 Lagrangian coordinates and quasi-coordinates. So far we have developed the theory of impulsive motion entirely in terms of Cartesian coordinates, in a manner similar to that in which the theory for finite forces was developed in Chapters I–IV.

We now introduce coordinates of more general type. The first point to notice is that these may be Lagrangian coordinates or quasi-coordinates; in the theory of impulsive motion we can use quasi-coordinates freely, just as we did in the theory of the Gibbs-Appell equations. We have

$$dx_r = \sum_{s=1}^{k} \alpha_{rs}\, dq_s + \alpha_r\, dt, \qquad r = 1, 2, \ldots, N, \tag{12.2.6}$$

where k is the number of freedoms of the system (or, in a problem involving the imposition of an inert constraint, the number of freedoms of the system before the constraint is imposed). The equations (12.2.7) are not required in the impulse theory. From (12.2.6) we have

$$u_r = \sum_{s=1}^{k} \alpha_{rs}\omega_s + \alpha_r, \qquad r = 1, 2, \ldots, N, \tag{14.8.1}$$

where ω_r is written for the velocity-component $\dot{q}_r$. From (14.8.1)

$$\Delta u_r = \sum_{s=1}^{k} \alpha_{rs}\, \Delta\omega_s, \tag{14.8.2}$$

$$u_r - u_{r0} = \sum_{s=1}^{k} \alpha_{rs}(\omega_s - \omega_{s0}), \tag{14.8.3}$$

where we recall that in the present context the coefficients α_{rs} are constants.

We return now to the fundamental equation (14.3.6) for impulses,

$$\sum_{r=1}^{N} m_r(u_r - u_{r0})\, \Delta u_r = \sum_{r=1}^{N} P_r\, \Delta u_r. \tag{14.8.4}$$

The second member of this equation is

$$\sum_{s=1}^{k}\left(\sum_{r=1}^{N} P_r\alpha_{rs}\right) \Delta\omega_s = \sum_{s=1}^{k} \Omega_s\, \Delta\omega_s, \tag{14.8.5}$$

where

$$\Omega_s = \sum_{r=1}^{N} P_r\alpha_{rs}, \tag{14.8.6}$$

and Ω_s is a generalized component of impulse. The Ω's can be found here exactly as the Q's were found (§ 12.3) in the theory of the Gibbs-Appell equations,

$$\sum_{r=1}^{N} P_r\, \delta x_r = \sum_{s=1}^{k} \Omega_s\, \delta q_s. \tag{14.8.7}$$

In the commonly-occurring case in which the coefficients α_r in (14.8.1) are all zero

$$\sum_{r=1}^{N} P_r u_r = \sum_{s=1}^{k} \Omega_s\omega_s. \tag{14.8.8}$$

Expressing the second member of (14.8.4) in terms of the k $\Delta\omega$'s we have

$$\sum_{r=1}^{N} m_r(u_r - u_{r0})\, \Delta u_r = \sum_{s=1}^{k} \Omega_s\, \Delta\omega_s, \tag{14.8.9}$$

which is a result for impulses strikingly similar to the fifth form of the fundamental equation (12.3.11) for finite forces.

We now introduce the function $\mathfrak{R}$, which is

$$\tfrac{1}{2} \sum_{r=1}^{N} m_r(u_r - u_{r0})^2 \tag{14.8.10}$$

expressed, by means of (14.8.3), in terms of $(\omega_1 - \omega_{10})$, $(\omega_2 - \omega_{20})$, . . . , $(\omega_k - \omega_{k0})$. We notice that $\mathfrak{R}$ is a homogeneous quadratic function of $(\omega_1 - \omega_{10})$, $(\omega_2 - \omega_{20})$, . . . , $(\omega_k - \omega_{k0})$. If the coefficients α_r all vanish, $\mathfrak{R}$ is the same function of the $(\omega_r - \omega_{r0})$'s that T is of the ω_r's; in any case $\mathfrak{R}$ can be found from the T_2 terms in T. Now the first member of (14.8.9) is

(14.8.11)
$$\sum_{s=1}^{k}\left\{\sum_{r=1}^{N} m_r(u_r - u_{r0})\alpha_{rs}\right\}\Delta\omega_s$$
$$= \sum_{s=1}^{k}\left\{\sum_{r=1}^{N} m_r(u_r - u_{r0})\frac{\partial u_r}{\partial \omega_s}\right\}\Delta\omega_s$$
$$= \sum_{s=1}^{k}\frac{\partial \mathfrak{R}}{\partial \omega_s}\Delta\omega_s,$$

and therefore (14.8.9) is equivalent to

(14.8.12)
$$\sum_{s=1}^{k}\frac{\partial \mathfrak{R}}{\partial \omega_s}\Delta\omega_s = \sum_{s=1}^{k}\Omega_s\,\Delta\omega_s.$$

To find the equations for the motion at $t_1 + 0$ it will suffice, as usual, to use infinitesimal variations, and (14.8.12) then becomes

(14.8.13)
$$\delta\mathfrak{R} = \sum_{s=1}^{k}\Omega_s\,\delta\omega_s.$$

In the free impulse problem, where $\delta\omega_1, \delta\omega_2, \ldots, \delta\omega_k$ are independent, (4.18.13) leads to the equations

(14.8.14)
$$\frac{\partial \mathfrak{R}}{\partial \omega_s} = \Omega_s, \qquad s = 1, 2, \ldots, k.$$

In the problem of an inert impulsive constraint, say for example an inert constraint defined by a single equation

(14.8.15)
$$b_1\omega_1 + b_2\omega_2 + \cdots + b_k\omega_k = 0,$$

the motion at $t_1 + 0$ is derived from the condition $\delta\mathfrak{R} = 0$ subject to (14.8.15), and the equations are

(14.8.16)
$$\frac{\partial \mathfrak{R}}{\partial \omega_s} = \lambda b_s, \qquad s = 1, 2, \ldots, k.$$

The multiplier λ is proportional to the magnitude of the impulse of constraint called into play by the impulsive constraint.

Now the equations of motion obtained from

(14.8.17)
$$\sum_{s=1}^{k}\left(\frac{\partial \mathfrak{R}}{\partial \omega_s} - \Omega_s\right)\delta\omega_s = 0$$

(with infinitesimal $\delta\omega_r$'s) are the first-order conditions for

(14.8.18)
$$\mathfrak{R} - \sum_{s=1}^{k}\Omega_s\omega_s$$

to be stationary. *It is in fact a minimum.* For

$$(14.8.19)\quad \Delta(\mathfrak{R} - \sum_{s=1}^{k} \Omega_s\omega_s) = \tfrac{1}{2}\sum_{s=1}^{N} m_r(u_r + \Delta u_r - u_{r0})^2 - \tfrac{1}{2}\sum_{r=1}^{N} m_r(u_r - u_{r0})^2 - \sum_{s=1}^{k} \Omega_s\,\Delta\omega_s$$
$$= \tfrac{1}{2}\sum_{r=1}^{N} m_r(\Delta u_r)^2 + \left\{\sum_{r=1}^{N} m_r(u_r - u_{r0})\,\Delta u_r - \sum_{s=1}^{N} \Omega_s\,\Delta\omega_s\right\},$$

which becomes, in virtue of (14.8.9),

$$(14.8.20)\qquad \Delta(\mathfrak{R} - \sum_{s=1}^{k} \Omega_s\omega_s) = \tfrac{1}{2}\sum_{r=1}^{N} m_r(\Delta u_r)^2 > 0.$$

This proves the result. The theorem bears the same relation to (14.5.3), $\Delta\mathfrak{C} > 0$, that (12.4.6) bears to Gauss's principle of Least Constraint.

14.9 Lagrange's form of the impulse equations. We can derive the equations of motion from the kinetic energy function T, expressed in terms of $\omega_1, \omega_2, \ldots, \omega_k$, instead of from the relative kinetic energy $\mathfrak{R}$ expressed in terms of $(\omega_1 - \omega_{10})$, $(\omega_2 - \omega_{20}), \ldots, (\omega_k - \omega_{k0})$. The function T is

$$(14.9.1)\qquad \tfrac{1}{2}\sum_{r=1}^{N} m_r u_r^2$$

expressed in terms of $\omega_1, \omega_2, \ldots, \omega_k$, by means of (14.8.1). Now

$$(14.9.2)\qquad \frac{\partial\mathfrak{R}}{\partial\omega_s} = \sum_{r=1}^{N} m_r(u_r - u_{r0})\frac{\partial u_r}{\partial\omega_s} = \frac{\partial T}{\partial\omega_s} - \left(\frac{\partial T}{\partial\omega_s}\right)_0,$$

since $\dfrac{\partial u_r}{\partial\omega_s}$ has the same value before and after the blows. Thus

$$(14.9.3)\qquad \frac{\partial\mathfrak{R}}{\partial\omega_s} = \left.\frac{\partial T}{\partial\omega_s}\right|,$$

where $\left.\dfrac{\partial T}{\partial\omega_s}\right|$ means the change in $\dfrac{\partial T}{\partial\omega_s}$, i.e. the value of $\dfrac{\partial T}{\partial\omega_s}$ at $t_1 + 0$ minus its value at $t_1 - 0$. The equations (14.8.14) and (14.8.16) can therefore be written

$$(14.9.4)\qquad \left.\frac{\partial T}{\partial\omega_s}\right| = \Omega_s, \qquad s = 1, 2, \ldots, k,$$

$$(14.9.5)\qquad \left.\frac{\partial T}{\partial\omega_s}\right| = \lambda b_s, \qquad s = 1, 2, \ldots, k,$$

and these equations (14.9.4) and (14.9.5) are Lagrange's form of the impulse equations. If the system starts from rest, $\mathfrak{R}$ is identical with T, and the equations are most simply comprehended in the formulation

$$(14.9.6)\qquad \delta T = \sum_{S=1}^{k} \Omega_s\,\delta\omega_s.$$

If we have a free impulse problem, and the system is initially at rest,

$$(14.9.7)\qquad p_s = \frac{\partial T}{\partial\omega_s} = \Omega_s,$$

where p_s denotes a generalized momentum component as defined in § 6.10 (though there the q's were strictly Lagrangian coordinates, and here they may be quasi-coordinates). Each generalized momentum component is equal to the corresponding generalized impulse-component needed to set up the motion from rest.

14.10 The energy theorems reconsidered. The proofs of the energy theorems established in § 14.6 and § 14.7 can also be established in terms of Lagrangian coordinates. It may be of interest to prove some of these theorems again from this point of view. For the sake of brevity we confine our attention to the case in which the terms α_r in (14.8.1) are all zero. In this case T is a homogeneous quadratic form in the ω's,

(14.10.1) $$T = \tfrac{1}{2}\sum_{r=1}^{k}\sum_{s=1}^{k} a_{rs}\omega_r\omega_s,$$

and

(14.10.2) $$p_r = \sum_{s=1}^{k} a_{rs}\omega_s.$$

Lagrange's equation for impulsive motion can be written

(14.10.3) $$\Omega_r = p_r - p_{r0}.$$

(i) To prove the superposition theorem of § 14.6, we have

(14.10.4) $$\Omega_r = \sum_{s=1}^{k} a_{rs}(\omega_s - \omega_{s0}), \qquad r = 1, 2, \ldots, k,$$

(14.10.5) $$\Omega_r' = \sum_{s=1}^{k} a_{rs}(\omega_s' - \omega_{s0}), \qquad r = 1, 2, \ldots, k,$$

where $\boldsymbol{\omega}$ is the velocity set up by the impulse $\boldsymbol{\Omega}$, $\boldsymbol{\omega}'$ is the velocity set up by Ω'. Hence

(14.10.6) $$\Omega_r + \Omega_r' = \sum_{s=1}^{k} a_{rs}\{(\omega_s + \omega_s' - \omega_{s0}) - \omega_{s0}\}, \qquad r = 1, 2, \ldots, k,$$

and the velocity set up by $\boldsymbol{\Omega} + \boldsymbol{\Omega}'$ is

(14.10.7) $$\boldsymbol{\omega} + \boldsymbol{\omega}' - \boldsymbol{\omega}_0.$$

This is equivalent to the theorem of § 14.6, since the u_r's are homogeneous linear functions of the ω's. In particular, if the system starts from rest, superposition of impulse-systems implies superposition of the velocity-systems set up.

(ii) If the system is set in motion from rest by given impulses we have

(14.10.8) $$T = \tfrac{1}{2}\sum_{r=1}^{k} \omega_r p_r = \tfrac{1}{2}\sum_{r=1}^{k} \Omega_r\omega_r,$$

in virtue of (14.10.3), and this is equivalent to (14.7.5), since the inner product $\sum_{r=1}^{k} \Omega_r\omega_r$ is invariant.

(iii) If the system is already moving when the impulses are applied

(14.10.9) $$\begin{aligned} T - T_0 &= \tfrac{1}{2}\sum_{r=1}^{k} (\omega_r p_r - \omega_{r0}p_{r0}) \\ &= \tfrac{1}{2}\sum_{r=1}^{k} (p_r - p_{r0})(\omega_r + \omega_{r0}) - \tfrac{1}{2}\sum_{r=1}^{k} (p_r\omega_{r0} - p_{r0}\omega_r). \end{aligned}$$

But

(14.10.10) $$\sum_{r=1}^{k} p_r\omega_{r0} = \sum_{r=1}^{k} p_{r0}\omega_r,$$

(a result that we shall need again later) so (14.10.9) becomes

$$T - T_0 = \sum_{r=1}^{k} \Omega_r \frac{\omega_r + \omega_{r0}}{2}, \tag{14.10.11}$$

which is equivalent to (14.7.4).

(iv) To prove Bertrand's theorem, let us suppose that the generalized impulse-components Ω_r vanish for $r > j$, and that the constraint imposed in the second experiment is $\omega_r = 0$ for $r > j$.

In the first experiment

$$\begin{cases} \Omega_r = p_r, & r \leqslant j, \\ 0 = p_r, & r > j, \end{cases} \tag{14.10.12}$$

and in the second experiment

$$\begin{cases} \Omega_r = p_r', & r \leqslant j, \\ 0 = \omega_r' & r > j, \end{cases} \tag{14.10.13}$$

where the accented symbols refer to the motion in the second (constrained) experiment. Now

(14.10.14)

$$\begin{aligned} T - T' &= \tfrac{1}{2} \sum_{r=1}^{k} (p_r\omega_r - p_r'\omega_r') \\ &= \tfrac{1}{2} \sum_{r=1}^{k} (p_r - p_r')(\omega_r - \omega_r') + \sum_{r=1}^{k} (p_r - p_r')\omega_r' - \tfrac{1}{2} \sum_{r=1}^{k} (p_r\omega_r' - p_r'\omega_r), \end{aligned}$$

and the second and third terms on the right vanish, the second since $p_r - p_r' = 0$ when $r \leqslant j$ and $\omega_r' = 0$ when $r > j$, the third in virtue of (14.10.10). Therefore

$$T - T' = R > 0. \tag{14.10.15}$$

(v) To prove Kelvin's theorem, let ω_r be prescribed for $r \leqslant j$, and let Ω_r vanish fo $r > j$. If $\boldsymbol{\omega}'$ refers to any other motion possible with the prescribed values of ω_1 $\omega_2, \ldots, \omega_j$, we have

(14.10.16)

$$\begin{aligned} T - T' &= \tfrac{1}{2} \sum_{r=1}^{k} (p_r\omega_r - p_r'\omega_r') \\ &= -\tfrac{1}{2} \sum_{r=1}^{k} (p_r - p_r')(\omega_r - \omega_r') + \sum_{r=r}^{k} p_r(\omega_r - \omega_r') + \tfrac{1}{2} \sum_{r=1}^{k} (p_r\omega_r' - p_r'\omega_r), \end{aligned}$$

and again the second and third terms on the right vanish, the second because $\omega_r > \omega_r'$ for $r \leqslant j$ and $p_r = 0$ for $r > j$, and the third in virtue of (14.10.10). Thus

$$T' - T = R > 0. \tag{14.10.17}$$

14.11 Examples of impulsive motion. We now consider some concrete problems illustrating the preceding theory.

Example 14.11*A*. A chain of rods is composed of three uniform rods AB, BC, CD, each of mass M, which are smoothly jointed together at B and C, and which lie at rest in line on a smooth table. The system is set in motion by a blow, in a horizontal direction at right angles to the rods, at A. To find the motion set up, and to illustrate Bertrand's, Kelvin's, and Taylor's theorems when the constraint is the fixing of the other end D of the chain.

In the free motion problem, using the notation shown in Fig. 14.11*a* for the velocities with which the points A, B, C, and D start to move, the motion set up by the impulse is given by (14.9.6), $\delta T = J\ \delta v$, where

$$T = \tfrac{1}{6}M\{(v^2 - vx + x^2) + (x^2 - xy + y^2) + (y^2 - yz + z^2)\} \tag{14.11.1}$$
$$= \tfrac{1}{6}M(v^2 - vx + 2x^2 - xy + 2y^2 - yz + z^2).$$

Thus

$$2v - x = 6J/M, \quad -v + 4x - y = 0, \quad -x + 4y - z = 0, \quad -y + 2z = 0, \tag{14.11.2}$$

giving

$$\frac{z}{1} = \frac{y}{2} = \frac{x}{7} = \frac{v}{26} = \frac{6J/M}{45} = \frac{2J}{15M}. \tag{14.11.3}$$

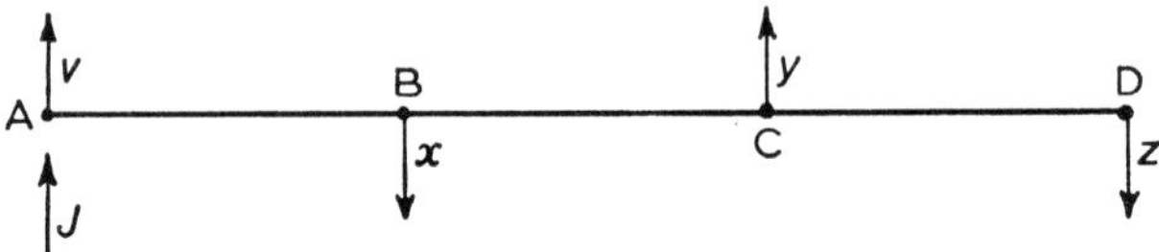

Figure 14.11*a*

The energy generated is, by (14.7.5),

$$\frac{1}{2}Jv = \frac{15}{104}Mv^2 = \frac{26}{15}\frac{J^2}{M}. \tag{14.11.4}$$

With the constraint $z = 0$ we have

$$T = \tfrac{1}{6}M(v^2 - vx + 2x^2 - xy + 2y^2) \tag{14.11.5}$$

and the principle $\delta T = J\ \delta v$ leads to the equations

$$2v - x = 6J/M, \quad -v + 4x - y = 0, \quad -x + 4y = 0, \tag{14.11.6}$$

whence

$$\frac{y}{1} = \frac{x}{4} = \frac{v}{15} = \frac{6J/M}{26} = \frac{3J}{13M}, \tag{14.11.7}$$

and the energy generated is

$$\frac{1}{2}Jv = \frac{13}{90}Mv^2 = \frac{45}{26}\frac{J^2}{M}. \tag{14.11.8}$$

(i) If J is the same in both experiments, and if the energy in the free problem exceeds the energy in the constrained problem by B, then

$$B = \left(\frac{26}{15} - \frac{45}{26}\right)\frac{J^2}{M} = \frac{1}{390}\frac{J^2}{M}, \tag{14.11.9}$$

or, in terms of the velocity v_0 of A in the free problem,

$$B = \frac{15}{70304}Mv_0^{\,2}. \tag{14.11.10}$$

(ii) If $v = v_0$ in both experiments, and the energy in the free problem is less than the energy in the constrained problem by K, then

$$K - \left(\frac{13}{90} - \frac{15}{104}\right) Mv_0^2 = \frac{1}{4680} Mv_0^2. \tag{14.11.11}$$

Finally

$$K - B = \left(\frac{1}{4680} - \frac{15}{70304}\right) Mv_0^2 = \frac{1}{3{,}163{,}680} Mv_0^2. \tag{14.11.12}$$

Example 14.11*B*. Twelve equal uniform rods, each of mass M, are freely hinged together at the ends to form a framework, whose form initially is that of the twelve edges of a cube. One vertex O is fixed, and the system is initially at rest. It is set in motion by an impulse applied to the opposite vertex D; the components of the impulse in the directions of the edges of the cube are X, Y, Z. How does the framework start to move, and what amount of energy is communicated to it?

We use the superposition theorem (§ 14.6) and consider first the effect of the simple component X. If the initial motion of the framework is as shown in Fig. 14.11*b*, we have

(14.11.13)

$$T = \tfrac{1}{6}M\{7u_2^2 + 7u_3^2 + 9(u_2 + u_3)^2\},$$

and the equation $\delta T = X\delta(u_2 + u_3)$ leads to

$$u_2 = u_3 = 3X/(25M). \tag{14.11.14}$$

Using the analogous notation for the other components, we have

$$v_3 = v_1 = 3Y/(25M), \tag{14.11.15}$$
$$w_1 = w_2 = 3Z/(25M).$$

The energy communicated is

(14.11.16)

$$\tfrac{1}{2}\{X(u_2 + u_3) + Y(v_3 + v_1) + Z(w_1 + w_2)\}$$
$$= 3(X^2 + Y^2 + Z^2)/(25M).$$

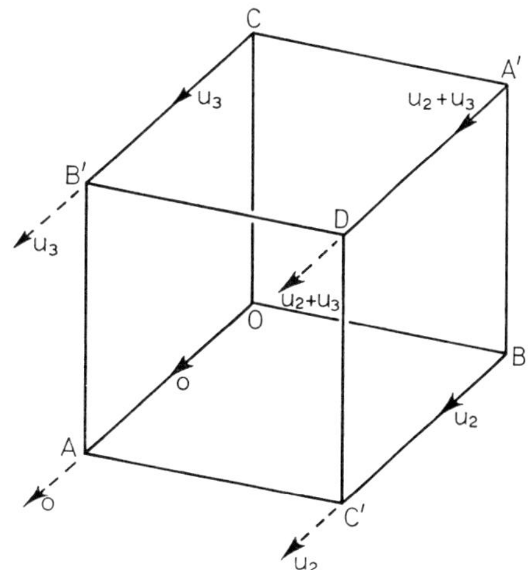

Figure 14.11*b*

Example 14.11*C*. A rhombus of mass M formed of four equal rods AB, BC, CD, DA, each of length $2a$, freely jointed at the corners, is moving, as if rigid, in the direction of the diagonal AC with velocity u. The angle at A is 2α. Suddenly a particle of mass m, originally at rest, is attached to A. Prove that the angular velocity suddenly acquired by each rod is

$$\omega = 3mu \sin \alpha/(2a\kappa),$$

and that the kinetic energy lost is $\tfrac{1}{2}Mmu^2/\kappa$, where

$$\kappa = M + m\,(1 + 3 \sin^2 \alpha).$$

If v is the velocity of the centre of mass G of the framework just after the impulse, the kinetic energy of the system is

$$(14.11.17)\qquad \tfrac{1}{2}Mv^2 + 4\left(\frac{1}{2}\frac{M}{4}a^2\omega^2 + \frac{1}{2}\frac{M}{4}\frac{a^2}{3}\omega^2\right) + \tfrac{1}{2}m(v - 2a\omega\sin\alpha)^2$$
$$= \tfrac{1}{2}Mv^2 + \tfrac{2}{3}Ma^2\omega^2 + \tfrac{1}{2}m(v - 2a\omega\sin\alpha)^2.$$

Hence

$$(14.11.18)\qquad \Re = \tfrac{1}{2}M(v-u)^2 + \tfrac{2}{3}Ma^2\omega^2 + \tfrac{1}{2}m(v - 2a\omega\sin\alpha)^2,$$

since the angular velocity of each rod, and the velocity of m, all vanish at $t_1 - 0$. The equation (14.8.13), $\delta\Re = 0$, leads to the equations

$$(14.11.19)\qquad M(v-u) + m(v - 2a\omega\sin\alpha) = 0,$$

$$(14.11.20)\qquad \tfrac{4}{3}Ma^2\omega - 2ma\sin\alpha(v - 2a\omega\sin\alpha) = 0.$$

We recognize the equation (14.11.19) as the expression of the conservation of linear momentum. From (14.11.19–20) we have

$$(14.11.21)\qquad \frac{2a\omega}{3m\sin\alpha} = \frac{v - 2a\omega\sin\alpha}{M} = \frac{v-u}{-m}$$
$$= \frac{v}{M + 3m\sin^2\alpha} = \frac{u}{M + m(1 + 3\sin^2\alpha)} = \frac{u}{\kappa},$$

whence

$$(14.11.22)\qquad \omega = 3mu\sin\alpha/(2a\kappa).$$

Finally the kinetic energy lost is, by Carnot's theorem, equal to the value of $\Re$ when v and ω have their values at $t_1 + 0$, and therefore the energy lost is

$$(14.11.23)\qquad \Re = \tfrac{1}{2}\left(u\frac{\partial\Re}{\partial u} + v\frac{\partial\Re}{\partial v} + \omega\frac{\partial\Re}{\partial\omega}\right) = \tfrac{1}{2}u\frac{\partial\Re}{\partial u} = -\tfrac{1}{2}Mu(v-u) = \tfrac{1}{2}Mmu^2/\kappa.$$

Example 14.11D. We consider a system for which the kinetic energy, expressed in terms of $\omega_1, \omega_2, \ldots, \omega_k$, contains only square terms,

$$(14.11.24)\qquad T = \tfrac{1}{2}\sum_{r=1}^{k}\omega_r{}^2/A_r.$$

We suppose the system to be set in motion by an impulse applied to the first j coordinates, $\Omega_r = \Omega_{r0}$ for $r \leqslant j$, $\Omega_r = 0$ for $r > j$. We first determine the motion set up by the impulses, and the energy generated. We then consider the system subjected to the (finite) constraint

$$(14.11.25)\qquad b_1\omega_1 + b_2\omega_2 + \cdots + b_k\omega_k = 0,$$

and we illustrate the energy theorems (§ 14.7) by finding the energy generated (i) when the blows are unchanged, (ii) when the first j velocities are unchanged.

We are here thinking in terms of a finite constraint imposed on the system before the impulses are applied; but the effect is the same if we consider instead an impulsive constraint imposed simultaneously with the impulses (cf. § 17.4 (iv)).

In the free impulse problem we have $\delta T = \sum_{r=1}^{j}\Omega_r\,\delta\omega_r$, so, if the velocity acquired is $\alpha_1, \alpha_2, \ldots, \alpha_k$, we have

$$(14.11.26)\qquad \alpha_r = A_r\Omega_{r0},\quad (r \leqslant j);\qquad \alpha_r = 0,\quad (r > j).$$

The kinetic energy generated is

$$T_0 = \tfrac{1}{2}\sum_{r=1}^{j} A_r\Omega_{r0}^2 = \tfrac{1}{2}\sum_{r=1}^{j}\frac{\alpha_r^2}{A_r}. \tag{14.11.27}$$

Let us now consider the constrained system.

(i) If the impulses are unchanged, we have

$$\omega_r = A_r\Omega_{r0} + \lambda A_r b_r, \quad (r \leqslant j); \qquad \omega_r = \lambda A_r b_r, \quad (r > j); \tag{14.11.28}$$

and we find λ from (14.11.25)

$$\sum_{r=1}^{j} A_r b_r \Omega_{r0} + \lambda \sum_{r=1}^{k} A_r b_r^2 = 0. \tag{14.11.29}$$

Thus the energy acquired is

$$\begin{aligned} T_1 &= \tfrac{1}{2}\sum_{r=1}^{j}\Omega_{r0}\omega_r \\ &= \tfrac{1}{2}\sum_{r=1}^{j}\Omega_{r0}(A_r\Omega_{r0} + \lambda A_r b_r) \\ &= \tfrac{1}{2}\sum_{r=1}^{j} A_r\Omega_{r0}^2 - \tfrac{1}{2}\left(\sum_{r=1}^{j} A_r b_r \Omega_{r0}\right)^2 \Big/ \left(\sum_{r=1}^{k} A_r b_r^2\right) \\ &= T_0 - B, \end{aligned} \tag{14.11.30}$$

where B, expressed in terms of $\alpha_1, \alpha_2, \ldots, \alpha_j$, is

$$B = \tfrac{1}{2}\left(\sum_{r=1}^{j} b_r\alpha_r\right)^2 \Big/ \left(\sum_{r=1}^{k} A_r b_r^2\right). \tag{14.11.31}$$

(ii) If the system is set in motion by a different impulse-system $\mathbf{\Omega}$, with $\Omega_r = 0$ for $r > j$, and if the impulses are such that $\omega_r = \alpha_r$ for $r \leqslant j$, we have

$$\alpha_r = A_r\Omega_r + \lambda A_r b_r, \quad (r \leqslant j); \qquad \omega_r = \lambda A_r b_r, \quad (r > j). \tag{14.11.32}$$

The energy set up is

$$T_2 = \tfrac{1}{2}\sum_{r=1}^{j}\Omega_r\alpha_r = \tfrac{1}{2}\left(\sum_{r=1}^{j}\alpha_r^2/A_r\right) - \tfrac{1}{2}\lambda\sum_{r=1}^{j} b_r\alpha_r, \tag{14.11.33}$$

and since also

$$T_2 = \tfrac{1}{2}\left(\sum_{r=1}^{j}\alpha_r^2/A_r\right) + \tfrac{1}{2}\left(\sum_{r=j+1}^{k}\omega_r^2/A_r\right) \tag{14.11.34}$$

we have

$$\lambda\sum_{r=1}^{j} b_r\alpha_r = -\sum_{r=j+1}^{k}\omega_r^2/A_r = -\lambda^2\left(\sum_{r=j+1}^{k} A_r b_r^2\right), \tag{14.11.35}$$

giving the value of λ,

$$\lambda = -\left(\sum_{r=1}^{j} b_r\alpha_r\right) \Big/ \left(\sum_{j+1}^{k} A_r b_r^2\right). \tag{14.11.36}$$

Thus

$$\begin{aligned} T_2 &= \tfrac{1}{2}\left(\sum_{r=1}^{j}\alpha_r^2/A_r\right) + \tfrac{1}{2}\left(\sum_{r=1}^{j} b_r\alpha_r\right)^2 \Big/ \left(\sum_{r=j+1}^{k} A_r b_r^2\right) \\ &= T_0 + K, \end{aligned} \tag{14.11.37}$$

where

$$K = \tfrac{1}{2}\left(\sum_{r=1}^{j} b_r\alpha_r\right)^2 \Big/ \left(\sum_{r=j+1}^{k} A_r b_r^2\right). \tag{14.11.38}$$

We easily verify the theorem $K > B$; in fact

$$K - B = \frac{1}{2}\frac{\left(\sum_{r=1}^{j} A_r b_r^2\right)\left(\sum_{r=1}^{j} b_r \alpha_r\right)^2}{\left(\sum_{r=1}^{k} A_r b_r^2\right)\left(\sum_{r=j+1}^{k} A_r b_r^2\right)}. \tag{14.11.39}$$

Example 14.11*E*. Finally, let us consider an example of a live constraint. We take the framework of four equal rods considered in *Example* 14.5, and suppose that initially it is moving as if rigid; if θ denotes the angle ADC, $\theta = \frac{1}{2}\pi$ and $\dot\theta = 0$ at $t_1 - 0$. Suppose now that, at the instant t_1, $\dot\theta$ is suddenly given the prescribed value φ; we may suppose that this is effected by a mischievous (but massless) insect sitting on the framework at D. With the notation of *Example* 14.5 the impulsive constraint is defined by the equations

$$\begin{cases} u - v + w - x = 0, & \text{at } t_1 - 0, \\ u - v + w - x = l\varphi, & \text{at } t_1 + 0, \end{cases} \tag{14.11.40}$$

and the equation $\delta\mathfrak{R} = 0$ is valid for variations such that

$$\delta u - \delta v + \delta w - \delta x = 0. \tag{14.11.41}$$

Thus the equations (14.5.8) hold in this problem also, and using (14.11.40) we have

$$\lambda = l\varphi. \tag{14.11.42}$$

Hence finally

$$\begin{cases} u - u_0 = w - w_0 = \frac{1}{4}l\varphi, \\ v - v_0 = x - x_0 = -\frac{1}{4}l\varphi. \end{cases} \tag{14.11.43}$$

The gain of energy is equal to the energy of the relative motion (§ 14.6 (iii)), namely $\frac{1}{6}Ml^2\varphi^2$, a result that is readily verified directly.

The problem is in a sense the converse of *Example* 14.5. There we had an inert constraint, and $\dot\theta$ was suddenly diminished from φ_0 to zero; here we have a live constraint, and $\dot\theta$ is suddenly increased from zero to φ.

14.12 Impulsive motion of a continuous system. We have already assumed, on physical grounds, that the fundamental equation for finite forces is applicable to continuous systems, and in § 3.9 we considered some concrete examples. We now make a similar assumption, that the fundamental equation for impulses (14.3.6) also applies to continuous systems, the summation being replaced by the corresponding integration.

(i) *Incompressible liquid.* We consider a mass of uniform incompressible perfect liquid. There are internal and external boundaries in motion. The boundaries are rigid surfaces, or if they are deformable they must move in such a way that the volume enclosed is constant. If the motion of the boundaries is discontinuous at t_1 (for example, if the liquid is at rest in a closed vessel which is suddenly jerked into motion) the motion of the liquid is discontinuous. The problem is to determine the instantaneous change of motion.

We denote the components of $\mathbf{q}$, the velocity, referred to fixed rectangular axes, by u, v, w, the (constant) density by ρ. An impulsive pressure ϖ is set up in the liquid, corresponding to the impulses of constraint in a system with a finite number of freedoms. The fundamental equation (14.3.6) becomes

$$\int \rho\{(u - u_0)\Delta u + (v - v_0)\,\Delta v + (w - w_0)\,\Delta w\}\,d\tau = -\int \varpi\,\Delta q_n\,dS, \tag{14.12.1}$$

where the volume integral extends through the liquid, and the surface integral over the bounding surfaces; q_n is the component of velocity along the normal drawn outwards from the liquid. The symbol Δ denotes a finite, not an infinitesimal, variation, possible at $t_1 + 0$. If l, m, n are direction cosines of the outward normal, the second member of (14.12.1) is

$$\begin{aligned} -\int \varpi(l\,\Delta u + m\,\Delta v + n\,\Delta w)\,dS = &-\int \left(\frac{\partial \varpi}{\partial x}\,\Delta u + \frac{\partial \varpi}{\partial y}\,\Delta v + \frac{\partial \varpi}{\partial z}\,dw\right) d\tau \\ &-\int \varpi\left(\frac{\partial}{\partial x}\,\Delta u + \frac{\partial}{\partial y}\,\Delta v + \frac{\partial}{\partial z}\,\Delta w\right) d\tau, \end{aligned} \tag{14.12.2}$$

and the last term on the right is zero, since $\operatorname{div}\mathbf{q} = \operatorname{div}(\mathbf{q} + \Delta\mathbf{q}) = 0$. From (14.12.1) and (14.12.2) we find

(14.12.3)

$$\int\left\{\left[\rho(u - u_0) + \frac{\partial \varpi}{\partial x}\right]\Delta u + \left[\rho(v - v_0) + \frac{\partial \varpi}{\partial y}\right]\Delta v + \left[\rho(w - w_0) + \frac{\partial \varpi}{\partial z}\right]\Delta w\right\} d\tau = 0,$$

and this holds for values of $\Delta\mathbf{q}$ arbitrary save for the conditions $\operatorname{div}\Delta\mathbf{q} = 0$, $\Delta q_n = 0$. Thus

$$\begin{cases} \rho(u - u_0) = -\dfrac{\partial \varpi}{\partial x}, \\ \rho(v - v_0) = -\dfrac{\partial \varpi}{\partial y}, \\ \rho(w - w_0) = -\dfrac{\partial \varpi}{\partial z}, \end{cases} \tag{14.12.4}$$

and these are the equations for the impulsive motion of a liquid. We see that if the motion at $t_1 - 0$ is irrotational, the motion at $t_1 + 0$ is also irrotational. If the motion is set up from rest it is irrotational, $\mathbf{q} = -\operatorname{grad}\varphi$, and the impulsive pressure ϖ is related to the velocity potential φ of the motion set up by the equation

$$\varpi = \rho\varphi. \tag{14.12.5}$$

All this refers only to the frictionless incompressible liquid of the classical hydrodynamics.

Some well-known theorems of classical hydrodynamics, usually proved by applications of Green's theorem, can now be established as simple illustrations of the general theorems on impulsive motion. Let us suppose that the motion is set up from rest by jerking the boundaries into motion. Then the energy of the system is (§ 14.7(i))

$$-\tfrac{1}{2}\int \varpi q_n\,dS = \tfrac{1}{2}\int \rho\varphi\,\frac{\partial \varphi}{\partial n}\,dS, \tag{14.12.6}$$

where the integral is taken over the boundaries, and dn refers to the outward normal. Again, the energy set up when the boundaries are set in motion is the least possible subject to the prescribed value of the normal velocity at points of the boundary. This follows from *Cor.* 1 to Kelvin's theorem (§ 14.7(v)), since at each point of the boundary the direction of the impulse, and the component of velocity in that direction, is prescribed.

(ii) *Inelastic string.* An inelastic string AB, lying on a smooth table, is jerked into motion by a tangential impulse J at the end B. How does the string start to move?

Let s be the arc-length from A to a point P of the string, and ψ the inclination of the tangent at P to the tangent at A. We assume that the radius of curvature ρ $(= ds/d\psi)$ is positive and finite, and a differentiable function of ψ, at all points of the arc AB. Let u, v be tangential and normal components of velocity at P (Fig. 14.12). If λ is the mass per unit length at P the fundamental equation (14.3.6) becomes

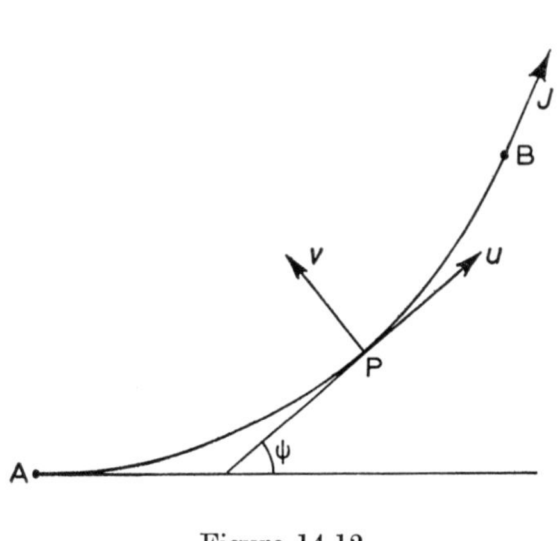

Figure 14.12

$$\int_A^B \lambda(u\,\Delta u + v\,\Delta v)\,ds = J\,\Delta u_B, \tag{14.12.7}$$

where Δ refers, as usual, to a finite, not an infinitesimal, variation, and u_B is the value of u at B.

Now, since the string is inextensible,

$$v = \frac{du}{d\psi}, \qquad \Delta v = \frac{d}{d\psi}\,\Delta u, \tag{14.12.8}$$

and (14.12.7) becomes

$$\int_0^\alpha \left\{\lambda u\,\Delta u + \lambda v\frac{d}{d\psi}(\Delta u)\right\}\rho\,d\psi = J\Delta u_B, \tag{14.12.9}$$

where α is the value of ψ at B. From (14.12.9), on integration by parts, we find

$$\lambda\rho v\,\Delta u\Big|_A^B + \int_0^\alpha \left\{\lambda\rho u - \frac{d}{d\psi}(\lambda\rho v)\right\}\Delta u\,d\psi = J\Delta u_B. \tag{14.12.10}$$

The end-conditions are

$$(\lambda\rho v)_A = 0, \quad (\lambda\rho v)_B = J, \tag{14.12.11}$$

and, since (14.12.10) holds for arbitrary Δu, we have

$$\lambda\rho u = \frac{d}{d\psi}(\lambda\rho v). \tag{14.12.12}$$

The differential equation to determine u is

$$\frac{d}{d\psi}\left(\lambda\rho\frac{du}{d\psi}\right) = \lambda\rho u. \tag{14.12.13}$$

To find the differential equation satisfied by v we have

$$v = \frac{du}{d\psi} = \frac{d}{d\psi}\left\{\frac{1}{\lambda\rho}\frac{d}{d\psi}(\lambda\rho v)\right\}, \tag{14.12.14}$$

which is equivalent to the homogeneous linear equation

$$v'' + \kappa v' + (\kappa' - 1)v = 0, \tag{14.12.15}$$

where $\kappa\left(= \dfrac{1}{\lambda\rho}\dfrac{d}{d\psi}(\lambda\rho)\right)$ is a given function of ψ, and in (14.12.15) accents denote differentiation with respect to ψ. We need the solution of (14.12.15) satisfying the end-conditions (14.12.11). We notice that the theory fails if the radius of curvature at B is zero, e.g. if B is at the cusp of a cycloidal arc.

Another situation that may arise is that in which the end A is not free, but is constrained to move in the direction of the normal at A to the curve. No other direction may be prescribed! The end-conditions are now

(14.12.16) $$u_A = 0, \quad (\lambda\rho v)_B = J.$$

We consider some concrete examples, with a uniform string, so that λ is constant, and $\kappa = \rho'/\rho$.

(*a*) A circular arc, from $\psi = 0$ to $\psi = \alpha$. The equation for v is

(14.12.17) $$v'' - v = 0,$$

and the solution is

(14.12.18) $$v = C \sinh \psi = \frac{J}{\lambda\rho}\frac{\sinh \psi}{\sinh \alpha} = \frac{J\alpha}{M}\frac{\sinh \psi}{\sinh \alpha},$$

where M is the mass of the string. Further, from (14.12.12),

(14.12.19) $$u = v' = \frac{J\alpha}{M}\frac{\cosh \psi}{\sinh \alpha},$$

and this completes the solution. The energy generated is

(14.12.20) $$\tfrac{1}{2}Ju_B = \frac{J^2}{2M}\alpha \coth \alpha.$$

It is interesting to observe that this is greater than $\frac{1}{2}(J^2/M)$, as we can foresee by Bertrand's theorem; for we could constrain the string to move in a smooth tube, and then the energy generated would be $\frac{1}{2}(J^2/M)$.

If, instead of being free, the end A is constrained to move normally, the solution is

(14.12.21) $$v = C \cosh \psi = \frac{J}{\lambda\rho}\frac{\cosh \psi}{\cosh \alpha} = \frac{J\alpha}{M}\frac{\cosh \psi}{\cosh \alpha},$$

and

(14.12.22) $$u = \frac{J\alpha}{M}\frac{\sinh \psi}{\cosh \alpha}.$$

Here the energy generated is

(14.12.23) $$\tfrac{1}{2}Ju_B = \frac{J^2}{2M}\alpha \tanh \alpha,$$

and this is less than (14.12.20), giving still another illustration of Bertrand's theorem.

(*b*) A catenary arc

(14.12.24) $$s = c \tan \psi,$$

from $\psi = 0$ to $\psi = \alpha$. In this case $\rho = c \sec^2 \psi$, $\kappa = 2 \tan \psi$, and the differential equation for v is

(14.12.25) $$v'' + 2v' \tan \psi + (2 \tan^2 \psi + 1)v = 0.$$

The solution is

(14.12.26) $$v = (C + D\psi) \cos \psi,$$

and therefore, from (14.12.12),

(14.12.27) $$u = (C + D\psi) \sin \psi + D \cos \psi.$$

If the string is free, the end-conditions (14.12.11) give

$$C = 0, \quad D = \frac{J}{\lambda c} \frac{\cos \alpha}{\alpha}. \tag{14.12.28}$$

If A is constrained to move on the normal, the end-conditions (14.12.16) give

$$C = \frac{J}{\lambda c} \cos \alpha, \quad D = 0. \tag{14.12.29}$$

In this case

$$u = C \sin \psi, \quad v = C \cos \psi, \tag{14.12.30}$$

and all points of the string move with the same speed C in the same direction, the direction of the normal to the curve at A.

Chapter XV

The sixth form of the fundamental equation

15.1 The sixth form of the fundamental equation. In Chapters XII and XIII we were concerned with dynamical systems of a high degree of generality. The systems with which we now deal are systems of a more restricted type, namely conservative holonomic systems. We choose Lagrangian coordinates $q_1, q_2, \ldots, q_n$, equal in number to the number of freedoms, and we recall that the virtual displacements are those given by arbitrary values of $\delta q_1, \delta q_2, \ldots, \delta q_n$. The fourth form of the fundamental equation (§ 6.1) can be written

$$\sum_{r=1}^{n}\left\{\frac{d}{dt}\left(\frac{\partial L}{\partial \dot{q}_r}\right) - \frac{\partial L}{\partial q_r}\right\}\delta q_r = 0, \tag{15.1.1}$$

and, since this holds for arbitrary values of $\delta q_1, \delta q_2, \ldots, \delta q_n$, it is equivalent to the n Lagrangian equations of motion.

We write p_r for the generalized momentum component $\partial L/\partial \dot{q}_r$ (§ 6.10), and denote by δL the differential consequent on arbitrary variations of q's and $\dot{q}$'s, t being unvaried,

$$\delta L = \sum_{r=1}^{n}\left(\frac{\partial L}{\partial q_r}\,\delta q_r + \frac{\partial L}{\partial \dot{q}_r}\,\delta \dot{q}_r\right) = \sum_{r=1}^{n}\left(\frac{\partial L}{\partial q_r}\,\delta q_r + p_r\,\delta \dot{q}_r\right). \tag{15.1.2}$$

Then, combining (15.1.1) and (15.1.2), we have

$$\sum_{r=1}^{n}(\dot{p}_r\,\delta q_r + p_r\,\delta \dot{q}_r) = \delta L. \tag{15.1.3}$$

This is the sixth form of the fundamental equation. It is valid for arbitrary values of δq's and $\delta \dot{q}$'s. If we use the summation convention, so that repeated suffixes imply summation from 1 to n, the equation takes the form

$$\dot{p}_r\,\delta q_r + p_r\,\delta \dot{q}_r = \delta L. \tag{15.1.4}$$

The sixth form of the fundamental equation is a compact and convenient repository of information about the motion of a dynamical system of the type under discussion. We shall show first how some of the results previously established by other methods can be derived from it. Then we shall proceed further to new and important results.

15.2 Immediate deductions. We derived the sixth form of the fundamental equation (15.1.4) from Lagrange's equations; the first and obvious application is, conversely, the deduction of Lagrange's equations from (15.1.4). Since (15.1.4) holds for arbitrary values of δq's and $\delta \dot{q}$'s we have

$$p_r = \frac{\partial L}{\partial \dot{q}_r}, \qquad \dot{p}_r = \frac{\partial L}{\partial q_r}, \qquad r = 1, 2, \ldots, n, \tag{15.2.1}$$

whence

$$\frac{d}{dt}\left(\frac{\partial L}{\partial \dot{q}_r}\right) = \frac{\partial L}{\partial q_r}, \qquad r = 1, 2, \ldots, n. \tag{15.2.2}$$

Next we write (15.1.4) in the form

$$\dot{q}_r\,\delta p_r - \dot{p}_r\,\delta q_r = \delta(p_r\dot{q}_r - L). \tag{15.2.3}$$

We denote by H the function $(p_r\dot{q}_r - L)$ when expressed in terms of q's and p's and t (§ 10.13). The equations defining the p's, namely

$$p_r = \frac{\partial L}{\partial \dot{q}_r}, \qquad r = 1, 2, \ldots, n,$$

are linear in the $\dot{q}$'s, and can be solved for the $\dot{q}$'s as functions of the q's and p's and t; these functions are linear in the p's. We can thus suppress the $\dot{q}$'s in the formula $(p_r\dot{q}_r - L)$ in favour of the p's, and the function so determined is H. Now in the original equation (15.1.4) the variations of q's and $\dot{q}$'s are arbitrary, which implies that, in the equation

$$\dot{q}_r\,\delta p_r - \dot{p}_r\,\delta q_r = \delta H, \tag{15.2.4}$$

the variations of q's and p's are arbitrary. We deduce therefore

$$\dot{q}_r = \frac{\partial H}{\partial p_r}, \qquad \dot{p}_r = -\frac{\partial H}{\partial q_r}, \qquad r = 1, 2, \ldots, n, \tag{15.2.5}$$

and these are Hamilton's equations.

As we have remarked already (§ 10.13) the equations (15.2.5) are $2n$ equations of the first order of the form

$$\dot{\mathbf{x}} = \mathbf{X},$$

where $\mathbf{x}$ and $\mathbf{X}$ are column matrices, or vectors, with $2n$ components. The component X_r of $\mathbf{X}$ is a function of $x_1, x_2, \ldots, x_{2n}$, and exceptionally also of t. The function H is a new descriptive function (cf. § 6.6) for the dynamical system, i.e. a function from which equations of motion can be constructed, so that it contains implicitly a complete description of the possible motions. Some extensions of (15.2.5) have already been discussed in § 10.13, and explicit formulae for H have been found in § 10.14.

The space of $2n$ dimensions whose points are defined by the $2n$ coordinates $q_1, q_2, \ldots, q_n, p_1, p_2, \ldots, p_n$ is called the *phase space*, and the motion of the dynamical system can be pictured as the motion of a representative point in the phase space. When it is desirable to give a structure to the phase space we can think of it as a Euclidean space of $2n$ dimensions in which $q_1, q_2, \ldots, q_n, p_1, p_2, \ldots, p_n$ are rectangular coordinates.

The Lagrangian and Hamiltonian functions are not the only possible descriptive functions, though they are certainly the most important. There are other forms of the equations of motion that can be derived from the sixth form of the fundamental equation. Thus, for example, we can write the equation in the form

$$q_r\,\delta\dot{p}_r + \dot{q}_r\,\delta p_r = \delta(\dot{p}_r q_r + p_r\dot{q}_r - L), \tag{15.2.6}$$

and if X is $(\dot{p}_r q_r + p_r\dot{q}_r - L)$ expressed in terms of p's and $\dot{p}$'s we have the equations of motion

$$q_r = \frac{\partial X}{\partial \dot{p}_r}, \quad \dot{q}_r = \frac{\partial X}{\partial p_r}, \qquad r = 1, 2, \ldots, n, \tag{15.2.7}$$

which are of Lagrangian type, and lead to

$$\frac{d}{dt}\left(\frac{\partial X}{\partial \dot{p}_r}\right) = \frac{\partial X}{\partial p_r}, \qquad r = 1, 2, \ldots, n. \tag{15.2.8}$$

But the process by which X is formed, though theoretically possible, is not practicable. We have to solve the equations

$$p_r = \frac{\partial L}{\partial \dot{q}_r}, \quad \dot{p}_r = \frac{\partial L}{\partial q_r}, \qquad r = 1, 2, \ldots, n, \tag{15.2.9}$$

for q's and $\dot{q}$'s (in terms of p's and $\dot{p}$'s) and this is not feasible except in very simple cases; the equations (15.2.9) are not in general linear in the q's. An example where the process *can* be carried out is afforded by the problem of small oscillations. If

$$L = \tfrac{1}{2} \sum_{r=1}^{n} (\dot{q}_r^{\,2} - n_r^{\,2} q_r^{\,2}),$$

the corresponding function X is

$$X = \tfrac{1}{2} \sum_{r=1}^{n} \left(-\frac{1}{n_r^{\,2}} \dot{p}_r^{\,2} + p_r^{\,2} \right),$$

and the equations of motion (15.2.7) are equivalent to Lagrange's equations for the system.

Similarly we can, in theory, find a descriptive function containing $\dot{q}$'s and $\dot{p}$'s. We write (15.1.4) in the form

$$q_r\, \delta \dot{p}_r - p_r\, \delta \dot{q}_r = \delta(\dot{p}_r q_r - L), \tag{15.2.10}$$

and if Y is $(\dot{p}_r q_r - L)$ expressed in terms of $\dot{q}$'s and $\dot{p}$'s the equations of motion are

$$q_r = \frac{\partial Y}{\partial \dot{p}_r}, \quad p_r = -\frac{\partial Y}{\partial \dot{q}_r}, \qquad r = 1, 2, \ldots, n. \tag{15.2.11}$$

This time we have to suppress the q's in favour of the $\dot{p}$'s by means of the equations

$$\dot{p}_r = \frac{\partial L}{\partial q_r}, \qquad r = 1, 2, \ldots, n,$$

and again the process is not usually practicable.

15.3 The Routhian function. We can find a descriptive function which enables us to write some of the equations, say the first m pairs, in Hamiltonian, and the rest in Lagrangian, form. This is easily achieved. We write (15.1.4), now giving up for the moment the summation convention, in the form

$$\sum_{r=1}^{n} (\dot{p}_r\, \delta q_r + p_r\, \delta \dot{q}_r) - \sum_{r=1}^{m} (p_r\, \delta \dot{q}_r + \dot{q}_r\, \delta p_r) = \delta\Big(L - \sum_{r=1}^{m} p_r \dot{q}_r\Big). \tag{15.3.1}$$

If R is the function $\left(L - \sum_{r=1}^{m} p_r \dot{q}_r\right)$ with the first m velocities $\dot{q}_1, \dot{q}_2, \ldots, \dot{q}_m$ suppressed in favour of the corresponding momenta $p_1, p_2, \ldots, p_m$, the equations of motion are

$$\dot{q}_r = -\frac{\partial R}{\partial p_r}, \quad \dot{p}_r = \frac{\partial R}{\partial q_r}, \qquad r = 1, 2, \ldots, m, \tag{15.3.2}$$

$$\dot{p}_r = \frac{\partial R}{\partial q_r}, \quad p_r = \frac{\partial R}{\partial \dot{q}_r}, \qquad r = m+1, m+2, \ldots, n. \tag{15.3.3}$$

The first m pairs of equations are of Hamiltonian form (with $-R$ in place of H), and the remaining $(n - m)$ pairs lead to equations of Lagrangian form (with R in place of L). To form R we need to solve the m linear equations

$$p_r = \frac{\partial L}{\partial \dot{q}_r}, \qquad r = 1, 2, \ldots, m,$$

for $\dot{q}_1, \dot{q}_2, \ldots, \dot{q}_m$ as functions of $p_1, p_2, \ldots, p_m, \dot{q}_{m+1}, \dot{q}_{m+2}, \ldots, \dot{q}_n$, and the q's and possibly t.

The most important case, and in fact the only case that was actually considered by Routh, is the case already considered in § 10.1 where the first m coordinates are ignorable. In this case the first m momenta $p_1, p_2, \ldots, p_m$ remain constant during the motion, and the function R plays the part of a Lagrangian function for a system with $(n - m)$ freedoms whose coordinates are $q_{m+1}, q_{m+2}, \ldots, q_n$. Some particular applications have already been discussed in § 10.1 *et seqq.*

15.4 The theorem $\frac{d}{dt}(p_r\, \delta q_r) = \delta L$. We now turn to a different interpretation of (15.1.4). We picture the motion of the system as the motion of a representative point in a space of n dimensions, the coordinates being $q_1, q_2, \ldots, q_n$. We begin with a natural orbit of the system, i.e. a path in the q-space satisfying the equations of motion. We consider at each instant a variation from the point $q_1, q_2, \ldots, q_n$ on the orbit to a contemporaneous position $q_1 + \delta q_1, q_2 + \delta q_2, \ldots, q_n + \delta q_n$ on a varied path. The varied path is not in general an orbit for the system, i.e. it does not satisfy the equations of motion. It *is* of course a geometrically possible path, since the system is holonomic. The variations are arbitrary, save for the limitation that each of the variations δq_r is a function of t of class C_2. Now, since the variations are contemporaneous,

$$\delta \dot{q}_r = \frac{d}{dt}\delta q_r, \qquad r = 1, 2, \ldots, n, \tag{15.4.1}$$

and (15.1.4) may be written

$$\frac{d}{dt}(p_r\, \delta q_r) = \delta L, \tag{15.4.2}$$

where we use the summation convention. *The time-rate of change of the inner product $p_r\, \delta q_r$ is equal to the variation in L arising from the contemporaneous variation $\delta\mathbf{q}$ and the consequent variation $\delta\dot{\mathbf{q}}$.*

Our first deduction from (15.4.2) is a new proof of Hamilton's principle; but this time the proof (unlike that given in § 3.7) applies only to holonomic conservative systems. We have

$$\int_{t_0}^{t_1} \delta L\, dt = p_{r1}\, \delta q_{r1} - p_{r0}\, \delta q_{r0}, \tag{15.4.3}$$

where q_{r0}, p_{r0} are the values of q_r, p_r at time t_0, and q_{r1}, p_{r1} are the values at time t_1. If $\delta\mathbf{q}$ vanishes both at t_0 and at t_1 we find

$$\int_{t_0}^{t_1} \delta L\, dt = 0, \tag{15.4.4}$$

and this is Hamilton's principle.

The equations (15.4.3–4) can also be written in the forms

$$\delta\int_{t_0}^{t_1} L\, dt = p_{r1}\, \delta q_{r1} - p_{r0}\, \delta q_{r0}, \tag{15.4.5}$$

$$\delta\int_{t_0}^{t_1} L\, dt = 0, \tag{15.4.6}$$

where the original integral is taken along an arc of an orbit in the q-space (i.e. a path satisfying the equations of motion), and the varied integral is taken along the varied path constructed in the way described above. As we have noticed already, the varied path is not in general an orbit.

The equation (15.4.2) is true when the varied path is arbitrary; we only demand that the related points on the original path and the varied path are contemporaneous, and that each $\delta q_r \in C_2$, not that the varied path is itself an orbit. But now let us impose a further restriction; *let us suppose that the varied path is itself an orbit*, the orbit arising from slightly varied initial conditions. The operator δ now brings us to the contemporaneous point on a neighbouring orbit.

As a first application, suppose that L does not contain t explicitly, so that if we start with given initial values of $\mathbf{q}$ and $\dot{\mathbf{q}}$ we get the same orbit whatever the instant of projection, and the position on the orbit depends only on the interval from the instant of projection. Now let δ denote a variation to the position occupied on the same orbit after a small constant time-interval τ. The varied path is the original orbit, but with each point occupied τ seconds earlier than in the original orbit. Then

$$\delta q_r = \tau \dot{q}_r, \quad \delta \dot{q}_r = \tau \ddot{q}_r, \quad \delta L = \tau \frac{dL}{dt}, \tag{15.4.7}$$

and (15.4.2) gives

$$\frac{d}{dt}(p_r \dot{q}_r - L) = 0, \tag{15.4.8}$$

which is equivalent to Jacobi's integral (§ 6.7).

As a second application, consider orbits starting from points on a closed curve γ_0 in the q-space at $t = 0$; the velocities of projection are assumed to vary continuously as we traverse the closed curve. After time t the representative points build up another closed curve γ. Now for two neighbouring orbits we have

$$\frac{d}{dt}(p_r \, \delta q_r) = \delta L, \tag{15.4.2}$$

so for the closed curve γ we have

$$\frac{d}{dt} \oint p_r \, \delta q_r = 0. \tag{15.4.9}$$

The line-integral $\oint p_r \, \delta q_r$ retains its initial value always if the curve γ moves in the way described, the motion of the curve in the q-space being correlated with the possible motions of the dynamical system. We notice a close analogy with the well-known theorem of the constancy of the circulation in classical hydrodynamics.

There is another aspect of the result that is actually more valuable; it comes from the interpretation in terms of the phase space (§ 15.2) rather than the q-space. If we start from a simple closed curve Γ_0 in the phase space there is a definite orbit starting from each point of Γ_0 at $t = 0$. The representative points on these orbits build up a closed curve Γ at time t, and the curve Γ at time t is completely defined when Γ_0 is prescribed. *The value of the line-integral $\oint p_r \, dq_r$ round Γ remains constant.* Such an integral is spoken of as an *integral-invariant* of the equations defining the motion, in this case the Hamiltonian equations. The integral remains constant only for a closed curve, not for an open arc, and in these circumstances we speak of a *relative* integral-invariant. The integral $\oint p_r \, dq_r$ is the famous linear integral-invariant of Poincaré; the existence of this integral-invariant is a fundamental property of

Hamiltonian systems. When we turn later to the detailed study of the Hamiltonian equations we shall consider this and other integral-invariants more fully.

15.5 The principal function. We now introduce the *principal function* of Hamilton. The idea of the principal function is suggested by a technique that is important in geometrical optics. It is a function from which the dynamically possible motions of the system can be derived.

Explicitly the principal function S is the integral $\int_{t_0}^{t_1} L\,dt$ taken along an orbit (i.e. a path in the q-space satisfying the equations of motion) and expressed in terms of the termini and the times of departure and arrival,

$$S = S(q_{10}, q_{20}, \ldots, q_{n0};\ q_{11}, q_{21}, \ldots, q_{n1};\ t_0, t_1), \tag{15.5.1}$$

or, compactly,

$$S = S(q_{r0};\ q_{r1};\ t_0, t_1). \tag{15.5.2}$$

To construct the function S we may proceed as follows. Let us suppose for the moment that the integrals of the Lagrangian equations of motion have been found, so that each q_r is a known uniform function of the n q_{r0}'s, the n ω_{r0}'s, t_0 and t. (Here ω_{r0} is the value of $\dot{q}_r$ at the instant t_0.) Thus

$$q_s = \varphi_s(q_{r0};\ \omega_{r0};\ t_0, t), \qquad s = 1, 2, \ldots, n. \tag{15.5.3}$$

We can thus express L in terms of the $2n + 1$ parameters $(q_{r0};\ \omega_{r0};\ t_0)$ and t, and, evaluating the integral, we express it as a function of the n q_{r0}'s, the n ω_{r0}'s, t_0 and t_1,

$$\int_{t_0}^{t_1} L\,dt = \sum (q_{r0};\ \omega_{r0};\ t_0, t_1). \tag{15.5.4}$$

Now consider the point $q_{11}, q_{21}, \ldots, q_{n1}$, which is the point reached at the instant t_1. We have

$$q_{s1} = \varphi_s(q_{r0};\ \omega_{r0};\ t_0, t_1), \qquad s = 1, 2, \ldots, n, \tag{15.5.5}$$

and by means of these equations we can suppress the ω_{r0}'s in (15.5.4) in favour of the q_{r1}'s, and we then obtain

$$\sum(q_{r0};\ \omega_{r0};\ t_0, t_1) = S(q_{r0};\ q_{r1};\ t_0, t_1). \tag{15.5.6}$$

The function S is the objective desired.

It is clear now that the ω_{r0}'s are, as it were, only a scaffolding, to be discarded when the structure is complete, and that any other equivalent set of parameters (for example the n p_{r0}'s or the n ω_{r1}'s) might be used instead in the calculation; the function S obtained ultimately will be the same whichever parameters we choose to employ in defining the orbits. Nevertheless it will make for clarity if, for the present, we think of S as being evaluated in one particular way, namely in the way just described. We observe that if L does not contain t explicitly the q's and $\dot{q}$'s are functions of $(t - t_0)$, and t_0, t_1 occur in S only in the expression $(t_1 - t_0)$.

We now consider how S varies with its $2n + 2$ arguments. If, to begin with, we leave t_0 and t_1 unvaried, and consider only variations in the terminal points, we have, from (15.4.5),

$$\delta S = p_{r1}\,\delta q_{r1} - p_{r0}\,\delta q_{r0}, \tag{15.5.7}$$

where p_{r0}, p_{r1} are components of momentum at t_0 and at t_1. The momentum-components at the terminal points of the orbit can be found from the principal function; they are the partial derivatives $-\partial S/\partial q_{r0}$ and $\partial S/\partial q_{r1}$.

We next consider a variation in t_1. If L_1 is the value of L on the orbit at time t_1, we have

$$L_1 = \frac{\partial \Sigma}{\partial t_1} = \frac{\partial S}{\partial t_1} + \frac{\partial S}{\partial q_{r1}} \frac{\partial q_{r1}}{\partial t_1}, \tag{15.5.8}$$

whence

$$\frac{\partial S}{\partial t_1} = -p_{r1}\omega_{r1} + L_1 = -H_1, \tag{15.5.9}$$

where H_1 is the value of the Hamiltonian function H at t_1 in the given motion.

Finally, from considerations of symmetry,

$$\frac{\partial S}{\partial t_0} = H_0, \tag{15.5.10}$$

where H_0 is the value of H at t_0 in the given motion. (A formal proof of this result is not entirely trivial if we think of the principal function as evaluated in the way described above; we shall return to this point in § 15.7. The difficulty can be avoided by using a different method of evaluation, with parameters other than the ω_{r0}'s previously used.) Thus *for a completely general variation of all the* $(2n + 2)$ *arguments we have the important formula*

$$dS = p_{r1}\, dq_{r1} - p_{r0}\, dq_{r0} - H_1\, dt_1 + H_0\, dt_0. \tag{15.5.11}$$

15.6 Reflexions on the principal function. The $(2n + 2)$ independent variables in terms of which the principal function is defined are the coordinates of the initial and the final points (in the q-space) and the times of departure and arrival. In the simplest cases (cf. (i) below) we can prescribe arbitrary values of these variables, and it is possible to project the mobile from $\mathbf{q}_0$ at t_0 in such a way that it hits the target $\mathbf{q}_1$ at t_1. In these cases S exists, and is a uniform (single-valued) differentiable function, for all real values of the arguments. This is not true in more complicated cases, but this does not invalidate the theory, because in practice we start from a given arc of a known orbit. This corresponds to a definite point

$$q_{10}, q_{20}, \ldots, q_{n0};\ q_{11}, q_{21}, \ldots, q_{n1};\ t_0, t_1, \tag{15.6.1}$$

in the $(2n + 2)$-fold for which a definite value of S is defined by the given orbit, and we are only concerned with the variation of S in a neighbourhood of the given point (15.6.1).

We illustrate these remarks by consideration of some concrete examples.

(i) *Motion of a particle in the plane* $z = 0$ *under the action of the uniform field* $(0, -g)$. If (u_0, v_0) is the velocity of projection from (x_0, y_0) we have

$$\begin{cases} x_1 - x_0 = u_0(t_1 - t_0), \\ y_1 - y_0 = v_0(t_1 - t_0) - \tfrac{1}{2}g(t_1 - t_0)^2. \end{cases} \tag{15.6.2}$$

Unless $(t_1 - t_0)$ vanishes the equations determine u_0 and v_0 uniquely. There is a unique solution for arbitrary positions of the terminal points, and for arbitrary unequal values of t_0 and t_1. Therefore S exists and is a uniform function of its six arguments.

(ii) *Harmonic oscillator on a line.* The equation of motion is

$$\ddot{x} + n^2 x = 0, \tag{15.6.3}$$

and the equation

$$x_1 = x_0 \cos n(t_1 - t_0) + \frac{u_0}{n} \sin n(t_1 - t_0) \tag{15.6.4}$$

determines u_0 uniquely *unless* $n(t_1 - t_0)$ *is an integral multiple of* π; apart from these exceptional values of $n(t_1 - t_0)$ there is a unique orbit for arbitrary values of the four arguments, and S is a uniform function of (x_0, x_1, t_0, t_1). This is evident from Fig. 15.6, which shows the motions starting from x_0 at t_0. But if $n(t_1 - t_0) = r\pi$ the problem is poristic; there is no orbit unless $x_1 = (-)^r x_0$, and in that case there are infinitely many orbits. Thus S is not defined in general if $n(t_1 - t_0)$ is an integral multiple of π.

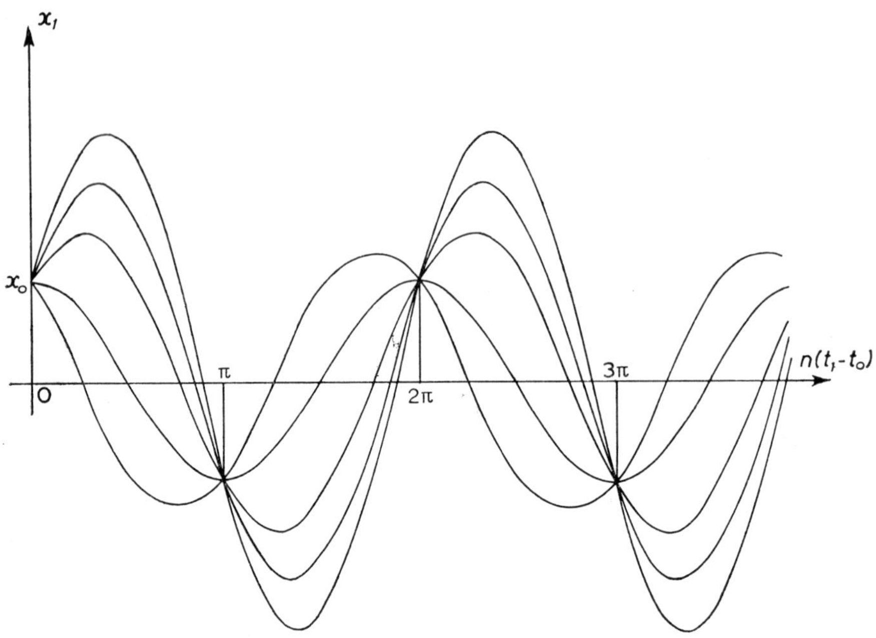

Figure 15.6

More generally, consider the theory of small oscillations about a position of stable equilibrium (§ 9.1). Using the normal coordinates we have

$$\xi_{r1} = \xi_{r0} \cos p_r(t_1 - t_0) + \frac{\omega_{r0}}{p_r} \sin p_r(t_1 - t_0), \qquad r = 1, 2, \ldots, n, \tag{15.6.5}$$

where ω_{r0} is the value of $\dot{\xi}_r$ at t_0. The equations determine $\omega_{10}, \omega_{20}, \ldots, \omega_{n0}$ uniquely, provided that none of the numbers $p_r(t_1 - t_0)$ is an integral multiple of π. With this exception the orbit is uniquely determined by the terminal points and the time of transit, and S is a uniform function.

(iii) *The simple pendulum.* For the sake of simplicity we take $t_0 = 0$ and $\theta_0 = 0$; the particle is projected from the lowest point of the circle. Fig. 5.2*c* shows how θ varies with t for different velocities of projection. If t_1 is arbitrary, and θ_1 is arbitrary in the range $-\pi < \theta_1 < \pi$, the orbit is clearly not unique. However we can ensure uniqueness if we impose certain restrictions on the orbits considered as follows: (*a*) only periodic orbits with amplitude less than π are considered, orbits in which θ varies monotonically being excluded, (*b*) only positive initial values of $\dot{\theta}$ are permitted, and (*c*) the terminal value θ_1 is reached in less than one complete period.

15.7 Proof that $\partial S/\partial t_0 = H_0$. We turn to the proof of (15.5.10), supposing S to have been constructed in the way described in § 15.5. We need the following *Lemma*:

Lemma. The functions φ_r *(see the equation* (15.5.3)*) are annihilated by the operator*

$$\frac{\partial}{\partial t_0} + \omega_{r0}\frac{\partial}{\partial q_{r0}} + \alpha_{r0}\frac{\partial}{\partial \omega_{r0}}, \tag{15.7.1}$$

where α_{r0} *is the value of* $\ddot{q}_r$ *when* $t = t_0$. (Repeated suffixes imply summation from 1 to n.)

The truth of the Lemma is evident if we consider varying the parameters determining the orbit to neighbouring parameters defining the same orbit. To construct a formal proof we notice that, for an arbitrary value of t_1 in some neighbourhood of t_0,

$$\varphi_s(q_{r0};\ \omega_{r0};\ t_0, t) = \varphi_s\{\varphi_r(q_{m0};\ \omega_{m0};\ t_0, t_1);\ \dot{\varphi}_r(q_{m0};\ \omega_{m0};\ t_0, t_1);\ t_1, t\}. \tag{15.7.2}$$

If we differentiate partially with respect to t_1, and then put $t_1 = t_0$, we obtain the desired result.

We easily deduce the result stated. For, in virtue of (15.5.4) and (15.5.6),

$$\frac{\partial \Sigma}{\partial t_0} = \frac{\partial S}{\partial t_0} + \frac{\partial S}{\partial q_{r1}}\frac{\partial q_{r1}}{\partial t_0} = \int_{t_0}^{t_1}\frac{\partial L}{\partial t_0}\,dt - L_0, \tag{15.7.3}$$

where L is expressed, as in (15.5.4), in terms of $q_{r0};\ \omega_{r0};\ t_0, t$. Further

$$\frac{\partial \Sigma}{\partial q_{s0}} = \frac{\partial S}{\partial q_{s0}} + \frac{\partial S}{\partial q_{r1}}\frac{\partial q_{r1}}{\partial q_{s0}} = \int_{t_0}^{t_1}\frac{\partial L}{\partial q_{s0}}\,dt, \tag{15.7.4}$$

$$\frac{\partial \Sigma}{\partial \omega_{s0}} = \frac{\partial S}{\partial q_{r1}}\frac{\partial q_{r1}}{\partial \omega_{s0}} = \int_{t_0}^{t_1}\frac{\partial L}{\partial \omega_{s0}}\,dt. \tag{15.7.5}$$

If we multiply these equations by 1, ω_{s0}, α_{s0} and sum we obtain

$$\begin{aligned}\frac{\partial S}{\partial t_0} + \omega_{s0}\frac{\partial S}{\partial q_{s0}} + \frac{\partial S}{\partial q_{r1}}\left(\frac{\partial q_{r1}}{\partial t_0} + \omega_{s0}\frac{\partial q_{r1}}{\partial q_{s0}} + \alpha_{s0}\frac{\partial q_{r1}}{\partial \omega_{s0}}\right)\\ = -L_0 + \int_{t_0}^{t}\left(\frac{\partial L}{\partial t_0} + \omega_{s0}\frac{\partial L}{\partial q_{s0}} + \alpha_{s0}\frac{\partial L}{\partial \omega_{s0}}\right)dt.\end{aligned} \tag{15.7.6}$$

Now q_{r1} is annihilated by the operator (15.7.1), in virtue of the Lemma, and consequently so also is L, and therefore

$$\frac{\partial S}{\partial t_0} = -\omega_{s0}\frac{\partial S}{\partial q_{s0}} - L_0 = p_{s0}\omega_{s0} - L_0 = H_0, \tag{15.7.7}$$

and this is the result we wished to prove.

15.8 Properties of the principal function. A knowledge of the function S would be of immense value to us in the study of the dynamical system if, by some inspiration or some exercise of ingenuity, we could determine it by a different method, i.e. without first finding the integrals of the Lagrangian equations of motion. Consider for example the equations

$$\frac{\partial S}{\partial q_{r0}} = -p_{r0}, \qquad r = 1, 2, \ldots, n. \tag{15.8.1}$$

They are n equations which determine the q_{r1}'s in terms of t_1 (and the parameters $q_{r0};\ p_{r0};\ t_0$). *They are the integrals of Lagrange's equations,* and determine the motion in the q-space. They give us the general solution of the Lagrange problem. Observe particularly that the equations (15.8.1) give the actual explicit expression of the motion in the q-space, not merely a new form of the differential equations to determine this motion. Again the equations

$$\frac{\partial S}{\partial q_{r1}} = p_{r1}, \qquad r = 1, 2, \ldots, n, \tag{15.8.2}$$

express the p_{r1}'s in terms of the q_{r1}'s (and the q_{r0}'s and t_0 and t_1). The two sets (15.8.1–2) together determine q_{r1}'s and p_{r1}'s in terms of t_1 (and the parameters q_{r0}; p_{r0}; t_0). *They are the integrals of Hamilton's equations*, and determine the motion in the phase-space. They give us the general solution of the Hamilton problem.

Some other important properties of S, and some other results derived from it, should be noticed at this point.

(i) If L does not contain t explicitly, t_0 and t_1 occur in S only in the combination $(t_1 - t_0)$. In this case $H_1 = H_0$ (as we know already, § 10.14) and (15.5.11) takes the form

$$dS = p_{r1}\, dq_{r1} - p_{r0}\, dq_{r0} - H_1\, d(t_1 - t_0). \tag{15.8.3}$$

(ii) S has continuous second derivatives, and the determinant

$$\begin{vmatrix} \dfrac{\partial^2 S}{\partial q_{10}\, \partial q_{11}} & \dfrac{\partial^2 S}{\partial q_{10}\, \partial q_{21}} & \cdots & \dfrac{\partial^2 S}{\partial q_{10}\, \partial q_{n1}} \\ \dfrac{\partial^2 S}{\partial q_{20}\, \partial q_{11}} & \dfrac{\partial^2 S}{\partial q_{20}\, \partial q_{21}} & \cdots & \dfrac{\partial^2 S}{\partial q_{20}\, \partial q_{n1}} \\ \cdot & \cdot & \cdots & \cdot \\ \dfrac{\partial^2 S}{\partial q_{n0}\, \partial q_{11}} & \dfrac{\partial^2 S}{\partial q_{n0}\, \partial q_{21}} & \cdots & \dfrac{\partial^2 S}{\partial q_{n0}\, \partial q_{n1}} \end{vmatrix} \tag{15.8.4}$$

or, briefly, the determinant $\left\| \dfrac{\partial^2 S}{\partial q_{r0}\, \partial q_{s1}} \right\|$, does not vanish identically. For, if it did vanish, there would be a functional relation connecting the $\dfrac{\partial S}{\partial q_{r1}}$'s and the q_{r1}'s (and t_0 and t_1). This would imply a relation connecting p_{r1}'s and q_{r1}'s (and t_0 and t_1), and this is impossible since these are independent variables.

(iii) *Liouville's theorem. The Jacobian*

$$\frac{\partial(q_{11}, q_{21}, \ldots, q_{n1}, p_{11}, p_{21}, \ldots, p_{n1})}{\partial(q_{10}, q_{20}, \ldots, q_{n0}, p_{10}, p_{20}, \ldots, p_{n0})} \tag{15.8.5}$$

has the value $+1$. If we consider the transformation from (q_{r0}, p_{r0}) to (q_{r1}, p_{r1}) defined by the integrals of Hamilton's equations (t_0 and t_1 being fixed) *the transformation has the property of preserving the extension (volume, measure) of the phase space.*

To prove Liouville's theorem we express all the variables in terms of the intermediate set q_{r0}, q_{r1}. We use the abbreviated formula

$$\frac{\partial(q_{r1};\ p_{r1})}{\partial(q_{r0};\ p_{r0})}$$

for the determinant (15.8.5), and then

$$\frac{\partial(q_{r1};\ p_{r1})}{\partial(q_{r0};\ p_{r0})} = \frac{\dfrac{\partial(q_{r1};\ p_{r1})}{\partial(q_{r0};\ q_{r1})}}{\dfrac{\partial(q_{r0};\ p_{r0})}{\partial(q_{r0};\ q_{r1})}} = \frac{(-)^n \dfrac{\partial(p_{r1})}{\partial(q_{s0})}}{\dfrac{\partial(p_{r0})}{\partial(q_{s1})}}, \tag{15.8.6}$$

where $\dfrac{\partial(p_{r1})}{\partial(q_{s0})}$ stands for the determinant in which the element in the rth row and sth column is $\dfrac{\partial p_{r1}}{\partial q_{s0}}$. But the expression on the right in (15.8.6) is equal to

$$\frac{(-)^n \left\| \dfrac{\partial^2 S}{\partial q_{s0}\, \partial q_{r1}} \right\|}{(-)^n \left\| \dfrac{\partial^2 S}{\partial q_{s1}\, \partial q_{r0}} \right\|} = 1,$$

and the proof is complete.

(iv) The solution of the Hamilton problem provided by (15.8.1–2) expresses q_{r1} and p_{r1} by formulae involving the $2n$ parameters q_{r0} and p_{r0}. But it is not always convenient to use this particular set of parameters. Suppose therefore that we introduce a new set of $2n$ parameters α_r, β_r which are restricted to having the following properties: they are $2n$ independent functions of the q_{r0}'s and p_{r0}'s, with continuous first derivatives, and they satisfy the condition

$$\beta_r\, d\alpha_r = p_{r0}\, dq_{r0}, \tag{15.8.7}$$

where the repeated suffix r implies summation from 1 to n. A transformation of this type from (q_{r0}, p_{r0}) to (α_r, β_r) is called a *homogeneous contact transformation.* Such transformations will appear frequently in the sequel.

Let us now express S in terms of the $(2n + 2)$ variables $(q_{r1};\ \alpha_r;\ t_0, t_1)$,

$$S(q_{r0};\ q_{r1};\ t_0, t_1) = S'(\alpha_r;\ q_{r1};\ t_0, t_1), \tag{15.8.8}$$

and then, from (15.5.11), we have

$$dS' = p_{r1}\, dq_{r1} - \beta_r\, d\alpha_r - H_1\, dt_1 + H_0\, dt_0. \tag{15.8.9}$$

We can derive from (15.8.9) the same sort of information that we previously derived from (15.5.11). Thus the equations

$$\frac{\partial S'}{\partial \alpha_r} = -\beta_r \qquad r = 1, 2, \ldots, n, \tag{15.8.10}$$

give the solution of the Lagrange problem. They allow us to express the q_{r1}'s in terms of the α's and β's and t_0 and t_1. If we add the equations

$$\frac{\partial S'}{\partial q_{r1}} = p_{r1}, \qquad r = 1, 2, \ldots, n, \tag{15.8.11}$$

the two sets (15.8.10–11) together give us the solution of the Hamilton problem. They allow us to express q_{r1}'s and p_{r1}'s in terms of α's and β's and t_0 and t_1.

The process just described is a little more subtle than would appear at first sight. We have to use the equations

$$\alpha_r = \alpha_r(q_{s0}, p_{s0}), \qquad r = 1, 2, \ldots, n, \tag{15.8.12}$$

$$p_{r0} = -\frac{\partial S}{\partial q_{r0}} = p_{r0}(q_{s0};\ q_{s1};\ t_0, t_1), \qquad r = 1, 2, \ldots, n, \tag{15.8.13}$$

to express q_{r0}'s and p_{r0}'s in terms of $(\alpha_r;\ q_{r1};\ t_0, t_1)$. It may be noticed in passing that the n functions in the second members of (15.8.12) cannot be chosen arbitrarily; they must satisfy certain conditions which we shall investigate later. By means of (15.8.12–13) we form S', suppressing the q_{r0}'s in S in favour of the α's; we have to substitute for each q_{r0} in S a formula

$$q_{r0} = q_{r0}(\alpha_s;\ q_{s1};\ t_0, t_1). \tag{15.8.14}$$

But now it appears odd at first sight that $\dfrac{\partial S}{\partial q_{r1}}$ and $\dfrac{\partial S'}{\partial q_{r1}}$ are equally valid expressions for p_{r1}. The resolution of the paradox is not far to seek; it depends on the condition (15.8.7). Thus

$$dS' = dS = \frac{\partial S}{\partial q_{r0}}\left(\frac{\partial q_{r0}}{\partial \alpha_s}\,d\alpha_s + \frac{\partial q_{r0}}{\partial q_{s1}}\,dq_{s1} + \frac{\partial q_{r0}}{\partial t_0}\,dt_0 + \frac{\partial q_{r0}}{\partial t_1}\,dt_1\right) + \frac{\partial S}{\partial q_{r1}}\,dq_{r1} + \frac{\partial S}{\partial t_0}\,dt_0 + \frac{\partial S}{\partial t_1}\,dt_1, \tag{15.8.15}$$

but the terms

$$\frac{\partial S}{\partial q_{r0}}\left(\frac{\partial q_{r0}}{\partial \alpha_s}\,d\alpha_s + \frac{\partial q_{r0}}{\partial q_{s1}}\,dq_{s1} + \frac{\partial q_{r0}}{\partial t_0}\,dt_0 + \frac{\partial q_{r0}}{\partial t_1}\,dt_1\right) \tag{15.8.16}$$

reduce to $-\beta_r d\alpha_r$ simply, in virtue of (15.8.7), so the coefficient of each dq_{s1} in (15.8.16) is identically zero. The apparent discrepancy now disappears.

(v) *The transformation from* (α_r, β_r) *to* (q_{r1}, p_{r1}) *is measure-preserving*;

$$\frac{\partial(q_{r1};\ p_{r1})}{\partial(\alpha_r;\ \beta_r)} = 1. \tag{15.8.17}$$

In fact the transformation from (α_r, β_r) to (q_{r0}, p_{r0}) is measure-preserving (by an argument similar to that used in (iii) above). So is the transformation, for any fixed values of t_0 and t_1, from (q_{r0}, p_{r0}) to (q_{r1}, p_{r1}). Therefore the product of these two transformations, i.e. the transformation from (α_r, β_r) to (q_{r1}, p_{r1}) is also measure-preserving.

(vi) *Periodic orbits.* We consider now a system for which there exists a family of periodic orbits.

In some systems, *all* the orbits are periodic. For example, as we have noticed (Chapter IX), if we have an oscillatory system in which the ratio of any two periods is rational, all motions are periodic. Let us denote the free periods by $2\pi/\mu_r$ ($r = 1, 2, \ldots, n$). If there are positive integers $m_1, m_2, \ldots, m_n$ such that

$$\frac{\mu_1}{m_1} = \frac{\mu_2}{m_2} = \cdots = \frac{\mu_n}{m_n} = \varpi, \tag{15.8.18}$$

then all motions are periodic with period $2\pi/\varpi$, and this is true whatever the initial conditions. A simple example is provided by the isotropic oscillator. In other systems all the orbits originating in a certain region of the phase space are periodic.

For example if a particle moves under a Newtonian attraction $\mu m/r^2$ to the origin the orbit originating at $t = 0$ at the point

$$x, y, z, p_x, p_y, p_z,$$

of the phase space is periodic if the starting point lies in the region

$$(x^2 + y^2 + z^2)(p_x^2 + p_y^2 + p_z^2)^2 < 4\mu^2. \tag{15.8.19}$$

In this example (the Newtonian orbit) the period varies with the initial conditions; in the preceding example (the oscillatory system) the period is the same whatever the initial conditions.

In other systems both periodic and non-periodic orbits occur.

Consider then a natural system which admits a one-parameter family of periodic orbits. Let us calculate S for a member of this family, i.e. for the complete closed orbit. Since now the initial and final points coincide (15.5.2) becomes

$$S = S(q_{r0};\ \sigma),$$

where σ is the period. But in fact S cannot depend on the q_{r0}'s, since the result is the same whatever point of the closed orbit we take as our starting point, so

$$S = S(\sigma). \tag{15.8.20}$$

If now we consider a variation to a neighbouring member of the family of periodic orbits, (15.5.11) becomes

$$dS = -h\, d\sigma,$$

where h is the (constant) value of H for the periodic orbit considered. Hence

$$h = -\frac{dS}{d\sigma}. \tag{15.8.21}$$

It follows that *in the family of periodic orbits the energy constant h is a function only of the period σ.*

15.9 Examples of the direct calculation of the principal function. We shall find it illuminating to determine the explicit form of S for a few simple concrete cases.

(i) *Uniform field.* A particle of mass m moves in a plane under the action of a uniform field $(0, -mg)$. The motion is determined by the formulae

$$\begin{cases} x - x_0 = u_0(t - t_0), \\ y - y_0 = v_0(t - t_0) - \tfrac{1}{2}g(t - t_0)^2, \end{cases} \tag{15.9.1}$$

as in (15.6.2). Here $V = gy$, and

$$S = \int_{t_0}^{t_1} \{\tfrac{1}{2}(\dot{x}^2 + \dot{y}^2) - gy\}\, dt, \tag{15.9.2}$$

where the result of the integration is to be expressed in terms of $(x_0, y_0, x_1, y_1, t_0, t_1)$. The calculation is simple, and yields

$$S = \frac{1}{2(t_1 - t_0)}\{(x_1 - x_0)^2 + (y_1 - y_0)^2\} - \tfrac{1}{2}g(t_1 - t_0)(y_1 + y_0) - \tfrac{1}{24}g^2(t_1 - t_0)^3. \tag{15.9.3}$$

We easily verify the properties of S already discussed. For example the equations (15.8.1) give us the solution of the Lagrange problem, the motion in the (x, y)-plane:

$$(15.9.4)\quad \begin{cases} -u_0 = \dfrac{\partial S}{\partial x_0} = -\dfrac{x_1 - x_0}{t_1 - t_0}, \\[2ex] -v_0 = \dfrac{\partial S}{\partial y_0} = -\dfrac{y_1 - y_0}{t_1 - t_0} - \tfrac{1}{2}g(t_1 - t_0). \end{cases}$$

(ii) *The harmonic oscillator.* Here

$$(15.9.5)\quad x = x_0 \cos n(t - t_0) + \frac{u_0}{n} \sin n(t - t_0),$$

and

$$(15.9.6)\quad S = \int_{t_0}^{t_1} \tfrac{1}{2}(\dot{x}^2 - n^2x^2)\, dt,$$

the result to be expressed in terms of x_0 and x_1. The integration is elementary, and we find

$$(15.9.7)\quad S = \tfrac{1}{2}n(x_1^2 + x_0^2) \cot n(t_1 - t_0) - \frac{nx_1x_0}{\sin n(t_1 - t_0)},$$

provided that $n(t_1 - t_0)$ is not an integral multiple of π. As we know (§ 15.6 (ii)) S does not exist in the excepted case unless $x_1 = (-)^r x_0$, when it has the value zero (this is the familiar theorem that for any integral number of half-periods of the harmonic oscillator, $\overline{T} = \overline{V}$).

Again we easily verify that the equations (15.8.1–2) yield the integrals of the Hamiltonian equations of motion. For example

$$(15.9.8)\quad -u_0 = \frac{\partial S}{\partial x_0} = nx_0 \cot n(t_1 - t_0) - \frac{nx_1}{\sin n(t_1 - t_0)},$$

which is precisely equivalent to the (t, x) relation from which we started.

(iii) We consider a simple case in which t appears explicitly in L, so that S is a function of t_0 and t_1, not merely of their difference. We consider a particle moving on a line in a uniform field which increases uniformly with the time. A concrete example is a magnetic pole in a varying magnetic field. The potential per unit mass is $-Atx$, where A is a constant, and we have

$$(15.9.9)\quad \ddot{x} = At,$$

$$(15.9.10)\quad \dot{x} = u_0 + \tfrac{1}{2}A(t^2 - t_0^2),$$

$$(15.9.11)\quad x = x_0 + u_0(t - t_0) + \tfrac{1}{6}A(t - t_0)^2(t + 2t_0).$$

We can thus express

$$(15.9.12)\quad L = \tfrac{1}{2}\dot{x}^2 + Atx$$

as a function of t, and if we evaluate the integral $\int_{t_0}^{t_1} L\, dt$, and suppress u_0 in the result in favour of x_0, we obtain the principal function

$$(15.9.13)\quad S = \frac{(x_1 - x_0)^2}{2(t_1 - t_0)} + \frac{1}{6}A(t_1 - t_0)\{x_1(2t_1 + t_0) + x_0(t_1 + 2t_0)\} - \frac{1}{360}A^2(t_1 - t_0)^3(4t_1^2 + 7t_1t_0 + 4t_0^2).$$

Again we readily verify that the function S has the characteristic properties already described.

(iv) *Periodic orbits*. We calculate S for a complete closed orbit. For the harmonic oscillator $S = 0$; this we might have expected, because here we have the exceptional case in which σ is *constant*, the same for all the periodic orbits. For the Newtonian elliptic orbit

$$h = -\frac{\mu}{2a}, \quad \sigma = 2\pi\sqrt{\left(\frac{a^3}{\mu}\right)}, \quad \bar{T} = \frac{\mu}{2a}, \quad \bar{V} = -\frac{\mu}{a}, \tag{15.9.14}$$

where $2a$ is the major axis of the ellipse, and $\bar{T}$, $\bar{V}$ denote the mean values of T, V with respect to time. Hence, for the complete orbit,

$$S = (\bar{T} - \bar{V})\sigma = \frac{3\mu}{2a}\sigma = \tfrac{3}{2}(2\pi\mu)^{2/3}\sigma^{1/3}. \tag{15.9.15}$$

The equation (15.8.21) is easily verified in this case, for

$$\frac{dS}{d\sigma} = \frac{1}{2}\left(\frac{2\pi\mu}{\sigma}\right)^{2/3} = \frac{\mu}{2a} = -h. \tag{15.9.16}$$

(There are many ways of establishing the formulae quoted in (15.9.14) for $\bar{T}$ and $\bar{V}$. We need only prove one of these formulae, since if one is found the other can be deduced from $\bar{T} + \bar{V} = h$. One simple method is to express r and t in terms of the eccentric angle φ,

$$r = a(1 - e\cos\varphi), \quad nt = \varphi - e\sin\varphi, \quad (n = 2\pi/\sigma).$$

Thus

$$\bar{V} = \frac{1}{\sigma}\int_0^\sigma \left(-\frac{\mu}{r}\right) dt = -\frac{\mu}{n\sigma}\int_0^{2\pi} \frac{1}{a}\,d\varphi = -\frac{\mu}{a}.)$$

Chapter XVI

The Hamilton-Jacobi theorem

16.1 Hamilton's partial differential equation. We have noticed already (§ 15.8) that the principal function would be of supreme value to us in the study of the dynamical system if we could determine it independently, without first finding the integrals of the equations of motion. To this search we now direct our attention. It will lead us to a method of finding, if not S itself, at least other functions that are equally valuable.

Our first step is the simple remark that, without loss of generality, we may put $t_0 = 0$ throughout. This is obvious in the usual case where L does not contain t, and S is a function of $(t_1 - t_0)$. It is true also in the general case when t occurs explicitly in L; if the point of projection in the q-space is arbitrary all possible motions are comprehended even though we think of $t = 0$ as the instant of projection.

Our next step is to allow greater freedom in the choice of parameters to define the orbit, as in § 15.8 (iv). Instead of using the initial values of coordinates and momenta (q_{r0}, p_{r0}) as the parameters defining the orbit in the phase space, we use instead parameters (α_r, β_r). These are functions of the q_{r0}'s and p_{r0}'s with continuous first derivatives; but they may not be chosen arbitrarily, they must in fact satisfy the condition mentioned in § 15.8, namely

(16.1.1) $$\beta_r\, d\alpha_r = p_{r0}\, dq_{r0}.$$

When we first introduced the principal function we thought of the orbit as determined by the initial and final coordinates and t_0 and t_1. We now move to another viewpoint, and think of the orbit as determined by the α's the q_{r1}'s and t_1 (t_0 being zero), and we express S in terms of these $(2n + 1)$ arguments, as in § 15.8 (iv). It will be convenient at this point to drop the suffix 1 in the coordinates of the upper terminus, and in the symbols t_1 and H_1; we now denote the upper terminus by $(q_1, q_2, \ldots, q_n, p_1, p_2, \ldots, p_n)$ and the time of transit by t. Thus

(16.1.2) $$S = S(q_1, q_2, \ldots, q_n;\ \alpha_1, \alpha_2, \ldots, \alpha_n;\ t),$$

and

(16.1.3) $$dS = p_r\, dq_r - \beta_r\, d\alpha_r - H\, dt,$$

the repeated suffix r implying summation from $r = 1$ to $r = n$. Hence

(16.1.4) $$\frac{\partial S}{\partial \alpha_r} = -\beta_r, \qquad r = 1, 2, \ldots, n,$$

(16.1.5) $$\frac{\partial S}{\partial q_r} = p_r, \qquad r = 1, 2, \ldots, n,$$

(16.1.6) $$\frac{\partial S}{\partial t} = -H.$$

As we have noticed already, the n equations (16.1.4) give the solution of the Lagrange problem, since by means of them we can express each q_r in terms of t and α's and β's; and the $2n$ equations (16.1.4) and (16.1.5) give the solution of the Hamilton problem, since by means of them we can express each q_r and each p_r in terms of t and α's and β's.

The Hamiltonian function H which appears in the second member of (16.1.6) is a known function of q's and p's and t,

$$H = H(q_1, q_2, \ldots, q_n;\ p_1, p_2, \ldots, p_n;\ t), \tag{16.1.7}$$

or, as we shall frequently write for the sake of brevity,

$$H = H(q;\ p;\ t). \tag{16.1.8}$$

If, using (16.1.5), we substitute $\dfrac{\partial S}{\partial q_r}$ for p_r in the second member of (16.1.6), we obtain a differential equation which is satisfied by S,

$$\frac{\partial S}{\partial t} + H\left(q_1, q_2, \ldots, q_n; \frac{\partial S}{\partial q_1}, \frac{\partial S}{\partial q_2}, \ldots, \frac{\partial S}{\partial q_n}; t\right) = 0, \tag{16.1.9}$$

or, concisely,

$$\frac{\partial S}{\partial t} + H\left(q; \frac{\partial S}{\partial q}; t\right) = 0. \tag{16.1.10}$$

This is *Hamilton's differential equation.* It is a non-linear partial differential equation of the first order. The principal function, expressed in terms of the q's and t and the n parameters α, is a complete integral.

Now there exist a great variety of complete integrals of a partial differential equation, and, if we started from Hamilton's differential equation and found a complete integral of it, we should have no guarantee that this integral would be an expression for the principal function which we seek. But the question suggests itself, will *any* complete integral serve our purpose? The answer is affirmative, and this fact is the heart of the Hamilton-Jacobi theorem.

We give two proofs of the theorem, the first a deliberate verification, the second depending on the equivalence of the system of Hamiltonian equations with a certain Pfaffian equation.

16.2 The Hamilton-Jacobi theorem, first proof. *If*

$$S = S(q_1, q_2, \ldots, q_n;\ \alpha_1, \alpha_2, \ldots, \alpha_n;\ t), \tag{16.2.1}$$

or briefly,

$$S = S(q;\ \alpha;\ t), \tag{16.2.2}$$

is a complete integral of Hamilton's partial differential equation

$$\frac{\partial S}{\partial t} + H\left(q; \frac{\partial S}{\partial q}; t\right) = 0, \tag{16.2.3}$$

then the integrals of Hamilton's equations of motion are given by the equations

$$\frac{\partial S}{\partial \alpha_r} = -\beta_r, \qquad r = 1, 2, \ldots, n, \tag{16.2.4}$$

$$\frac{\partial S}{\partial q_r} = p_r, \qquad r = 1, 2, \ldots, n, \tag{16.2.5}$$

where the β's are n new arbitrary constants. These equations (16.2.4–5) determine the q's and p's as functions of t involving the $2n$ arbitrary constants α and β. The equations (16.2.4) alone determine the motion in the q-space, the solution of the Lagrange problem. The equations (16.2.4–5) determine the motion in the phase space, the solution of the Hamilton problem.

A complete integral is a function of class C_2 containing n independent arbitrary constants $\alpha_1, \alpha_2, \ldots, \alpha_n$ (as well as the purely additive constant α_{n+1}) and such that the determinant

(16.2.6) $$\left\| \frac{\partial^2 S}{\partial q_r\, \partial \alpha_s} \right\|,$$

(i.e. the determinant in which the element in the rth row and the sth column is $\left.\dfrac{\partial^2 S}{\partial q_r\, \partial \alpha_s}\right)$, is nowhere zero in the relevant domain of $\mathbf{q}$ and $\boldsymbol{\alpha}$.

We have to show that the functions

(16.2.7) $$q_r = q_r(\alpha;\ \beta;\ t),$$

(16.2.8) $$p_r = p_r(\alpha;\ \beta;\ t),$$

determined from (16.2.4–5) satisfy Hamilton's equations for arbitrary values of the α's and β's, or at least for arbitrary values in some domain of $(\alpha;\ \beta)$.

Now S satisfies (16.2.3) for all values of $q;\ \alpha;\ t$ in the appropriate domain, so substituting the complete integral in (16.2.3), and differentiating partially with respect to α_1, we have

(16.2.9) $$\frac{\partial^2 S}{\partial \alpha_1\, \partial t} + \sum_{r=1}^{n} \frac{\partial^2 S}{\partial \alpha_1\, \partial q_r} H_{p_r}\left(q;\ \frac{\partial S}{\partial q};\ t\right) = 0.$$

(H_{p_r} stands for the partial derivative $\partial H/\partial p_r$.) Also the equation

(16.2.10) $$\frac{\partial S}{\partial \alpha_1} = -\beta_1$$

is satisfied identically if we substitute for each q from (16.2.7), so substituting these values, and differentiating partially with respect to t, we have

(16.2.11) $$\frac{\partial^2 S}{\partial t\, \partial \alpha_1} + \sum_{r=1}^{n} \frac{\partial^2 S}{\partial q_r\, \partial \alpha_1} \frac{\partial q_r}{\partial t} = 0.$$

The symbol $\dfrac{\partial q_r}{\partial t}$ is the velocity formerly denoted by $\dfrac{dq_r}{dt}$; the partial derivative is needed here because we are thinking now of q_r as a function of the parameters α and β as well as of t. In other words we are now contemplating the totality of orbits instead of one particular orbit. Now since $S \in C_2$ we have

(16.2.12) $$\frac{\partial^2 S}{\partial \alpha_1\, \partial t} = \frac{\partial^2 S}{\partial t\, \partial \alpha_1}, \qquad \frac{\partial^2 S}{\partial \alpha_1\, \partial q_r} = \frac{\partial^2 S}{\partial q_r\, \partial \alpha_1},$$

so from (16.2.9) and (16.2.11) we have

(16.2.13) $$\sum_{r=1}^{n} \frac{\partial^2 S}{\partial q_r\, \partial \alpha_1} \left\{ \frac{\partial q_r}{\partial t} - H_{p_r}\left(q;\ \frac{\partial S}{\partial q};\ t\right) \right\} = 0.$$

Moreover there are n such equations, one corresponding to each α, and the determinant (16.2.6) of the coefficients is non-vanishing, whence

(16.2.14) $$\frac{\partial q_r}{\partial t} = H_{p_r}\left(q;\ \frac{\partial S}{\partial q};\ t\right), \qquad r = 1, 2, \ldots, n.$$

Next we again substitute the complete integral in (16.2.3), and now we differentiate partially with respect to q_1,

(16.2.15) $$\frac{\partial^2 S}{\partial q_1\, \partial t} + H_{q_1}\left(q;\ \frac{\partial S}{\partial q};\ t\right) + \sum_{r=1}^{n} \frac{\partial^2 S}{\partial q_1\, \partial q_r} H_{p_r}\left(q;\ \frac{\partial S}{\partial q};t\right) = 0.$$

Now the equation

(16.2.16) $$p_1 = \frac{\partial S}{\partial q_1}$$

is satisfied identically if we substitute for p_1 and for the q's their values in terms of α's and β's and t; so substituting these values, and differentiating partially with respect to t, we have

(16.2.17) $$\frac{\partial p_1}{\partial t} = \frac{\partial^2 S}{\partial t\, \partial q_1} + \sum_{r=1}^{n} \frac{\partial^2 S}{\partial q_r\, \partial q_1} \frac{\partial q_r}{\partial t}.$$

Now

(16.2.18) $$\frac{\partial^2 S}{\partial q_1\, \partial t} = \frac{\partial^2 S}{\partial t\, \partial q_1}, \qquad \frac{\partial^2 S}{\partial q_1\, \partial q_r} = \frac{\partial^2 S}{\partial q_r\, \partial q_1},$$

and therefore, in virtue of (16.2.15) and (16.2.14), (16.2.17) is equivalent to

(16.2.19) $$\frac{\partial p_1}{\partial t} = -H_{q_1}\left(q;\ \frac{\partial S}{\partial q};\ t\right).$$

The same method establishes the n similar equations

(16.2.20) $$\frac{\partial p_r}{\partial t} = -H_{q_r}\left(q;\ \frac{\partial S}{\partial q};\ t\right), \qquad r = 1, 2, \ldots, n.$$

The equations (16.2.14) and (16.2.20) prove that the functions q_r and p_r defined by (16.2.7–8) satisfy Hamilton's equations

(10.13.8) $$\frac{\partial q_r}{\partial t} = \frac{\partial H}{\partial p_r}, \qquad \frac{\partial p_r}{\partial t} = -\frac{\partial H}{\partial q_r}, \qquad r = 1, 2, \ldots, n,$$

for arbitrary values of the α's and β's, and the theorem is proved.

The upshot of the matter is that *from any one complete integral of Hamilton's partial differential equation we can derive the complete solution of the Hamilton problem,* i.e. the integrals of Hamilton's equations of motion. The differential equation for S was first given by Hamilton in 1834, and the proof of the complete theorem was given by Jacobi in 1837.

16.3 The equivalence theorem. The principal function S,

(16.3.1) $$S = S(q_1, q_2, \ldots, q_n;\ q_{10}, q_{20}, \ldots, q_{n0};\ t) = S(q;\ q_0;\ t),$$

has the property (cf.(15.5.11))

(16.3.2) $$dS = p_r\, dq_r - p_{r0}\, dq_{r0} - H\, dt,$$

where H, the Hamiltonian function, is a known function of $(q_1, q_2, \ldots, q_n;\ p_1, p_2, \ldots, p_n;\ t)$. If in (16.3.1) we substitute for each q_r its value as a function of q_{r0}'s and p_{r0}'s and t we get a function ψ

$$S(q;\ q_0;\ t) = \psi(q_0;\ p_0;\ t), \tag{16.3.3}$$

and (16.3.2) leads to the equation

$$p_r\, dq_r - H\, dt = d\psi + p_{r0}\, dq_{r0}. \tag{16.3.4}$$

The Pfaffian form $p_r\, dq_r - H\, dt$, when expressed in terms of q_{r0}'s and p_{r0}'s and t, is the sum of a complete differential $d\psi$ (where $\psi = \psi(q_0;\ p_0;\ t)$) and a Pfaffian form $p_{r0}\, dq_{r0}$ not containing the time.

More generally if we suppose the orbit (in the phase-space) to be defined by the values of any $2n$ convenient parameters $\gamma_1, \gamma_2, \ldots, \gamma_{2n}$, instead of by the value of the particular parameters, which are the q_{r0}'s and p_{r0}'s, we have a similar relation

$$\sum_{r=1}^{n} p_r\, dq_r - H\, dt = d\psi + \sum_{s=1}^{2n} K_s\, d\gamma_s, \tag{16.3.5}$$

where $\psi = \psi(\gamma;\ t)$, and the K's are functions only of the γ's. The γ's are $2n$ independent functions of the q_{r0}'s and p_{r0}'s, and the values of the γ's define the orbit as effectively as the values of the q_{r0}'s and p_{r0}'s. The form $\sum_{s=1}^{2n} K_s\, d\gamma_s$ is simply the form $\sum_{r=1}^{n} p_{r0}\, dq_{r0}$ expressed in terms of the new parameters. We moved towards this result earlier, in § 15.8 (iv), when we replaced the form $\sum_{r=1}^{n} p_{r0}\, dq_{r0}$ by the form $\sum_{r=1}^{n} \beta_r\, d\alpha_r$; but this required a restriction on the choice of the new parameters α and β, namely the restriction to a homogeneous contact transformation. No such restriction applies to the choice of the γ's. On the other hand it must be observed that the form $\sum_{s=1}^{2n} K_s\, d\gamma_s$ is not essentially more general than the form $\sum_{r=1}^{n} \beta_r\, d\alpha_r$, since in virtue of Pfaff's theorem the first of these can always be reduced to the second.

The Pfaffian equation (16.3.5) is precisely equivalent to the 2n differential equations of Hamilton. Our study of the principal function has shown us that the solutions of Hamilton's equations do in fact satisfy (16.3.5), and it only remains to prove conversely that the functions

$$q_r(\gamma;\ t), \qquad p_r(\gamma;\ t), \tag{16.3.6}$$

which satisfy (16.3.5), also satisfy Hamilton's equations. But it is perhaps more satisfying at this stage to exhibit a self-contained proof of the complete theorem.

The equivalence theorem. The functions

$$\begin{cases} q_r = q_r(\gamma_1, \gamma_2, \ldots, \gamma_{2n};\ t), & r = 1, 2, \ldots, n, \\ p_r = p_r(\gamma_1, \gamma_2, \ldots, \gamma_{2n};\ t), & r = 1, 2, \ldots, n, \end{cases} \tag{16.3.7}$$

are $2n$ functions of the γ's and t: q_r, $\partial q_r/\partial t$, p_r, $\partial p_r/\partial t$ are of class C_1 in a domain Δ of $(\gamma_1, \gamma_2, \ldots, \gamma_{2n})$ and an interval I of t, and the Jacobian

$$\frac{\partial(q_1, q_2, \ldots, q_n, p_1, p_2, \ldots, p_n)}{\partial(\gamma_1, \gamma_2, \quad . \quad . \quad . \quad , \gamma_{2n})} \neq 0 \tag{16.3.8}$$

for $(\gamma_1, \gamma_2, \ldots, \gamma_{2n}) \in \Delta$ and $t \in I$.

(1) *If $H(q;\ p;\ t)$ is a given function of its $(2n+1)$ arguments, of class C_1 (in the (q, p)-domains on which Δ is mapped by (16.3.7) for each t in I), and the q's and p's satisfy, identically for all values of the γ's in Δ, the differential equations*

(16.3.9) $$\frac{\partial q_r}{\partial t} = \frac{\partial H}{\partial p_r}, \qquad \frac{\partial p_r}{\partial t} = -\frac{\partial H}{\partial q_r}, \qquad r = 1, 2, \ldots, n,$$

then

(16.3.10) $$p_r\, dq_r - H\, dt = d\psi + K_s\, d\gamma_s,$$

where $\psi(=\psi(\gamma;\ t)) \in C_2$, and the coefficients K_s are functions only of the γ's. The terms with repeated suffix r are summed from 1 to n, and the terms with repeated suffix s are summed from 1 to $2n$.

(2) *If there exists a function $H(q;\ p;\ t) \in C_1$ such that the Pfaffian form $p_r\, dq_r - H\, dt$, when expressed in terms of the γ's and t, has the form $d\psi + K_s\, d\gamma_s$, where $\psi(=\psi(\gamma;\ t)) \in C_2$, and K_s is a function only of the γ's, then q_r, p_r satisfy the differential equations*

(16.3.9) $$\frac{\partial q_r}{\partial t} = \frac{\partial H}{\partial p_r}, \qquad \frac{\partial p_r}{\partial t} = -\frac{\partial H}{\partial q_r}, \qquad r = 1, 2, \ldots, n,$$

identically, for all values of the γ's in Δ.

Proof of (1), the direct theorem. Denote the form $p_r\, dq_r - H\, dt$, when expressed in terms of γ's and t, by $U\, dt + U_s\, d\gamma_s$, so that

(16.3.11) $$U = p_r \frac{\partial q_r}{\partial t} - H,$$

(16.3.12) $$U_s = p_r \frac{\partial q_r}{\partial \gamma_s}, \qquad s = 1, 2, \ldots, 2n,$$

where, as before, the repeated suffix r implies summation from 1 to n.

We now prove that

(16.3.13) $$\frac{\partial U}{\partial \gamma_s} = \frac{\partial U_s}{\partial t}.$$

From (16.3.11)

(16.3.14) $$\frac{\partial U}{\partial \gamma_s} = \frac{\partial p_r}{\partial \gamma_s}\frac{\partial q_r}{\partial t} + p_r \frac{\partial^2 q_r}{\partial \gamma_s\, \partial t} - \frac{\partial H}{\partial q_r}\frac{\partial q_r}{\partial \gamma_s} - \frac{\partial H}{\partial p_r}\frac{\partial p_r}{\partial \gamma_s}$$
$$= p_r \frac{\partial^2 q_r}{\partial \gamma_s\, \partial t} + \frac{\partial p_r}{\partial t}\frac{\partial q_r}{\partial \gamma_s},$$

since q_r, p_r satisfy (16.3.9). Thus, since

(16.3.15) $$\frac{\partial^2 q_r}{\partial \gamma_s\, \partial t} = \frac{\partial^2 q_r}{\partial t\, \partial \gamma_s},$$

we have

(16.3.16) $$\frac{\partial U}{\partial \gamma_s} = p_r \frac{\partial^2 q_r}{\partial t \partial \gamma_s} + \frac{\partial p_r}{\partial t}\frac{\partial q_r}{\partial \gamma_s} = \frac{\partial U_s}{\partial t}.$$

We now introduce a function $\psi = \psi(\gamma;\ t)$ such that

$$\frac{\partial\psi}{\partial t} = U. \tag{16.3.17}$$

Then

$$\frac{\partial U_s}{\partial t} = \frac{\partial U}{\partial \gamma_s} = \frac{\partial^2\psi}{\partial\gamma_s\,\partial t} = \frac{\partial^2\psi}{\partial t\,\partial\gamma_s}, \tag{16.3.18}$$

whence

$$U_s = \frac{\partial\psi}{\partial\gamma_s} + K_s, \tag{16.3.19}$$

where K_s is a function of the γ's only, independent of t. Thus finally

$$p_r\,dq_r - H\,dt = \frac{\partial\psi}{\partial t}\,dt + \left(\frac{\partial\psi}{\partial\gamma_s} + K_s\right)d\gamma_s = d\psi + K_s\,d\gamma_s, \tag{16.3.10}$$

which is the result stated.

Proof of (2), the converse theorem. Since

$$p_r\,dq_r - H\,dt = d\psi + K_s\,d\gamma_s \tag{16.3.20}$$

we have

$$p_r\frac{\partial q_r}{\partial t} - H = \frac{\partial\psi}{\partial t}, \tag{16.3.21}$$

$$p_r\frac{\partial q_r}{\partial\gamma_s} = \frac{\partial\psi}{\partial\gamma_s} + K_s, \qquad s = 1, 2, \ldots, 2n, \tag{16.3.22}$$

whence

$$\frac{\partial}{\partial t}\left(p_r\frac{\partial q_r}{\partial\gamma_s}\right) - \frac{\partial}{\partial\gamma_s}\left(p_r\frac{\partial q_r}{\partial t}\right) = -\frac{\partial H}{\partial\gamma_s} = -\left(\frac{\partial H}{\partial q_r}\frac{\partial q_r}{\partial\gamma_s} + \frac{\partial H}{\partial p_r}\frac{\partial p_r}{\partial\gamma_s}\right), \tag{16.3.23}$$

where we have used the property

$$\frac{\partial^2\psi}{\partial t\,\partial\gamma_s} = \frac{\partial^2\psi}{\partial\gamma_s\,\partial t}.$$

But we have also

$$\frac{\partial^2 q_r}{\partial t\,\partial\gamma_s} = \frac{\partial^2 q_r}{\partial\gamma_s\,\partial t},$$

so (16.3.23) becomes

$$\frac{\partial q_r}{\partial\gamma_s}\left(\frac{\partial p_r}{\partial t} + \frac{\partial H}{\partial q_r}\right) + \frac{\partial p_r}{\partial\gamma_s}\left(-\frac{\partial q_r}{\partial t} + \frac{\partial H}{\partial p_r}\right) = 0. \tag{16.3.24}$$

There are $2n$ equations of this type, one for each γ, and the determinant of the coefficients is non-zero: it follows that

$$\frac{\partial q_r}{\partial t} = \frac{\partial H}{\partial p_r}, \qquad \frac{\partial p_r}{\partial t} = -\frac{\partial H}{\partial q_r}, \tag{16.3.9}$$

and this is the required result. This completes the proof of the equivalence theorem.

16.4 The Hamilton-Jacobi theorem, second proof. We deduce the Hamilton-Jacobi theorem as an immediate corollary of the equivalence theorem. Let $S = S(q;\ \alpha;\ t)$ be a complete integral of Hamilton's partial differential equation

$$\frac{\partial S}{\partial t} + H\left(q;\ \frac{\partial S}{\partial q}\ ;\ t\right) = 0. \tag{16.4.1}$$

If we take the equations

$$p_r = \frac{\partial S}{\partial q_r}, \qquad r = 1, 2, \ldots, n, \tag{16.4.2}$$

$$-\beta_r = \frac{\partial S}{\partial \alpha_r}, \qquad r = 1, 2, \ldots, n, \tag{16.4.3}$$

and from them express the q's and p's in terms of α's and β's and t, these formulae constitute the general solution of Hamilton's equations. To prove this we take the form $p_r\, dq_r - H\, dt$ and express it in terms of α's and β's and t,

$$\begin{aligned} p_r\, dq_r - H\, dt &= \frac{\partial S}{\partial q_r}\, dq_r + \frac{\partial S}{\partial t}\, dt \\ &= dS - \frac{\partial S}{\partial \alpha_r}\, d\alpha_r \\ &= d\psi + \beta_r\, d\alpha_r, \end{aligned} \tag{16.4.4}$$

where ψ is S expressed in terms of α's and β's and t. Now the q's and p's are independent functions of $(\alpha;\ \beta;\ t)$; in fact

$$\frac{\partial(q_r;\ p_r)}{\partial(\alpha_r;\ \beta_r)} = 1, \tag{16.4.5}$$

as we prove by an argument similar to that used in § 15.8 (iii). It now follows from (16.4.4), in virtue of the second part of the equivalence theorem, that q_r, p_r satisfy Hamilton's equations of motion. This completes the proof.

16.5 Reflexions on the Hamilton-Jacobi theorem. The beautiful theorem established in § 16.2 and § 16.4 is of far-reaching importance, both as a working tool for the solution of concrete problems, and in its theoretical implications. Hitherto, in the study of a particular dynamical system, we have set up the equations of motion, and then we have had to face the problem of integration. In the Hamilton-Jacobi method this process is short-circuited. So soon as we have found one complete integral of Hamilton's partial differential equation the *integrals* of the equations of motion can be written down. The only doubt that arises is whether a complete integral can be found easily, but this doubt is readily dispelled by a few experiments; we shall find in fact that, for the most familiar problems of classical dynamics, a complete integral can be found immediately.

Before turning to the solution of particular problems it will be useful to consider certain classes of dynamical system for which the technique can be simplified. The most important, and the one most commonly occurring, is that in which L and H do not contain t explicitly,

$$H = H(q_1, q_2, \ldots, q_n;\ p_1, p_2, \ldots, p_n) = H(q;\ p), \tag{16.5.1}$$

and an integral of energy exists

$$H = h. \tag{16.5.2}$$

To determine a complete integral we write

$$S = -ht + K, \tag{16.5.3}$$

where $h(=\alpha_1)$ is one of the arbitrary constants, and K is a function of $(q_1, q_2, \ldots, q_n)$ involving $h(=\alpha_1)$ and $(n-1)$ additional arbitrary constants $\alpha_2, \alpha_3, \ldots, \alpha_n$. In this case Hamilton's partial differential equation leads to

$$H\left(q; \frac{\partial K}{\partial q}\right) = h, \tag{16.5.4}$$

and we need a complete integral of this equation, one involving $(n-1)$ new arbitrary constants, none of which is merely additive. The integrals of the equations of motion are

$$t - t_0 = \frac{\partial K}{\partial h}, \tag{16.5.5}$$

$$-\beta_r = \frac{\partial K}{\partial \alpha_r}, \qquad r = 2, 3, \ldots, n, \tag{16.5.6}$$

$$p_r = \frac{\partial K}{\partial q_r}, \qquad r = 1, 2, \ldots, n, \tag{16.5.7}$$

where t_0 is written in place of β_1.

The solution is given in a particularly simple form. The equations (16.5.6) determine the path in the q-space, without reference to the rate of travel on the path; the equation (16.5.5) then determines the relation between the position on the path and the time. The solution of the Lagrange problem is thus conveniently presented in two stages. The equations (16.5.7) complete the solution of the Hamilton problem.

The constant $h(=\alpha_1)$ is the value of the conserved energy of the system, and the constant $t_0(=\beta_1)$ is an epoch constant depending merely on the instant from which t is measured in the time scale.

Most of the systems with which we deal are conservative, and the form of the Hamilton-Jacobi theorem just described is the one most frequently used. In practice we usually start from the *modified partial differential equation* (16.5.4) rather than from Hamilton's differential equation.

Next, if H does not contain t, and if one coordinate, say q_n, is ignorable, we can simplify the procedure still further. In (16.5.3) we write

$$K = \gamma q_n + K', \tag{16.5.8}$$

where K' depends on $(q_1, q_2, \ldots, q_{n-1})$, on $h(=\alpha_1)$, on $\gamma(=\alpha_n)$, and on $(n-2)$ other arbitrary constants $\alpha_2, \alpha_3, \ldots, \alpha_{n-1}$. The coordinate q_n does not occur in H, and K' is a complete integral of the equation

$$H\left(q_1, q_2, \ldots, q_{n-1}; \frac{\partial K'}{\partial q_1}, \frac{\partial K'}{\partial q_2}, \ldots, \frac{\partial K'}{\partial q_{n-1}}, \gamma\right) = h. \tag{16.5.9}$$

The integrals of the Hamiltonian equations of motion are given by the equations

$$t - t_0 = \frac{\partial K'}{\partial h}, \tag{16.5.10}$$

$$-\beta_r = \frac{\partial K'}{\partial \alpha_r}, \qquad r = 2, 3, \ldots, n-1, \tag{16.5.11}$$

$$q_{n0} = q_n + \frac{\partial K'}{\partial \gamma}, \tag{16.5.12}$$

$$p_r = \frac{\partial K'}{\partial q_r}, \qquad r = 1, 2, \ldots, n-1, \tag{16.5.13}$$

$$p_n = \gamma, \tag{16.5.14}$$

where q_{n0} has been written in place of $-\beta_n$. The constant $\gamma(=\alpha_n)$ is clearly the value of the conserved momentum corresponding to the ignorable coordinate q_n, and the constant $q_{n0}(=-\beta_n)$ merely depends on the choice of the point from which q_n is measured. In practice we are not usually interested in the value of q_n at time t, and then the equation (16.5.12) is not required.

Finally, it frequently happens that we can determine K as a sum of functions of the separate coordinates, each function involving just one of the q's (and of course the α's, or some of them). If such a complete integral of (16.5.4) exists the system is said to be *separable* in the coordinates chosen. Nearly all the systems familiar in elementary dynamics belong to this category. Separability is a property jointly of the system and of the Lagrangian coordinates chosen to describe it.

16.6 Uniform field. We turn now to the applications of the Hamilton-Jacobi theorem in its first aspect, as a working tool for the solution of concrete problems. We begin with three elementary examples, namely the three systems for which the explicit form of the principal function was found in § 15.9. The principal function is itself a complete integral of Hamilton's partial differential equation; but in each case the complete integral that we shall find is not in fact the principal function.

For a particle moving in a plane (x, y) under the action of a uniform field $(0, -g)$ we have, taking a particle of unit mass,

$$H = \tfrac{1}{2}(p_x^2 + p_y^2) + gy, \tag{16.6.1}$$

and Hamilton's partial differential equation is

$$\frac{\partial S}{\partial t} + \frac{1}{2}\left(\frac{\partial S}{\partial x}\right)^2 + \frac{1}{2}\left(\frac{\partial S}{\partial y}\right)^2 + gy = 0. \tag{16.6.2}$$

We need a solution containing two arbitrary constants, and we easily verify that the principal function found in § 15.9, namely

$$\frac{1}{2t}\{(x-x_0)^2 + (y-y_0)^2\} - \frac{1}{2}gt(y+y_0) - \frac{1}{24}g^2t^3, \tag{16.6.3}$$

satisfies (16.6.2) for arbitrary values of x_0 and y_0.

Our present purpose however is to *find* a complete integral. Since H does not contain t, and x is ignorable, we write

$$S = -ht + \alpha x + \varphi(y), \tag{16.6.4}$$

and substituting in (16.6.2) we find

$$\varphi'^2 = 2h - 2gy - \alpha^2 = 2g(k - y), \tag{16.6.5}$$

where

$$h = \tfrac{1}{2}\alpha^2 + gk. \tag{16.6.6}$$

(We can foresee that the geometrical significance of the parameter k is that it is the greatest height reached by the projectile.) Thus we can take for φ

$$\varphi = \int_y^k \sqrt{\{2g(k - z)\}}\, dz = \sqrt{(2g)} \int_0^{k-y} \sqrt{u}\, du. \tag{16.6.7}$$

(We can of course evaluate the last integral if we wish, but there is no need to do so.) We have thus determined a complete integral, the two parameters being α and k,

$$S = -(\tfrac{1}{2}\alpha^2 + gk)t + \alpha x + \sqrt{(2g)} \int_0^{k-y} \sqrt{u}\, du. \tag{16.6.8}$$

The equations giving the motion in the (x, y)-plane are

$$\begin{cases} -\beta = \dfrac{\partial S}{\partial \alpha} = -\alpha t + x, \\[2ex] -\gamma = \dfrac{\partial S}{\partial k} = -gt + \sqrt{\{2g(k - y)\}}, \end{cases} \tag{16.6.9}$$

and these equations are of course equivalent to the well-known elementary solution. We can write (16.6.9) in the form

$$\begin{cases} x + \beta = \alpha t, \\[1ex] y - \left(k - \dfrac{\gamma^2}{2g}\right) = \gamma t - \tfrac{1}{2}gt^2, \end{cases} \tag{16.6.10}$$

and the significance of the parameters is clear,

$$\begin{cases} \alpha = u_0, & \gamma = v_0, \\ \beta = -x_0, & k = y_0 + (v_0^2/2g), \end{cases} \tag{16.6.11}$$

where (x_0, y_0) is the point of projection at $t = 0$, and (u_0, v_0) is the velocity of projection. We notice that

$$h = \tfrac{1}{2}\alpha^2 + gk = \tfrac{1}{2}(u_0^2 + v_0^2) + gy_0, \tag{16.6.12}$$

and that

$$(k - y) = \frac{1}{2g}(\gamma - gt)^2, \tag{16.6.13}$$

and k, as we expect, is the greatest height attained.

16.7 The harmonic oscillator. Here

$$H = \tfrac{1}{2}(p^2 + n^2x^2), \tag{16.7.1}$$

and Hamilton's partial differential equation is

$$\frac{\partial S}{\partial t} + \frac{1}{2}\left(\frac{\partial S}{\partial x}\right)^2 + \tfrac{1}{2}n^2x^2 = 0. \tag{16.7.2}$$

First, we easily verify that the principal function already found,

$$\tfrac{1}{2}n(x^2 + a^2) \cot nt - \frac{nxa}{\sin nt}, \tag{16.7.3}$$

satisfies (16.7.2) for all values of a. Here a $(= x_0)$ is the initial value of x, and we will suppose $a > 0$.

Next, to *find* a complete integral, put

$$S = -\tfrac{1}{2}n^2\alpha^2 t + \varphi(x). \tag{16.7.4}$$

This satisfies (16.7.2) if

$$\varphi'^2 = n^2(\alpha^2 - x^2), \tag{16.7.5}$$

and we can take for φ the expression

$$\varphi = n\int_0^x \sqrt{(\alpha^2 - y^2)}\, dy. \tag{16.7.6}$$

Thus

$$S = -\tfrac{1}{2}n^2\alpha^2 t + n\int_0^x \sqrt{(\alpha^2 - y^2)}\, dy. \tag{16.7.7}$$

The Hamilton-Jacobi theorem gives

$$-\beta = \frac{\partial S}{\partial \alpha} = -n^2\alpha t + n\alpha \int_0^x \frac{1}{\sqrt{(\alpha^2 - y^2)}}\, dy, \tag{16.7.8}$$

and we can write this in the familiar form

$$x = \alpha \sin n(t - t_0), \tag{16.7.9}$$

where $\beta = n^2\alpha t_0$.

What is the relation between the two complete integrals that we have found? We start with the solution

$$S_0 = \tfrac{1}{2}n(x^2 + a^2) \cot nt - \frac{nxa}{\sin nt} + a' \tag{16.7.10}$$

and substitute

$$a' = \Phi(a, \alpha, \alpha'), \tag{16.7.11}$$

where $\Phi \in C_1$ but is otherwise arbitrary, and we thus obtain from (16.7.10) say $F(x, t, a, \alpha, \alpha')$. Now we know (from the theory of partial differential equations of the first order) that if we solve the equation

$$\frac{\partial F}{\partial a} = 0 \tag{16.7.12}$$

for a, and substitute this value in F, we obtain a new complete integral. If we make the right choice for Φ we shall arrive at (16.7.7) with the additive constant α'.

Let us put

$$a' = n\int_0^a \sqrt{(\alpha^2 - y^2)}\,dy + \alpha', \qquad (\alpha > a > 0). \tag{16.7.13}$$

Then (16.7.12) is

$$a \cot nt - \frac{x}{\sin nt} + \sqrt{(\alpha^2 - a^2)} = 0, \tag{16.7.14}$$

and we have to solve this for a, and substitute in F. We rewrite (16.7.14) in the form

$$x = a \cos nt + \sqrt{(\alpha^2 - a^2)} \sin nt, \tag{16.7.15}$$

and if we put $a = \alpha \sin \theta$ this is

$$x = \alpha \sin (nt + \theta) = \alpha \sin \psi, \tag{16.7.16}$$

where $\psi = nt + \theta$. Thus

$$\begin{aligned} F &= \tfrac{1}{2}nx^2 \cot nt + \tfrac{1}{2}na^2 \cot nt - \frac{nx\alpha}{\sin nt} + \tfrac{1}{4}n\alpha^2(2\theta + \sin 2\theta) + \alpha' \\ &= \tfrac{1}{2}n\alpha^2 \sin^2 \psi \cot nt + \tfrac{1}{2}n\alpha^2 \sin^2 \theta \cot nt - \frac{n\alpha^2}{\sin nt} \sin \theta \sin \psi \\ &\qquad + \tfrac{1}{4}n\alpha^2(2\theta + \sin 2\theta) + \alpha'. \end{aligned} \tag{16.7.17}$$

Now

$$\begin{aligned} \tfrac{1}{2}n\alpha^2 \sin^2 \theta \cot nt + \tfrac{1}{4}n\alpha^2 \sin 2\theta &= \tfrac{1}{2}n\alpha^2 \sin \theta(\sin \theta \cot nt + \cos \theta) \\ &= \frac{n\alpha^2}{2 \sin nt} \sin \theta \sin \psi, \end{aligned} \tag{16.7.18}$$

so (16.7.17) becomes

$$\begin{aligned} F &= \tfrac{1}{2}n\alpha^2 \sin^2 \psi \cot nt - \frac{n\alpha^2}{2 \sin nt} \sin \theta \sin \psi + \tfrac{1}{4}n\alpha^2(2\theta) + \alpha' \\ &= \frac{n\alpha^2 \sin \psi}{2 \sin nt}(\sin \psi \cos nt - \sin \theta) + \tfrac{1}{4}n\alpha^2(2\theta) + \alpha' \\ &= \frac{n\alpha^2 \sin \psi}{2 \sin nt} \cos \psi \sin nt + \tfrac{1}{4}n\alpha^2(2\psi - 2nt) + \alpha' \\ &= -\tfrac{1}{2}n^2\alpha^2 t + \tfrac{1}{4}n\alpha^2(2\psi + \sin 2\psi) + \alpha' \\ &= -\tfrac{1}{2}n^2\alpha^2 t + n\int_0^x \sqrt{(\alpha^2 - y^2)}\,dy + \alpha' \\ &= S + \alpha'. \end{aligned} \tag{16.7.19}$$

The substitution of the value of a obtained from (16.7.14) in (16.7.17) has led us to a new complete integral, and it is in fact the complete integral desired.

Before leaving this problem we take the opportunity to mention a point of great importance in the applications of the Hamilton-Jacobi theorem. We found that $-\tfrac{1}{2}n^2\alpha^2 t + \varphi(x)$ is a complete integral of (16.7.2) if

$$\varphi'^2 = n^2(\alpha^2 - x^2), \tag{16.7.5}$$

and we chose for φ the function defined by the integral on the right in (16.7.6) in which the lower limit of integration is zero. We could equally well have taken as the lower limit one of the zeros of the function under the radical sign, say $-\alpha$. More generally, we shall frequently find a term $\varphi(q)$ in the complete integral, where φ satisfies an equation of the form

$$\varphi'^2 = f(q).$$

(The function $f(q)$ of course involves the α's.) Thus

$$\varphi = \int^q \sqrt{f(x)}\, dx,$$

and we can take as the lower limit of integration either an absolute constant, or a *simple* zero a of $f(q)$. We usually adopt the second alternative. If we do so, the lower limit of integration a is a function of the α's. But when we form $\partial S/\partial \alpha_r$ we merely differentiate under the integral sign as before; there is no term arising from the fact that the lower limit is a function of α_r, because the integrand vanishes at a.

The operation of differentiating under the integral sign with respect to α_r leads to an improper integral, in which the integrand has an infinity at one end of the range of integration. (For example the integral in the second member of (16.7.8) is improper if the lower limit of integration is $-\alpha$.) But the integral is convergent, and the rule that the derivative is obtained by differentiating under the integral sign is still valid.* Actually, convergent improper integrals have already appeared in this problem, since in (16.7.8) x can take the values α and $-\alpha$, and for these values of x the integral in the second member is improper; the equation (16.7.8) still holds when x has the value α or the value $-\alpha$.

16.8 Particle in varying field At. For the system considered in § 15.9(iii) we have

$$H = \tfrac{1}{2}p^2 - Atx, \tag{16.8.1}$$

and Hamilton's partial differential equation is

$$\frac{\partial S}{\partial t} + \frac{1}{2}\left(\frac{\partial S}{\partial x}\right)^2 - Atx = 0. \tag{16.8.2}$$

We easily verify that the principal function calculated in § 15.9,

$$\frac{1}{2t}(x - x_0)^2 + \frac{1}{6}At^2(2x + x_0) - \frac{1}{90}A^2t^5, \tag{16.8.3}$$

satisfies (16.8.2) for all values of x_0.

If we start from (16.8.2) we easily find a complete integral. One way is to put

$$S = \tfrac{1}{2}At^2x + \alpha x - \varphi(t), \tag{16.8.4}$$

which is a complete integral if

$$\varphi' = \tfrac{1}{2}(\tfrac{1}{2}At^2 + \alpha)^2, \quad \varphi = \tfrac{1}{40}A^2t^5 + \tfrac{1}{6}A\alpha t^3 + \tfrac{1}{2}\alpha^2 t. \tag{16.8.5}$$

The solution of the Lagrange problem is given by

$$-\beta = \frac{\partial S}{\partial \alpha} = x - \alpha t - \tfrac{1}{6}At^3, \tag{16.8.6}$$

which is equivalent to (15.9.11) (with $t_0 = 0$).

* See for example Ch.-J. de la Vallée Poussin, Cours d'Analyse Infinitésimal, Tome II, Chapter 1, § 23.

16.9 Central orbit. We now turn to the solution of some well-known problems by the Hamilton-Jacobi method. The routine application of the method is very simple. We begin with the problem of a particle moving in a plane under a central attraction to O whose potential per unit mass is $V(r)$. Here, using polar coordinates (r, θ) as the Lagrangian coordinates,

$$H = \frac{1}{2}\left(p_r^2 + \frac{1}{r^2}p_\theta^2\right) + V. \tag{16.9.1}$$

(We recall that, for a natural system,

$$H = T + V,$$

and that when the coordinates are orthogonal (§ 10.14) T can be written at once in terms of p's.) The modified partial differential equation (16.5.4) is

$$\left(\frac{\partial K}{\partial r}\right)^2 + \frac{1}{r^2}\left(\frac{\partial K}{\partial \theta}\right)^2 = 2(h - V), \tag{16.9.2}$$

and we need a solution containing one arbitrary constant α in addition to h. Now θ is ignorable, so we put

$$K = \alpha\theta + R, \tag{16.9.3}$$

where R is a function of r, and (16.9.3) satisfies (16.9.2) if

$$R'^2 = 2h - 2V - \frac{\alpha^2}{r^2}. \tag{16.9.4}$$

We denote the second member of (16.9.4) by $f(r)$, and then

$$K = \alpha\theta + \int_a^r \sqrt{\left(2h - 2V(\xi) - \frac{\alpha^2}{\xi^2}\right)}\, d\xi = \alpha\theta + \int_a^r \sqrt{f(\xi)}\, d\xi. \tag{16.9.5}$$

Here a is a simple zero of $f(r)$ (cf. § 16.7); in most cases there is a libration in r between two simple zeros a, b of $f(r)$, and in the range $a < r < b$, $f(r) > 0$. The solution of the Lagrange problem, the motion of the particle in the plane, is given by

$$t - t_0 = \frac{\partial K}{\partial h} = \int_a^r \frac{d\xi}{\sqrt{f(\xi)}}, \tag{16.9.6}$$

and

$$-\beta = \theta - \alpha\int_a^r \frac{d\xi/\xi^2}{\sqrt{f(\xi)}}. \tag{16.9.7}$$

We thus recover the solution already found in *Example* 5.2B; the equation (16.9.6) is the equation (5.2.41), and (16.9.7) is equivalent to (5.2.43).

A matter of notation should be noticed at this point. In the integrals appearing in (16.9.5–6–7) the symbol r is sometimes used for the variable of integration as well as for the upper limit. Thus, for example, (16.9.6) sometimes appears in the form

$$t - t_0 = \int_a^r \frac{dr}{\sqrt{f(r)}}.$$

This usage is really indefensible, since the symbol r is used in two different senses in the same formula. But the convention is accepted and convenient, and will not lead to confusion if the double usage is clearly recognized.

16.10 The spherical pendulum. With the same notation as before (*Example* 5.2*D*), measuring θ from the upward vertical.

$$T = \tfrac{1}{2}ma^2(\dot{\theta}^2 + \sin^2\theta\dot{\varphi}^2), \qquad V = mga\cos\theta = ma^2n^2\cos\theta, \tag{16.10.1}$$

where $n^2 = g/a$. Thus, removing the positive factor ma^2, we can write

$$T = \tfrac{1}{2}(\dot{\theta}^2 + \sin^2\theta\dot{\varphi}^2), \qquad V = n^2\cos\theta, \tag{16.10.2}$$

and

$$H = \frac{1}{2}\left(p_\theta{}^2 + \frac{1}{\sin^2\theta}p_\varphi{}^2\right) + n^2\cos\theta. \tag{16.10.3}$$

The modified partial differential equation is

$$\left(\frac{\partial K}{\partial\theta}\right)^2 + \frac{1}{\sin^2\theta}\left(\frac{\partial K}{\partial\varphi}\right)^2 = 2(h - n^2\cos\theta), \tag{16.10.4}$$

and

$$K = \alpha\varphi + \Theta \tag{16.10.5}$$

is a solution if

$$\Theta'^2 = 2h - 2n^2\cos\theta - \frac{\alpha^2}{\sin^2\theta}. \tag{16.10.6}$$

We denote the second member of (16.10.6) by $f(\theta)$, and then the complete integral is

$$K = \alpha\varphi + \int^\theta \sqrt{f(\xi)}\,d\xi, \tag{16.10.7}$$

where the lower limit of integration is either an absolute constant or a simple zero of $f(\theta)$. The integrals of Lagrange's equations of motion are

$$\begin{cases} t - t_0 = \dfrac{\partial K}{\partial h} = \displaystyle\int^\theta \frac{d\xi}{\sqrt{f(\xi)}}, \\ -\beta = \dfrac{\partial K}{\partial\alpha} = \varphi - \displaystyle\int^\theta \frac{(\alpha/\sin^2\xi)}{\sqrt{f(\xi)}}\,d\xi. \end{cases} \tag{16.10.8}$$

To reconcile these formulae with those already found (§ 5.2) we put $h = n^2h'$, $\alpha^2 = 2n^2\alpha'$, and then we have

$$\begin{cases} \sqrt{\dfrac{2g}{a}}\,(t - t_0) = \displaystyle\int^\theta \frac{d\xi}{\sqrt{F(\xi)}}, \\ \varphi + \beta = \sqrt{\alpha'}\displaystyle\int^\theta \frac{d\xi}{\sin^2\xi\sqrt{F(\xi)}}, \end{cases} \tag{16.10.9}$$

where

$$F(\theta) = h' - \cos\theta - \frac{\alpha'}{\sin^2\theta}, \tag{16.10.10}$$

and these are equivalent to the results found in § 5.2.

20

16.11 The spinning top. Using Euler's angles to describe the orientation, as in § 8.6, we have, taking Oz vertically upwards,

(16.11.1) $$T = \tfrac{1}{2}A(\dot{\theta}^2 + \sin^2\theta\dot{\varphi}^2) + \tfrac{1}{2}C(\dot{\psi} + \dot{\varphi}\cos\theta)^2, \qquad V = Mgl\cos\theta.$$

The coordinates are not orthogonal, so the expression of T in terms of p's is not immediate; we have

(16.11.2) $$p_\theta = A\dot{\theta},$$

(16.11.3) $$p_\varphi = A\sin^2\theta\dot{\varphi} + C\cos\theta(\dot{\psi} + \dot{\varphi}\cos\theta),$$

(16.11.4) $$p_\psi = C(\dot{\psi} + \dot{\varphi}\cos\theta),$$

whence

(16.11.5) $$A\sin^2\theta\dot{\varphi} = p_\varphi - p_\psi\cos\theta.$$

Thus

(16.11.6) $$H = T + V = \frac{1}{2A}p_\theta^{\ 2} + \frac{1}{2A\sin^2\theta}(p_\varphi - p_\psi\cos\theta)^2 + \frac{1}{2C}p_\psi^{\ 2} + Mgl\cos\theta,$$

and the modified partial differential equation is

(16.11.7) $$\frac{1}{A}\left(\frac{\partial K}{\partial\theta}\right)^2 + \frac{1}{A\sin^2\theta}\left(\frac{\partial K}{\partial\varphi} - \frac{\partial K}{\partial\psi}\cos\theta\right)^2 + \frac{1}{C}\left(\frac{\partial K}{\partial\psi}\right)^2 = 2(h - Mgl\cos\theta).$$

Now φ and ψ are ignorable, and we seek a solution of the form

(16.11.8) $$K = \alpha_2\varphi + \alpha_3\psi + \Theta,$$

which satisfies (16.11.7) if

(16.11.9) $$\Theta'^2 = 2A(h - Mgl\cos\theta) - \left(\frac{\alpha_2 - \alpha_3\cos\theta}{\sin\theta}\right)^2 - \frac{A}{C}\alpha_3^{\ 2}.$$

We denote the second member of (16.11.9) by $f(\theta)$, and the required complete integral is

(16.11.10) $$K = \alpha_2\varphi + \alpha_3\psi + \int_{\theta_0}^{\theta}\sqrt{f(\xi)}\,d\xi,$$

where, as usual, θ_0 is an absolute constant or a simple zero of $f(\theta)$.

The solution of the Lagrange problem is given by

(16.11.11) $$t - t_0 = \frac{\partial K}{\partial h} = A\int_{\theta_0}^{\theta}\frac{d\xi}{\sqrt{f(\xi)}},$$

(16.11.12) $$-\beta_2 = \frac{\partial K}{\partial\alpha_2} = \varphi - \int_{\theta_0}^{\theta}\frac{\alpha_2 - \alpha_3\cos\xi}{\sin^2\xi}\frac{d\xi}{\sqrt{f(\xi)}},$$

(16.11.13) $$-\beta_3 = \frac{\partial K}{\partial\alpha_3} = \psi - \int_{\theta_0}^{\theta}\left\{\frac{A}{C}\alpha_3 - \frac{\cos\xi}{\sin^2\xi}(\alpha_2 - \alpha_3\cos\xi)\right\}\frac{d\xi}{\sqrt{f(\xi)}}.$$

The path of the axis in space, the relation connecting θ and φ, is given by (16.11.12), and the relation between θ and t is given by (16.11.11). The equation (16.11.13) giving ψ in terms of θ is not usually of particular interest.

The (t, θ) relation (16.11.11) can be written

$$A^2\dot{\theta}^2 = f(\theta), \tag{16.11.14}$$

and, if we write z for $\cos\theta$, this becomes

$$\dot{z}^2 = 2\left(\frac{h}{A} - \frac{\alpha_3^2}{2CA} - \frac{Mgl}{A}z\right)(1 - z^2) - \frac{(\alpha_2 - \alpha_3 z)^2}{A^2}. \tag{16.11.15}$$

To recover the notation of § 8.6 we put

$$\alpha_3 = p_\psi = Cn = 2Ap, \quad Mgl = Aq, \quad \alpha_2 = p_\varphi = 2A\lambda, \quad h - \frac{\alpha_3^2}{2C} = A\mu, \tag{16.11.16}$$

and then (16.11.15) reduces to (8.6.9).

16.12 Rod in rotating plane. As a further example we consider the system already discussed in § 8.11. A rod is constrained to move in a smooth plane which rotates uniformly about a horizontal line fixed in the plane. In this case the solution by Lagrange's equations is simpler, but the solution by the Hamilton-Jacobi method is not without interest. From the Lagrangian function (8.11.1) we have

$$H = T_2 + V - T_0 = \frac{1}{2}\left(p_\xi^2 + p_\eta^2 + \frac{1}{k^2}p_\theta^2\right) - \tfrac{1}{2}\omega^2\eta^2 - \tfrac{1}{2}k^2\omega^2\sin^2\theta - g\eta\sin\omega t, \tag{16.12.1}$$

and Hamilton's differential equation is

$$2\frac{\partial S}{\partial t} + \left(\frac{\partial S}{\partial \xi}\right)^2 + \left(\frac{\partial S}{\partial \eta}\right)^2 + \frac{1}{k^2}\left(\frac{\partial S}{\partial \theta}\right)^2 - \omega^2\eta^2 - k^2\omega^2\sin^2\theta - 2g\eta\sin\omega t = 0. \tag{16.12.2}$$

We see that

$$S = \alpha_1\xi + \Theta + F(\eta, t) \tag{16.12.3}$$

is a complete integral if

$$\Theta'^2 = k^2(\alpha_3^2 + k^2\omega^2\sin^2\theta), \tag{16.12.4}$$

and if F satisfies

$$2\frac{\partial F}{\partial t} + \left(\frac{\partial F}{\partial \eta}\right)^2 + \alpha_1^2 + \alpha_3^2 - \omega^2\eta^2 - 2g\eta\sin\omega t = 0. \tag{16.12.5}$$

A solution of (16.12.5) is

$$F = \tfrac{1}{2}\omega\eta^2 + \eta\varphi + \psi, \tag{16.12.6}$$

where φ and ψ are functions of t satisfying

$$\dot{\varphi} + \omega\varphi = g\sin\omega t, \tag{16.12.7}$$

and

$$2\dot{\psi} + \varphi^2 + \alpha_1^2 + \alpha_3^2 = 0. \tag{16.12.8}$$

Thus

$$\varphi = \alpha_2 e^{-\omega t} + \frac{g}{2\omega}(\sin\omega t - \cos\omega t), \tag{16.12.9}$$

and the complete integral is

$$\begin{aligned} S = \alpha_1\xi &+ k\int_0^\theta \sqrt{(\alpha_3^2 + k^2\omega^2\sin^2\theta)}\,d\theta + \tfrac{1}{2}\omega\eta^2 \\ &+ \left\{\alpha_2 e^{-\omega t} + \frac{g}{2\omega}(\sin\omega t - \cos\omega t)\right\}\eta - \tfrac{1}{2}(\alpha_1^2 + \alpha_3^2)t - \tfrac{1}{2}\int_0^t \varphi^2\,dt, \end{aligned} \tag{16.12.10}$$

where we have used the notation mentioned at the end of § 16.9. The solution of the Lagrange problem is given by

$$-\beta_1 = \frac{\partial S}{\partial \alpha_1} = \xi - \alpha_1 t, \tag{16.12.11}$$

$$-\beta_2 = \frac{\partial S}{\partial \alpha_2} = e^{-\omega t}\eta - \int_0^t \varphi \frac{\partial \varphi}{\partial \alpha_2}\, dt, \tag{16.12.12}$$

$$-\beta_3 = \frac{\partial S}{\partial \alpha_3} = k\alpha_3 \int_0^\theta \frac{d\theta}{\sqrt{(\alpha_3^2 + k^2\omega^2 \sin^2 \theta)}} - \alpha_3 t. \tag{16.12.13}$$

The equation (16.12.11) gives the expected uniform motion in ξ, and (16.12.13) gives

$$\dot{\theta}^2 = \omega^2 \sin^2 \theta + (\alpha_3^2/k^2), \tag{16.12.14}$$

from which

$$\ddot{\theta} = \omega^2 \cos \theta \sin \theta, \tag{16.12.15}$$

as in (8.11.2). It remains to find how η varies with t. Now (16.12.12) gives

$$\eta = -\beta_2 e^{\omega t} + \frac{\alpha_2}{\omega} \sinh \omega t - \frac{g}{2\omega^2} \sin \omega t, \tag{16.12.16}$$

which is equivalent to (8.11.3).

16.13 Electron under a central attraction. Suppose that an electron, of variable mass (11.1.1) moves in a plane in a field of attraction to the origin whose potential is $V(r)$. The Hamiltonian function, using polar coordinates, is given by (11.4.12),

$$H = c\sqrt{\left(m_0^2c^2 + p_r^2 + \frac{1}{r^2} p_\theta^2\right)} - m_0c^2 + V. \tag{16.13.1}$$

This is not of the familiar type in which H is a quadratic form in the p's, but this does not affect the validity of the Hamilton-Jacobi theorem. The modified partial differential equation is

$$c\sqrt{\left\{m_0^2c^2 + \left(\frac{\partial K}{\partial r}\right)^2 + \frac{1}{r^2}\left(\frac{\partial K}{\partial \theta}\right)^2\right\}} = h - V + m_0c^2. \tag{16.13.2}$$

To find a complete integral we put

$$K = \alpha\theta + R, \tag{16.13.3}$$

which satisfies (16.13.2) if

$$R'^2 = 2m_0(h - V) + \left(\frac{h - V}{c}\right)^2 - \frac{\alpha^2}{r^2}. \tag{16.13.4}$$

We denote the second member of (16.13.4) by $f(r)$, and we then find the complete integral

$$K = \alpha\theta + \int^r \sqrt{f(r)}\, dr, \tag{16.13.5}$$

where we have used the notation mentioned at the end of § 16.9. The solution of the Hamilton problem is given by

(16.13.6)
$$\begin{cases} t - t_0 = \dfrac{\partial K}{\partial h} = \dfrac{1}{c^2}\displaystyle\int^r \dfrac{m_0c^2 + h - V}{\sqrt{f(r)}}\, dr, \\[2ex] -\beta = \dfrac{\partial K}{\partial \alpha} = \theta - \displaystyle\int^r \dfrac{(\alpha/r^2)}{\sqrt{f(r)}}\, dr, \\[2ex] p_r = \dfrac{\partial K}{\partial r} = \sqrt{f(r)}, \\[2ex] p_\theta = \dfrac{\partial K}{\partial \theta} = \alpha. \end{cases}$$

We recall the formulae (11.4.9)

(16.13.7)
$$p_r = \frac{m_0\dot{r}}{\sqrt{\left(1 - \dfrac{v^2}{c^2}\right)}}, \quad p_\theta = \frac{m_0 r^2\dot{\theta}}{\sqrt{\left(1 - \dfrac{v^2}{c^2}\right)}}.$$

Let us consider more particularly the problem of a Newtonian attraction, $V = -\mu/r$, where $\mu = Ze^2 > 0$. Then $f(r)$ takes the form

(16.13.8)
$$h\left(2m_0 + \frac{h}{c^2}\right) + 2\mu\left(m_0 + \frac{h}{c^2}\right)\frac{1}{r} - \alpha^2\left(1 - \frac{\mu^2}{c^2\alpha^2}\right)\frac{1}{r^2}.$$

We will assume $h < 0$; if the particle is projected with speed u from a point at distance k from O we have, from (11.4.5),

(16.13.9)
$$h = m_0c^2\left\{\frac{1}{\sqrt{\left(1 - \dfrac{u^2}{c^2}\right)}} - 1\right\} - \frac{\mu}{k},$$

and $h < 0$ if

(16.13.10)
$$u^2 < \frac{2\mu}{km_0}\,\frac{\left(1 + \dfrac{\mu}{2m_0kc^2}\right)}{\left(1 + \dfrac{\mu}{m_0kc^2}\right)^2}.$$

(If we let $c \to \infty$ we recover the well-known condition for an elliptic orbit if the mass does not vary, $m_0ku^2 < 2\mu$). We may assume $2m_0 + (h/c^2) > 0$ and $c\alpha > \mu$, conditions which are fulfilled in all ordinary circumstances on account of the largeness of c. In these circumstances the function $f(r)$, quadratic in $1/r$, has two real positive zeros, and

(16.13.11)
$$f(r) = \alpha^2\lambda^2\left(\frac{1}{r_1} - \frac{1}{r}\right)\left(\frac{1}{r} - \frac{1}{r_2}\right),$$

where

(16.13.12)
$$\lambda^2 = 1 - \frac{\mu^2}{c^2\alpha^2}.$$

The equation of the orbit is

$$\lambda(\theta + \beta) = \int_{r_1}^{r} \frac{(1/r^2)\,dr}{\sqrt{\left\{\left(\dfrac{1}{r_1} - \dfrac{1}{r}\right)\left(\dfrac{1}{r} - \dfrac{1}{r_2}\right)\right\}}}. \tag{16.13.13}$$

If we put

$$\frac{1}{r} = \frac{1}{2}\left(\frac{1}{r_1} + \frac{1}{r_2}\right) + \frac{1}{2}\left(\frac{1}{r_1} - \frac{1}{r_2}\right)\cos\psi \tag{16.13.14}$$

we find

$$\lambda(\theta + \beta) = \psi, \tag{16.13.15}$$

and the equation of the orbit is

$$\frac{1}{r} = \frac{1}{2}\left(\frac{1}{r_1} + \frac{1}{r_2}\right) + \frac{1}{2}\left(\frac{1}{r_1} - \frac{1}{r_2}\right)\cos\lambda(\theta + \beta). \tag{16.13.16}$$

This would be the equation of an ellipse if λ had the value 1. In fact $\lambda < 1$, and the orbit does not close; to recover the same value of r the angle θ must increase by $2\pi/\lambda(> 2\pi)$.

If the point of projection, at distance k from O, is an apse, the formulae become simpler; k is one of the apsidal distances, r_1 or r_2, and we take it as the lower limit in the integrals; $t_0 = 0$, $\beta = 0$,

$$\alpha = \frac{m_0 k u}{\sqrt{\left(1 - \dfrac{u^2}{c^2}\right)}}, \tag{16.13.17}$$

and

$$\lambda^2 = 1 - \frac{\mu^2(c^2 - u^2)}{m_0{}^2 k^2 u^2 c^4}. \tag{16.13.18}$$

The apsidal distance k is the perihelion if

$$u^2 > \frac{\mu}{m_0 k}\sqrt{\left(1 + \frac{\mu^2}{4 m_0{}^2 k^2 c^4}\right)} - \frac{\mu^2}{2 m_0{}^2 k^2 c^2},$$

which reduces to the well-known condition $m_0 k u^2 > \mu$ if $c \to \infty$.

16.14 The Pfaffian form $p_r\,dq_r - H\,dt$. We return for a moment to the equivalence theorem (§ 16.3). We saw that the Pfaffian equation

$$p_r\,dq_r - H\,dt = d\psi + \omega \tag{16.14.1}$$

is implied by, and implies, the Hamiltonian equations of motion. The equations have been solved, for the q's and p's, in terms of $2n$ independent parameters $\gamma_1, \gamma_2, \ldots, \gamma_{2n}$, and ω is a Pfaffian form

$$\omega = \sum_{s=1}^{2n} K_s\,d\gamma_s, \tag{16.14.2}$$

where the K's are functions of the γ's. In virtue of Pfaff's theorem we can, if we wish, reduce the form ω to one with only n terms,

$$\omega = \sum_{r=1}^{n} \beta_r\,d\alpha_r \tag{16.14.3}$$

where the α's and β's are suitable functions of the γ's. They are new parameters replacing the γ's, and the particular orbit in the phase space is defined as effectively by the numerical values of the α's and β's as it is by the numerical values of the γ's.

The Pfaffian form which is the first member of (16.14.1) is of great importance in the theory of the motion in the phase space. If we have a general Pfaffian form

$$\Omega = \sum_{r=1}^{m} X_r\, dx_r, \tag{16.14.4}$$

where the coefficients X_r are functions, of class C_1, of the m independent variables $x_1, x_2, \ldots, x_m$, the system of Pfaffian equations

$$\sum_{s=1}^{m} a_{rs}\, dx_s = 0, \qquad r = 1, 2, \ldots, m, \tag{16.14.5}$$

where

$$a_{rs} = \frac{\partial X_r}{\partial x_s} - \frac{\partial X_s}{\partial x_r}, \tag{16.14.6}$$

is of fundamental importance in the study of the Pfaffian form Ω. (It is the system called S_1 by Goursat.) In our case, where $m = 2n + 1$, the variables are $q_1, q_2, \ldots, q_n$; $p_1, p_2, \ldots, p_n$; t, and

$$\Omega = \sum_{r=1}^{n} p_r\, dq_r - H\, dt. \tag{16.14.7}$$

The skew-symmetric matrix (a_{rs}) is

(16.14.8)

$$\left[\begin{array}{cccc|cccc|c}
 & & & & 1 & & & & \frac{\partial H}{\partial q_1}\\
 & \mathbf{0} & & & & 1 & & & \frac{\partial H}{\partial q_2}\\
 & & & & & & & 1 & \frac{\partial H}{\partial q_n}\\
\hline
-1 & & & & & & & & \frac{\partial H}{\partial p_1}\\
 & -1 & & & & \mathbf{0} & & & \frac{\partial H}{\partial p_2}\\
 & & & -1 & & & & & \frac{\partial H}{\partial p_n}\\
\hline
-\frac{\partial H}{\partial q_1} & -\frac{\partial H}{\partial q_2} & & -\frac{\partial H}{\partial q_n} & -\frac{\partial H}{\partial p_1} & -\frac{\partial H}{\partial p_2} & & -\frac{\partial H}{\partial p_n} & 0
\end{array}\right]$$

The equations (16.14.5) for the Pfaffian form (16.14.7) are therefore

$$(16.14.9)\quad \begin{cases} dp_r + \dfrac{\partial H}{\partial q_r}\,dt = 0, & r = 1, 2, \ldots, n, \\[2ex] -dq_r + \dfrac{\partial H}{\partial p_r}\,dt = 0, & r = 1, 2, \ldots, n, \\[2ex] \displaystyle\sum_{r=1}^{n}\left(\frac{\partial H}{\partial q_r}\,dq_r + \frac{\partial H}{\partial p_r}\,dp_r\right) = 0. & \end{cases}$$

The first $2n$ equations are Hamilton's equations for the dynamical system. The last is not independent of them, since the determinant of the matrix is a skew-symmetric determinant of odd order, and vanishes. If H does not contain t the last equation is equivalent to the energy integral $H = h$.

Chapter XVII

Separable systems with two degrees of freedom

17.1 The idea of separability. It may happen that a dynamical system, described by a particular set of Lagrangian coordinates, is separable, i.e. the system is such that the modified partial differential equation (16.5.4) possesses a complete integral which is the sum of n separate functions of the n separate coordinates. Such systems have important and interesting properties which we shall now study. Separability is a property jointly of the system and of the chosen coordinates. What are the conditions for separability, and what are the particular characteristics of a system when these conditions are satisfied? Throughout the discussion we shall be concerned with a natural system which has n freedoms and which is described by n Lagrangian coordinates.

The separable system *par excellence* occurs in the theory of small oscillations (Chapter IX) when the Lagrangian coordinates chosen are the normal coordinates. In that case the motion in each coordinate is completely independent of the motion in the other coordinates; the system is in effect broken up into n independent systems. The same complete separability occurs occasionally in other problems (an example has been given in § 8.11). In separable systems in general, however, this is no longer true. We cannot isolate one particular coordinate and study its variation as for a system with only one freedom. Nevertheless, for any separable system we can make some progress towards this ideal separation. We shall find that *to some extent* we can study the variation of one coordinate without reference to the behaviour of the other coordinates; this somewhat imprecise statement will be clarified a little later (§ 17.3).

We have already considered the motion of a conservative system with one degree of freedom; the typical problem of this class is that of the rectilinear motion of a particle in a field of force. The fundamental differential equation controlling the motion (§ 1.2) has the form

$$\dot{x}^2 = f(x),$$

and we found that a glance at the graph of $f(x)$ enables us to tell the character of the motion. The theory of this differential equation is relevant again here; but whereas in the case of one freedom $f(x)$ contains only one parameter, in the general case (of a separable system with n freedoms) there are n parameters which occur linearly in $f(x)$.

17.2 Two degrees of freedom, conditions for separability. We begin with a discussion of an important special case, that of a system with two freedoms. We shall confine our attention to orthogonal systems (i.e. T contains only square terms, no product term). We first establish necessary and sufficient conditions for separability; then, assuming that these conditions are satisfied, we determine what are the characteristic properties of the motions that are possible for such a system.

We denote the Lagrangian coordinates by x, y, and the Hamiltonian function has the form

$$H = \tfrac{1}{2}(ap_x{}^2 + bp_y{}^2) + V, \tag{17.2.1}$$

where a, b, V are given functions of (x, y); we assume that these functions are of class C_1 in the appropriate domain of (x, y). We first establish conditions that are *necessary* for separability. If the system is separable the modified partial differential equation

$$\frac{1}{2}\left\{a\left(\frac{\partial K}{\partial x}\right)^2 + b\left(\frac{\partial K}{\partial y}\right)^2\right\} + V = h \tag{17.2.2}$$

admits a complete integral

$$F(x, h, \alpha) + G(y, h, \alpha), \tag{17.2.3}$$

where α is a second arbitrary constant. Thus

$$\frac{1}{2}\left\{a\left(\frac{\partial F}{\partial x}\right)^2 + b\left(\frac{\partial G}{\partial y}\right)^2\right\} = h - V \tag{17.2.4}$$

identically for the relevant domain of values of (x, y, h, α). We write this for the moment in the simpler form

$$a\theta + b\varphi = h - V, \tag{17.2.5}$$

where $\theta\left(= \frac{1}{2}\left(\frac{\partial F}{\partial x}\right)^2\right)$ involves only x (and h and α), and $\varphi\left(= \frac{1}{2}\left(\frac{\partial G}{\partial y}\right)^2\right)$ involves only y (and h and α). From (17.2.5) we have

$$a\theta_1 + b\varphi_1 = 1, \tag{17.2.6}$$

$$a\theta_2 + b\varphi_2 = 0, \tag{17.2.7}$$

where, for the moment, the suffix 1 denotes differentiation with respect to h, and the suffix 2 denotes differentiation with respect to α. We recall that a and b are positive for all values of (x, y) since they are coefficients in the formula for the kinetic energy. We see from (17.2.7) that neither θ_2 nor φ_2 can vanish identically, and from (17.2.6) that θ_1 and φ_1 cannot both vanish identically. Further

$$\theta_1\varphi_2 - \theta_2\varphi_1 = \frac{\partial(\theta, \varphi)}{\partial(h, \alpha)} = \frac{\partial F}{\partial x}\frac{\partial G}{\partial y}\frac{\partial\left(\frac{\partial F}{\partial x}, \frac{\partial G}{\partial y}\right)}{\partial(h, \alpha)} \tag{17.2.8}$$

does not vanish identically, since $F + G$ is a complete integral of the equation (17.2.2). We now choose any convenient fixed values of h and α; they must be such that none of θ_2, φ_2, $\theta_1\varphi_2 - \theta_1\varphi_1$ vanishes for all values of x and y, and such that θ_1 and φ_1 do not both vanish for all values of x and y. We then solve the linear equations (17.2.5–7) for a, b, and V. We find

$$V = \frac{\dfrac{h\theta_1 - \theta}{\theta_2} - \dfrac{h\varphi_1 - \varphi}{\varphi_2}}{\dfrac{\theta_1}{\theta_2} - \dfrac{\varphi_1}{\varphi_2}} = \frac{\xi + \eta}{X + Y}, \tag{17.2.9}$$

where ξ, X are functions of x only, and η, Y are functions of y only. These values must be independent of the fixed values of h and α we have chosen, and this suggests that h and α will occur linearly in θ and φ; we shall find that this surmise is in fact correct. Further

$$a = \frac{\dfrac{1}{\theta_2}}{\dfrac{\theta_1}{\theta_2} - \dfrac{\varphi_1}{\varphi_2}} = \frac{P}{X + Y}, \tag{17.2.10}$$

$$b = \frac{-\dfrac{1}{\varphi_2}}{\dfrac{\theta_1}{\theta_2} - \dfrac{\varphi_1}{\varphi_2}} = \frac{Q}{X + Y}, \tag{17.2.11}$$

where $P = P(x)$ and $Q = Q(y)$; and P and Q also must be independent of the values assigned to h and α.

Thus, finally, *if the system is separable, H must have the form*

$$H = \frac{1}{2(X + Y)}(Pp_x{}^2 + Qp_y{}^2) + \frac{\xi + \eta}{X + Y}, \tag{17.2.12}$$

where X, P, ξ are functions of x only, and Y, Q, η are functions of y only.

We now prove that these conditions are *sufficient*, i.e. a system for which

$$\begin{cases} T = \dfrac{1}{2}(X + Y)\left(\dfrac{\dot{x}^2}{P} + \dfrac{\dot{y}^2}{Q}\right) = \dfrac{1}{2(X + Y)}(Pp_x{}^2 + Qp_y{}^2), \\ V = \dfrac{\xi + \eta}{X + Y}, \end{cases} \tag{17.2.13}$$

is separable. The modified partial differential equation for such a system is

$$\frac{1}{(X + Y)}\left\{\frac{1}{2}P\left(\frac{\partial K}{\partial x}\right)^2 + \frac{1}{2}Q\left(\frac{\partial K}{\partial y}\right)^2 + \xi + \eta\right\} = h, \tag{17.2.14}$$

and we can find a complete integral of the required form $F + G$ if we put

$$\frac{1}{2}P\left(\frac{\partial F}{\partial x}\right)^2 = hX - \xi + \alpha, \tag{17.2.15}$$

$$\frac{1}{2}Q\left(\frac{\partial G}{\partial y}\right)^2 = hY - \eta - \alpha. \tag{17.2.16}$$

We thus obtain the required complete integral

$$K = \int\sqrt{\left\{\frac{2}{P}(hX - \xi + \alpha)\right\}}\,dx + \int\sqrt{\left\{\frac{2}{Q}(hY - \eta - \alpha)\right\}}\,dy, \tag{17.2.17}$$

where the integrals are to be interpreted in the usual way; for example, in the first integral the upper limit is x, and the lower limit is either an absolute constant or a simple zero of the function under the radical sign. Glancing back for a moment at the proof of necessity, we notice that, with the notation used there,

$$\theta = (hX - \xi + \alpha)/P, \quad \varphi = (hY - \eta - \alpha)/Q, \tag{17.2.18}$$

and the formulae (17.2.9–11) are verified.

17.3 Study of the motion. The integrals of the equations of motion are

$$t - t_0 = \frac{\partial K}{\partial h} = \int \frac{X}{\sqrt{2P(hX - \xi + \alpha)}}\,dx + \int \frac{Y}{\sqrt{2Q(hY - \eta - \alpha)}}\,dy, \tag{17.3.1}$$

$$-\beta = \frac{\partial K}{\partial \alpha} = \int \frac{1}{\sqrt{2P(hX - \xi + \alpha)}}\,dx - \int \frac{1}{\sqrt{2Q(hY - \eta - \alpha)}}\,dy, \tag{17.3.2}$$

$$p_x = \frac{\partial K}{\partial x} = \sqrt{\left\{\frac{2}{P}(hX - \xi + \alpha)\right\}}, \tag{17.3.3}$$

$$p_y = \frac{\partial K}{\partial y} = \sqrt{\left\{\frac{2}{Q}(hY - \eta - \alpha)\right\}}. \tag{17.3.4}$$

For the solution of the Lagrange problem, the motion in the (x, y)-space, we need only the equations (17.3.1–2), and we can write these compactly in the form

$$\frac{dx}{\sqrt{R}} = \frac{dy}{\sqrt{S}} = \frac{dt}{X + Y}, \tag{17.3.5}$$

where

$$R = R(x) = 2P(hX - \xi + \alpha), \tag{17.3.6}$$

and

$$S = S(y) = 2Q(hY - \eta - \alpha). \tag{17.3.7}$$

The equations (17.3.5), correctly interpreted, reduce the finding of the integrals of the Lagrangian equations to quadratures. We notice that the arbitrary constants h, α occur linearly in R and S.

We write

$$\frac{dt}{X + Y} = d\tau. \tag{17.3.8}$$

We can interpret τ as an artificial time measured on a clock travelling with the representative point in the (x, y)-space. The rate of this clock depends on the position in the space, and $X + Y$ is always positive, so τ always increases with t. Now

$$\frac{dx}{\sqrt{R}} = d\tau, \quad \frac{dy}{\sqrt{S}} = d\tau, \tag{17.3.9}$$

so that

$$\left(\frac{dx}{d\tau}\right)^2 = R, \quad \left(\frac{dy}{d\tau}\right)^2 = S, \tag{17.3.10}$$

and we can interpret these equations in part in the light of our previous discussion of the case of one freedom (§ 1.2); the relation here between x and τ is of the same form as the relation between x and t in the theory of § 1.2. But we must remember that the relation between t and τ depends on x and y, so the motions in x and y are not really independent. Nevertheless to some extent the motions can be discussed independently. They would be completely independent if $X + Y$ were constant (which would require of course that X and Y should be separately constant); they are partially independent if $X + Y$ does not vary too violently. This is the interpretation of the somewhat imprecise statement made in § 17.1.

Let us suppose that $X + Y$, which we know to be positive, is bounded above for all values of x and y, or at least for all values attained in the motion under discussion; there is a constant A such that

$$0 < X + Y \leqslant A \tag{17.3.11}$$

for all values of t. Then $\tau \to \infty$ with t. In this case it is easy to see what is the general nature of the motion in each coordinate. Thus if x, for example, lies initially between consecutive simple real zeros a_1, b_1 of R, there is an oscillatory motion in x, persisting for all time, between the limiting values a_1 and b_1. We shall extend the use of the term *libration* to include this case, though here the motion is not periodic in t (though it is periodic in τ). We see that the sign of the radical $\sqrt{R}$ in (17.3.5) must be interpreted as in the case of one freedom, *plus* when x is increasing, *minus* when x is decreasing. The two-valued function is not an awkwardness that could have been avoided; it is inherent in the nature of the problem. If x approaches a double zero c of R, then $x \to c$ as t and τ tend to infinity, and we can speak of this as a *limitation motion*. Similar remarks apply of course to the coordinate y.

The argument may need modification if $X + Y$ is unbounded. Let us suppose that, in the motion under discussion, $X + Y$ tends to infinity with t. In practice this happens most frequently if x or y tends to infinity with t. It may happen that the integral

$$\int^{\infty} \frac{dt}{X + Y}$$

is convergent, and in that case τ tends to a finite limit τ_0 as $t \to \infty$; the (artificial) time τ must have a stop! It is easy to see how the former conclusions must be modified in this case. If x lies initially between consecutive simple real zeros a, b of R we get, not the expected libration continuing indefinitely, but x tends to a limit l $(a \leqslant l \leqslant b)$, possibly after a finite number of oscillations, as t tends to infinity. And if x approaches a double zero c of R we see that x tends to a limit short of c. Such motions may be called *pseudo-limitation motions*.

If there is a libration in each coordinate the motion is periodic if μ,

$$\mu = \oint \frac{dx}{\sqrt{R}} \Big/ \oint \frac{dy}{\sqrt{S}}, \tag{17.3.12}$$

is rational. If $\mu = p/q$, where p and q are integers with no common factor, then after q x-librations and p y-librations the system has returned to its original state, both in position and velocity. The period is

$$q \oint \frac{X}{\sqrt{R}}\, dx + p \oint \frac{Y}{\sqrt{S}}\, dy. \tag{17.3.13}$$

If μ is irrational the motion is not periodic, and the orbit, lying in the rectangular box $(a_1 \leqslant x \leqslant b_1,\ a_2 \leqslant y \leqslant b_2)$ in the (x, y)-plane, does not close (Fig. 17.3). The motion is said to be *quasi-periodic*. For a more penetrating study of quasi-periodic motions it is expedient to introduce the so-called *angle variables*, but it will be convenient to postpone the study of this technique until we deal with the general

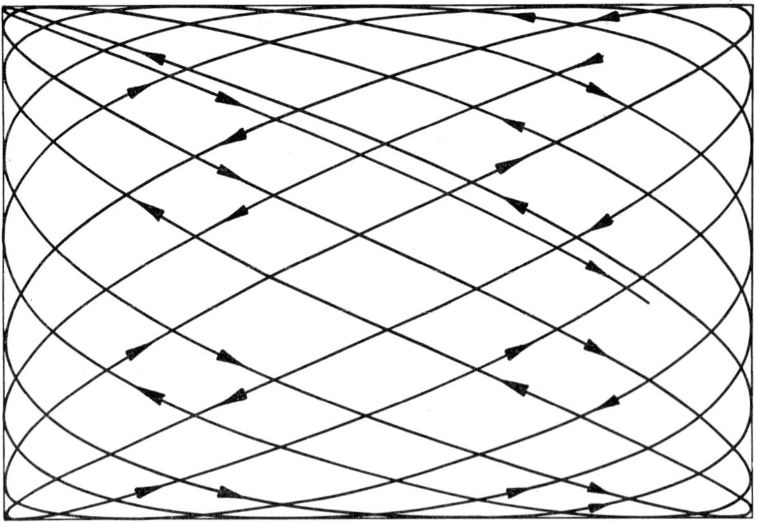

Figure 17.3

case of n variables. (One simple example of an angle variable has already been noticed, for a system with one freedom, in § 1.3.)

It is plausible to suppose, since R and S both contain h and α, that we can always obtain both periodic and aperiodic motions by adjustment of the initial conditions. But this supposition turns out to be false. There are, as we know, systems for which the motion is always periodic, and there are systems for which the motion is never periodic. Both possibilities are illustrated in the theory of small oscillations. If the ratio of the periods is rational the orbit is always periodic, whatever the circumstances of projection; and if the ratio of the periods is irrational, the orbit is never periodic (unless of course the system oscillates in a normal mode). Another conspicuous example is furnished by the Newtonian orbit, which is always periodic whatever the direction and speed of projection of the planet (provided that the speed of projection is less than the velocity from infinity for the point of projection). We shall return to this point later (§ 18.8) and discover the source of the anomaly.

17.4 Classification of the orbits. As we have seen, the general nature of the orbit in the (x, y)-space can be inferred from a study of the real zeros of R and S. If x lies initially between two consecutive simple real zeros a_1, b_1, of R we have, in general a libration between a_1 and b_1; and if x approaches a double zero of R we have, in general, a limitation motion. Similar remarks apply to the other Lagrangian coordinate y. We recall that an anomaly arises if $\int^{\infty} \frac{1}{X + Y}\,dt$ converges.

A question naturally arises at this point which deserves consideration. The functions R and S involve only two constants h and α, whereas, since the system has two freedoms, four constants must occur in the general solution of the Lagrangian or of the Hamiltonian equations of motion. What is the significance of the missing constants, and why do they play only a minor role in the theory of the classification?

For one of these constants the answer is immediate; it is the epoch constant whose value merely indicates the instant that has been chosen as the zero of the time-scale. If $x = \varphi(t)$, $y = \psi(t)$ satisfy the equations of motion so do $x = \varphi(t - t_0)$, $y = \psi(t - t_0)$, and the value of

t_0 does not affect the orbit, nor the rate at which it is traversed. The other missing constant is a phase constant which appears in the integration of the equation defining the orbit,

$$\frac{dx}{\sqrt{R}} = \frac{dy}{\sqrt{S}}.$$

The value of this constant does affect the form of the orbit. (And in fact in general, h and α being prescribed, there are *two* orbits through a suitable initial point x, y. Suppose for example that h and α are such that a_1, b_1 are consecutive simple real zeros of R, and $R > 0$ between a_1 and b_1, and a_2, b_2 are consecutive simple real zeros of S, and $S > 0$ between a_2 and b_2. Then we can start from any point x_0, y_0 in the rectangle

$$a_1 \leqslant x \leqslant b_1, \quad a_2 \leqslant y \leqslant b_2,$$

and two orbits through x_0, y_0 satisfy (17.4.1). If the denominators were uniform (single-valued) there would be only one. But we are dealing here with the q-space, not the phase space. There are an infinity of orbits through a given point of projection, and two of these correspond to the prescribed values of h and α.) Nevertheless the general character of the orbit depends only on the zeros of R and S, and thus only on h and α. These two constants h and α therefore play the major role in the classification of the orbits.

Consider first motion on one of the coordinate curves, say on the curve $x = a$. We expect such an orbit to be of particular interest because the chosen coordinates are such that the system possesses the distinctive property of separability. Now for motion on $x = a$ we need that $\dot{x}$ and $\ddot{x}$ both vanish for $x = a$, and this requires that a is a *double zero of R*. For

$$(17.4.1) \qquad (X + Y)^2\dot{x}^2 = R,$$

$$(17.4.2) \qquad (X + Y)^2\ddot{x} = \tfrac{1}{2}R' - (X + Y)(X'\dot{x} + Y'\dot{y})\dot{x},$$

(the formula for $\ddot{x}$ being valid even when $\dot{x} = 0$) so R and R' must both vanish at $x = a$. Thus if a coordinate curve $x =$ constant is an orbit, the values of h and α must be such that R has a double zero. The condition that R should have a double zero is that h and α satisfy a certain relation $\Delta(h, \alpha) = 0$.

We can now classify the orbits in the (x, y)-space by reference to a subsidiary diagram in which h, α are taken as coordinates. If we take a definite point in this (h, α)-diagram the corresponding functions R and S are thereby determined. And though, as we have seen, this does not determine a unique orbit, at least all the orbits so determined are of the same type or types, with the same limits of libration (if there is a libration motion). The condition that R has a double zero is represented by the curve or curves

$$(17.4.3) \qquad \Delta(h, \alpha) = 0,$$

which are called *critical curves*; and there are also critical curves representing coincidences between pairs of zeros of S. The diagram is divided into regions by these critical curves, and the orbits represented by points in the interior of the same region are of the same general type, though the limits of libration (if there is a libration motion) are not the same for all the points in the region. The types of orbit only change when we cross a critical curve from one region to another.

Some regions may be of no interest from the point of view of dynamics because no real orbits correspond to points (h, α) in them. Such *excluded regions* will occur if the values of (h, α) in the region are such that, for these values of (h, α), R (or S) is negative for all values of x (or y). (Another way in which excluded regions arise will be noticed in § 17.6.)

17.5 Stability. We consider now the effect of a small disturbance represented by small changes in the values of h and α. If the orbit corresponds to a point h, α in the interior of a region (i.e. not a point on a critical curve) a small disturbance leads to neighbouring orbits of similar type. In this context such orbits are said to be *stable*; but this is a broad use of the term stability, and does not necessarily imply that the disturbed orbit lies in the neighbourhood of the original orbit. In this broad sense stability merely means that the disturbed orbit is a neighbouring orbit of the same type as the original orbit.

If the orbit corresponds to a point h, α on a critical curve, then either R or S has a double zero, say

(17.5.1) $$R = (x - a)^2\varphi(x),$$

where $\varphi(a) \neq 0$. If now a small disturbance occurs, represented by small changes in h and α, the second member of (17.5.1) becomes

(17.5.2) $$(x - a_1)(x - a_2)\psi(x),$$

where a_1 and a_2 are nearly equal to a, and $\psi(x)$ is nearly equal to $\varphi(x)$ for values of x near to a. In general for displacements of (h, α) on one side $\mathfrak{A}$ of the critical curve, a_1, a_2 will be real and different; and for displacements on the other side $\mathfrak{B}$ of the critical curve, a_1, a_2 will be complex.

It is easy to see that the phenomena are quite different according as $\varphi(a) < 0$ or $\varphi(a) > 0$.

(i) Suppose first that $\varphi(a) < 0$. Then, for this value of (h, α), the motion on $x = a$ is the only motion possible in the neighbourhood of $x = a$, since no motion is possible at a point (x, y) for which $R < 0$. If there is a small disturbance, $\psi(x) < 0$ for values of x sufficiently near to a, so if a_1, a_2 are real the disturbed motion is a libration between a_1 and a_2, and if a_1, a_2 are complex, no motion is possible near $x = a$. Two consequences follow from this remark. The first is that the disturbed orbit (in the (x, y)-space) lies between the curves $x = a_1$ and $x = a_2$, and a_1, a_2 are both nearly equal to a. In the important special case where the curves $x =$ constant are closed oval curves, the disturbed orbit lies in a narrow belt in the neighbourhood of the undisturbed orbit $x = a$. The undisturbed orbit is stable, not merely in the broad sense mentioned above, but also in the more exacting sense that the disturbed orbit lies near the undisturbed orbit for all values of t. The second consequence is that, as we cross the critical curve from the side $\mathfrak{A}$ to the side $\mathfrak{B}$, a set of orbits disappears; the orbits lie in zones which narrow down to single curves as the representative point in the (h, α)-diagram approaches the critical curve, and these orbits do not exist beyond the critical curve. As we have noticed already, there may be excluded regions in the (h, α)-diagram such that no real orbits correspond to the interior points.

(ii) If $\varphi(a) > 0$ everything is changed. To begin with, the motion corresponding to such a value of (h, α) may be either *on* $x = a$, or a limitation motion in which $x \to a$ as $t \to \infty$; the orbit approximates, for large values of t, to the curve $x = a$. If we consider the effect of a small disturbance, $\psi(x) > 0$ near $x = a$. If the disturbance takes the point (h, α) to the side $\mathfrak{A}$ of the critical curve, so that a_1, a_2 are real, x must lie, throughout the motion, *outside* the range (a, a_2); two orbits are possible, one with $x \leqslant a_1$ and one with $x \geqslant a_2$. If the disturbance takes the point (h, α) to the side $\mathfrak{B}$, so that a_1, a_2 are complex, the expression (17.5.2) is positive near $x = a$, and there is no relevant zero, and no boundary to the x-motion, in the neighbourhood of $x = a$. Thus again as we pass from the side $\mathfrak{A}$ to the side $\mathfrak{B}$ of the critical curve, a set of orbits is lost; the two distinct sets merge into a single set. The original motion, whether a motion on $x = a$ or a limitation motion, is unstable, even in the broad sense of stability mentioned above; a small disturbance gives rise to orbits of a completely different type.

It remains to consider a point (h, α) which gives R a triple zero,

$$(X + Y)^2\dot{x}^2 = (x - a)^3\chi(x). \tag{17.5.3}$$

A motion *on* $x = a$ is possible, but so also is a limitation motion having $x = a$ as the limit curve—from above if $\chi(a) > 0$, from below if $\chi(a) < 0$. Let us suppose for definiteness that $\chi(a) > 0$. The effect of a small disturbance is to replace the second member of (17.5.3) by

$$(x - a_1)(x - a_2)(x - a_3)\rho(x). \tag{17.5.4}$$

If a_1, a_2, a_3 are all real, $a_1 < a_2 < a_3$, we must have, for values of x in the neighbourhood of a, either

$$x > a_3 \quad \text{or} \quad a_2 > x > a_1. \tag{17.5.5}$$

If a_1, a_2 are complex only the alternative $x > a_3$ is permissible. It is true that in the first case (a_1, a_2, a_3 all real) a libration between a_1 and a_2 is possible; but so also is a *non-local* motion having a_3 as its lower bound. And only this non-local motion is possible in the second case. The original motion is unstable.

Finally there may be points at which critical curves of R and critical curves of S intersect. At such a point (h, α) both R and S have double zeros, and the point is a point of equilibrium; the system can rest in this position. If (h, α) is such that

$$\begin{cases} R = (x - a)^2\varphi(x), \\ S = (y - b)^2\psi(y), \end{cases} \tag{17.5.6}$$

then $x = a$, $y = b$ is a point of equilibrium, and the equilibrium is stable (in the ordinary sense of statics) if $\varphi(a) < 0$ and $\psi(b) < 0$.

17.6 Application of the theory. The preceding theory gives a general idea of the types of orbit that occur, and of a method of classification. In applying it to concrete examples the physical meaning of the chosen coordinates must be kept in mind. For example, the theory applied uncritically can be misleading in the following case. It may happen that one of the Lagrangian coordinates is bounded, values outside a certain range having no physical significance; for example, in the familiar theory of central orbits the radius vector r is always non-negative. The occurrence of such bounded coordinates may give rise to further excluded regions in the (h, α) diagram, regions for which real orbits appear to exist, but orbits involving values of one coordinate outside the physically admissible range. Further, such bounded coordinates may necessitate some modification of the stability theory. Suppose, by way of illustration, that R has a triple zero a, and that a is a boundary value for x, $x \leqslant a$. If $\chi(a) > 0$ only the motion on $x = a$, not the limitation motion, is possible, and it is stable. But for a double zero the stability theory is unaffected if the double zero is a boundary value.

One application of this method of classification of orbits has already been given in advance of the general theory. This is the problem of the spherical pendulum (§5.3). The diagram Fig. 5.3*b* is precisely the (h, α)-plane of the present theory. The critical curves are the curves $\alpha = 0$, $\alpha = \varphi(h)$, and there are, as we saw, three types of orbit, according as (h, α) lies in the interior of the one admissible region, or on one of the critical curves which bound it.

17.7 Central attraction k/r^{n+1}. A particle moves in a plane under a central attraction derived from the potential $-\mu/r^n$ per unit mass, where n is an integer greater than 2. The equations corresponding to (17.3.5) are, with $u = 1/r$,

$$\frac{du}{\sqrt{f(u)}} = \frac{d\theta}{\sqrt{\alpha}} = \sqrt{2u^2}\, dt, \tag{17.7.1}$$

where

$$f(u) = \mu u^n - \alpha u^2 + h. \tag{17.7.2}$$

These are easily derived from the general theory of § 17.3, or, with a suitable change of notation, from (5.2.14). The graph of $f(u)$ for positive values of u has the form shown in Fig. 17.7*a*. If we consider a fixed (positive) value of α, the effect of a change in the value of h is to move the graph bodily up or down. There are two critical values of h. These are (i) $h = 0$, for which $f(u)$ has two coincident zeros $u = 0$ and one positive zero $u = b$, where

$$b^{n-2} = \frac{\alpha}{\mu}, \tag{17.7.3}$$

and (ii) $h = h_1$, where

$$h_1^{n-2} = (n - 2)^{n-2} \left(\frac{2}{\mu}\right)^2 \left(\frac{\alpha}{n}\right)^n, \tag{17.7.4}$$

for which $f(u)$ has two coincident zeros $u = a$, where

$$a^{n-2} = \frac{2\alpha}{n\mu}. \tag{17.7.5}$$

The critical curves in the (h, α) diagram (Fig. 17.7*b*) are

$$h = 0, \quad h = h_1(\alpha), \tag{17.7.6}$$

where $h_1(\alpha)$ is given by (17.7.4). The half-plane $\alpha < 0$ is excluded, and in the upper half-plane we have three regions to consider and the boundary curves. Let us consider a definite value of α (i.e. the points on a certain horizontal line in Fig. 17.7*b*) and consider how the situation changes as h increases from $-\infty$ to $+\infty$. On $h = 0$, $\varphi(0) < 0$, and as we cross from left to right (i.e. from the region $\mathfrak{B}$ to the region $\mathfrak{A}$ in the notation of § 17.5) a set of orbits splits into two sets. But this is a case where the general theory must be used with caution; if applied uncritically it would predict, for $h = 0$, a stable circular orbit on $u = 0$. But this has no physical meaning, since $u = 1/r$, and moreover the stability theory is inapplicable here, since small changes in u do not represent small displacements in space. As we have noticed (§ 17.6) we must be alive to the possibility of this kind of anomaly arising from the properties of the coordinates

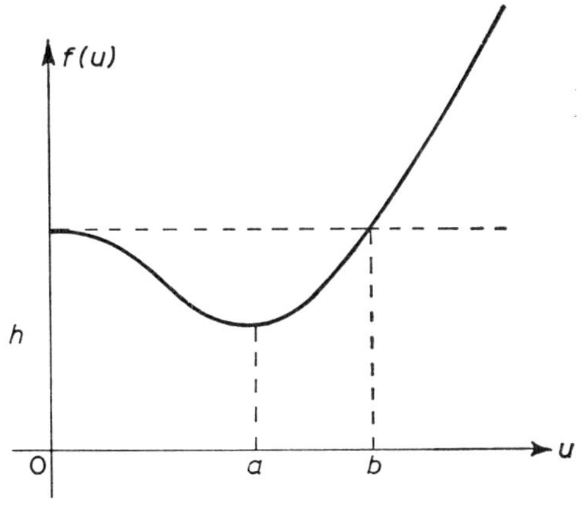

Figure 17.7a

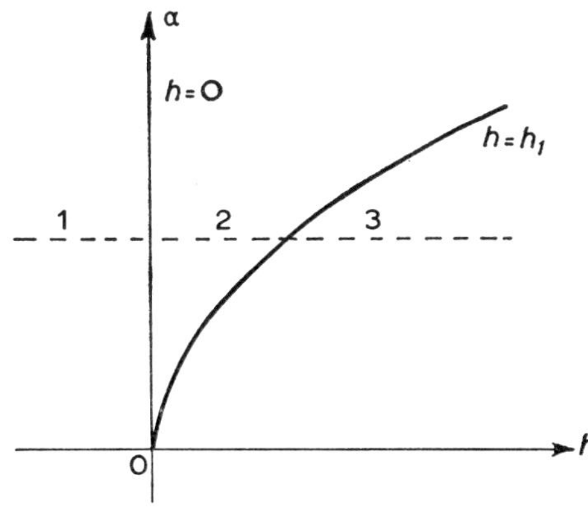

Figure 17.7b

chosen. On $h = h_1$, $\varphi(a) > 0$ ($\varphi(a)$ has the same sign as $f''(a)$) and as we cross from left to right (i.e. from $\mathfrak{A}$ to $\mathfrak{B}$) a set of orbits is lost.

Before enumerating the possible types of orbit in the plane, we may notice that $\int \frac{du}{\sqrt{f(u)}}$ is convergent at 0 and at ∞; thus, θ tends to a limit if the orbit goes to infinity or to the centre of attraction. Further, any orbit that goes to infinity has an asymptote, since the subtangent $d\theta/du$ tends to a limit as u tends to zero.

We are now in a position to classify the orbits; we denote the three regions by the figures 1, 2, 3 (Fig. 17.7b), and we denote the dividing curves by 12 and 23.

1. $h < 0$, u varies from a lower limit u_0 to ∞, where $u_0 > b$. There is one type of orbit, a rosette orbit lying inside the circle $r = 1/u_0$ (Fig. 17.7c). The angle φ is given by the formula

$$\varphi = \int_{u_0}^{\infty} \frac{\sqrt{\alpha}\, du}{\sqrt{f(u)}} . \tag{17.7.7}$$

12. $h = 0$. This is the anomaly already mentioned. There is merely the rosette orbit inserted in the circle $r = 1/b$. Its equation is

$$\theta = \int_{1}^{1/(br)} \frac{dx}{x\sqrt{(x^{n-2} - 1)}} . \tag{17.7.8}$$

For $n = 4$ (the problem of an attraction proportional to r^{-5}) this is the circle

$$r = \frac{1}{b} \cos \theta.$$

2. $0 < h < h_1$. There are two orbits corresponding to any point in the region, a rosette orbit with $u \geqslant u_2$ and a hyperbola-type orbit with $u \leqslant u_1$ (only the latter is shown in Fig. 17.7d). The hyperbola-type orbit touches the circle $r = 1/u_1$ externally and goes to infinity; if h and α are large the path is nearly straight.

23. $h = h_1$. The orbit is either an unstable circular motion on $r = 1/a$, or a limitation motion, a spiral up or down to this circle as the limit curve (Fig. 17.7e).

3. $h > h_1$. The orbit goes to infinity in one direction, and to the centre of attraction in the other (Fig. 17.7f). A limiting case is a straight line through the centre of attraction.

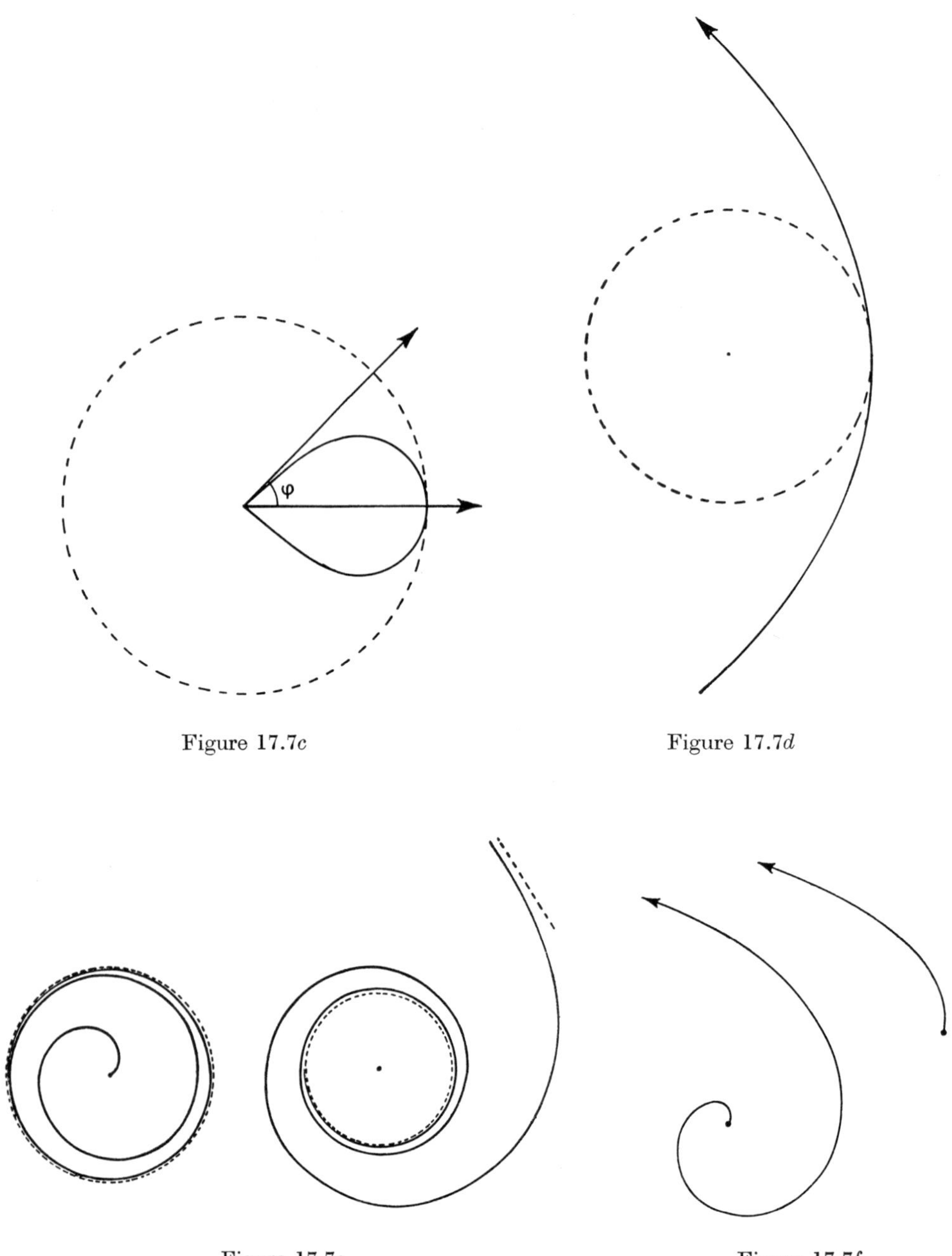

Figure 17.7*c*

Figure 17.7*d*

Figure 17.7*e*

Figure 17.7*f*

Perhaps the most striking feature of this investigation is the fact that the possible orbits are of essentially the same types for all values of n greater than 2. In the next section we shall consider the exact form of the orbits in the case $n = 4$.

17.8 Central attraction k/r^5. In problems of this kind, when we have completed our survey of the possible types of orbit, we can proceed to the actual integration; it is advantageous to postpone the detailed calculations until after the classification has been achieved. For the problem of a central attraction with $V = -\mu/r^n$ the cases $n = -2, -1, 1, 2$ are integrable in terms of circular or exponential functions, and the cases $n = -6, -4, 3, 4, 6$ are integrable in terms of elliptic functions. (Of course the theory in the preceding section applies only to values of n greater than 2.) Let us consider the particular case of an attraction proportional to r^{-5}, $n = 4$. Here

(17.8.1) $$f(u) = \mu u^4 - \alpha u^2 + h,$$

where

(17.8.2) $$h_1 = \frac{\alpha^2}{4\mu}, \qquad b = \sqrt{\left(\frac{\alpha}{\mu}\right)}, \qquad a = \sqrt{\left(\frac{\alpha}{2\mu}\right)}.$$

The critical curve $h = h_1$ is the parabola $\alpha^2 = 4\mu h$. To illustrate the theory we shall be content to discuss the central region 2 (Fig. 17.7b) and its boundaries, $0 \leqslant h \leqslant h_1$, or say $0 \leqslant \beta \leqslant \frac{1}{4}$, where we write $h = \alpha^2\beta/\mu$. It will be convenient in this case to work with r rather than u, and the equations (17.7.1) become

(17.8.3) $$\frac{dr}{\sqrt{\left(\frac{\alpha\beta}{\mu}r^4 - r^2 + \frac{\mu}{\alpha}\right)}} = d\theta = \frac{\sqrt{(2\alpha)}}{r^2}\,dt,$$

where we have changed the sign of the first radical (which involves no loss of generality).

Let us now determine the orbits for the range $0 \leqslant \beta \leqslant \frac{1}{4}$.

12. $\beta = 0$. The differential equation of the orbit in the (r, θ)-plane can be written in the form

(17.8.4) $$\left(\frac{dr}{d\theta}\right)^2 = c^2 - r^2,$$

where $c = 1/b$; the orbit, of the rosette type, is the circle

(17.8.5) $$r = c \cos\theta.$$

2. $0 < \beta < \frac{1}{4}$. Here

(17.8.6) $$\left(\frac{dr}{d\theta}\right)^2 = \frac{\alpha\beta}{\mu}r^4 - r^2 + \frac{\mu}{\alpha} = \frac{\alpha\beta}{\mu}(r^2 - r_1^2)(r^2 - r_2^2),$$

where $0 < r_1 < r_2$,

(17.8.7) $$r_1^2 = \frac{\mu}{2\alpha\beta}(1 - \delta), \quad r_2^2 = \frac{\mu}{2\alpha\beta}(1 + \delta), \quad \delta = \sqrt{(1 - 4\beta)}.$$

There are two orbits, a rosette orbit lying inside $r = r_1$, and an open hyperbola-like orbit, lying outside $r = r_2$.

(i) The rosette orbit, $0 \leqslant r \leqslant r_1$. We substitute $r = r_1 \operatorname{sn} v$, with $k = r_1/r_2$,

(17.8.8) $$k^2 = \frac{1 - \delta}{1 + \delta}, \quad \beta = \left(k + \frac{1}{k}\right)^{-2}.$$

Then

(17.8.9) $$r_1^2 - r^2 = r_1^2 \operatorname{cn}^2 v, \quad r_2^2 - r^2 = r_2^2 \operatorname{dn}^2 v, \quad \frac{dr}{dv} = r_1 \operatorname{cn} v \operatorname{dn} v,$$

and (17.8.6) becomes

(17.8.10) $$\left(\frac{dv}{d\theta}\right)^2 = \frac{\alpha\beta}{\mu}r_2^2 = \tfrac{1}{2}(1 + \delta) = \frac{1}{1 + k^2} = \lambda^2, \text{ say,}$$

and the equation of the orbit is

(17.8.11) $$r = r_1 \operatorname{sn} \lambda\theta.$$

We notice that r reaches its maximum value r_1 when $\theta = \theta_0$, where

(17.8.12) $$\theta_0 = K/\lambda = K\sqrt{(1 + k^2)}.$$

Now $\theta_0 \to \infty$ as $k \to 1$, and the orbit approximates to the spiral orbit, approaching the circular boundary from inside, as $\beta \to \frac{1}{4}$.

Numerical example. If $\beta = 4/25$, $k = 1/2$, $\lambda^2 = 4/5$,

(17.8.13) $$K = 1{\cdot}6857, \quad \lambda = 0{\cdot}8944, \quad r_2{}^2 = 4r_1{}^2 = 5\mu/\alpha,$$

and θ_0 is approximately 108° (Fig. 17.8).

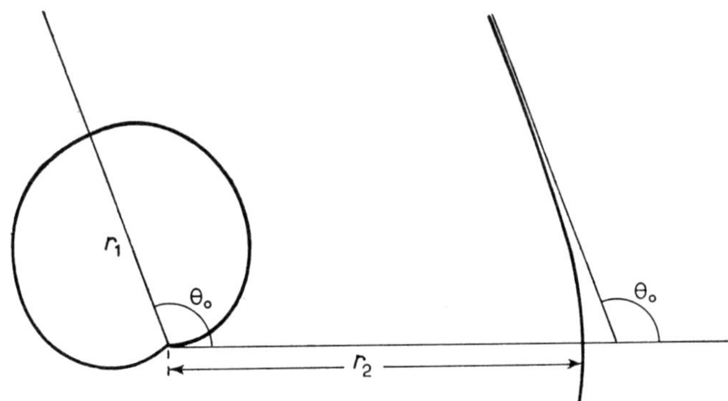

Figure 17.8

(ii) The open orbit, $r \geqslant r_2$. To complete the integration we make a substitution in which $r^2 - r_2{}^2$ is proportional to $s^2/(1 - s^2)$, where $s = \operatorname{sn} v$; explicitly, supplying the appropriate coefficient, and taking $k = r_1/r_2$ as before, we put

(17.8.14) $$r^2 - r_2{}^2 = (r_2{}^2 - r_1{}^2)\frac{\operatorname{sn}^2 v}{\operatorname{cn}^2 v}.$$

Then

(17.8.15) $$r^2 - r_1{}^2 = (r_2{}^2 - r_1{}^2)\frac{1}{\operatorname{cn}^2 v},$$

and

(17.8.16) $$r = r_2 \frac{\operatorname{dn} v}{\operatorname{cn} v}.$$

Thus

(17.8.17) $$\frac{dr}{dv} = \frac{1}{r_2}(r_2{}^2 - r_1{}^2)\frac{\operatorname{sn} v}{\operatorname{cn}^2 v},$$

and, substituting in the differential equation of the orbit (17.8.6), we find $v = \lambda\theta$ as before. The equation of the orbit is

(17.8.18) $$r = r_2 \frac{\operatorname{dn} \lambda\theta}{\operatorname{cn} \lambda\theta}.$$

Here $r \to \infty$ as $\theta \to \theta_0$. The orbit for the numerical example quoted above is shown in Fig. 17.8.

We can express the equations in terms of $\wp$-functions instead of Jacobian elliptic functions. In the equation (17.8.6)

(17.8.19) $$\left(\frac{dr}{d\theta}\right)^2 = \frac{\alpha\beta}{\mu} r^4 - r^2 + \frac{\mu}{\alpha}$$

we put

(17.8.20) $$r^2 = \frac{\mu}{\alpha\beta}(v + \tfrac{1}{3}).$$

Then

(17.8.21) $$\left(\frac{dv}{d\theta}\right)^2 = \left(\frac{dr}{d\theta}\right)^2 \Big/ \left(\frac{dr}{dv}\right)^2 = \left(\frac{2r\alpha\beta}{\mu}\right)^2\left(\frac{dr}{d\theta}\right)^2 = 4(v + \tfrac{1}{3})\{v^2 - \tfrac{1}{3}v + (\beta - \tfrac{2}{9})\}$$
$$= 4(v - e_1)(v - e_2)(v - e_3),$$

where

(17.8.22) $$e_1 = \tfrac{1}{6} + \tfrac{1}{2}\delta, \quad e_2 = \tfrac{1}{6} - \tfrac{1}{2}\delta, \quad e_3 = -\tfrac{1}{3},$$

so that $e_1 > \frac{1}{6} > e_2 > -\frac{1}{3}$. For the rosette orbit

(17.8.23) $$v = \wp(\theta - \omega_2),$$

and v has its maximum value e_2 when $\theta = \omega_1$. The equation of the orbit is

(17.8.24) $$r^2 = \frac{\mu}{\alpha\beta}\{\wp(\theta - \omega_2) + \tfrac{1}{3}\}.$$

For the open orbit

(17.8.25) $$v = \wp(\theta - \omega_1),$$

and v has its minimum value e_1 when $\theta = 0$, while $v \to \infty$ as $\theta \to \omega_1$. The equation of the orbit is

(17.8.26) $$r^2 = \frac{\mu}{\alpha\beta}\{\wp(\theta - \omega_1) + \tfrac{1}{3}\}.$$

Finally (returning to the systematic classification of the orbits) we consider points (h, α) on the boundary 23 of Fig. 17.7*b*.

23. $\beta = \frac{1}{4}$, and the differential equation of the orbit can be written in the form

(17.8.27) $$\left(\frac{dr}{d\theta}\right)^2 = \frac{1}{2r_1^2}(r^2 - r_1^2)^2.$$

There are three possibilities:

(i) If $r = r_1$ initially the orbit is the circle $r = r_1$.

(ii) If $r < r_1$ initially, and we suppose for definiteness that r increases with θ,

(17.8.28) $$r_1 \frac{dr}{d\varphi} = r_1^2 - r^2,$$

where $\varphi = \theta/\sqrt{2}$. The orbit is the spiral

(17.8.29) $$r = r_1 \tanh \varphi = r_1 \tanh(\theta/\sqrt{2}).$$

approaching the circle $r = r_1$, from within.

(iii) If $r > r_1$ initially, and r decreases as θ increases,

(17.8.30) $$r_1 \frac{dr}{d\varphi} = -(r^2 - r_1^2),$$

and the orbit is the spiral

(17.8.31) $$r = r_1 \coth \varphi = r_1 \coth (\theta/\sqrt{2}),$$

approaching the circle $r = r_1$ from without.

The reader may find it of interest to complete the investigation by determining the equations of the orbits corresponding to values of (h, α) in the regions 1 and 3 of Fig. 17.7*b*.

17.9 Newtonian centre and uniform field. A particle moves in the (x, y)-plane under the action of an attraction $m\mu/r^2$ to the origin and of a uniform field $(-mg, 0)$. The potential per unit mass is $-\dfrac{\mu}{r} + gx$. We introduce the parabolic coordinates u, v, where

(17.9.1) $$u = \tfrac{1}{2}(r + x), \quad v = \tfrac{1}{2}(r - x).$$

The curve $u = c$ is the parabola with focus at O and vertex at $(c, 0)$. The curve $v = c$ is the parabola with focus at O and vertex at $(-c, 0)$. The two families of parabolas intersect orthogonally. The relevant ranges of values for u and v are $0 \leqslant u < \infty$, $0 \leqslant v < \infty$. Now

(17.9.2) $$x = u - v, \quad y^2 = 4uv, \quad r = u + v,$$

so (omitting the positive multiplier m) we have

(17.9.3) $$T = \tfrac{1}{2}(\dot{x}^2 + \dot{y}^2) = \tfrac{1}{2}(\dot{u} - \dot{v})^2 + \frac{1}{2uv}(v\dot{u} + u\dot{v})^2 = \tfrac{1}{2}(u + v)\left(\frac{\dot{u}^2}{u} + \frac{\dot{v}^2}{v}\right),$$

(17.9.4) $$V = -\frac{\mu}{r} + gx = -\frac{\mu}{u + v} + g(u - v) = \frac{1}{u + v}\{gu^2 - g(v^2 + b^2)\},$$

where $b^2 = \mu/g$. (The equilibrium point in the field is given by $x = -b$, $y = 0$.) Thus

(17.9.5) $$H = \frac{1}{2(u + v)}(up_u{}^2 + vp_v{}^2) + \frac{1}{u + v}\{gu^2 - g(v^2 + b^2)\},$$

and this is of the form (17.2.12) with

(17.9.6) $$X = P = u, \quad \xi = gu^2; \quad Y = Q = v, \quad \eta = -g(v^2 + b^2).$$

The system therefore satisfies the conditions for separability, with the chosen coordinates, and the integrals of the equations of motion are derived from the formulae

(17.9.7) $$\frac{du}{\sqrt{R}} = \frac{dv}{\sqrt{S}} = \frac{dt}{u + v},$$

where

(17.9.8) $$R = -2u(gu^2 - hu - \alpha),$$

(17.9.9) $$S = 2v(gv^2 + hv + gb^2 - \alpha).$$

We now turn to the problem of classification of orbits. We can use the (h, α)-plane as in the general theory (§ 17.4), but in this case a simpler method is available, as follows. The cubic polynomial R must have all its zeros real; for if the quadratic form

$$gu^2 - hu - \alpha$$

had complex zeros, R would be negative for all positive values of u, and no motion could occur. Thus the zeros of R are u_1, u_2, 0, where u_1 and u_2 are real, $u_1 \geqslant u_2$, and we can use the (u_1, u_2)-plane as the basis of our classification, instead of the (h, α)-plane of the general theory.

The critical curves are easy to determine, but the remarks in § 17.5 about the effect of crossing a critical curve refer to the (h, α)-plane, and are not immediately applicable here.

Let us now find the critical curves. For R, these are $u_1 = 0$, $u_2 = 0$, $u_1 = u_2$. The region $u_1 < 0$ is excluded, since $u_1 < 0$ would imply $R < 0$ for all positive values of u. Thus $u_1 \geqslant 0$, and if $u_1 > 0$ there is a libration between u_1 and u_2 if $u_2 > 0$, and between u_1 and 0 if $u_2 < 0$. The critical curves for S are $v_1 = 0$, $v_2 = 0$, $v_1 = v_2$, and we have to interpret these in the (u_1, u_2)-plane. Now v_1, v_2 are the roots of the equation

(17.9.10) $$v^2 + (u_1 + u_2)v + (u_1u_2 + b^2) = 0.$$

Thus v_1 or v_2 vanishes if (u_1, u_2) lies on the hyperbola

(17.9.11) $$u_1u_2 + b^2 = 0.$$

Also v_1 and v_2 are real and unequal if

(17.9.12) $$u_1 - u_2 > 2b,$$

real and equal if

(17.9.13) $$u_1 - u_2 = 2b,$$

and complex if

(17.9.14) $$u_1 - u_2 < 2b.$$

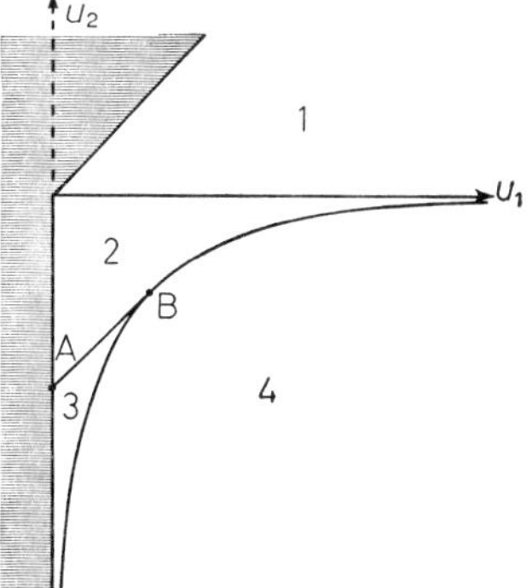

Figure 17.9a

We thus obtain the curves shown in Fig. 17.9a. The equation (17.9.13) represents the tangent to the hyperbola (17.9.11) at $(b, -b)$.

For the classification of the orbits there are four regions to consider and the curves bounding them. The relevant information about the zeros of R and S is given in the following table:

Region 1. $u_1 > u_2 > 0$; v_1, v_2 complex, or $0 > v_1 > v_2$;

2. $u_1 > 0 > u_2$; v_1, v_2 complex, or $0 > v_1 > v_2$;

3. $u_1 > 0 > u_2$; $v_1 > v_2 > 0$;

4. $u_1 > 0 > u_2$; $v_1 > 0 > v_2$.

We can now see the range of values through which u varies when the point (u_1, u_2) lies in the interior of one of the four regions; and similarly we can see what is the range of values for v. Thus, in the region 1, u suffers a libration between u_1 and u_2: in the regions 2, 3, and 4, u has a libration between u_1 and 0. For v, in the regions 1 and 2, v decreases from ∞ to 0 (for the complete orbit) and then increases to ∞: in the region 3 there are two possibilities, (a) there is a libration between v_2 and 0, (b) v decreases from ∞ to v_1 and then increases to ∞: in the region 4 the v-motion is as in 3(b).

The only case of a bounded orbit, and the case of particular interest, is that denoted by 3(a), and exhibited in Fig. 17.9b. The conditions required for this case are

(17.9.15) $$h < 0, \quad 0 < \alpha < gb^2,$$

and initially

(17.9.16) $$0 < v < v_2.$$

The first condition $h < 0$ is equivalent to

(17.9.17) $$\tfrac{1}{2}W^2 < \frac{\mu}{r} - gx,$$

where W is the velocity of projection, and (x, y) is the point of projection. The condition (17.9.17) reduces to the familiar condition for the Newtonian elliptic orbit if $g = 0$. The condition (17.9.17) cannot be satisfied if

$$rx > b^2, \tag{17.9.18}$$

i.e. if the point of projection lies to the right of the curve $rx = b^2$.

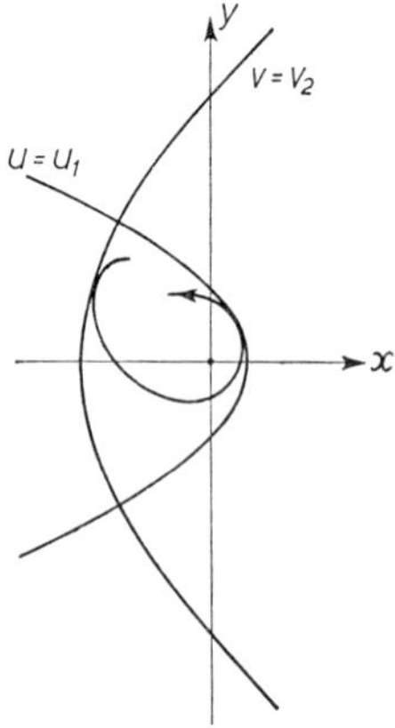

Figure 17.9*b*

We can express the form of the orbit parametrically in terms of $\wp$-functions with one real period $2\omega_1$ and one pure-imaginary period $2\omega_3$. We can write

$$\frac{du}{\sqrt{\{4u(u_1 - u)(u - u_2)\}}} = \frac{dv}{\sqrt{\{4v(v_1 - v)(v_2 - v)\}}} = d\theta, \tag{17.9.19}$$

say, and we need the $\wp$-function with

$$g_2 = \frac{4}{g}\left(\frac{h^2}{3g} + \alpha\right), \quad g_3 = \frac{4h}{3g^2}\left(\frac{2h^2}{9g} + \alpha\right), \tag{17.9.20}$$

for u, and the $\wp$-function with

$$g_2 = \frac{4}{g}\left(\frac{h^2}{3g} + \alpha - gb^2\right), \quad g_3 = -\frac{4h}{3g^2}\left(\frac{2h^2}{9g} + \alpha - gb^2\right), \tag{17.9.21}$$

for v. The curve of the orbit is represented parametrically by the equations

$$u = \frac{h}{3g} + \wp(\omega_1 + i\theta), \quad v = -\frac{h}{3g} + \wp(\omega_3 + \theta - \theta_0), \tag{17.9.22}$$

where the parameter θ is real, and the first $\wp$-function refers to (17.9.20), the second to (17.9.21).

We consider very briefly the orbits corresponding to points on the boundaries of the region 3 in Fig. 17.9*a*. These points correspond to motions on the parabolas $u =$ constant or $v =$ constant, or to limitation motions approximating to motions on these curves.

On the boundary curve 23 (i.e. the curve dividing the region 2 from the region 3) we have

$$R = 2gu\{(b - k) - u\}\{u + (b + k)\}, \quad S = 2gv(v - k)^2, \tag{17.9.23}$$

where $0 < k < b$. A possible motion is motion on the arc of the parabola $v = k$ lying inside the parabola $u = b - k$. The motion is unstable, and so is the limitation motion to this arc.

On the boundary curve 34

$$R = 2gu(be^{-\theta} - u)(u + be^{\theta}), \quad S = 2gv^2(v - 2b\sinh\theta), \tag{17.9.24}$$

where $\theta > 0$. The particle moves on $v = 0$, the positive x-axis, between $x = 0$ and $x = be^{-\theta}$; it is not a libration, because of the discontinuity of the field at O.

On the part of the negative u_2-axis bounding the region 3 we have

$$R = -2gu^2(u + 2b\cosh\theta), \quad S = 2gv(be^{-\theta} - v)(be^{\theta} - v), \tag{17.9.25}$$

where $\theta > 0$. There is a stable motion on $u = 0$, the negative x-axis, between $x = -be^{-\theta}$ and $x = 0$; but again it is not a libration motion because of the discontinuity in the field at O.

Finally we consider the special points A and B in Fig. 17.9a. At A,

$$R = -2gu^2(u + 2b), \quad S = 2gv(v - b)^2, \tag{17.9.26}$$

giving the unstable equilibrium at the neutral point $u = 0$, $v = b$ (i.e. $x = -b, y = 0$). Or we can have a motion on the negative x-axis in which $x \to -b$ as $t \to \infty$; the particle has been projected from one side or the other towards the neutral point with just enough energy to reach it.

At B,

$$R = 2gu(b^2 - u^2), \quad S = 2gv^3. \tag{17.9.27}$$

The motion is such that, if u increases initially, it reaches the value b and then decreases to zero. The v-motion is on $v = 0$, the positive x-axis, or a limitation motion to $v = 0$. But all these are unstable.

The reader may find it of interest to complete the classification for the other regions in Fig. 17.9a and the bounding curves.

If $g = 0$ the problem becomes the problem of a single Newtonian centre of attraction. We notice that this problem is separable in the parabolic coordinates, as well as in polar coordinates (§ 17.14).

17.10 Two fixed Newtonian centres. We consider the motion of a planet, of mass m_0, attracted by two fixed suns of masses m and m'; the motion takes place in a plane through the suns. The problem is of particular interest as an approach to the problem of three bodies. It was first considered in detail by Legendre in connexion with his researches on the elliptic functions. We denote by r, r' the distances of the planet from m, m' respectively, and we use confocal coordinates λ and μ,

$$\lambda = \tfrac{1}{2}(r + r'), \quad \mu = \tfrac{1}{2}(r - r'), \tag{17.10.1}$$

so that the curve $\lambda =$ constant is an ellipse with the suns in the foci, and $\mu =$ constant is one branch of a hyperbola with the same foci. We denote the distance between the suns by $2c$. The coordinate λ is bounded below, $\lambda \geqslant c$, and the coordinate μ is bounded both above and below, $c \geqslant \mu \geqslant -c$.

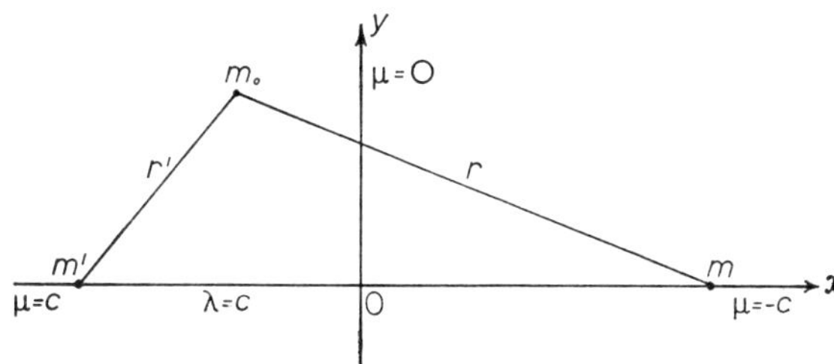

Figure 17.10a

Taking the Cartesian coordinates of the suns to be $(c, 0)$ and $(-c, 0)$, as shown in Fig. 17.10a, we have

$$r^2 = (x - c)^2 + y^2, \quad r'^2 = (x + c)^2 + y^2, \tag{17.10.2}$$

whence

$$x^2 + y^2 + c^2 = \tfrac{1}{2}(r'^2 + r^2) = \lambda^2 + \mu^2, \tag{17.10.3}$$

$$cx = \tfrac{1}{4}(r'^2 - r^2) = -\lambda\mu, \tag{17.10.4}$$

and therefore

(17.10.5) $$c^2y^2 = (\lambda^2 - c^2)(c^2 - \mu^2).$$

Hence

(17.10.6) $$\frac{\dot{y}}{y} = \frac{\lambda\dot{\lambda}}{\lambda^2 - c^2} - \frac{\mu\dot{\mu}}{c^2 - \mu^2},$$

and

(17.10.7) $$c^2\dot{y}^2 = (\lambda^2 - c^2)(c^2 - \mu^2)\left(\frac{\lambda\dot{\lambda}}{\lambda^2 - c^2} - \frac{\mu\dot{\mu}}{c^2 - \mu^2}\right)^2.$$

Thus

(17.10.8)

$$T = \tfrac{1}{2}m_0(\dot{x}^2 + \dot{y}^2) = \frac{m_0}{2c^2}\left\{(\lambda\dot{\mu} + \dot{\lambda}\mu)^2 + (\lambda^2 - c^2)(c^2 - \mu^2)\left(\frac{\lambda\dot{\lambda}}{\lambda^2 - c^2} - \frac{\mu\dot{\mu}}{c^2 - \mu^2}\right)^2\right\}$$
$$= \tfrac{1}{2}m_0(\lambda^2 - \mu^2)\left(\frac{\dot{\lambda}^2}{\lambda^2 - c^2} + \frac{\dot{\mu}^2}{c^2 - \mu^2}\right),$$

and, further,

(17.10.9) $$V = -\gamma m_0\left(\frac{m}{r} + \frac{m'}{r'}\right) = -\gamma m_0\left(\frac{m}{\lambda + \mu} + \frac{m'}{\lambda - \mu}\right)$$
$$= -m_0\frac{k\lambda - k'\mu}{\lambda^2 - \mu^2},$$

where

(17.10.10) $$k = \gamma(m + m'), \quad k' = \gamma(m - m').$$

We shall suppose, for definiteness, that $m > m'$, and then

(17.10.11) $$k > k' > 0.$$

Thus finally, omitting the positive factor m_0, we have

(17.10.12) $$H = \frac{1}{2}\left(\frac{1}{\lambda^2 - \mu^2}\right)\{(\lambda^2 - c^2)p_\lambda{}^2 + (c^2 - \mu^2)p_\mu{}^2\} - \frac{k\lambda - k'\mu}{\lambda^2 - \mu^2},$$

and this is of the separable type (17.2.12).

The integrals of the Lagrangian equations of motion can be written in the form (17.3.5),

(17.10.13) $$\frac{d\lambda}{\sqrt{R}} = \frac{d\mu}{\sqrt{S}} = \frac{dt}{\lambda^2 - \mu^2},$$

where

(17.10.14) $$R = 2(\lambda^2 - c^2)(h\lambda^2 + k\lambda + \alpha),$$

(17.10.15) $$S = -2(c^2 - \mu^2)(h\mu^2 + k'\mu + \alpha).$$

We write

(17.10.16) $$L = h\lambda^2 + k\lambda + \alpha,$$

(17.10.17) $$M = h\mu^2 + k'\mu + \alpha.$$

and we observe that, throughout the motion,

(17.10.18) $$L \geqslant 0, \quad M \leqslant 0.$$

We denote by λ_1, λ_2 the zeros of L, and by μ_1, μ_2 the zeros of M. Then λ_1, λ_2 are certainly real. For if λ_1, λ_2 are complex, then $k^2 < 4\alpha h$, and *a fortiori* $k'^2 < 4\alpha h$, so that μ_1, μ_2 are complex also. But this is impossible, because if both L and M have complex zero, both are definite forms with the sign of h, so one or other of the conditions (17.10.18) is violated. We shall use the fact that λ_1, λ_2 are real as the basis of classification, using the (λ_1, λ_2)-plane in place of the (h, α)-plane of the general theory of § 17.4.

The conditions (17.10.18) imply that if $h < 0$, λ must lie inside the range (λ_1, λ_2) and μ must lie outside the range (μ_1, μ_2) if μ_1 and μ_2 are real; while if $h > 0$, λ must lie outside the range (λ_1, λ_2), and μ must lie inside the range (μ_1, μ_2), complex values of μ_1 and μ_2 being prohibited when $h > 0$.

We now find the critical curves in the (λ_1, λ_2) diagram, supposing always $\lambda_1 \geqslant \lambda_2$. Now μ_1 and μ_2 are the roots of the equation

(17.10.19) $$x^2 - \frac{k'}{k}(\lambda_1 + \lambda_2)x + \lambda_1\lambda_2 = 0,$$

and $\mu_1 = \mu_2$ if

(17.10.20) $$(\lambda_1 + \lambda_2)^2 = 4\lambda_1\lambda_2(k/k')^2.$$

If we write

(17.10.21) $$\cosh\theta = \frac{k}{k'},$$

which implies

(17.10.22) $$\frac{m'}{m} = \tanh^2 \tfrac{1}{2}\theta,$$

the equation (17.10.20) becomes

(17.10.23) $$\frac{\lambda_1}{\lambda_2} = e^{\pm 2\theta},$$

representing a pair of lines in the (λ_1, λ_2)-plane equally inclined to the axes. These are two of the critical curves.

Next, either $\mu_1 = c$ or $\mu_2 = c$ if

(17.10.24) $$c^2 - \frac{k'}{k}(\lambda_1 + \lambda_2)c + \lambda_1\lambda_2 = 0,$$

i.e. if the point (λ_1, λ_2) lies on the hyperbola

(17.10.25) $$(\lambda_1 - ck'/k)(\lambda_2 - ck'/k) = -c^2\tanh^2\theta.$$

The tangents from the origin are the lines (17.10.23), and $\lambda_1 = \lambda_2 e^{2\theta}$ touches the lower branch at $(ce^{\theta}, ce^{-\theta})$. We must determine also (taking $\mu_1 \geqslant \mu_2$) which part of the curve (17.10.25) corresponds to $\mu_1 = c$ and which to $\mu_2 = c$. Now if $\mu_2 = c$, $\mu_1 + \mu_2 \geqslant 2c$, and $\lambda_1 + \lambda_2 \geqslant 2ck/k' = 2c\cosh\theta$, so that $\mu_2 = c$ to the right of $(ce^{\theta}, ce^{-\theta})$. A similar argument proves that $\mu_1 = -c$, $\mu_2 = -c$ correspond to parts of a branch of the hyperbola

(17.10.26) $$(\lambda_1 + ck'/k)(\lambda_2 + ck'/k) = -c^2\tanh^2\theta.$$

Both hyperbolas (17.10.25) and (17.10.26) go through the point $(c, -c)$.

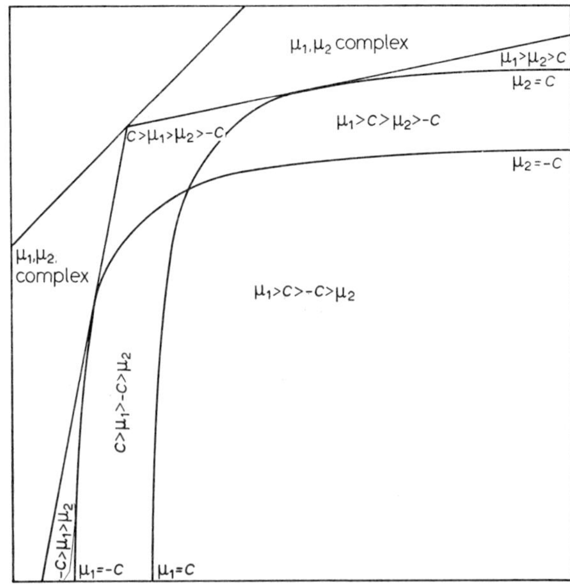

Figure 17.10*b*

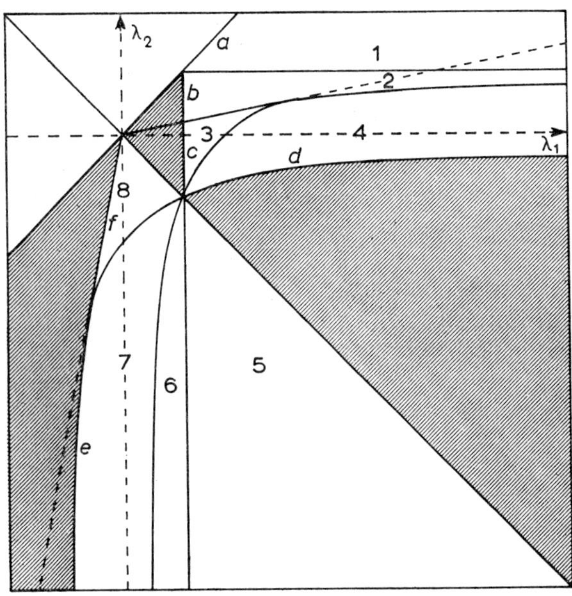

Figure 17.10*c*

This completes the critical curves relevant to the zeros of S (Fig. 17.10*b*). For the zeros of R we have also the critical curves $\lambda_1 = \lambda_2$, $\lambda_1 = c$, $\lambda_2 = c$, and this completes the set. But some of the regions are excluded.

If $h < 0$, λ lies in the range (λ_1, λ_2), and since $\lambda \geqslant c$, the region $\lambda_1 < c$ is excluded. If $h < 0$, μ lies outside the range (μ_1, μ_2), and since $c \geqslant \mu \geqslant -c$ we must exclude the region in which $\mu_1 > c > -c > \mu_2$: of these two conditions $\mu_1 > c$ is necessarily satisfied if $-c > \mu_2$, since $\mu_1 + \mu_2 > 0$.

If $h > 0$, complex values of μ_1, μ_2 are excluded (as we have noticed already). If μ_1, μ_2 are real, μ lies between them, so the regions $\mu_2 > c$, $-c > \mu_1$ are excluded; but $\mu_2 > c$ does not arise, since $\mu_1 + \mu_2 < 0$.

When the excluded regions have been blocked out the half-plane $\lambda_1 \geqslant \lambda_2$ is divided into eight regions by the critical curves. There are therefore eight fundamental types of orbit. We number the regions 1, 2, . . . , 8 as in Fig. 17.10*c*. In addition to the eight fundamental types there are a number of other types corresponding to certain special points in the Fig. 17.10*c*. These are points *on* the critical curves, isolated points for which *three* zeros of R or of S coincide, and points at which critical curves of R and S intersect (i.e. points such that the corresponding forms of R and S both possess double zeros).

We recall that for motion to take place on the ellipse $\lambda = \lambda_0$, λ_0 must be a double zero of R. Thus for motion on $\lambda = \lambda_0 > c$, λ_0 must be a double zero of L, while for motion on $\lambda = c$ (the line joining the suns) c must be a simple zero of L. Similarly for motion on $\mu = \mu_0$, where $|\mu_0| < c$, μ_0 must be a double zero of M, while for motion on $\mu = c$ (or on $\mu = -c$), c (or $-c$) must be a simple zero of M.

17.11 The bounded orbits. We shall be content, for the sake of brevity, to consider in detail only the case $h < 0$. In this case $\lambda_1 > c$, and the orbit lies inside the ellipse $\lambda = \lambda_1$. If μ_1, μ_2 are real, μ lies outside the range (μ_1, μ_2). With these remarks in mind the forms of the four types of orbit are evident. In the region 1, $\lambda_1 > \lambda_2 > c$, and the λ-motion is a libration between λ_1 and λ_2. In the regions 2, 3, 4, $\lambda_1 > c > \lambda_2$, and the λ-motion is a libration between λ_1 and c. In the regions 1 and 2 the zeros of M are either complex, or real with $\mu_1 > \mu_2 > c$, and the μ-motion is a libration between $+c$ and $-c$. In the region 3, $c > \mu_1 > \mu_2 > -c$, and there are two possibilities for the μ-motion, (*a*) a libration between c and μ_1, (*b*) a libration between μ_2 and $-c$. In the region 4, $\mu_1 > c > \mu_2 > -c$, and the μ-motion is a libration between μ_2 and $-c$.

Thus in the region 1 the orbit is an oval curve, not in general closed, lying in the annulus between the ellipses $\lambda = \lambda_1$ and $\lambda = \lambda_2$ (Fig. 17.11*a*). The curve is closed, and the motion is periodic, if

$$\frac{\int_{\lambda_1}^{\lambda_2} d\lambda/\sqrt{R}}{\int_{-c}^{c} d\mu/\sqrt{S}} \tag{17.11.1}$$

is rational.

In the region 2 the orbit is a figure-of-eight curve about the two suns (Fig. 17.11*b*).

In the region 3 the planet is a satellite of one sun or the other (Fig. 17.11*c*). The figure-of-eight type has split into two distinct curves in passing from region 2 to region 3, and in passing from region 3 to region 4 one of these disappears. In region 4 the planet is a satellite of m.

To complete the classification for $h < 0$ we must also consider points on the boundaries of the regions in Fig. 17.10*c*. This task may be conveniently divided into three parts, as follows.

(i) The curve 23 separating the regions 2 and 3 is the critical curve for which $\mu_1 = \mu_2$, the values of the double zero lying between a certain value μ_0 and c. Now M has two zeros equal to μ_0 when $\lambda_1 = c$, $\lambda_2 = ce^{-2\theta}$, so

$$\mu_0 = \frac{k'}{2k}(\lambda_1 + \lambda_2) = ce^{-\theta}.$$

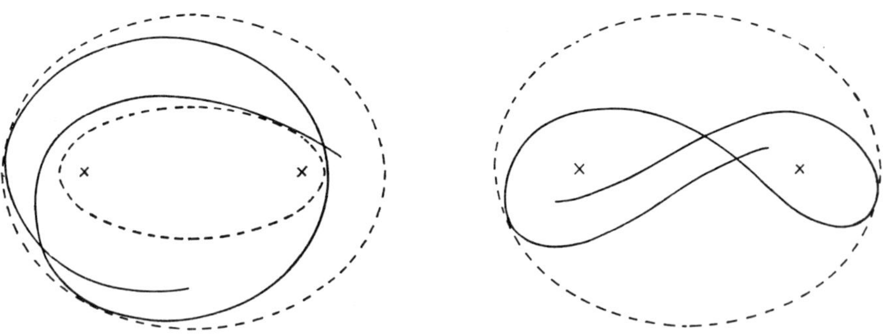

Figure 17.11*a* Figure 17.11*b*

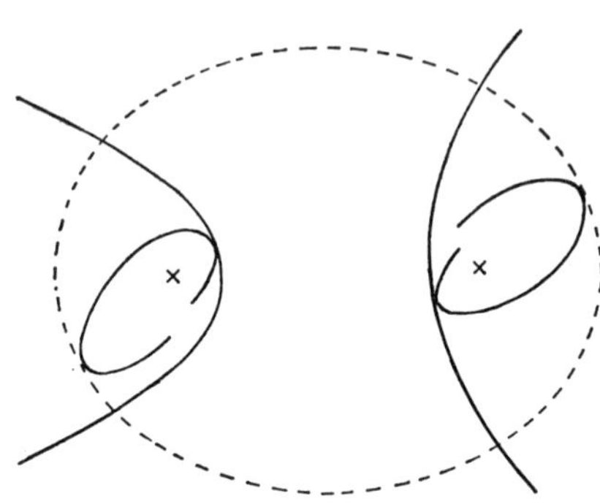

Figure 17.11*c*

In fact the equilibrium point on the line joining the suns is the point $\lambda = c$, $\mu = \mu_0$; for at the equilibrium point

$$\frac{\sqrt{m}}{r} = \frac{\sqrt{m'}}{r'} = \frac{\sqrt{m}+\sqrt{m'}}{2c} = \frac{\sqrt{m}-\sqrt{m'}}{2\mu}, \tag{17.11.2}$$

whence

$$\mu = c\,\frac{\sqrt{m}-\sqrt{m'}}{\sqrt{m}+\sqrt{m'}} = ce^{-\theta} = \mu_0. \tag{17.11.3}$$

We now consider briefly the results for points on the critical curves 12, 23, 34, 42.

12. Here μ_1, μ_2 are complex, or real and greater than c, and the μ-motion is a libration between c and $-c$. Further $\lambda_1 > \lambda_2 = c$, and

$$R = 2h'(\lambda - c)^2(\lambda + c)(\lambda_1 - \lambda),$$

where $h' = -h > 0$. The λ-motion is a motion on $\lambda = c$, or a limitation motion from above with $\lambda = c$ as the limit curve. The former is a motion on the line joining the suns, not a genuine libration because of the discontinuities of the field at the suns: the latter is a spiral curve lying inside the ellipse $\lambda = \lambda_1$, which it touches. But these orbits are unstable and cannot occur in practice.

23, 34, 42. For these curves $\lambda_1 > c > \lambda_2$, and the λ-motion is a libration between λ_1 and c.

23. $$c > \mu_1 = \mu_2 > \mu_0,$$

and

$$S = 2h'(c^2 - \mu^2)(\mu - \mu_1)^2.$$

The μ-motion is a motion on $\mu = \mu_1$, which is a hyperbola cutting the axis between m' and the equilibrium point, or a limitation motion from either side to $\mu = \mu_1$. The former is an oscillation bounded by the ellipse $\lambda = \lambda_1$. But these orbits also are unstable.

34.
$$\mu_1 = c > \mu_2 > -c$$
and
$$S = 2h'(c - \mu)^2(\mu + c)(\mu_2 - \mu).$$

There are two possibilities. (a) The μ-motion is a libration between μ_2 and $-c$, the planet being a satellite of m: this type of orbit occurs on both sides of the boundary, as well as on the boundary, and the squared factor in M is irrelevant to it. (b) The μ-motion is an isolated stable motion on $\mu = c$; the planet is a satellite of m'. The λ-motion is not a genuine libration, because the satellite collides with the sun m'.

42.
$$\mu_1 > \mu_2 = c,$$
and
$$S = 2h'(c - \mu)^2(c + \mu)(\mu_1 - \mu).$$

The μ-motion is again a motion on $\mu = c$, as in the case just considered, but this time the motion is unstable; or it may be a limitation motion from below to $\mu = c$, a motion similar to that in 23.

(ii) We next consider the critical curves labelled a, b, c, d in Fig. 17.10c. On a and b, μ_1 and μ_2 are complex, and the μ-motion is a libration between c and $-c$.

a.
$$\lambda_1 = \lambda_2 > c$$
and
$$R = -2h'(\lambda^2 - c^2)(\lambda - \lambda_1)^2,$$
an isolated stable periodic motion on the ellipse $\lambda = \lambda_1$. The ellipse is a possible orbit for motion in the field of either sun alone: it has long been known that it is also a possible orbit under the action of the two suns together. The reader may be interested to construct a proof independent of the general theory.

b.
$$c = \lambda_1 > \lambda_2,$$
and
$$R = -2h'(\lambda - c)^2(\lambda + c)(\lambda - \lambda_2),$$
an isolated stable motion on the line joining the suns, ending in a collision with one sun or the other.

c.
$$c = \lambda_1 > \lambda_2,$$
and
$$R = -2h'(\lambda - c)^2(\lambda + c)(\lambda - \lambda_2),$$
$$c > \mu_1 > \mu_0 > \mu_2 > -c,$$
and
$$S = 2h'(c^2 - \mu^2)(\mu - \mu_1)(\mu - \mu_2).$$

The λ-motion is an isolated stable motion on $\lambda = c$, as for b. The μ-motion is linear between c and μ, or between μ_2 and $-c$. The planet is a satellite of one sun or the other, being projected from a point near one sun towards the other, but never reaching the equilibrium point. The planet falls back into the sun from which it was projected.

d. $\lambda_1 > c > \lambda_2$, and the λ-motion is a libration between λ_1 and c. Also

$$\mu_1 > c > \mu_2 = -c,$$

and

$$S = -2h'(\mu + c)^2(\mu - c)(\mu - \mu_1),$$

and the μ-motion is an isolated stable motion on $\mu = -c$: the planet is a satellite of m.

(iii) Finally it remains to consider a number of special points in Fig. 17.10*c*.

Consider first the point where the regions 2, 3, 4 meet. Here $\lambda_1 = ce^{\theta}$, $\lambda_2 = ce^{-\theta}$, and the λ-motion is a libration between λ_1 and c. Further $\mu_1 = \mu_2 = c$, giving

$$S = 2h'(c - \mu)^3(c + \mu).$$

The motion is on $\mu = c$, or a limitation motion from below, with $\mu = c$, as the limit curve. These motions are unstable. The point in question may be considered to belong to 42, which branches here into the two types 23 and 34.

For the point *ab*, μ_1 and μ_2 are complex, the μ-motion being a libration between c and $-c$. Further, $\lambda_1 = \lambda_2 = c$, and

$$R = -2h'(\lambda + c)(\lambda - c)^3.$$

The motion takes place on the line joining the suns, and it is stable, in spite of the cubed factor, since λ is a bounded coordinate; this is an example of the anomaly mentioned in § 17.6.

For the point *bc* we have critical curves of R and S intersecting, with $\lambda_1 = c$ and $\mu_1 = \mu_2 = \mu_0$. For this point

$$R = -2h'(\lambda - c)^2(\lambda + c)(\lambda - \lambda_2),$$

$$S = 2h'(c^2 - \mu^2)(\mu - \mu_0)^2.$$

The λ-motion is an isolated motion on $\lambda = c$, and either $\mu = \mu_0$ or $\mu \to \mu_0$ from above or from below. Either the planet rests at the equilibrium point, or it approaches this point as a limit from one side or the other, having been projected from a point near one sun towards the other with just enough energy to carry it to the equilibrium point. The equilibrium and the limitation motion are both unstable.

17.12 The equations of the orbits. When we have completed our survey of the possible types of orbit (but not sooner) we may proceed to the actual integration. Consider as a specific example the region 1 (Fig. 17.11*a*) where the orbit, not in general closed, encircles both suns, and lies in the annulus $\lambda_1 \geqslant \lambda \geqslant \lambda_2$. The form of the curve traversed by the planet is derived from the equation

$$\text{(17.12.1)} \quad \frac{d\lambda}{\sqrt{\{(\lambda_1 - \lambda)(\lambda - \lambda_2)(\lambda - c)(\lambda + c)\}}} = \frac{d\mu}{\sqrt{\{(c - \mu)(\mu + c)(\mu_1 - \mu)(\mu_2 - \mu)\}}},$$

where $\lambda_1 > \lambda_2 > c > -c$ and $\mu_1 > \mu_2 > c > -c$. The λ motion is a libration between λ_1 and λ_2, the μ-motion is a libration between c and $-c$.

If we equate each member of (17.12.1) to $2d\theta$ we can express λ and μ in terms of θ, using either Jacobian or Weierstrassian elliptic functions, in a great variety of ways. We thus find a parametric representation of the curve in the form $\lambda = \lambda(\theta)$, $\mu = \mu(\theta)$. As an illustration, we give one method of integration, as follows.

If we use the substitution

$$\text{(17.12.2)} \quad \frac{\lambda - \lambda_2}{\lambda_1 - \lambda} = \frac{\lambda_2 - c}{\lambda_1 - c}\frac{x^2}{1 - x^2},$$

the first member of (17.12.1) takes the form

$$\frac{2}{\sqrt{\{(\lambda_1 - c)(\lambda_2 + c)\}}}\frac{dx}{\sqrt{\{(1 - x^2)(1 - k^2x^2)\}}}, \tag{17.12.3}$$

where

$$k^2 = \frac{2c(\lambda_1 - \lambda_2)}{(\lambda_1 - c)(\lambda_2 + c)}. \tag{17.12.4}$$

Thus

$$x = \text{sn } u, \quad \text{where } u = \sqrt{\{(\lambda_1 - c)(\lambda_2 + c)\}}\theta, \tag{17.12.5}$$

and

$$\lambda = \frac{\lambda_1(\lambda_2 - c)\text{sn}^2 u + \lambda_2(\lambda_1 - c)\text{cn}^2 u}{(\lambda_2 - c)\text{sn}^2 u + (\lambda_1 - c)\text{cn}^2 u}. \tag{17.12.6}$$

Similarly, if we use the substitution

$$\frac{\mu + c}{c - \mu} = \frac{\mu_1 + c}{\mu_1 - c}\frac{y^2}{1 - y^2}, \tag{17.12.7}$$

the second member of (17.12.1) becomes

$$\frac{2}{\sqrt{\{(\mu_1 - c)(\mu_2 + c)\}}}\frac{dy}{\sqrt{\{(1 - y^2)(1 - \kappa^2y^2)\}}}, \tag{17.12.8}$$

where

$$\kappa^2 = \frac{2c(\mu_1 - \mu_2)}{(\mu_1 - c)(\mu_2 + c)}. \tag{17.12.9}$$

Thus,

$$y = \text{sn } v, \quad \text{where } v = \sqrt{\{(\mu_1 - c)(\mu_2 + c)\}}(\theta - \theta_0), \tag{17.12.10}$$

and

$$\mu = c\,\frac{(\mu_1 + c)\text{sn}^2 v - (\mu_1 - c)\text{cn}^2 v}{(\mu_1 + c)\text{sn}^2 v + (\mu_1 - c)\text{cn}^2 v}. \tag{17.12.11}$$

We have thus expressed the curve in the form $\lambda = \lambda(\theta)$, $\mu = \mu(\theta)$. The parameter k^2 for the Jacobian elliptic functions in (17.12.6) is given by (17.12.4), and the corresponding parameter κ^2 in (17.12.11) is given by (17.12.9).

17.13 The unbounded orbits. We now turn to the orbits corresponding to positive values of h, i.e. the orbits corresponding to points in the regions 5, 6, 7, 8 in Fig. 17.10*c*. In these cases μ_1 and μ_2 are real, and λ_2 and μ_2 are negative. During the motion, λ lies outside the range (λ_1, λ_2), and μ lies within the range (μ_1, μ_2). There is no upper bound to the value of λ, and the lower limit is the greater of λ_1 and c. With one trivial exception (which occurs when $\lambda_1 = c$, and, if λ decreases originally, we have an unstable limitation motion to $\lambda = c$) λ eventually increases with t. Moreover, $\lambda \to \infty$ with t. To prove this we have only to observe that

$$t - t_0 = \int \frac{(\lambda^2 - \mu^2)\,d\lambda}{\sqrt{\{2(\lambda^2 - c^2)(h\lambda^2 + k\lambda + \alpha)\}}} > \int \frac{\sqrt{(\lambda^2 - c^2)}}{\sqrt{\{2(h\lambda^2 + k\lambda + \alpha)\}}}\,d\lambda, \tag{17.13.1}$$

and the last integral diverges.

The behaviour of μ requires careful consideration. We have

$$\int \pm \frac{d\mu}{\sqrt{S}} = \int \frac{d\lambda}{\sqrt{R}}, \tag{17.13.2}$$

and the integral on the right in (17.13.2) *converges* as $\lambda \to \infty$. We have here examples of pseudo-limitation motions (§ 17.3). If the relevant zeros of S are simple we get, after a finite number (which may be zero) of oscillations, a pseudo-limitation motion to some value lying between them; and if one of the relevant zeros of S is double, we get a pseudo-limitation motion to some value short of the double zero.

Apart from the trivial exception already mentioned (which occurs when $\lambda_1 = c$ and R has a double zero) all the orbits for $h > 0$ are unbounded. They are of less interest than the bounded orbits, and we shall be content to consider only one of the cases in detail.

Consider by way of illustration a point in the interior of the region 5 of Fig. 17.10*c*. Here $\lambda_1 > c$, the orbit lies outside the ellipse $\lambda = \lambda_1$, and λ ultimately increases indefinitely, perhaps after first falling (if $\dot{\lambda} < 0$ initially) to the value λ_1. For this case $\mu_1 > c > -c > \mu_2$, and at first sight we might expect for μ a libration between c and $-c$; but this is fallacious because, as we have seen, the μ-motion is a pseudo-limitation motion, and μ, after a finite number of oscillations between c and $-c$, tends to a limit μ_l. Thus the orbit is a spiral touching the ellipse $\lambda = \lambda_1$ externally and, after a finite number of convolutions, moving off to infinity and approximately to one of the confocal hyperbolas.

17.14 Systems that are separable in more than one way. As we have noticed (§ 17.1) separability is a property jointly of the dynamical system and of the Lagrangian coordinates chosen to describe it. It may happen, for a particular system, that we can choose the Lagrangian coordinates in more than one way to obtain a separable system.

A simple example of this phenomenon is provided by the Newtonian orbit, i.e. the problem of a particle moving in a plane, attracted to a fixed centre of attraction in the plane by a force varying as the inverse square of the distance. The system is separable if we use polar coordinates with the centre of attraction as origin (§ 16.9). But it is also separable if we use the parabolic coordinates introduced in § 17.9; the problem considered there was that of a Newtonian attraction with a uniform field superposed, but the system is clearly still separable if the uniform field is absent. There is still a third possibility. The system is separable if we use confocal coordinates; to obtain the problem of a single Newtonian centre we have only to put $m' = 0$ in § 17.10.

The solution in terms of polar coordinates has already been considered in *Example* 5.2*B*, and we shall return to the problem and discuss it more fully in § 18.12 *et seq*. The solution in terms of parabolic coordinates is not without interest. We have

$$T = \tfrac{1}{2}(u+v)\left(\frac{\dot{u}^2}{u} + \frac{\dot{v}^2}{v}\right), \quad V = -\frac{\mu}{u+v}, \tag{17.14.1}$$

and the system is of the type (17.2.13) with

$$X = P = u, \quad Y = Q = v, \quad \xi + \eta = -\mu. \tag{17.14.2}$$

Thus R and S have the forms

$$R = 2hu(u - c), \quad S = 2hv(v - k), \tag{17.14.3}$$

where $c + k = -\mu/h$. We consider the case in which the motion is not rectilinear motion on a line through O, and in which $h < 0$, say $h = -\mu/(2a)$; then c and k are positive, and $c + k = 2a$. The differential equation of the orbit is

$$\frac{du}{\sqrt{\{u(c-u)\}}} = \frac{dv}{\sqrt{\{v(k-v)\}}}. \tag{17.14.4}$$

If we define the parameters φ and ψ by the equations

$$u = \tfrac{1}{2}c(1 - \cos\varphi), \quad v = \tfrac{1}{2}k(1 - \cos\psi), \tag{17.14.5}$$

the equation (17.14.4) becomes $d\varphi = \pm d\psi$, so $\varphi \mp \psi$ is constant, say

$$\varphi \mp \psi = 2\kappa, \tag{17.14.6}$$

and κ is not zero, nor a multiple of π, because this would imply motion on a straight line through 0. Thus

$$\cos\varphi\cos\psi \pm \sin\varphi\sin\psi = \cos 2\kappa, \tag{17.14.7}$$

and substituting the values

$$\begin{cases} \tfrac{1}{2}c\cos\varphi = \tfrac{1}{2}c - u, & \tfrac{1}{2}c\sin\varphi = \sqrt{\{u(c-u)\}}, \\ \tfrac{1}{2}k\cos\psi = \tfrac{1}{2}k - v, & \tfrac{1}{2}k\sin\psi = \sqrt{\{v(k-v)\}}, \end{cases} \tag{17.14.8}$$

and rationalizing, we find

$$(ku + cv - ck\sin^2\kappa)^2 = 4ckuv\cos^2\kappa = cky^2\cos^2\kappa. \tag{17.14.9}$$

The equation of the orbit is therefore

$$ku + cv - ck\sin^2\kappa = \pm\sqrt{(ck)}y\cos\kappa, \tag{17.14.10}$$

which (since $u = \tfrac{1}{2}(r + x)$ and $v = \tfrac{1}{2}(r - x)$) is equivalent to

$$\tfrac{1}{2}(c + k)r = \tfrac{1}{2}(c - k)x \pm \sqrt{(ck)}y\cos\kappa + ck\sin^2\kappa. \tag{17.14.11}$$

Now (17.14.11) is equivalent to

$$r = ep, \tag{17.14.12}$$

where p is the length of the perpendicular from (x, y) on to the line λ,

$$\tfrac{1}{2}(c - k)x \pm \sqrt{(ck)}y\cos\kappa + ck\sin^2\kappa = 0, \tag{17.14.13}$$

p being taken as positive for points on the same side of λ as O. Further,

$$e^2 = \frac{c^2 + k^2 + 2ck\cos 2\kappa}{c^2 + k^2 + 2ck} < 1. \tag{17.14.14}$$

The orbit is an ellipse, with O as focus and λ as directrix.

Chapter XVIII

Separable systems with n degrees of freedom

18.1 Liouville's system. We found (§ 17.2) that a system with two degrees of freedom is separable if its kinetic and potential energy functions have the forms

$$(18.1.1)\qquad \begin{cases} T = \dfrac{1}{2}(X + Y)\left(\dfrac{\dot{x}^2}{P} + \dfrac{\dot{y}^2}{Q}\right) = \dfrac{1}{2(X + Y)}(Pp_x{}^2 + Qp_y{}^2), \\ V = \dfrac{\xi + \eta}{X + Y}, \end{cases}$$

where X, P, ξ are functions of x, and Y, Q, η are functions of y. The immediate generalization is a system with n degrees of freedom for which

$$(18.1.2)\qquad \begin{cases} T = \dfrac{1}{2}(X_1 + X_2 + \cdots + X_n)\left(\dfrac{\dot{q}_1{}^2}{P_1} + \dfrac{\dot{q}_2{}^2}{P_2} + \cdots + \dfrac{\dot{q}_n{}^2}{P_n}\right) \\ \quad = \dfrac{1}{2(X_1 + X_2 + \cdots + X_n)}(P_1p_1{}^2 + P_2p_2{}^2 + \cdots + P_np_n{}^2), \\ V = \dfrac{\xi_1 + \xi_2 + \cdots + \xi_n}{X_1 + X_2 + \cdots + X_n}, \end{cases}$$

where X_r, P_r, ξ_r are functions of q_r. This system is called *Liouville's system*, and it is natural to ask if this system also is separable.

It is easy to see that the answer is affirmative. The modified partial differential equation for the system (18.1.2) can be written in the form

$$(18.1.3)\qquad \sum_{r=1}^{n}\left\{\tfrac{1}{2}P_r\left(\frac{\partial K}{\partial q_r}\right)^2 + \xi_r\right\} = \alpha_1\sum_{r=1}^{n} X_r.$$

We have at once a complete integral

$$(18.1.4)\qquad K = K_1 + K_2 + \cdots + K_n,$$

where $K_r = K_r(q_r)$, if we put

$$(18.1.5)\qquad \tfrac{1}{2}P_1\left(\frac{\partial K_1}{\partial q_1}\right)^2 = \alpha_1X_1 - \xi_1 + \alpha_0,$$

$$(18.1.6)\qquad \tfrac{1}{2}P_r\left(\frac{\partial K_r}{\partial q_r}\right)^2 = \alpha_1X_r - \xi_r - \alpha_r, \qquad r = 2, 3, \ldots, n,$$

where α_0 here stands for $\alpha_2 + \alpha_3 + \cdots + \alpha_n$. The n arbitrary constants are α_1, $\alpha_2, \ldots, \alpha_n$, and of these the energy constant α_1 $(= h)$ has a special role. We thus have the complete integral

$$(18.1.7)\qquad K = \int\sqrt{\left\{\frac{2}{P_1}(\alpha_1X_1 - \xi_1 + \alpha_0)\right\}}\,dq_1 + \sum_{r=2}^{n}\int\sqrt{\left\{\frac{2}{P_r}(\alpha_1X_r - \xi_r - \alpha_r)\right\}}\,dq_r,$$

where we have used the notation mentioned at the end of § 16.9. The system is separable, and the integrals of the Lagrangian equations of motion are

$$(18.1.8)\qquad \begin{cases} t - \beta_1 = \displaystyle\int \frac{X_1\,dq_1}{\sqrt{\varphi_1(q_1)}} + \sum_{r=2}^{n} \int \frac{X_r\,dq_r}{\sqrt{\varphi_r(q_r)}}, \\ -\beta_s = \displaystyle\int \frac{dq_1}{\sqrt{\varphi_1(q_1)}} - \int \frac{dq_s}{\sqrt{\varphi_s(q_s)}}, \qquad s = 2, 3, \ldots, n, \end{cases}$$

where

$$(18.1.9)\qquad \begin{cases} \varphi_1(q_1) = 2P_1(\alpha_1 X_1 - \xi_1 + \alpha_0), \\ \varphi_r(q_r) = 2P_r(\alpha_1 X_r - \xi_r - \alpha_r), \qquad r = 2, 3, \ldots, n. \end{cases}$$

The integrals of the Hamiltonian equations of motion are found by combining (18.1.8) with the equations

$$(18.1.10)\qquad p_r = \frac{\partial K}{\partial q_r} = \frac{1}{P_r}\sqrt{\varphi_r(q_r)}.$$

The line of thought is thus closely parallel to that already followed in the case of two freedoms. The integrals of the Lagrangian equations of motion can be written compactly in the form

$$(18.1.11)\qquad \frac{dq_1}{\sqrt{\varphi_1(q_1)}} = \frac{dq_2}{\sqrt{\varphi_2(q_2)}} = \cdots = \frac{dq_n}{\sqrt{\varphi_n(q_n)}} = \frac{dt}{X_1 + X_2 + \cdots + X_n} = d\tau,$$

say, where τ is an artificial time-measure, as in § 17.3. (The equations (18.1.11) follow from (18.1.8), or even more simply by comparing (18.1.10) with

$$(18.1.12)\qquad p_r = \frac{X_1 + X_2 + \cdots + X_n}{P_r}\,\dot{q}_r.\,\Big)$$

The general character of the motion can be seen in just the same way as for the simple case of two freedoms. The radicals in the denominators in (18.1.11) are not unexpected. In the case, which occurs frequently, of a libration motion, the ambiguous signs are determined, the positive sign of $\sqrt{\varphi_r(q_r)}$ being taken when q_r is increasing, and the negative sign when q_r is decreasing. But Liouville's system is not the most general separable system, and we reserve a detailed study for the more general system which follows.

18.2 Stäckel's theorem. We now turn to the central theorem in the theory of separable systems. It is natural to ask, what is the most general separable system? The complete answer to this question is not known, but if we confine our attention to orthogonal systems (i.e. systems for which T contains only square terms, and no product terms, in $\dot{q}$'s or p's) the answer is contained in Stäckel's theorem now to be proved. Liouville's system just discussed is a separable orthogonal system, but it is not the most general separable orthogonal system.

We consider a system for which

$$(18.2.1)\qquad T = \tfrac{1}{2}\sum_{r=1}^{n} c_r p_r^2 = \tfrac{1}{2}\sum_{r=1}^{n} \frac{1}{c_r}\dot{q}_r^2.$$

We notice that $\dot{q}_r = c_r p_r$. The coefficients c_r and the potential function V are given functions of the Lagrangian coordinates $q_1, q_2, \ldots, q_n$, of class C_1 in the appropriate domain of the q-space, and $c_r \geqslant 0$.

Stäckel's theorem asserts that *the system is separable if and only if there exists a regular* $n \times n$ *matrix* (u_{rs}), *where* u_{rs} *is a function of* q_r *only, and a column matrix* $\{w_1, w_2, \ldots, w_n\}$, *where* w_r *is a function of* q_r *only, such that*

(18.2.2) $$\sum_{r=1}^{n} c_r u_{rs} = \delta_1^{\ s}, \qquad s = 1, 2, \ldots, n,$$

(18.2.3) $$\sum_{r=1}^{n} c_r w_r = V.$$

Before proving the theorem it will be helpful to consider a little more closely what is implied. The condition (18.2.2) can be written

(18.2.4) $$\mathbf{c}'\mathbf{u} = (1, 0, 0, \ldots, 0),$$

where $\mathbf{u}$ is the matrix (u_{rs}) and $\mathbf{c}$ is the column matrix $\{c_1, c_2, \ldots, c_n\}$. In the matrices $\mathbf{u}$ and $\mathbf{w}$ the rth row contains only the one coordinate q_r. If $\mathbf{v}$ is the matrix inverse to $\mathbf{u}$ the explicit formulae for c_r and V are

(18.2.5) $$c_r = v_{1r}, \quad V = \sum_{r=1}^{n} v_{1r} w_r.$$

We now proceed to the proof of the theorem. We show first that the conditions (18.2.2–3) are *necessary* for separability. Let us assume that the system is separable, i.e. that the modified partial differential equation

(18.2.6) $$\frac{1}{2}\sum_{r=1}^{n} c_r \left(\frac{\partial K}{\partial q_r}\right)^2 + V = \alpha_1$$

admits a complete integral of the required form

(18.2.7) $$K = K_1 + K_2 + \cdots + K_n,$$

where

(18.2.8) $$K_r = K_r(q_r, \alpha_1, \alpha_2, \ldots, \alpha_n).$$

We substitute this complete integral in (18.2.6), which is then satisfied identically for all values of q's and α's in the relevant domain. Differentiating partially with respect to each α in turn we have

(18.2.9) $$\begin{cases} \displaystyle\sum_{r=1}^{n} c_r \frac{\partial K}{\partial q_r} \frac{\partial^2 K}{\partial \alpha_1\, \partial q_r} = 1, \\ \displaystyle\sum_{r=1}^{n} c_r \frac{\partial K}{\partial q_r} \frac{\partial^2 K}{\partial \alpha_s\, \partial q_r} = 0, \qquad s = 2, 3, \ldots, n. \end{cases}$$

The coefficient of c_r in each of these equations is a function of q_r only, since K has the form (18.2.7), and the determinant of the coefficients is

(18.2.10) $$\Delta = \frac{\partial K}{\partial q_1}\frac{\partial K}{\partial q_2}\cdots\frac{\partial K}{\partial q_n}\left\| \frac{\partial^2 K}{\partial \alpha_r\, \partial q_s} \right\|$$

and does not vanish identically, since K is a complete integral.

We now choose a particular set of values for $\alpha_1, \alpha_2, \ldots, \alpha_n$ such that Δ does not vanish, and the equations (18.2.9) take the form

$$\text{(18.2.11)} \qquad \begin{cases} \sum_{r=1}^{n} c_r u_{r1} = 1, & \\ \sum_{r=1}^{n} c_r u_{rs} = 0, & s = 2, 3, \ldots, n, \end{cases}$$

which are of the form (18.2.2) with $||u_{rs}|| \neq 0$. Further

$$\text{(18.2.12)} \qquad V = \alpha_1 - \frac{1}{2}\sum_{r=1}^{n} c_r\left(\frac{\partial K}{\partial q_r}\right)^2 = \sum_{r=1}^{n} c_r\left\{\alpha_1 u_{r1} - \frac{1}{2}\left(\frac{\partial K_r}{\partial q_r}\right)^2\right\}$$

which is of the form $\sum_{r=1}^{n} c_r w_r$. This completes the proof that the conditions stated are necessary for separability.

We next prove that the conditions are also *sufficient*; and then, assuming that the conditions are satisfied, we go on to find the integrals of the equations of motion and to study the motion.

The modified partial differential equation is

$$\text{(18.2.13)} \qquad \frac{1}{2}\sum_{r=1}^{n} c_r\left(\frac{\partial K}{\partial q_r}\right)^2 + V = \alpha_1,$$

where $\alpha_1(= h)$ is one of the arbitrary constants in the complete integral. Now, since the conditions (18.2.2–3) are satisfied, we can write (18.2.13) in the form

(18.2.14)

$$\frac{1}{2}\sum_{r=1}^{n} c_r\left(\frac{\partial K}{\partial q_r}\right)^2 + \sum_{r=1}^{n} c_r w_r = \alpha_1\left(\sum_{r=1}^{n} c_r u_{r1}\right) + \alpha_2\left(\sum_{r=1}^{n} c_r u_{r2}\right) + \cdots + \alpha_n\left(\sum_{r=1}^{n} c_r u_{rn}\right),$$

where $\alpha_2, \alpha_3, \ldots, \alpha_n$ are arbitrary constants, and (18.2.14) can be written

$$\text{(18.2.15)} \qquad \sum_{r=1}^{n} c_r\left\{\frac{1}{2}\left(\frac{\partial K}{\partial q_r}\right)^2 - (\alpha_1 u_{r1} + \alpha_2 u_{r2} + \cdots + u_n u_{rn} - w_r)\right\} = 0.$$

It is now evident that

$$\text{(18.2.16)} \qquad K_1 + K_2 + \cdots + K_n$$

is a complete integral, where

$$\text{(18.2.17)} \qquad \left(\frac{\partial K_r}{\partial q_r}\right)^2 = 2(\alpha_1 u_{r1} + \alpha_2 u_{r2} + \cdots + \alpha_n u_{rn} - w_r).$$

We denote the second member of (18.2.17) by $f_r(q_r)$. We notice that $f_r(q_r)$ contains only the rth coordinate, that the constants $\alpha_1, \alpha_2, \ldots, \alpha_n$ appear linearly in $f_r(q_r)$, and that

$$\text{(18.2.18)} \qquad K_r = \int \sqrt{f_r(q_r)}\, dq_r,$$

or, more precisely,

$$\text{(18.2.19)} \qquad K_r = \int^{q_r} \sqrt{f_r(x)}\, dx,$$

where the lower limit of integration is chosen in the usual way, either as an absolute constant, or as a simple zero of $f_r(q_r)$.

The integrals of the equations of motion are

$$t - \beta_1 = \frac{\partial K}{\partial \alpha_1} = \sum_{r=1}^{n} \int \frac{u_{r1}\, dq_r}{\sqrt{f_r(q_r)}}, \tag{18.2.20}$$

$$-\beta_s = \frac{\partial K}{\partial \alpha_s} = \sum_{r=1}^{n} \int \frac{u_{rs}\, dq_r}{\sqrt{f_r(q_r)}}, \qquad s = 2, 3, \ldots, n, \tag{18.2.21}$$

$$p_s = \frac{\partial K}{\partial q_s} = \sqrt{f_s(q_s)}, \qquad s = 1, 2, \ldots, n. \tag{18.2.22}$$

The solution of the dynamical problem is reduced to quadratures. The equations (18.2.21) determine the path in the q-space (without reference to the time). The equations (18.2.20–21) give the solution of the Lagrange problem, the motion in the q-space. The complete equations (18.2.20–22) give the solution of the Hamilton problem, the motion in the phase space.

Some features of the solution should be noticed at this point. The constant α_1 is anomalous; it is the energy constant, and will play a special role in the sequel. The rth momentum-component p_r is a function of the rth coordinate q_r; in the familiar case of a libration motion it is a two-valued function of q_r. The rth velocity-component $\dot{q}_r$ is given by the formula

$$\dot{q}_r = c_r p_r = c_r \sqrt{f_r(q_r)}. \tag{18.2.23}$$

It is *not* a function of q_r only, and if the motion is a libration motion it is a two-valued function having the same sign as p_r.

18.3 Discussion of the integrals. From (18.2.23) we have

$$\frac{dq_r}{\sqrt{f_r(q_r)}} = c_r\, dt = d\tau_r, \qquad r = 1, 2, \ldots, n, \tag{18.3.1}$$

where τ_r is a local time-measure as in § 17.3, only here we need a different clock for each coordinate. Since $c_r \geqslant 0$ the sign of the radical is positive if q_r increases with t, negative if q_r decreases as t increases. If c_r is bounded away from zero, $c_r \geqslant A_r > 0$, and if $f_r(q_r)$ is continuous, the general character of the q_r-motion can be inferred from (18.3.1). The artificial time τ_r tends to infinity with t, and the nature of the variation of q_r depends upon the real zeros of $f_r(q_r)$. If q_r lies initially between consecutive simple real zeros a_r, b_r of $f_r(q_r)$ (so that $f_r(q_r) > 0$ for $a_r < q_r < b_r$) we have a libration motion in q_r; and if q_r approaches a double zero a_r of $f_r(q_r)$, then we have a limitation motion in which $q_r \to a_r$ as $t \to \infty$. The libration motion, when it occurs, is an oscillation, continuing indefinitely, between a_r and b_r, but it is not in general periodic in t. We see that, as in the special case of two degrees of freedom (§ 17.3), the motion in one coordinate can be discussed to some extent independently of the others; and this is the essential characteristic of the separable system.

The equations (18.3.1) can be established in another way which is not without interest. The equations (18.2.20–21) lead to

$$\sum_{r=1}^{n} \frac{u_{r1}\dot{q}_r}{\sqrt{f_r(q_r)}} = 1, \quad \sum_{r=1}^{n} \frac{u_{rs}\dot{q}_r}{\sqrt{f_r(q_r)}} = 0, \qquad s = 2, 3, \ldots, n, \tag{18.3.2}$$

and comparing these equations with (18.2.2) we recover (18.3.1).

Some divergences from the simple theory occur if c_r is not bounded away from zero. It may happen that $c_r \to 0$ as $t \to \infty$, or that c_r actually vanishes for a particular point $\mathbf{q}$, usually a point on the boundary of that region of the q-space for which $\mathbf{q}$ has a physical significance.

Suppose first that $c_r \to 0$ (in the actual motion) as $t \to \infty$. Then t_r may tend to a finite limit as $t \to \infty$ (cf. § 17.3) and in that case the q_r-motion is a pseudo-limitation motion. If q_r lies initially between consecutive simple real zeros a_r, b_r of $f_r(q_r)$, q_r does not execute the expected libration continuing indefinitely, but instead, perhaps after a finite number of oscillations, q_r tends to a limit l ($a_r \leqslant l \leqslant b_r$) as t tends to infinity. In the same way, if q_r approaches a multiple zero of $f_r(q_r)$, then q_r tends to a limit short of the multiple zero.

Again, we know that $c_r \geqslant 0$, and in general c_r (which is a function of all the q's, not of q_r only) is positive. But there may be a point $\mathbf{q}$ at which c_r actually vanishes, and then the conclusions about the q_r-motion drawn from (18.3.1) may need to be modified. As an illustration, suppose that c_r has the form $(q_r - q_{r0})\psi_r$, where $\psi_r(q_1, q_2, \ldots, q_n) \geqslant A_r > 0$. Then in general each of the elements u_{rs} in the rth row of the matrix $\mathbf{u}$ has a simple pole at q_{r0}, in virtue of (18.2.2). The function $f_r(q_r)$ is no longer continuous, but has a simple pole at q_{r0}. Now in this case (18.3.1) becomes

$$\frac{d\,q_r}{\sqrt{\{(q_r - q_{r0})^2 f_r(q_r)\}}} = \psi_r\,dt, \tag{18.3.3}$$

and the function under the radical sign has a simple zero at q_{r0}. In consequence, q_{r0} may appear as one limit of a libration motion for q_r, though q_{r0} is a pole and not a zero of $f_r(q_r)$.

An illustration of this situation appears in the problem of two fixed Newtonian centres (§ 17.10). The equation (18.3.1) for λ takes the form

$$\frac{d\lambda}{\sqrt{\left\{\dfrac{2(\alpha_1\lambda^2 + k\lambda + \alpha_2)}{\lambda^2 - c^2}\right\}}} = \frac{\lambda^2 - c^2}{\lambda^2 - \mu^2}\,dt. \tag{18.3.4}$$

Here $\lambda = c$, for example, is a simple zero of c_1 and a simple pole of $f_1(\lambda)$, and (18.3.4) is reconciled with (17.10.13) in which c is a simple zero of R.

In practice these anomalous cases are fairly conspicuous, and not likely to be overlooked.

18.4 Further comments on Stäckel's theorem. (i) Stäckel's theorem can be exhibited in the form of n first integrals of Lagrange's equations of motion for a system of the type defined by (18.2.1–3). For (18.2.23) can be written in the form

$$\frac{1}{2}\frac{\dot{q}_r^2}{c_r^2} + w_r = \alpha_1 u_{r1} + \alpha_2 u_{r2} + \cdots + \alpha_n u_{rn}, \tag{18.4.1}$$

whence

$$\sum_{r=1}^{n} v_{sr}\left(\frac{1}{2}\frac{\dot{q}_r^2}{c_r^2} + w_r\right) = \alpha_s, \qquad s = 1, 2, \ldots, n, \tag{18.4.2}$$

where $\mathbf{v}$ is the matrix inverse to $\mathbf{u}$ as in (18.2.5).

(ii) To exhibit Liouville's system (18.1.2) as a special case of Stäckel's system, we put $w_r = \xi_r/P_r$, and the matrix $\mathbf{u}$ is

$$\begin{pmatrix} X_1/P_1 & 1/P_1 & 1/P_1 & 1/P_1 \\ X_2/P_2 & -1/P_2 & 0 & 0 \\ X_3/P_3 & 0 & -1/P_3 & 0 \\ & & & \\ X_n/P_n & 0 & 0 & -1/P_n \end{pmatrix}. \tag{18.4.3}$$

(iii) If $T = \frac{1}{2}\sum_{r=1}^{n} c_r p_r^2$, as in (18.2.1), we can satisfy the conditions for Stäckel's theorem if

$$c_1 = 1, \quad c_2 = \varphi_1, \quad c_3 = \varphi_1\varphi_2, \quad c_4 = \varphi_1\varphi_2\varphi_3, \ldots, c_n = \varphi_1\varphi_2\cdots\varphi_{n-1}, \tag{18.4.4}$$

where φ_r is a function of q_r; the matrix $\mathbf{u}$ is

$$\begin{pmatrix} 1 & \varphi_1 & 0 & 0 & & 0 \\ 0 & -1 & \varphi_2 & 0 & & 0 \\ 0 & 0 & -1 & \varphi_3 & & 0 \\ & & & & & \\ 0 & 0 & 0 & 0 & & \varphi_{n-1} \\ 0 & 0 & 0 & 0 & & -1 \end{pmatrix}. \tag{18.4.5}$$

The system is separable if V has the form

$$w_1 + \varphi_1 w_2 + \varphi_1\varphi_2 w_3 + \cdots + \varphi_1\varphi_2 \cdots \varphi_{n-1} w_n. \tag{18.4.6}$$

(iv) Stäckel's theorem can be exhibited in a form in which the formulae bear a close resemblance to those occurring in Liouville's system (§ 18.1). For, since $\sum_{r=1}^{n} c_r u_{r1} = 1$, we can write

$$\left\{\begin{aligned} T &= \frac{1}{2(c_1u_{11} + c_2u_{21} + \cdots + c_nu_{n1})}(c_1p_1^2 + c_2p_2^2 + \cdots + c_np_n^2) \\ &= \frac{1}{2}(c_1u_{11} + c_2u_{21} + \cdots + c_nu_{n1})\left(\frac{\dot{q}_1^2}{c_1} + \frac{\dot{q}_2^2}{c_2} + \cdots + \frac{\dot{q}_n^2}{c_n}\right), \\ V &= \frac{c_1w_1 + c_2w_2 + \cdots + c_nw_n}{c_1u_{11} + c_2u_{21} + \cdots + c_nu_{n1}}, \end{aligned}\right. \tag{18.4.7}$$

and the affinity to (18.1.2) is evident. But these formulae have no practical advantage.

18.5 Quasi-periodic motions. We consider a system of Stäckel's type, and discuss more particularly the simplest (and commonest) case in which there is a libration motion in each coordinate. The coefficients c_r are assumed to be bounded away from zero, and the functions $f_r(q_r)$ are continuous. Each q_r lies initially between consecutive simple real zeros a_r, b_r of $f_r(q_r)$, where $a_r < b_r$, and q_r oscillates between the values a_r, b_r for all time. We take a_r as the lower limit of integration in the formula (18.2.19) for K_r. During the motion

$$\frac{dq_r}{\sqrt{f_r(q_r)}} = c_r\, dt, \tag{18.5.1}$$

and the sign of the radical is positive when q_r is increasing, and negative when q_r is decreasing. Also, as in (18.2.22),

$$p_r^2 = f_r(q_r), \tag{18.5.2}$$

and each p_r is a (two-valued) function of the corresponding q_r; the kind of relation connecting q_r and p_r is illustrated roughly in Fig. 18.5a. The motion of the representative point in the q-space takes place in the rectangular box

$$a_r \leqslant q_r \leqslant b_r, \qquad r = 1, 2, \ldots, n.$$

The motion of the representative point in the phase space takes place in a region defined by associating with the values of q_r in $a_r \leqslant q_r \leqslant b_r$ the values of p defined in (18.5.2) and shown in Fig. 18.5a. Motion of this type is called *quasi-periodic*; the origin of this nomenclature will shortly become clear.

We consider now a transformation from the Lagrangian coordinates q_r to new coordinates θ_r defined by the equations

$$\theta_s = \sum_{r=1}^{n} \int \frac{u_{rs}\,dq_r}{\sqrt{f_r(q_r)}}, \qquad s = 1, 2, \ldots, n, \tag{18.5.3}$$

or, more precisely,

$$\theta_s = \sum_{r=1}^{n} \int_{a_r}^{q_r} \frac{u_{rs}(x_r)}{\sqrt{f_r(x_r)}}\, dx_r, \qquad s = 1, 2, \ldots, n. \tag{18.5.4}$$

The Lagrangian coordinate q_r lies in the range $a_r \leqslant q_r \leqslant b_r$, and the transformation is of a special type in which each q_r is assumed to oscillate between a_r and b_r (as in

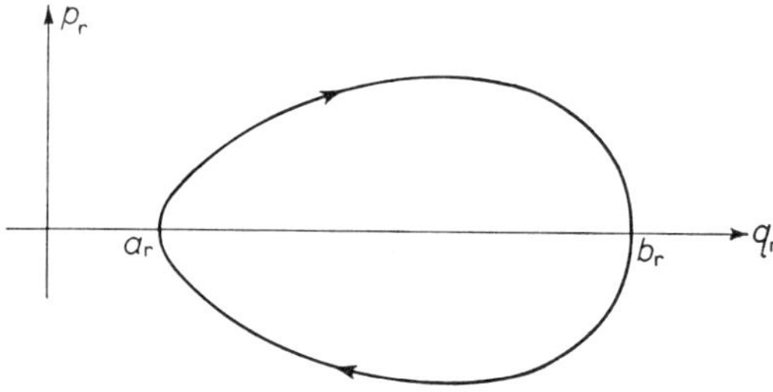

Figure 18.5*a*

the actual motion). The radical $\sqrt{f_r(x_r)}$ is to be taken positive when x_r is increasing, negative when x_r is decreasing. Thus $\boldsymbol{\theta}$ is not a uniform function of $\mathbf{q}$, but it has a discrete set of values, depending on the path by which the representative point $\mathbf{x}$ has moved from $\mathbf{a}$ to $\mathbf{q}$.

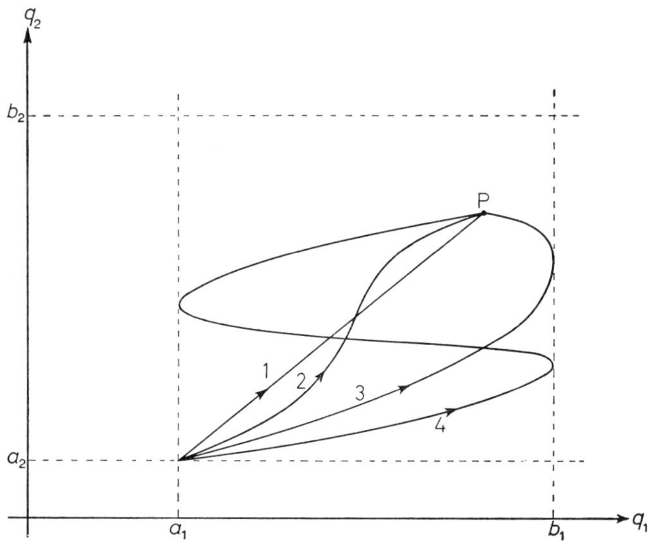

Figure 18.5*b*

As a simple illustration take $n = 2$ and consider the four paths from (a_1, a_2) to $P(q_1, q_2)$ shown in Fig. 18.5*b*. In each path x_2 increases steadily from a_2 to q_2. In 1 and 2, x_1 increases steadily from a_1 to q_1, and the value of (θ_1, θ_2) is the same for both these paths. But it is different for 3 (in which x_1 has first increased to b_1, and then decreased to a_1), and different again for 4 (in which x_1 has increased to b_1, decreased to a_1, and then increased to q_1).

Suppose now that one coordinate q_r goes through a complete cycle of its values and returns to the starting point, the other q's remaining unchanged. Then θ_s increases by

$$\omega_{rs} = \oint \frac{u_{rs}\, dq_r}{\sqrt{f_r(q_r)}}, \tag{18.5.5}$$

which we may also write as

$$\omega_{rs} = 2\int_{a_r}^{b_r} \frac{u_{rs}\, dq_r}{\sqrt{f_r(q_r)}}. \tag{18.5.6}$$

Thus if $\theta_1, \theta_2, \ldots, \theta_n$ increase respectively by $\omega_{r1}, \omega_{r2}, \ldots, \omega_{rn}$ we return to the original point in the q-box, and moreover to the same velocities. If we write

$$q_r = \varphi_r(\theta_1, \theta_2, \ldots, \theta_n), \tag{18.5.7}$$

the functions φ_r have the property

$$\varphi_r(\theta_1, \theta_2, \ldots, \theta_n) = \varphi_r(\theta_1 + \omega_{s1}, \theta_2 + \omega_{s2}, \ldots, \theta_n + \omega_{sn}), \tag{18.5.8}$$

and there are n such sets of periods. We shall assume that these sets are linearly independent, i.e. $||\omega_{rs}|| \neq 0$. Thus two points in the θ-space are equivalent to one and the same point in the q-space, and even to one and the same point in the phase space, if their relative positions are described by one of the vectors $\mathbf{\Omega}_r$ (whose components are $\omega_{r1}, \omega_{r2}, \ldots, \omega_{rn}$). These n vectors $\mathbf{\Omega}_1, \mathbf{\Omega}_2, \ldots, \mathbf{\Omega}_n$ are linearly independent. Moreover we can go further; it is clear that two points P_1, P_2 in the θ-space are equivalent to the same point in the phase space if the position of P_2 relative to P_1 is described by the vector $\sum_{r=1}^{n} m_r\mathbf{\Omega}_r$, where the m's are integers, positive, negative, or zero.

We can thus divide up the θ-space into period cells, the lattice points being the points defined by $\sum_{r=1}^{n} m_r\mathbf{\Omega}_r$ for all integral values of $m_1, m_2, \ldots, m_n$. The cells have the property that congruent points in any two cells represent the same configuration and velocity of the dynamical system. The relation between q's and θ's is not symmetrical; for example if q_r increases from q_{r0} to b_r, and then decreases to q_{r0} (the other q's remaining unchanged) we get to a different point in the θ-cell, which represents the same q-point but with different velocity. In fact each point in the q-box corresponds to 2^n points in a θ-cell, and each of these θ-points represents one of the 2^n possible velocity-systems. We notice that a θ-cell provides a more precise representation of the motion than the q-box, because each point in it represents both a definite configuration and a definite velocity of the system.

Since congruent points in different θ-cells are equivalent, it is natural to confine our attention to one standard cell, and to replace each point occupied by the mobile in the θ-space by the congruent point in the standard cell. For the standard cell we can take one vertex at the origin (corresponding to the point **a** in the q-space) and we can take the edges through this vertex to be the vectors $\mathbf{\Omega}_r$.

It will perhaps make for clarity if we consider for a moment the simple case when $n = 2$. The representative point moves in a rectangle in the (q_1, q_2)-plane (Fig. 17.3), and the corresponding representative point in the (θ_1, θ_2)-plane can be transferred throughout to the standard cell. Now in the (θ_1, θ_2)-plane the motion is very simply described, for the representative point moves with unit velocity parallel to the θ_1-axis,

$$\begin{cases} \theta_1 = t - \beta_1, \\ \theta_2 = -\beta_2, \end{cases} \tag{18.5.9}$$

and we are to replace the various segments of this line by the congruent segments in the standard cell (Fig. 18.5*c*). In general these will not overlap, but will cover the standard cell more and more thickly as more segments are transferred to it. But the segments will overlap and repeat after a time if ω_{22}/ω_{12} is rational. In this case the orbit in the standard θ-cell consists of a finite number of segments which are traversed again and again; the orbit in the q-box is a closed periodic orbit. We shall find shortly the condition for periodicity in the general case, of which this is a particular example.

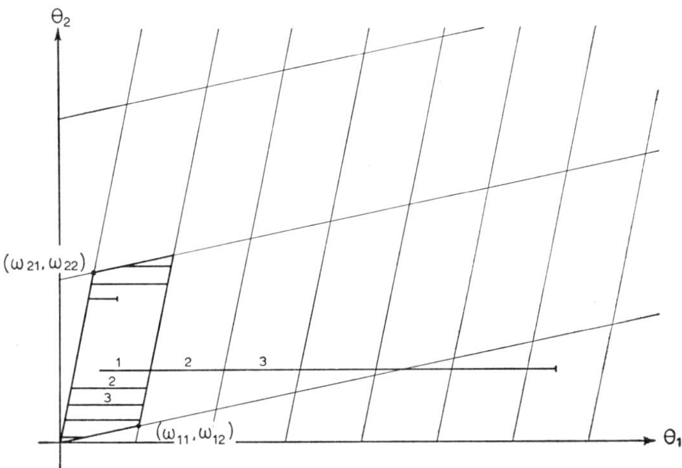

Figure 18.5*c*

18.6 Angle variables. We return to the problem of n freedoms. The coordinates θ_r introduced in § 18.5 are not themselves of primary importance, but certain linear functions of the θ's, the so-called *angle variables*, play a fundamental part in the theory; the main purpose of the θ's is as a scaffolding to facilitate the introduction of the angle variables.

Consider the non-singular linear transformation

$$\theta_s = \omega_{1s}v_1 + \omega_{2s}v_2 + \cdots + \omega_{ns}v_s = \sum_{r=1}^{n} \omega_{rs}v_r, \qquad s = 1, 2, \ldots, n. \tag{18.6.1}$$

Expressed in matrix notation this is

$$\boldsymbol{\theta} = \boldsymbol{\omega}'\mathbf{v}, \tag{18.6.2}$$

where $\boldsymbol{\theta}$ is the column matrix $\{\theta_1, \theta_2, \ldots, \theta_n\}$, $\mathbf{v}$ is the column matrix $\{v_1, v_2, \ldots, v_n\}$, and $\boldsymbol{\omega}$ is the $n \times n$ matrix (ω_{rs}).

If v_r increases by 1, the other v's remaining unchanged, $\theta_1, \theta_2, \ldots, \theta_n$ increase respectively by $\omega_{r1}, \omega_{r2}, \ldots, \omega_{rn}$, i.e. by a set of periods, and the q's and $\dot{q}$'s and p's do not change. The q's and $\dot{q}$'s and p's are periodic functions of the v's, with period 1 in each v. The v's are called *angle variables* (though the name would be more appropriate to the variables $w_r = 2\pi v_r$, with period 2π in each w). We can think of $2\pi v_r$ as an angular variable on an n-dimensional torus, and then there is a 1–1 correlation between points of the torus and the relevant region of the phase space. In general the q's can be expressed as multiple Fourier series in the v's

$$q_r = \psi_r(v_1, v_2, \ldots, v_n) = \sum c^r_{\nu_1, \nu_2, \ldots, \nu_n} e^{2\pi i(\nu_1 v_1 + \nu_2 v_2 + \cdots + \nu_n v_n)}, \tag{18.6.3}$$

where the ν's take all integral values, positive, negative and zero.

The motion in the v-space is a uniform rectilinear motion,

$$v_s = \mu_{1s}\theta_1 + \mu_{2s}\theta_2 + \cdots + \mu_{ns}\theta_n = \sum_{r=1}^{n} \mu_{rs}\theta_r, \qquad s = 1, 2, \ldots, n, \tag{18.6.4}$$

where (μ_{rs}) is the matrix inverse to (ω_{rs}). If we substitute for the θ's their values at time t, namely

$$\begin{cases} \theta_1 = t - \beta_1, \\ \theta_s = -\beta_s, \end{cases} \qquad s = 2, 3, \ldots, n, \tag{18.6.5}$$

we have

$$v_s = \mu_s t + \delta_s, \tag{18.6.6}$$

where μ_s is written for μ_{1s}, and

$$\delta_s = -\sum_{r=1}^{n} \mu_{rs}\beta_r. \tag{18.6.7}$$

The constants $\mu_1, \mu_2, \ldots, \mu_n$ are called the *frequencies* for the motion. If we think of $2\pi v_r$ as an angle, the inclination of a rotating indicator-line to a fixed line, μ_r is the number of rotations per second.

The configuration of the system at time t is given by the formulae

$$q_r = \psi_r(\mu_1 t + \delta_1, \mu_2 t + \delta_2, \ldots, \mu_n t + \delta_n), \tag{18.6.8}$$

and each of the functions ψ_r is periodic in each of its arguments, with period 1 in each. But, as we have noticed earlier, q_r is not in general a periodic function of t. The q's would be periodic functions of t, with period σ, if the numbers

$$\sigma\mu_1, \sigma\mu_2, \ldots, \sigma\mu_n$$

were all integers. Such a multiplier exists only if all the ratios $\mu_2/\mu_1, \mu_3/\mu_1, \ldots, \mu_n/\mu_1$ are rational. Only if the frequencies are connected by $(n - 1)$ independent linear relations, with integral coefficients, do we get a closed periodic orbit.

Unless this condition is fulfilled the original position in the v-space never recurs; the same is true of the phase-space. Nevertheless, although, if the condition is not fulfilled, there is no number τ for which the numbers $\tau\mu_1, \tau\mu_2, \ldots, \tau\mu_n$ are all integers, yet we can find values of τ, and indeed arbitrarily large values of τ, to make them as near to integers as we please. This is one form of Dirichlet's theorem. In virtue of the uniform continuity of the q's and p's (as functions of the v's) a similar result holds in the phase space. We can find a time τ, and indeed an arbitrarily large τ, after which the representative point in the phase space comes within a prescribed distance ϵ of its initial position. The origin of the name *quasi-periodic motion* is now clear.

18.7 The standard cube. It is now evident that we have in the v-space a periodic structure similar to that in the θ-space. Two points in the v-space correspond to the same point in the phase space if their relative displacement is a vector $\sum_{r=1}^{n} m_r \mathbf{U}_r$, where the m's are integers, and the $\mathbf{U}$'s are unit vectors parallel to the coordinate axes. Thus we can divide the space into unit cubes such that congruent points in any two cubes are equivalent, i.e. they correspond to the same point in the phase space. It is natural therefore to concentrate our attention on a standard unit cube, and to transfer the segment of the orbit in any cube to the congruent segment in the standard cube. The orbit consists of a number of parallel linear segments running across the standard cube.

Let us take the point P_0 $(\delta_1, \delta_2, \ldots, \delta_n)$, the point occupied at $t = 0$, as a corner of the standard cube. The pairs of opposite faces of the standard cube are the flat $(n - 1)$-folds defined by

$$v_r = \delta_r, \quad v_r = \delta_r + 1, \qquad r = 1, 2, \ldots, n, \tag{18.7.1}$$

the position of the representative point relative to P_0 at time t being

$$v_r - \delta_r = (\mu_r t), \qquad r = 1, 2, \ldots, n, \tag{18.7.2}$$

where in this context (x) $(= x - [x])$ denotes the fractional part of the number x. The initial position P_0 will not recur unless, as we saw, the frequencies μ_r are connected by $(n - 1)$ linear relations with integer coefficients.

In fact if there are n_0 linear relations of this type, where $0 < n_0 < (n - 1)$, the motion is of exceptional character, and is said to be *degenerate*. Suppose first, to fix the ideas, that $n_0 = 1$, i.e. there is just one relation

$$\nu_1\mu_1 + \nu_2\mu_2 + \cdots + \nu_n\mu_n = 0, \tag{18.7.3}$$

where the ν's are integers, not all zero. It is easy to see what is the physical implication of this relation, namely that the orbit (in the q-space) is confined to a manifold of fewer dimensions than the n dimensions normally appropriate to a system with n freedoms. For

$$0 = \left\{\sum_{r=1}^{n} \nu_r\mu_r\right\} t = \sum_{r=1}^{n} \nu_r[\mu_r t] + \sum_{r=1}^{n} \nu_r(\mu_r t), \tag{18.7.4}$$

so that $\sum_{r=1}^{n} \nu_r(\mu_r t)$ is an integer, positive, negative, or zero, and the representative point, in virtue of (18.7.2), lies on one of the planes

$$\sum \nu_r(v_r - \delta_r) = 0, \pm 1, \pm 2, \ldots \tag{18.7.5}$$

The segments which represent the orbit, instead of coming near to all points of the cube, are confined to a set, finite in number, of equidistant parallel planes. Fig. 18.7 illustrates the case $n = 3$, when there is just one relation of the type (18.7.3). Similarly (for a system with n degrees of freedom) if there are n_0 independent relations the segments are confined to a manifold of $(n - n_0)$ dimensions.

If there is no relation of the type (18.7.3) the orbit is dense in the standard cube. If $\lambda_1, \lambda_2, \ldots, \lambda_n$ is an arbitrary point in the unit cube, and ϵ is a prescribed positive

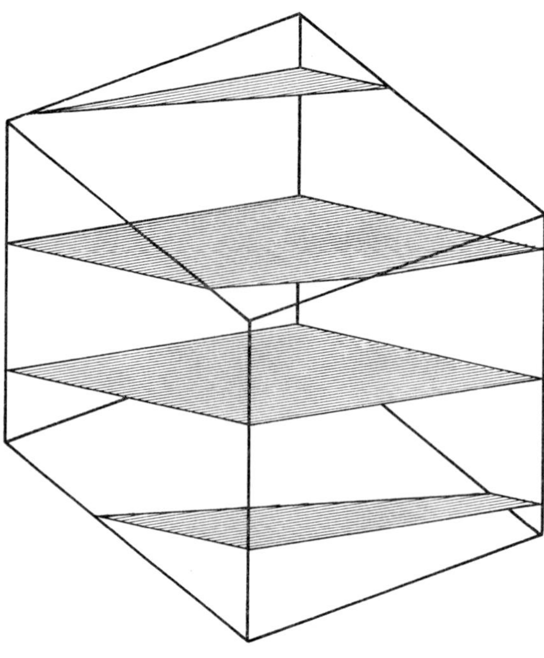

Figure 18.7

number, however small, we can find a number τ, and indeed an arbitrarily large number τ, such that

$$|(\mu_r\tau) - \lambda_r| < \epsilon, \qquad r = 1, 2, \ldots, n.$$

This is Kronecker's theorem. The representative point comes infinitely often arbitrarily near to any given point of the unit cube. A similar statement is true of the representative point in the relevant region of the phase space. We thus recover the result already proved in § 18.6. If the motion is degenerate, the path of the representative point is dense in the appropriate manifold (such as the manifold illustrated in Fig. 18.7) of the v-space.

18.8 The constants I_r. The general nature of the motion is determined by the real zeros of the functions $f_r(q_r)$, and these zeros depend in turn on the values of the constants $\alpha_1, \alpha_2, \ldots, \alpha_n$. Although $2n$ parameters α_r, β_r are required to determine the orbit, the α's alone determine the general nature of the orbit. We have noticed this already in the two-dimensional problem, where the constants h, α were of primary importance (§ 17.4). In the n-dimensional problem the epoch-constant β_1 depends only on the choice of the zero of the time-scale, and the phase constants $\beta_r (r > 1)$ do not affect the limits of the librations, and so do not influence the overall character of the motion.

Let us now consider the frequencies μ_r. They were determined from the constants ω_{rs}, in fact $\mu_r = \mu_{1r}$, where (μ_{rs}) is the matrix inverse to (ω_{rs}). Now

$$\omega_{rs} = \oint \frac{u_{rs}\, dq_r}{\sqrt{f_r(q_r)}}, \tag{18.8.1}$$

which is determined so soon as the α's, and consequently the limits of libration for q_r, are fixed. Thus the elements of the matrices (ω_{rs}) and (μ_{rs}) are known functions of the α's, and in particular the frequencies μ_r are known functions of the α's. The question arises, to what extent can we give the frequencies prearranged values by suitably adjusting the initial conditions? For example, do motions of the dynamical system occur in which the μ_r's are proportional to integers? In other words, do there exist periodic motions?

To study this question it is convenient to introduce new constants I_r in place of the α's. The constant I_r is the increment in K_r when q_r goes through a complete cycle of its values,

$$I_r = \oint \sqrt{f_r(q_r)}\, dq_r. \tag{18.8.2}$$

The I's are a new set of parameters which are functions of the original α's, and we see from (18.8.1) that

$$\omega_{rs} = \frac{\partial I_r}{\partial \alpha_s}. \tag{18.8.3}$$

If therefore we express the α's as functions of the I's we have

$$\mu_{sr} = \frac{\partial \alpha_s}{\partial I_r}, \tag{18.8.4}$$

and in particular

$$\mu_r = \frac{\partial \alpha_1}{\partial I_r}. \tag{18.8.5}$$

We are not surprised to see α_1 playing here a special role; as we have noticed already, α_1 is the energy constant, and it plays a special part throughout.

We have thus arrived at the following simple rule in the theory of quasi-periodic motions of a system of Stäckel's type: *if we express the energy constant α_1 in terms of the I's, the frequencies are given by the values of the partial derivatives $\partial\alpha_1/\partial I_r$.*

We should expect in general to be able to solve the equations (18.8.5) for the I's with prescribed values of the μ's, or at least for prescribed values of the μ's in some domain. This means that we should be able to give arbitrary values to the frequencies by suitably adjusting the initial conditions. This is true in general, but there is an important exception. It may happen that α_1 turns out to be a function of a linear combination of the I's, $\alpha_1 = F(z)$, where

$$z = k_1 I_1 + k_2 I_2 + \cdots + k_n I_n, \tag{18.8.6}$$

and the coefficients k_r are fixed absolute constants. In this case, whatever the initial conditions, we have

$$\frac{\mu_1}{k_1} = \frac{\mu_2}{k_2} = \cdots = \frac{\mu_n}{k_n}. \tag{18.8.7}$$

The ratios of pairs of frequencies are predetermined once for all, and cannot be altered by altering the initial conditions. In this situation, therefore, the degree of degeneracy of the system is predetermined and beyond our control. In the extreme case in which the ratio of every pair of k's is rational, the motion is always periodic; in this case there exist $(n - 1)$ linear relations connecting the k's of the form

$$\nu_1 k_1 + \nu_2 k_2 + \cdots + \nu_n k_n = 0, \tag{18.8.8}$$

where the coefficients ν_r are integers. In the other extreme case there exists *no* relation of the form (18.8.8), and the motion is never periodic (apart from such exceptions as normal oscillation of a vibrating system). In the intermediate case, where there are n_0 independent linear relations of the form (18.8.8), where $0 < n_0 < n - 1$, the degree of degeneracy of the system is independent of the initial conditions.

Two well-known examples of this phenomenon have already been mentioned in § 17.3:

(i) In the theory of small oscillations (Chapter IX), where

$$L = \tfrac{1}{2}(\dot{\xi}_1^2 + \dot{\xi}_2^2 + \cdots + \dot{\xi}_n^2) + \tfrac{1}{2}(m_1^2\xi_1^2 + m_2^2\xi_2^2 + \cdots + m_n^2\xi_n^2), \tag{18.8.9}$$

the motion is always periodic if the ratio of every pair of m's is rational, and never periodic (except for oscillation in a normal mode) if there is no homogeneous linear relation with integral coefficients connecting $m_1, m_2, \ldots, m_n$. In fact in this case α_1 is a function of $m_1I_1 + m_2I_2 + \cdots + m_nI_n$, and

$$\frac{\mu_1}{m_1} = \frac{\mu_2}{m_2} = \cdots = \frac{\mu_n}{m_n}. \tag{18.8.10}$$

(ii) The second example is that of a planet moving in space under a Newtonian attraction to a fixed sun. The question why the orbit (if it is bounded) should always be periodic naturally arose when the general dynamical system began to be studied. We shall find that in this problem α_1 is a function of $I_1 + I_2 + I_3$, and that therefore

$$\mu_1 = \mu_2 = \mu_3 \tag{18.8.11}$$

whatever the initial conditions.

Another special case is that in which α_1 is a function, not of a single linear form z, but of p independent linear forms $z_1, z_2, \ldots, z_p$,

$$z_r = k_{r1}I_1 + k_{r2}I_2 + \cdots + k_{rn}I_n, \qquad n = 1, 2, \ldots, p, \tag{18.8.12}$$

where $0 < p < n - 1$. In this case there are $(n - p)$ independent linear relations connecting the μ's,

$$\nu_{r1}\mu_1 + \nu_{r2}\mu_2 + \cdots + \nu_{rn}\mu_n = 0, \qquad r = 1, 2, \ldots, (n - p). \tag{18.8.13}$$

If the coefficients k_{rs} are rational, the coefficients ν_{rs} are also rational, and we can take them to be integers; the motion has this degree of degeneracy whatever the initial conditions.

18.9 Relations connecting q's and v's. The q's are functions of the v's with period 1 in each v. To find the explicit relations we can start from the two formulae (18.5.4) and (18.6.1) for θ_s, giving

$$\sum_{r=1}^{n} \int_{a_r}^{q_r} \frac{u_{rs}(x_r)}{\sqrt{f_r(x_r)}}\,dx_r = \sum_{r=1}^{n} \omega_{rs}v_r, \qquad s = 1, 2, \ldots, n. \tag{18.9.1}$$

If we solve these linear equations for the v's we have

$$v_l = \sum_{r=1}^{n} \int_{a_r}^{q_r} \frac{\left\{\sum_{s=1}^{n} \mu_{sl}u_{rs}(x_r)\right\}}{\sqrt{f_r(x_r)}}\,dx_r, \qquad l = 1, 2, \ldots, n. \tag{18.9.2}$$

We easily verify from (18.9.2) the characteristic property that if q_m goes through a cycle of its values and returns to the starting point v_l increases by $\delta_m{}^l$.

The relations between q's and v's can be expressed much more simply, however, if we introduce the constants I_r. Let us substitute for the α's in K their values in terms of the I's. We thus obtain a function of q's and I's, say $K'(q_1, q_2, \ldots, q_n; I_1, I_2, \ldots, I_n)$,

(18.9.3) $$K(q;\ \alpha) = K'(q;\ I).$$

Now

(18.9.4) $$\theta_s = \frac{\partial K}{\partial \alpha_s} = \sum_{r=1}^{n} \frac{\partial K'}{\partial I_r}\frac{\partial I_r}{\partial \alpha_s} = \sum_{r=1}^{n} \omega_{rs}\frac{\partial K'}{\partial I_r}, \qquad s = 1, 2, \ldots, n,$$

where we have quoted (18.8.3). But also

(18.9.5) $$\theta_s = \sum_{r=1}^{n} \omega_{rs} v_r, \qquad s = 1, 2 \ \ldots, n,$$

and comparing (18.9.4) and (18.9.5) we have

(18.9.6) $$v_r = \frac{\partial K'}{\partial I_r}, \qquad r = 1, 2, \ldots, n.$$

The equations (18.9.6) *present the relations between q's and v's in a strikingly simple form.*

18.10 Small oscillations. We now consider the application of the theory of quasi-periodic motions to some concrete dynamical systems.

We begin with the *completely* separable system, a vibrating system referred to normal coordinates (Chapter IX). It is true that this case is elementary, but it may serve nevertheless to give concreteness to some of the concepts introduced in the preceding sections.

The kinetic and potential energy functions are

(18.10.1) $$T = \tfrac{1}{2}\sum_{r=1}^{n} \dot{q}_r^{\,2} = \tfrac{1}{2}\sum_{r=1}^{n} p_r^{\,2}, \qquad V = \tfrac{1}{2}\sum_{r=1}^{n} m_r^{\,2} q_r^{\,2}.$$

The modified partial differential equation is

(18.10.2) $$\sum_{r=1}^{n}\left\{\left(\frac{\partial K}{\partial q_r}\right)^2 + m_r^{\,2} q_r^{\,2}\right\} = 2\alpha_1,$$

and we have at once a complete integral of the form $K_1 + K_2 + \cdots + K_n$ if we put

(18.10.3) $$\left(\frac{\partial K_r}{\partial q_r}\right)^2 = m_r^{\,2}(a_r^{\,2} - q_r^{\,2}),$$

where

(18.10.4) $$\tfrac{1}{2}\sum_{r=1}^{n} m_r^{\,2} a_r^{\,2} = \alpha_1,$$

and $(n - 1)$ further parameters $\alpha_2, \alpha_3, \ldots, \alpha_n$ are present, say by taking

(18.10.5) $$\begin{cases} \tfrac{1}{2}m_1^{\,2}a_1^{\,2} = \alpha_1 - \alpha_2 - \alpha_3 \cdots - \alpha_n, \\ \tfrac{1}{2}m_r^{\,2}a_r^{\,2} = \alpha_r, \end{cases} \qquad r = 2, 3, \ldots, n.$$

Thus

(18.10.6) $$K_r = m_r \int_0^{q_r} \sqrt{(a_r^{\,2} - x^2)}\, dx,$$

whence

(18.10.7) $$I_r = \pi m_r a_r^{\,2}.$$

Thus, from (18.10.4) and (18.10.7), we have

(18.10.8) $$\alpha_1 = \frac{1}{2\pi}(m_1 I_1 + m_2 I_2 + \cdots + m_n I_n),$$

and we have an example of the anomalous case mentioned in § 18.8. The frequencies are

(18.10.9) $$\mu_r = \frac{\partial \alpha_1}{\partial I_r} = \frac{m_r}{2\pi}, \qquad r = 1, 2, \ldots, n$$

To find the explicit relation between q's and v's we can use the method of § 18.9. We have

(18.10.10) $$K_r' = m_r \int_0^{q_r} \sqrt{\left(\frac{I_r}{\pi m_r} - x^2\right)} dx,$$

and therefore

(18.10.11) $$v_r = \frac{\partial K'}{\partial I_r} = \frac{\partial K_r'}{\partial I_r} = \frac{1}{2\pi} \int_0^{q_r} \frac{dx}{\sqrt{\left(\frac{I_r}{\pi m_r} - x^2\right)}} = \frac{1}{2\pi} \int_0^{q_r} \frac{dx}{\sqrt{(a_r^2 - x^2)}} = \frac{\theta_r}{2\pi},$$

where $q_r = a_r \sin \theta_r$. The explicit formula for q_r in terms of the angle variables is

(18.10.12) $$q_r = \sqrt{\left(\frac{I_r}{\pi m_r}\right)} \sin 2\pi v_r.$$

In this simple case each q_r is a function of the corresponding v_r, but this of course is not true in general.

From (18.10.5) and (18.10.7) we easily find the expression for I's in terms of α's

(18.10.13) $$\begin{cases} I_1 = \dfrac{2\pi}{m_1}(\alpha_1 - \alpha_2 - \alpha_3 \cdots - \alpha_n), \\ I_r = \dfrac{2\pi}{m_r}\alpha_r, \qquad r = 2, 3, \ldots, n, \end{cases}$$

and for α's in terms of I's

(18.10.14) $$\begin{cases} \alpha_1 = \dfrac{1}{2\pi}(m_1 I_1 + m_2 I_2 + \cdots + m_n I_n), \\ \alpha_r = \dfrac{1}{2\pi} m_r I_r, \qquad r = 2, 3, \ldots, n. \end{cases}$$

The matrices $\boldsymbol{\omega}$ and $\boldsymbol{\mu}$ are easily constructed, either from the definition of ω_{rs}, or from (18.8.3–4),

(18.10.15) $$\boldsymbol{\omega} = \begin{bmatrix} \dfrac{2\pi}{m_1} & -\dfrac{2\pi}{m_1} & -\dfrac{2\pi}{m_1} & & -\dfrac{2\pi}{m_1} \\ 0 & \dfrac{2\pi}{m_2} & 0 & & 0 \\ 0 & 0 & \dfrac{2\pi}{m_3} & & 0 \\ & & & & \\ 0 & 0 & 0 & & \dfrac{2\pi}{m_n} \end{bmatrix},$$

(18.10.16) $$\boldsymbol{\mu} = \begin{bmatrix} \dfrac{m_1}{2\pi} & \dfrac{m_2}{2\pi} & \dfrac{m_3}{2\pi} & & \dfrac{m_n}{2\pi} \\ 0 & \dfrac{m_2}{2\pi} & 0 & & 0 \\ 0 & 0 & \dfrac{m_3}{2\pi} & & 0 \\ & & & & \\ 0 & 0 & 0 & & \dfrac{m_n}{2\pi} \end{bmatrix}.$$

The values of the v's at time t are

(18.10.17)
$$\begin{cases} v_1 = \dfrac{m_1}{2\pi}(t - \beta_1), \\ v_s = \dfrac{m_s}{2\pi}(t - \beta_1 - \beta_s), \qquad s = 2, 3, \ldots, n, \end{cases}$$

and of the q's

(18.10.18)
$$q_1 = \sqrt{\left(\frac{I_1}{\pi m_1}\right)} \sin m_1(t - \beta_1),$$
$$q_s = \sqrt{\left(\frac{I_s}{\pi m_s}\right)} \sin m_s(t - \beta_1 - \beta_s), \qquad s = 2, 3, \ldots, n.$$

18.11 The spherical pendulum. Let us reconsider the motion of a spherical pendulum (§ 5.3) in the light of the theory of quasi-periodic motions. We are here concerned with the case in which there is a libration in each coordinate. An anomaly occurs in this problem, and in similar problems, if we use the azimuthal angle φ as one of the coordinates. For φ does not oscillate between two limiting values, but continually increases. However, we readily bring the problem into the scope of the general theory if we think in terms of the coordinate $s(= \sin \varphi)$ which has a libration between the limits $+1$ and -1. In practice we need not discard φ completely, but we must bear in mind the slight modification of the theory that is required.

We have, as in § 5.3,

(18.11.1)
$$T = \tfrac{1}{2}ma^2(\dot{\theta}^2 + \sin^2 \theta\dot{\varphi}^2), \quad V = mga \cos \theta,$$

where θ is measured from the upward vertical. If we write z for $\cos \theta$ as before, and introduce a new dimensionless time-variable $\tau(= t\sqrt{(g/2a)})$, we can write (omitting a positive multiplier)

(18.11.2)
$$T = \frac{1}{4}(1 - z^2)\left\{\varphi'^2 + \frac{z'^2}{(1 - z^2)^2}\right\}, \quad V = z,$$

where the accent denotes differentiation with respect to τ. The system thus has the standard form (17.2.13) for a separable system with two degrees of freedom, and if we write φ, z for the coordinates x, y of the general theory, we have

(18.11.3) $X = 0, \quad P = 2, \quad \xi = 0; \quad Y = 1 - z^2, \quad Q = 2(1 - z^2)^2, \quad \eta = z(1 - z^2).$

Thus

(18.11.4)
$$R = 4\alpha, \quad S = 4(1 - z^2)^2\{(h - z)(1 - z^2) - \alpha\} = 4(1 - z^2)^2 f(z),$$

and

(18.11.5)
$$K = \sqrt{\alpha}\varphi + \int \frac{\sqrt{f}}{1 - z^2}\, dz.$$

The integrals of the Lagrangian equations of motion are

(18.11.6)
$$\begin{cases} \tau - \tau_0 = 0 + \displaystyle\int \frac{dz}{2\sqrt{f}}, \\ -\beta = \dfrac{1}{2\sqrt{\alpha}}\varphi - \displaystyle\int \frac{dz}{2(1 - z^2)\sqrt{f}}. \end{cases}$$

We are dealing with a libration motion, and the sign of the radical $\sqrt{f(z)}$ is to be interpreted in the usual way, positive for z increasing, negative for z decreasing. The coordinate φ continually increases, and, as we have noticed, to bring the problem into line with the general theory we should strictly use say $s(=\sin\varphi)$ as a coordinate rather than φ. It will make for clarity if we introduce for a moment a special notation for the integrals containing $\sqrt{f(z)}$, say

$$A = \int \frac{dz}{\sqrt{f}}, \quad B = \int \frac{dz}{(1-z^2)\sqrt{f}},$$

or, expressed more precisely,

$$A(z) = \int_{z_3}^{z} \frac{dx}{\sqrt{f(x)}}, \quad B(z) = \int_{z_3}^{z} \frac{dx}{(1-x^2)\sqrt{f(x)}}. \tag{18.11.7}$$

These functions of z continually increase as z oscillates between z_3 and z_2. They are many-valued functions, in accordance with the conventions introduced in § 18.5; the value of A (or of B) depends not only on the value of z, but on the number of oscillations already executed, and on whether z is increasing or decreasing. We write also

$$A_0 = \oint \frac{dz}{\sqrt{f}} = 2\int_{z_3}^{z_2} \frac{dz}{\sqrt{f(z)}}, \quad B_0 = \oint \frac{dz}{(1-z^2)\sqrt{f}} = 2\int_{z_3}^{z_2} \frac{dz}{(1-z^2)\sqrt{f(z)}}. \tag{18.11.8}$$

We can now calculate the elements of the matrix (ω_{rs}),

$$\begin{cases} \omega_{11} = 0, & \omega_{21} = \tfrac{1}{2}A_0, \\ \omega_{12} = \dfrac{\pi}{\sqrt{\alpha}}, & \omega_{22} = -\tfrac{1}{2}B_0. \end{cases} \tag{18.11.9}$$

Hence

$$\mu_1 = \frac{\sqrt{\alpha}}{\pi}\frac{B_0}{A_0}, \quad \mu_2 = \frac{2}{A_0}. \tag{18.11.10}$$

The condition for a periodic motion is that μ_1/μ_2 should be rational, and this agrees with (5.3.13). The I's, the increments in the partial action components K_1, K_2, are given by

$$I_1 = 2\pi\sqrt{\alpha}, \quad I_2 = \oint \frac{\sqrt{f}}{(1-z^2)}\,dz. \tag{18.11.11}$$

It is interesting to verify by deliberate calculation the formulae $\mu_r = \partial h/\partial I_r$. The relation defining h implicitly as a function of I_1 and I_2 is

$$I_2 = \oint \frac{1}{(1-z^2)}\sqrt{\left\{(h-z)(1-z^2) - \frac{I_1^2}{4\pi^2}\right\}}\,dz. \tag{18.11.12}$$

Differentiating partially with respect to I_1 and with respect to I_2 we have

$$\begin{cases} 0 = \oint \dfrac{1}{2(1-z^2)\sqrt{f}}\left\{(1-z^2)\mu_1 - \dfrac{I_1}{2\pi^2}\right\}dz = \tfrac{1}{2}\mu_1 A_0 - \dfrac{I_1}{4\pi^2}B_0, \\ 1 = \oint \dfrac{\mu_2}{2\sqrt{f}}\,dz = \tfrac{1}{2}\mu_2 A_0, \end{cases} \tag{18.11.13}$$

and these lead again to (18.11.10).

Let us now find the explicit formulae for the angle variables. The equations (18.6.1) are

$$\begin{cases} 0 + \tfrac{1}{2}A = 0 + \tfrac{1}{2}A_0 v_2, \\ \dfrac{1}{2\sqrt{\alpha}}\varphi - \tfrac{1}{2}B = \dfrac{\pi}{\sqrt{\alpha}}v_1 - \tfrac{1}{2}B_0 v_2, \end{cases} \tag{18.11.14}$$

giving

$$v_1 = \frac{1}{2\pi}\varphi + \frac{B_0\sqrt{\alpha}}{2\pi}\left(\frac{A}{A_0} - \frac{B}{B_0}\right), \quad v_2 = \frac{A}{A_0}. \tag{18.11.15}$$

These formulae possess the expected property, that v_r increases by 1 when q_r goes through a cycle of its values, the other q's remaining unchanged; but we must remember that in this context to say that φ goes through a cycle of its values merely means that φ increases by 2π.

We can also find the relations between v's and q's by the method of § 18.9. Thus

(18.11.16) $$K' = \frac{1}{2\pi} I_1\varphi + \int_{z_3}^{z} \frac{1}{(1-z^2)} \sqrt{F}\, dz,$$

where

(18.11.17) $$F = (h' - z)(1 - z^2) - (I_1/2\pi)^2,$$

and h' denotes h expressed as a function of I_1 and I_2 by means of (18.11.12). We easily verify that the equations $v_r = \partial K'/\partial I_r$ lead again to (18.11.15).

Finally, if we put

(18.11.18) $$z - \frac{h}{3} = \wp(\tau + \omega_3),$$

as in (5.2.40), taking $z = z_3$ when $t = \tau = 0$, we have

(18.11.19) $$A = \int \frac{dz}{\sqrt{f}} = 2\tau, \quad A_0 = 4\omega_1.$$

Thus, using (18.11.15), we have $v_2 = A/A_0 = \tau/(2\omega_1)$, and we therefore verify directly the relation $v_2 = \mu_2\tau$, since $\mu_2 = 1/(2\omega_1)$.

18.12 The problem of two bodies. If two particles, a sun S of mass M and a planet P of mass m_1, move in space under their gravitational attraction $\gamma M m_1/r^2$, the motion of the planet relative to the sun is the same as if the sun were fixed and the acceleration of the planet were $\gamma(M + m_1)/r^2$ in the line PS. The relative orbit is a conic with the sun in one focus. An elementary discussion of this problem has already appeared in § 5.4. Our purpose in this and the following sections is to reconsider the problem in the light of the theory of quasi-periodic motions. We shall find that the various concepts appearing in the theory are aptly illustrated in this problem when we confine our attention to elliptic orbits.

For the motion of P relative to S we have

(18.12.1) $$H = \frac{1}{2}\left(p_r^{\,2} + \frac{1}{r^2} p_\theta^{\,2} + \frac{1}{r^2\cos^2\theta} p_\varphi^{\,2}\right) - \frac{\mu}{r},$$

where $\mu = \gamma(M + m_1)$, and the coordinates are spherical polar coordinates, except that θ is measured from the equator (following the usage of astronomers) instead of from the pole. We take $r, \theta, \varphi = q_1, q_2, q_3$, and we can find the complete integral K, either by direct solution of the modified partial differential equation, or as an application of Stäckel's theorem. Taking the first of these courses we have the equation for K,

(18.12.2) $$\frac{1}{2}\left\{\left(\frac{\partial K}{\partial r}\right)^2 + \frac{1}{r^2}\left(\frac{\partial K}{\partial \theta}\right)^2 + \frac{1}{r^2\cos^2\theta}\left(\frac{\partial K}{\partial \varphi}\right)^2\right\} - \frac{\mu}{r} = \alpha_1.$$

We seek a solution of the form

(18.12.3) $$K = \alpha_3\varphi + R + \Theta,$$

where $R = R(r)$ and $\Theta = \Theta(\theta)$. Substituting this formula in (18.12.2) we find

(18.12.4) $$r^2\left(R'^2 - \frac{2\mu}{r} - 2\alpha_1\right) + \left(\Theta'^2 + \frac{\alpha_3^{\,2}}{\cos^2\theta}\right) = 0.$$

The first member of this equation is the sum of a function of r and a function of θ, so each must be constant. The function of θ is clearly positive, so we write

$$\Theta'^2 + \frac{\alpha_3{}^2}{\cos^2\theta} = \alpha_2{}^2, \quad r^2\left(R'^2 - \frac{2\mu}{r} - 2\alpha_1\right) = -\alpha_2{}^2, \tag{18.12.5}$$

and therefore

$$R'^2 = 2\alpha_1 + \frac{2\mu}{r} - \frac{\alpha_2{}^2}{r^2}, \quad \Theta'^2 = \alpha_2{}^2 - \frac{\alpha_3{}^2}{\cos^2\theta}. \tag{18.12.6}$$

We can now find at once the required complete integral. We may assume, without any serious loss of generality, that α_2 and α_3 are positive, and the formula for Θ'^2 shows that $\alpha_2 > \alpha_3$. The case in which we are interested is that in which $\alpha_1 < 0$; the quadratic form $2\alpha_1 r^2 + 2\mu r - \alpha_2{}^2$ has two real positive zeros r_1, r_2 $(0 < r_1 < r_2)$, and the r-motion is a libration between the limits r_1 and r_2. In what follows

$$\alpha_2 > \alpha_3 > 0 > \alpha_1. \tag{18.12.7}$$

Supplying now appropriate lower limits in the integrals in the usual way we have

$$K = \int_{r_1}^{r} \sqrt{\left(2\alpha_1 + \frac{2\mu}{r} - \frac{\alpha_2{}^2}{r^2}\right)}\,dr + \int_0^\theta \sqrt{\left(\alpha_2{}^2 - \frac{\alpha_3{}^2}{\cos^2\theta}\right)}\,d\theta + \alpha_3\varphi. \tag{18.12.8}$$

The integrals of the Lagrangian equations of motion are

$$t - \beta_1 = \int_{r_1}^{r} \frac{dr}{\sqrt{\left(2\alpha_1 + \frac{2\mu}{r} - \frac{\alpha_2{}^2}{r^2}\right)}}, \tag{18.12.9}$$

$$-\beta_2 = -\int_{r_1}^{r} \frac{\alpha_2\,dr/r^2}{\sqrt{\left(2\alpha_1 + \frac{2\mu}{r} - \frac{\alpha_2{}^2}{r^2}\right)}} + \int_0^\theta \frac{\alpha_2\,d\theta}{\sqrt{\left(\alpha_2{}^2 - \frac{\alpha_3{}^2}{\cos^2\theta}\right)}}, \tag{18.12.10}$$

$$-\beta_3 = -\int_0^\theta \frac{\alpha_3\,d\theta/\cos^2\theta}{\sqrt{\left(\alpha_2{}^2 - \frac{\alpha_3{}^2}{\cos^2\theta}\right)}} + \varphi. \tag{18.12.11}$$

These equations form the basis of the subsequent theory. The coordinates r and θ have proper libration motions, but φ continually increases; we have met this phenomenon before (§18.11) and again we can bring the formulae into the same form as that appearing in the general theory by using say s $(= \sin\varphi)$ instead of φ as the coordinate. If we adopt this device the last term in the second member of (18.12.11) is

$$\int \frac{ds}{\sqrt{(1 - s^2)}},$$

exhibiting the libration in s between the values $+1$ and -1.

It may be of interest to pause for a moment and ask how the solution we have found differs from that given by a direct application of Stäckel's theorem. One essential difference is evident at once; in the solution by Stäckel's theorem the α's appear linearly under the radicals. We have

$$\mathbf{u} = \begin{pmatrix} 1 & -1/r^2 & 0 \\ 0 & 1 & -1/\cos^2\theta \\ 0 & 0 & 1 \end{pmatrix}, \quad \mathbf{w} = \begin{pmatrix} -\mu/r \\ 0 \\ 0 \end{pmatrix}, \tag{18.12.12}$$

and

$$K = \int_{r_1}^{r} \sqrt{\left\{2\left(\alpha_1' + \frac{\mu}{r} - \frac{\alpha_2'}{r^2}\right)\right\}}\, dr + \int_0^\theta \sqrt{\left\{2\left(\alpha_2' - \frac{\alpha_3'}{\cos^2\theta}\right)\right\}}\, d\theta + \sqrt{(2\alpha_3')}\varphi, \tag{18.12.13}$$

where we have used accents for the parameters in this solution to avoid confusion with the former. Actually

$$\begin{cases} \alpha_1' = \alpha_1, & \alpha_2' = \tfrac{1}{2}\alpha_2^2, & \alpha_3' = \tfrac{1}{2}\alpha_3^2, \\ \beta_1' = \beta_1, & \beta_2' = \beta_2/\alpha_2, & \beta_3' = \beta_3/\alpha_3. \end{cases} \tag{18.12.14}$$

We notice that the transformation from (α, β) to (α', β') is a homogeneous contact transformation (§ 15.8),

$$\sum_{r=1}^{3} \beta_r' d\alpha_r' = \sum_{r=1}^{3} \beta_r d\alpha_r, \tag{18.12.15}$$

a fact whose significance will become clear later.

18.13 Interpretation of the α's and β's. We can write (18.12.11) in the form

$$\varphi + \beta_3 = \int_0^\theta \frac{\sec^2\theta\, d\theta}{\sqrt{\left(\dfrac{\alpha_2^2}{\alpha_3^2} - \sec^2\theta\right)}} = \int_0^\theta \frac{d(\tan\theta)}{\sqrt{\left\{\left(\dfrac{\alpha_2^2}{\alpha_3^2} - 1\right) - \tan^2\theta\right\}}}, \tag{18.13.1}$$

whence

$$\tan\theta = \sqrt{\left(\frac{\alpha_2^2}{\alpha_3^2} - 1\right)} \sin(\varphi + \beta_3). \tag{18.13.2}$$

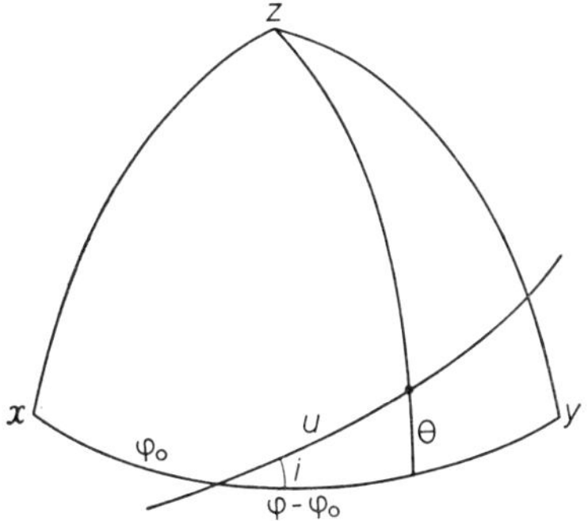

Figure 18.13

This shows that the orbit is plane, since it is a linear relation connecting the direction cosines $(\cos\theta\cos\varphi, \cos\theta\sin\varphi, \sin\theta)$. The fact that the orbit is plane is of course evident by elementary considerations. If φ_0 is the longitude of the ascending node and i the inclination of the orbit (i.e. i is the inclination of the plane of the orbit to the equatorial plane $z = 0$) we have, from the theory of the right-angled spherical triangle (Fig. 18.13),

$$\tan\theta = \tan i \sin(\varphi - \varphi_0). \tag{18.13.3}$$

Thus, comparing (18.13.2) and (18.13.3),

$$\beta_3 = -\varphi_0, \quad \alpha_3/\alpha_2 = \cos i. \tag{18.13.4}$$

We now turn to (18.12.10), and we find that each of the integrals on the right has a very simple meaning. Thus

(18.13.5) $$\int_{r_1}^{r} \frac{\alpha_2\, dr/r^2}{\sqrt{\left(2\alpha_1 + \dfrac{2\mu}{r} - \dfrac{\alpha_2{}^2}{r^2}\right)}} = \int_{r_1}^{r} \frac{dr/r^2}{\sqrt{\left(\dfrac{1}{r_1} - \dfrac{1}{r}\right)\left(\dfrac{1}{r} - \dfrac{1}{r_2}\right)}} = \psi,$$

where

(18.13.6) $$\frac{1}{r} = \frac{1}{2}\left(\frac{1}{r_1} + \frac{1}{r_2}\right) + \frac{1}{2}\left(\frac{1}{r_1} - \frac{1}{r_2}\right) \cos \psi.$$

Again, if in the integral

(18.13.7) $$\int_{\delta}^{\theta} \frac{\alpha_2\, d\theta}{\sqrt{(\alpha_2{}^2 - \alpha_3{}^2 \sec^2 \theta)}}$$

we write

(18.13.8) $$\sin \theta = \sin i \sin u,$$

so that u is the angular displacement from the ascending node measured in the plane of the orbit, we have

(18.13.9)
$$\int_{0}^{\theta} \frac{\alpha_2\, d\theta}{\sqrt{(\alpha_2{}^2 - \alpha_3{}^2 \sec^2 \theta)}} = \int_{0}^{\theta} \frac{\cos \theta\, d\theta}{\sqrt{(\cos^2 \theta - \cos^2 i)}} = \int_{0}^{u} \frac{\sin i \cos u\, du}{\sqrt{(\sin^2 i - \sin^2 \theta)}} = u.$$

Thus (18.12.10) takes the simple form

(18.13.10) $$\psi = u + \beta_2,$$

and since $\psi = 0$ when $r = r_1$,

(18.13.11) $$\beta_2 = -u_0,$$

where u_0 is the value of u at perihelion. From (18.13.6) and (18.13.10) we see that the equation of the orbit in its plane is

(18.13.12) $$\frac{1}{r} = \frac{1}{2}\left(\frac{1}{r_1} + \frac{1}{r_2}\right) + \frac{1}{2}\left(\frac{1}{r_1} - \frac{1}{r_2}\right) \cos (u - u_0),$$

which is the equation of an ellipse. Introducing the usual notation a,e for the semi-axis major and the eccentricity of the ellipse, we have

(18.13.13) $$r_1 = a(1 - e), \quad r_2 = a(1 + e),$$

and since r_1, r_2 are the zeros of $2\alpha_1 r^2 + 2\mu r - \alpha_2{}^2$ we see that

(18.13.14) $$-\frac{\mu}{\alpha_1} = r_1 + r_2 = 2a, \quad -\frac{\alpha_2{}^2}{2\alpha_1} = r_1 r_2 = a^2(1 - e^2),$$

whence

(18.13.15) $$\alpha_1 = -\mu/(2a), \quad \alpha_2 = \sqrt{(\mu p)},$$

where $p = a(1 - e^2)$ is the semi-latus rectum of the ellipse.

We have now interpreted all the constants α, β except β_1, and we see from (18.12.9) that $\beta_1 = t_0$, the value of t when the planet is at perihelion. So finally we have the table:

(18.13.16) $$\begin{cases} \alpha_1 = -\mu/(2a), & \beta_1 = t_0, \\ \alpha_2 = \sqrt{(\mu p)}, & \beta_2 = -u_0, \\ \alpha_3 = \sqrt{(\mu p)} \cos i, & \beta_3 = -\varphi_0. \end{cases}$$

The α's depend only upon a, e and i. We speak of the six parameters $a, e, i, t_0, u_0, \varphi_0$ as the *elliptic elements*.

18.14 Expression of r as a function of t. The equation (18.12.9) contains only t and r, and we can use the technique developed for one freedom (in § 1.3) to express r as a function of t; historically, the present problem is the one for which this technique was originally devised.

We can write (18.12.9) in the form

(18.14.1)
$$t - t_0 = \int_{r_1}^{r} \frac{r\,dr}{\sqrt{(-2\alpha_1)}\,\sqrt{\{(r_2 - r)(r - r_1)\}}} = \sqrt{\left(\frac{a}{\mu}\right)} \int_{r_1}^{r} \frac{r\,dr}{\sqrt{\{(r_2 - r)(r - r_1)\}}}.$$

We write

(18.14.2) $$r = r_1 \cos^2 \tfrac{1}{2}w + r_2 \sin^2 \tfrac{1}{2}w = a(1 - e\cos w),$$

so that w can be interpreted as the eccentric angle in the ellipse ($w = 0$ at perihelion); in the technical language of astronomy, w is the *eccentric anomaly*. Then (18.14.1) becomes

(18.14.3) $$t - t_0 = \sqrt{\left(\frac{a}{\mu}\right)} \int_0^w r\,dw = \sqrt{\left(\frac{a^3}{\mu}\right)} (w - e \sin w),$$

and the relation between position on the ellipse and the time is given by *Kepler's equation*

(18.14.4) $$w - e \sin w = n(t - t_0),$$

where $n = \sqrt{(\mu/a^3)}$. The period of the elliptic motion is $2\pi/n$, and n, the *mean motion*, is the mean value (with respect to time) of the angular velocity of the radius vector to the planet; a line rotating with uniform angular velocity n would complete one rotation in the period of the planetary motion. Kepler's equation has been noticed earlier, in (5.2.65) and in (5.5.6).

To find the explicit relation connecting t and r we express r as a Fourier series

(18.14.5) $$\frac{r}{a} = \tfrac{1}{2}b_0 + \sum_{s=1}^{\infty} b_s \cos sl,$$

where l stands for $n(t - t_0)$, and

(18.14.6)
$$\begin{aligned} b_s &= \frac{2}{\pi}\int_0^{\pi} \frac{r}{a} \cos sl\,dl \\ &= \frac{2}{\pi}\left[\frac{r}{as}\sin sl\right]_0^{\pi} - \frac{2}{\pi}\int_{a(1-e)}^{a(1+e)} \frac{1}{as} \sin sl\,dr \\ &= -\frac{2}{\pi a s}\int_0^{\pi} \sin sl\,(ae \sin w)\,dw \\ &= \frac{e}{\pi s}\int_0^{\pi} \{\cos(sl + w) - \cos(sl - w)\}\,dw, \end{aligned}$$

and, since $l = w - e \sin w$, by (18.14.4), the coefficients b_s are determined. Explicitly

(18.14.7)
$$\begin{aligned} b_s &= \frac{e}{\pi s}\int_0^{\pi} \{\cos[(s+1)w - se\sin w] - \cos[(s-1)w - se\sin w]\}\,dw \\ &= \frac{e}{s}\{J_{s+1}(se) - J_{s-1}(se)\}, \end{aligned}$$

where $J_n(x)$ is the Bessel coefficient

$$(18.14.8)\qquad J_n(x) = \frac{1}{\pi}\int_0^\pi \cos(n\theta - x\sin\theta)\,d\theta$$
$$= \frac{(x/n)^n}{n!}\left\{1 - \frac{(x/2)^2}{1\,.\,(n+1)} + \frac{(x/2)^4}{1\,.\,2\,.\,(n+1)(n+2)} - \cdots\right\}.$$

This completes the task of expressing r as a function of t.

For some elementary purposes it suffices to use the relations (18.14.2) and (18.14.4) —expressing r in terms of t through the intermediary variable w—instead of the explicit relation. Similarly we can express u in terms of w,

$$(18.14.9)\qquad \tan\frac{u - u_0}{2} = \sqrt{\left(\frac{1+e}{1-e}\right)}\tan\tfrac{1}{2}w,$$

and hence indirectly in terms of t.

18.15 The angle variables. The elements of the matrix (ω_{rs}) can all be written down from (18.12.9–11). A cycle of values for r is from r_1 to r_2 and back: a cycle for θ is from $-i$ to $+i$ and back: and a cycle for φ simply means that φ increases by 2π. Hence, referring to (18.12.9–11), we have

$$(18.15.1)\qquad \begin{cases} \omega_{11} = 2\pi/n, & \omega_{21} = 0, & \omega_{31} = 0,\\ \omega_{12} = -2\pi, & \omega_{22} = 2\pi, & \omega_{32} = 0,\\ \omega_{13} = 0, & \omega_{23} = -2\pi, & \omega_{33} = 2\pi. \end{cases}$$

Introducing the angle variables (§ 18.6) we have

$$(18.15.2)\qquad \begin{cases} n\theta_1 = l = 2\pi v_1,\\ \theta_2 = u_0 = -2\pi v_1 + 2\pi v_2,\\ \theta_3 = \varphi_0 = \qquad\quad - 2\pi v_2 + 2\pi v_3, \end{cases}$$

whence

$$(18.15.3)\qquad \begin{cases} 2\pi v_1 = l,\\ 2\pi v_2 = l + u_0,\\ 2\pi v_3 = l + u_0 + \varphi_0. \end{cases}$$

The frequencies μ_1, μ_2, μ_3 are all equal, each has the value $n/2\pi$. The coordinates r, θ, φ are functions of the v's with periods 1 in each, so they are all functions of t with period $2\pi/n$, a result which was of course already evident. A given function of r, θ, φ can be expressed as a function of l, u_0, φ_0 with periods 2π in each.

18.16 The constants I_r. We can determine the I's from (18.12.8) as functions of the α's, and hence also as functions of the elliptic elements a, e, i.

First, to find I_1, we have

$$(18.16.1)\qquad I_1 = 2\int_{r_1}^{r_2} \sqrt{(-2\alpha_1)}\,\sqrt{\{(r_2 - r)(r - r_1)\}}\,\frac{dr}{r}.$$

We can effect the integration in various ways. If we use the eccentric anomaly we have

$$(18.16.2)\qquad r = a(1 - e\cos w),\quad r - r_1 = ae(1 - \cos w),\quad r_2 - r = ae(1 + \cos w),$$

and the integral is

$$(18.16.3)\qquad I_1 = \sqrt{(-2\alpha_1)}\int_0^{2\pi} \frac{(ae\sin w)^2}{a(1 - e\cos w)}\,dw = 2\pi\{\sqrt{(\mu a)} - \sqrt{(\mu p)}\}.$$

In terms of the α's this becomes

(18.16.4) $$I_1 = 2\pi\left(\frac{\mu}{\sqrt{(-2\alpha_1)}} - \alpha_2\right).$$

Another method of integration may be of interest as an illustration of technique, though it is in fact not particularly advantageous for the present problem. We use the method of contour integration, taking r now as a complex variable. To obtain an integrand that is one-valued we make a cut in the plane from r_1 to r_2. We take the radical as positive immediately below the cut. We may interpret the formula (18.16.1) for I_1 as an integral round a simple closed contour C enclosing the cut (Fig. 18.16),

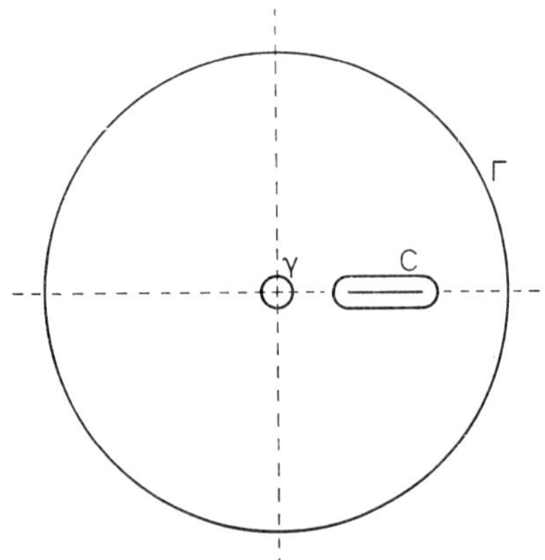

Figure 18.16

(18.16.5) $$I_1 = \sqrt{(-2\alpha_1)}\int_C \sqrt{\{(r_2 - r)(r - r_1)\}}\,\frac{dr}{r}.$$

If Γ is a large circle with O as centre, and γ is a small circle with O as centre, the integrand is regular in the closed region bounded externally by Γ and internally by γ and C. Therefore

(18.16.6) $$\int_C = \int_\Gamma - \int_\gamma,$$

the integrals being taken anti-clockwise round the contours. Now

(18.16.7) $$\int_\gamma \sqrt{\{(r_2 - r)(r - r_1)\}}\,\frac{dr}{r} = -i\int_\gamma \sqrt{\{(r_2 - r)(r_1 - r)\}}\,\frac{dr}{r}.$$

There is a simple pole at the origin with residue $\sqrt{(r_1 r_2)}$, so the value of the integral is

(18.16.8) $$-i\,.\,2\pi i\sqrt{(r_1 r_2)} = 2\pi\sqrt{(r_1 r_2)}.$$

For the integral round the large circle

(18.16.9)
$$\int_\Gamma \sqrt{\{(r_2 - r)(r - r_1)\}}\,\frac{dr}{r} = i\int_\Gamma \sqrt{\{(r - r_1)(r - r_2)\}}\,\frac{dr}{r} = i\int_{\gamma'} \sqrt{\{(1 - r_1 t)(1 - r_2 t)\}}\,\frac{dt}{t^2},$$

where we have used the transformation $r = 1/t$, and γ' is a small circle about $t = 0$. There is a pole of order 2 at the origin, and the residue is $\frac{1}{2}(r_1 + r_2)$, so the integral (18.16.9) has the value

(18.16.10) $$-i\,.\,2\pi i\,.\,\tfrac{1}{2}(r_1 + r_2) = \pi(r_1 + r_2).$$

Thus finally

(18.16.11)
$$\begin{aligned} I_1 &= \sqrt{(-2\alpha_1)}\{\pi(r_1 + r_2) - 2\pi\sqrt{(r_1 r_2)}\} \\ &= \sqrt{(-2\alpha_1)}\left\{\frac{2\pi\mu}{(-2\alpha_1)} - 2\pi\,\frac{\alpha_2}{\sqrt{(-2\alpha_1)}}\right\} = 2\pi\left(\frac{\mu}{\sqrt{(-2\alpha_1)}} - \alpha_2\right), \end{aligned}$$

as before.

Next

(18.16.12) $$I_2 = 2\int_{-i}^{i} \sqrt{(\alpha_2{}^2 - \alpha_3{}^2\sec^2\theta)}\,d\theta,$$

and, using again the substitution

(18.13.8) $$\sin\theta = \sin i \sin u,$$

we have

$$I_2 = 2\alpha_2 \int_{-i}^{i} \sqrt{(\sin^2 i - \sin^2 \theta)} \frac{d\theta}{\cos\theta} \tag{18.16.13}$$

$$= 2\alpha_2 \int_{-\frac{1}{2}\pi}^{\frac{1}{2}\pi} \frac{\sin^2 i \cos^2 u}{1 - \sin^2 i \sin^2 u} du$$

$$= 2\alpha_2 \int_{-\frac{1}{2}\pi}^{\frac{1}{2}\pi} \left(1 - \frac{\cos^2 i}{1 - \sin^2 i \sin^2 u}\right) du$$

$$= 2\alpha_2 \pi(1 - \cos i) = 2\pi(\alpha_2 - \alpha_3).$$

In terms of the elliptic elements this is

$$I_2 = 2\pi\sqrt{(\mu p)}(1 - \cos i). \tag{18.16.14}$$

Finally

$$I_3 = 2\pi\alpha_3 = 2\pi\sqrt{(\mu p)} \cos i. \tag{18.16.15}$$

Collecting the results we have

$$I_1 = 2\pi\left(\frac{\mu}{\sqrt{(-2\alpha_1)}} - \alpha_2\right), \quad I_2 = 2\pi(\alpha_2 - \alpha_3), \quad I_3 = 2\pi\alpha_3. \tag{18.16.16}$$

Hence

$$I_1 + I_2 + I_3 = 2\pi\mu/\sqrt{(-2\alpha_1)}, \tag{18.16.17}$$

and therefore

$$\alpha_1 = -2\pi^2\mu^2/(I_1 + I_2 + I_3)^2. \tag{18.16.18}$$

We have here an example of the anomalous case mentioned in § 18.8. The energy constant α_1, when expressed as a function of the I's, contains only a single linear form in the I's, and the periodicity or non-periodicity of the motion is independent of the initial conditions and beyond our control. Actually, of course, in this case all the frequencies are equal, and (so long as $\alpha_1 < 0$) the motion is always periodic. Explicitly

$$\mu_1 = \mu_2 = \mu_3 = \frac{\partial \alpha_1}{\partial I_1} = \frac{4\pi^2\mu^2}{(I_1 + I_2 + I_3)^3}, \tag{18.16.19}$$

and this is equal to

$$\frac{4\pi^2\mu^2}{(2\pi\mu)^3}(-2\alpha_1)^{3/2} = \frac{1}{2\pi}\sqrt{\left(\frac{\mu}{a^3}\right)} = \frac{n}{2\pi}, \tag{18.16.20}$$

and we recover a result already established in § 18.15.

We can express the v's in terms of the position of the planet by writing $w - e \sin w$ in place of l in the formulae (18.15.3),

$$\begin{cases} 2\pi v_1 = w - e \sin w, \\ 2\pi v_2 = w - e \sin w + u_0, \\ 2\pi v_3 = w - e \sin w + u_0 + \varphi_0. \end{cases} \tag{18.16.21}$$

These formulae are equivalent to the relations connecting q's and v's, and they are readily recovered by the theory of § 18.9. To find K' we have only to substitute for the α's in (18.12.8) their values in terms of the I's,

$$\alpha_1 = -\frac{2\pi^2\mu^2}{(I_1 + I_2 + I_3)^2}, \quad \alpha_2 = \frac{1}{2\pi}(I_2 + I_3), \quad \alpha_3 = \frac{1}{2\pi} I_3, \tag{18.16.22}$$

and the formulae (18.16.21) are given immediately by the equations (18.9.6).

18.17 Perturbation. So far we have considered the motion of a single planet relative to the sun. What is the effect of the presence of a second planet?

The orbit of the first planet relative to the sun is no longer an ellipse. But, if the second planet is sufficiently small (as to its mass) and sufficiently remote, its influence will be correspondingly small, and instead of discarding entirely the idea of the elliptic orbit we can think of the motion at each instant as motion in an ellipse which is being slowly modified by the presence of the second planet. This is a fundamental problem of Celestial Mechanics, which we cannot pursue in detail in this book, though a few introductory observations will appear later (§ 25.3). For the moment we content ourselves with finding an expression for the *disturbing function R*.

We denote the mass of the sun by M and the mass of the first planet by m_1, as in § 18.12; we denote the mass of the second planet by m_2. The distances of m_1 and m_2 from the sun are denoted by r_1 and r_2, and the distance between m_1 and m_2 is denoted by r_{12}. The accelerations of the sun and of the first planet are indicated, each as a sum of vectors, in Fig. 18.17a; and the acceleration of m_1 relative to the sun is indicated similarly in Fig. 18.17b. Thus, if we denote the positions of the planets relative to the sun by (x_1, y_1, z_1) and (x_2, y_2, z_2), we have

$$(18.17.1)\quad \ddot{x}_1 = -\frac{\gamma(M+m_1)}{r_1{}^2}\frac{x_1}{r_1} - \frac{\gamma m_2}{r_2{}^2}\frac{x_2}{r_2} - \frac{\gamma m_2}{r_{12}{}^2}\frac{x_1-x_2}{r_{12}} = \frac{\partial}{\partial x_1}(U+R),$$

where the "gravitation potential" $U(=-V)$ is given by

$$(18.17.2)\qquad U = \frac{\gamma(M+m_1)}{r_1},$$

and

$$(18.17.3)\qquad R = \gamma m_2\left(\frac{1}{r_{12}} - \frac{x_1x_2+y_1y_2+z_1z_2}{r_2{}^3}\right).$$

There are equations of similar form for y_1 and z_1; and there are three similar equations relating to the motion of the second planet.

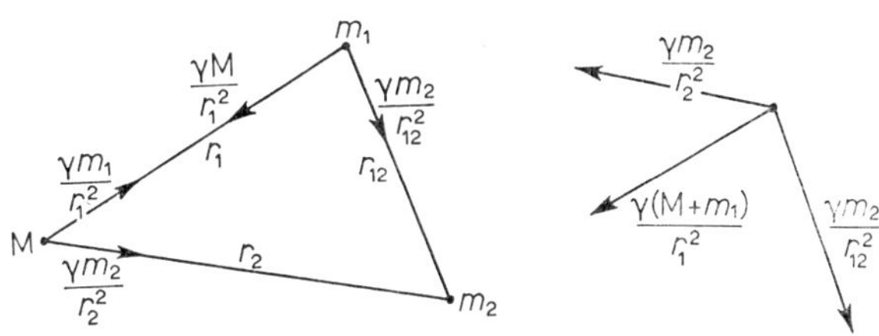

Figure 18.17a Figure 18.17b

If $m_2 = 0$ the disturbing function R is absent, and we have the two-body problem already discussed. If m_2 is small, and the distances r_2 and r_{12} do not become dangerously small during the motion, the effect of the additional function R on the motion of m_1 is a gradual modification of the elliptic motion. We shall return to this topic in § 25.3.

18.18 Non-orthogonal and non-natural separable systems. The system considered in Stäckel's theorem is *natural* and *orthogonal*. The kinetic energy function T is a homogeneous quadratic function of $\dot{q}$'s or p's, and moreover this quadratic function contains only square terms. But non-orthogonal, and even non-natural systems (in which T has the form $T_2 + T_1 + T_0$) exist, which are separable.

We have already met an example of a natural, but non-orthogonal, system which is soluble by separation, namely the spinning top (§ 16.11). If we use the Eulerian angles as coordinates, and if V is a function of θ only (as for example in the ordinary problem, when the top moves under gravity, and the axis OZ is taken vertically upwards) the system is separable. In this problem both φ and ψ are ignorable, and a glance at the details of the calculation shows how largely the property of separability depends upon this fact.

If we form the Routhian function by ignoration of ψ only, we obtain a non-natural system with two freedoms. *This system is also separable*, assuming again that V is a function of θ only. We have, as in (10.5.12),

(18.18.1)
$$R = \tfrac{1}{2}A(\dot{\theta}^2 + \sin^2\theta\,\dot{\varphi}^2) + \beta\dot{\varphi}\cos\theta - V.$$

To derive the Hamiltonian function we have

(18.18.2)
$$p_\theta = A\dot{\theta}, \quad p_\varphi = A\sin^2\theta\,\dot{\varphi} + \beta\cos\theta,$$

and

(18.18.3)
$$H = \tfrac{1}{2}A(\dot{\theta}^2 + \sin^2\theta\,\dot{\varphi}^2) + V$$
$$= \frac{1}{2A}{p_\theta}^2 + \frac{1}{2A\sin^2\theta}(p_\varphi - \beta\cos\theta)^2 + V.$$

The modified partial differential equation is

(18.18.4)
$$\frac{1}{2A}\left(\frac{\partial K}{\partial\theta}\right)^2 + \frac{1}{2A\sin^2\theta}\left(\frac{\partial K}{\partial\varphi} - \beta\cos\theta\right)^2 + V = \alpha_1,$$

and there is a complete integral of the form

(18.18.5)
$$K = \alpha_2\varphi + f(\theta),$$

where

(18.18.6)
$$f'(\theta)^2 = 2A(\alpha_1 - V) - \left(\frac{\alpha_2 - \beta\cos\theta}{\sin\theta}\right)^2.$$

Thus the non-natural system (18.18.1) is separable.

Chapter XIX

Systems with one degree of freedom, motion near a singular point

19.1 The differential equations. In the preceding chapters we have established certain principles that enable us to solve many problems of dynamics, or at least to make substantial progress towards a solution. Some of these problems are concerned with systems which possess some special property whose presence simplifies the discussion. Such a property is that of separability, discussed in Chapters XVII and XVIII. We now turn to the general problem presented by a system of differential equations, a system of the type that confronts us in the classical dynamics.

The equations of motion for a holonomic system can be written compactly in the vector form (6.4.4),

$$\dot{\mathbf{x}} = \mathbf{X}, \tag{19.1.1}$$

where $\mathbf{x} = \{x_1, x_2, \ldots, x_m\}$, $\mathbf{X} = \{X_1, X_2, \ldots, X_m\}$, and $X_r = X_r(x_1, x_2, \ldots, x_m; t)$. The number $m(= 2n)$ is twice the number of degrees of freedom of the dynamical system. The equations written *in extenso* take the form

$$\dot{x}_r = X_r, \qquad r = 1, 2, \ldots, m. \tag{19.1.2}$$

In the equations as they arise in dynamics, the set of m variables is composed of n associated pairs. In Lagrange's equations, the pairs are q's and ω's, and the equations have the form (6.4.3),

$$\dot{q}_r = \omega_r, \quad \dot{\omega}_r = \psi_r, \qquad r = 1, 2, \ldots, n.$$

In Hamilton's equations the pairs are q's and p's, and the equations have the form (10.3.8),

$$\dot{q}_r = \partial H/\partial p_r, \quad \dot{p}_r = -\partial H/\partial q_r, \qquad r = 1, 2, \ldots, n.$$

But for our immediate purpose, for the theory discussed in the present and the following Chapter, the division of the m variables into n related pairs is usually irrelevant.

In most problems of practical interest the functions X_r are functions of the x's only, not of t. When this happens the system is said to be *autonomous*. A non-autonomous system (19.1.2) with m dependent variables can be regarded as an autonomous system with $(m + 1)$ dependent variables.

$$\begin{cases} \dot{x}_r = X_r(x_1, x_2, \ldots, x_m; x_{m+1}), \qquad r = 1, 2, \ldots, m, \\ \dot{x}_{m+1} = 1. \end{cases} \tag{19.1.3}$$

The properties of the solutions of the system (19.1.2) will depend on the properties of the functions X_r; in general, the more assumptions we make about the X's, the more we can assert about the solutions. We recall briefly some of the relevant fundamental results in the theory of the differential equations. In the first instance the variables are real, but sometimes we must extend the scope of the discussion to include complex values.

(i) The fundamental existence theorem for the equations (19.1.2) was first established by Peano in 1885. We assume that the X's are single-valued and continuous in R, which is a domain (an open connected set) of the real Euclidean $(m + 1)$-dimensional space of $(x_1, x_2, \ldots, x_m; t)$. Let $(\alpha_1, \alpha_2, \ldots, \alpha_m; \tau)$ be any point of R. The fundamental result is that there is a solution through $(\alpha_1, \alpha_2, \ldots, \alpha_m; \tau)$. More precisely, there exist a positive number κ, and m functions $x_1(t), x_2(t), \ldots, x_m(t)$, defined in the time-interval I,

$$|t - \tau| < \kappa,$$

with the properties

(*a*) $x_r(\tau) = \alpha_r$,
(*b*) $\dot{x}_r(t)$ exists and is continuous in I,
(*c*) the point $[x_1(t), x_2(t), \ldots, x_m(t); t]$ lies in R if $t \in I$,
(*d*) the functions $x_r(t)$ satisfy (19.1.2).

The time-interval I can be taken closed if we interpret the derivatives $\dot{x}_r(t)$ at the ends of the interval as one-sided derivatives.

In this enunciation we are thinking in terms of a fixed initial point $(\alpha_1, \alpha_2, \ldots, \alpha_m; \tau)$ in R. More generally, if we contemplate as initial points all the points of some sub-set of R, we must think of x_r as a function, not merely of the single variable t, but of the $(m + 2)$ variables $t; \alpha_1, \alpha_2, \ldots, \alpha_m; \tau$. We write

$$x_r = \varphi_r(t; \alpha_1, \alpha_2, \ldots, \alpha_m; \tau), \qquad r = 1, 2, \ldots, m.$$

(ii) The fundamental existence theorem does not assert uniqueness. In fact the solution is not unique unless we impose further restrictions on the X's. To prove this assertion, it will suffice to consider the simple example, with $m = 1$,

$$\dot{x} = \sqrt{|x|}.$$

Here R is the whole (t, x) plane. In the half-plane $x \geqslant 0$ we have the solutions

$$x = \tfrac{1}{4}(t - t_1)^2, \qquad t \geqslant t_1,$$

and in the half-plane $x \leqslant 0$ we have the solutions

$$x = -\tfrac{1}{4}(t - t_2)^2, \qquad t \leqslant t_2.$$

We have also the solution $x = 0$ for all t. The dependence of x upon t in these solutions is shown in Fig. 19.1, and it is clear that the solution through a given initial point (τ, α) is not unique. (One solution through a particular initial point is given by the firm line in the figure.) If $\alpha \neq 0$ the solution is unique in a certain neighbourhood of (τ, α), but if $\alpha = 0$ there is no neighbourhood of (τ, α) in which the solution is unique.

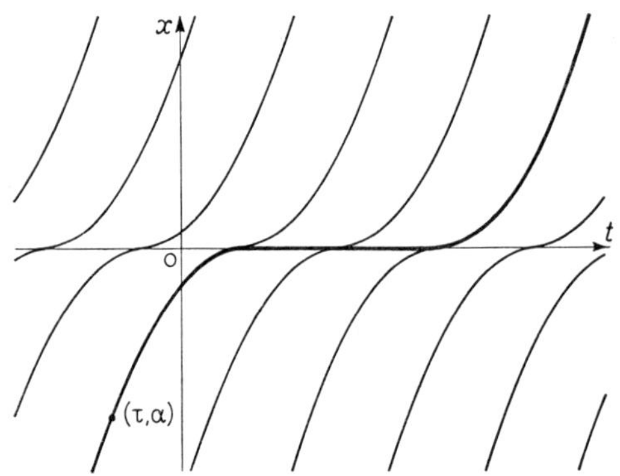

Figure 19.1

(iii) The time-interval I that occurs in the statement of the fundamental existence theorem is not in general the longest interval in which this solution through $(\alpha_1, \alpha_2, \ldots, \alpha_m; \tau)$ exists. Usually the interval in which the solution is defined can be extended to right and left, and we finally arrive at a solution defined in a maximal open interval, $a < t < b$, called the *natural interval of definition* for the solution; the numbers a and b depend on $(\alpha_1, \alpha_2, \ldots, \alpha_m; \tau)$ and on the particular solution considered in those cases where the solution is not unique. Here a can be $-\infty$ and b can be $+\infty$, so there are four types of natural interval of definition.

If the functions $X_r(x_1, x_2, \ldots, x_m; t)$ are bounded in R, then as t approaches a finite end-point of the natural interval of definition (if there is one) the point $[x_1(t), x_2(t), \ldots, x_m(t); t]$ approaches a point of the boundary of R.

(iv) The situation is at once greatly simplified if we make the additional assumption that the functions X_r are of class C_1 in R. This assumption has three important consequences, as follows:

(*a*) It ensures that the solution through $(\alpha_1, \alpha_2, \ldots, \alpha_m; \tau)$,

$$x_r = \varphi_r(t; \alpha_1, \alpha_2, \ldots, \alpha_m; \tau),$$

is unique.

(*b*) Let us consider, not one particular solution, but all the solutions through the points $(\alpha_1, \alpha_2, \ldots, \alpha_m; \tau)$ of a sub-domain D of R. The assumption (that each $X_r \in C_1$ in R) ensures certain properties of the solutions *qua* functions of $(\alpha_1, \alpha_2, \ldots, \alpha_m; \tau)$, namely that the functions φ_r possess first derivatives $\partial\varphi_r/\partial\alpha_s$ and $\partial\varphi_r/\partial\tau$, and these derivatives are continuous in the domain E defined by

$$(\alpha_1, \alpha_2, \ldots, \alpha_m; \tau) \in D, \quad a < t < b.$$

(*c*) It ensures that the second derivatives $\partial^2\varphi_r/\partial t^2$ and $\partial^2\varphi_r/\partial t\,\partial\alpha_s (= \partial^2\varphi_r/\partial\alpha_s\,\partial t)$ exist and are continuous in E.

(v) In some problems the X's contain parameters $\lambda_1, \lambda_2, \ldots, \lambda_p$. We are usually concerned with values $(\lambda_1, \lambda_2, \ldots, \lambda_p)$ lying in a domain L, which may be, for example, a neighbourhood of a particular value $(\lambda_1^0, \lambda_2^0, \ldots, \lambda_p^0)$. The solutions now depend on the λ's (as well as on t and the α's and τ),

$$x_r = \varphi_r(t; \alpha_1, \alpha_2, \ldots, \alpha_m; \tau; \lambda_1, \lambda_2, \ldots, \lambda_p), \qquad r = 1, 2, \ldots, m,$$

the solution being valid for $a < t < b$, where a and b now depend on the λ's as well as on the α's and τ. If now we assume that the functions X_r are of class C_1 in the domain F defined by

$$(\alpha_1, \alpha_2, \ldots, \alpha_m; \tau) \in D, \quad a < t < b, \quad (\lambda_1, \lambda_2, \ldots, \lambda_p) \in L,$$

then the first derivatives $\partial\varphi_r/\partial t$, $\partial\varphi_r/\partial\alpha_s$, $\partial\varphi_r/\partial\tau$, $\partial\varphi_r/\partial\lambda_s$, and the second derivatives $\partial^2\varphi_r/\partial t^2$, $\partial^2\varphi_r/\partial t\,\partial\alpha_s (= \partial^2\varphi_r/\partial\alpha_s\,\partial t)$, and $\partial^2\varphi_r/\partial t\,\partial\lambda_s (= \partial^2\varphi_r/\partial\lambda_s\,\partial t)$ exist and are continuous in F.

In this book we shall assume, unless the contrary is explicitly stated, that the functions X_r satisfy the conditions demanded in (iv) and (v) above. The solutions φ_r may therefore be assumed to possess the corresponding differentiability properties.

From this brief resumé of the theory, we return to the equations (19.1.2). It is useful to think of the equations as defining the motion of a *representative point* or *mobile* $(x_1, x_2, \ldots, x_m)$ in a space of m dimensions; the motion of the mobile pictures the motion of the dynamical system (in the phase space, not merely in the q-space). We may regard the space as a Euclidean space in which $x_1, x_2, \ldots, x_m$ are rectangular coordinates.

It is sometimes convenient to think of the equations (19.1.2) as defining the motion of a *fluid* in the m-fold space rather than the motion of a single particle or mobile; the fluid velocity at the point $\{x_1, x_2, \ldots, x_m\}$ at time t is $\{X_1, X_2, \ldots, X_m\}$. This device enables us to contemplate the totality of possible motions (or at any rate all the motions originating in some region of the $(m + 1)$-fold space of $\mathbf{x}$ and t) instead of one individual motion. The usefulness of this device is most marked when the system is autonomous, and then the fluid motion is *steady*, i.e. the fluid velocity at any given point is the same for all values of t.

It is sometimes convenient to write the equations (19.1.2) in the form

$$\frac{dx_1}{X_1} = \frac{dx_2}{X_2} = \cdots = \frac{dx_m}{X_m} = dt. \tag{19.1.4}$$

Again, this form is especially useful in the autonomous case.

The solutions of the equations (19.1.2) are of the form

$$x_r = \varphi_r(t;\ \alpha_1, \alpha_2, \ldots, \alpha_m;\ \tau), \qquad r = 1, 2, \ldots, m. \tag{19.1.5}$$

There is (assuming that the X's have the prescribed properties) a unique motion of the mobile in which $\mathbf{x}$ has the value $\boldsymbol{\alpha}$ at the instant $t = \tau$. The curves in the $(m + 1)$-dimensional $(\mathbf{x}, t)$-space defined by (19.1.5) are called *characteristics*.

In the autonomous case we usually take $\tau = 0$ (which involves no loss of generality) so that $\mathbf{x} = \boldsymbol{\alpha}$ at $t = 0$. The functions $X_1, X_2, \ldots, X_m$ define a vector field in the m-dimensional space of $\mathbf{x}$. The paths of the mobile in the $\mathbf{x}$-space, without reference to the times at which the different points are occupied, are called *trajectories*. The trajectories are the projections of the characteristics onto the $\mathbf{x}$-space. The equations (19.1.5), which define the characteristics, also provide a parametric representation of the trajectories (in terms of the parameter t).

The curves defined by the equations

$$\frac{dx_1}{X_1} = \frac{dx_2}{X_2} = \cdots = \frac{dx_m}{X_m} \tag{19.1.6}$$

are called *lines of force*. A unique line of force passes through each ordinary point of the field, but there may be several lines of force through a singular point (i.e. a point at which $X_1 = X_2 = \cdots = X_m = 0$).

The trajectories are arcs of the lines of force, but strictly speaking the trajectories are not identical with the lines of force. For example, if $\boldsymbol{\alpha}$ is a singular point, the trajectory originating in $\boldsymbol{\alpha}$ is the point $\boldsymbol{\alpha}$ itself; and a line of force may pass through a singular point, whereas the corresponding trajectory never reaches it. It is natural to think of the problem of determining the characteristics as falling into two stages, first the determination of the trajectories, and second the finding of the relation between position on the trajectory and the time. The second step is simple, at least in theory, if the trajectory has been found. Let us suppose that the trajectory is expressed in the form

$$x_r = \psi_r(x_1), \qquad r = 2, 3, \ldots, m. \tag{19.1.7}$$

Then the relation between the position on the trajectory and the time is found from

$$\frac{dx_1}{X} = dt, \tag{19.1.8}$$

where

$$X = X(x_1) = X_1(x_1, \psi_1, \psi_2, \ldots, \psi_m). \tag{19.1.9}$$

In the autonomous case, if the characteristic leaving $\boldsymbol{\alpha}$ at $t = 0$ is defined by the equations

$$x_r = \varphi_r(t;\ \alpha_1, \alpha_2, \ldots, \alpha_m), \qquad r = 1, 2, \ldots, m, \tag{19.1.10}$$

another characteristic is given by

$$x_r = \varphi_r(t - t_0;\ \alpha_1, \alpha_2, \ldots, \alpha_m), \qquad r = 1, 2, \ldots, m. \tag{19.1.11}$$

All the characteristics (19.1.11) for different values of t_0 follow the same trajectory; they only differ from one another because in different characteristics a given point of the trajectory is occupied at different times.

In the autonomous case, if the mobile starts from a point A of the m-fold space at $t = 0$, the points occupied by the mobile for $t \geqslant 0$ constitute the *positive semi-characteristic* originating at A. Similarly the points occupied for $t \leqslant 0$ by a mobile arriving at A at $t = 0$ constitute the *negative semi-characteristic* originating at A.*

Many interesting and important properties of the solutions of the equations (19.1.2), mostly referring to the autonomous case, are known, and some of these we shall establish in Chapter XXI. But the only case for which a fairly complete theory exists at present is the simple case where the system is autonomous and $m = 2$. It is this case that we shall consider in this Chapter and the next. The simplest example is provided by a particle moving on a straight line when the force acting on it is a function of x and $\dot{x}$ (but not of t). If we ask, "Why cannot the theory for $m = 2$ be extended to systems with $m > 2$?", the answer is, broadly speaking, that parts of the discussion depend essentially on Jordan's curve theorem, that a simple closed curve Γ in a plane Π divides $\Pi - \Gamma$ into two disjoint regions, interior and exterior, whose common boundary is Γ. There is no analogous theorem for curves in space of more than two dimensions.

19.2 Particle moving on a straight line. We denote the displacement of the particle at time t, measured from a fixed origin O on the line and in a definite sense, by x. If the mass of the particle is m, and the force acting on it is mF, where

$$F = F(x, \dot{x}, t), \tag{19.2.1}$$

the equation of motion is

$$\ddot{x} = F. \tag{19.2.2}$$

We replace this equation by the two first-order equations, of the type (19.1.2),

$$\dot{x} = y, \quad \dot{y} = F(x, y, t). \tag{19.2.3}$$

The system is autonomous if F does not contain t.

Some particular examples are familiar. The problem of motion in a field of force, where F is a function of x only, has been discussed already in § 1.2. The problem of motion under the action of a force which is a function of the speed, for example motion in a resisting medium, is also very simple. The equation of motion is now

$$\ddot{x} = f(\dot{x}), \tag{19.2.4}$$

and, if the force arises from a resisting medium, $f(\dot{x})$ vanishes with $\dot{x}$ and is monotone decreasing. But other cases are of interest, e.g. cases in which the condition $\dot{x}f(\dot{x}) \leqslant 0$ is not fulfilled; in such cases we speak of *negative friction*. The equation (19.2.4) leads to

$$\dot{x} = y, \quad \dot{y} = f(y), \tag{19.2.5}$$

* There is a slight awkwardness of terminology at this point. Since these curves are curves in the $\mathbf{x}$-space, not the $(\mathbf{x}, t)$-space, it would be more logical to speak of positive or negative semi-trajectories rather than positive or negative semi-characteristics. But the term semi-characteristic seems to be established in this context.

of which the second is self-contained, since it involves only the variables y and t. We can find the trajectories in the (x, y)-plane from the equation

$$\frac{d}{dx}(\tfrac{1}{2}y^2) = f(y). \tag{19.2.6}$$

Moreover

$$\frac{d}{dt}(\tfrac{1}{2}y^2) = yf(y), \tag{19.2.7}$$

and for a resisting medium the second member is negative (unless $y = 0$) and the kinetic energy always decreases as t increases.

A classical problem of the type (19.2.1) is that of a particle moving under the action of a uniform field in a medium offering a resistance proportional to the speed. The equation of motion is

$$\ddot{x} = -g - k\dot{x}, \tag{19.2.8}$$

where x is measured in the direction opposite to that of the field. The solution, with $x = x_0$ and $\dot{x} = y_0$ at $t = 0$, is

$$k(x - x_0) = (c + y_0)(1 - e^{-kt}) - c(kt), \tag{19.2.9}$$

where c is the *terminal velocity* g/k. The trajectory in the (x, y)-plane is given by the equation

$$k(x - x_0) = y_0 - y - c \log\left(\frac{c + y_0}{c + y}\right). \tag{19.2.10}$$

The problem of motion in a resisting medium under the action of a general (non-uniform) field of force merits a little consideration before we turn to the general theory. Here the function F is the sum of a function of x and a function of $\dot{x}$, and the equation of motion has the form

$$\ddot{x} = -\frac{dV}{dx} + f(\dot{x}). \tag{19.2.11}$$

We see that

$$\frac{d}{dt}(\tfrac{1}{2}\dot{x}^2 + V) = \dot{x}f(\dot{x}), \tag{19.2.12}$$

and if the force $mf(\dot{x})$ arises from a resisting medium the second member of this equation is negative, and the energy $T + V$ continually decreases. A familiar example is that of a harmonic oscillator in a medium offering a resistance proportional to the speed. The equation of motion is then of the form

$$\ddot{x} + 2k\dot{x} + n^2x = 0, \tag{19.2.13}$$

and we consider the case of "light" damping, with $0 < k < n$. If $x = a$ and $\dot{x} = u$ at $t = 0$ the solution is

$$x = e^{-kt}\left(a \cos pt + \frac{ka + u}{p} \sin pt\right), \tag{19.2.14}$$

where $p = \sqrt{(n^2 - k^2)}$. With a suitable change of the origin for t we can write this in the form

$$x = Ae^{-kt} \sin pt, \tag{19.2.15}$$

and then

$$y = \dot{x} = Ae^{-kt}(p \cos pt - k \sin pt). \tag{19.2.16}$$

If we define an acute angle α by means of the equations

$$\frac{\cos\alpha}{p} = \frac{\sin\alpha}{k} = \frac{1}{n}, \tag{19.2.17}$$

we can write the solution in the form

$$x = Ae^{-\theta\tan\alpha}\sin\theta, \quad y = nAe^{-\theta\tan\alpha}\cos(\theta + \alpha), \tag{19.2.18}$$

where $\theta = pt$. This represents a spiral curve converging to O (Fig. 19.2a); it has the property

$$\frac{x(\theta+\pi)}{x(\theta)} = \frac{y(\theta+\pi)}{y(\theta)} = -e^{-\pi\tan\alpha}. \tag{19.2.19}$$

The oscillations on the straight line are damped out, and the motion tends finally to rest at O.

The problem of forced oscillations of the damped harmonic oscillator has already been considered in § 9.10.

The motion is similar in a wider class of problem of which the prototype is the problem just considered. We suppose that $X(x)$ is an attraction towards O, and that $f(\dot{x})$ is a frictional resistance; the function $X(x)$ vanishes with x and is monotone decreasing, the function $f(\dot{x})$ vanishes with $\dot{x}$ and is monotone decreasing. We may suppose $V(0) = 0$, and then $V(x) > 0$ for $x \neq 0$, and $V(x)$ steadily increases as x increases or decreases from zero. Then the motion is a damped-out oscillation as in the special case just considered. To prove this, we notice that, as t increases, the energy $\frac{1}{2}y^2 + V$ steadily decreases, and tends to a limit $(C \geqslant 0)$ as $t \to \infty$. But $C > 0$ is impossible. For suppose on the contrary that $C > 0$. If this limiting value were actually attained we should have

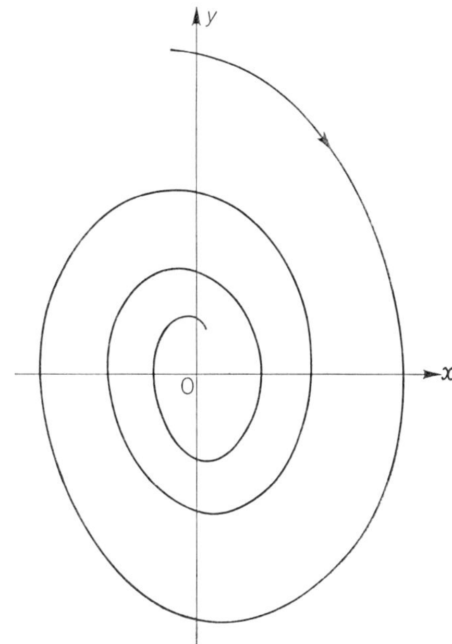

Figure 19.2a

$$\tfrac{1}{2}y^2 + V = C, \tag{19.2.20}$$

and this corresponds to a periodic oscillation, with constant energy C, on a stretch (x_1, x_2) of the x-axis, where $x_1 < 0 < x_2$; the corresponding trajectory in the (x, y)-plane would be a closed oval curve, such as the curve Γ, shown by a firm line in Fig. 19.2b. Now if $\frac{1}{2}y^2 + V$ decreases steadily to the value C, the trajectory in the (x, y)-plane is a spiral tending to Γ, as shown by the dotted line in Fig. 19.2b, and the decrease of energy during an interval between two successive minima of x is greater than K,

$$K = -2\int_{x_1}^{x_2} f(y)\,dx, \tag{19.2.21}$$

where the symbol y in this formula is the positive-valued function of x whose graph is the part of Γ in the upper half-plane. Now $K > 0$, so after a finite number of to-and-fro swings (between one minimum of x and the next) the energy, whatever its initial value, will have fallen below the value C. Thus $C > 0$ leads to a contradiction, and the only alternative is $C = 0$. The trajectory in the (x, y)-plane is a spiral converging to O, of the same general character as Fig. 19.2a; the motion of the particle on the x-axis tends ultimately to rest at O. All this of course bears out the expectation of untutored common sense.

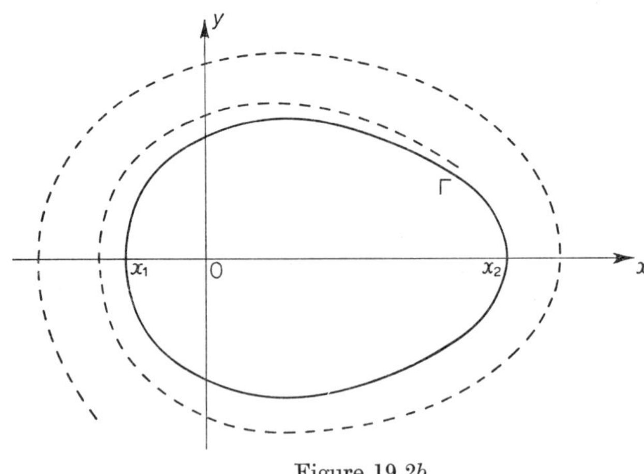

Figure 19.2b

19.3 System with one freedom. We turn now from these simple special cases to the general autonomous system with $m = 2$. We have a vector field $\mathbf{F}$ (the field that was called $\mathbf{X}$ in the general case) whose components P, Q are of class C_1 in a domain D of the (x, y)-plane. The equations controlling the motion are

$$\dot{x} = P(x, y), \quad \dot{y} = Q(x, y), \tag{19.3.1}$$

and we picture the motion of the system as the motion of a mobile in the (x, y)-plane.

A point (x, y) at which $P^2 + Q^2 > 0$ is called an *ordinary* or *regular point*; a point at which $P = Q = 0$ is called a *singular point* or *singularity*. We shall restrict the discussion to the case of a field in which there are only isolated singular points, at each of which the Jacobian $\dfrac{\partial(P, Q)}{\partial(x, y)}$ is different from zero.

The trajectories are arcs of the lines of force defined by the equation

$$\frac{dx}{P} = \frac{dy}{Q}, \tag{19.3.2}$$

and, as we have noticed, through each regular point there is just one line of force. Given any point A of D there is a unique motion of the mobile in which the mobile is at A at $t = 0$. If A is a singular point this "motion" is rest at A; the trajectory degenerates into a single point. If A is a regular point the mobile moves away from A along the line of force through A, and the trajectory is a genuine curve.

We shall find that the singular points (giving positions of equilibrium) and the closed lines of force (giving periodic orbits), if any exist, are of particular significance in the study of the motion. We begin by considering the motion in the neighbourhood of a singular point.

19.4 Motion in the neighbourhood of a singular point, the linear approximation. It will be convenient to change the notation so that the singular point in question is the origin of coordinates. If we expand for small values of $r(= \sqrt{(x^2 + y^2)})$ we have

$$\begin{cases} P = ax + by + \epsilon(x, y), \\ Q = cx + dy + \eta(x, y), \end{cases} \tag{19.4.1}$$

where $ad - bc \neq 0$, and ϵ/r and η/r tend to zero with r. (In the simple cases, ϵ and η are $O(r^2)$.) It is natural to expect that the *linear approximation* (i.e. the approximation given by the linear terms alone, omitting the terms ϵ and η) will give us some guidance as to the motion in the general case. We therefore start with a discussion of the simpler problem in which the equations are

$$\begin{cases} \dot{x} = ax + by, \\ \dot{y} = cx + dy, \end{cases} \tag{19.4.2}$$

which we can write in the matrix form

$$\dot{\mathbf{x}} = \mathbf{A}\mathbf{x}, \tag{19.4.3}$$

where $\mathbf{x}$ is the column matrix $\{x, y\}$, and $\mathbf{A}$ is the non-singular matrix

$$\begin{pmatrix} a & b \\ c & d \end{pmatrix}.$$

We shall find that the discussion depends essentially on the *eigenvalues* or *latent roots*, λ_1, λ_2, of the matrix $\mathbf{A}$, i.e. the roots of the equation

$$|\lambda\mathbf{1} - \mathbf{A}| = 0, \tag{19.4.4}$$

which is equivalent to

$$\lambda^2 - \lambda(a + d) + (ad - bc) = 0. \tag{19.4.5}$$

If we make the linear transformation

$$\mathbf{x} = \mathbf{C}\mathbf{u}, \tag{19.4.6}$$

where $\mathbf{C}$ is a non-singular matrix, and $\mathbf{u}$ is the vector (column matrix) $\{u, v\}$, the equation (19.4.3) becomes

$$\mathbf{u} = \mathbf{B}\mathbf{u}, \tag{19.4.7}$$

where $\mathbf{B}$ is the matrix $\mathbf{C}^{-1}\mathbf{A}\mathbf{C}$. We can choose $\mathbf{C}$ to give a simple form, the *Jordan normal form*, to $\mathbf{B}$, as follows:

(*a*) If λ_1, λ_2 are real and different we can find a real linear transformation such that $\mathbf{B}$ has the form

$$\begin{pmatrix} \lambda_1 & 0 \\ 0 & \lambda_2 \end{pmatrix}. \tag{19.4.8}$$

(We are reminded of the transformation to normal coordinates in the theory of vibrations, § 9.2.)

(*b*) If λ_1, λ_2 are real and equal we can find a real linear transformation such that $\mathbf{B}$ has either the form

$$\begin{pmatrix} \lambda_1 & 0 \\ 0 & \lambda_1 \end{pmatrix}, \tag{19.4.9}$$

or the form

$$\begin{pmatrix} \lambda_1 & 1 \\ 0 & \lambda_1 \end{pmatrix}. \tag{19.4.10}$$

(*c*) If λ_1, λ_2 are complex, and $\lambda_2 = \bar{\lambda}_1$, we can find a linear transformation (with complex coefficients) such that **B** has the form

$$\begin{pmatrix} \lambda_1 & 0 \\ 0 & \bar{\lambda}_1 \end{pmatrix}. \tag{19.4.11}$$

But this is equivalent to the statement that we can find a real linear transformation such that **B** has the form

$$\begin{pmatrix} \alpha & -\beta \\ \beta & \alpha \end{pmatrix}, \tag{19.4.12}$$

where $\lambda_1 = \alpha + i\beta$.

Let us consider the nature of the motion that takes place in the various cases.

(i) The eigenvalues are real and of the same sign. We must consider separately the cases of unequal and of equal roots.

(i*a*) The eigenvalues are real, unequal, and of the same sign. We will suppose for definiteness that they are negative, say $\lambda_1 < \lambda_2 < 0$. The transformed system is

$$\dot{u} = \lambda_1 u, \quad \dot{v} = \lambda_2 v, \tag{19.4.13}$$

and the solution is

$$u = u_0 e^{\lambda_1 t} = u_0 e^{-\mu_1 t}, \quad v = v_0 e^{\lambda_2 t} = v_0 e^{-\mu_2 t}, \tag{19.4.14}$$

where $\mu_i = -\lambda_i$, and $\mu_1 > \mu_2 > 0$.

Now $\sqrt{(x^2 + y^2)}$ is small when $\sqrt{(u^2 + v^2)}$ is small, and $\sqrt{(x^2 + y^2)} \to 0$ when $\sqrt{(u^2 + v^2)} \to 0$, so the distance of the mobile from O tends to zero as $t \to \infty$. When this happens we say that the trajectory *approaches O*. Further, the direction of the tangent to the path tends to a definite limiting direction as $t \to \infty$ and $r \to 0$, and when this happens we say that the trajectory *enters O*. To prove that the direction tends to a limiting direction, we notice that

$$\frac{\dot{v}}{\dot{u}} = \frac{\mu_2 v_0}{\mu_1 u_0} e^{(\mu_1 - \mu_2)t}, \tag{19.4.15}$$

and, if $v_0 \neq 0$, this tends to $+\infty$ or to $-\infty$. The trajectories enter O along the positive or along the negative v-axis. If $v_0 = 0$ the trajectory is the segment of the u-axis between $u = u_0$ and $u = 0$. Thus two trajectories (or, more precisely, two sets of semi-trajectories, since the mobile travels along the positive u-axis towards O for all positive values of u_0, not merely for one particular value) enter O along the u-axis. Here we have an example of a phenomenon mentioned in § 19.1 above. A trajectory enters O; but O itself is not a point of the trajectory, but only a limit point.

To sum up, if $\lambda_1 < \lambda_2 < 0$, all the positive semi-characteristics enter O, two (or, more precisely, two sets) along the u-axis and the rest along the v-axis (Fig. 19.4*a*). (If we return to the original coordinates (x, y), the directions in which the curves enter O are no longer at right angles.) A singularity of this type is called a *stable node*. If $\lambda_1 > \lambda_2 > 0$ we have an *unstable node*; in that case the negative semi-characteristics enter O.

(i*b*) The eigenvalues are real and equal, and the matrix

$$\begin{pmatrix} a - \lambda_1 & b \\ c & d - \lambda_1 \end{pmatrix} \tag{19.4.16}$$

has rank 0. Thus $b = c = 0$, $a = d = \lambda_1$. The equations are

(19.4.17) $$\dot{x} = \lambda_1 x, \quad \dot{y} = \lambda_1 y,$$

and if $\lambda_1 < 0$, say $\lambda_1 = -\mu_1$, the solution is

(19.4.18) $$x = x_0 e^{-\mu_1 t}, \quad y = y_0 e^{-\mu_1 t}.$$

The trajectories are the straight lines

(19.4.19) $$\frac{y}{x} = \frac{y_0}{x_0},$$

and all the positive semi-characteristics enter O. We again have a stable node, but in this case, in contrast to (i*a*), the positive semi-characteristics enter O in all directions (Fig. 19.4*b*). If $\lambda_1 > 0$ we have an unstable node. It may be mentioned that a singularity of this type occurs only rarely in the practical applications.

(i*c*) The eigenvalues are real and equal, and the matrix

(19.4.20) $$\begin{pmatrix} a - \lambda_1 & b \\ c & d - \lambda_1 \end{pmatrix}$$

has rank 1. We can reduce the matrix to the form

(19.4.21) $$\mathbf{B} = \begin{pmatrix} \lambda_1 & 1 \\ 0 & \lambda_1 \end{pmatrix},$$

and the equations take the form

(19.4.22) $$\dot{u} = \lambda_1 u + v, \quad \dot{v} = \lambda_1 v.$$

If $\lambda_1 < 0$, say $\lambda_1 = -\mu_1$, the solution is

(19.4.23) $$u = (u_0 + v_0 t)e^{-\mu_1 t}, \quad v = v_0 e^{-\mu_1 t},$$

and the positive semi-characteristics approach O. If $v_0 = 0$, the trajectory is part of the u-axis. If $v_0 \neq 0$,

(19.4.24) $$\frac{v}{u} = \frac{v_0}{u_0 + v_0 t},$$

which $\to 0$ as $t \to \infty$, and the positive semi-characteristic enters O along Ou. We again have a stable node, and all the positive semi-characteristics enter O along the u-axis (Fig. 19.4*c*). If $\lambda_1 > 0$ we have an unstable node.

The upshot is that if the eigenvalues are real and negative we have a stable node, and if they are real and positive we have an unstable node.

(ii) The eigenvalues are real and of different signs, say $\lambda_1 < 0 < \lambda_2$. The equations are

(19.4.25) $$\dot{u} = -\mu_1 u, \quad \dot{v} = \lambda_2 v,$$

and the solution is

(19.4.26) $$u = u_0 e^{-\mu_1 t}, \quad v = v_0 e^{\lambda_2 t}.$$

The only positive semi-characteristics that approach O are those for which $v_0 = 0$. The other trajectories are hyperbola-like curves (actually rectangular hyperbolas if $\lambda_1 = \mu_1$) and (if $u_0 = 0$) the v-axis, and the mobile moves to infinity (Fig. 19.4*d*). A singularity of this type is called a *saddle point* or *col*.

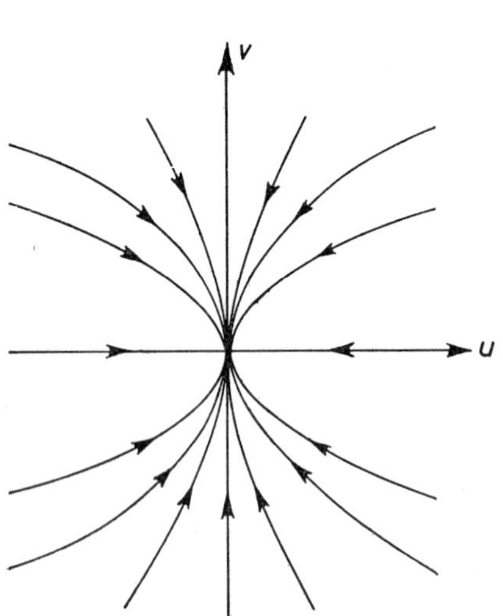

Figure 19.4a

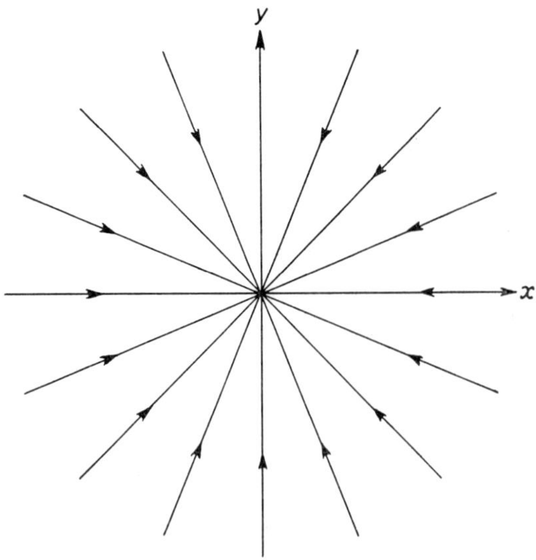

Figure 19.4b

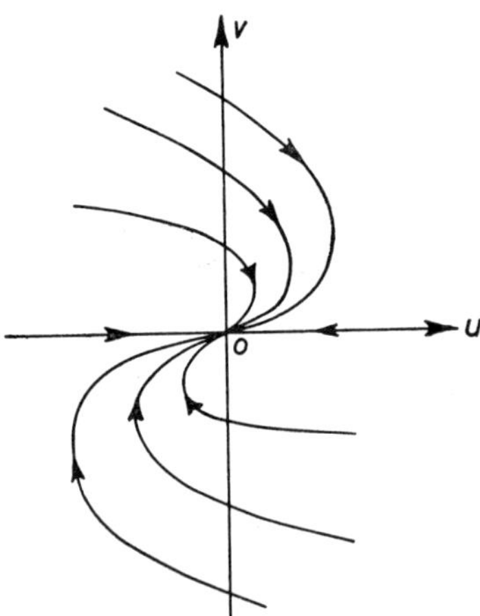

Figure 19.4c

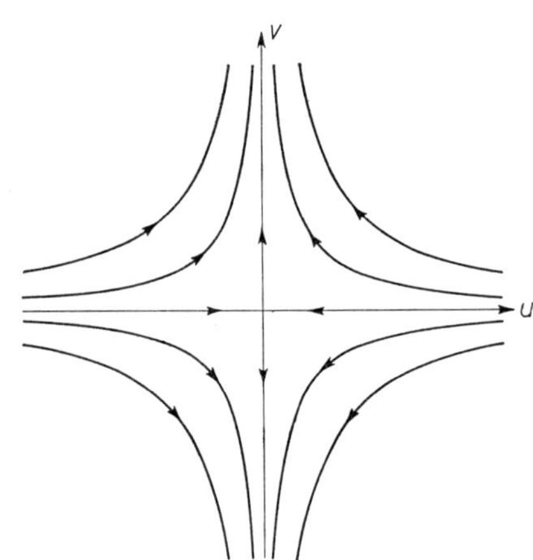

Figure 19.4d

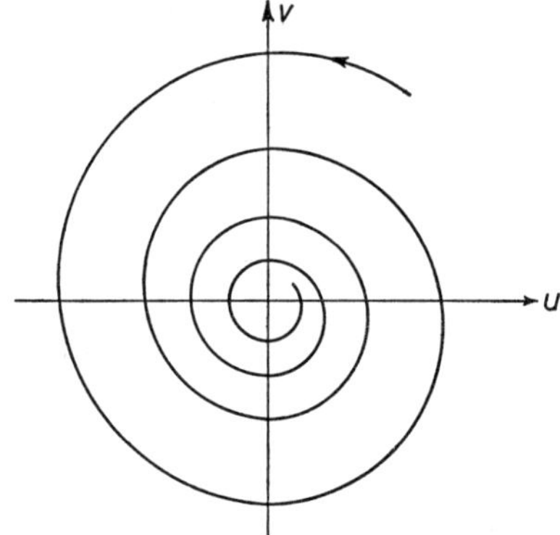

Figure 19.4e

(iii) The eigenvalues are conjugate complex numbers $\alpha \pm i\beta$, and $\alpha \neq 0$. In this case a real linear transformation leads to the equations

(19.4.27) $$\dot{u} = \alpha u - \beta v, \quad \dot{v} = \beta u + \alpha v.$$

We can write these compactly as the single equation

(19.4.28) $$\dot{w} = (\alpha + i\beta)w,$$

where $w = u + iv$, and the solution is

(19.4.29) $$w = w_0 e^{(\alpha+i\beta)t} = \rho e^{\alpha t} e^{i\beta(t-t_0)},$$

where ρ and t_0 are real, $w_0 = \rho e^{-i\beta t_0}$. If we replace the rectangular coordinates (u, v) by the polar coordinates (r, θ) we have

(19.4.30) $$r = \rho e^{\alpha t}, \quad \theta = \beta(t - t_0).$$

If $\alpha < 0$, $r \to 0$ as $t \to \infty$; the trajectories approach O, but they do not enter O. The path is a spiral curve (actually a logarithmic spiral if the coordinates are rectangular) about O, and it is described in the positive sense if $\beta > 0$ (Fig. 19.4*e*).

A singularity of this type is a *spiral point* or *focus*. It is stable if $\alpha < 0$. If $\alpha > 0$ we have an unstable focus, and the negative semi-characteristic approaches O; $r \to 0$ as $t \to -\infty$.

Example 19.4*A*. A familiar example of a stable focus is provided by the theory of damped harmonic motion. This problem has already been discussed in § 19.2, but it may be of interest to reconsider it briefly as an illustration of the general theory. The equations are

(19.4.31) $$\dot{x} = y, \quad \dot{y} = -n^2 x - 2ky,$$

and the eigenvalues are $-k \pm ip$, where $p = \sqrt{(n^2 - k^2)}$. If we put

(19.4.32) $$u = kx + y, \quad v = px,$$

the equations become

(19.4.33) $$\dot{u} = -ku - pv, \quad \dot{v} = pu - kv,$$

and expressed in polar coordinates (with $u = r \cos \theta$, $v = r \sin \theta$) the equations are

(19.4.34) $$\dot{r} = -kr, \quad \dot{\theta} = p.$$

The solution is

(19.4.35) $$r = r_0 e^{-kt}, \quad \theta = pt,$$

if $\theta = 0$ at $t = 0$. Thus

(19.4.36) $$u = r_0 e^{-kt} \cos pt, \quad v = r_0 e^{-kt} \sin pt,$$

and hence

(19.4.37) $$x = v/p = Ae^{-kt} \sin pt,$$

(19.4.38) $$y = u - (kv/p) = Ae^{-kt} (p \sin pt - k \cos pt),$$

where $A = r_0/p$. These are the formulae previously found in (19.2.15–16); the trajectory in the (x, y)-plane is shown in Fig. 19.2*a*.

(iv) The eigenvalues are pure imaginary numbers $\pm i\beta$. The analysis is as in (iii) with α replaced by zero, and the equations are

(19.4.39) $$\dot{u} = -\beta v, \quad \dot{v} = \beta u.$$

The solution is

(19.4.40) $$r = r_0, \quad \theta = \beta(t - t_0),$$

and the trajectories in the (u, v)-plane are circles. The trajectories in the (x, y)-plane are ellipses. Here we have the exceptional case in which all the trajectories are cyclic; all the orbits are periodic orbits.

A singularity of this type is called a *vortex point* or *centre*.

Example 19.4*B*. A familiar example of a vortex point is provided by the harmonic oscillator (*Example* 1.2*A*) for which

(19.4.41) $$\ddot{x} + n^2x = 0.$$

The equivalent first-order equations are

(19.4.42) $$\dot{x} = y, \quad \dot{y} = -n^2x.$$

The eigenvalues are $\pm i$. If we put $u = nx$, $v = y$, the equations become

(19.4.43) $$\dot{u} = nv, \quad \dot{v} = -nu,$$

and the solution in the (u, v)-plane (with $u = r\cos\theta$, $v = r\sin\theta$) is

(19.4.44) $$r = r_0, \quad \theta = -n(t - t_0).$$

This leads to the well-known solution in the (x, y)-plane

(19.4.45) $$\begin{cases} x = c\cos n(t - t_0), \\ y = -nc\sin n(t - t_0). \end{cases}$$

The trajectories in the (x, y)-plane are the ellipses

(19.4.46) $$n^2x^2 + y^2 = \text{constant}.$$

Example 19.4*C*. For the system

(19.4.47) $$\dot{x} = x + y, \quad \dot{y} = -2x - y,$$

the eigenvalues are $\pm i$. To find the trajectories we have

(19.4.48) $$(2x + y)\dot{x} + (x + y)\dot{y} = 0,$$

giving as the trajectories (Fig. 19.4*f*) the ellipses

(19.4.49) $$2x^2 + 2xy + y^2 = \text{constant}.$$

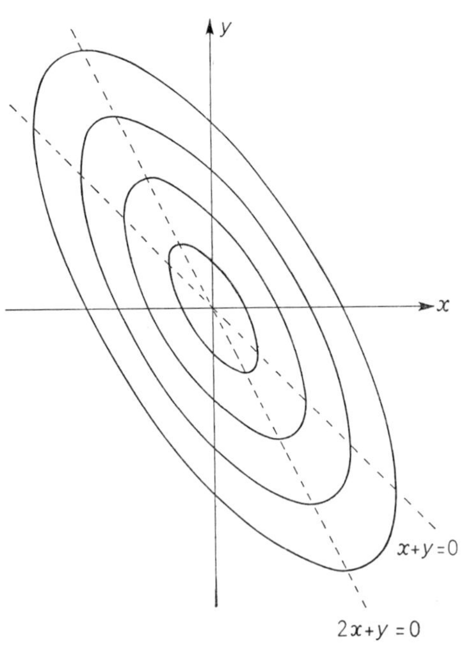

Figure 19.4*f*

(To draw the figure we may notice that

$$\frac{1}{4}(2x^2 + 2xy + y^2) = \frac{(x\sin\alpha - y\cos\alpha)^2}{(\sqrt{5}+1)^2} + \frac{(x\cos\alpha + y\sin\alpha)^2}{(\sqrt{5}-1)^2},$$

where $\tan\alpha = \frac{1}{2}(\sqrt{5} - 1)$.)

The system is in fact equivalent to the preceding, since the equations can be written

(19.4.50) $$\dot{u} = v, \quad \dot{v} = -u,$$

where $u = x$ and $v = x + y$. The solution is

(19.4.51) $$u = c\cos(t - t_0), \quad v = -c\sin(t - t_0),$$

and the trajectories in the (u, v)-plane are the circles

(19.4.52) $$u^2 + v^2 = \text{constant}.$$

Of course (19.4.52) is equivalent to (19.4.49).

19.5 Stability of equilibrium, complete stability, and instability. The singular points, or equilibrium points, in the field are points at which the mobile can stay at rest. We now consider further the notion of stability, which we have already encountered in the theory of small oscillations (Chapter IX).

We say that a position of equilibrium corresponding to the singular point O is stable if a trajectory originating near O remains near O for ever afterwards. Let us denote the distance of the mobile from O at time t by $r(t)$,

$$r(t) = |\mathbf{x}(t)| = \sqrt{(x^2 + y^2)}.$$

Then the precise definition of stability is as follows: The equilibrium is *stable* if, given $\varepsilon > 0$, there exists a positive number $\kappa(= \kappa(\varepsilon))$ such that, if $r(0) < \kappa$, then $r(t) < \varepsilon$ for $t \geqslant 0$.*

In the definition, the number $\kappa(\varepsilon)$ is not precisely defined, but if we take for $\kappa(\varepsilon)$ the greatest possible value, then $\kappa(\varepsilon)$ is a monotonic function of ε, and $\kappa(\varepsilon) \to 0$ with ε. If the equilibrium at O is stable, corresponding to any sufficiently small positive number κ, there is a positive number ε, with the property that $r(0) < \kappa$ implies $r(t) < \varepsilon$ for $t \geqslant 0$.

In the theory of small oscillations, we started from Lagrange's equations of motion, which are equations of the second order. Here, on the contrary, we have equations of the first order, and in interpreting the definition of stability we must remember that smallness of r implies smallness of the velocity of the dynamical system as well as smallness of displacement. Consider in particular the simple case in which x is a Lagrangian coordinate of a dynamical system with one freedom, and the first of the equations (19.3.1) is $\dot{x} = y$. The singular points $(x_0, 0)$ give the configurations $x = x_0$ in which the system can stay at rest, and smallness of $r\ (= \sqrt{\{(x - x_0)^2 + \dot{x}^2\}})$ implies not only smallness in the displacement of the system from the equilibrium position, but also smallness of velocity.

In some of the problems that we have discussed an even more stringent condition than that of stability is fulfilled, namely that the trajectories originating near O approach O; the motion is damped out, the mobile tends to rest at the singularity. In such cases we speak of complete stability. The equilibrium is *completely stable* (or *convergently stable*, or *asymptotically stable*) if it is stable, and if, in addition, there exists a positive number κ such that, if $r(0) < \kappa$, then $r(t) \to 0$ as $t \to \infty$.

Instability means lack of stability. Thus the equilibrium at O is *unstable* if and only if there exists a positive number κ with the property that there exist trajectories originating in points arbitrarily near to O such that $r(t) > \kappa$ for some positive values of t.

Notice that this definition of instability does not require $r(t) > \kappa$ for all sufficiently large values of t, nor even for some arbitrarily large values of t; but in fact one or other of these conditions is satisfied in many concrete examples.

* There is a more exacting definition of stability which demands that, if $r(0) < \kappa$, then $r(t) < \varepsilon$ for *all* values of t (i.e. for $t < 0$ as well as for $t \geqslant 0$), but this notion does not seem to be of great value in dynamics, and we shall not consider it in this book.

Examples of all the various possibilities occur in the singular points for the linear system studied in § 19.4. A vortex point or centre is stable. In this case the trajectories are a family of similar ellipses with O as centre, and if we consider the ellipse for which ε is the major semi-axis we can take for $\kappa(\varepsilon)$ the minor semi-axis of the same ellipse. The stable nodes and stable foci are completely stable. The saddle points and unstable nodes and unstable foci are unstable. (To obtain the equations in the form used in § 19.4 we have used a linear transformation

$$\mathbf{x} = \mathbf{C}\mathbf{u}, \tag{19.4.6}$$

where $\mathbf{C}$ is a real non-singular 2×2 matrix. To reach the conclusions just stated regarding stability in the various cases we must observe that $|\mathbf{x}| = 0$ if and only if $|\mathbf{u}| = 0$, and that $|\mathbf{x}|$ is small if and only if $|\mathbf{u}|$ is small.)

All of this refers to the linear approximation, and the crucial question that insistently suggests itself is this: "Is the stability correctly determined by the linear approximation?". We shall find that, in the case $m = 2$ at present under discussion, the answer is affirmative, with one conspicuous exception; a vortex point, which appears to be stable when we deal with the linear approximation, may be stable or unstable when we deal with the complete equations.*

We shall find that the definitions of stability and of complete stability and of instability can be extended to problems in m dimensions, where $m > 2$. Later (§ 23.7) we shall consider also the extension of the notion of stability to the *motion* of a dynamical system, i.e. to proper trajectories instead of to the degenerate trajectories consisting of isolated equilibrium points. (One particular problem of stability of motion has already been considered in § 9.6.)

19.6 Motion in the neighbourhood of a singular point, the general theory. We now turn to the general theory of the motion near an isolated singularity of the field $\mathbf{F}$. We take the singularity as origin, as in § 19.4, and we have the equations

$$\begin{cases} \dot{x} = ax + by + \varepsilon(x, y), \\ \dot{y} = cx + dy + \eta(x, y), \end{cases} \tag{19.6.1}$$

where $ad - bc \neq 0$, and ε/r and $\eta/r \to 0$ with r. We denote by $\mathbf{F}_0$ the field defined by the linear terms alone

$$P_0 = ax + by, \quad Q_0 = cx + dy. \tag{19.6.2}$$

Now $\mathbf{F}$ differs only slightly from $\mathbf{F}_0$ near O; more precisely, $|\mathbf{F}|/|\mathbf{F}_0| \to 1$, and $\psi \to 0$, as $r \to 0$, where ψ is the angle between $\mathbf{F}_0$ and $\mathbf{F}$. These statements are almost obvious. To prove them formally we notice that

$$\mathbf{F}_0(r, \theta) = r\mathbf{F}_0(1, \theta), \tag{19.6.3}$$

and $|\mathbf{F}_0|/r$ is bounded away from zero; in fact $|\mathbf{F}_0|/r \geqslant c > 0$, where c is the infimum of $|\mathbf{F}_0|$ on the unit circle. Further

$$|\mathbf{F} - \mathbf{F}_0|/r = \sqrt{(\varepsilon^2 + \eta^2)}/r \to 0 \tag{19.6.4}$$

as $r \to 0$. Thus $|\mathbf{F} - \mathbf{F}_0|/|\mathbf{F}_0| \to 0$ as $r \to 0$. Now

$$|\mathbf{F}| = |\mathbf{F}_0 + \mathbf{F} - \mathbf{F}_0| = |\mathbf{F}_0| + \lambda|\mathbf{F} - \mathbf{F}_0|, \tag{19.6.5}$$

* The case of a zero eigenvalue, hitherto excluded from the discussion, is another case in which the linear approximation gives no clue to the actual behaviour; cf. *Examples* 19.11B and 19.11C below.

where $|\lambda| \leqslant 1$, and

(19.6.6) $$\frac{|\mathbf{F}|}{|\mathbf{F}_0|} = 1 + \lambda \frac{|\mathbf{F} - \mathbf{F}_0|}{|\mathbf{F}_0|} \to 1.$$

This is the first of the two results stated. To prove the second,

(19.6.7) $$\sin \psi \leqslant \frac{|\mathbf{F} - \mathbf{F}_0|}{|\mathbf{F}_0|} \to 0,$$

and this completes the proof.

We shall sometimes wish to consider the radial and transverse components of $\mathbf{F}$, and we shall denote these by R and S. The corresponding components of $\mathbf{F}_0$ are denoted by R_0 and S_0.

We know the results for the field $\mathbf{F}_0$ (§ 19.4), and it is natural to ask if the motion near O is similar for $\mathbf{F}$ to the motion for $\mathbf{F}_0$. In this theory (in contrast to the theory for the field $\mathbf{F}_0$) we are only concerned with characteristics originating in points near O.

We shall find that in the neighbourhood of a node, a saddle point, or a focus, the motion near the singularity is similar to the motion for the field $\mathbf{F}_0$. The exception is the vortex point. In this case the linear terms alone are not sufficient to settle the question of stability. This comes as something of a shock, especially as the problem of small oscillations (Chapter IX) comes under this heading. However in that case we have the additional information derived from the energy equation; the fact of stability is known in advance, and the linear theory does provide a good approximation to the actual motion. In the general case, however, we have no such assurance.

Consider first a positive semi-characteristic that approaches *and enters O*. If $\dot{y}/\dot{x} \to l$ as $t \to \infty$, then $y/x \to l$ also, and since

(19.6.8) $$\frac{\dot{y}}{\dot{x}} = \frac{cx + dy + \eta}{ax + by + \varepsilon},$$

we have

(19.6.9) $$l = \frac{c + dl}{a + bl},$$

and $\{1, l\}$ is an eigenvector of the matrix $\mathbf{A}$. Thus if λ_1 and λ_2 are real and unequal there can be only two directions (or four if we take account of different senses) in which the trajectories enter O, and no trajectory can enter O if the eigenvalues are not real.

We now consider the motion near a singular point of one of the four types.

19.7 Motion near a node. By a suitable affine transformation we obtain the equations

(19.7.1) $$\begin{cases} \dot{x} = \lambda_1 x + \varepsilon(x, y), \\ \dot{y} = \lambda_2 y + \eta(x, y), \end{cases}$$

where we now use (x, y) instead of (u, v) for the new variables, and ε/r and $\eta/r \to 0$ with r. We will consider more particularly the case $\lambda_1 < \lambda_2 < 0$.

Using polar coordinates (in the new (x, y)-plane) we have, for the radial component of the field,

(19.7.2) $$R_0/r = -(\mu_1 \cos^2 \theta + \mu_2 \sin^2 \theta) < -\mu_2 < 0,$$

where $\mu_i = -\lambda_i$, as in (19.4.14). Hence there is a length r_0, and a positive number μ, such that

$$R/r < -\mu < 0 \tag{19.7.3}$$

for $r < r_0$.

Now consider a characteristic $(r(t),\, \theta(t))$ starting at a point inside the circle of radius r_0, $r(0) < r_0$. Since $\dot{r} = R < 0$ the mobile lies inside the circle for $t > 0$, and

$$\frac{1}{r}\frac{dr}{dt} = \frac{R}{r} < -\mu, \tag{19.7.4}$$

whence

$$r(t) < r(0)e^{-\mu t}. \tag{19.7.5}$$

Thus $r(t) \to 0$ as $t \to \infty$, and every positive semi-characteristic originating in a sufficiently small neighbourhood of O *approaches* O.

But we can go further. The trajectory actually *enters* O, either along Oy or along Ox; we find that $y(t)/x(t)$ tends to $+\infty$, or to $-\infty$, or to zero, as $t \to \infty$. To prove this, we choose an angle δ, and consider the angular regions A_i $(= A_i(\delta))$, each of angle 2δ, as shown in Fig. 19.7. Now, for the transverse component,

$$S_0/r = (\mu_1 - \mu_2)\cos\theta\sin\theta, \tag{19.7.6}$$

so that, outside the regions A_i,

$$|S_0|/r > (\mu_1 - \mu_2)\cos\delta\sin\delta > 0. \tag{19.7.7}$$

Hence there is a length r_1 $(= r_1(\delta))$, $r_1 \leqslant r_0$, and a positive number μ', such that at points outside the regions A_i, and inside the circle of radius r_1,

$$|S|/r > \mu' > 0. \tag{19.7.8}$$

In general, the smaller value we take for δ, the smaller the value we need for r_1. The regions inside the circle of radius r_1, but outside the sectors A_i, we call B_1, B_2, B_3, B_4 (Fig. 19.7). The angular velocity $\dot{\theta}$ of the mobile is equal to S/r, and in B_1 and B_3

$$\dot{\theta} > \mu' > 0, \tag{19.7.9}$$

while in B_2 and B_4

$$\dot{\theta} < -\mu' < 0. \tag{19.7.10}$$

We now consider a positive semi-characteristic originating at a point of B_1. Since $r_1 \leqslant r_0$ the trajectory approaches O, and since $\dot{\theta} > \mu'$ in B_1, the mobile enters A_2. But once the mobile gets inside A_2 it stays inside for good. To prove this we have only to notice the direction of the field $\mathbf{F}$ at points on the boundary of the sector. The trajectory may cross Oy.

The rest is simple. We replace δ by $\frac{1}{2}\delta$, and consider a point on the same trajectory at a time t so large that $r(t) < r_1(\frac{1}{2}\delta)$. By the same argument as before, if the mobile is not already in the region $A_2(\frac{1}{2}\delta)$ it will penetrate this region and then stay inside for ever.

Thus, by repeated application of the same method, we see that, given any $\eta > 0$ however small, there exists a time τ $(= \tau(\eta))$ such that

$$\tfrac{1}{2}\pi - \eta < \theta(t) < \tfrac{1}{2}\pi + \eta \tag{19.7.11}$$

for $t > \tau$, and the trajectory enters O along the positive y-axis.

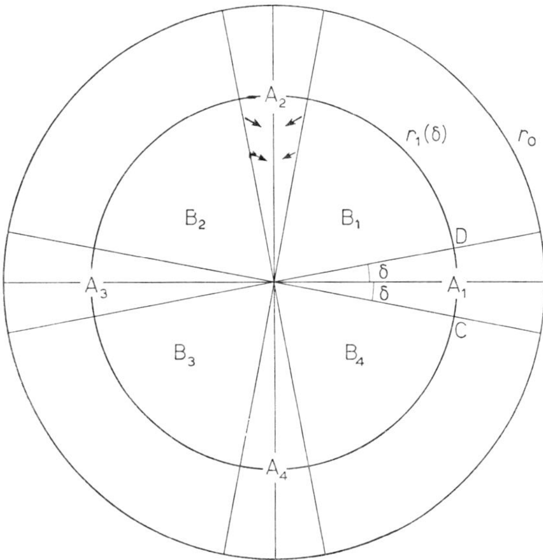

Figure 19.7

If the mobile starts in B_2 at $t = 0$ the trajectory again enters O along the positive y-axis. If it starts in B_3 or B_4 the trajectory enters O along the negative y-axis. Every positive semi-characteristic which does not enter O along the x-axis enters O along the y-axis.

This leaves open the question whether there is a trajectory which enters O along the x-axis. The answer is affirmative. To prove this, consider the arc CD of the circle $r = r_1$ lying in A_1. Suppose the mobile starts at $t = 0$ from a point of CD. If none of the positive semi-characteristics originating in points of CD enters O along Ox they will all enter O along Oy, from above or from below. Some will penetrate A_2 (and enter O along the positive y-axis) and some will penetrate A_4 (and enter O along the negative y-axis). Thus we can find on the arc CD two non-vacuous sets, points belonging to one or the other according as the trajectory enters A_2 or A_4. These are open sets, since the solution varies continuously with the initial point, so there is at least one point of CD which is not in either set. The trajectory originating in this point must enter O along Ox. (There is however an important difference from the linear case, namely that the trajectory entering O along Ox is not necessarily unique.* As an illustration, the system

$$\dot{x} = -2x, \qquad \dot{y} = -y - 3x^2 \sin (\pi y/2x^2), \tag{19.7.12}$$

has infinitely many trajectories entering O along Ox, for example the curves $y = 0$ and $y = x^2$.)

Thus finally *the behaviour near the node is essentially the same as for the linear approximation* discussed previously.

The case where $\lambda_1 = \lambda_2$ can be handled in a similar way; the stability of the node is determined by the linear terms alone. In the usual case where ε and η are $O(r^2)$ the node remains a node. But with the less exacting conditions $\varepsilon/r \to 0$, $\eta/r \to 0$, the node may become a spiral point.

* There is uniqueness if $\partial\eta/\partial y \to 0$ with r.

Example 19.7. Consider the case in which

(19.7.13) $$\dot{x} = -\mu x + \varepsilon, \quad \dot{y} = -\mu y + \eta,$$

where $\mu > 0$, and

(19.7.14) $$\varepsilon = -\sin\theta\, f(r) \qquad \eta = \cos\theta\, f(r),$$

where $$f(r) = \frac{kr}{\sqrt{\left(\log \dfrac{r_1}{r}\right)}}.$$

If initially $r = r_0 < r_1$, we have

(19.7.15) $$\dot{r} = -\mu r, \quad r = r_0 e^{-\mu t},$$

and the trajectory approaches O. Further

(19.7.16) $$\dot{\theta} = \frac{k}{\sqrt{\left(\log \dfrac{r_1}{r}\right)}} = \frac{k}{\sqrt{\left(\log \dfrac{r_1}{r_0} + \log \dfrac{r_0}{r}\right)}} = \frac{k}{\sqrt{\left(\mu t + \log \dfrac{r_1}{r_0}\right)}},$$

whence

(19.7.17) $$\theta - \theta_0 = \frac{2k}{\mu}\sqrt{\left(\mu t + \log \frac{r_1}{r_0}\right)},$$

and the singularity for the complete field is a spiral point. For the linear approximation the singularity is a stable node.

19.8 Motion near a saddle point. We reduce the equations to the form

(19.8.1) $$\begin{cases} \dot{x} = \lambda_1 x + \varepsilon(x, y), \\ \dot{y} = \lambda_2 y + \eta(x, y), \end{cases}$$

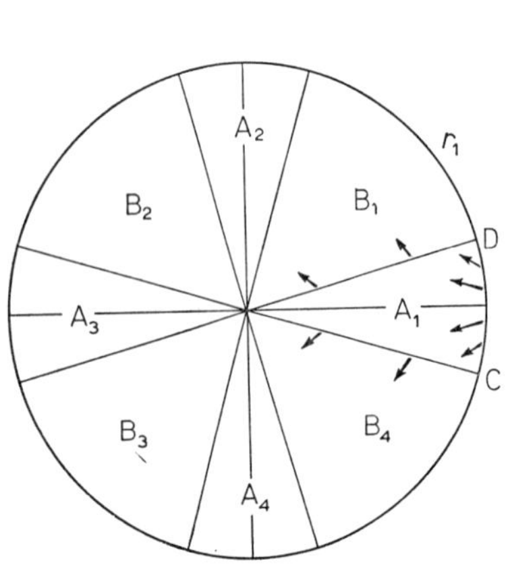

Figure 19.8*a*

where $\lambda_1 < 0 < \lambda_2$. Then

(19.8.2) $$\begin{aligned} R_0/r &= \lambda_2 \sin^2\theta - \mu_1 \cos^2\theta \\ &= (\mu_1 + \lambda_2)\sin^2\theta - \mu_1 \\ &= \lambda_2 - (\mu_1 + \lambda_2)\cos^2\theta, \end{aligned}$$

and we can find an angle δ and a positive constant K such that (with the notation of Fig. 19.8*a*)

(19.8.3) $$\begin{cases} R_0/r > K > 0, & \text{in } A_2 \text{ and } A_4, \\ R_0/r < -K < 0, & \text{in } A_1 \text{ and } A_3. \end{cases}$$

Further

(19.8.4) $$S_0/r = (\mu_1 + \lambda_2)\cos\theta\sin\theta,$$

so

(19.8.5) $$\begin{cases} S_0/r > (\mu_1 + \lambda_2)\cos\delta\sin\delta > 0, & \text{in } B_1 \text{ and } B_3, \\ S_0/r < -(\mu_1 + \lambda_2)\cos\delta\sin\delta < 0, & \text{in } B_2 \text{ and } B_4. \end{cases}$$

Similar statements are true of R/r and S/r if we consider only points sufficiently near to O. There is a number r_1 $(= r_1(\delta))$, and positive numbers k, k', such that, if $r < r_1$,

$$(19.8.6)\qquad \begin{cases} \dot{r} = R > kr > 0, & \text{in } A_2 \text{ and } A_4, \\ \dot{r} = R < -kr < 0, & \text{in } A_1 \text{ and } A_3, \end{cases}$$

while

$$(19.8.7)\qquad \begin{cases} \dot{\theta} = S/r > k' > 0, & \text{in } B_1 \text{ and } B_3, \\ \dot{\theta} = S/r < -k' < 0, & \text{in } B_2 \text{ and } B_4. \end{cases}$$

Consider then a trajectory originating in B_1. Since $\dot{\theta} > k'$ the mobile enters A_2 (unless it has previously left the circle $r = r_1$) and, as before, once in A_2 it stays in A_2 for good. But in A_2

$$(19.8.8)\qquad \dot{r} > kr, \quad r > r_0 e^{kt},$$

and the mobile leaves the circle. The trajectory either enters A_2 and then leaves the circle $r = r_1$, or it leaves the circle before reaching A_2. *The singularity is unstable*, just as it is for the linear approximation.

There is however (as for the linear approximation) one trajectory entering O along the positive x-axis. To prove this statement, consider the trajectories originating in points of the arc CD of the circle $r = r_1$. The trajectory starting at D enters B_1, and then leaves the circle at a point above Ox (as we saw above). Similarly the trajectory starting at C enters B_4, and leaves the circle at a point below Ox. If now we suppose that all the trajectories starting from points of CD do one or other of these things (i.e. either they leave the circle above Ox or they leave it below Ox) we are led to a contradiction. We have two open sets on CD, and there is at least one dividing point, which belongs to neither set; the trajectory originating in this point behaves in neither of the ways described. Therefore this particular trajectory stays in A_1, and so it must enter O along Ox. By the same argument there is at least one trajectory entering O from the left along Ox.

Example 19.8*A*. *Simple pendulum.* A familiar example is provided by the problem of the simple pendulum near the position of unstable equilibrium. The equation of motion, if we measure from the highest point of the circle, is

$$(19.8.9)\qquad \ddot{\theta} - n^2 \sin\theta = 0, \qquad n^2 = g/a,$$

and writing this as two first-order equations, we have

$$(19.8.10)\qquad \dot{\theta} = \varphi, \quad \dot{\varphi} = n^2 \sin\theta.$$

The linear approximation is

$$(19.8.11)\qquad \dot{\theta} = \varphi, \quad \dot{\varphi} = n^2\theta,$$

and the eigenvalues are $\pm n$; the singularity is a saddle point. The fact that one trajectory enters the singularity from each side is familiar; these are the limitation motions in which the particle just reaches the highest point of the circle.

The trajectories for the general problem, not merely for motion near the singularity, are shown in Fig. 19.8b. The singularities lie on the line $\varphi = 0$ at the points $\theta = 0$ and $\theta = \pm n\pi$; $\theta = 0$ (and also $\theta = \pm n\pi$, where n is even) is a saddle point, a point of unstable equilibrium, and $\theta = \pi$ (and $\theta = \pm n\pi$, where n is odd) is a vortex point, a point of stable equilibrium. The equations of the trajectories are

$$\varphi^2 = \omega^2 - 4n^2 \cos^2 \tfrac{1}{2}\theta, \tag{19.8.12}$$

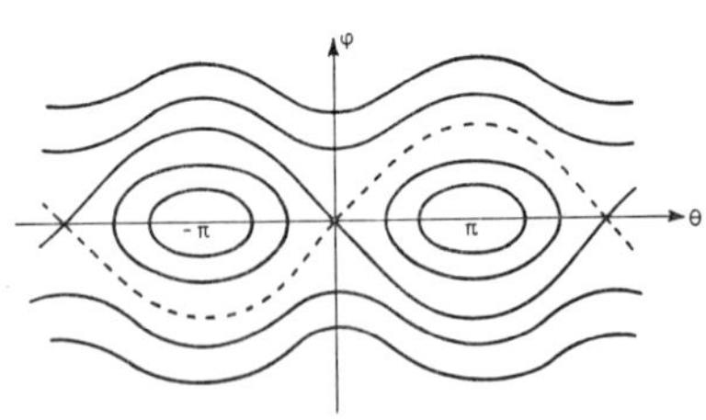

Figure 19.8b

where ω is the angular velocity at the lowest point of the circle; the equation (19.8.12) is of course equivalent to the energy equation. For the oscillatory motions, $|\omega| < 2n$; for the motions in which θ continually increases or continually decreases, $|\omega| > 2n$. In the critical, case in which the energy level is the tangent at the highest point of the circle, $|\omega| = 2n$. The dividing trajectory, or *separatrix* is the curve $\varphi = -2n \sin \frac{1}{2}\theta$. (The curve $\varphi = 2n \sin \frac{1}{2}\theta$, represented in the figure by a broken line, represents a motion in which $\theta \to 2\pi$ from below as $t \to \infty$; physically this is the same motion as the limitation motion in which $\theta \to 0$ from below as $t \to \infty$, so the broken curve is effectively also part of the separatrix.)

Example 19.8B. *Pendulum in a resisting medium.* A slightly more elaborate example is provided by the motion of a simple pendulum in a resisting medium; a bead slides on a smooth wire in the form of a circle in a vertical plane, and there is a resistance to motion proportional to the speed. Measuring from the highest point of the circle we have the equation of motion

$$\ddot{\theta} + 2k\dot{\theta} - n^2 \sin \theta = 0 \tag{19.8.13}$$

and, writing this as usual in the form of two first-order equations, we have

$$\dot{\theta} = \varphi, \quad \dot{\varphi} = n^2 \sin \theta - 2k\varphi. \tag{19.8.14}$$

The linear approximation is

$$\dot{\theta} = \varphi, \quad \dot{\varphi} = n^2\theta - 2k\varphi, \tag{19.8.15}$$

and the eigenvalues are $-k \pm p$, where $p = \sqrt{(k^2 + n^2)}$. We have a saddle point at $\theta = \varphi = 0$. There is one trajectory entering the singularity from either side. We can project the bead from any point of the circle with an initial velocity which will just carry it to the top, though it does not reach the highest point in a finite time. This agrees with the expectation of common sense. We should expect that there is a critical value of the velocity of projection dividing the motions in which the head fails to reach the highest point from those in which it overshoots the highest point.

The trajectories for the general problem (not merely near the saddle point) are again of great interest. If we write x in place of θ and make an appropriate change in the time-scale, the equation becomes

$$\ddot{x} + \dot{x} - p \sin x = 0, \tag{19.8.16}$$

where $p = n^2/(4k^2)$, so the first-order equations are

$$\dot{x} = y, \quad \dot{y} = p \sin x - y. \tag{19.8.17}$$

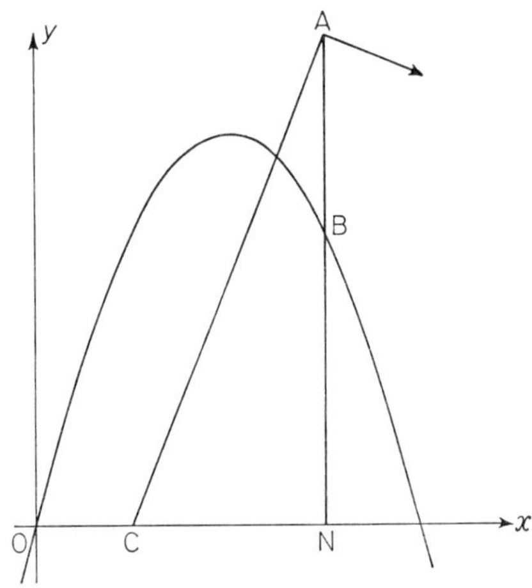

Figure 19.8c

In problems of this type the lines of force can usually be constructed graphically. We begin (Fig. 19.8*c*) by drawing the curve $y = p \sin x$. Let the perpendicular to Ox from an arbitrary point A cut the sine-curve in B and the axis Ox in N. Take a point C on Ox at distance AB from N, to the left (right) of N if A is above (below) B. Then the field at A is perpendicular to CA. The lines of force for this field, which are the trajectories in the dynamical problem,

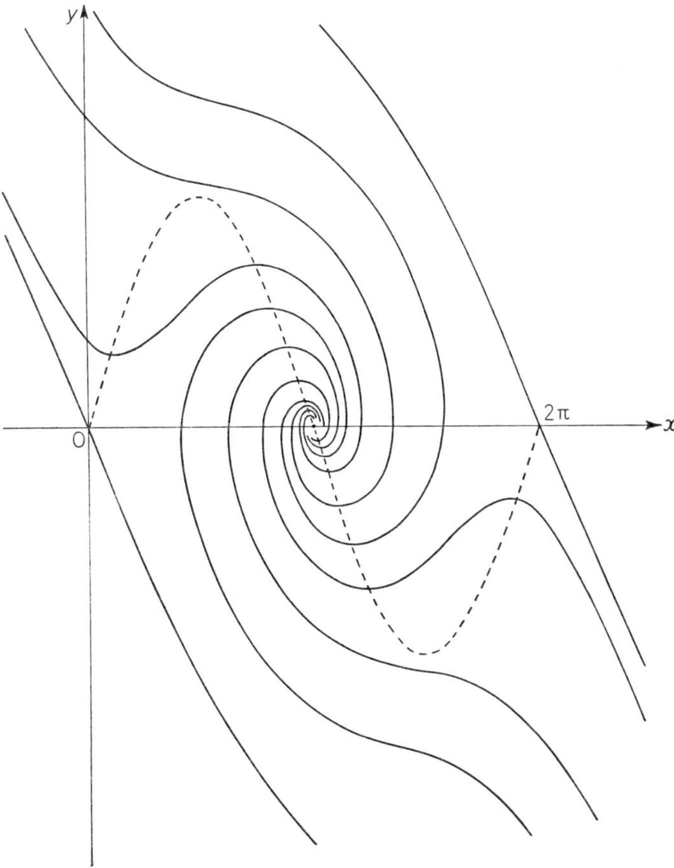

Figure 19.8*d*

are shown in Fig. 19.8*d*. The point of unstable equilibrium ($\theta = \varphi = 0$) is a saddle point, the point of stable equilibrium ($\theta = \pi$, $\varphi = 0$) is a stable focus.

19.9 Motion near a spiral point. We reduce the equations to the normal form

$$\begin{cases} \dot{x} = \alpha x - \beta y + \varepsilon(x, y), \\ \dot{y} = \beta x + \alpha y + \eta(x, y), \end{cases} \tag{19.9.1}$$

where $\alpha \pm i\beta$ are the eigenvalues, and ε/r, $\eta/r \to 0$ with r. We will suppose, for definiteness, $\alpha < 0$ and $\beta > 0$. Now $R_0 = \alpha r$, $S_0 = \beta r$, and the trajectories for the field $\mathbf{F}_0$ are spirals winding in the positive sense to O. At points sufficiently near to O the field $\mathbf{F}$ differs only slightly from $\mathbf{F}_0$, so for $r < r_0$ we have

$$R/r < -k < 0, \quad S/r > k' > 0. \tag{19.9.2}$$

Thus a positive semi-characteristic originating in $r < r_0$ is again a spiral about O, in which $r(t) \to 0$ and $\theta(t) \to \infty$ as $t \to \infty$. We see again that *the nature of the trajectories near the singularity is determined by the linear terms alone.* The singularity is stable if $\alpha < 0$, unstable if $\alpha > 0$.

The *Example* 19.8*B* provides an illustration of this case also. If we measure from the lowest point of the circle the equation of motion is

$$\ddot{\theta} + 2k\dot{\theta} + n^2 \sin \theta = 0. \tag{19.9.3}$$

The first-order equations are

$$\dot{\theta} = \varphi, \quad \dot{\varphi} = -n^2 \sin \theta - 2k\varphi, \tag{19.9.4}$$

and the eigenvalues are $-k \pm ip$, where $p = \sqrt{(n^2 - k^2)}$. The trajectories are seen in Fig. 19.8*d*, where however the singularity with which we are here concerned is not the origin, but is the point $(\pi, 0)$.

19.10 Motion near a vortex point. We now come to the critical case. We have found that for a node, a saddle point, or a spiral point the motion near the singularity is similar to the motion determined by the linear terms alone. This is no longer true for a vortex point. The motion determined by the linear approximation is stable; the motion determined by the complete field may be stable, or completely stable, or unstable.

The equations in the normalized form are

$$\begin{cases} \dot{x} = -\beta y + \varepsilon(x, y), \\ \dot{y} = \beta x + \eta(x, y). \end{cases} \tag{19.10.1}$$

It is frequently advantageous to use polar coordinates; recalling the relations $r\dot{r} = x\dot{x} + y\dot{y}$, $r^2\dot{\theta} = x\dot{y} - y\dot{x}$, we easily find the following formulae for $\dot{r}$ and $\dot{\theta}$,

$$\begin{cases} \dot{r} = \dfrac{x\varepsilon + y\eta}{r}, \\ \dot{\theta} = \beta + \dfrac{x\eta - y\varepsilon}{r^2}. \end{cases} \tag{19.10.2}$$

The solution for the linear approximation is

$$r = r_0, \quad \theta = \theta_0 + \beta t.$$

It is worthy of notice that the formula for θ remains valid for the complete equations in any problem in which $\varepsilon/x = \eta/y$.

Example 19.10*A*. Let us start with the linear field

$$\dot{x} = y, \quad \dot{y} = -x, \tag{19.10.3}$$

which is essentially the problem of the harmonic oscillator. The origin is a vortex point, $\beta = -1$, and the solution is

$$r = r_0, \quad \theta = \theta_0 - t. \tag{19.10.4}$$

Let us now consider what happens when we add second-order terms in the field: we give one example of each of the three possibilities. (In each of these examples $\varepsilon/x = \eta/y$, and the equation $\theta = \theta_0 - t$ persists in each case.)

(i) If the equations are

(19.10.5) $$\dot{x} = y - xy, \quad \dot{y} = -x - y^2,$$

we have $$\dot{r} = -ry = -r^2 \sin(\theta_0 - t),$$

and

$$\frac{1}{r} - \frac{1}{r_0} = \cos(\theta_0 - t) - \cos\theta_0 = \cos\theta - \cos\theta_0.$$

The trajectories are the conics $r = e(1 - x)$ with O as focus and the line $x = 1$ as directrix. For small values of r_0 the trajectories are ellipses, and in this problem the stability persists when we add the second-order terms in the equations. Given a positive number ε $(< \frac{1}{2})$ we can take $\kappa(\varepsilon) = \frac{1}{2}\varepsilon$, where the symbols ε and κ refer to the definition of stability given in § 19.5. The trajectories cutting $y = 0$ at $x = 0{\cdot}1$, $0{\cdot}2$. $0{\cdot}3$, $0{\cdot}4$, $0{\cdot}5$, $0{\cdot}6$, $0{\cdot}7$ are shown in Fig. 19.10a.

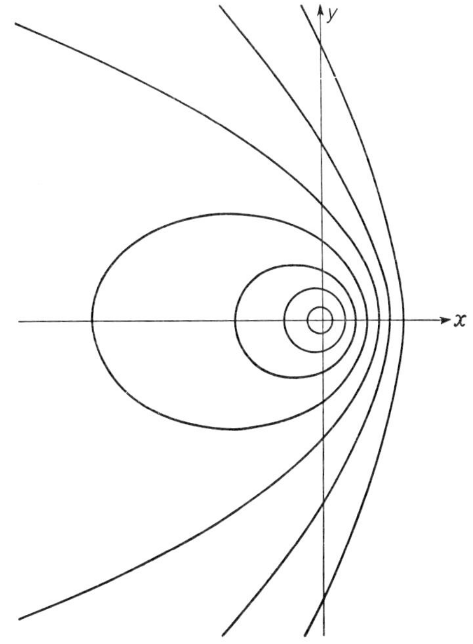

Figure 19.10a

(ii) If the equations are

(19.10.6) $$\dot{x} = y - xr, \quad \dot{y} = -x - yr,$$

we have $$\dot{r} = -r^2,$$

and therefore

$$\frac{1}{r} - \frac{1}{r_0} = t,$$

and $r \to 0$ as $t \to \infty$. The stability not only persists, but is enhanced, and we now have complete stability.

(iii) If the equations are

(19.10.7) $$\dot{x} = y + xr, \quad \dot{y} = -x + yr,$$

we have $$\dot{r} = r^2,$$

and therefore $$\frac{1}{r} - \frac{1}{r_0} = -t.$$

In this case $r \to \infty$ as $t \to 1/r_0$, and the singularity is unstable. (This example has been noticed already, in § 9.9.)

In (ii) and (iii) the trajectories are hyperbolic spirals.

Example 19.10B. We reconsider, in the light of the present theory, the problem of a harmonic oscillator in a resisting medium, which has already been noticed in § 19.2. The equation of motion

(19.10.8) $$\ddot{x} + f(\dot{x}) + x = 0$$

leads to the two first-order equations

(19.10.9) $$\dot{x} = y, \quad \dot{y} = -x - f(y),$$

where $f(y)$ vanishes with y and is monotone increasing, so $yf(y) > 0$ unless $y = 0$, and $yf(y)$ increases steadily as y increases or decreases from zero. The origin is a vortex point. Now

$$r\dot{r} = x\dot{x} + y\dot{y} = -yf(y),$$

and r continually decreases and tends to a limit l ($l \geqslant 0$) as $t \to \infty$. But, as we have seen already (§ 19.2), $l > 0$ is impossible, so $r \to 0$, and the singularity is completely stable.

Example 19.10*C*. The system just considered is not necessarily completely stable if we relinquish the condition that $f(y)$ has the same sign as y.

Consider for example the motion defined by the equation

$$\ddot{x} + \dot{x}^2 + x = 0. \tag{19.10.10}$$

The first-order equations are

$$\dot{x} = y, \quad \dot{y} = -x - y^2. \tag{19.10.11}$$

The origin is a vortex point, with $\beta = -1$, and

$$r\dot{r} = -y^3, \quad \dot{\theta} = -1 - (xy^2/r^2).$$

If we replace t by $-t$ and y by $-y$ the system is unchanged, so there is symmetry about the axis Ox. Let us consider the trajectory originating in $(-b, 0)$, where $b > 0$. The mobile moves into the upper half-plane, and so long as it remains in this half-plane $\dot{x} > 0$ (so $x > -b$) and $\dot{r} < 0$ (so $r < b$). Also, for small values of b, θ continually decreases; if we suppose for definiteness that $b < \frac{1}{2}$, then $\dot{\theta} < -\frac{1}{2}$. The trajectory cannot enter O, so the trajectory meets Ox again to the right of O. By the symmetry the path in the lower half-plane is the mirror image of that in the upper half-plane, and the trajectories are closed oval curves. In this case the stability indicated by the linear approximation persists as ordinary stability, in contrast to the complete stability of the previous example.

In this case we can find the trajectories explicitly, and it is interesting to investigate the complete solution, not merely the solution for a small disturbance from equilibrium. The equation (19.10.10) is equivalent to

$$\frac{d}{dx}\left(\tfrac{1}{2}y^2\right) + y^2 + x = 0, \tag{19.10.12}$$

which is a linear differential equation of the first order for y^2. The characteristic through $(a, 0)$ is

$$y^2 = \tfrac{1}{2} - x - \left(\tfrac{1}{2} - a\right)e^{2(a-x)}, \tag{19.10.13}$$

which we can also write in the form

$$y^2 = (a - x) + \left(a - \tfrac{1}{2}\right)\{e^{2(a-x)} - 1\}. \tag{19.10.14}$$

A glance at the graph of the second member shows that we have a libration in x, and a closed trajectory in the (x, y)-plane, if $0 < a < \frac{1}{2}$. In that case the motion is periodic; x oscillates between two values, $a \geqslant x \geqslant -b$ (where $b > 0$), and the relation between a and b is

$$(1 + 2b)e^{-2b} = (1 - 2a)e^{2a}.$$

(When a is small and positive, the value of b is approximately $a + \frac{4}{3}a^2 + \frac{16}{9}a^3$, and the period is approximately $2\pi(1 + \frac{1}{6}a^2)$*.) We notice that $b \to \infty$ as $a \to \frac{1}{2}$. For the critical value $a = \frac{1}{2}$ the trajectory is the parabola $y^2 + x = \frac{1}{2}$, and $x \to -\infty$ as $t \to \infty$. For $a > \frac{1}{2}$ the trajectories are not closed, and $x \to -\infty$ as t tends to a finite limit t_0. The trajectories are shown in Fig. 19.10*b* for $a = 0{\cdot}1, 0{\cdot}2, 0{\cdot}3, 0{\cdot}4, 0{\cdot}5, 0{\cdot}6, 0{\cdot}7$ (cf. Fig. 19.10*a*).

* Cf. the footnote on p. 10.

In drawing the figure we notice that the closed trajectories have horizontal tangents on the parabola $y^2 + x = 0$, and that the maximum value of y is w where

$$2w^2 = \log\left(\frac{1}{1 - 2a}\right) - 2a,$$

$$\left(\frac{w}{a}\right)^2 = 1 + \tfrac{2}{3}(2a) + \tfrac{2}{4}(2a)^2 + \tfrac{2}{5}(2a)^3 + \cdots.$$

For the unclosed trajectories, $\dot\theta = 0$ on the curve $x^2 + y^2 + xy^2 = 0$.

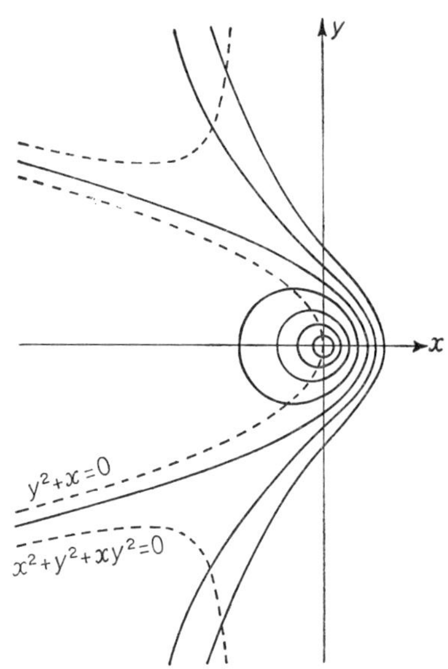

Figure 19.10*b*

Example 19.10*D*. As a final example of motion near a vortex point we consider the system

$$(19.10.15)\qquad \begin{cases} \dot x = y + xf(r), \\ \dot y = -x + yf(r). \end{cases}$$

Here $\theta = \theta_0 - t$ whatever the form of $f(r)$, and $\dot r = rf(r)$. The cases $f(r) = \pm r$ have been noticed already (in *Example* 19.10*A*) and we now consider three further cases:

(i) $f(r) = r(a - r)$, where $a > 0$. If initially $r = r_0$, where $0 < r_0 < a$, then $\dot r > 0$, and $r \to a$ as $t \to \infty$. The trajectory is a spiral approximating to the circle $r = a$ from the inside. Explicitly,

$$a^2t = a^2(\theta_0 - \theta) = \log\frac{\rho_0}{\rho} + \rho_0 - \rho,$$

where ρ is written for $\dfrac{a}{r} - 1$. The vortex point at the origin is unstable. If $r_0 > a$, then $\dot r < 0$, and $r \to a$ as $t \to \infty$; the trajectory is a spiral approximating to the circle $r = a$ from the outside.

(ii) $f(r) = r\sin(\pi/r)$. In this case $\dot r = r^2\sin(\pi/r)$, and there exists a family of periodic orbits, namely the circles $r = 1/n$, where n is a positive integer. If $r_0 = 1/n$ the trajectory is the circle $r = 1/n$.

If $r_0 > 1$, $\dot r > 0$, and $r \to \infty$ with t. If $1 > r_0 > \frac{1}{2}$, $\dot r < 0$, and $r \to \frac{1}{2}$ as $t \to \infty$; the trajectory is a spiral approaching the circle $r = \frac{1}{2}$ from the outside. If $\frac{1}{2} > r_0 > \frac{1}{3}$, $\dot r > 0$, and $r \to \frac{1}{2}$ as $t \to \infty$; the trajectory is a spiral approaching the circle $r = \frac{1}{2}$ from the inside. And generally, if $0 < r_0 < 1$, and r_0 is not of the form $1/n$, the trajectory is a spiral inwards or outwards to the nearest circle whose radius is the inverse of an even integer. The ordinary stability indicated by the linear approximation persists when we add the extra terms; it is not replaced by complete stability. The trajectories near O are not all periodic orbits (as they were in *Example* 19.10*A*(i) and in *Example* 19.10*C*). The reader may find it of interest to consider the equation $\dot r^2 = r^4\sin^2\dfrac{\pi}{r}$ in the light of the theory of equation (1.2.10).

(iii) $f(r) = r^2$. Here $\dfrac{1}{r^2} = 2(t_0 - t)$, and $r \to \infty$ as $t \to t_0 = \dfrac{1}{2r_0^{\,2}}$. The trajectory is the spiral $r^2(\theta - \theta_1) = \frac{1}{2}$, where $\theta_1 = \theta_0 - t_0$. The vortex point is unstable (cf. *Example* 19.10*A*(iii)).

If we write $\xi = x - iy$, $\eta = x + iy$, the equations become

$$\dot\xi = i\xi + \xi^2\eta, \quad \dot\eta = -i\eta + \xi\eta^2.$$

Then

$$\frac{d}{dt}(\xi\eta) = \xi\dot\eta + \dot\xi\eta = 2\xi^2\eta^2, \quad \frac{d}{dt}\left(\frac{\eta}{\xi}\right) = \frac{\xi\dot\eta - \eta\dot\xi}{\xi^2} = -2i\frac{\eta}{\xi},$$

whence

$$\frac{1}{\xi\eta} = 2(t_0 - t), \quad \frac{\eta}{\xi} = e^{2i(\theta_0 - t)},$$

which is of course equivalent to the solution already found. We can deal in a similar way with the more general system

$$\dot{\xi} = \lambda\xi + \mu\xi(\xi\eta)^n, \quad \dot{\eta} = -\lambda\eta + \mu\eta(\xi\eta)^n.$$

19.11 Relation of the linear approximation to the general theory. In the preceding sections we have considered the question of the stability of a position of equilibrium in relation to the problem presented by the linear approximation. We found that, if complete stability is indicated by the linear approximation, this persists when we add the non-linear terms. Similarly, if instability is indicated by the linear approximation, this also persists. But ordinary stability does not always persist.

We conclude with three further examples. In the first, the system contains two singular points, a vortex point and a saddle point, and the trajectories are divided into three classes by the *separatrix*, which is the line of force through the saddle point. The second and third are examples of the exceptional case in which the Jacobian vanishes at the singularity.

Example 19.11*A*. A particle of unit mass moves on a straight line under the action of a force

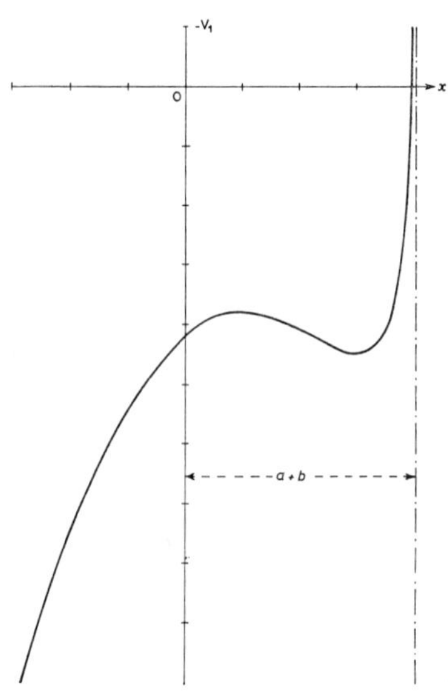

Figure 19.11*a*

(19.11.1) $$-x + \frac{ab}{a + b - x},$$

where $0 < a < b$, and we are concerned with the domain $x < a + b$. The equations are

(19.11.2) $$\dot{x} = y, \quad \dot{y} = -x + \frac{ab}{a + b - x}.$$

The second member of (19.11.2) vanishes at a and at b; there are two singular points in the field, a vortex point at A $(a, 0)$ and a saddle point at B $(b, 0)$. The potential function is given by

(19.11.3) $$V = \tfrac{1}{2}x^2 + ab \log\left(\frac{a + b - x}{a}\right),$$

and the trajectories are defined by the energy equation

(19.11.4) $$\tfrac{1}{2}y^2 = C - V.$$

The graph of $-V$ has the form shown in Fig. 19.11*a*, and (as in § 1.2) we can read off from this graph the nature of the motion for all values of C. The trajectories are shown in Fig. 19.11*b*. The stability of the vortex point A persists as ordinary stability (as in *Example* 19.10*A*(i) and in *Example* 19.10*C*) when we move from the linear approximation to the complete equations. We verify the theory of § 19.8; the motion near the saddle point for the complete equations is of the same type as the motion for the linear approximation.

The *separatrix*, which is the line of force through the saddle point B, has a double point at B. The saddle point itself is a point trajectory; it is also the limit point of trajectories entering it, which are arcs of the separatrix. The equation of the separatrix is

(19.11.5)
$$x^2 + y^2 + 2ab \log\left(\frac{a+b-x}{a}\right) = b^2.$$

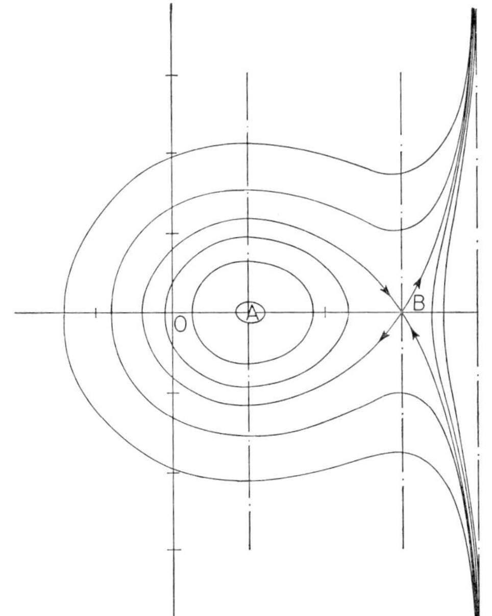

Figure 19.11b

It cuts $y = 0$ again, either to the right or to the left of the origin according to the value of b/a. The critical case in which it actually passes through the origin occurs when $(a + b)/a$ satisfies the equation

$$\log x = \tfrac{1}{2}(x - 1),$$

giving $x = 3{\cdot}51$, $b/a = 2{\cdot}51$, approximately. If b/a is greater than this critical value the other intersection of the separatrix with Ox lies to the left of O; this is so in Fig. 19.11b, which is drawn for the case $b = 3a$.

Example 19.11B. So far we have confined attention to systems with only isolated singular points at each of which the Jacobian $\partial(P, Q)/\partial(x, y)$ does not vanish. We conclude this Chapter with two examples of the exceptional case where the Jacobian does vanish at the singularity, and the preceding theory is no longer applicable.

Let us consider the system

(19.11.6)
$$\dot{x} = x^2 - y^2, \quad \dot{y} = 2xy.$$

There are no linear term on the right in the equations, and the solution for the linear approximations is $x = x_0$, $y = y_0$. The singularity given by the linear approximation is stable, and in the definition of stability (§ 19.5) we can take $\kappa = \varepsilon$.

Let us now consider the complete field. The equations (19.10.2) give

(19.11.7)
$$\dot{r} = xr, \quad \dot{\theta} = y,$$

and we easily find the equation of the trajectory, namely $r = k \sin\theta$. The position on the trajectory at time t is given by $\dot{\theta} = k \sin^2\theta$. The path is a circle touching Ox at O, and the position on the circle at time t is given by

(19.11.8)
$$kt = \cot\theta_0 - \cot\theta.$$

The mobile ultimately returns to O, for θ steadily increases and tends to π as t tends to infinity. Nevertheless the singularity is unstable, and indeed we can find an initial point arbitrarily near to O such that during the subsequent motion the mobile moves to a point arbitrarily remote from O; for example if θ_0 is a small positive number, and $r_0 = \sqrt{(\sin\theta_0)}$, then $k = 1/\sqrt{(\sin\theta_0)}$, which is large.

What happens if the starting point is *on* the x-axis? If the initial point is $(x_0, 0)$ the characteristic is defined by the equations

(19.11.9)
$$\frac{1}{x} = \frac{1}{x_0} - t, \quad y = 0.$$

If $x_0 > 0$, x continually increases and tends to infinity as t tends to $1/x_0$. If $x_0 < 0$, x continually increases, and tends to zero as t tends to infinity.

Example 19.11 *C*. The theorem that, if instability is indicated by the linear approximation this instability persists when we consider the complete equations, is not valid if we relinquish the condition that the Jacobian does not vanish at the singularity. As an illustration, consider the system

$$\dot{x} = y - x^3, \quad \dot{y} = 0. \tag{19.11.10}$$

The motion defined by the linear approximation is clearly unstable. But the motion defined by the complete equations is stable; if initially $y = y_0$, then $y = y_0$ always, and $x \to {y_0}^{1/3}$ as $t \to \infty$.

Chapter XX

Systems with one degree of freedom, the cyclic characteristics

20.1 Index of a curve, and index of a singular point. We now turn to the study of the periodic motions that are possible for the system

$$\dot{x} = P(x, y), \quad \dot{y} = Q(x, y). \tag{20.1.1}$$

The trajectories for the periodic motions are simple closed curves; they are the closed lines of force, if any exist, for the field (P, Q).

In some familiar cases all the lines of force are closed. If we have a particle moving on a straight line in a field of force, the equation of a trajectory is

$$\tfrac{1}{2}y^2 = C - V, \tag{20.1.2}$$

and if $V = \frac{1}{2}n^2x^2$ (the harmonic oscillator) or if V has the same general form (i.e. as x increases from $-\infty$ to $+\infty$, V decreases steadily from $+\infty$ to a minimum, and then increases steadily to $+\infty$) all the lines of force are closed, and all possible motions are periodic. But this is exceptional. In many important cases there exists just one cyclic trajectory, and almost all trajectories are spirals approximating to it; the system tends to settle down to the periodic motion.

We speak of *cyclic* rather than of *closed* trajectories because the proofs in the present Chapter require some appeal to the theory of sets of points, and it will make for clarity if in general we confine the term *closed* to its usual meaning in the theory of sets.

The singular points discussed in the preceding Chapter are degenerate cases of cyclic characteristics.

Consider a simple closed curve Γ which does not pass through any singularity, and let the point p traverse the curve completely in the positive (anticlockwise) sense. Let $\theta(p)$ be the inclination of the field $\mathbf{F}$ to Ox at p. As p moves once completely round the curve, in the prescribed sense, $\theta(p)$ (which is assumed to vary continuously with p) increases by $2n\pi$, where n is an integer, positive, negative, or zero. The number n is the *index* of the curve for the given field. We can picture the variation of θ as p moves round Γ in terms of the mapping of Γ on a unit circle; if $\mathbf{u}(p)$ is the unit vector $\dfrac{1}{|\mathbf{F}|}\mathbf{F}$, the index is the number of revolutions of the vector $\mathbf{u}$ as p moves once round Γ.

If the curve Γ is fixed and we change the vector field $\mathbf{F}$ continuously, but in such a way that there is never a singularity on Γ, then the index does not change. Or again, if we keep the field unchanged, but continuously deform Γ in such a way that it is always a simple closed curve and never passes through a singularity, then the index does not change. These results follow from the simple observation that a variable capable of taking only a discrete set of values, and varying continuously, can only remain constant.

Let us now consider an isolated singularity q. Let us draw a small circle γ about q; the radius of the circle is so small that there is no singularity on γ, and no singularity other than q inside γ. Then the index of the field for γ is well-defined and independent of the radius; indeed it is the same for all simple closed curves with only the one singularity q inside. This number is *the index of the singularity* q.

In the theory of functions of a complex variable z, if the regular function $f(z)$ defines a vector field $\mathbf{F}$,

$$f(z) = P + iQ, \tag{20.1.3}$$

the index of Γ is the number N of zeros of $f(z)$, each counted to its proper order, inside Γ. If $f(z)$ is regular on and inside Γ, save for a finite number of poles inside Γ, the index is $N - M$, where M is the number of poles, each counted to its proper order, inside Γ.

We can easily find the index for each of the types of singularity considered in the preceding Chapter. Taking the origin at the singularity as before, we have

$$P = ax + by + \varepsilon, \quad Q = cx + dy + \eta, \tag{20.1.4}$$

where $ad - bc$, the value J_0 of $\dfrac{\partial(P, Q)}{\partial(x, y)}$ at O, is not zero. To find the index we can work with the field $\mathbf{F}_0$ instead of $\mathbf{F}$, since the angle ψ between $\mathbf{F}$ and $\mathbf{F}_0$ tends to zero with the distance from O (§ 19.6). Consider then a small circle γ about O as centre, and the field

$$P_0 = ax + by, \quad Q_0 = cx + dy. \tag{20.1.5}$$

The mapping

$$(x, y) \to (P_0, Q_0), \tag{20.1.6}$$

where (P_0, Q_0) are interpreted as rectangular coordinates in a subsidiary diagram, transforms the circle γ (in the (x, y)-plane) into an ellipse (in the (P_0, Q_0)-plane), and a positive circuit of the circle corresponds to a positive or negative circuit of the ellipse according as $J_0 > 0$ or $J_0 < 0$, where

$$J_0 = \frac{\partial(P_0, Q_0)}{\partial(x, y)} = \left[\frac{\partial(P, Q)}{\partial(x, y)}\right]_{(0,0)}. \tag{20.1.7}$$

Thus the index of the singularity is $+1$ or -1 according as $J_0 > 0$ or $J_0 < 0$. But J_0 is equal to the product of the eigenvalues of the matrix $\mathbf{A}$ (§ 19.4); it is positive at a node or spiral point or vortex point, and negative at a saddle point. *Thus the index of any singularity of the permitted type (with* $J_0 \neq 0$*) is* ± 1, *being* $+1$ *for a node or spiral point or vortex point, and* -1 *for a saddle point.*

If a closed path Γ in the field $\mathbf{F}$ lies in a simply-connected region without singularities, its index is zero. For we can continuously deform Γ into a point without changing the index. If Γ is a simple closed curve, with no singularities on Γ and only isolated singularities of the permitted type inside, *the index for* Γ *is the sum of the indices for the singularities inside* Γ. The number of the singularities inside must be finite, and to prove the result stated we have only to consider a path such as that shown in Fig. 20.1 for which the index is zero; but this is the index for Γ minus the sum of the indices for the separate loops. Thus the index for Γ is $N - S$, where S is the number of saddle points inside Γ, and N is the number of singularities of other types inside Γ.

An important special case is that in which Γ is a cyclic trajectory; its index is 1 (whether the *motion* on it is clockwise or anticlockwise) and therefore, for a cyclic trajectory,

$$N - S = 1. \tag{20.1.8}$$

It is clear, therefore, that we cannot have a cyclic trajectory with no singularities inside, nor with only saddle points inside. The simplest case is that in which there is just one singularity, not a saddle point, inside; in that case $N = 1$ and $S = 0$.

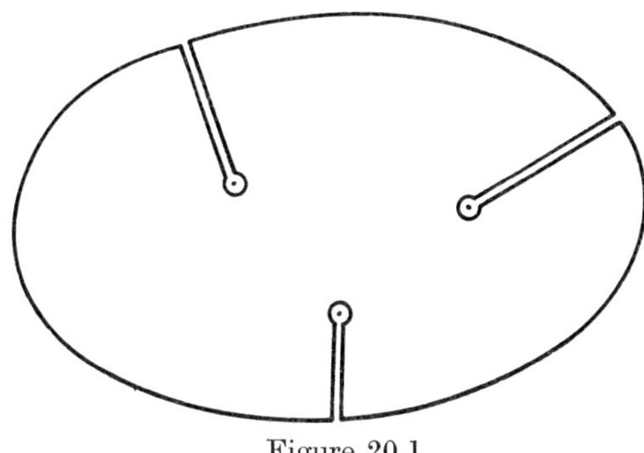

Figure 20.1

20.2 The positive limiting set. We consider a bounded positive semi-characteristic C lying in the domain D (§ 19.3). We denote the position of the mobile on C at time t by the vector $p(t)$, $p(t) = \{x(t), y(t)\}$, so $p(t) \in D$ and $|p(t)| < K$ for $t \geqslant 0$.

Let l be a point such that

$$l = \lim_{n\to\infty} p(t_n), \tag{20.2.1}$$

where the sequence $\{t_n\}$ is such that

$$0 \leqslant t_1 < t_2 < t_3 \ldots, \tag{20.2.2}$$

and $t_n \to \infty$ with n. The set of such points l is the *positive limiting set* for the trajectory in question, and we denote it by Λ. The points l of Λ are called Λ-points. We notice that the Λ-points of C are limit (cluster) points of C, but that not all limit points of C are Λ-points.

A Λ-point of C may or may not lie on C. In some simple cases the positive limiting set is easy to find. If $p(t)$ approaches a stable singularity p_0 as $t \to \infty$, then $\Lambda \equiv p_0$. If C is cyclic, every point of C is a Λ-point, and there are no others; thus, if C is cyclic, $\Lambda \equiv C$. We shall find that, in many cases, Λ is itself a cyclic trajectory, and C is a spiral approximating to Λ as t tends to infinity.

We now consider the essential properties of the positive limiting set Λ. They are as follows: Λ is (i) non-vacuous, (ii) closed, and (iii) connected; further (iv) if $l \in \Lambda$ the entire trajectory through l (i.e. both the positive semi-characteristic and the negative semi-characteristic originating in l) lies in Λ.

We have noticed already that (i) is true if C is cyclic. If C is not cyclic, consider the set of points $p(1)$, $p(2)$, $p(3)$, ... This is a bounded infinite set, all different, and there exists at least one limit point of the set; this point is a Λ-point of C. The proof of (ii) is similar to the well-known proof that the derived set of a given set is closed.

To prove (iii) we have to show that Λ cannot consist of two (or more) non-vacuous closed sets with no point in common. Suppose on the contrary that Λ consists of two disjoint non-vacuous sets A and B. Then there is a non-zero distance δ between the sets A and B. Let a be a point of A and b a point of B, and let t_0 be an arbitrary positive number. Then there is a number t_1 greater than t_0 such that

$$d\{a, p(t_1)\} < \tfrac{1}{2}\delta, \tag{20.2.3}$$

and there is a number t_2 greater than t_1 such that

$$d\{b, p(t_2)\} < \tfrac{1}{2}\delta. \tag{20.2.4}$$

Now (20.2.3) implies

$$d\{p(t_1), A\} < \tfrac{1}{2}\delta, \tag{20.2.5}$$

and therefore

$$d\{p(t_1), B\} > \tfrac{1}{2}\delta, \tag{20.2.6}$$

and therefore

$$d\{p(t_1), A\} - d\{p(t_1), B\} < 0. \tag{20.2.7}$$

Similarly

$$d\{p(t_2), A\} - d\{p(t_2), B\} > 0, \tag{20.2.8}$$

so the function

$$\varphi(t) = d\{p(t), A\} - d\{p(t), B\} \tag{20.2.9}$$

is negative at t_1 and positive at t_2. Thus, since $\varphi(t)$ is continuous, there is a number θ between t_1 and t_2 at which $\varphi(\theta) = 0$; for any choice of t_0 there is a number θ greater than t_0 at which

$$d\{p(\theta), A\} = d\{p(\theta), B\}. \tag{20.2.10}$$

Thus, we can find an increasing sequence $\theta_1, \theta_2, \theta_3, \ldots$ tending to infinity, with the property

$$d\{p(\theta_n), A\} = d\{p(\theta_n), B\}. \tag{20.2.11}$$

Let p_0 be a limit point of the set $\{p(\theta_n)\}$; then $p_0 \in \Lambda$, and

$$d(p_0, A) = d(p_0, B). \tag{20.2.12}$$

But this is impossible, since p_0 belongs either to A or to B. Thus the supposition that Λ consists of two disjoint sets is untenable, and a similar argument shows that Λ cannot consist of more than two disjoint sets. Thus Λ is a non-vacuous, closed, connected set.

Finally, to prove (iv), let the trajectory originating in l at $t = 0$ be $\bar{p}(t)$, so that $\bar{p}(0) = l$. Consider a sequence $\{t_n\}$, increasing steadily to infinity, such that $\lim_{n\to\infty} p(t_n) = l$, and let t be a fixed real number, positive or negative. Now

$$\lim_{n\to\infty} p(t_n) = \bar{p}(0), \tag{20.2.13}$$

and therefore

$$\lim_{n\to\infty} p(t_n + t) = \bar{p}(t), \tag{20.2.14}$$

since the solutions of the differential equations depend continuously on the initial values for all finite t. Thus $\tilde{p}(t) \in \Lambda$ for all values of t, and this completes the proof.

To sum up, if Λ is not a singular point, it is a non-vacuous closed connected set, which is built up of entire trajectories.

20.3 Segment without contact. A *segment without contact* is a finite closed segment of a straight line with the property that at no point of the segment does the component of **F** normal to the segment vanish. Thus a segment without contact does not touch any trajectory nor pass through any singular point. A segment without contact *through* p_0 means a segment without contact of which p_0 is an interior point. It is clear that through any regular point we can draw infinitely many segments without contact. We shall now establish the principal properties of segments without contact.

(i) *If a positive semi-characteristic C crosses a segment without contact S more than once, it always crosses in the same sense.* For if C crossed S in opposite senses at P_1 and P_2 the normal component of **F** would have opposite senses at P_1 and P_2, and therefore, since it varies continuously on S, it would vanish at some point between P_1 and P_2; but this is impossible since S is a segment without contact.

(ii) *In a finite time-interval a trajectory C cannot cross S more than a finite number of times.* For suppose, on the contrary, that there is an infinity of values $\{t_n\}$ in the range $\alpha \leqslant t \leqslant \beta$ such that $p(t_n) \in S$. Then no two points $p(t_r)$, $p(t_s)$ coincide. For if they did the trajectory would be either a singular point on S, which is prohibited, or a cyclic trajectory, and in that case it would have a period σ, and the number of crossings of S in the interval $[\alpha, \beta]$ would be finite. Thus the points $p(t_n)$ are all distinct.

The values $\{t_n\}$ have a limit point t_0, $\alpha \leqslant t_0 \leqslant \beta$, and $p(t_0) \in S$. We can find t_n as near to t_0 as we wish, so the chord $p(t_0)p(t_n)$ tends to the direction of the tangent to C at $p(t_0)$. Thus C touches S at $p(t_0)$, and this is impossible since S does not touch any trajectory. The hypothesis of an infinity of intersections in a finite time is therefore untenable.

(iii) *If p_0 is a point near to a segment without contact S, the trajectory through p_0 intersects S.* Let us first put the theorem into a more precise form. Let q be an interior point of S, and let ε be a given positive number. Then there is a positive number δ $(= \delta(\varepsilon))$ such that if $d(q, p_0) < \delta$ the positive or the negative semi-characteristic originating in p_0 will intersect S at a time in the interval $(-\varepsilon, \varepsilon)$; if $p(t)$ is the trajectory for which $p(0) = p_0$, there is a number θ such tha t $-\varepsilon < \theta < \varepsilon$ and such that $p(\theta) \in S$.

To prove this, it is convenient to change the variables by an affine transformation so that S is the segment $x_1 \leqslant x \leqslant x_2$ of the x-axis, where $x_1 < 0 < x_2$, and q is the origin. The trajectory originating at $t = 0$ in p_0 $(= (x_0, y_0))$ is the curve $p(t;\ x_0, y_0)$, whose components are denoted by

$$x(t;\ x_0, y_0), \quad y(t;\ x_0, y_0).$$

We wish to prove that the equation

$$y(t;\ x_0, y_0) = 0 \tag{20.3.1}$$

has a solution

$$t = \varphi(x_0, y_0) \tag{20.3.2}$$

if $\sqrt{(x_0^2 + y_0^2)}$ is small enough; and, further, that for this solution $|t| < \varepsilon$ and $x(\varphi;\ x_0, y_0)$ lies in (x_1, x_2). Now

$$\frac{\partial}{\partial t}\, y(t;\ x_0, y_0)$$

does not vanish when $t = x_0 = y_0 = 0$, so the solution certainly exists when $\sqrt{(x_0^2 + y_0^2)}$ is sufficiently small. Moreover $\varphi(0, 0) = 0$, and the function φ is a continuous function of (x_0, y_0), so $|\varphi(x_0, y_0)|$ is small when $\sqrt{(x_0^2 + y_0^2)}$ is small. Further, x is small when t and $\sqrt{(x_0^2 + y_0^2)}$ are small, and this completes the proof.

20.4 Segment without contact through a point of Λ. Let C be a positive semi-characteristic whose limiting set Λ is not merely a singular point. Let l be a regular point of Λ, and S a segment without contact through l. Now, given a positive number ε, there exists a positive number $\delta(\varepsilon)$ such that a trajectory originating, at $t = \tau$, at a point whose distance from l is less than δ intersects S at some instant in the interval $(\tau - \varepsilon, \tau + \varepsilon)$ (§ 20.3(iii)). Further, given t_0, however large, there is a number t' greater than t_0 such that

$$d\{p(t'), l\} < \delta,$$

so C must intersect S in the interval $(t' - \varepsilon, t' + \varepsilon)$. Thus there are infinitely many values of t for which $p(t)$ lies on S. In a finite time-interval there are only a finite number of intersections; therefore the instants of intersection $t_1, t_2, t_3, \ldots$ can be ordered so that

$$t_1 < t_2 < t_3 \ldots,$$

and t_n tends to infinity with n. Let us denote the point $p(t_r)$ on S by p_r.

Now there are two possibilities. If (i) p_2 coincides with p_1, the trajectory C is cyclic, and all the points $p_1, p_2, p_3, \ldots$ coincide. If (ii) p_2 is distinct from p_1, then p_3 is distinct from p_1 and p_2, and p_2 *lies between* p_1 *and* p_3. It is here that we need an appeal to Jordan's theorem. Consider the simple closed curve Γ consisting of the arc p_1p_2 of C and the segment p_2p_1 of S. If the mobile enters the interior region bounded by Γ it stays inside for good, for it cannot cross either the arc p_1p_2 of C or the rectilinear boundary p_2p_1. Thus p_2 lies between p_1 and p_3 (Fig. 20.4*a*). Similarly if the mobile enters the exterior region bounded by Γ it stays outside for good, and again p_2 lies between p_1 and p_3 (Fig. 20.4*b*).

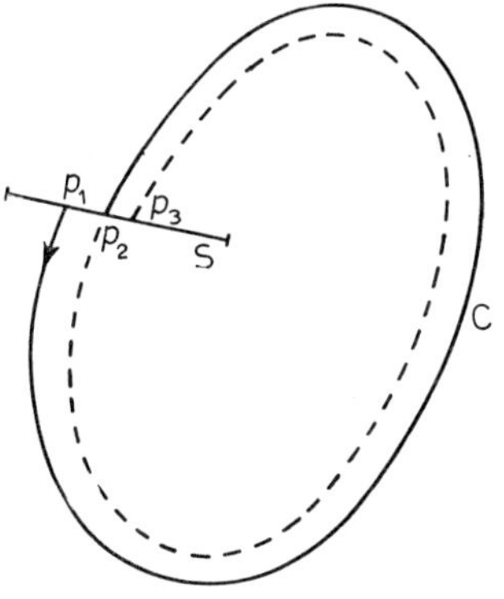

Figure 20.4*a*

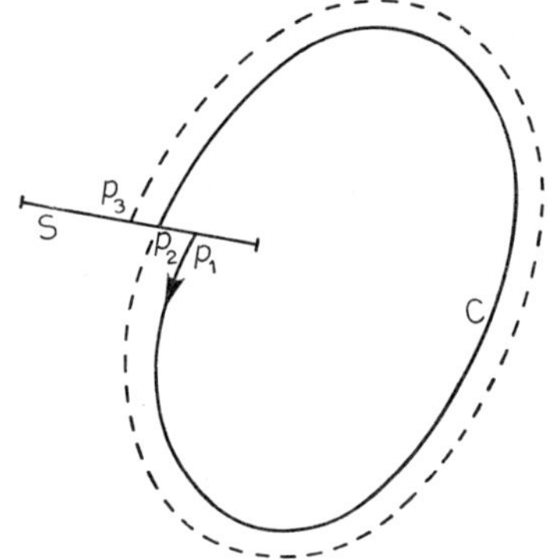

Figure 20.4*b*

Thus the points $p_1, p_2, p_3, \ldots$ on S are all the same or all different, and if they are all different the sequence is monotonic. Therefore the sequence, monotonic and bounded, tends to a limit, and this limit, which is a Λ-point, can only be l. Moreover S can contain no point of Λ other than l, since the limit is unique.

The results established in this section can be summed up in the following theorem. *Let l be a regular point of Λ, which is the positive limiting set of a trajectory C, and let S be a segment without contact through l; then (i) no point of Λ other than l lies on S, and (ii) C is cyclic if and only if it has precisely one point of intersection with S.*

20.5 The structure of Λ. We suppose again that the limiting set Λ of the positive semi-characteristic C is not a singular point. Now we know that the entire trajectory originating in a point of Λ lies wholly in Λ; let us now assume that there is an entire trajectory C' lying in Λ whose positive limiting set, or whose negative limiting set, is not a singular point. Then *C' is cyclic, and $\Lambda \equiv C'$.*

We first prove that C' is cyclic. Let p be a regular point of (say) the positive limiting set Λ' of C'. Now Λ' lies in Λ (since C' lies in Λ and Λ is closed) so $p \in \Lambda$. Let S be a segment without contact through p; then S intersects Λ in only the one point p. Therefore S intersects C' in only the one point p, and it follows that C' is cyclic.

We next prove that $C' \equiv \Lambda$. For suppose on the contrary that the statement is not true, and let E be the set of points of Λ not in C'. Since Λ and C' are closed sets, E is open, and there exists a limit (cluster) point q of E which does not lie in E. But q lies in Λ, since Λ is closed, so $q \in C'$. Consider now a segment without contact S' through q (which lies on C' and is a regular point), and let p' be a point of E sufficiently near to q. Then p' is a regular point, and the characteristic through p' will intersect S' in a point q'; and q' is distinct from q, since characteristics do not intersect. But $q' \in \Lambda$, because $p' \in \Lambda$ and therefore the entire characteristic through p' lies in Λ. Thus S' contains two distinct points, q and q', belonging to Λ, and this we have seen to be impossible. Thus E must be empty, and $C' \equiv \Lambda$. The set Λ is a cyclic trajectory.

If C is cyclic, $C \equiv \Lambda$. If C is not cyclic, consider a segment without contact $\bar{S}$ through a point $\bar{p}$ of Λ. The successive intersections $\bar{p}_1, \bar{p}_2, \bar{p}_3, \ldots$ of C with $\bar{S}$ converge to $\bar{p}$ (§ 20.4), and C is therefore a spiral approximating to Λ as $t \to \infty$. In this case the cyclic trajectory Λ is called a *limit cycle*.

It remains to consider briefly the exceptional case in which Λ is not a singular point, but is such that every entire trajectory lying in Λ has the property that its positive limiting set is a singular point, and its negative limiting set is a singular point. In this exceptional case Λ is a *pseudo-cyclic trajectory*, i.e. it is a closed curve built up of trajectories each of which begins and ends in a singular point. These singular points are saddle points. The simplest case of a pseudo-cyclic trajectory is that of a single trajectory which leaves and re-enters a saddle point. Another simple case is that in which there are two distinct saddle points, and two distinct trajectories joining one to the other. Concrete examples of both these types have appeared already; the separatrix in Fig. 19.11*b* is an example of the first case, and the separatrix in Fig. 19.8*b* is an example of the second.

20.6 The Poincaré-Bendixson theorem. The results of the preceding discussion can be summed up in the following theorem. *We consider a bounded positive semi-characteristic C lying in D whose positive limiting set Λ is not a singular point. Then* *either C is cyclic, and $\Lambda \equiv C$; or Λ is a cyclic trajectory (or, exceptionally, a pseudo-cyclic trajectory) and C is a spiral approximating to Λ as $t \to \infty$.*

We consider some results ancillary to the Poincaré-Bendixson theorem; but a complete and detailed discussion would take us too far afield, and would be out of place in this book. We recall that, throughout the discussion, we are concerned with a field of the type considered in § 19.3, in which there are only isolated singularities at each of which $\partial(P, Q)/\partial(x, y) \neq 0$.

(i) As we have seen, the positive limiting set of a trajectory C may consist of a single singular point l, and the trajectory approaches, and perhaps enters l, as $t \to \infty$. We may regard this as a special case of the Poincaré-Bendixson theorem, the singular point l being regarded as a degenerate form of a limit cycle.

(ii) If there is a closed region R containing no singular points, and such that at each point of the boundary of R the field vector $\mathbf{F}$ is directed *into* the region, the region contains at least one cyclic trajectory. (It is assumed that the boundary consists of curves with a continuously turning tangent, except for a finite number of corners.) For any positive semi-characteristic originating in R remains inside it for all $t \geqslant 0$, and this positive semi-characteristic is either cyclic, or it approaches a limit cycle. The same conclusion holds if at all points of the boundary the vector $\mathbf{F}$ is directed *outwards*; to establish the result in this case we must consider a negative semi-characteristic originating in a point of R. Of course it does not follow that the region contains only one cyclic trajectory. (The region R cannot be simply connected. If for example we have a region R consisting of a simple closed curve Γ and its interior, and $\mathbf{F}$ is directed inwards at all points of Γ, then the index (§ 20.1) of Γ is 1, and the interior of Γ must contain at least one singular point.)

(iii) Suppose that the positive semi-characteristic C approaches a limit cycle Λ spirally from inside. Then if p_0 is any point inside Λ, and sufficiently near to Λ, the positive semi-characteristic originating in p_0 approaches Λ.

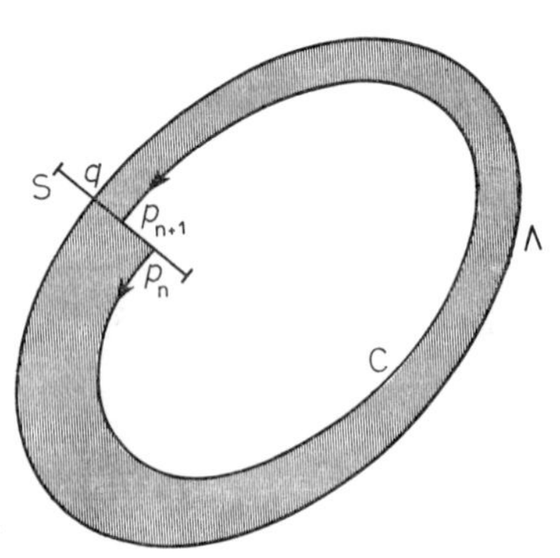

Figure 20.6

To prove this, let q be a point of Λ, S a segment without contact through q, and p_n, p_{n+1} two successive intersections of C with S for a given large value of n. We consider the annular region bounded externally by Λ and internally by the simple closed curve consisting of the arc $p_n p_{n+1}$ of C and the segment p_{n+1}, p_n of S (Fig. 20.6). The region is free from singularities for a sufficiently large n, and if we take any point p_0 inside it the positive semi-characteristic C' originating in p_0 will stay inside always. As C spirals out towards Λ, so also does C'; in fact the successive intersections of C' with S lie in the intervals $p_n p_{n+1}, p_{n+1} p_{n+2}, p_{n+2} p_{n+3}, \ldots$, since two trajectories cannot intersect one another. It follows that C' approaches Λ as $t \to \infty$.

(iv) If the limit cycle Λ is approached from inside by a positive semi-characteristic, it cannot also be approached from inside by a negative semi-characteristic. If, as in (iii), we consider a segment without contact S through a point q of Λ, the successive intersections $p_1, p_2, p_3, \ldots$ of a positive semi-characteristic with S approach q, and therefore the successive intersections for a negative semi-characteristic move away from q. In this case the limit cycle Λ is said to be *stable from inside*.

(v) If there is a cyclic trajectory Γ which is not approached from inside by any semi-characteristic, positive or negative, then there is a cyclic trajectory inside Γ and near to it.

To prove this, let us consider a point q on Γ, and a segment without contact S through q. Let p_0 be a point on S inside Γ and near to q, and let us consider the positive semi-characteristic originating in p_0. Either the mobile returns to p_0, in which case the theorem is proved, or it meets S again in a point p_1. If p_1 lies between p_0 and q, the next intersection p_2 must lie between p_1 and q, and so on. Then the sequence $\{p_n\}$ tends to a limit point on the segment p_0q. This limit cannot be q, because in that case the positive semi-characteristic through p_0 would approach Γ, which is prohibited. Therefore p_n tends to a limit l between p_0 and q, and the trajectory converges to a limit cycle Λ through l. (If p_1 does not lie between p_0 and q we must use instead the negative semi-characteristic originating in p_0.)

(vi) Let us consider the case where Γ is a cyclic trajectory, and there is just one singular point p_0 inside Γ, and p_0 is a node or a spiral point. Let q be a point near p_0. If the singularity is unstable, the positive semi-characteristic originating in q cannot approach p_0, and it must approach a limit cycle, which is either Γ itself, or another cyclic trajectory lying inside Γ. The negative semi-characteristic originating in q approaches, and perhaps enters, p_0.

If the limit cycle for the positive semi-characteristic originating in q is Γ itself, there cannot be any cyclic trajectory inside Γ, because if there were, the positive semi-characteristic originating in q would approach it instead of Γ. In this case Γ is said to be the smallest cyclic trajectory enclosing p_0. It is easy to see, by an argument similar to that in (iii) above, that, if q' is any point other than p_0 inside Γ, the positive semi-characteristic originating in q' approaches Γ, and the negative semi-characteristic originating in q' approaches p_0.

The situation is similar if p_0 is stable. In that case the positive-semi characteristic originating in q' approaches p_0, and the negative semi-characteristic approaches Γ.

(vii) Other possible cases exhibit a finite number of cyclic trajectories about the single singularity p_0, or an enumerable infinity of cyclic trajectories; and further, as we have seen, if p_0 is a vortex point, *all* the trajectories may be cyclic.

If the number of cyclic trajectories about p_0 is finite, and p_0 is unstable, the smallest cyclic trajectory enclosing p_0 must be stable from inside. Exceptionally it may be *semi-stable*, i.e. stable from inside and unstable from outside. But this phenomenon is exceptional, and except for rather artificial examples it is *stable*, i.e., stable from both sides. In general the successive cyclic trajectories are alternately stable and unstable.

20.7 Application to a particular system. In the problem of damped harmonic oscillations (§ 19.2) the motion is determined by an equation of the form

$$\ddot{x} + 2k\dot{x} + n^2x = 0, \qquad n > k > 0, \tag{20.7.1}$$

and we have the familiar phenomenon of oscillations decaying exponentially as t increases. If we replace (20.7.1) by the equivalent pair of first-order equations, the origin is a stable focus, or spiral point (§ 19.4). If however we consider instead the equation (20.7.1) with a negative value of k, $n > 0 > k$, we have negative friction, and the oscillations increase indefinitely in amplitude. The origin, for the equivalent-pair of first-order equations, is an unstable focus, or spiral point.

By a suitable choice of the time-scale we can, without loss of generality, take $n = 1$ in (20.7.1) and in similar cases.

Suppose now that in (20.7.1) we replace the positive or negative constant k by a function of x and $\dot{x}$ which is sometimes positive and sometimes negative; we then have a problem in which there is sometimes damping and sometimes stimulation. In such problems it may happen (i) that the motion is periodic for sufficiently small disturbances from equilibrium, or (ii) that the motion tends to settle down to a periodic motion in which the net loss of energy is zero.

An example of the first possibility (i) is given by *Example* 19.10*C*. As a simple example of (ii), consider the problem of a particle moving on a straight line, for which the equation of motion is

$$\ddot{x} + \mu(x^2 + \dot{x}^2 - a^2)\dot{x} + x = 0, \tag{20.7.2}$$

where $\mu > 0$ and $a > 0$. The friction is damping if $r > a$ (where $r = \sqrt{(x^2 + \dot{x}^2)}$) and stimulating if $r < a$. It is natural to expect that the system will tend ultimately to settle down to a harmonic oscillation of amplitude a, in which $x^2 + \dot{x}^2 = a^2$, and the friction is permanently zero. That this expectation is fulfilled follows easily from the theory. The first-order equations are $\dot{x} = P$, $\dot{y} = Q$, where

$$P = y, \quad Q = -x - \mu(r^2 - a^2)y, \tag{20.7.3}$$

and the radial component of the field is

$$R = -\mu(r^2 - a^2)r \sin^2 \theta. \tag{20.7.4}$$

If we consider the annulus $\alpha < r < \beta$, where $0 < \alpha < a < \beta$, we see that the field is directed outwards on the inner circle $r = \alpha$ and inwards on the outer circle $r = \beta$ (except indeed at the points on $y = 0$) so a positive semi-characteristic originating at a point in the annulus is either cyclic (which happens if $r = a$ initially) or it approaches a limit cycle (§ 20.6(ii)) which must clearly be the circle $r = a$.

A much more important example is provided by *van der Pol's equation*

$$\ddot{x} + \mu(x^2 - 1)\dot{x} + x = 0, \qquad \mu > 0. \tag{20.7.5}$$

There is damping if $|x| > 1$, stimulation if $|x| < 1$, and we may expect that the motion will tend to settle down to a periodic motion in which the two tendencies counterbalance one another. In fact we shall find that in this case, for the equivalent first-order equations, there is just one limit cycle.

Let us consider instead of (20.7.5) the more general equation

$$\ddot{x} + f(x)\dot{x} + x = 0, \tag{20.7.6}$$

where $f(x) \in C_1$, $f(x)$ is an even function, and $f(x)$ is such that, if $F(x) = \int_0^x f(\xi)\, d\xi$, then there is a positive number b such that $F(x)$ is negative for $0 < x < b$, and $F(x)$ is positive and monotonically increasing for $x > b$.* (For the particular case (20.7.5)

$$F(x) = \tfrac{1}{3}\mu x(x^2 - 3),$$

and $b = \sqrt{3}$.)

It will be convenient to consider the equation

$$\ddot{z} + F(\dot{z}) + z = 0, \tag{20.7.7}$$

which is effectively equivalent to (20.7.6). For if z is a solution of (20.7.7), $\dot{z}$ is a solution of (20.7.6); while if x is a solution of (20.7.6),

$$z = \dot{x} + F(x) \tag{20.7.8}$$

* The discussion can be extended to the more general equation

$$\ddot{x} + f(x)\dot{x} + g(x) = 0,$$

where $g(x)$ is an odd function, and $\int_0^\infty g(x)\, dx$ diverges. But in this book we shall be content to discuss the special case in which $g(x) = x$.

is a solution of (20.7.7). To prove this, we notice that

$$\dot{z} = \ddot{x} + f(x)\dot{x} = -x, \tag{20.7.9}$$

and therefore

$$\ddot{z} + F(\dot{z}) + z = -\dot{x} + F(-x) + \dot{x} + F(x), \tag{20.7.10}$$

which is zero, since $F(x)$ is an odd function. The two equations (20.7.6) and (20.7.7) are so related that, corresponding to a periodic solution of one of them, there is a periodic solution of the other with the same period.

20.8 Existence of the limit cycle. We consider the equation (20.7.7), now writing x for the dependent variable instead of z,

$$\ddot{x} + F(\dot{x}) + x = 0, \tag{20.8.1}$$

and we replace it as usual by the two first-order equations $\dot{x} = P$, $\dot{y} = Q$, where

$$P = y, \quad Q = -x - F(y). \tag{20.8.2}$$

There is only one singular point, the origin, and it is either an unstable node or an unstable spiral point. We shall find that there is just one cyclic line of force, and that all positive semi-characteristics approach the same limit cycle. However the motion starts (apart from the trivial exception when $x = \dot{x} = 0$ initially) the motion tends to settle down to a periodic oscillation.

One way of proving the existence of a limit cycle is to find a closed curve enclosing O such that $\mathbf{F}$ is directed inwards at all points of the curve. Then, as in § 20.6, the existence of the limit cycle follows from the Poincaré-Bendixson theorem. We choose instead a different attack which also proves uniqueness.

We can determine the direction of the field at any point by a graphical construction similar to that used in § 19.8. We draw the *leading curve* L, which is defined by the equation

$$x = -F(y). \tag{20.8.3}$$

We then find the direction of the field at any point A by the following construction. Let the horizontal line through A meet the leading curve in B, and let the vertical line through B meet Ox in N. Then the field at A is perpendicular to NA.

We can now observe the general character of the field. The horizontal component P is to the right in the upper half-plane, to the left in the lower. The vertical component Q is upwards to the left of L, and downwards to the right. The field is horizontal on L, and vertical on Ox.

Consider now the trajectory through an arbitrary initial point (x_0, y_0) say for definiteness a point to the left of L in the upper half-plane. An arc of the trajectory leads from a point $(x_1, 0)$ on the negative x-axis to a point $(x_2, 0)$ on the positive x-axis. It intersects L in one point, the highest point of the arc, rising to a height ζ at the intersection and then falling (Fig. 20.8a). This is almost evident from the general character of the field. To prove it formally, we notice that, as the mobile moves away from (x_0, y_0), x and y increase; thus $\dot{x} \geqslant y_0 > 0$, and the mobile crosses L. At the crossing $\dot{y}$ changes sign, from positive to negative, for

$$\ddot{y} = -y - f(y)\dot{y}, \tag{20.8.4}$$

and at the crossing $\ddot{y} = -\zeta < 0$. The mobile can only cross L once in the upper half-plane, since the crossing must be from left to right, and it cannot touch L, since at a point of L the tangent to the trajectory is horizontal. Thus the horizontal displacement from L, $x + F(y)$, is bounded away from zero when once it attains a positive value. But $x + F(y) = -\dot{y}$, and at a short time τ after the crossing $\dot{y} < -\frac{1}{2}\zeta\tau$, $x + F(y) > \frac{1}{2}\zeta\tau > 0$. On the arc to the right of L, $\dot{y}(< 0)$ is bounded away from zero, and the mobile reaches Ox

After crossing Ox the path continues in the lower half-plane with again just one crossing of L, and it again crosses the negative x-axis.

Let us then consider an arc of a trajectory in the upper half-plane joining the point $(x_1, 0)$, where $x_1 < 0$, to the point $(x_2, 0)$, where $x_2 > 0$. This arc is determined by the ordinate ζ of its highest point (where it crosses L). Let us call the arc C_ζ, and

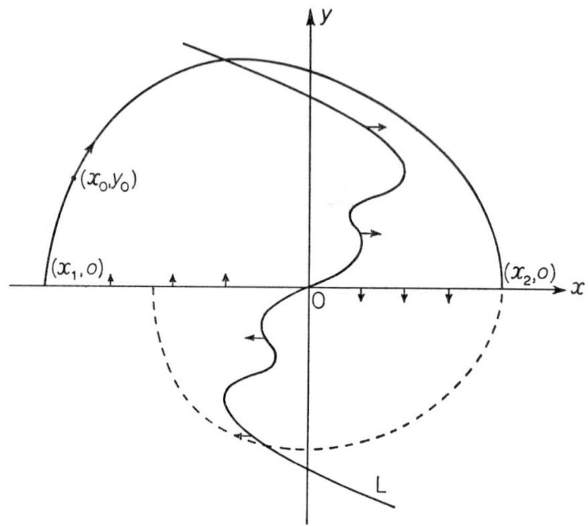

Figure 20.8a

write $x_1 = x_1(\zeta)$, $x_2 = x_2(\zeta)$. The functions $x_1(\zeta)$, $x_2(\zeta)$ are monotonic (since trajectories do not intersect) and they vary continuously with ζ, x_1 varying from 0 to $-\infty$, and x_2 from 0 to $+\infty$, as ζ increases from 0 to ∞.

Now if we replace x by $-x$ and y by $-y$ the equations do not change, so the point-image of C_ζ in O is also an arc of a trajectory. It follows that *the trajectory is cyclic if and only if* $x_2 = -x_1$.

Returning now to the equations $\dot{x} = P$, $\dot{y} = Q$, where P and Q are given by (20.8.2), we have

$$x\dot{x} + y\dot{y} = -F(y)y = -F(y)\dot{x}, \tag{20.8.5}$$

whence

$$d\{\tfrac{1}{2}(x^2 + y^2)\} = -F(y)\,dx. \tag{20.8.6}$$

(This is, of course, the third form of the equation of energy. § 3.5.) Integrating along the arc C_ζ we have

$$\tfrac{1}{2}({x_2}^2 - {x_1}^2) = -\int_{x_1}^{x_2} F(y)\,dx, \tag{20.8.7}$$

and we write $\lambda(\zeta)$ for $-\int_{x_1}^{x_2} F(y)\,dx$. *We have a cyclic trajectory if and only if* $\lambda(\zeta) = 0$.

We shall show that $\lambda(\zeta)$ vanishes for just one positive value of ζ. We prove successively:

(i) for $\zeta < b$, $\lambda(\zeta) > 0$;

(ii) for $\zeta_2 > \zeta_1 > b$, $\lambda(\zeta_2) < \lambda(\zeta_1)$, so that $\lambda(\zeta)$ decreases monotonically as ζ increases for $\zeta > b$;

(iii) $\lambda(\zeta) \to -\infty$ as $\zeta \to \infty$.

From these results it will follow that $\lambda(\zeta)$ passes just once through the value zero.

We now prove the three results stated.

(i) If $\zeta < b$, $y < b$ and $F(y) < 0$ on C_ζ. Hence

(20.8.8) $$\lambda(\zeta) = -\int_x^{x_2} F(y)\,dx > 0.$$

(ii) Take $\zeta_2 > \zeta_1 > b$, and let us use the notation indicated in Fig. 20.8*b*. We first consider

(20.8.9) $$-\int_{A_1}^{B_1} F(y)\,dx = -\int_0^b F(y)\frac{dx}{dy}\,dy.$$

Now on a trajectory

(20.8.10) $$\frac{dx}{dy} = \frac{\dot{x}}{\dot{y}} = \frac{y}{-x - F(y)},$$

and the second member is positive at P_1 and at P_2, with a smaller value at P_2 than at P_1,

(20.8.11) $$\left(\frac{dx}{dy}\right)_{P_2} < \left(\frac{dx}{dy}\right)_{P_1}.$$

Hence

(20.8.12) $$-\int_{A_2}^{B_2} F(y)\,dx < -\int_{A_1}^{B_1} F(y)\,dx,$$

and by a similar argument

(20.8.13) $$-\int_{C_2}^{D_2} F(y)\,dx < -\int_{C_1}^{D_1} F(y)\,dx.$$

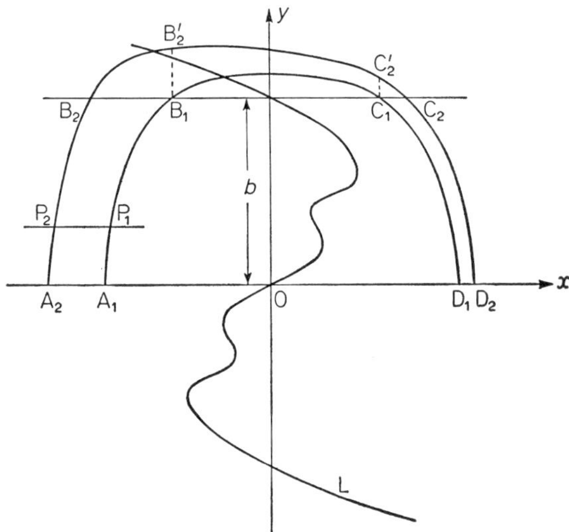

Figure 20.8*b*

It remains to compare the integrals for B_1C_1 and for B_2C_2. On these arcs $F(y) > 0$, and

$$\int_{B_2}^{C_2} F(y)\,dx > \int_{B_2'}^{C_2'} F(y)\,dx > \int_{B_1}^{C_1} F(y)\,dx, \tag{20.8.14}$$

since, for $y > b$, $F(y)$ increases monotonically with y.

Adding the results, we have

$$\lambda(\zeta_2) = -\int_{A_2}^{D_2} F(y)\,dx < -\int_{A_1}^{D_1} F(y)\,dx = \lambda(\zeta_1), \tag{20.8.15}$$

and this completes the proof of the second result.

(iii) Consider now a large value of ζ. The contributions to $-\int F(y)\,dx$ for A_2B_2 and C_2D_2 are positive and bounded; the contribution for B_2C_2 tends to $-\infty$ as $\zeta \to \infty$. To prove this, take a fixed number $c > b$, and let $y = c$ cut C_{ζ_2} (assuming $\zeta_2 > c$) in M_2 and N_2. Then

$$\int_{B_2}^{C_2} F(y)\,dx > \int_{M_2}^{N_2} F(y)\,dx > F(c)M_2N_2, \tag{20.8.16}$$

and M_2N_2 tends to infinity with ζ (since, given any point on $y = c$, we can find a trajectory through it). Thus $\lambda(\zeta) \to -\infty$ as $\zeta \to \infty$.

This completes the proof that $\lambda(\zeta)$ vanishes for just one positive value of ζ, and this implies that just one cyclic trajectory Γ exists. Every positive semi-characteristic approaches Γ as $t \to \infty$. The origin is an unstable singularity, and a trajectory originating at a point inside Γ approaches Γ from inside. For a trajectory originating outside Γ, $x_2 < (-x_1)$, and the trajectory approaches a limit cycle as $t \to \infty$; this limit cycle can only be Γ, because no other cyclic trajectory exists.

The existence of a unique limit cycle, which is approached by all positive semi-characteristics, has been established for the first-order equations derived from the equation (20.8.1). It follows that the same property holds for the equation (20.7.6); in particular it holds for van der Pol's equation (20.7.5).

20.9 Van der Pol's equation. We conclude our study of the Poincaré-Bendixson theorem with a brief discussion of the application of the theory of the preceding section to the important special case of Van der Pol's equation (20.7.5),

$$\ddot{x} + \mu(x^2 - 1)\dot{x} + x = 0, \qquad \mu > 0. \tag{20.9.1}$$

The equation corresponding to (20.7.7) is

$$\ddot{x} + \mu(\tfrac{1}{3}\dot{x}^3 - \dot{x}) + x = 0, \tag{20.9.2}$$

and the corresponding first-order equations are

$$\dot{x} = y, \quad \dot{y} = -x - \mu(\tfrac{1}{3}y^3 - y). \tag{20.9.3}$$

We know that there is a unique limit cycle for (20.9.3). The motion defined by (20.9.2) tends to settle down to a certain periodic oscillation.

It is interesting to find approximations to the form of the limit cycle in the two extreme cases, when μ is very small and when μ is very large.

(i) If μ is very small, the equation (20.9.2) is very nearly the same as the equation for harmonic motion. If μ were zero, the trajectories for (20.9.3) would be circles, and if μ is very small the one surviving cyclic trajectory will be nearly circular. We can find its radius R from considerations of energy, as in (20.8.6); the integral $\int F(y)\,dx$ for a complete period must vanish. Thus

(20.9.4) $$\int (\tfrac{1}{3}y^3 - y)\,dx = 0,$$

where the integral is taken along the semi-circle of radius R in the upper half-plane, and this gives, for the radius of the nearly-circular limit cycle, $R = 2$. This is the amplitude of the oscillation for x (and also of the oscillation for y). The trajectories are spirals approximating slowly to the limit cycle (Fig. 20.9a), the x-motion is a nearly-harmonic oscillation of amplitude slowly increasing (or decreasing) to the value 2 (Fig. 20.9b).

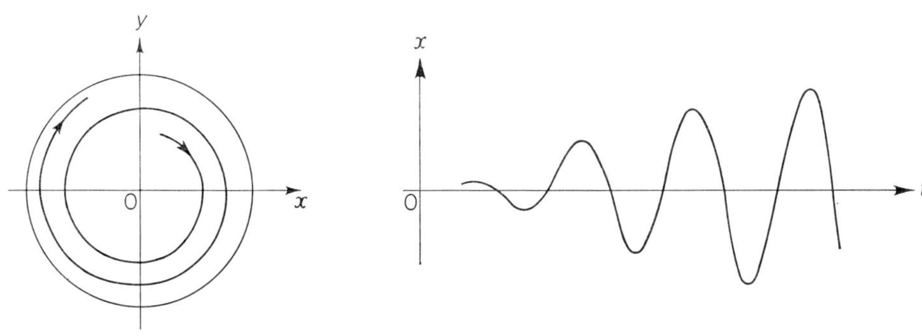

Figure 20.9a Figure 20.9b

(ii) If μ is very large we can find an approximation to the form of the limit cycle by a geometrical argument. On the leading curve L,

(20.9.5) $$x = -\mu(\tfrac{1}{3}y^3 - y),$$

the field **F** is horizontal. As we move away from L the direction of the field rapidly becomes steep, because μ is large, upwards to the left of L and downwards to the right. If the mobile starts at a point R to the left of L in the upper half-plane (Fig. 20.9c) its motion to begin with

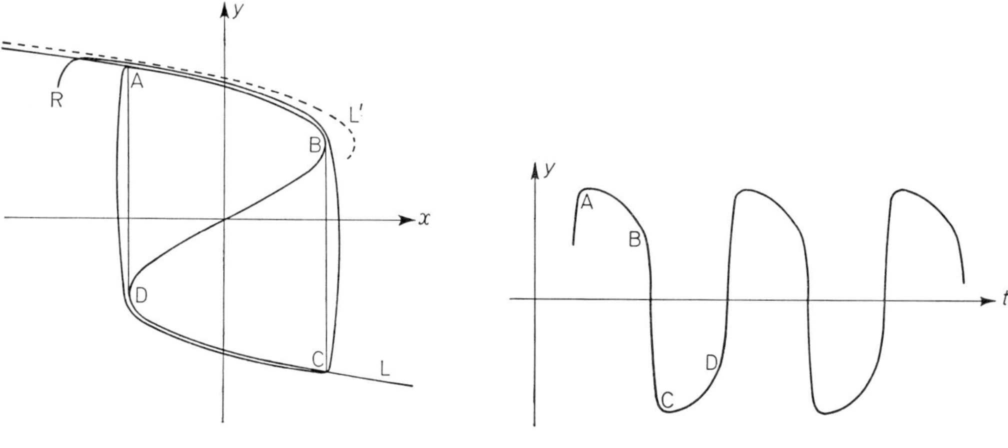

Figure 20.9c Figure 20.9d

is nearly vertical and upwards, until it gets near to L, on which its motion is horizontal. On the curve L', which is L shifted bodily a small distance to the right, the field vector $\mathbf{F}$ points steeply downwards, so the mobile remains in the strip between L and L'. It will therefore nearly follow the leading curve until it comes near to the extreme point $B(\frac{2}{3}\mu, 1)$. After this it moves nearly vertically downwards, until it again comes near to L. After crossing L near $C(\frac{2}{3}\mu, -2)$ it again nearly follows the leading curve until it reaches the neighbourhood of $D(-\frac{2}{3}\mu, -1)$, and then the motion is nearly vertical until L is reached again near $A(-\frac{2}{3}\mu, 2)$. The upshot is that, if μ is large, the limit cycle is very near to the curve $ABCD$ consisting of two vertical lines and two arcs of the leading curve.

The variation of y with t in the periodic motion on the limit cycle is shown in Fig. 20.9d. The time taken on the nearly-vertical pieces is small, and since $dt = dx/y$ the period σ is given approximately by

$$\sigma = 2\int_A^B \frac{1}{y}\,dx = 2\int_1^2 \frac{\mu}{y}(y^2 - 1)\,dy = \mu(3 - 2\log 2), \tag{20.9.6}$$

and σ is approximately $1{\cdot}6\mu$. This is also the period of the limiting periodic motion in van der Pol's equation (20.9.1).

Chapter XXI

Systems with n degrees of freedom, properties of the characteristics

21.1 Integrals of the system of differential equations. We now turn from the special case (of an autonomous system with $m = 2$) of the equations (19.1.2),

$$\dot{x}_r = X_r(x_1, x_2, \ldots, x_m;\ t), \qquad r = 1, 2, \ldots, m, \tag{21.1.1}$$

and consider the general case. Many interesting and important properties of the characteristics are known, and some of these will be studied in the present Chapter. But (as we have noticed already) the theory for a general value of m, even in the autonomous case, is less complete than the theory for the special case considered in the preceding two Chapters.

The number m is twice the number of degrees of freedom of the system, $m = 2n$. To begin with, all the variables are real, though occasionally it will be necessary to extend the discussion to include complex variables as well. It is often convenient to write the equations in the form (19.1.4),

$$\frac{dx_1}{X_1} = \frac{dx_2}{X_2} = \cdots = \frac{dx_m}{X_m} = dt. \tag{21.1.2}$$

The solutions have the form

$$x_r = \varphi_r(t;\ \alpha_1, \alpha_2, \ldots, \alpha_m;\ \tau), \qquad r = 1, 2, \ldots, m, \tag{21.1.3}$$

where $\boldsymbol{\alpha}$ is the value of $\mathbf{x}$ at $t = \tau$. As we have noticed, the more exacting the assumptions we make about the functions X_r, the more we can assert about the solutions (§ 19.1). We shall assume that the functions X_r are of class C_1 in a certain domain R of $x_1, x_2, \ldots, x_m, t$, and that therefore the functions φ_r have the corresponding differentiability properties. Occasionally we shall make still further assumptions—for example, that the functions X_r are analytic functions in a certain domain of the $(m + 1)$ complex variables $x_1, x_2, \ldots, x_m, t$; in that case the solutions are analytic functions of the $(m + 2)$ complex variables $t, \alpha_1, \alpha_2, \ldots, \alpha_m, \tau$, in a suitably restricted domain.

The most important case, and by far the commonest, is that in which the system is autonomous; the functions X_r do not contain t,

$$X_r = X_r(x_1, x_2, \ldots, x_m), \qquad r = 1, 2, \ldots, m, \tag{21.1.4}$$

and we assume also that they have continuous first derivatives (at least) in a domain D of $x_1, x_2, \ldots, x_m$. We can put $\tau = 0$ once for all without any effective loss of generality, so that $\boldsymbol{\alpha}$ is the value of $\mathbf{x}$ at $t = 0$. If the mobile starts at a point $\boldsymbol{\alpha}$ of D at $t = 0$, it reaches a point $\mathbf{x}$ of D at time t (if $|t|$ is not too large) and the characteristic is defined by formulae of the type (19.1.10),

$$x_r = \varphi_r(t;\ \alpha_1, \alpha_2, \ldots, \alpha_m), \qquad r = 1, 2, \ldots, m. \tag{21.1.5}$$

The trajectories (i.e. the curves traversed by the mobile, the projections of the characteristics onto the $\mathbf{x}$-space) are arcs of the lines of force for the vector field. These curves are defined by the equations

$$\frac{dx_1}{X_1} = \frac{dx_2}{X_2} = \cdots = \frac{dx_m}{X_m}. \tag{21.1.6}$$

If $\boldsymbol{\alpha}$ is a regular point of D, the trajectory through $\boldsymbol{\alpha}$ is unique, at least in some neighbourhood of $\boldsymbol{\alpha}$; if $\boldsymbol{\alpha}$ is a singular point, the trajectory originating in $\boldsymbol{\alpha}$ is the point-trajectory $\boldsymbol{\alpha}$, but there may be many lines of force through $\boldsymbol{\alpha}$ (cf. Figs. 19.4*a*, *b*, *c*). We can think of the problem of determining the characteristics as divided into two stages, the determination of the trajectories, and then the determination of the position of the mobile on its trajectory at time t. The last step is simple, at least in theory, when the trajectories are known (cf. § 19.1 above and § 21.2 below).

If we solve the equations (21.1.5) for $\alpha_1, \alpha_2, \ldots, \alpha_m$ we find

$$\alpha_r = \varphi_r(-t;\ x_1, x_2, \ldots, x_m), \qquad r = 1, 2, \ldots, m, \tag{21.1.7}$$

and the reciprocal property of the functions φ_r exhibited in the equations (21.1.5) and (21.1.7) is an important and distinctive property of the autonomous system.

Returning now to the general (non-autonomous) case, consider a function $f(x_1, x_2, \ldots, x_m;\ t)$, of class C_1 in a suitable domain, which has the property that it remains constant in virtue of the differential equations (21.1.1). This means that, as the mobile moves in accordance with the differential equations, its position at time t being $(x_1, x_2, \ldots, x_m)$,

$$f(x_1, x_2, \ldots, x_m;\ t) = c, \tag{21.1.8}$$

and this property holds for all the characteristics, the constant c having different values for different characteristics. Such a function f is called an *integral* of the system of differential equations (21.1.1) or (21.1.2). An integral f satisfies the partial differential equation

$$\frac{\partial f}{\partial t} + X_1\frac{\partial f}{\partial x_1} + X_2\frac{\partial f}{\partial x_2} + \cdots + X_m\frac{\partial f}{\partial x_m} = 0, \tag{21.1.9}$$

and conversely any solution of (21.1.9) is an integral of the system (21.1.1). An integral which is a function of $(x_1, x_2, \ldots, x_m)$ only, not of t, satisfies the equation

$$X_1\frac{\partial f}{\partial x_1} + X_2\frac{\partial f}{\partial x_2} + \cdots + X_m\frac{\partial f}{\partial x_m} = 0. \tag{21.1.10}$$

We shall speak of such an integral as a *space-integral*.

If the system is autonomous, the space-integrals of the system (21.1.2) are the integrals of the system (21.1.6); any solution of (21.1.10) is an integral of (21.1.6) and a space-integral of (21.1.2). It is clear that (in the autonomous case) if f is an integral containing t of the system (21.1.2), then $\dfrac{\partial f}{\partial t}$ is also an integral. Similarly $\dfrac{\partial^2 f}{\partial t^2}$ is also an integral, and so on, provided that these partial derivatives of f are themselves of class C_1.

There are of course functions which are constant on particular characteristics, but not on all characteristics; these functions are not included in the class of integrals. As a trivial example, consider the equations

$$\frac{dx}{u} = \frac{dy}{v} = \frac{du}{0} = \frac{dv}{g} = dt,$$

where g is constant. We have the integrals

$$f = u, \quad f = \tfrac{1}{2}(u^2 + v^2) - gy.$$

In addition, on any characteristic for which $u = 0$ initially, $f = x$ remains constant; but this is not true for all the characteristics, and $f = x$ is not an integral.

The linear operator

$$X_1 \frac{\partial}{\partial x_1} + X_2 \frac{\partial}{\partial x_2} + \cdots + X_m \frac{\partial}{\partial x_m} \tag{21.1.11}$$

appearing in (21.1.9) and (21.1.10) is denoted by Ω. The space-integrals of (21.1.2), satisfy the condition

$$\Omega f = 0; \tag{21.1.12}$$

they are the functions of $(x_1, x_2, \ldots, x_m)$ which are annihilated by the operator Ω. The integrals, including those containing t, satisfy the condition

$$\left(\frac{\partial}{\partial t} + \Omega\right) f = 0. \tag{21.1.13}$$

The system of equations (21.1.1) or (21.1.2) can be written also in the form

$$\dot{x}_r = \Omega x_r, \qquad r = 1, 2, \ldots, m, \tag{21.1.14}$$

or, in a form similar to (21.1.13),

$$\left(\frac{\partial}{\partial t} - \Omega\right) x_r = 0, \qquad r = 1, 2, \ldots, m. \tag{21.1.15}$$

As we have noticed already (§ 19.1) it is sometimes useful to think of the equations (21.1.1) as defining the motion of a fluid rather than the motion of a single mobile (cf. § 19.1). The value of the idea of a fluid motion is that it allows us to contemplate the totality of possible motions, or at least all the motions originating in some domain, instead of merely one possible motion of the dynamical system. This idea is especially important when the system is autonomous, and the fluid motion is a steady motion. The stream-lines in the steady fluid motion coincide with the trajectories, and these curves are also the lines of force in the field **X**. If $f(x_1, x_2, \ldots, x_m)$ is a space-integral of the autonomous system, the equations $f = c$ represent (for a certain range of values of c) manifolds containing the stream-lines. It is sometimes convenient to denote the linear operator $\dfrac{\partial}{\partial t} + \Omega$ by the symbol $\dfrac{D}{Dt}$, as in the classical hydrodynamics. The meaning of $\dfrac{Df}{Dt}$ is the time-rate of change of the function $f(x_1, x_2, \ldots, x_m; t)$ at the variable point occupied by the mobile. The integrals of (21.1.1) satisfy the condition

$$\frac{Df}{Dt} = 0, \tag{21.1.16}$$

and the manifolds $f =$ constant *move with the fluid.*

If the autonomous system is sufficiently simple, we may be able to find more than one solution of (21.1.10), even as many as $(m - 1)$ independent solutions, $f_1, f_2, \ldots,$ f_{m-1}. Each trajectory is then the intersection of $(m - 1)$ manifolds defined by equations of the form $f_r = c_r$. There cannot be more than $(m - 1)$ independent space-integrals. But in general we have no assurance that $(m - 1)$ single-valued, or finitely many-valued, space-integrals exist. If we *can* find $(m - 1)$ independent solutions of (21.1.10) the knowledge of one solution containing t of (21.1.9) will enable us to complete the solution of the problem.

Consider for example the oscillatory system with two freedoms

(21.1.17) $$\dot{x} = u, \quad \dot{u} = -p^2x, \quad \dot{y} = v, \quad \dot{v} = -q^2y,$$

where p and q are positive constants, and $m = 4$. The equations determining the trajectories,

(21.1.18) $$\frac{dx}{u} = \frac{dy}{v} = \frac{du}{-p^2x} = \frac{dv}{-q^2y},$$

possess the familiar integrals

(21.1.19) $$p^2x^2 + u^2 = \text{constant}, \quad q^2y^2 + v^2 = \text{constant}.$$

There is a third space-integral, an algebraic function of (x, y, u, v) if p/q is rational, but not if p/q is irrational.

If we express the equations in terms of new variables x, y, ξ, η, where

(21.1.20) $$p^2\xi^2 = p^2x^2 + u^2, \quad q^2\eta^2 = q^2y^2 + v^2,$$

the equations (21.1.16) become

(21.1.21) $$\frac{d\xi}{0} = \frac{d\eta}{0} = \frac{dx}{p\sqrt{(\xi^2 - x^2)}} = \frac{dy}{q\sqrt{(\eta^2 - y^2)}},$$

giving $\xi = a$, $\eta = b$, and

(21.1.22) $$\frac{dx}{p\sqrt{(a^2 - x^2)}} = \frac{dy}{q\sqrt{(b^2 - y^2)}}.$$

If p/q is irrational the curve defined by (21.1.22) is dense in the rectangle bounded by $x = \pm a$, $y = \pm b$ (cf. Fig. 17.3), and no finitely many-valued integral of (21.1.22) exists.

The same problem will serve to illustrate another point. We saw that if we have an integral f containing t, then $\partial f/\partial t$ is also an integral, and so is $\partial^2 f/\partial t^2$, and so on. It might appear that from a single integral containing t we could find m independent integrals and so solve the problem completely. But of course the integrals produced in this way are not necessarily independent. Thus

(21.1.23) $$f = px \sin pt + u \cos pt$$

is an integral of (21.1.15), and

(21.1.24) $$\partial f/\partial t = p(px \cos pt - u \sin pt)$$

is an independent integral. In fact these two integrals serve to determine x and u as functions of t. But $\partial^2 f/\partial t^2$ is merely a multiple of f; it is not independent of the integrals already found.

We shall sometimes write $\varphi_r(t;\ \boldsymbol{\alpha})$, for the sake of brevity, instead of

$$\varphi_r(t;\ \alpha_1, \alpha_2, \ldots, \alpha_m).$$

We denote the partial derivative $\partial\varphi_r/\partial\alpha_s$ by φ_{rs}; the functions $\varphi_{rs}(t;\ \alpha_1, \alpha_2, \ldots, \alpha_m)$, or briefly $\varphi_{rs}(t;\ \boldsymbol{\alpha})$, are uniquely determined by the differential equations (21.1.1) from which we start.

If we substitute the formulae (21.1.7) for $\alpha_1, \alpha_2, \ldots, \alpha_m$ in the second member of (21.1.3), we obtain an identity involving the functions φ_r,

(21.1.25) $$x_r = \varphi_r\{t;\ \varphi_1(-t;\ \mathbf{x}),\quad \varphi_2(-t;\ \mathbf{x}), \ldots, \varphi_m(-t;\ \mathbf{x})\}.$$

If we differentiate partially with respect to t, and remember that

(21.1.26) $$\frac{\partial}{\partial t}\varphi_r(t;\ \boldsymbol{\alpha}) = X_r(\mathbf{x}),\quad \frac{\partial}{\partial t}\varphi_r(-t;\ \mathbf{x}) = -X_r(\boldsymbol{\alpha}),$$

we obtain the theorem

(21.1.27) $$X_r(\mathbf{x}) = \sum_{s=1}^{m} \varphi_{rs}(t;\ \boldsymbol{\alpha})X_s(\boldsymbol{\alpha}).$$

Another proof of this theorem will be given in § 21.5; see the equation (21.5.4).

21.2 Transformation to new coordinates. Let us express the equations (21.1.1) in terms of new coordinates $y_1, y_2, \ldots, y_m$. The transformation to be considered is defined by the equations

(21.2.1) $$y_r = F_r(x_1, x_2, \ldots, x_m), \qquad r = 1, 2, \ldots, m.$$

The functions F_r are of class C_2 in a suitable domain D of $\mathbf{x}$; in the autonomous case, this may be the same as the domain D relevant to (21.1.4). The Jacobian $\dfrac{\partial(F_1, F_2, \ldots, F_m)}{\partial(x_1, x_2, \ldots, x_m)}$ does not vanish in D. Then the transformation represents a mapping of the domain D of $\mathbf{x}$ onto a domain E of $\mathbf{y}$; if D is not too extensive, the correlation is a one-one relation, continuous and twice-differentiable in both directions. The equations (21.1.2),

(21.2.2) $$\frac{dx_1}{X_1} = \frac{dx_2}{X_2} = \cdots = \frac{dx_m}{X_m} = dt,$$

are transformed into

(21.2.3) $$\frac{dy_1}{Y_1} = \frac{dy_2}{Y_2} = \cdots = \frac{dy_m}{Y_m} = dt,$$

where Y_r denotes ΩF_r expressed in terms of the y's and of t.

The important property relating the equations (21.2.2) to the equations (21.2.3) is that the two *motions*, in the x-space and the y-space, correspond. Explicitly, let $\mathbf{x}_0$ be any point of D and $\mathbf{y}_0$ the corresponding point of E. Let $\mathbf{x}$ be the point reached at time t on the trajectory of (21.2.2) originating at $\mathbf{x}_0$, and let $\mathbf{y}$ be the point reached at time t on the trajectory of (21.2.3) originating at $\mathbf{y}_0$. Then $\mathbf{x}$ and $\mathbf{y}$ are corresponding points for all values of t at which $\mathbf{x} \in D$.

Suppose now that F_1 is a space-integral of (21.2.2). Then $Y_1 = 0$, and in the motion in the y-space y_1 remains constant, say $y_1 = \beta_1$. Then the system (21.2.3) can be replaced by the system

(21.2.4) $$\frac{dy_2}{Y_2'} = \frac{dy_3}{Y_3'} = \cdots = \frac{dy_m}{Y_m'} = dt,$$

where Y_r' is found from Y_r by replacing y_1 by β_1. We have used a known integral of (21.2.2) to reduce the number of coordinates from m to $(m - 1)$. Similarly if we know μ independent space-integrals $F_1, F_2, \ldots, F_\mu$, we can use these functions as the first μ components in the transformation (21.1.1), and thus we can reduce the number of coordinates effectively from m to $(m - \mu)$.

Consider the particular case of an autonomous system for which $(m - 1)$ independent space-integrals, $F_1, F_2, \ldots, F_{m-1}$, are known. As we have noticed, the trajectories are defined by the intersections of the varieties $F_r = \beta_r$. If we consider the trajectory corresponding to a particular set of values of $\beta_1, \beta_2, \ldots, \beta_{m-1}$, it remains to find the relation connecting position on the trajectory with the time. The relation is defined by

(21.2.5) $$\frac{dx_m}{X_m'} = dt,$$

where X_m' is X_m expressed in terms of $(\beta_1, \beta_2, \ldots, \beta_{m-1}, x_m)$ by means of the equations

(21.2.6) $$F_r = \beta_r, \qquad r = 1, 2, \ldots, (m - 1).$$

This is evident by elementary reasoning, or by using the transformation

(21.2.7) $$\begin{cases} y_r = F_r, & r = 1, 2, \ldots, (m - 1), \\ y_m = x_m. \end{cases}$$

21.3 The operator T_t. Let us consider an autonomous system. The characteristics represented by the equations (21.1.5) define a transformation from $\boldsymbol{\alpha}$ to $\mathbf{x}$, a transformation depending on t,

(21.3.1) $$\mathbf{x} = T_t\boldsymbol{\alpha}.$$

The operator T_t transforms the point $\boldsymbol{\alpha}$ occupied by the mobile at $t = 0$ into the point $\mathbf{x}$ occupied by the mobile at time t. We assume that the Jacobian

$$\frac{\partial(\varphi_1, \varphi_2, \ldots, \varphi_m)}{\partial(\alpha_1, \alpha_2, \ldots, \alpha_m)}$$

does not vanish for any relevant value of $\boldsymbol{\alpha}$ and any value of t. (We shall see later that in the important case of the Hamiltonian equations this Jacobian has the value 1.) If we consider a region E_0 of the domain D (relevant to (21.1.4)), and $\boldsymbol{\alpha} \in E_0$, the transformation T_t defines, for sufficiently small values of t, a topological mapping of E_0 onto a region E_t. The transformation defined by the operator T_0 is the identity, and there is an inverse transformation T_{-t} which defines a mapping of E_t onto E_0. Two successive transformations defined by the operators T_{t_1}, T_{t_2}, are commutative, and they are equivalent to the single transformation defined by the operator $T_{t_1+t_2}$,

(21.3.2) $$T_{t_2}T_{t_1} = T_{t_1+t_2}.$$

Further, the operator T_t satisfies the associative law,

(21.3.3) $$T_{t_3}(T_{t_2}T_{t_1}) = (T_{t_3}T_{t_2})T_{t_1}.$$

We have thus a one-parameter continuous group of transformations of the x-space onto itself.

In the important special case of Hamilton's equations the $2n$ variables are grouped in n pairs (q_r, p_r), and the transformation is of a particular type called a *contact transformation*. Transformations of this type will be studied in Chapter XXIV.

21.4 Solution in power series. We consider an autonomous system with the property that the functions X_r possess derivatives of all orders in D. If we define a function of t by $f(\mathbf{x})$, where $\mathbf{x}$ is the position of the mobile at time t, we have

$$\frac{\partial}{\partial t} f = \sum_{r=1}^{m} \frac{\partial f}{\partial x_r} \dot{x}_r = \sum_{r=1}^{m} X_r \frac{\partial f}{\partial x_r} = \Omega f. \tag{21.4.1}$$

Now

$$\frac{\partial x_r}{\partial t} = X_r = \Omega x_r, \tag{21.4.2}$$

whence

$$\frac{\partial^2 x_r}{\partial t^2} = \Omega(\Omega x_r) = \Omega^2 x_r, \tag{21.4.3}$$

and, generally,

$$\frac{\partial^n x_r}{\partial t^n} = \Omega^n x_r. \tag{21.4.4}$$

Hence, by Taylor's theorem, if $\mathbf{x} = \boldsymbol{\alpha}$ at $t = 0$, we have, if the series is convergent,

$$\begin{aligned} x_r &= (x_r)_0 + t(\Omega x_r)_0 + \frac{t^2}{2!} (\Omega^2 x_r)_0 + \cdots \\ &= \alpha_r + t\omega\alpha_r + \frac{t^2}{2!} \omega^2 \alpha_r + \cdots, \end{aligned} \tag{21.4.5}$$

where ω denotes the operator

$$\sum_{r=1}^{m} X_r(\alpha_1, \alpha_2, \ldots, \alpha_m) \frac{\partial}{\partial \alpha_r}. \tag{21.4.6}$$

We can write (21.4.5) *symbolically in the compact form*

$$x_r = e^{t\omega}\alpha_r, \qquad r = 1, 2, \ldots, m, \tag{21.4.7}$$

and this is the solution of the equations $\dot{x}_r = X_r(\mathbf{x})$.

The series for x_r will certainly converge if $\Omega^n x_r$ is bounded, for all n, on the trajectory joining $\boldsymbol{\alpha}$ to $\mathbf{x}$. Thus in general the series will converge ($\boldsymbol{\alpha}$ being fixed) inside the circle of convergence $|t| = \rho_r$. The solution is valid for all the coordinates $x_1, x_2, \ldots, x_m$ if $|t| < \rho(\boldsymbol{\alpha})$, where ρ is the least of the numbers $\rho_1, \rho_2, \ldots, \rho_m$.

More generally we may be concerned, not with a fixed initial point $\boldsymbol{\alpha}$, but with all the points in a certain region R_0. Then we need $|t|$ to be less than the infimum of the values of $\rho(\boldsymbol{\alpha})$ for $\boldsymbol{\alpha}$ in R_0.

An alternative proof of the solution in power series (21.4.5) is not without interest. In virtue of (21.1.7), $\varphi_r(-t;\ x_1, x_2, \ldots, x_m)$ is an integral of the equations (21.1.1), and therefore, by (21.1.13),

$$\left(\frac{\partial}{\partial t} + \Omega\right) \varphi_r(-t;\ x_1, x_2, \ldots, x_m) = 0. \tag{21.4.8}$$

Hence

$$\left(\frac{\partial}{\partial t} - \Omega\right) \varphi_r(t;\ x_1, x_2, \ldots, x_m) = 0, \tag{21.4.9}$$

or again

(21.4.10) $$\left(\frac{\partial}{\partial t} - \omega\right) \varphi_r(t;\ \alpha_1, \alpha_2, \ldots, \alpha_m) = 0.$$

Thus $\varphi_r(t;\ \alpha_1, \alpha_2, \ldots, \alpha_m)$ satisfies the equation

(21.4.11) $$\frac{\partial \varphi_r}{\partial t} = \omega\varphi_r.$$

But this equation is clearly satisfied (the X_r's being infinitely differentiable) by

(21.4.12) $$\alpha_r + t\omega\alpha_r + \frac{t^2}{2!}\omega^2\alpha_r + \cdots,$$

and this solution has the value α_r at $t = 0$; so (21.4.12) is equal to x_r, and we recover (21.4.5).

The solution in power series gives us, for sufficiently small values of t, an explicit expression for the operator T_t,

(21.4.13) $$T_t = e^{t\omega},$$

and the fundamental group property is evident. If we have any analytic function $f(x_1, x_2, \ldots, x_m)$, and wish to investigate how it varies as $\mathbf{x}$ moves on a trajectory, we have

(21.4.14) $$f(\mathbf{x}) = e^{t\omega}f(\boldsymbol{\alpha}) = f(\boldsymbol{\alpha}) + t\omega f(\boldsymbol{\alpha}) + \frac{t^2}{2!}\omega^2 f(\boldsymbol{\alpha}) + \cdots,$$

and the function is invariant if and only if

(21.4.15) $$\omega f(\alpha_1, \alpha_2, \ldots, \alpha_m) = 0,$$

i.e. if and only if $f(\mathbf{x})$ satisfies (21.1.12). The invariants are the integrals of (21.1.6), i.e. they are the space-integrals of (21.1.2). This is a re-statement, from a different point of view, of the remark that the integrals of (21.1.6) define manifolds containing the trajectories.

In the simplest cases the power-series converge for all values of t, as in the *Examples* 21.4*A*, *B* below. But in general the solution is valid only for sufficiently small values of t.

Example 21.4*A*. *The harmonic oscillator*. The equations are

(21.4.16) $$\dot{x} = u, \quad \dot{u} = -n^2x,$$

and we seek the solution having $x = \alpha$, $u = \beta$, at $t = 0$. Here

(21.4.17) $$\omega = \beta\frac{\partial}{\partial\alpha} - n^2\alpha\frac{\partial}{\partial\beta},$$

and the solution is

(21.4.18) $$\begin{cases} x = (1 + t\omega + \dfrac{t^2}{2!}\omega^2 + \cdots)\alpha, \\ u = (1 + t\omega + \dfrac{t^2}{2!}\omega^2 + \cdots)\beta. \end{cases}$$

Now

(21.4.19) $$\begin{cases} \omega\alpha = \beta, \\ \omega^2\alpha = -n^2\alpha, \\ \omega^3\alpha = -n^2\beta, \\ \omega^4\alpha = (-n^2)^2\alpha, \end{cases}$$

and so on. Thus

$$x = \alpha\left(1 - \frac{n^2t^2}{2!} + \frac{n^4t^4}{4!} - \cdots\right) + \beta\left(t - \frac{n^2t^3}{3!} + \frac{n^4t^5}{5!} - \cdots\right) \tag{21.4.20}$$

$$= \alpha \cos nt + \frac{\beta}{n} \sin nt.$$

Similarly

$$u = -n\alpha \sin nt + \beta \cos nt, \tag{21.4.21}$$

though this can be found more simply, of course, from $u = \dot{x}$. We thus recover the familiar solution. We notice that the solutions possess the reciprocal property described by (21.1.5) and (21.1.7),

$$\begin{cases} \alpha = x \cos nt - \dfrac{u}{n} \sin nt, \\ \beta = nx \sin nt + u \cos nt. \end{cases} \tag{21.4.22}$$

Actually in this simple case the whole is evident by elementary arguments (cf. *Example* 19.4*B*). If we put $u = ny$ the equations become

$$\dot{x} = ny, \quad \dot{y} = -nx, \tag{21.4.23}$$

and the transformation T_t is simply a clockwise rotation through an angle nt. Thus to find the explicit formulae we have only to rotate the axes anticlockwise through an angle nt and write the coordinates of the initial point referred to the new axes,

$$\begin{cases} x = x_0 \cos nt + y_0 \sin nt, \\ y = -x_0 \sin nt + y_0 \cos nt, \end{cases} \tag{21.4.24}$$

which is equivalent to (21.4.20–21).

Example 21.4*B*. *Uniform field*. This is even simpler, because in this case the series are finite. Here

$$\dot{x}_1 = x_4, \quad \dot{x}_2 = x_5, \quad \dot{x}_3 = x_6, \quad \dot{x}_4 = 0, \quad \dot{x}_5 = 0, \quad \dot{x}_6 = g, \tag{21.4.25}$$

and

$$\omega = \alpha_4 \frac{\partial}{\partial \alpha_1} + \alpha_5 \frac{\partial}{\partial \alpha_2} + \alpha_6 \frac{\partial}{\partial \alpha_3} + g \frac{\partial}{\partial \alpha_6}. \tag{21.4.26}$$

Thus

$$\begin{cases} \omega\alpha_1 = \alpha_4, \quad \omega^2\alpha_1 = 0; \\ \omega\alpha_2 = \alpha_5, \quad \omega^2\alpha_2 = 0; \\ \omega\alpha_3 = \alpha_6, \quad \omega^2\alpha_3 = g, \quad \omega^3\alpha_3 = 0; \\ \omega\alpha_4 = 0; \\ \omega\alpha_5 = 0; \\ \omega\alpha_6 = g, \quad \omega^2\alpha_6 = 0; \end{cases} \tag{21.4.27}$$

giving the familiar solution

$$\begin{cases} x_1 = \alpha_1 + \alpha_4 t, \\ x_2 = \alpha_2 + \alpha_5 t, \\ x_3 = \alpha_3 + \alpha_6 t + \tfrac{1}{2}gt^2. \\ x_4 = \alpha_4, \\ x_5 = \alpha_5, \\ x_6 = \alpha_6 + gt. \end{cases} \tag{21.4.28}$$

We notice again the reciprocal property of the solutions; if we express α in terms of $(\mathbf{x}, t)$ we get similar formulae with $\mathbf{x}$ and $\boldsymbol{\alpha}$ interchanged, and $-t$ in place of t.

Example 21.4*C*. *Newtonian orbit.* Here

$$H = \tfrac{1}{2}\left(\xi^2 + \frac{1}{r^2}\eta^2\right) - \frac{\mu}{r}, \tag{21.4.29}$$

where we write ξ, η for p_r, p_θ. We suppose that initially

$$(r, \theta, \xi, \eta) = (\alpha, \beta, \gamma, \delta). \tag{21.4.30}$$

The Hamiltonian equations of motion are

$$\begin{cases} \dot{r} = \xi, \quad \dot{\theta} = \dfrac{\eta}{r^2}, \\ \dot{\xi} = \dfrac{\eta^2}{r^3} - \dfrac{\mu}{r^2}, \quad \dot{\eta} = 0, \end{cases} \tag{21.4.31}$$

and

$$\omega = \gamma\frac{\partial}{\partial\alpha} + \frac{\delta}{\alpha^2}\frac{\partial}{\partial\beta} + \left(\frac{\delta^2}{\alpha^3} - \frac{\mu}{\alpha^2}\right)\frac{\partial}{\partial\gamma}. \tag{21.4.32}$$

To find the value of r at time t we have

$$\begin{cases} \omega\alpha = \gamma, \\ \omega^2\alpha = \dfrac{\delta^2}{\alpha^3} - \dfrac{\mu}{\alpha^2}, \\ \omega^3\alpha = \gamma\left(-\dfrac{3\delta^2}{\alpha^4} + \dfrac{2\mu}{\alpha^3}\right), \end{cases} \tag{21.4.33}$$

and so on. Thus

$$r = \alpha + \gamma t + \left(\frac{\delta^2}{2\alpha^3} - \frac{\mu}{2\alpha^2}\right)t^2 + \left(-\frac{\gamma\delta^2}{2\alpha^4} + \frac{\mu\gamma}{3\alpha^3}\right)t^3 + \cdots, \tag{21.4.34}$$

which gives an approximation to the value of r for small values of t. But in general the expression as a Fourier series (§ 18.14) is more useful.

To find the value of θ at time t we have

$$\begin{cases} \omega\beta = \dfrac{\delta}{\alpha^2}, \\ \omega^2\beta = -\dfrac{2\gamma\delta}{\alpha^3}, \\ \omega^3\beta = \gamma\left(\dfrac{6\gamma\delta}{\alpha^4}\right) + \left(\dfrac{\delta^2}{\alpha^3} - \dfrac{\mu}{\alpha^2}\right)\left(-\dfrac{2\delta}{\alpha^3}\right) = \dfrac{6\gamma^2\delta}{\alpha^4} + \dfrac{2\mu\delta}{\alpha^5} - \dfrac{2\delta^3}{\alpha^6}, \end{cases} \tag{21.4.35}$$

and so on. Thus

$$\theta = \beta + \frac{\delta}{\alpha^2}t - \frac{\gamma\delta}{\alpha^3}t^2 + \left(\frac{\gamma^2\delta}{\alpha^4} + \frac{\mu\delta}{3\alpha^5} - \frac{\delta^3}{3\alpha^6}\right)t^3 + \cdots. \tag{21.4.36}$$

The solution for ξ is found from $\xi = \dot{r}$, and the solution for η is simply $\eta = \delta$.

21.5 A formula for X(x) − X(α). The solutions of the equations (21.1.1) are given by (21.1.5), where $\boldsymbol{\alpha}$ is the value of $\mathbf{x}$ at $t = 0$, and we assume that the functions φ are of class C_2. As usual we think of the equations as defining the motion of a mobile which starts from $\boldsymbol{\alpha}$ at $t = 0$ and arrives at $\mathbf{x}$ at time t. We denote the partial derivative $\partial\varphi_r/\partial\alpha_s$ by φ_{rs}, as in § 21.1.

Let us suppose that at time $t = \theta$ the mobile arrives at the point $\boldsymbol{\xi}$,

$$\xi_r = \varphi_r(\theta;\ \alpha_1, \alpha_2, \ldots, \alpha_m). \tag{21.5.1}$$

Now the motion starting at $\boldsymbol{\alpha}$ at $t = 0$ is the same motion as the motion starting at $\boldsymbol{\xi}$ at $t = \theta$, so that

$$\varphi_r(\theta + t;\ \boldsymbol{\alpha}) = \varphi_r(t;\ \boldsymbol{\xi}). \tag{21.5.2}$$

Differentiating partially with respect to θ we have

$$X_r\{\boldsymbol{\varphi}(\theta + t;\ \boldsymbol{\alpha})\} = \sum_{s=1}^{m} \varphi_{rs}(t;\ \boldsymbol{\xi})X_s\{\varphi(\theta;\ \boldsymbol{\alpha})\}. \tag{21.5.3}$$

Putting $\theta = 0$ in this result we have

$$X_r(\mathbf{x}) = \sum_{s=1}^{m} \varphi_{rs}(t;\ \boldsymbol{\alpha})X_s(\boldsymbol{\alpha}), \tag{21.5.4}$$

a result which has been found already by a different method in § 21.1. Hence

$$X_r(\mathbf{x}) - X_r(\boldsymbol{\alpha}) = \sum_{s=1}^{m} \{\varphi_{rs}(t;\ \boldsymbol{\alpha}) - \delta_{rs}\}X_s(\boldsymbol{\alpha}). \tag{21.5.5}$$

If now we denote by $\mathbf{F}$ $(= \mathbf{F}(t;\boldsymbol{\alpha}))$ the $m \times m$ matrix for which the typical element is

$$f_{rs} = \varphi_{rs}(t;\boldsymbol{\alpha}) - \delta_{rs}, \tag{25.5.6}$$

we have

$$\mathbf{X}(\mathbf{x}) - \mathbf{X}(\boldsymbol{\alpha}) = \mathbf{F}(t;\boldsymbol{\alpha})\mathbf{X}(\boldsymbol{\alpha}), \tag{21.5.7}$$

and this is the desired result.

21.6 Integral-invariants. We consider an autonomous system. The transformation defined by the operator T_t transforms a point $\boldsymbol{\alpha}$, occupied by the mobile at $t = 0$, into the point $\mathbf{x}$ occupied by the mobile at time t. Consider now, not a single initial point $\boldsymbol{\alpha}$, but the points of a curve γ_0. The curve γ_0 is assumed to have a continuously turning tangent, except at a finite number of corners. The transformation T_t, which is defined by the differential equations (21.1.1), transforms each point $\boldsymbol{\alpha}$ on γ_0 at $t = 0$ into a point $\mathbf{x}$ at time t, and these points $\mathbf{x}$ trace out a curve γ. If we think of the equations (21.1.1) as defining the motion of a fluid (cf. § 21.1), the curve γ is a curve *moving with the fluid*, and γ_0 is its position at $t = 0$.

Suppose now that there exists a vector field $\mathbf{P}(= \mathbf{P}(\mathbf{x}))$, with components $P_1, P_2, \ldots, P_m$, where $P_r \in C_1$, such that

$$\int_{\gamma_0} P_1\,dx_1 + P_2\,dx_2 + \cdots + P_m\,dx_m = \int_{\gamma} P_1dx_1 + P_2\,dx_2 + \cdots + P_m\,dx_m \tag{21.6.1}$$

for all values of t and for all choices of γ_0. Then the line-integral

$$\int_{\gamma} \mathbf{P}\,.\,d\mathbf{x} = \int_{\gamma} \sum_{r=1}^{m} P_r\,dx_r \tag{21.6.2}$$

is said to be a linear *integral-invariant* of the equations (21.1.1). If the invariance holds for all curves, open or closed, the line-integral is an *absolute* integral-invariant. If the invariance holds only for closed curves, the line-integral is a *relative* integral-invariant.

A trivial example of a relative integral-invariant arises when the field $\mathbf{P}$ is derived from a uniform potential function; in that case the integral $\oint \mathbf{P}\,.\,d\mathbf{x}$ is zero for any closed curve at any time. Another familiar example occurs in the classical hydrodynamics. We suppose the motion to be steady, so that the components u, v, w of the fluid velocity are functions of (x, y, z), and we suppose that the body forces acting on the fluid are derived from a uniform potential function. Then the *circulation*

$$\oint u\,dx + v\,dy + w\,dz \tag{21.6.3}$$

taken round a closed curve moving with the fluid remains constant for all time.

We now find necessary and sufficient conditions that $\int \mathbf{P} \,.\, d\mathbf{x}$ should be an integral-invariant. To achieve this end, we introduce a parameter u, and we define the curve γ in terms of u as u runs from 0 to 1. The parameter u is so chosen that the points for any fixed value of u refer to the same trajectory for all values of t. Thus

$$x_r = x_r(t, u), \qquad r = 1, 2, \ldots, m, \tag{21.6.4}$$

where the functions on the right are of class C_2. For a fixed value of t, the equations (21.6.4) define the curve γ as u runs from 0 to 1, and for a fixed value of u the equations define a trajectory, and

$$\frac{\partial x_r}{\partial t} = X_r, \qquad r = 1, 2, \ldots m. \tag{21.6.5}$$

In other words, the curves u = constant are the trajectories, the curves t = constant are the instantaneous positions of the curve γ moving with the fluid.

Consider then the line-integral

$$I = \int_\gamma^1 \mathbf{P} \,.\, d\mathbf{x} = \int_\gamma P_r\,dx_r = \int_0^1 P_r \frac{\partial x_r}{\partial u}\,du, \tag{21.6.6}$$

where we use the convention that repeated suffixes imply summation. We have

$$\begin{aligned} \frac{DI}{Dt} &= \int_0^1 \frac{\partial}{\partial t}\left(P_r \frac{\partial x_r}{\partial u}\right) du \\ &= \int_0^1 \left(\frac{\partial P_r}{\partial x_s} X_s \frac{\partial x_r}{\partial u} + P_r \frac{\partial X_r}{\partial u}\right) du \\ &= \int_0^1 \left(\frac{\partial P_r}{\partial x_s} X_s \frac{\partial x_r}{\partial u} + P_r \frac{\partial X_r}{\partial x_s}\frac{\partial x_s}{\partial u}\right) du \\ &= \int_0^1 \left(\frac{\partial P_r}{\partial x_s} X_s + P_s \frac{\partial X_s}{\partial x_r}\right) \frac{\partial x_r}{\partial u}\,du. \end{aligned} \tag{21.6.7}$$

We can express the second member as a line-integral along γ,

$$\begin{aligned} \frac{DI}{Dt} &= \int_\gamma \left(\frac{\partial P_r}{\partial x_s} X_s + P_s \frac{\partial X_s}{dx_r}\right) dx_r \\ &= \int_\gamma \left\{\frac{\partial}{\partial x_r}(P_s X_s) + \left(\frac{\partial P_r}{\partial x_s} - \frac{\partial P_s}{\partial x_r}\right) X_s\right\} dx_r \\ &= P_s X_s \Big| + \int_\gamma Q_r\,dx_r, \end{aligned} \tag{21.6.8}$$

where

$$Q_r = \sum_{s=1}^m \left(\frac{\partial P_r}{\partial x_s} - \frac{\partial P_s}{\partial x_r}\right) X_s. \tag{21.6.9}$$

The necessary and sufficient condition for I to be an absolute integral-invariant is that

$$P_s X_s \Big| + \int_\gamma Q_r \, dx_r \tag{21.6.10}$$

should vanish for all choices of γ; I is a relative integral-invariant if $\oint Q_r \, dx_r$ vanishes for all closed curves, i.e. if $\sum_{r=1}^{m} Q_r \, dx_r$ is a perfect differential of a uniform function of $(x_1, x_2, \ldots, x_m)$.

The argument can be expressed very concisely in a form which makes use of the idea of a fluid in motion. We consider a line-element $d\mathbf{x}$ moving with the fluid. Then

$$\frac{D}{Dt}(P_r \, dx_r) = \frac{DP_r}{Dt} dx_r + P_r \frac{D}{Dt} dx_r. \tag{21.6.11}$$

Now

$$\frac{DP_r}{Dt} = \frac{\partial P_r}{\partial x_s} X_s, \tag{21.6.12}$$

and

$$\frac{D}{Dt} dx_r = dX_r = \frac{\partial X_r}{\partial x_s} dx_s. \tag{21.6.13}$$

Hence

$$\frac{D}{Dt}(P_r \, dx_r) = \frac{\partial P_r}{\partial x_s} X_s \, dx_r + P_r \frac{\partial X_r}{\partial x_s} dx_s, \tag{21.6.14}$$

leading again to the result already found.

As a simple concrete example consider the system

$$\frac{dx}{u} = \frac{dy}{v} = \frac{du}{0} = \frac{dv}{-n^2 y} = dt. \tag{21.6.15}$$

The line-integral $\oint u \, dx + v \, dy$ is a relative integral-invariant. We can prove this easily, either from the fact that $\sum_{r=1}^{4} Q_r \, dx_r$ is a perfect differential, or directly from the explicit solution

$$x = x_0 + u_0 t, \quad y = y_0 \cos nt + \frac{1}{n} v_0 \sin nt, \quad u = u_0, \quad v = -ny_0 \sin nt + v_0 \cos nt. \tag{21.6.16}$$

So far we have spoken only of integral-invariants of order 1, but we can also have integral-invariants of higher order, 2, 3, . . . , m, where the domain of integration is a manifold of 2, 3, . . . , m dimensions moving with the fluid. For the classical dynamics the most important cases are the extreme cases, where the manifold of integration has dimensions 1 or m.

To a relative integral-invariant of order r there corresponds an absolute integral-invariant of order $(r + 1)$. This follows from the generalization of Stokes's theorem.

The theory of linear integral-invariants can be extended to the case in which the system is not autonomous, and in which the functions P_r contain t. The formula (21.6.10) must be replaced by

$$P_s X_s \Big| + \int_\gamma \left(\frac{\partial P_r}{\partial t} + Q_r \right) dx_r, \tag{21.6.17}$$

and the integral I is an absolute integral-invariant if (21.6.17) vanishes for all choices of γ; it is a relative integral-invariant if $\sum_{r=1}^{m}\left(\frac{\partial P_r}{\partial t}+Q_r\right)dx_r$ is a perfect space-differential.

As a trivial example in which the P's contain t, we may consider again the system (21.6.15). For this system the line-integral $\int dx - t\,du$ is an absolute integral-invariant. We can see this either from the general criterion, the vanishing of (21.6.17), or directly from the explicit solution (21.6.16).

21.7 Integral-invariants of order m. We consider in the first instance an autonomous system. The theory depends on the following lemma.

Lemma. Let J denote the Jacobian

$$\frac{\partial(x_1, x_2, \ldots, x_m)}{\partial(\alpha_1, \alpha_2, \ldots, \alpha_m)}, \tag{21.7.1}$$

and Δ the divergence of the vector field $\mathbf{X}$,

$$\Delta = \frac{\partial X_1}{\partial x_1} + \frac{\partial X_2}{\partial x_2} + \cdots + \frac{\partial X_m}{\partial x_m}. \tag{21.7.2}$$

Then

$$\frac{\partial J}{\partial t} = J\Delta. \tag{21.7.3}$$

The derivative of a determinant can be represented as the sum of the m determinants obtained by differentiating the elements of each row in turn. Thus $\partial J/\partial t$ can be represented as the sum of m determinants, of which the first is

$$\frac{\partial(\dot{x}_1, x_2, \ldots, x_m)}{\partial(\alpha_1, \alpha_2, \ldots, \alpha_m)} = \frac{\partial(X_1, x_2, \ldots, x_m)}{\partial(\alpha_1, \alpha_2, \ldots, \alpha_m)}. \tag{21.7.4}$$

The rth element in the first row of this determinant is

$$\frac{\partial X_1}{\partial \alpha_r} = \sum_{s=1}^{m} \frac{\partial X_1}{\partial x_s}\frac{\partial x_s}{\partial \alpha_r}. \tag{21.7.5}$$

If we subtract from the elements of the first row the corresponding elements of the sth row multiplied by $\partial X_1/\partial x_s$, for each s from 2 to m, we do not alter the value of the determinant. In the determinant so found the rth element in the first row is $\frac{\partial X_1}{\partial x_1}\frac{\partial x_1}{\partial \alpha_r}$, so the first of the m determinants obtained by differentiation is $\frac{\partial X_1}{\partial x_1}J$. Proceeding similarly with the other $(m-1)$ determinants we have

$$\frac{\partial J}{\partial t} = \left(\frac{\partial X_1}{\partial x_1} + \frac{\partial X_2}{\partial x_2} + \cdots + \frac{\partial X_m}{\partial x_m}\right) J, \tag{21.7.6}$$

and the lemma is proved.

Consider now a closed region E_0 of finite volume (extension) A_0, and let E_t be the region into which E_0 is transformed by the transformation T_t. If A is the volume of E_t, we have

$$A = \int_{E_t} dx_1\,dx_2 \cdots dx_m = \int_{E_0} J\,d\alpha_1\,d\alpha_2 \cdots d\alpha_m, \tag{21.7.7}$$

the x-space being here taken to be Euclidean. Thus

(21.7.8)
$$\frac{DA}{Dt} = \int_{E_0} \frac{\partial J}{\partial t}\, d\alpha_1\, d\alpha_2 \cdots d\alpha_m = \int_{E_0} \Delta J\, d\alpha_1\, d\alpha_2 \cdots d\alpha_m = \int_{E_t} \Delta\, dx_1\, dx_2 \cdots dx_m.$$

The equation (21.7.8) gives us a useful geometrical interpretation of the significance of the divergence Δ of the field $\mathbf{x}$. By applying the result to a *small* volume E_t of the m-fold space we see that, if V is the *specific volume* of the fluid at the point $\mathbf{x}$,

(21.7.9)
$$\Delta = \frac{1}{V}\frac{DV}{Dt}.$$

The result for the case $m = 3$ is familiar in the classical hydrodynamics.

Let us now find the necessary and sufficient condition for the integral

(21.7.10)
$$I = \int_E M\, dx_1\, dx_2 \cdots dx_m$$

to be an integral-invariant, M being a scalar function of $(x_1, x_2, \ldots, x_m)$ of class C_1. We have

(21.7.11)
$$I = \int_{E_t} M\, dx_1\, dx_2 \cdots dx_m = \int_{E_0} MJ\, d\alpha_1\, d\alpha_2 \cdots d\alpha_m,$$

and therefore

(21.7.12)
$$\frac{DI}{Dt} = \int_{E_0} \frac{\partial}{\partial t}(MJ)\, d\alpha_1\, d\alpha_2 \cdots d\alpha_m.$$

Now, using (21.7.3),

(21.7.13)
$$\frac{\partial}{\partial t}(MJ) = \left(\sum_{r=1}^{m} \frac{\partial M}{\partial x_r} X_r\right)J + M\left(\sum_{r=1}^{m} \frac{\partial X_r}{\partial x_r}\right)J = J\sum_{r=1}^{m} \frac{\partial}{\partial x_r}(MX_r),$$

and (21.7.12) becomes

(21.7.14)
$$\frac{DI}{Dt} = \int_{E_0}\left\{\sum_{r=1}^{m} \frac{\partial}{\partial x_r}(MX_r)\right\} J\, d\alpha_1\, d\alpha_2 \cdots d\alpha_m = \int_{E_t}\left\{\sum_{r=1}^{m} \frac{\partial}{\partial x_r}(MX_r)\right\} dx_1\, dx_2 \cdots dx_m.$$

Thus, finally, $\dfrac{DI}{Dt} = 0$ *for an arbitrary choice of* E_t *if and only if*

(21.7.15)
$$\frac{\partial}{\partial x_1}(MX_1) + \frac{\partial}{\partial x_2}(MX_2) + \cdots + \frac{\partial}{\partial x_m}(MX_m) = 0.$$

The functions $M(x_1, x_2, \ldots, x_m)$ satisfying the linear partial differential equation (21.7.15) were called by Jacobi the *multipliers* for the system (21.1.1). We can write the equation satisfied by the multipliers in either of the forms

(21.7.16)
$$\operatorname{div}(M\mathbf{X}) = 0,$$

(21.7.17)
$$M \operatorname{div} \mathbf{X} + \Omega M = 0.$$

The argument can be written in a very concise form if we use the result (21.7.9). If we consider an infinitesimal region of the x-space of volume V, we have

$$\frac{D}{Dt}(MV) = \frac{DM}{Dt}V + M\frac{DV}{dt} \tag{21.7.18}$$

$$= \left(\sum_{r=1}^{m}\frac{\partial M}{\partial x_r}X_r + M\Delta\right)V$$

$$= \left\{\sum_{r=1}^{m}\frac{\partial}{\partial x_r}(MX_r)\right\}V,$$

and the result follows as before.

To furnish a simple concrete example of an integral-invariant of order m, let us consider again the system (21.6.15). The integral

$$\iiiint\sqrt{(n^2y^2 + v^2)}\,dx\,dy\,du\,dv \tag{21.7.19}$$

is an integral-invariant. This follows from (21.7.15), or directly from the explicit solution (21.6.16).

Again, the theory can be generalized to include non-autonomous systems, and integrands M which are functions of t as well as of $(x_1, x_2, \ldots, x_m)$. The result (21.7.3) is still valid for non-autonomous systems, and if M contains t the condition (21.7.15) must be replaced by

$$\frac{\partial M}{\partial t} + \frac{\partial}{\partial x_1}(MX_1) + \frac{\partial}{\partial x_2}(MX_2) + \cdots + \frac{\partial}{\partial x_m}(MX_m) = 0. \tag{21.7.20}$$

We shall, however, reserve the term *multiplier* for functions M not involving t.

21.8 Properties of the multipliers. We consider an autonomous system; the functions X_r in the second members of (21.1.1) do not contain t. A number of important properties of the system follow from the results just proved.

(i) If we can find an explicit expression $\chi(x_1, x_2, \ldots, x_m)$ for the specific volume V, then $1/\chi$ is a multiplier.

(ii) If we can find two independent multipliers M_1, M_2, their ratio M_1/M_2 is an integral of the system of differential equations. This follows from the fact that M_1V and M_2V both remain constant on a trajectory, as in (21.7.18), so M_1/M_2 also remains constant. Or, expressing the argument more formally, from (21.7.17) we have

$$\frac{1}{M_2}\Omega M_2 - \frac{1}{M_1}\Omega M_1 = 0, \tag{21.8.1}$$

whence

$$\Omega\left(\frac{M_1}{M_2}\right) = 0. \tag{21.8.2}$$

(iii) If $\Delta = 0$, then $M = 1$ is a multiplier; the extension of the x-space is itself an integral-invariant. (This holds also for non-autonomous systems in which $\Delta = 0$.)

The differential equation satisfied by the multipliers is simply

$$\Omega M = 0, \tag{21.8.3}$$

and the multipliers are precisely the space-integrals. We can look at the identity of multipliers and space-integrals in another way. If M is a space-integral, M is constant on a trajectory; and (since $\Delta = 0$) V also is constant on a trajectory; therefore MV is constant on a trajectory, and it follows that $\int M\, dx_1\, dx_2 \cdots dx_m$ is an integral-invariant.

(iv) If $m = 2$ the multipliers are the integrating factors for the equation

$$X_2\, dx_1 - X_1\, dx_2 = 0. \tag{21.8.4}$$

For the integrating factors μ satisfy the equation

$$\frac{\partial}{\partial x_1}(\mu X_1) + \frac{\partial}{\partial x_2}(\mu X_2) = 0, \tag{21.8.5}$$

so the integrating factors are identified with the multipliers.

In particular, if $m = 2$ and $\Delta = 0$, then 1 is a multiplier, and therefore 1 is an integrating factor, i.e. $X_2\, dx_1 - X_1\, dx_2$ is a perfect differential $d\psi$. The function ψ is the *stream function* of Lagrange, which is important in the study of the two-dimensional motion of an incompressible fluid.

(v) We now consider a transformation to new variables $y_1, y_2, \ldots, y_m$, as in § 21.2. In the equations of transformation

$$y_r = F_r(x_1, x_2, \ldots, x_m), \qquad r = 1, 2, \ldots, m, \tag{21.8.6}$$

the functions F_r are of class C_2 in a domain D of $\mathbf{x}$, and the Jacobian

$$J = \frac{\partial(y_1, y_2, \ldots, y_m)}{\partial(x_1, x_2, \ldots, x_m)} \tag{21.8.7}$$

does not vanish in D. The transformation defines a one-one correlation between the domain D of $\mathbf{x}$ and the corresponding domain E of $\mathbf{y}$.

We shall prove that, *if M is a multiplier for the original system, then $(M/J)'$ is a multiplier for the transformed system, where the accent denotes expression in terms of $y_1, y_2, \ldots, y_m$.*

The theorem is not difficult to prove by deliberate calculation,* but it is much simpler to use the hydrodynamical ideas introduced above. We recall that there is a correlation not only between the two *spaces*, but also between the two *motions* (§ 21.2); two mobiles $\mathbf{x}$ and $\mathbf{y}$ in the two spaces, which occupy related positions at $t = 0$ and move with the respective fluids, occupy related positions for all time. Thus, in virtue of (21.7.18).

$$\operatorname{div}(M\mathbf{X}) = \frac{1}{V}\frac{D}{Dt}(MV) = \frac{J'}{V'}\frac{D}{Dt}\left(\frac{M'}{J'}V'\right) = J' \operatorname{div}'\left(\frac{M'}{J'}\mathbf{Y}\right), \tag{21.8.8}$$

where accents denote expression in terms of $(y_1, y_2, \ldots, y_m)$; and the theorem follows.

21.9 Jacobi's last multiplier. Consider the equations defining the trajectories of an autonomous system,

$$\frac{dx_1}{X_1} = \frac{dx_2}{X_2} = \cdots = \frac{dx_m}{X_m}, \tag{21.9.1}$$

and let us suppose that we have found $(m - 2)$ space-integrals

$$f_r = c_r, \qquad r = 1, 2, \ldots, (m - 2), \tag{21.9.2}$$

* See for example Whittaker, "Analytical Dynamics" **(27)**, Cambridge, 1937, p. 277.

of these equations. To complete the determination of the trajectories we need to integrate

$$X_m' \, dx_{m-1} - X'_{m-1} \, dx_m = 0, \tag{21.9.3}$$

where X_m', X'_{m-1} are found by expressing X_m, X_{m-1} in terms of $c_1, c_2, \ldots, c_{m-2}, x_{m-1}, x_m$ by means of (21.9.2).

Jacobi's famous theorem of *the last multiplier* provides a rule for finding an integrating factor for (21.9.3), provided we know a multiplier for the original system. The rule is as follows. *If M is a multiplier for the original system* (21.9.1), *an integrating factor of* (21.9.3) *is given by* $(M/K)'$, *where*

$$K = \frac{\partial(f_1, f_2, \ldots, f_{m-2})}{\partial(x_1, x_2, \ldots, x_{m-2})}, \tag{21.9.4}$$

and the accent denotes expression in terms of $c_1, c_2, \ldots, c_{m-2}, x_{m-1}, x_m$. Thus a further integral, the $(m - 1)$th, is given by

$$f_{m-1} = \int (M/K)' \, (X_m' \, dx_{m-1} - X'_{m-1} \, dx_m), \tag{21.9.5}$$

and this completes the solution of the equations (21.9.1); the trajectories are determined.

The proof of Jacobi's rule is simple. If we transform to new variables y_r, where

$$y_1 = f_1, \; y_2 = f_2, \; \ldots, \; y_{m-2} = f_{m-2}, \; y_{m-1} = x_{m-1}, \; y_m = x_m, \tag{21.9.6}$$

the motion in the y-space takes place in the planes

$$y_1 = c_1, \; y_2 = c_2, \; \ldots, \; y_{m-2} = c_{m-2}, \tag{21.9.7}$$

and $Y_1, Y_2, \ldots, Y_{m-2}$ all vanish identically. Moreover, for the transformation (21.9.6), $J = K$. The transformed system is

$$\frac{dy_1}{0} = \frac{dy_2}{0} = \cdots = \frac{dy_{m-2}}{0} = \frac{dx_{m-1}}{X'_{m-1}} = \frac{dx_m}{X_m'},$$

and if M is a multiplier for the original system, $(M/K)'$ is a multiplier for the transformed system (§ 21.8(v)). Thus $(M/K)'$ is an integrating factor for (21.9.3), in virtue of § 21.8(iv), and this completes the proof.

It is easy to over-estimate the importance of the elegant result just proved. As we have seen, we have no assurance that $(m - 2)$ independent uniform space-integrals exist; and if they do exist, the integration of (21.9.3) may not be very formidable, even in the absence of a specific rule for finding an integrating factor.

The theorem is easily extended to finding an mth integral of the equations for any system, whether autonomous or not, when $(m - 1)$ integrals are known, and one multiplier satisfying (21.7.20) is known. Indeed, as we have noticed, a non-autonomous system with m coordinates can be regarded as an autonomous system with $(m + 1)$ coordinates. The equations, replacing (21.9.1), are now

$$\frac{dx_1}{X_1} = \frac{dx_2}{X_2} = \cdots = \frac{dx_m}{X_m} = \frac{dt}{1},$$

and the X's may now contain t. Jacobi's rule provides an integrating factor for

$$dx_m - X_m' \, dt = 0,$$

where the accent denotes expression in terms of x_m and t and $(m - 1)$ constants $c_1, c_2, \ldots, c_{m-1}$.

21.10 The linear system. We now turn from the general system

(21.1.1) $$\dot{x}_r = X_r, \qquad r = 1, 2, \ldots, m,$$

to the special case in which the second members X_r are homogeneous linear functions of $(x_1, x_2, \ldots, x_m)$ with coefficients which are prescribed real-valued functions of t, with continuous first derivatives,

(21.10.1) $$X_r = a_{r1}x_1 + a_{r2}x_2 + \cdots + a_{rm}x_m, \qquad r = 1, 2, \ldots, m.$$

We can write the equations compactly in the form

(21.10.2) $$\dot{\mathbf{x}} = \mathbf{A}\mathbf{x},$$

where $\mathbf{x}$ is the column matrix $\{x_1, x_2, \ldots, x_m\}$, and $\mathbf{A}$ is the $m \times m$ matrix whose typical element is a_{rs} $(= a_{rs}(t))$.

Later (Chapter XXIII) we shall find the solution of the equation (21.10.2) in the general case, but for the moment we confine our attention to *the special case in which the elements a_{rs} are constants*; the system is autonomous. In this case *the solution is easily seen to be*

(21.10.3) $$\mathbf{x} = e^{t\mathbf{A}}\boldsymbol{\alpha},$$

where $\boldsymbol{\alpha}$ is the value of $\mathbf{x}$ at $t = 0$, and $e^{t\mathbf{A}}$ is the matrix

(21.10.4) $$\mathbf{I}_m + t\mathbf{A} + (t^2/2!)\mathbf{A}^2 + (t^3/3!)\mathbf{A}^3 + \cdots.$$

For (21.10.3) clearly satisfies (21.10.2) and makes $\mathbf{x} = \boldsymbol{\alpha}$ at $t = 0$. The question of convergence presents no difficulty. If $|a_{rs}| < K$ for all values of r and s, then if $a_{rs}^{(p)}$ is the typical element of $\mathbf{A}^p$, $|a_{rs}^{(p)}| < m^{p-1} K^p$, and therefore each element of $e^{t\mathbf{A}}$ (for $t > 0$) is numerically less than

(21.10.5) $$1 + Kt + mK^2(t^2/2!) + m^2K^3(t^3/3!) + \cdots = (m - 1 + e^{mKt})/m.$$

The series is majorized by an exponential series, and it is therefore uniformly convergent in any interval $0 \leqslant t \leqslant t_1$.

The rth component of the formula on the right in (21.10.3) is of course the special case (when X_r is a homogeneous linear function of $x_1, x_2, \ldots, x_m$) of the power series for x_r already found by another method in § 21.4.

21.11 Stability of equilibrium. We now return from the linear system to the general autonomous case of motion defined by the equations

(21.1.1) $$\dot{x}_r = X_r(x_1, x_2, \ldots, x_m), \qquad r = 1, 2, \ldots, m,$$

and consider more particularly the motion originating in the neighbourhood of a singular point of the field (i.e. a point at which $X_1 = X_2 = \cdots = X_m = 0$). We shall take the singular point as origin, as we did for the special case $m = 2$ in Chapter XIX. We shall assume that X_r, which vanishes at O, can be expanded in the form

(21.11.1) $$X_r = a_{r1}x_1 + a_{r2}x_2 + \cdots + a_{rm}x_m + \theta_r,$$

where θ_r $(= \theta_r(x_1, x_2, \ldots, x_m))$ is such that $\theta_r/R \to 0$ with R, where $R = |\mathbf{x}| = \sqrt{(x_1^2 + x_2^2 + \cdots + x_m^2)}$. In many cases θ_r can be expanded in a multiple power-series beginning with terms of the second degree, and convergent for $R < R_0$.

The symbol R represents the distance of $(x_1, x_2, \ldots, x_m)$ from the singularity O in the real (Euclidean) space of $(x_1, x_2, \ldots, x_m)$. If the x's can take complex values we replace the formula for R by $\sqrt{(|x_1|^2 + |x_2|^2 + \cdots + |x_m|^2)}$. Or we can use (in both cases, when the x's take only real values and when they take complex values) instead of R the function R', where $R' = |x_1| + |x_2| + \cdots + |x_m|$. In the present context, R and R' serve our purpose equally well; for R' is small if and only if R is small, and $R' = 0$ if and only if $R = 0$.

The definition of stability, and the related definitions, are similar to those for the special case treated in § 19.5. We denote the value of R for the point $(x_1, x_2, \ldots, x_m)$ occupied at time t during the motion (in other words, the distance of the mobile from O at time t) by $R(t)$.

The equilibrium is *stable* if, given $\varepsilon > 0$, there exists a positive number $\kappa(= \kappa(\varepsilon))$ such that, if $R(0) < \kappa$, then $R(t) < \varepsilon$ for $t \geqslant 0$. The definition implies that if the equilibrium at O is stable, then, corresponding to any sufficiently small positive number κ, there is a positive number ε with the property that $R(0) < \kappa$ implies $R(t) < \varepsilon$ for $t \geqslant 0$.

The equilibrium is *completely stable* if it is stable, and if in addition there exists a positive number κ such that, if $R(0) < \kappa$, then $R(t) \to 0$ as $t \to +\infty$.

Instability means lack of stability. In other words, the equilibrium at O is *unstable* if there exists a positive number κ with the property that there exist characteristics originating in points arbitrarily near to O such that $R(t) > \kappa$ for some positive values of t.

We begin, as in § 19.4, by considering the linear approximation, i.e. we replace X_r in (21.1.1) by the linear terms only, $\sum_{s=1}^{m} a_{rs}x_s$. The equations take the form

$$\dot{\mathbf{x}} = \mathbf{A}\mathbf{x}. \tag{21.10.2}$$

Let us consider first the case in which the matrix $\mathbf{A}$ can be reduced, by a non-singular transformation, to diagonal form. If we make the linear transformation $\mathbf{x} = \mathbf{C}\mathbf{u}$ the equations become

$$\dot{\mathbf{u}} = \mathbf{C}^{-1}\mathbf{A}\mathbf{C}\mathbf{u}, \tag{21.11.2}$$

and we choose $\mathbf{C}$ such that $\mathbf{C}^{-1}\mathbf{A}\mathbf{C}$ is the diagonal matrix $\mathbf{\Lambda}$ whose diagonal elements are the eigenvalues $\lambda_1, \lambda_2, \ldots, \lambda_m$ of $\mathbf{A}$. Since the elements of $\mathbf{C}$ may be complex the u's may have complex values even though the x's are real. We denote the distance of $\mathbf{u}$ from O by S $(= \sqrt{(|u_1|^2 + |u_2|^2 + \cdots + |u_m|^2)})$, and we notice that S is small if and only if R is small, and that $S = 0$ if and only if $R = 0$. (Or, again, we may use S' instead of S, where $S' = |u_1| + |u_2| + \cdots + |u_m|$.) The equations (21.11.2) have the form

$$\dot{u}_r = \lambda_r u_r, \qquad r = 1, 2, \ldots, m, \tag{21.11.3}$$

and the solutions are

$$u_r = a_r e^{\lambda_r t}, \qquad r = 1, 2, \ldots, m, \tag{21.11.4}$$

where a_r is the value of u_r when $t = 0$.

It is clear that in this case (i.e. when **A** can be diagonalized) the conditions for stability are the same as in § 19.5. If the eigenvalues of **A** have real parts which are negative or zero the equilibrium is stable. If the eigenvalues all have real parts which are negative, the equilibrium is completely stable. If one eigenvalue has its real part positive, the equilibrium is unstable.

One classical problem, the problem of small oscillations about a point of the q-space at which V has a minimum value, has been discussed already (Chapter IX) from a somewhat different point of view. From the point of view of the present theory we have a problem in which $m = 2n$, the matrix can be diagonalized, the eigenvalues are the pure-imaginary numbers $\pm ip_1, \pm ip_2, \ldots, \pm ip_n$, and the equilibrium is stable.

There are however cases in which the stability theory for $m > 2$ diverges from that for $m = 2$. If **A** cannot be diagonalized, which happens if there are repeated eigenvalues and the invariant factors are not simple, instability may occur if one repeated eigenvalue is a pure-imaginary number, even if all the other eigenvalues have real parts which are negative or zero. For in this case terms of the form $t^N \cos \beta t$ and $t^N \sin \beta t$ may occur in the formulae for the x's. We postpone the formal proof (to § 23.3) and content ourselves for the moment with a simple illustration.

Example 21.11. Consider as a simple example the system, with $m = 4$,

(21.11.5) $$\dot{x}_1 = x_2, \quad \dot{x}_2 = x_3, \quad \dot{x}_3 = x_4, \quad \dot{x}_4 = -n^4 x_1 - 2n^2 x_3,$$

where n is real and positive. The eigenvalues are in, in, $-in$, $-in$, and the solution contains terms $\cos nt$, $\sin nt$, $t \cos nt$, $t \sin nt$. Explicitly

(21.11.6) $$x_1 = \frac{1}{2}(2 \cos nt + nt \sin nt)\alpha_1 + \frac{1}{2n}(3 \sin nt - nt \cos nt)\alpha_2 + \frac{1}{2n^2}(nt \sin nt)\alpha_3 + \frac{1}{2n^3}(\sin nt - nt \cos nt)\alpha_4,$$

and the formulae for $x_2(=\dot{x}_1)$ and $x_3(=\dot{x}_2)$ and $x_4(=\dot{x}_3)$ can be derived immediately. It is clear that the origin is a point of unstable equilibrium. If, for example, $\alpha_1 = \alpha_2 = \alpha_4 = 0$, we have

$$x_1 = \frac{1}{2n^2}(nt \sin nt)\alpha_3,$$

and for $nt = (N + \frac{1}{2})\pi$, where N is a positive integer,

$$|\mathbf{x}| \geqslant |x_1| = (N + \tfrac{1}{2})\frac{\pi}{2n^2}|\alpha_3|,$$

which can be made as large as we wish by choice of N however small $|\boldsymbol{\alpha}|(= |\alpha_3|)$ may be.

We notice here (and in many similar contexts) that the fact that O is a point of unstable equilibrium does not imply that $R(t)$ takes large values for *all* small values of $|\boldsymbol{\alpha}|$. If $\alpha_3 = -n^2\alpha_1$ and $\alpha_4 = -n^2\alpha_2$ we have

$$x_1 = \alpha_1 \cos nt + \frac{\alpha_2}{n} \sin nt, \quad x_2 = -n\alpha_1 \sin nt + \alpha_2 \cos nt,$$

$$x_3 = -n^2\alpha_1 \cos nt - n\alpha_2 \sin nt, \quad x_4 = n^3\alpha_1 \sin nt - n^2\alpha_2 \cos nt,$$

and $|\mathbf{x}| < \varepsilon$ for all time if $|\boldsymbol{\alpha}|$ is sufficiently small.

21.12 Discrete stability. We leave the linear approximation and return to the complete equations (21.1.1). Suppose that, in the definitions of stability and of instability given in § 21.11, we consider, not all non-negative values of t, but only the discrete values $0, \tau, 2\tau, 3\tau, \ldots$, where τ is a positive constant, fixed once for all. The point $\mathbf{x}(k\tau)$ on the trajectory originating in $\mathbf{x}(0)$ is sometimes called the $k\tau$-consequent of $\mathbf{x}(0)$. If we consider only these discrete instants we arrive at a new notion of stability as follows.

The equilibrium is *stable* if, given $\varepsilon > 0$, there exists a positive number κ $(= \kappa(\varepsilon))$ such that, if $R(0) < \kappa$, then $R(k\tau) < \varepsilon$ for all positive integral values of k.

The equilibrium is *completely stable* if it is stable, and if in addition there exists a positive number κ such that, if $R(0) < \kappa$, then $R(k\tau) \to 0$ as $k \to \infty$ through positive integral values.

Instability means lack of stability. Thus the equilibrium is *unstable* if there exists a positive number κ with the property that there exist trajectories originating in points arbitrarily near to O such that $R(k\tau) > \kappa$ for some positive integral value of k.

We may for the moment distinguish the old notion (described in § 21.11) as C-stability (C implying continuous values of t) and the new notion as D-stability (D implying discrete values of t).

We now prove that *the two definitions mean precisely the same thing*; C-stability implies D-stability, and D-stability implies C-stability, and a similar statement holds for complete stability and for instability. To prove this we need the following lemma. Let $\mathbf{x}(t)$, as before, be the trajectory originating in $\mathbf{x}(0)$; if the mobile is at $\mathbf{x}(0)$ at $t = 0$ it is at $\mathbf{x}(t)$ for a later value of t. In the interval $0 \leqslant t \leqslant \tau$ the mobile traces out a segment of the trajectory, which we speak of as the τ-segment originating in $\mathbf{x}(0)$. Let r be a positive number, and let $S(r)$ be the set of points consisting of the points of all the τ-segments originating in points $\mathbf{x}(0)$ inside the hypersphere of radius r about O. Let r' be the supremum (least upper bound) of the distance of points of $S(r)$ from O. Then r' is a continuous monotone increasing function of r, which vanishes with r. Therefore $r = f(r')$, where $f(r')$ is a continuous monotone increasing function of r', with the properties $f(0) = 0$, and $0 < f(r') \leqslant r'$ if $r' > 0$. (In the special case of the linear approximation $f(r') = Kr'$, where K is a constant, and $0 < K < 1$.)

With the aid of this lemma the equivalence of the two notions of stability is almost evident; stated formally, the proof is as follows.

Stability. It is clear that C-stability implies D-stability; it remains to prove that D-stability implies C-stability. Suppose then that there is D-stability. Then, given $\varepsilon > 0$, let $\kappa(\varepsilon)$ be the number occurring in the definition of D-stability (i.e. κ is such that $R(0) < \kappa$ implies $R(k\tau) < \varepsilon$ for positive integral values of k). Let $\kappa' = f(\kappa)$ and let $\mathbf{x}(0)$ be any point such that $|\mathbf{x}(0)| < \kappa'$.

The τ-segment originating in $\mathbf{x}(0)$ lies inside the sphere about O of radius κ, so the trajectory originating in $\mathbf{x}(\theta)$, where $0 \leqslant \theta < \tau$, has the property $|\mathbf{x}(\theta + k\tau)| < \varepsilon$ for all positive integral values of k. Thus if $|\mathbf{x}(0)| < \kappa'$, $|\mathbf{x}(t)| < \varepsilon$ for all positive values of t, and this proves C-stability.

Complete stability. It is clear that complete C-stability implies complete D-stability; it remains to prove that complete D-stability implies complete C-stability. Suppose then that there is complete D-stability, and let κ be the number occurring in the definition (i.e. $R(0) < \kappa$ implies $R(k\tau) \to 0$ as k tends to infinity through positive integral values). Let $\kappa' = f(\kappa)$, and let $\mathbf{x}(0)$ be any point such that $|\mathbf{x}(0)| < \kappa'$.

The τ-segment originating in $\mathbf{x}(0)$ lies inside the hypersphere about O of radius κ, so the trajectory originating in $\mathbf{x}(\theta)$ where $0 \leqslant \theta < \tau$, has the property that

$|\mathbf{x}(\theta + k\tau)| \to 0$ as k tends to infinity through integral values. Thus, if $|\mathbf{x}(0)| < \kappa'$, $|\mathbf{x}(t)| \to 0$ as $t \to +\infty$, and this proves complete C-stability.

Instability. It is clear that D-instability implies C-instability; it remains to prove that C-instability implies D-instability. Suppose then that there is C-instability; then there is a positive number κ such that, given $\varepsilon(> 0)$ however small, there is a point $\mathbf{x}(0)$ with $|\mathbf{x}(0)| < \varepsilon'$, where $\varepsilon' = f(\varepsilon)$, such that $|\mathbf{x}(\theta + k\tau)| > \kappa$ for some value of θ in $0 \leqslant \theta < \tau$ and some positive integral value of k. Now the τ-segment originating in $\mathbf{x}(0)$ lies inside the hypersphere about O of radius ε, so $\mathbf{x}(\theta)$ is a point whose distance from O is less than the prescribed number ε. But the $k\tau$-consequent of $\mathbf{x}(\theta)$ lies outside the circle about O of radius κ, and this proves D-instability.

The proof of the equivalence of the two notions of stability is now complete, and we can discard the terms C-stability and D-stability and speak merely of stability. To establish (say) stability in a particular problem we can apply whichever criterion is more convenient, using either continuous or discrete values of t. The fundamental interval τ is at our disposal; in some cases a convenient choice may suggest itself naturally, and in other cases we can take $\tau = 1$.

21.13 Stability of transformations. We consider a continuous transformation that correlates a point $\mathbf{x}$ with a point $\mathbf{y}$; we denote the operator that transforms $\mathbf{x}$ into $\mathbf{y}$ by T,

$$T\mathbf{x} = \mathbf{y}. \tag{21.13.1}$$

The operator T is defined for points $\mathbf{x}$ belonging to a domain D. For the operators with which we shall be concerned D contains the origin, and the origin is a fixed point of the transformation, $T\mathbf{0} = \mathbf{0}$. We can frame a definition of stability analogous to the definition of discrete stability in § 21.12; roughly speaking, the operator T is stable if $|T^n\mathbf{x}|$ is small when $|\mathbf{x}|$ is small. Stated formally, the definitions are as follows.

The transformation defined by the operator T is *stable* (or, briefly, the operator T is stable) if, given $\varepsilon > 0$, there is a positive number $\kappa = \kappa(\varepsilon)$ such that, if $|\mathbf{x}| < \kappa$, then $|T^n\mathbf{x}| < \varepsilon$ for all positive integral values of n.

The transformation is *completely stable* if it is stable, and if in addition there is a positive number κ such that, if $|\mathbf{x}| < \kappa$, then $|T^n\mathbf{x}| \to 0$ as $n \to \infty$.

If the transformation is not stable, it is said to be unstable. Thus the transformation is *unstable* if and only if there is a positive number κ with the property that there are points $\mathbf{x}$ with $|\mathbf{x}|$ arbitrarily small such that $|T^n\mathbf{x}| > \kappa$ for some positive integral value of n.

Consider for example the linear transformation

$$\mathbf{y} = \mathbf{B}\mathbf{x}, \tag{21.13.2}$$

where $\mathbf{B}$ is a non-singular $m \times m$ matrix whose elements b_{rs} are constants. Let us consider the case in which $\mathbf{B}$ can be diagonalized. If $\mathbf{x} = \mathbf{C}\mathbf{u}$ and $\mathbf{y} = \mathbf{C}\mathbf{v}$, where $\mathbf{C}$ is non-singular, the equation (21.13.2) takes the form

$$\mathbf{v} = \mathbf{C}^{-1}\mathbf{B}\mathbf{C}\mathbf{u}, \tag{21.13.3}$$

and we choose $\mathbf{C}$ such that $\mathbf{C}^{-1}\mathbf{B}\mathbf{C}$ is the diagonal matrix $\mathbf{M}$ whose diagonal elements are the eigenvalues $\mu_1, \mu_2, \ldots, \mu_m$ of **B**. The transformation now has the simple form $\mathbf{v} = \mathbf{Mu}$, the rth equation is

$$v_r = \mu_r u_r, \tag{21.13.4}$$

and the rth component of $T^n\mathbf{u}$ is $\mu_r{}^n u_r$. The conditions for stability (and for complete stability and for instability) of the transformation are now clear. The transformation defined by the operator T is stable if $|\mu_r| \leqslant 1$ for all values of r in the range $1, 2, \ldots, m$; it is completely stable if $|\mu_r| < 1$ for all these values of r; and it is unstable if $|\mu_r| > 1$ for some value of r.

We add two simple illustrations, both one-dimensional.

Example 21.13*A*. Consider the transformation

$$Tx = x + x^2.$$

The origin is a fixed point for this transformation (it is the only fixed point) and it is unstable. We write x_n for $T^n\alpha$.

(i) If $\alpha > 0$, $x_n \to \infty$ with n. The sequence $\alpha, x_1, x_2, \ldots$ is monotone increasing, and, for $n > 1$,

$$\frac{x_n}{x_{n-1}} = 1 + x_{n-1} > 1 + \alpha,$$

whence

$$x_n > \alpha(1 + \alpha)^n,$$

and $x_n \to \infty$ with n.

(ii) If $\alpha = 0$, $x_1 = x_2 = \cdots = 0$

(iii) If $0 > \alpha > -1$, $x_n \to 0$ as $n \to \infty$. For, writing $-\beta$ for α, we have

$$x_1 = -\beta(1 - \beta),$$

so

$$0 > x_1 \geqslant -\tfrac{1}{4} > -1,$$

and similarly

$$0 > x_n > -1,$$

for all values of n. The sequence $\alpha, x_1, x_2, \ldots$ is monotone increasing and bounded, so $x_n \to l$ as $n \to \infty$; letting $n \to \infty$ in the equation

$$x_n = x_{n-1} + x_{n-1}^2$$

we find $l = 0$.

(iv) If $\alpha = -1$, $x_1 = x_2 = \cdots = 0$.

(v) If $-1 > \alpha$, $x_1 > 0$, and $x_n \to \infty$ as in (i).

Thus $x_n \to 0$ if $0 \geqslant \alpha \geqslant -1$, but otherwise $x_n \to \infty$.

Example 21.13*B*. Consider the bilinear transformation

$$Tx = \frac{ax + b}{cx + d}, \qquad c \neq 0, \quad ad - bc \neq 0.$$

In general there are two fixed points p and q which are the roots of the equation

$$cx^2 + (d - a)x - b = 0,$$

and we can write the relation between x_{n-1} and x_n in the form

$$\frac{x_n - p}{x_n - q} = \lambda \frac{x_{n-1} - p}{x_{n-1} - q},$$

where $\lambda = \dfrac{cq + d}{cp + d}$.

Let us consider in particular the case in which $(d - a)^2 + 4bc > 0$ and $a + d \neq 0$. Then p and q are real and different, and $|\lambda| \neq 1$, and we may so order the fixed points p and q that $|\lambda| < 1$. Now

$$\frac{x_n - p}{x_n - q} = \lambda^n \frac{\alpha - p}{\alpha - q},$$

so (unless $\alpha = q$) $x_n \to p$ as $n \to \infty$. Thus one fixed point p is completely stable, and the other fixed point q is unstable.

In the anomalous case, where $(d - a)^2 + 4bc > 0$ and $a + d = 0$, $\lambda = -1$; then $x_n = \alpha$ when n is even, and $x_n = \dfrac{a\alpha + b}{c\alpha + d}$ when n is odd. Both fixed points are stable, but neither is completely stable.

21.14 Application to the differential equations. We return to the differential equations (21.1.1), $\dot{x}_r = X_r$. The system is autonomous, and we suppose, as in § 21.11, that the origin is a singular point. The motion defined by these differential equations sets up the transformation defined by the operator T_t (§ 21.3),

$$\mathbf{x} = T_t \boldsymbol{\alpha}, \tag{21.3.1}$$

where $\boldsymbol{\alpha}$ is the value $\mathbf{x}(0)$ of $\mathbf{x}$ at $t = 0$, and $\mathbf{x}$ is the value at time $t(t \geqslant 0)$. If we consider a positive value τ of t, fixed once for all, we obtain a transformation T $(= T_\tau)$ which has O as a fixed point. We know that, to test for stability, we can use the discrete values $0, \tau, 2\tau, 3\tau, \ldots$ of t. Therefore stability of the equilibrium at O is the same thing as stability of the transformation T; and similarly for complete stability and for instability.

For the case of the linear approximation to the differential equations

$$\dot{\mathbf{x}} = \mathbf{A}\mathbf{x} \tag{21.10.2}$$

this equivalence merely confirms results already found. The corresponding transformation is the linear transformation

$$\mathbf{x} = \mathbf{B}\boldsymbol{\alpha}, \tag{21.14.1}$$

where, as in (21.10.3),

$$\mathbf{B} = \mathbf{e}^{\tau \mathbf{A}}. \tag{21.14.2}$$

If a typical eigenvalue of $\mathbf{A}$ is λ_r, the corresponding eigenvalue of $\mathbf{B}$ is $\mu_r = e^{\tau\lambda_r}$. Taking the case in which $\mathbf{A}$ and $\mathbf{B}$ can be diagonalized, and using ρ_r to denote the real part of λ_r, we can (reducing $\mathbf{B}$ to diagonal form) express the conditions either in terms of ρ_r or in terms of $|\mu_r|$ as follows:

for stability, $\rho_r \leqslant 0$, $|\mu_r| \leqslant 1$, for all values of r:

for complete stability, $\rho_r < 0$, $|\mu_r| < 1$, for all values of r:

for instability, $\rho_r > 0$, $|\mu_r| > 1$, for some value of r.

These are simply the results already found in § 21.11 and in § 21.13.

If $\mathbf{A}$ cannot be diagonalized, the matter is less simple. In that case, as we have noticed, the condition $\rho_r \leqslant 0$ (or, equivalently, $|\mu_r| \leqslant 1$) for all r is no longer sufficient to ensure stability; a repeated pure-imaginary eigenvalue λ_r can give rise to instability.

But the other conditions are unchanged. There is complete stability if all $\rho_r < 0$ (or, equivalently, all $|\mu_r| < 1$), and there is instability if one $\rho_r > 0$ (or, equivalently, one $|\mu_r| > 1$). We omit the proof, which is implicit in the theory to be developed later (§ 23.3).

21.15 The Poincaré-Liapounov theorem. We now turn from the linear approximation (for motion near the singularity O)

(21.10.2) $$\dot{\mathbf{x}} = \mathbf{A}\mathbf{x},$$

where the transformation has the form

(21.14.1) $$\mathbf{x} = \mathbf{B}\boldsymbol{\alpha},$$

to the exact equations

(21.1.1) $$\dot{x}_r = X_r, \qquad r = 1, 2, \ldots, m,$$

where the transformation has the form $\mathbf{x} = T_\tau \boldsymbol{\alpha}$

(21.15.1) $$x_r = \varphi_r(\tau;\ \alpha_1, \alpha_2, \ldots, \alpha_m), \qquad r = 1, 2, \ldots, m,$$

and the functions φ_r are of class C_2.

The eigenvalues for the linear approximation to the transformation $\mathbf{x} = T\boldsymbol{\alpha}$ do not depend on the choice of coordinates. To prove this, we notice that if we take a new coordinate system, with

$$\mathbf{y} = \boldsymbol{\psi}(\mathbf{x}), \quad \boldsymbol{\beta} = \boldsymbol{\psi}(\boldsymbol{\alpha}),$$

where $\boldsymbol{\psi}(0) = \mathbf{0}$, and the component functions ψ_r are of class C_2, the transformation becomes say $\mathbf{y} = U\boldsymbol{\beta}$. Let $\mathbf{A}$ be the matrix for the linear approximation to T,

$$\mathbf{A} = \left(\frac{\partial x_r}{\partial \alpha_s}\right)_0,$$

where the suffix 0 indicates the value at $\boldsymbol{\alpha} = 0$. Let $\mathbf{B}$ be the matrix for the linear approximation to U,

$$\mathbf{B} = \left(\frac{\partial y_r}{\partial \beta_s}\right)_0,$$

and let $\mathbf{C}$ be the matrix

$$\mathbf{C} = \left(\frac{\partial y_r}{\partial x_s}\right)_0 = \left(\frac{\partial \beta_r}{\partial \alpha_s}\right)_0.$$

Then

$$\mathbf{B} = \mathbf{C}\mathbf{A}\mathbf{C}^{-1},$$

and the matrices $\mathbf{A}$ and $\mathbf{B}$ have the same eigenvalues and the same invariant factors.

We now turn to the Poincaré-Liapounov theorem. We shall be concerned only with transformations for which the matrix $\mathbf{A}$ of the linear approximation can be diagonalized. The theorem asserts that in this case *the stability is determined by the linear approximation, except in the critical case where some λ's are pure-imaginary numbers.* There is complete stability if all $\rho_r < 0$, and instability if at least one $\rho_r > 0$.

This is, of course, precisely what we should expect from the results found for the special case $m = 2$ (Chapter XIX). In that case, if the eigenvalues for the linear approximation $\mathbf{F}_0$ are pure-imaginary numbers the singularity for the field $\mathbf{F}_0$ is stable; but for the complete field $\mathbf{F}$ there may be stability or instability. To test for stability we may use the transformation T ($= T_\tau$) as mentioned in § 21.14.

(1) *Complete stability.* We suppose that all $\rho_r < 0$, all $|\mu_r| < 1$ (where $\lambda_r = \rho_r + i\sigma_r$ is an eigenvalue of $\mathbf{A}$, and $\mu_r = e^{\tau\lambda_r}$ is an eigenvalue of $\mathbf{B}$). For the linear approximation the transformation T is linear,

(21.14.1) $$\mathrm{x} = \mathbf{B}\boldsymbol{\alpha},$$

and we suppose that $\mathbf{B}$ has been reduced, by a suitable transformation, to diagonal form, so that the equations (21.14.1) are equivalent to

(21.15.2) $$x_r = \mu_r\alpha_r, \qquad r = 1, 2, \ldots, m.$$

This transformation has the property

(21.15.3) $$|\mathbf{B}\boldsymbol{\alpha}| < k|\boldsymbol{\alpha}|,$$

where $k(< 1)$ is a number between the greatest $|\mu_r|$ and 1. We notice first the simple lemma that if

(21.15.4) $$|\mathbf{B}\boldsymbol{\alpha}| < l|\boldsymbol{\alpha}|,$$

where $0 < l < 1$, then $|\mathbf{B}^n\boldsymbol{\alpha}| \to 0$ as $n \to \infty$. For

(21.15.5) $$|\mathbf{B}^2\boldsymbol{\alpha}| < l|\mathbf{B}\boldsymbol{\alpha}| < 1^2|\alpha|,$$

and generally

(21.15.6) $$|\mathbf{B}^n\boldsymbol{\alpha}| < l^n|\boldsymbol{\alpha}|,$$

which tends to zero as n tends to infinity.

The transformation

(21.15.7) $$\mathrm{x} = T\boldsymbol{\alpha},$$

giving the solution of the exact equations for $t = \tau$, is such that

(21.15.8) $$|T\boldsymbol{\alpha} - \mathbf{B}\boldsymbol{\alpha}| = o\,|\boldsymbol{\alpha}|.$$

This is true since the φ's have continuous second derivatives (and is in fact also true under less exacting conditions). Then there is a positive number ε_0 such that, if $|\boldsymbol{\alpha}| < \varepsilon_0$,

(21.15.9) $$|T\boldsymbol{\alpha} - \mathbf{B}\boldsymbol{\alpha}| < \frac{1-k}{2}|\boldsymbol{\alpha}|,$$

and in that case

(21.15.10) $$|T\boldsymbol{\alpha}| \leqslant |T\boldsymbol{\alpha} - \mathbf{B}\boldsymbol{\alpha}| + |\mathbf{B}\boldsymbol{\alpha}| < \frac{1+k}{2}|\boldsymbol{\alpha}| = l|\alpha|,$$

where $0 < l < 1$. Hence, by the lemma, $|T^n\boldsymbol{\alpha}| \to 0$, and we have complete stability.

(2) *Instability.* We suppose now that at least one $\rho_r > 0$, so that the corresponding $|\mu_r| > 1$. We assume as before that $\mathbf{B}$ has been reduced to diagonal form.

To establish the instability of the operator T we proceed as follows. We introduce the real-valued quadratic form

(21.15.11) $$Q(\mathrm{x}) = \sum_{r=1}^{n} (1 - |\mu_r|^2)\,|x_r|^2.$$

Then

(21.15.12) $$Q(\mathrm{x}) - Q(\mathbf{B}\mathrm{x}) = \sum_{r=1}^{n} (1 - |\mu_r|^2)^2\,|x_r|^2$$

is a positive definite form, and there exists a positive constant c such that

(21.15.13) $$Q(\mathbf{x}) - Q(\mathbf{Bx}) > 2c\,|\mathbf{x}|^2$$

for all values of $\mathbf{x}$. Now the properties

(21.15.14) $$|T\mathbf{x}| - |\mathbf{Bx}| = o|\mathbf{x}|, \quad |\mathbf{Bx}| = O|\mathbf{x}|,$$

imply that

(21.15.15) $$Q(T\mathbf{x}) - Q(\mathbf{Bx}) = o|\mathbf{x}|^2,$$

and it now follows, from (21.15.13) and (21.15.15), that

(21.15.16) $$Q(\mathbf{x}) - Q(T\mathbf{x}) > c|\mathbf{x}|^2$$

for small values of $|\mathbf{x}|$, say for $|\mathbf{x}| < \kappa$.

Next, since at least one $|\mu_r|$ is greater than unity, we can find a point $\boldsymbol{\alpha}$, with $|\boldsymbol{\alpha}|$ arbitrarily small, such that $Q(\boldsymbol{\alpha})$ is negative, say $Q(\boldsymbol{\alpha}) < -a < 0$. We then use *reductio ad absurdum*. We suppose that $|\boldsymbol{\alpha}|$, $|T\boldsymbol{\alpha}|$, $|T^2\boldsymbol{\alpha}|, \ldots,$ are all less than κ, and we find that this hypothesis leads to a contradiction.

From (21.15.16), since $|T^n\boldsymbol{\alpha}| < \kappa$ for all values of n,

(21.15.17) $$-a > Q(\boldsymbol{\alpha}) > Q(T\boldsymbol{\alpha}) > \cdots > Q(T^n\boldsymbol{\alpha})$$

for all values of n; and since $Q(\mathbf{x}) < -a$ implies $|\mathbf{x}| > b$, where b is a positive number, $|T^n\boldsymbol{\alpha}| > b$ for all values of n. Hence, appealing again to (21.15.16),

(21.15.18) $$Q(T^r\boldsymbol{\alpha}) - Q(T^{r+1}\boldsymbol{\alpha}) > c\,|T^r\boldsymbol{\alpha}|^2 > cb^2$$

for all values of r.

We now write the inequality (21.15.18) for $r = 0, 1, 2, \ldots, (n-1)$ and sum, and we obtain

(21.15.19) $$-Q(T^n\boldsymbol{\alpha}) > -Q(\boldsymbol{\alpha}) + ncb^2 > a + ncb^2,$$

and therefore $Q(T^n\boldsymbol{\alpha}) \to -\infty$ as $n \to \infty$. But this is inconsistent with the hypothesis $|T^n\boldsymbol{\alpha}| < \kappa$, since $|x| < \kappa$ implies that $|Q(\mathbf{x})|$ is bounded; and this completes the proof.

The theorem just proved gives sufficient conditions for complete stability and for instability. We may notice at this point a necessary condition for stability. If the linear transformation is $\mathbf{x} = \mathbf{B}\boldsymbol{\alpha}$ (where $\mathbf{B}$ is not necessarily itself a diagonal matrix, though it *is* a matrix that can be diagonalized) the product of the eigenvalues of $\mathbf{B}$ is $|\mathbf{B}|$, the determinant of $\mathbf{B}$; so a necessary condition for stability is $|\mathbf{B}| \leqslant 1$. For the linear approximation to the transformation (21.15.1) the elements b_{rs} of $\mathbf{B}$ are the values of the derivatives $\partial\varphi_r/\partial\alpha_s$ at $\boldsymbol{\alpha} = 0$. So a necessary condition for the stability of the transformation (21.15.1) is that the Jacobian

$$\frac{\partial(\varphi_1, \varphi_2, \ldots, \varphi_m)}{\partial(\alpha_1, \alpha_2, \ldots, \alpha_n)}$$

should be not greater than 1 in absolute value when $\boldsymbol{\alpha} = 0$.

Corollary. Consider a transformation T which is such that the matrix $\mathbf{A}$ for the linear approximation has eigenvalues all of which are numerically less than 1, $|\mu_r| < 1$ for $r = 1, 2, \ldots, m$. Then T is completely stable. Let k be a number between the greatest $|\mu_r|$ and 1. Then there exists a positive number η and a positive number c such that

(21.15.20) $$|T^n\mathbf{x}| < ck^n$$

for $n = 1, 2, 3, \ldots,$ if $|\mathbf{x}| < \eta$.

To prove this, we introduce the transformation U, where

$$U\mathbf{x} = \frac{1}{k} T\mathbf{x}, \tag{21.15.21}$$

and then

$$U^n\mathbf{x} = \frac{1}{k^n} T^n\mathbf{x}. \tag{21.15.22}$$

The matrix for the linear approximation to U is $\frac{1}{k}\mathbf{A}$, and its eigenvalues are μ_r/k, all numerically less than 1. Thus U is stable, and we can find η, c such that

$$|U^n\mathbf{x}| < c \tag{21.15.23}$$

for all positive integral values of n; and (21.15.20) follows in virtue of (21.15.22).

21.16 The critical case. The Poincaré-Liapounov theorem gives us no information about the critical case where some λ_r's are pure-imaginary numbers.

If $m = 2$, the critical case is that of a vortex point, and, as we saw (§ 19.4), although the linear approximation $\mathbf{F}_0$ gives stability, the complete field $\mathbf{F}$ may give stability or instability. The case $m > 2$ differs from the case $m = 2$ because, when there are multiple pure-imaginary roots λ_r, even the linear approximation may give instability (§21.11). Even when the linear approximation gives stability, the complete field may give either stability or instability. We give one example of each possibility for $m = 4$. The first of these is a problem of small oscillations about a position at which the potential energy V has a minimum value, and, as we know, the equilibrium is stable (Chapter IX).

Example 21.16*A*. *The elastic pendulum.* The problem is the same as that of a simple pendulum swinging in a vertical plane, except that the inelastic string of the ordinary simple pendulum is replaced by an elastic string or spring obeying Hooke's law. The system has two degrees of freedom, and $m = 4$.

Let a be the unstretched length of the string, $(a + c)$ the stretched length when the particle hangs at rest. If r is the length of the string at time t, and θ is its inclination to the downward vertical, we have

$$T = \tfrac{1}{2}(\dot{r}^2 + r^2\dot{\theta}^2) = \frac{1}{2}\left(\xi^2 + \frac{1}{r^2}\eta^2\right), \tag{21.16.1}$$

$$V = -gr\cos\theta + \frac{g}{2c}(r - a)^2, \tag{21.16.2}$$

where ξ is written for p_r and η for p_θ. The Hamiltonian function H is equal to $T + V$, and the Hamiltonian equations of motion are

$$\begin{cases} \dot{r} = \xi, & \dot{\theta} = \dfrac{\eta}{r^2}, \\ \dot{\xi} = \dfrac{\eta^2}{r^3} + g\cos\theta - \dfrac{g}{c}(r - a), & \dot{\eta} = -gr\sin\theta. \end{cases} \tag{21.16.3}$$

For the equilibrium position $\theta = \xi = \eta = 0$, $r = a + c$, so writing $r = a + c + s$ we have for the linear approximation

(21.16.4)
$$\begin{cases} \dot{s} = \xi & \dot{\theta} = \dfrac{1}{(a+c)^2}\eta, \\ \dot{\xi} = -\dfrac{g}{c}s, & \dot{\eta} = -g(a+c)\theta. \end{cases}$$

The eigenvalues are $\pm i\sqrt{\left(\frac{g}{c}\right)}$ and $\pm i\sqrt{\left(\frac{g}{a+c}\right)}$, as we expect. (We do not need the fourth-order determinant here, since in this case the equations for the linear approximation fall into two groups, one containing only s and ξ, the other containing only θ and η; in fact we find immediately

(21.16.5)
$$\ddot{s} + \frac{g}{c}s = 0, \quad \ddot{\theta} + \frac{g}{a+c}\theta = 0.)$$

We now turn to the complete field **F**. The potential energy V has a minimum value V_0 in the position of equilibrium, and the curves $V = V_0 + \varepsilon$, for small positive values of ε, are simple closed oval curves about the equilibrium point $r = a + c$, $\theta = 0$. If the energy constant is $V_0 + \varepsilon$, throughout the motion

(21.16.6)
$$V - V_0 \leqslant \varepsilon, \quad T \leqslant \varepsilon,$$

so the particle remains inside the curve $V = V_0 + \varepsilon$, and the kinetic energy remains small; thus θ, s, ξ, η all remain small, and the equilibrium is stable.

The explicit equation of the curve $V = V_0 + \varepsilon$ is

(21.16.7)
$$r(1 - \cos\theta) + \frac{1}{2c}(r - b)^2 = \frac{1}{2c}k^2,$$

where $b = a + c$, and $\varepsilon = gk^2/(2c)$. The extreme values of r on the curve are $b \pm k$ (attained when $\theta = 0$), and θ lies between the values $\pm\theta_0$, where

(21.16.8)
$$1 - \cos\theta_0 = \frac{b - \sqrt{(b^2 - k^2)}}{c},$$

($\theta = \pm\theta_0$ when $r = \sqrt{(b^2 - k^2)}$). If we use a string (not a spring) the string will surely remain taut during the motion if $k < c$. The curves (21.16.7) for $\frac{k}{c} = \frac{1}{2}, 1, \frac{3}{2}, 2$ are shown in Fig. 21.16. If we introduce rectangular coordinates (u, v), with the position of equilibrium as origin, and u vertically downwards, the equation (21.16.7) becomes

(21.16.9)
$$2(b - c)(r - u) = u^2 + v^2 + 2b^2 - 2bc - k^2,$$

which we can express by means of the expansion

(21.16.10)
$$u^2 + \frac{c}{b}v^2 = k^2 - \frac{a}{b^2}uv^2 + \frac{a}{4b^3}v^2(4u^2 - v^2) - \cdots.$$

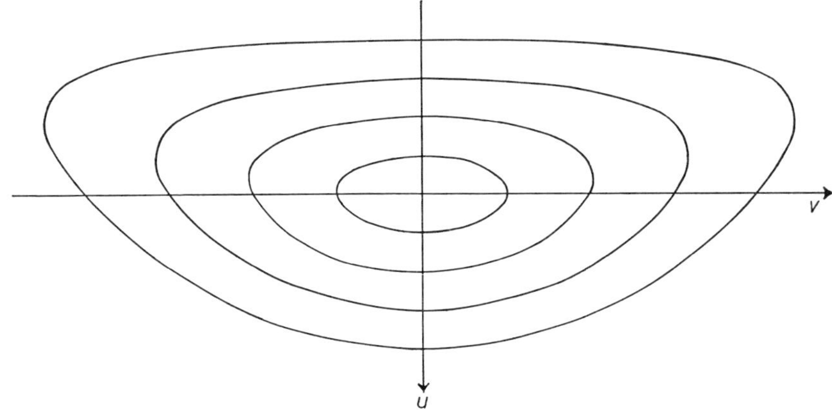

Figure 21.16

Example 21.16*B*. We consider the system, with $m = 4$, for which the Hamiltonian function is

$$H = \tfrac{1}{2}n(q_1^2 + p_1^2) - n(q_2^2 + p_2^2) + \tfrac{1}{2}\alpha(q_1^2 q_2 - q_2 p_1^2 - 2q_1 p_1 p_2). \tag{21.16.11}$$

The parameters n and α are real and positive. The equations of motion are

$$\begin{cases} \dot{q}_1 = np_1 - \alpha(q_1 p_2 + q_2 p_1), \\ \dot{q}_2 = -2np_2 - \alpha q_1 p_1, \\ \dot{p}_1 = -nq_1 - \alpha(q_1 q_2 - p_1 p_2), \\ \dot{p}_2 = 2nq_2 - \tfrac{1}{2}\alpha(q_1^2 - p_1^2). \end{cases} \tag{21.16.12}$$

For the linear approximation $\mathbf{F}_0$ the eigenvalues are $\pm in$, $\pm 2in$, and the motion is given by the formulae

$$\begin{cases} q_1 = a_1 \cos nt + b_1 \sin nt, \\ q_2 = a_2 \cos 2nt - b_2 \sin 2nt, \\ p_1 = b_1 \cos nt - a_1 \sin nt, \\ p_2 = b_2 \cos 2nt + a_2 \sin 2nt, \end{cases} \tag{21.16.13}$$

where (a_1, a_2, b_1, b_2) are the values of (q_1, q_2, p_1, p_2) at $t = 0$. The solution can also be written in the form

$$\begin{aligned} q_1 &= A \sin (nt + \beta), \quad q_2 = B \sin (2nt + \gamma), \\ p_1 &= A \cos (nt + \beta), \quad p_2 = -B \cos (2nt + \gamma). \end{aligned} \tag{21.16.14}$$

All these orbits are periodic, with period $2\pi/n$, and the singularity has first-order stability.

Let us now turn to the complete field $\mathbf{F}$. The equations (21.16.12) are satisfied by

$$\begin{cases} q_1 = \dfrac{\sqrt{2}}{\alpha(t - t_0)} \sin (nt + \delta), \quad q_2 = \dfrac{1}{\alpha(t - t_0)} \sin 2(nt + \delta), \\ p_1 = \dfrac{\sqrt{2}}{\alpha(t - t_0)} \cos (nt + \delta), \quad p_2 = -\dfrac{1}{\alpha(t - t_0)} \cos 2(nt + \delta), \end{cases} \tag{21.16.15}$$

for all values of t_0 and δ. If t_0 is large, the mobile is near O at $t = 0$, but its distance from O is large for values of t near t_0. The singularity for the complete field is unstable. As a concrete illustration, if $q_1 = q_2 = p_1 = -a$, $p_2 = 0$, at $t = 0$, the solution is. (21.16.15) with $\alpha t_0 = 1/a$ and $\delta = \pi/4$,

$$(21.16.16)\qquad \begin{cases} q_1 = \dfrac{1}{\alpha(t - t_0)}(\cos nt + \sin nt), & q_2 = \dfrac{1}{\alpha(t - t_0)}\cos 2nt, \\ p_1 = \dfrac{1}{\alpha(t - t_0)}(\cos nt - \sin nt), & p_2 = \dfrac{1}{\alpha(t - t_0)}\sin 2nt. \end{cases}$$

We shall return to this problem later (§ 30.4).

Chapter XXII

Hamilton's equations

22.1 Hamilton's equations. In the preceding Chapter we considered the system of differential equations

(22.1.1) $$\dot{x}_r = X_r, \qquad r = 1, 2, \ldots, m.$$

The equations of motion for a holonomic system with n freedoms can be put in this form, with $m = 2n$, in various ways. The most important of these (cf. § 10.13) leads to Hamilton's equations

(22.1.2) $$\dot{q}_r = \frac{\partial H}{\partial p_r}, \quad \dot{p}_r = -\frac{\partial H}{\partial q_r}, \qquad r = 1, 2, \ldots, n.$$

The $2n$ variables, to be determined as functions of t, are

$$q_1, q_2, \ldots, q_n; \ p_1, p_2, \ldots, p_n,$$

so that the two notations are connected by the relations

$$x_r = q_r, \quad x_{n+r} = p_r, \qquad r = 1, 2, \ldots, n.$$

The $2n$ functions X_r are

$$\frac{\partial H}{\partial p_1}, \ \frac{\partial H}{\partial p_2}, \ldots, \frac{\partial H}{\partial p_n}; \ -\frac{\partial H}{\partial q_1}, \ -\frac{\partial H}{\partial q_2}, \ldots, -\frac{\partial H}{\partial q_n},$$

so that

$$X_r = \frac{\partial H}{\partial p_r}, \quad X_{n+r} = -\frac{\partial H}{\partial q_r}, \qquad r = 1, 2, \ldots, n.$$

We shall be concerned more particularly with the autonomous case in which H does not contain t,

(22.1.3) $$H = H(q_1, q_2, \ldots, q_n; \ p_1, p_2, \ldots, p_n),$$

and $H \in C_2$ in a domain D of $(q_1, q_2, \ldots, q_n; \ p_1, p_2, \ldots, p_n)$. As we have noticed (§ 10.14) *if the system is autonomous, H is an integral.* This is a famous and important result. The proof is immediate, for

(22.1.4) $$\frac{dH}{dt} = \sum_{r=1}^{n} \left(\frac{\partial H}{\partial q_r} \dot{q}_r + \frac{\partial H}{\partial p_r} \dot{p}_r \right),$$

which vanishes in virtue of (22.1.2). Thus H = constant $= h$ throughout the motion. The trajectories lie on the manifolds $H = h$.

We can write the Hamiltonian equations of motion in the matrix form

(22.1.5) $$\dot{\mathbf{x}} = \mathbf{Z}\mathbf{H}_x,$$

where $\mathbf{x}$ is the column matrix, or vector, $\{q_1, q_2, \ldots, q_n; p_1, p_2, \ldots, p_n\}$, $\mathbf{H}_x$ is the vector $\left\{\frac{\partial H}{\partial q_1}, \frac{\partial H}{\partial q_2}, \ldots, \frac{\partial H}{\partial q_n}; \frac{\partial H}{\partial p_1}, \frac{\partial H}{\partial p_2}, \ldots, \frac{\partial H}{\partial p_n}\right\}$, and $\mathbf{Z}$ is the $2n \times 2n$ matrix

(22.1.6) $$\begin{pmatrix} \mathbf{0} & \mathbf{I}_n \\ -\mathbf{I}_n & \mathbf{0} \end{pmatrix}.$$

We notice that the matrix $\mathbf{Z}$ has the properties

(22.1.7) $$\mathbf{Z}' = \mathbf{Z}^{-1} = -\mathbf{Z}, \quad |\mathbf{Z}| = 1.$$

22.2 Poisson brackets. The integrals F of Hamilton's equations satisfy the condition

(22.2.1) $$\frac{\partial F}{\partial t} + \Omega F = 0,$$

and the linear operator Ω is defined by the equation

(22.2.2) $$\Omega F = \sum_{r=1}^{n} \left(\frac{\partial F}{\partial q_r}\frac{\partial H}{\partial p_r} - \frac{\partial F}{\partial p_r}\frac{\partial H}{\partial q_r}\right) = \sum_{r=1}^{n} \frac{\partial(F, H)}{\partial(q_r, p_r)}.$$

If u and v are functions of $(q_1, q_2, \ldots, q_n; p_1, p_2, \ldots, p_n; t)$—or, as we shall often write, for the sake of brevity, functions of $(q; p; t)$—of class C_2, the expression

(22.2.3) $$\sum_{r=1}^{n} \frac{\partial(u, v)}{\partial(q_r, p_r)},$$

which is the sum of n Jacobians, is called a *Poisson bracket*, and it is written (u, v). Thus

(22.2.4) $$\Omega F = (F, H),$$

and the integrals of Hamilton's equations satisfy

(22.2.5) $$\frac{\partial F}{\partial t} + (F, H) = 0.$$

The Hamiltonian equations themselves can be written in terms of Poisson brackets in the form

(22.2.6) $$\dot{x}_r = \Omega x_r = (x_r, H), \qquad r = 1, 2, \ldots, 2n.$$

The Poisson brackets are important, both in classical dynamics and in quantum theory, and we now consider their principal properties. The symbols u, v, w denote functions of $(q; p; t)$ of class C_2, and c is a constant. The following properties of the Poisson brackets are evident:

(22.2.7) $$\begin{cases} (u, u) = (u, c) = (c, u) = 0, \\ (v, u) = (-u, v) = (u, -v) = -(u, v), \\ \dfrac{\partial}{\partial t}(u, v) = \left(\dfrac{\partial u}{\partial t}, v\right) + \left(u, \dfrac{\partial v}{\partial t}\right). \end{cases}$$

In dealing with Poisson brackets we must remember that the order in which the functions are written is material, since $(v, u) = -(u, v)$.

A more substantial property of Poisson brackets is expressed in the theorem known as *Poisson's, or Jacobi's, identity*, namely

$$(u, (v, w)) + (v, (w, u)) + (w, (u, v)) = 0. \tag{22.2.8}$$

To prove this we observe first that if A, B are two linear operators defined as follows,

$$Af = \sum_{r=1}^{m} A_r \frac{\partial f}{\partial x_r}, \quad Bf = \sum_{r=1}^{m} B_r \frac{\partial f}{\partial x_r}, \tag{22.2.9}$$

where the coefficients A_r, B_r are of class C_1, and the function $f \in C_2$, then

$$ABf - BAf \tag{22.2.10}$$

is a linear expression in the first derivatives of f, and contains no second derivatives. To deduce the theorem (22.2.8) we observe that, when the brackets on the left are expanded, each term is the product of two first-order derivatives and one second-order derivative. It will suffice therefore to prove that the coefficient of each second-order derivative is zero. Let us fix attention on the second-order derivatives of u; these occur only in the second and third terms on the left in (22.2.8). Moreover

$$(v, u) = Vu, \quad (w, u) = Wu, \tag{22.2.11}$$

where V and W are linear operators of the type mentioned. Now

$$(v, (w, u)) + (w, (u, v)) = (v, (w, u)) - (w, (v, u)) = VWu - WVu, \tag{22.2.12}$$

and the expression on the right contains no second-order derivatives of u. The theorem follows.

22.3 Poisson's theorem. *If φ, ψ are integrals, of class C_2, of the Hamiltonian equations, (φ, ψ) also is an integral.*

The proof of this result is simple. We have

$$\frac{\partial \varphi}{\partial t} + (\varphi, H) = 0, \quad \frac{\partial \psi}{\partial t} + (\psi, H) = 0, \tag{22.3.1}$$

and therefore

$$\begin{aligned} &\frac{\partial}{\partial t}(\varphi, \psi) + ((\varphi, \psi), H) \\ &= \left(\frac{\partial \varphi}{\partial t}, \psi\right) + \left(\varphi, \frac{\partial \psi}{\partial t}\right) + ((\varphi, \psi), H) \\ &= -((\varphi, H), \psi) - (\varphi, (\psi, H)) + ((\varphi, \psi), H) \\ &= (\psi, (\varphi, H)) + (\varphi, (H, \psi)) + (H, (\psi, \varphi)), \end{aligned} \tag{22.3.2}$$

which is identically zero in virtue of Poisson's identity (22.2.8). Therefore (φ, ψ) is an integral.

Poisson's theorem is not quite so fruitful as it seems to be at first sight. It might appear that from two known integrals we could produce a third, then a fourth from the third and the first or second, and so on. But sometimes the new integral obtained is identically zero, and when it is not identically zero it is not always independent of those already found. It is evident that we cannot go on producing new integrals indefinitely, since not more than $2n$ independent integrals can exist.

Suppose that H does not contain t, so that H itself is a known integral. If φ is a second space-integral, then (φ, H) vanishes identically; and Poisson's theorem is fruitless. If φ is an integral containing t,

$$(\varphi, H) = -\frac{\partial\varphi}{\partial t}, \tag{22.3.3}$$

and we merely recover the result already noticed (§ 21.1), that $\frac{\partial\varphi}{\partial t}$ is an integral.

Sometimes however Poisson's theorem does provide an integral independent of those from which we start. As an illustration, consider the problem of a particle moving in space under the action of a central attraction to O; the attraction is a function of r, the distance from O. We take rectangular coordinates q_1, q_2, q_3, with the origin at the centre of attraction O, and then

$$H = \tfrac{1}{2}(p_1^2 + p_2^2 + p_3^2) + V, \tag{22.3.4}$$

where we have taken the mass of the particle as unity, and V is a function of r. If

$$\varphi_1 \equiv q_2p_3 - q_3p_2, \tag{22.3.5}$$

then $(\varphi_1, H) = 0$, and φ_1 is an integral of the Hamiltonian equations; and similarly

$$\varphi_2 \equiv q_3p_1 - q_1p_3 \tag{22.3.6}$$

is also an integral. These two integrals are of course two of the integrals of angular momentum. Poisson's theorem tells us that (φ_1, φ_2) is also an integral, and

$$(\varphi_1, \varphi_2) = \frac{\partial(\varphi_1, \varphi_2)}{\partial(q_3, p_3)} \tag{22.3.7}$$

since the other two determinants obviously vanish. Now

$$\frac{\partial(\varphi_1, \varphi_2)}{\partial(q_3, p_3)} = q_1p_2 - q_2p_1, \tag{22.3.8}$$

and the new integral is the third integral of angular momentum.

22.4 Use of a known integral. We have seen (§ 21.2) that we can make use of a known integral to depress the order of the system, i.e. to replace the original equations by a system with one less dependent variable than the original system. In the special case with which we are now concerned, where the original equations are of Hamiltonian form, we can sometimes do more; we can not only depress the order of the system, but we can also preserve the Hamiltonian form of the equations. Of the new equations, $2(n - 1)$ are of Hamilton's type, and one is anomalous.

The simplest example arises from the integral of momentum corresponding to an ignorable coordinate. Let us suppose that q_1 does not occur in H,

$$H = H(q_2, q_3, \ldots, q_n; p_1, p_2, \ldots, p_n; t). \tag{22.4.1}$$

Then p_1 is constant throughout the motion,

$$p_1 = \beta, \tag{22.4.2}$$

and the system is reduced immediately to a Hamiltonian system with $2(n - 1)$ dependent variables

$$\frac{dq_2}{\dfrac{\partial H'}{\partial p_2}} = \frac{dq_3}{\dfrac{\partial H'}{\partial p_3}} = \cdots = \frac{dp_2}{-\dfrac{\partial H'}{\partial q_2}} = \frac{dp_3}{-\dfrac{\partial H'}{\partial q_3}} = \cdots = dt, \tag{22.4.3}$$

where H' is obtained from H by writing β in place of p_1. There is also the anomalous equation giving the value of q_1 at time t, namely $q_1 = \int \frac{\partial H'}{\partial \beta}\, dt$.

Next, when the system is autonomous, we can use the integral of energy,

$$H(q_1, q_2, \ldots, q_n;\ p_1, p_2, \ldots, p_n) = h, \tag{22.4.4}$$

to depress the order of the system. Let us suppose that q_1 is not ignorable, and that we can solve the equation (22.4.4) for q_1,

$$q_1 = \varphi(q_2, q_3, \ldots, q_n;\ p_2, p_3, \ldots, p_n;\ h;\ p_1). \tag{22.4.5}$$

If we substitute φ for q_1 in (22.4.4) the equation so obtained is satisfied identically, and differentiating partially with respect to $p_r (r = 2, 3, \ldots, n)$ we find

$$\frac{\partial H}{\partial p_r} + \frac{\partial H}{\partial q_1}\frac{\partial \varphi}{\partial p_r} = 0. \tag{22.4.6}$$

Therefore

$$\frac{dq_r}{dp_1} = \frac{\dot{q}_r}{\dot{p}_1} = -\frac{\dfrac{\partial H}{\partial p_r}}{\dfrac{\partial H}{\partial q_1}} = \frac{\partial \varphi}{\partial p_r}. \tag{22.4.7}$$

Similarly, substituting φ for q_1 in (22.4.4), and differentiating with respect to q_r $(r = 2, 3, \ldots, n)$ we have

$$\frac{\partial H}{\partial q_r} + \frac{\partial H}{\partial q_1}\frac{\partial \varphi}{\partial q_r} = 0, \tag{22.4.8}$$

whence

$$\frac{dp_r}{dp_1} = \frac{\dot{p}_r}{\dot{p}_1} = \frac{\dfrac{\partial H}{\partial q_r}}{\dfrac{\partial H}{\partial q_1}} = -\frac{\partial \varphi}{\partial q_r}. \tag{22.4.9}$$

Thus *we can use φ as a new Hamiltonian function of the $2(n-1)$ dependent variables $q_2, q_3, \ldots, q_n;\ p_2, p_3, \ldots, p_n$, the variable p_1 being the independent variable* (playing the part usually taken by t). The new system is not autonomous, since φ contains the new independent variable. The remaining equation is simply the energy equation itself, given by (22.4.4) or (22.4.5).

The method is practicable if, for example, q_1 appears linearly in H. As a simple illustration suppose that

$$H = \tfrac{1}{2}(\xi^2 + \eta^2) - ky\xi + (\tfrac{1}{2}k^2y^2 - gx), \tag{22.4.10}$$

where x, y are Lagrangian coordinates, $\xi = p_x$, $\eta = p_y$, and k, g are positive constants. If we solve the equation $H = h$ for x in the form $x = \varphi(y;\ \eta;\ h;\ \xi)$ we have

$$\varphi = \frac{1}{2g}\{(\xi - ky)^2 + \eta^2\} - \frac{h}{g}. \tag{22.4.11}$$

We can use φ as a Hamiltonian function for a system with one freedom; the dependent variables are y and η $(= p_y)$, and the independent variable is ξ. The equations are

$$\frac{dy}{d\xi} = \frac{\partial\varphi}{\partial\eta} = \frac{\eta}{g}, \tag{22.4.12}$$

$$\frac{d\eta}{d\xi} = -\frac{\partial\varphi}{\partial y} = \frac{k}{g}(\xi - ky), \tag{22.4.13}$$

and the solution is elementary. From (22.4.12) and (22.4.13) we have

$$\frac{d^2\eta}{d\xi^2} = \frac{k}{g} - \frac{k^2}{g}\frac{dy}{d\xi} = \frac{k}{g} - \frac{k^2}{g^2}\eta, \tag{22.4.14}$$

and therefore

$$\eta = \frac{g}{k} + A\cos\frac{k}{g}\xi + B\sin\frac{k}{g}\xi. \tag{22.4.15}$$

Then y is given by (22.4.13), and the solution of the secondary problem (finding y and η as functions of ξ) is complete. To find the solution of the original problem we have

$$\dot{\xi} = g, \quad \xi = \xi_0 + gt, \tag{22.4.16}$$

and x is given by $x = \varphi$. (The direct solution is equally simple.)

In the same way, if we solve the equation $H = h$ for p_1, say,

$$p_1 = -\psi(q_2, q_3, \ldots, q_n;\ p_2, p_3, \ldots, p_n;\ h;\ q_1), \tag{22.4.17}$$

we easily see, by the same sort of argument, that *we can use ψ as a new Hamiltonian function for a system with $(n-1)$ freedoms, q_1 being the new independent variable,*

$$\frac{dq_r}{dq_1} = \frac{\partial\psi}{dp_r}, \quad \frac{dp_r}{dq_1} = -\frac{\partial\psi}{\partial q_r}, \qquad r = 2, 3, \ldots, n. \tag{22.4.18}$$

But, since the equation $H = h$ is a quadratic equation for p_1, the formula for ψ contains an irrationality and is not very convenient.

If q_1 were absent from the original Hamiltonian function H, ψ would not contain q_1, and the derived system would possess an "energy integral"

$$\psi = \beta_1. \tag{22.4.19}$$

This new integral is of course the integral of momentum corresponding to the ignorable coordinate q_1.

There is another way of establishing the theorems just proved (about depression of the order of the system by means of the energy integral) that is not without interest. It involves an appeal to the equivalence theorem (§ 16.3). Let us consider for definiteness the first case considered above, where the new Hamiltonian function is found by solving the equation $H = h$ for q_1, as in (22.4.5).

If the problem is solved by the Hamilton-Jacobi theorem, the solution is given in terms of $2n$ parameters α_r, β_r, where α_1 is the energy constant h, and β_1 is the epoch constant t_0 (§ 16.5). Then (§ 16.3)

$$\sum_{r=1}^{n} p_r\,dq_r - H\,dt = d\psi + \sum_{r=1}^{n}\beta_r\,d\alpha_r, \tag{22.4.20}$$

which we now write in the form

$$\sum_{r=2}^{n} p_r\,dq_r - q_1\,dp_1 = d(\psi + ht - q_1 p_1) + \sum_{r=2}^{n}\beta_r\,d\alpha_r + (H - h)\,dt - (t - t_0)\,dh. \tag{22.4.21}$$

We now consider, not the totality of possible motions, but only those with prescribed energy constant h, so that h now takes on the role of an absolute constant. All the trajectories considered lie on the manifold $H = h$, and our attention is now directed to this manifold instead of to the whole phase space. Then we have

$$\sum_{r=2}^{n} p_r\,dq_r - q_1\,dp_1 = d(\psi + ht - q_1p_1) + \sum_{r=2}^{n} \beta_r\,d\alpha_r, \tag{22.4.22}$$

and therefore, by the equivalence theorem, the variables $q_2, q_3, \ldots, q_n;\ p_2, p_3, \ldots, p_n$ satisfy Hamiltonian equations with q_1 as Hamiltonian function, and with p_1 replacing t as the independent variable. The function q_1 is to be expressed in the form (22.4.5) by means of the equation $H = h$. We thus recover the desired result.

22.5 Poincaré's linear integral-invariant. We now establish a famous theorem of Poincaré; *the line-integral* $\oint \sum_{r=1}^{n} p_r\,dq_r$ *is a relative integral-invariant of Hamilton's equations.* We can prove this from the general theory of § 21.5, or directly. With the notation of § 21.5, now writing ϖ_{rs} for $\dfrac{\partial p_r}{\partial x_s} - \dfrac{\partial p_s}{\partial x_r}$, we have

$$(\varpi_{rs}) = \mathbf{Z}, \tag{22.5.1}$$

and therefore

$$Q_r = -\frac{\partial H}{\partial q_r}, \quad Q_{n+r} = -\frac{\partial H}{\partial p_r}, \qquad r = 1, 2, \ldots, n, \tag{22.5.2}$$

so the Pfaffian form $\sum_{r=1}^{2n} Q_r\,dx_r$ is a perfect differential $-dH$. The result follows from § 21.5. The direct proof is equally simple, using either a parameter u on the closed circuit γ (as in (21.5.7)), or working with the line-element (as in (21.5.15)). Using the former we have

$$I = \oint_\gamma p_r\,dq_r = \int_0^1 p_r \frac{\partial q_r}{\partial u}\,du, \tag{22.5.3}$$

where the summation convention is used. Thus

$$\begin{aligned}\frac{DI}{Dt} &= \int_0^1 \left\{\frac{\partial p_r}{\partial t}\frac{\partial q_r}{\partial u} + p_r \frac{\partial}{\partial u}\left(\frac{\partial H}{\partial p_r}\right)\right\} du \\ &= \int_0^1 \left\{-\frac{\partial H}{\partial q_r}\frac{\partial q_r}{\partial u} + \frac{\partial}{\partial u}\left(p_r \frac{\partial H}{\partial p_r}\right) - \frac{\partial H}{\partial p_r}\frac{\partial p_r}{\partial u}\right\} du \\ &= \int_0^1 \frac{\partial}{\partial u}\left(p_r \frac{\partial H}{\partial p_r} - H\right) du = 0.\end{aligned} \tag{22.5.4}$$

We can deduce from Poincaré's relative integral-invariant an absolute integral-invariant of order 2, namely

$$\iint dq_1\,dp_1 + dq_2\,dp_2 + \cdots + dq_n\,dp_n. \tag{22.5.5}$$

This follows from Stokes's theorem. The integral (22.5.5) is taken over an area on one side of a two-sided surface moving with the fluid.

The converse of Poincaré's theorem is true. If there exists a relative integral-invariant $\oint p_r\, dq_r$ the $2n$ variables satisfy equations of Hamiltonian form. To prove this we introduce a parameter u as before, and we have

$$\frac{DI}{Dt} = \frac{D}{Dt}\oint p_r\, dq_r = \int_0^1 \frac{\partial}{\partial t}\left(p_r \frac{\partial q_r}{\partial u}\right) du \tag{22.5.6}$$

$$= \int_0^1 \left\{\left(\frac{\partial p_r}{\partial t}\frac{\partial q_r}{\partial u} - \frac{\partial q_r}{\partial t}\frac{\partial p_r}{\partial u}\right) + \frac{\partial}{\partial u}\left(p_r \frac{\partial q_r}{\partial t}\right)\right\} du.$$

The last term in the integrand gives zero contribution, since we are dealing with a closed curve, so since $\dfrac{DI}{Dt} = 0$ we have (now discarding the parameter u)

$$\oint \dot{p}_r\, dq_r - \dot{q}_r\, dp_r = 0. \tag{22.5.7}$$

This holds for any closed curve at any instant. It follows by a familiar argument that $\dot{p}_r\, dq_r - \dot{q}_r\, dp_r$ is a perfect space-differential $-d_sH$, where $H = H(q;\ p;\ t)$. Thus during the motion q_r, p_r vary in such a way that

$$\dot{q}_r = \frac{\partial H}{\partial p_r}, \quad \dot{p}_r = -\frac{\partial H}{\partial q_r}, \qquad r = 1, 2, \ldots, n, \tag{22.5.8}$$

and this is the result stated.

The result implies that any system of differential equations of the form

$$\dot{x}_r = X_r, \qquad r = 1, 2, \ldots, m, \tag{22.5.9}$$

for which a linear integral-invariant exists, can be transformed, or partially transformed, into the Hamiltonian form. This result depends on Pfaff's theorem on the reduction of a linear differential form. For suppose the system to possess the relative integral-invariant $\oint \omega$, where ω denotes the Pfaffian form.

$$\xi_1\, dx_1 + \xi_2\, dx_2 + \cdots + \xi_m\, dx_m, \tag{22.5.10}$$

and each $\xi_r(x_1, x_2, \ldots, x_m)$ is of class C_1. Now, in virtue of Pfaff's theorem, ω can be reduced, by a suitable choice of variables, to one of the forms

$$p_1\, dq_1 + p_2\, dq_2 + \cdots + p_v\, dq_v \tag{22.5.11}$$

or

$$p_1\, dq_1 + p_2\, dq_2 + \cdots + p_v\, dq_v + dq_{v+1} \tag{22.5.12}$$

according as the *class* of ω has an even value $2v$ or an odd value $2v + 1$. If ω is non-singular, the class of ω is m: if ω is singular, the class of ω is less than m.

We now consider a transformation from $x_1, x_2, \ldots, x_m$ to new variables $q_1, q_2, \ldots, q_n;$ $p_1, p_2, \ldots, p_n$ if $m(= 2n)$ is even, or to new variables $q_1, q_2, \ldots, q_n;\ p_1, p_2, \ldots, p_n;\ q_{n+1}$ if $m(= 2n + 1)$ is odd. Then $\oint \sum_{r=1}^{v} p_r\, dq_r$ is a relative integral-invariant for the transformed equations, and, in terms of the new variables, $2v$ of the differential equations can be written in Hamiltonian form.

22.6 Liouville's theorem. For the Hamiltonian equations the divergence Δ of the field is zero. It follows (§ 21.8, (iii)) that *the volume (extension) of the phase space is itself invariant under the transformation defined by the equations.* "The fluid is incompressible." This is the famous theorem of Liouville, which is of fundamental importance in the kinetic theory of gases. The multipliers are the space-integrals, and satisfy the condition

$$\Omega M \equiv (M, H) = 0. \tag{22.6.1}$$

If M is a space-integral, the integral $\int M\,dV$ is an absolute integral-invariant of order $2n$; this follows from § 21.8(iii). (We write $\int M\,dV$, for the sake of brevity, for $\int\int \cdots \int M\,dq_1, dq_2 \cdots dq_n\,dp_1\,dp_2 \cdots dp_n$.)

22.7 Poincaré's recurrence theorem. We consider an autonomous system

$$\dot{x}_r = X_r, \qquad r = 1, 2, \ldots, m, \tag{22.7.1}$$

which possesses the following two properties:

(i) $\Delta = 0$, so that the extension of the space is invariant under the transformation T_t defined by the solutions of the equations (22.7.1): "the fluid is incompressible." As we have noticed, this condition is certainly satisfied in the case in which we are primarily interested, that of Hamilton's equations:

(ii) There is a closed region Ω, of finite extension $m\Omega$, with the property that the characteristics originating in points of Ω lie entirely in Ω: "the fluid moves in a closed vessel." Such a region is transformed into itself by the transformation T_t, and is called an *invariant region*.

Poincaré's theorem states that *if α is any closed region of Ω, however small, there exist characteristics which traverse α infinitely often;* more precisely, for any value of t_1, however large, there exist motions of the system for which the mobile lies in α for some instant $t > t_1$.

To prove the theorem, let A be any closed region of Ω, and consider the mobiles (or fluid particles) which lie in A at $t = 0$; let B be the set of points occupied by these mobiles at $t = \theta (> 0)$, so that $B = T_\theta A$. Then we shall speak of B as the θ-consequent of A, and of A as the θ-antecedent of B (cf. § 21.12). We recall that B is uniquely determined by the number θ when A is given, and that A is uniquely determined by the number θ when B is given. Moreover, since the motion is steady, the mobiles which lie in A at $t = t_0$ lie in B at $t = t_0 + \theta$, and the mobiles which lie in B at $t = t_0$ lie in A at $t = t_0 - \theta$.

Consider then the given closed region α, and choose an arbitrary positive number τ. We might for example take $\tau = 1$. We denote the $\tau, 2\tau, 3\tau, \ldots$ antecedents of α by $\alpha_1, \alpha_2, \alpha_3, \ldots$. We recall that $\alpha, \alpha_1, \alpha_2, \ldots$ all have the same extension $m\alpha$, and that all are contained in Ω. Now if $N > m\Omega/m\alpha$ the regions $\alpha, \alpha_1, \alpha_2, \ldots, \alpha_{N-1}$ cannot all be external to one another. At least one pair, say α_r, α_s $(r > s)$ must have in common a region β of non-zero extension $m\beta$.

It follows that α, α_p $(p = r - s)$ have in common a region α' of the same extension $m\beta$. For α_p is the $s\tau$-consequent of α_r, and α is the $s\tau$-consequent of α_s.

Now repeat the argument, starting this time from α' instead of α, and using the same fundamental time-interval τ as before. There is an integer p' such that α' and its $p'\tau$-antecedent $\alpha_{p'}'$ have in common a region α'' of finite extension.

Proceeding in this way we construct a nest of regions $\alpha, \alpha', \alpha'', \ldots$ each of which is contained in the preceding. The sequence converges to a limit set λ, which may be a point or a closed region, and λ is contained in all the regions $\alpha, \alpha', \alpha'', \ldots$. Now the regions $\alpha, \alpha', \alpha'', \ldots$ have the property that the mobiles which lie in $\alpha^{(n+1)}$ at $t = t_0$ all lie in $\alpha^{(n)}$ at $t = t_0 + p^{(n)}\tau$.

Consider then the characteristic originating in a point P_0 of λ; the mobile P is at P_0 at $t = 0$. Since P lies in α' at $t = 0$, it lies in α at $t = p\tau$. Since P lies in α'' at $t = 0$, it lies in α' at $t = p'\tau$, and therefore it lies in α at $t = (p + p')\tau$. Since P lies in α''' at $t = 0$, it lies in α'' at $t = p''\tau$, in α' at $t = (p' + p'')\tau$, and in α at $t = (p + p' + p'')\tau$. Thus, repeating the argument, we see that P lies in α at $t = 0$, at $t = p\tau$, at $t = (p + p')\tau$, at $t = (p + p' + p'')\tau$, and generally at $t = (p + p' + \cdots + p^{(n)})\tau$. Now $(p + p' + \cdots + p^{(n)})$ tends to infinity with n, since all the p's are positive integers. The mobile returns into α infinitely often, and this is the result we set out to prove.

In the proof just given we have considered the position of the mobile P at the discrete instants $0, \tau, 2\tau, \ldots,$ but the theorem is evidently true *a fortiori* if we consider t varying continuously.

Poincaré spoke of such a motion, in which the system returns infinitely often to the neighbourhood of its initial state, as "stable in the sense of Poisson."

Notice again that the central idea of the proof is Liouville's theorem, the measure-preserving property of the operator T_t. No other special property of the Hamiltonian equations has been used.

We have already encountered a theorem of similar character to Poincaré's theorem in the special case of a quasi-periodic motion, § 18.6. We found that in that problem the mobile in the phase-space comes infinitely often arbitrarily near to its initial position.

Poincaré's theorem may be regarded as the starting point of a new approach to the problems of classical dynamics. In the original approach to the subject we hope to *solve* our problem in the sense of finding explicitly the configuration of the system at time t in terms of t and the prescribed configuration and velocity at $t = 0$. But in this sense most problems are not soluble exactly. The realization of this fact is the motive from which Poincaré's theorem, and the development of the theory subsequent to it, arise. The emphasis shifts from the attempt to determine the individual characteristics towards the discussion of the statistical properties of the characteristics as a whole.

22.8 Examples of invariant regions. Let us consider a problem in which H is bounded below in the phase space. Then we may suppose that the infimum of H is zero: this only amounts to adding a suitable constant to the Hamiltonian function (which does not alter the equations of motion), or to adjusting suitably the arbitrary constant in V. Let us assume also that the "surface" $H = h$, for $h > 0$, is closed. Now H is an integral of the Hamiltonian equations, so the surface $H = h$ (for $h > 0$) is an invariant region. Further the closed region bounded by two such surfaces (i.e. the set of points $\mathbf{x}$ for which $h_1 \leqslant H(\mathbf{x}) \leqslant h_2$) is also an invariant region.

As a trivial illustration, consider the harmonic oscillator

$$\dot{q} = p, \quad \dot{p} = -q, \tag{22.8.1}$$

where we have chosen the unit of time to give the value 2π for the period. There is one degree of freedom, the phase space is two-dimensional, and the trajectories are the curves $H =$ constant, i.e. they are the circles

$$\tfrac{1}{2}(q^2 + p^2) = h \tag{22.8.2}$$

for $h > 0$. The motion on each circle is a uniform clockwise motion with unit angular velocity. The circle $r = R$ (where $r^2 = q^2 + p^2$) for $R > 0$ is an invariant region: it contains in fact just one trajectory. The region $R_1 \leqslant r \leqslant R_2$ is also an invariant region. The fluid motion is a motion in which the fluid rotates like a rigid body, and we can take for the invariant region Ω any circle $R = R_1$, or any circular disc $R \leqslant R_1$, or any annulus $R_1 \leqslant r \leqslant R_2$.

22.9 Ergodic theorems. Poincaré's recurrence theorem asserts the existence of motions in which the mobile re-enters α infinitely often. We now turn to the deeper question, "For what proportion of the time does the mobile lie in α?" A similar question presents itself if we deal with the discrete instants $n\tau$: "For what proportion of these instants does the mobile lie in α?"* Theorems dealing with this topic, and with similar topics, are called *ergodic theorems*.

In this connexion we need the idea of integration over a set of points. We must now use the Lebesgue measure of a set of points instead of the simpler notion of volume or extension that has sufficed hitherto, and for the present (up to the end of § 22.17) the integrals will be Lebesgue integrals instead of the Riemann integrals that are usually sufficient in other parts of the classical dynamics.

We consider the transformation T_t defined by the solutions of the autonomous system

$$\dot{x}_r = X_r, \qquad r = 1, 2, \ldots, m. \tag{22.9.1}$$

We assume that $\operatorname{div} \mathbf{X} = 0$, so the transformation is measure-preserving. We consider an invariant region Ω, of finite measure $m\Omega$. Let $f(P)$ be a function of position, defined in Ω and summable over Ω. Let us denote the point into which the point P is carried by the transformation T_t by P_t. In other words, if the mobile whose motion is defined by (22.9.1) starts from P at $t = 0$, it arrives at P_t at time t.

We shall be concerned with the average value (with respect to time) of the function $f(P)$ on the part of a trajectory (say the trajectory originating in a point A) occupied by the mobile from time $t = a$ to time $t = b$, where $a < b$. Let us write

$$\mu_a{}^b(A) = \frac{1}{b - a}\int_a^b f(A_t)\, dt. \tag{22.9.2}$$

The existence of $\mu_a{}^b(A)$ for almost all points A of Ω follows from the summability of $f(P)$ in virtue of Fubini's Theorem; and in the sequel we exclude from consideration the nul set of points A for which it fails to exist. The fundamental result, which we shall speak of in the sequel as *the ergodic theorem*, is that $\mu_0{}^b(A)$ *tends to a limit* $\varphi(A)$ *as* $b \to \infty$ *for almost all points* A *of* Ω.

In particular if $f(P)$ is the characteristic function of a region α (i.e. $f(P)$ has the value 1 if P lies in α, and the value zero if P lies in $\Omega - \alpha$), then $\varphi(A)$ is the proportion of the time during which the mobile, starting from A at $t = 0$, lies in α.

The first point to notice is that if $\varphi(A)$ exists for a particular point A, then $\varphi(A_\theta)$ exists for all points A_θ on the trajectory through A, and indeed has the same value at all these points. To prove that, for a given fixed value of θ, $\varphi(A_\theta)$ exists we have to prove that

$$\frac{1}{b}\int_\theta^{\theta+b} f(A_t)\, dt \tag{22.9.3}$$

* Cf. the notions of C-stability and D-stability in § 21.12.

tends to a limit as $b \to \infty$. Now

$$(22.9.4) \qquad \frac{1}{b}\int_{\theta}^{\theta+b} f(A_t)\,dt = \frac{1}{b}\int_{0}^{\theta+b} f(A_t)\,dt - \frac{1}{b}\int_{0}^{\theta} f(A_t)\,dt$$

$$= \left(\frac{\theta+b}{b}\right)\left(\frac{1}{\theta+b}\int_{0}^{\theta+b} f(A_t)\,dt\right) - \frac{1}{b}\int_{0}^{\theta} f(A_t)\,dt.$$

The first term on the right in (22.9.4) tends to $\varphi(A)$, and the second term tends to zero, as $b \to \infty$. We see therefore that $\varphi(A_\theta)$ exists, and that $\varphi(A_\theta) = \varphi(A)$.

We shall find that, in certain circumstances, we can go further, and assert not only that $\varphi(P)$ is constant along a trajectory, but that $\varphi(P)$ is constant throughout Ω. This property of an invariant region is fundamental in statistical mechanics. It was first suggested, as a plausible hypothesis, in the Kinetic Theory of Gases, the subject in which a speculation on the lines of the ergodic theorem first appeared. It is easy to see that the property in question (that $\varphi(P)$ is constant throughout Ω) does not hold for Hamilton's equations in the classical dynamics. For it to hold, the system must possess a particular property that we shall introduce later (§ 22.15).

22.10 Concrete illustrations. It will perhaps make for clarity if, before proving the ergodic theorem, we consider some simple special examples.

Take first the very simple case in which the mobile P moves (clockwise) on a circle, the angular velocity being constant and equal to unity. (i) If we deal with the continuous variable t, and take for the region α an arc of angle β, Poincaré's recurrence theorem is trivial. Further, if $\chi(t)$ is the proportion of the time-interval $(0, t)$ during which the mobile lies in α, it is evident that $\chi(b)/b$ tends to the limit $\beta/2\pi$, and that this limit is independent of the position of the initial point A on the circle. (ii) If we consider the discrete instants $t = 0, \tau, 2\tau, \ldots$, as in § 22.7, and denote by $\nu(n)$ the number of the points $A, A_\tau, A_{2\tau}, \ldots, A_{(n-1)\tau}$ which lie in α, then $\nu(n)/n$ tends to the same limit $\beta/2\pi$ as n tends to infinity, provided that $\tau/2\pi$ is irrational. For if $\tau/2\pi$ is irrational the points $A, A_\tau, A_{2\tau}, \ldots$, at angular distances $0, \tau, 2\tau, \ldots$ from A tend to uniform distribution on the circle. The limit is independent of the position of A on the circle, and it is also independent of the choice of the fundamental interval τ, provided always that τ is not a rational multiple of 2π.

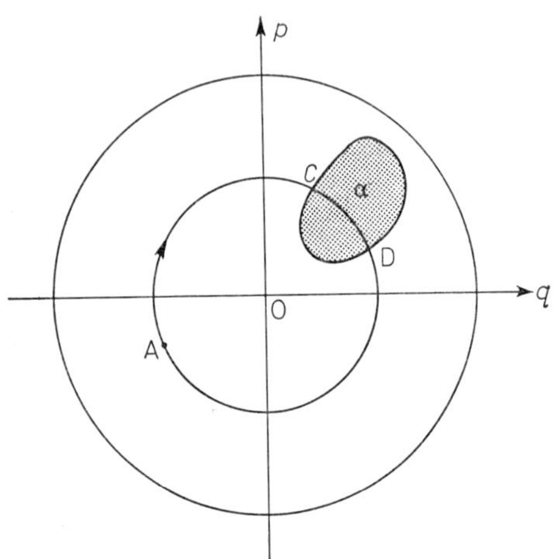

Figure 22.10

Consider now the simple example of the harmonic oscillator mentioned at the end of § 22.8. Let Ω be the circle of radius R about O, and its interior, and let A be any interior point. The characteristic through A is circular, and the proportion of the time during which the mobile lies in the given closed region α tends to the limit $\beta/2\pi$, where β is the angle subtended at O by the arc CD of the circle through A (Fig. 22.10). The limit is, as we have seen, independent of the position of A on the characteristic. The result is the same if we take the limit of $\nu(n)/n$, where $\nu(n)$ is the number of the points $A, A_\tau, A_{2\tau}, \ldots, A_{(n-1)\tau}$ which lie in α, provided that $\tau/2\pi$ is irrational. The result is independent of the position of A on the characteristic and of the value of τ.

But in this case the limit is different for different characteristics: it is not constant throughout Ω.

It may be of interest to consider also for the same system an example where $f(P)$ is not the characteristic function of α. Let us choose for $f(P)$ the simple function q^2. If A is the point (q_1, p_1) the point A_t is

$$\begin{cases} q = q_1 \cos t + p_1 \sin t, \\ p = -q_1 \sin t + p_1 \cos t, \end{cases} \tag{22.10.1}$$

and the mean value of $f(P)$ on the characteristic is

$$\begin{aligned} &\frac{1}{b}\int_0^b (q_1^2 \cos^2 t + 2q_1p_1 \cos t \sin t + p_1^2 \sin^2 t)\, dt \\ &= \tfrac{1}{2}(q_1^2 + p_1^2) + \frac{1}{4b}\{(q_1^2 - p_1^2) \sin 2b + 2q_1p_1(1 - \cos 2b)\}, \end{aligned} \tag{22.10.2}$$

which tends to the limit $\frac{1}{2}(q_1^2 + p_1^2)$ as $b \to \infty$.* We notice again that the limit is the same for all positions of A on the characteristic, but is not the same throughout Ω. The result is the same if we take the discrete points $A, A_\tau, \ldots, A_{(n-1)\tau}$: the average value of q^2 at these points tends to the same limit $\frac{1}{2}(q_1^2 + p_1^2)$, provided that τ is not an integral multiple of π.

22.11 The set K_s. We now turn to the proof of the ergodic theorem. The proof is in two stages. In the first stage we prove that $\mu_0{}^b(P)$ tends to a limit, for almost all P of Ω, when b tends to infinity *through integral values*. In the second stage we remove the restriction to integral values, and prove that the limit exists when b tends to infinity *continuously*.

To begin with, then, we consider $\mu_0{}^n(P)$, where n is an integer. We wish to prove that $\mu_0{}^n(P)$ tends to a limit for almost all P. Let us suppose on the contrary that there is a set L in Ω, of positive measure mL, such that $\mu_0{}^n(P)$ does not tend to a limit when $P \in L$. We then have the two lemmas following.

Lemma 1. *There exist two real numbers α and β, with $\alpha < \beta$, and a part K of L with finite positive measure mK, such that, if $P \in K$,*

$$\underline{\lim}\ \mu_0{}^n(P) < \alpha, \quad \overline{\lim}\ \mu_0{}^n(P) > \beta. \tag{22.11.1}$$

To prove this we consider the set of all intervals with rational end-points. This set is enumerable, and we can arrange the members in order, the nth interval δ_n having end-points α_n, β_n. If $P \in L$,

$$\underline{\lim}\ \mu_0{}^n(P) < \overline{\lim}\ \mu_0{}^n(P),$$

and therefore among the intervals δ_n there is a first one, say δ_p, for which

$$\underline{\lim}\ \mu_0{}^n(P) < \alpha_p < \beta_p < \overline{\lim}\ \mu_0{}^n(P).$$

Let L_p be the set of those points of L associated in this way with the interval δ_p. Then the sets L_i, L_j are disjoint if $i \neq j$, and

$$L = \bigcup_{p=1}^{\infty} L_p.$$

Since $mL > 0$ it follows that $mL_p > 0$ for at least one p, say for $p = q$. We can take for K the set L_q, with $\alpha = \alpha_q$ and $\beta = \beta_q$.

Lemma 2. *Let s be a positive integer. Starting from the set K of Lemma* 1, *let us denote by K_s the set of points P of K for which the inequality*

$$\mu_0{}^n(P) > \beta$$

* The result is evident also from the well-known property of a harmonic motion, $\bar{T} = \bar{V} = \frac{1}{2}C$.

holds for at least one $n \leqslant s$. Then

(22.11.2) $$mK_s > 0$$

for sufficiently large values of s.

For every $P \in K$ belongs to all K_s when s is sufficiently large, so

$$K = \bigcup_{s=1}^{\infty} K_s.$$

But

$$K_s \subset K_{s+1},$$

so

$$mK = \lim_{s \to \infty} mK_s.$$

Since $mK > 0$ it follows that $mK_s > 0$ when s is sufficiently large. This completes the proof of Lemma 2.

In what follows s is some *fixed* positive integer for which the condition $mK_s > 0$ is fulfilled.

22.12 Proper segments. We now introduce the notion of a *proper segment,* more precisely, a proper segment of P for the number β (of Lemmas 1 and 2). Let P be a point of K, and let a be an integer, positive, negative, or zero. We consider the numbers $\mu_a^{a+1}(P)$, $\mu_a^{a+2}(P)$, $\mu_a^{a+3}(P)$, ... If $\mu_a^{b}(P)$ is the first of these numbers which is greater than β we call (a, b) a *proper segment* of P. Thus a proper segment (a, b) has the properties

$$\mu_a^{b}(P) > \beta, \quad \mu_a^{c}(P) \leqslant \beta,$$

where c is any integer between a and b.

Lemma 3. *Two proper segments* (a_1, b_1) *and* (a_2, b_2) *of P cannot partially overlap one another.* For suppose, for example, that $a_1 < a_2 < b_1 < b_2$. Then it would follow that

$$(b_1 - a_1)\mu_{a_1}{}^{b_1} = (a_2 - a_1)\mu_{a_1}{}^{a_2} + (b_1 - a_2)\mu_{a_2}{}^{b_1},$$

and this cannot be true, since the first member is greater than $(b_1 - a_1)\beta$, and the second is less than (or equal to)

$$(a_2 - a_1 + b_1 - a_2)\beta = (b_1 - a_1)\beta.$$

We call a proper segment of P a *maximal segment* of rank s if its length does not exceed s, and if it is not contained in any other proper segment of P whose length does not exceed s.

Lemma 4. *Every proper segment of P whose length does not exceed s is contained in one and only one maximal proper segment of rank s.* To prove this, we notice that among all proper segments of length not exceeding s and containing the given segment, there is one of maximal length. It is clear that this must be a maximal segment of rank s. There cannot be two such segments, because if so they would have points in common, since both contain the given segment. But in that case one would be contained in the other, and would not be a maximal segment of rank s, or they would partially overlap, which we have seen to be impossible. This completes the proof of Lemma 4.

Lemma 5. *In order that P may belong to the set* K_s *it is necessary and sufficient that P should have a maximal segment* (a, b) *of rank s with* $a \leqslant 0 < b$. The condition is necessary. For let $P \in K_s$, and let n be the smallest positive integer for which $\mu_0{}^n(P) > \beta$, so that $n \leqslant s$. Then $(0, n)$ is a proper segment of P, and the unique maximal segment of rank s which contains it satisfies the conditions of the Lemma.

The condition is sufficient. Suppose that P has a maximal segment (a, b) of rank s, with $a \leqslant 0 < b$. We shall prove that $\mu_0{}^b(P) > \beta$, and it then follows that $P \in K_s$, since $b \leqslant b - a \leqslant s$.

If $a = 0$ the statement $\mu_0{}^b(P) > \beta$ is immediate, since (a, b) is a proper segment of P. Suppose then that $a < 0$. If $\mu_0{}^b(P) \leqslant \beta$ there exists a proper segment $(0, b')$, with $b' > b$, and this partially overlaps the proper segment (a, b), which is impossible by Lemma 3. Thus $\mu_0{}^b(P) > \beta$, and this completes the proof of Lemma 5.

22.13 Proof of the ergodic theorem, first stage. With reference to the maximal segments of rank s in Lemma 5, with $a \leqslant 0 < b$, it is convenient to introduce a change of notation. We write

$$a = -p, \quad b - a = q, \tag{22.13.1}$$

and since

$$a \leqslant 0, \quad b - a \leqslant s, \tag{22.13.2}$$

we have

$$0 \leqslant p < q \leqslant s. \tag{22.13.3}$$

For any pair of integers (p, q) satisfying (22.13.3) we denote by K_{pq} the set of those points of K_s which are associated with the segment $(-p, -p + q)$ in the sense of Lemma 5. We notice that the sets K_{pq} for different pairs of integers are disjoint. Moreover, the set K_{0q} goes over, after p units of time, into the set K_{pq},

$$T_p K_{0q} = K_{pq}, \tag{22.13.4}$$

so that

$$mK_{0q} = mK_{pq}, \tag{22.13.5}$$

and further, for any summable function $\varphi(P)$,

$$\int_{K_{pq}} \varphi(P)\, dV = \int_{K_{0q}} \varphi(P_p)\, dV. \tag{22.13.6}$$

Thus, bearing these relations in mind, we have

$$\begin{aligned}
\int_{K_s} \mu_0{}^1(P)\, dV &= \sum_{q=1}^{s} \sum_{p=0}^{q-1} \int_{K_{pq}} \mu_0{}^1(P)\, dV \\
&= \sum_{q=1}^{s} \sum_{p=0}^{q-1} \int_{K_{0q}} \mu_0{}^1(P_p)\, dV \\
&= \sum_{q=1}^{s} \sum_{p=0}^{q-1} \int_{K_{0q}} dV \int_0^1 f(P_{p+t})\, dt \\
&= \sum_{q=1}^{s} \sum_{p=0}^{q-1} \int_{K_{0q}} dV \int_p^{p+1} f(P_t)\, dt \\
&= \sum_{q=1}^{s} \int_{K_{0q}} dV \int_0^q f(P_t)\, dt \\
&= \sum_{q=1}^{s} \int_{K_{0q}} q\mu_0{}^q(P)\, dV \\
&> \beta \sum_{q=1}^{s} q(mK_{0q}) \\
&= \beta \sum_{q=1}^{s} \sum_{p=0}^{q-1} mK_{pq} \\
&= \beta(mK_s).
\end{aligned} \tag{22.13.7}$$

Up to this point s is a fixed positive integer. But (22.13.7) holds for all sufficiently large values of s, and letting $s \to \infty$ we have

(22.13.8) $$\int_K \mu_0^{\,1}(P)\,dV \geqslant \beta(mK).$$

We now consider the corresponding theory for the lower limit α of Lemma 1. Since

(22.13.9) $$\underline{\lim}\ \mu_0^{\,n}(P) < \alpha$$

we prove, by a similar argument to that used above, that

(22.13.10) $$\int_K \mu_0^{\,1}(P)\,dV \leqslant \alpha(mK).$$

But (22.13.8) and (22.13.10) are contradictory, since $\alpha < \beta$, and therefore the assumption

$$m(L) > 0$$

is false. In other words *$\mu_0^{\,n}(P)$ tends to a limit $\varphi(P)$ for almost all P in Ω.*

22.14 Proof of the ergodic theorem, second stage. It remains to prove that $\mu_0^{\,b}(P)$ tends to a limit when b tends to infinity continuously instead of through integral values.

We shall need to consider the average value of $|f(P)|$ on the part of the characteristic occupied by the mobile from time $t = n$ to $t = n + 1$, say

(22.14.1) $$\theta_n(P) = \int_n^{n+1} |f(P_t)|\,dt.$$

We notice at once that

(22.14.2) $$\theta_n(P) = \theta_0(P_n).$$

We first establish the following lemma.

Lemma 6. *For almost all points P of Ω, $\theta_n(P)/n$ tends to zero as n tends to infinity.*

Let ε be an arbitrary fixed positive number and n a positive integer. Let $E_{n,n}$ be the set of points of Ω for which

(22.14.3) $$\theta_n(P) > \varepsilon n,$$

and let $E_{n,0}$ be the set of points of Ω for which

(22.14.4) $$\theta_0(P) > \varepsilon n.$$

Now in the transformation T_n, defining the displacement of the mobile in time $t = n$, the set $E_{n,n}$ goes over into the set $E_{n,0}$, so that

(22.14.5) $$mE_{n,n} = mE_{n,0}.$$

We first prove that the series

(22.14.6) $$\sum_{n=1}^{\infty} mE_{n,n},$$

which is the same as the series

(22.14.7) $$\sum_{n=1}^{\infty} mE_{n,0},$$

is convergent. If s is a positive integer, and if F_s is the set of points of Ω for which

(22.14.8) $$s\varepsilon < \theta_0(P) \leqslant (s + 1)\varepsilon,$$

we see that

$$E_{n,0} = \bigcup_{s=n}^{\infty} F_s. \tag{22.14.9}$$

Thus the series (22.14.7) can be written

$$\begin{aligned}\sum_{n=1}^{\infty}\sum_{s=n}^{\infty} mF_s &= \sum_{s=1}^{\infty}\sum_{n=1}^{s} mF_s = \sum_{s=1}^{\infty} s(mF_s)\\ &= \frac{1}{\varepsilon}\sum_{s=1}^{\infty} s\varepsilon(mF_s) \leqslant \frac{1}{\varepsilon}\sum_{s=1}^{\infty}\int_{s\varepsilon<\theta_0(P)\leqslant(s+1)\varepsilon}\theta_0(P)\,dV\\ &\leqslant \frac{1}{\varepsilon}\int_{\Omega}\theta_0(P)\,dV = \frac{1}{\varepsilon}\int_{\Omega}dV\int_0^1|f(P_t)|\,dt\\ &= \frac{1}{\varepsilon}\int_0^1 dt\int_{\Omega}|f(P_t)|\,dV.\end{aligned} \tag{22.14.10}$$

Since Ω is an invariant region, and since the transformation T_t is measure-preserving, the last expression is equal to

$$\frac{1}{\varepsilon}\int_0^1 dt\int_{\Omega}|f(P)|\,dV = \frac{1}{\varepsilon}\int_{\Omega}|f(P)|\,dV, \tag{22.14.11}$$

which is finite since $f(P)$ is summable over Ω. This proves the convergence of the series (22.14.6).

It follows that every point of Ω, except at most a set of measure zero, belongs to no more than a finite number of the sets $E_{n,n}$ $(n = 1, 2, 3, \ldots)$. Thus for almost all points P of Ω there exists a number $N = N(P)$ such that, for each $n > N$,

$$\theta_n(P) \leqslant \varepsilon n. \tag{22.14.12}$$

Lemma 6 follows from (22.14.12), since ε is arbitrary.

The ergodic theorem, for the case when $b \to \infty$ continuously, now follows easily. Let n be the greatest integer not greater than b: then $n/b \to 1$ as $b \to \infty$. Now

$$\begin{aligned}|b\mu_0{}^b(P) - n\mu_0{}^n(P)| = \left|\int_n^b f(P_t)\,dt\right| &\leqslant \int_n^b |f(P_t)|\,dt\\ &\leqslant \int_n^{n+1}|f(P_t)|\,dt = \theta_n(P),\end{aligned} \tag{22.14.13}$$

whence

$$\left|\mu_0{}^b(P) - \frac{n}{b}\,\mu_0{}^n(P)\right| \leqslant \frac{1}{b}\,\theta_n(P) = \frac{n}{b}\cdot\frac{\theta_n(P)}{n}, \tag{22.14.14}$$

and the expression on the right tends to zero as b tends to infinity in virtue of Lemma 6. Thus

$$\mu_0{}^b(P) - \frac{n}{b}\,\mu_0{}^n(P) \tag{22.14.15}$$

tends to zero as b tends to ∞, and it follows that $\mu_0{}^b(P)$ has the same limit $\varphi(P)$ as $\mu_0{}^n(P)$.

22.15 Metric indecomposability. We have seen that the limit

$$\varphi(P) = \lim_{b\to\infty}\mu_0{}^b(P) = \lim_{b\to\infty}\frac{1}{b}\int_0^b f(P_t)\,dt \tag{22.15.1}$$

exists for almost all points P of the invariant region Ω, and that $\varphi(P)$ is constant along a trajectory. We have mentioned that, under certain conditions, $\varphi(P)$ is constant throughout Ω, though the examples in § 22.10 show that this is not true in general in the classical dynamics. We now turn to the discussion of the conditions that must be satisfied in order that $\varphi(P)$ should be constant throughout Ω.

We call the invariant region Ω *metrically indecomposable* if it cannot be represented in the form

(22.15.2) $$\Omega = \Omega_1 \cup \Omega_2,$$

where Ω_1 and Ω_2 are disjoint invariant regions of positive measure. We shall prove that, *if* Ω *is metrically indecomposable, then* (1) $\varphi(P)$ *is constant almost everywhere in* Ω, *and* (2) *this constant value is given by*

(22.15.3) $$\varphi(P) = \frac{1}{m\Omega}\int_\Omega f(P)\,dV.$$

The significance of the second result is the substitution of a space-average through Ω for the time-average on the characteristics.

We prove first that $\varphi(P)$ is constant almost everywhere in Ω. Let us divide the real numbers x into segments

(22.15.4) $$\frac{k}{2^n} < x \leqslant \frac{k+1}{2^n}$$

where k is an integer (not necessarily positive), and let us call such a segment an *essential segment* if the set of points P of Ω for which the values of $\varphi(P)$ lie in the segment has a positive measure. If for every n there exists only one essential segment δ_n, then δ_{n+1} is contained in δ_n, and the sequence of segments δ_n $(n = 1, 2, \ldots)$ has a single common point α. In this case $\varphi(P) = \alpha$ almost everywhere in Ω. On the other hand if for some n there exist two essential segments, then there is a number β with the property that Ω is divided into two parts Ω_1 and Ω_2, with the property that $\varphi(P) > \beta$ on Ω_1 and $\varphi(P) \leqslant \beta$ on Ω_2. But the sets Ω_1 and Ω_2 are disjoint invariant regions, since $\varphi(P)$ is constant along a characteristic, and this contradicts the assumption that Ω is metrically indecomposable. Therefore $\varphi(P)$ is constant throughout Ω, say

(22.15.5) $$\varphi(P) = a$$

at almost all points of Ω.

It remains to prove that $a = A$, where

(22.15.6) $$A = \frac{1}{m\Omega}\int_\Omega f(P)\,dV.$$

The result is almost evident intuitively. To prove it formally we notice first that, for any positive value of b,

(22.15.7) $$\int_\Omega \mu_0{}^b(P)\,dV = \frac{1}{b}\int_0^b dt\int_\Omega f(P_t)\,dV.$$

But, since Ω is an invariant region, we have, in virtue of Liouville's theorem,

(22.15.8) $$\int_\Omega f(P_t)\,dV = \int_\Omega f(P)\,dV,$$

and from (22.15.7) and (22.15.8) we have

(22.15.9) $$\int_{\Omega} \mu_0{}^b(P)\, dV = \int_{\Omega} f(P)\, dV = A(m\Omega).$$

Thus $\int_{\Omega} \mu_0{}^b(P)\, dV$ is in fact independent of b, and to prove that $a = A$ it will suffice to prove that

(22.15.10) $$\int_{\Omega} \{a - \mu_0{}^b(P)\}\, dV$$

tends to zero as $b \to \infty$; then, since (22.15.10) is independent of b, its value can only be zero.

Let ε be a given positive number. Let $\Omega_1(b)$ be the set of those points P of Ω for which

(22.15.11) $$|a - \mu_0{}^b(P)| < \varepsilon,$$

and $\Omega_2(b)$ the set of those points P of Ω for which

(22.15.12) $$|a - \mu_0{}^b(P)| \geqslant \varepsilon.$$

Then

(22.15.13) $$\left| \int_{\Omega} \{a - \mu_0{}^b(P)\}\, dV \right| \leqslant \int_{\Omega_1(b)} |a - \mu_0{}^b(P)|\, dV + \int_{\Omega_2(b)} |a - \mu_0{}^b(P)|\, dV$$
$$\leqslant \varepsilon(m\Omega) + |a|\,(m\Omega_2(b)) + \int_{\Omega_2(b)} |\mu_0{}^b(P)|\, dV.$$

Now $\mu_0{}^b(P) - a$ tends to zero almost everywhere on Ω as $b \to \infty$, and since convergence almost everywhere implies convergence in measure, $m\Omega_2(b) \to 0$ as $b \to \infty$.

Further, taking the last term on the right in (22.15.13), we have

(22.15.14) $$\int_{\Omega_2(b)} |\mu_0{}^b(P)|\, dV \leqslant \frac{1}{b}\int_0^b dt \int_{\Omega_2(b)} |f(P_t)|\, dV = \frac{1}{b}\int_0^b dt \int_{\Omega_2'(b)} |f(P)|\, dV,$$

where $\Omega_2'(b)$ is the set into which $\Omega_2(b)$ is transformed in time t by the motion. Now $m\Omega_2'(b) = m\Omega_2(b)$, and $m\Omega_2(b)$ tends to zero as b tends to infinity, so the integral $\int_{\Omega_2(b)} |\mu_0{}^b(P)|\, dV$ can be made less than ε by taking b large enough. Thus, finally, there is a number b_0 such that, for $b > b_0$,

(22.15.15) $$m\Omega_2(b) < \varepsilon, \quad \int_{\Omega_2(b)} |\mu_0{}^b(P)|\, dV < \varepsilon,$$

and therefore

(22.15.16) $$\left| \int_{\Omega} \{a - \mu_0{}^b(P)\}\, dV \right| \leqslant (m\Omega + |a| + 1)\varepsilon$$

if $b > b_0$. Since the first member is independent of b its value can only be zero, and this completes the proof.

The condition of metrical indecomposability is essential for the constancy of $\varphi(P)$ throughout Ω. A simple example in which the condition is emphatically *not* satisfied is provided by the harmonic oscillator considered in § 22.10. If we take any concentric circle of radius R_1, where $0 < R_1 < R$, the region $\Omega(r \leqslant R)$ is divided into two invariant regions $\Omega_1(0 \leqslant r \leqslant R_1)$ and $\Omega_2(R_1 < r \leqslant R)$, each of non-zero measure. In this example, as we have noticed already, $\varphi(P)$ is constant along a characteristic, but $\varphi(P)$ is not constant throughout Ω.

22.16 Integrals of the equations of motion. The theorem of § 22.15 requires that the invariant region considered is metrically indecomposable. If there is a one-valued integral ψ of the equations of motion, the region $a \leqslant \psi \leqslant b$ is an invariant region; but it is clearly not metrically indecomposable, since it is the union of the invariant regions $a \leqslant \psi \leqslant c$, $c < \psi \leqslant b$, where c is any number between a and b. The existence of such an integral however allows us to replace the m-fold integral in Liouville's theorem by an integral over a region of $(m - 1)$ dimensions.

Consider for example an autonomous Hamiltonian system for which the coordinate q_n is ignorable. Then p_n is an integral, and the trajectories lie in the planes $p_n =$ constant. Let us consider the plane ϖ defined by $p_n = \beta$. The motion of the system defines a transformation from a point P_0 of ϖ to a point P of ϖ, P_0 being the point occupied by the mobile at $t = 0$, and P being the point occupied by it at time t. Thus a region U_0 of ϖ is transformed, for a given value of t, into a region U of ϖ.

Now this transformation, in the $(2n - 1)$-dimensional plane ϖ, is a measure-preserving transformation; in other words, Liouville's theorem still holds in the $(2n - 1)$-dimensional space. To prove this, we consider the cylinder on U_0 as base which is bounded by the planes $p_n = \beta$ and $p_n = \beta + \varepsilon$. The volume of the cylinder is invariant, by Liouville's theorem, and hence $mU = mU_0$.

More generally, if ψ is a one-valued integral of the equations of motion, let dv be an element of volume of the manifold $\psi = \beta$. Then, by the same argument, the integral

$$\int \frac{1}{|\text{grad } \psi|} \, dv$$

is invariant under the transformation defined by the motion. The most important case is that in which ψ is the Hamiltonian function H. In these problems $\int dv$ is not itself invariant; but the existence of an invariant integral $\int \varphi \, dv$, with positive integrand φ, may be nearly as valuable as the volume-invariance of Liouville's theorem.

22.17 A corollary to Liouville's theorem. In the preceding paragraph we used the existence of a one-valued integral of the equations of motion to obtain an invariant integral over a region of $(2n - 1)$ dimensions. We now consider a situation in which we can find an invariant integral over a region of $(2n - 2)$ dimensions.

We consider an autonomous Hamiltonian system which is such that there exists a periodic orbit. We suppose that the periodic orbit starts from a point A of the phase space at $t = 0$, and returns to A at $t = \sigma$; A is the point $(\alpha_1, \alpha_2, \ldots, \alpha_n, \beta_1, \beta_2, \ldots, \beta_n)$. We assume that $\partial H/\partial q_1$ does not vanish at A, so the trajectory is not tangent to the plane ϖ defined by $p_1 = \beta_1$.

Now let U_0 denote a small neighbourhood of A in the plane ϖ, and let us consider the trajectory starting from a point P_0 of U_0 at $t = 0$. The mobile will return to the plane ϖ, at a point P, after time τ, where P is near to P_0, and τ is nearly equal to σ, if P_0 is near to A. The trajectory originating in P_0 may return to the plane ϖ more than once, but the point P is defined precisely by the continuity property just mentioned. As P_0 takes all positions in U_0, P traverses a region U of ϖ, and the motion defines a topological mapping of U_0 on U. This mapping has a fixed point at A.

If we consider an interval of time from $t = 0$ to $t = t_0$, the trajectories originating in points of U_0 at $t = 0$ build up in this interval a cylinder C_0 on U_0 as base; and similarly the trajectories originating in points of U at $t = 0$ build up in the interval $(0, t_0)$ a cylinder C on U as base. If we denote by R the tube built up by the trajectories from P_0 to P, then, by Liouville's theorem, $R + C - C_0$ has the same volume ($2n$-fold measure) as R, so C has the same volume as C_0. Hence, letting t_0 tend to zero, we see that the integral

$$\int_U -\frac{\partial H}{\partial q_1}\, dq_1\, dq_2 \cdots dq_n\, dp_2\, dp_3 \cdots dp_n \tag{22.17.1}$$

is invariant under the transformation.

We now make use of the fact that H is an integral of the equations of motion. Let us for the moment replace the variables $q_1, q_2, \ldots, q_n, p_2, p_3, \ldots, p_n$ by $H, q_2, q_3, \ldots, q_n, p_2, p_3, \ldots, p_n$, and let us take for U_0 the product space of a $(2n - 2)$-dimensional region Δ_0 of $(q_2, q_3, \ldots, q_n, p_2, p_3, \ldots, p_n)$ and an interval $(H_0 - \delta, H_0 + \delta)$ of H. The region Δ_0 is a small region in the neighbourhood of $(\alpha_2, \alpha_3, \ldots, \alpha_n, \beta_2, \beta_3, \ldots, \beta_n)$, and H_0 is the value of H at A. Now H is constant along a trajectory, and therefore U is the product of a $(2n - 2)$-dimensional region Δ of $(q_2, q_3, \ldots, q_n, p_2, p_3, \ldots, p_n)$ and the interval $(H_0 - \delta, H_0 + \delta)$ of H. The integral (22.17.1) is

$$-2\delta \int_\Delta dq_2\, dq_3 \cdots dq_n\, dp_2\, dp_3 \cdots dp_n, \tag{22.17.2}$$

and therefore the integral

$$\int_\Delta dq_2\, dq_3 \cdots dq_n\, dp_2\, dp_3 \cdots dp_n \tag{22.17.3}$$

is invariant. This is the Corollary to Liouville's theorem that we set out to prove.

The proof can be shortened a little by appealing to the theorem of § 22.4. The system can be reduced to a Hamiltonian system with the Hamiltonian function (22.4.5); the dependent variables are $q_2, q_3, \ldots, q_n, p_2, p_3, \ldots, p_n$, and the independent variable is p_1. The system is not autonomous, since the Hamiltonian function φ contains p_1, but this does not invalidate Liouville's theorem, and the corollary just established is a special case of Liouville's theorem for the reduced system.

22.18 The last multiplier. We now turn to the application of the theorem of Jacobi's last multiplier (§ 21.9) to an autonomous Hamiltonian system. For a Hamiltonian system 1 is a multiplier, and the simplest one to use. We are concerned in the first instance with the determination of the trajectories, and the theorem asserts that if $(m - 2)$ integrals of the system

$$\frac{dx_1}{X_1} = \frac{dx_2}{X_2} = \cdots = \frac{dx_m}{X_m} \tag{22.18.1}$$

are known, and if by means of these we reduce the problem to that of integrating a single equation

$$X_m'\, dx_{m-1} - X'_{m-1}\, dx_m = 0, \tag{22.18.2}$$

then Jacobi's rule determines an integrating factor. We consider the application of this result to an autonomous Hamiltonian system with two freedoms.

Consider then the system of equations

$$\frac{dq_1}{\dfrac{\partial H}{\partial p_1}} = \frac{dq_2}{\dfrac{\partial H}{\partial p_2}} = \frac{dp_1}{-\dfrac{\partial H}{\partial q_1}} = \frac{dp_2}{-\dfrac{\partial H}{\partial q_2}}, \tag{22.18.3}$$

where $H = H(q_1, q_2, p_1, p_2)$.

We can find the trajectories, i.e. the paths of the mobile in the phase space, if we can determine three integrals of (22.18.3). We know one such integral immediately, namely Jacobi's integral $H = h$. Suppose then that we know a second space-integral $F = \alpha$, where

$$F = F(q_1, q_2, p_1, p_2).$$

Then Jacobi's rule enables us to find a third integral. We shall find, in fact, that the final step can be put into a particularly elegant form.

Consider then the two known integrals

$$\begin{cases} H(q_1, q_2, p_1, p_2) = h, \\ F(q_1, q_2, p_1, p_2) = \alpha, \end{cases} \tag{22.18.4}$$

where we assume that $H \in C_1$, $F \in C_1$, in a domain D of the phase space, and that the Jacobian

$$J = \frac{\partial(H, F)}{\partial(p_1, p_2)} \tag{22.18.5}$$

does not vanish in D. Jacobi's rule gives us the third integral

$$\int \frac{1}{J}\left(\frac{\partial H}{\partial p_2}\, dq_1 - \frac{\partial H}{\partial p_1}\, dq_2\right) = \text{constant}, \tag{22.18.6}$$

where the coefficients in the integral are expressed in terms of q_1, q_2, h, α.

Suppose then that the equations (22.18.4) are solved for p_1, p_2 in the form

$$p_1 = f_1(q_1, q_2, h, \alpha), \quad p_2 = f_2(q_1, q_2, h, \alpha). \tag{22.18.7}$$

If we differentiate with respect to α the identities obtained by substituting f_1, f_2 for p_1, p_2 in (22.18.4) we obtain

$$\begin{cases} \dfrac{\partial H}{\partial p_1}\dfrac{\partial f_1}{\partial \alpha} + \dfrac{\partial H}{\partial p_2}\dfrac{\partial f_2}{\partial \alpha} = 0, \\[2ex] \dfrac{\partial F}{\partial p_1}\dfrac{\partial f_1}{\partial \alpha} + \dfrac{\partial F}{\partial p_2}\dfrac{\partial f_2}{\partial \alpha} = 1, \end{cases} \tag{22.18.8}$$

whence

$$\frac{\dfrac{\partial f_1}{\partial \alpha}}{\dfrac{\partial H}{\partial p_2}} = \frac{\dfrac{\partial f_2}{\partial \alpha}}{-\dfrac{\partial H}{\partial p_1}} = \frac{1}{-J}, \tag{22.18.9}$$

and the third integral (22.18.6) can be written

$$\int \frac{\partial f_1}{\partial \alpha}\, dq_1 + \frac{\partial f_2}{\partial \alpha}\, dq_2 = \text{constant}. \tag{22.18.10}$$

It follows that

$$f_1\, dq_1 + f_2\, dq_2, \tag{22.18.11}$$

considered as a Pfaffian form in q_1, q_2, is a perfect differential, and it is not difficult to prove this independently, without appealing to Jacobi's rule. For if we again substitute f_1, f_2 for q_1, q_2 in (22.18.4), and now differentiate the identities so obtained with respect to q_1, we find

$$\left\{\begin{aligned} &\frac{\partial H}{\partial q_1} + \frac{\partial H}{\partial p_1}\frac{\partial f_1}{\partial q_1} + \frac{\partial H}{\partial p_2}\frac{\partial f_2}{\partial q_1} = 0, \\ &\frac{\partial F}{\partial q_1} + \frac{\partial F}{\partial p_1}\frac{\partial f_1}{\partial q_1} + \frac{\partial F}{\partial p_2}\frac{\partial f_2}{d q_1} = 0, \end{aligned}\right. \tag{22.18.12}$$

whence, eliminating $\dfrac{\partial f_1}{\partial q_1}$,

$$\frac{\partial f_2}{\partial q_1} = \frac{\dfrac{\partial(H, F)}{\partial(q_1, p_1)}}{J}. \tag{22.18.13}$$

By a similar argument,

$$\frac{\partial f_1}{\partial q_2} = \frac{\dfrac{\partial(H, F)}{\partial(q_2, p_2)}}{-J}, \tag{22.18.14}$$

and therefore

$$\frac{\partial f_2}{\partial q_1} - \frac{\partial f_1}{\partial q_2} = \frac{(H, F)}{J} = 0, \tag{22.18.15}$$

where we have used the fact that (H, F) vanishes, which is true since F is an integral. Thus $f_1\, dq_1 + f_2\, dq_2$ is a perfect differential dK, where

$$K = K(q_1, q_2, h, \alpha), \tag{22.18.16}$$

and the third integral (22.18.10) can be written in the form

$$\frac{\partial K}{\partial \alpha} = \text{constant}. \tag{22.18.17}$$

This completes the determination of the trajectories. Actually in this problem we can go further and complete the solution by finding still another integral, which must of course contain t. We have, by a method exactly similar to that used to establish (22.18.9),

$$\frac{\dfrac{\partial f_1}{\partial h}}{\dfrac{\partial F}{\partial p_2}} = \frac{\dfrac{\partial f_2}{\partial h}}{-\dfrac{\partial F}{\partial p_1}} = \frac{1}{J}, \tag{22.18.18}$$

so, equating the expressions (22.18.3) to dt, we find

$$dt = \frac{dq_1}{\dfrac{\partial H}{\partial p_1}} = \frac{dq_2}{\dfrac{\partial H}{\partial p_2}} = \frac{\dfrac{\partial F}{\partial p_2}dq_1 - \dfrac{\partial F}{\partial p_1}dq_2}{J} = \frac{\partial f_1}{\partial h}dq_1 + \frac{\partial f_2}{\partial h}dq_2. \tag{22.18.19}$$

We thus obtain the fourth integral of the Hamiltonian system,

$$\frac{\partial K}{\partial h} = t + \text{constant}. \tag{22.18.20}$$

The result we have arrived at can be summed up very simply: *if we solve the equations* (22.18.4) *for* p_1 *and* p_2, *then* $p_1\,dq_1 + p_2\,dq_2$ *is a perfect differential* dK, *and the remaining integrals are*

(22.18.21)
$$\begin{cases} \dfrac{\partial K}{\partial h} = t - t_0, \\ \dfrac{\partial K}{\partial \alpha} = -\beta. \end{cases}$$

The form (22.18.21) of the solution, derived from Jacobi's rule, is very striking. It is precisely the form in which the solution would appear if we solved the problem by means of the Hamilton-Jacobi theorem. The connecting link between the two methods is the fact that $K(q_1, q_2, h, \alpha)$ is a complete integral of the modified partial differential equation (16.5.6).

In many concrete applications the second integral is an integral of momentum corresponding to an ignorable coordinate q_2. In this case the known integrals from which we start are

(22.18.22)
$$H(q_1, p_1, p_2) = h, \quad p_2 = \alpha,$$

and then

(22.18.23)
$$dK = \psi\,dq_1 + \alpha\,dq_2,$$

where ψ $(= \psi(q_1, h, \alpha))$ is found by solving the equation

(22.18.24)
$$H(q_1, p_1, \alpha) = h$$

for p_1 to obtain

(22.18.25)
$$p_1 = \psi(q_1, h, \alpha).$$

The two further integrals required to complete the solution of the problem are determined by the theorem just proved, and they are

(22.18.26)
$$\int \frac{\partial \psi}{\partial h}\,dq_1 = t - t_0, \quad \int \frac{\partial \psi}{\partial \alpha}\,dq_1 + q_2 = -\beta.$$

Example 22.18*A*. *Central orbit, polar coordinates.* In this problem

(22.18.27)
$$H = \frac{1}{2}\left(p_r^{\,2} + \frac{1}{r^2}\,p_\theta^{\,2}\right) + V,$$

where $V = V(r)$. We have the well-known integrals of energy and of angular momentum $H = h$, $p_\theta = \alpha$, and

(22.18.28)
$$\psi(r, h, \alpha) = \sqrt{\left(2h - 2V - \frac{\alpha^2}{r^2}\right)} = \sqrt{f(r)}, \quad \text{say}.$$

The integrals (22.18.26) give the familiar results

(22.18.29)
$$t - t_0 = \int_{r_1}^{r} \frac{d\xi}{\sqrt{f(\xi)}}, \quad \theta + \beta = \int_{r_1}^{r} \frac{(\alpha/\xi^2)}{\sqrt{f(\xi)}}\,d\xi,$$

already found in *Example* 5.2*B*.

Example 22.18*B*. *Central orbit, Cartesian coordinates.* It is an interesting exercise to solve the same problem in Cartesian coordinates by Jacobi's rule. Here

$$H = \tfrac{1}{2}(u^2 + v^2) + V, \tag{22.18.30}$$

where we write u, v for p_x, p_y. The known integrals are

$$\tfrac{1}{2}(u^2 + v^2) + V = h, \tag{22.18.31}$$

$$xv - yu = \alpha. \tag{22.18.32}$$

The theorem just proved asserts that if we solve these equations for u and v, then $u\,dx + v\,dy$ is a perfect differential dK, and the remaining integrals are given by (22.18.21).

To effect the solution, let us introduce for a moment the expression $xu + yv$, which we denote by γ. Then

$$u = \frac{\gamma x - \alpha y}{r^2}, \quad v = \frac{\gamma y + \alpha x}{r^2}, \tag{22.18.33}$$

and the formulae for u and v are found if we express γ in terms of x, y, h, α. Now

$$(xu + yv)^2 + (xv - yu)^2 = r^2(u^2 + v^2), \tag{22.18.34}$$

so, using (22.18.31),

$$\gamma^2 = r^2\left(2h - 2V - \frac{\alpha^2}{r^2}\right) = r^2 f(r), \tag{22.18.35}$$

and hence

$$dK = \frac{\Gamma x - \alpha y}{r^2}\,dx + \frac{\Gamma y + \alpha x}{r^2}\,dy, \tag{22.18.36}$$

where Γ stands for $r\sqrt{f(r)}$. Thus

$$dK = \sqrt{f(r)}\,dr + \alpha\,d\theta, \tag{22.18.37}$$

and we recover the same solution as before.

Example 22.18*C*. *The spherical pendulum.* Using spherical polar coordinates (as in § 5.3), and omitting the positive constant factor mga from L, we have

$$H = \frac{n^2}{2}\left(p_\theta{}^2 + \frac{1}{\sin^2\theta}\,p_\varphi{}^2\right) + \cos\theta, \tag{22.18.38}$$

where $n^2 = g/a$. The known integrals are

$$H = h, \quad p_\varphi = \alpha, \tag{22.18.39}$$

so, using the notation of (22.18.25),

$$\psi(\theta, h, \alpha) = \sqrt{\left\{\frac{2}{n^2}(h - \cos\theta) - \frac{\alpha^2}{\sin^2\theta}\right\}} = \sqrt{f(\theta)}, \tag{22.18.40}$$

and

$$K = \int \sqrt{f(\theta)}\,d\theta + \alpha\varphi. \tag{22.18.41}$$

The integrals (22.18.26) are

$$\text{(22.18.42)} \qquad \begin{cases} t - t_0 = \dfrac{1}{n^2}\displaystyle\int \dfrac{d\theta}{\sqrt{f(\theta)}}, \\ \varphi + \beta = \displaystyle\int \dfrac{(\alpha/\sin^2\theta)}{\sqrt{f(\theta)}}\, d\theta, \end{cases}$$

which are equivalent to the results found in § 5.3. (To recover the same form as that obtained previously we must write $2\alpha/n^2$ in place of α^2.)

Chapter XXIII

Motion in the neighbourhood of a given motion, stability of motion

23.1 The variational equations. The equations of motion for a dynamical system (for example, Hamilton's equations) have the form (19.1.1), $\dot{\mathbf{x}} = \mathbf{X}$. In this Chapter the system from which we start is an autonomous system, so that $\mathbf{X} = \mathbf{X}(\mathbf{x})$, and taking the separate components, we get equations of the form (21.1.3),

$$\dot{x}_r = X_r(x_1, x_2, \ldots, x_m), \qquad r = 1, 2, \ldots, m. \tag{23.1.1}$$

The functions X_r are of class C_1 in a certain domain D of $\mathbf{x}$. We think of the equations (23.1.1) as defining the motion of a mobile in the m-fold space of $(x_1, x_2, \ldots, x_m)$. If the mobile starts from a point $\boldsymbol{\alpha}$ of D at $t = 0$, its position at time t is given, for a certain interval $a < t < b$ of values of t, by formulae of the type $\mathbf{x} = \boldsymbol{\varphi}(t;\ \boldsymbol{\alpha})$, or, in the notation of (21.1.4),

$$x_r = \varphi_r(t;\ \alpha_1, \alpha_2, \ldots, \alpha_m), \qquad r = 1, 2, \ldots, m. \tag{23.1.2}$$

The functions φ_r have continuous first derivatives $\partial\varphi_r/\partial t$, $\partial\varphi_r/\partial\alpha_s$ in the domain E defined by

$$\boldsymbol{\alpha} \in D, \quad a < t < b,$$

and continuous second derivatives $\partial^2\varphi_r/\partial t^2$, $\partial^2\varphi_r/\partial t\,\partial\alpha_s$ $(= \partial^2\varphi_r/\partial\alpha_s\,\partial t)$ in the same domain (§ 19.1). Solving the problem, in the most complete sense, means determining the functions φ_r. In a few simple cases these functions can be determined. But in general the solution, in this complete sense, is not feasible; though in many astronomical applications we can find approximations to the solution with a high degree of accuracy.

Since many problems are intractable, in the sense that we cannot determine the functions φ_r explicitly, it is important to consider classes of problem for which the solution is made easier by the presence of some simplifying factor. An important case is that of the characteristics in the neighbourhood of a known characteristic. The situation is that we know the value of $\mathbf{x}$ for all positive values of t for a particular value of the initial point $\boldsymbol{\alpha}$, but we do not know the functions φ_r for any range of values of $\boldsymbol{\alpha}$. We then attempt to determine, or to determine approximately, the characteristic originating in a point $\boldsymbol{\alpha} + \boldsymbol{\delta}$ in the neighbourhood of $\boldsymbol{\alpha}$.

Let us for the moment denote the known solution, often spoken of as the *undisturbed characteristic*, by $\mathbf{x}$; thus $x_r = \alpha_r$ at $t = 0$, and $\dot{x}_r = X_r(x_1, x_2, \ldots, x_m)$. Let us denote the neighbouring characteristic, or *disturbed characteristic* by $\mathbf{x} + \mathbf{y}$; then $y_r = \delta_r$ at $t = 0$, and

$$\dot{x}_r + \dot{y}_r = X_r(x_1 + y_1, x_2 + y_2, \ldots, x_m + y_m), \quad r = 1, 2, \ldots, m. \tag{23.1.3}$$

Thus the displacement $\mathbf{y}$ from the undisturbed characteristic is such that the variables y_r satisfy the equations

(23.1.4) $$\dot{y}_r = Y_r(y_1, y_2, \ldots, y_m; t), \qquad r = 1, 2, \ldots, m,$$

where

(23.1.5)
$$Y_r(y_1, y_2, \ldots, y_m; t) = X_r(x_1 + y_1, x_2 + y_2, \ldots, x_m + y_m) - X_r(x_1, x_2, \ldots, x_m).$$

In the formulae on the right in (23.1.5) the symbols $x_1, x_2, \ldots, x_m$ denote known functions of t, namely the values at time t on the undisturbed characteristic. The system (23.1.4), in contrast to the system (23.1.1), is of course not autonomous.

We write $|\mathbf{y}|$ for $\sqrt{(|y_1|^2 + |y_1|^2 + \cdots + |y_m|^2)}$; in particular $|\boldsymbol{\delta}|$ stands for $\sqrt{(|\delta_1|^2 + |\delta_2|^2 + \cdots + |\delta_m|^2)}$.* Let us suppose that $|\boldsymbol{\delta}|$ is small. Since the solution of the differential equations (23.1.1) varies continuously with the initial values, $|\mathbf{y}|$ is also small, at least for a sufficiently small range of values of t. In some particular cases $|\mathbf{y}|$ will remain small for all positive values of t.

Later (§ 23.7) we shall return to the equations (23.1.4), but our immediate purpose is the study, not of the exact equations, but of the linear approximation. If we expand the second member of (23.1.5), and retain only terms of the first order in the y_r's, we obtain the linear approximation

(23.1.6) $$\dot{\xi}_r = \sum_{s=1}^{m} a_{rs}\xi_s, \qquad r = 1, 2, \ldots, m,$$

where we have written ξ_r in place of y_r (to distinguish between $\mathbf{y}$, which satisfies the exact equations (23.1.4), and $\boldsymbol{\xi}$, which satisfies the linear approximation (23.1.6)). The coefficient a_{rs} is a known function of t; it is the value of $\partial X_r/\partial x_s$ at the point $(x_1, x_2, \ldots, x_m)$ occupied by the mobile at time t on the undisturbed characteristic.

The equations (23.1.6) are the *variational equations*, sometimes called the variational equations of Jacobi or of Poincaré. They bear the same relation to the exact equations (23.1.4) that the linear approximation bears to the exact equations for motion near a singular point (§ 21.11). The equations can be written in the matrix form

(23.1.7) $$\dot{\boldsymbol{\xi}} = \mathbf{A}\boldsymbol{\xi},$$

where $\boldsymbol{\xi}$ is the column matrix $\{\xi_1, \xi_2, \ldots, \xi_m\}$, and $\mathbf{A}$ is the $m \times m$ matrix whose elements a_{rs} are known functions of t.

In the next section we shall find the solution $\boldsymbol{\xi}$ of the equation (23.1.7) which takes the value $\boldsymbol{\delta}$ at $t = 0$. If this solution is such that $|\boldsymbol{\xi}|$ remains small for all time when $|\boldsymbol{\delta}|$ is small, we say that the undisturbed characteristic has *first-order stability*, or that it is *infinitesimally stable*.

There are two special cases, of great importance, in which the elements a_{rs} of the matrix $\mathbf{A}$ are constants. The first is the problem of the motion in the neighbourhood of a singular point; this includes as a special case the classical theory of small oscillations about a position of stable equilibrium. The second occurs when the undisturbed motion is a steady motion (§ 9.6); in a steady motion the palpable coordinates and the momenta are all constants, and the ignorable coordinates (which

* We notice, as in § 21.11, that the function $|y_1| + |y_2| + \cdots + |y_m|$ has much the same range of usefulness as $|\mathbf{y}|$.

are not constant) do not occur in the formulae defining the elements a_{rs}. The solution of the variational equations (23.1.7) for the case in which the elements of $\mathbf{A}$ are constants has been found already in § 21.10.

We could, of course, easily find the solution of the variational equations (23.1.7), with the given initial value $\boldsymbol{\delta}$ of $\boldsymbol{\xi}$, if we knew the complete solutions (23.1.2) of the equations of motion. The variational equations are satisfied by

$$\xi_r = \frac{\partial \varphi_r}{\partial \alpha_s}, \qquad r = 1, 2, \ldots, m, \tag{23.1.8}$$

where s has any of the values $1, 2, \ldots, m$. This is evident if we substitute φ_r for x_r in (23.1.1) and differentiate partially with respect to α_s, remembering that $\partial^2\varphi_r/\partial t\, \partial\alpha_s = \partial^2\varphi_r/\partial\alpha_s\, \partial t$. The geometric significance is evident. If therefore we denote the matrix $(\partial\varphi_r/\partial\alpha_s)$ by $\mathbf{S}$, each column of $\mathbf{S}$ satisfies (23.1.7), and therefore

$$\dot{\mathbf{S}} = \mathbf{AS}. \tag{23.1.9}$$

($\dot{\mathbf{S}}$ denotes as usual the matrix obtained from $\mathbf{S}$ by differentiating each element with respect to t.) Thus $\boldsymbol{\xi} = \mathbf{S}\boldsymbol{\delta}$ is a solution of the variational equations, and, since $\mathbf{S} = \mathbf{I}_m$ when $t = 0$, this is precisely the solution for which $\boldsymbol{\xi} = \boldsymbol{\delta}$ at $t = 0$.

23.2 Solution of the variational equations. We now find the solution of the equations (23.1.6) with the prescribed initial value $\boldsymbol{\xi} = \boldsymbol{\delta}$ at $t = 0$. The method is suggested by successive approximation. Consider the matrix $\mathbf{R}(t)$,

$$\mathbf{R}(t) = \mathbf{D}_0 + \mathbf{D}_1(t) + \mathbf{D}_2(t) + \cdots, \tag{23.2.1}$$

where

$$\mathbf{D}_0 = \mathbf{I}_m, \tag{23.2.2}$$

and the successive members of the sequence of matrices are determined by the rule

$$\dot{\mathbf{D}}_{r+1} = \mathbf{AD}_r, \tag{23.2.3}$$

with

$$\mathbf{D}_{r+1}(0) = \mathbf{0}. \tag{23.2.4}$$

($\dot{\mathbf{D}}_{r+1}$ is the matrix obtained by differentiating each element of $\mathbf{D}_{r+1}$.) Then

$$\mathbf{R}(0) = \mathbf{D}_0 = \mathbf{I}_m, \tag{23.2.5}$$

and

$$\dot{\mathbf{R}}(t) = \mathbf{AR}(t). \tag{23.2.6}$$

Thus $\mathbf{R}(t)\,\boldsymbol{\delta}$ has the value $\boldsymbol{\delta}$ at $t = 0$ and it satisfies (23.1.6), so the required solution is

$$\boldsymbol{\xi} = \mathbf{R}(t)\,\boldsymbol{\delta}. \tag{23.2.7}$$

The relation expressing $\boldsymbol{\xi}$ in terms of $\boldsymbol{\delta}$ is linear, as we expect. (The matrix $\mathbf{R}(t)$ is in fact the matrix $\mathbf{S}$ $(=(\partial\varphi_r/\partial\alpha_s))$ mentioned in § 23.1.)

The elements of $\mathbf{R}$ are defined by infinite series, and we must consider the question of convergence. Consider an interval $0 \leqslant t \leqslant t_1$, and let K be a number such that, for all the m^2 elements a_{rs} of $\mathbf{A}$,

$$|a_{rs}(t)| < K \tag{23.2.8}$$

for $0 \leqslant t \leqslant t_1$. If we denote the typical element of $\mathbf{D}_r(t)$ by $d_{uv}^{(r)}$ we have

(23.2.9) $$\dot{d}_{uv}^{(1)} = a_{uv}, \quad d_{uv}^{(1)} = \int_0^t a_{uv}(\theta)\, d\theta,$$

whence, if $0 \leqslant t \leqslant t_1$,

(23.2.10) $$|d_{uv}^{(1)}| < Kt.$$

Similarly

(23.2.11) $$|\dot{d}_{uv}^{(2)}| = |\sum_w a_{uw} d_{wv}^{(1)}| < mK^2 t,$$

and

(23.2.12) $$|d_{uv}^{(2)}| < mK^2 t^2/2!.$$

Proceeding in this way we see that, for $0 \leqslant t \leqslant t_1$,

(23.2.13) $$m\, |d_{uv}^{(r)}| < (mKt)^r/r!.$$

The series defining the elements of $\mathbf{R}$ are therefore majorized by exponential series with constant terms, and so the series are convergent, and in fact uniformly convergent, for $0 \leqslant t \leqslant t_1$.

Some properties of the Jacobian J should be noticed, where

(23.2.14) $$J = \det \mathbf{R} = \frac{\partial(\xi)}{\partial(\delta)} = \frac{\partial(\varphi)}{\partial(\alpha)}\,.$$

$\left(\text{Here } \dfrac{\partial(\xi)}{\partial(\delta)}\right.$, for example, is written, for the sake of brevity, instead of $\left.\dfrac{\partial(\xi_1, \xi_2, \ldots, \xi_m)}{\partial(\delta_1, \delta_2, \ldots, \delta_m)}.\right)$ We have, as in § 21.7,

(23.2.15) $$\frac{\dot{J}}{J} = a_{11} + a_{22} + \cdots + a_{mm} = tr\mathbf{A} = \rho(t), \quad \text{say},$$

so

(23.2.16) $$J = e^{\int_0^t \rho(\theta) d\theta}.$$

(Alternatively, instead of quoting § 21.7, we can derive (23.2.16) from (23.2.6).) The interpretation of $\rho(t)$ is that it represents the value of the divergence Δ of the vector field $\mathbf{X}$ at the point occupied at time t in the original motion. In a system, such as a Hamiltonian system, for which Δ is identically zero, $J = 1$ for all time (as we know already, § 22.6).

In the special case in which the elements a_{rs} of $\mathbf{A}$ are constants

(23.2.17) $$\mathbf{D}_r = (t^r/r!)\mathbf{A}^r,$$

and

(23.2.18) $$\mathbf{R} = \mathbf{I}_m + t\mathbf{A} + (t^2/2!)\mathbf{A}^2 + (t^3/3!)\mathbf{A}^3 + \cdots = e^{t\mathbf{A}}.$$

In this case (when the elements of $\mathbf{A}$ are constants) the solution (23.2.7) takes the form

(23.2.19) $$\boldsymbol{\xi} = e^{t\mathbf{A}}\, \boldsymbol{\delta},$$

as we have noticed earlier (§ 21.10).

We consider some simple concrete applications of the solution (23.2.7), in particular of the solution (23.2.19), of the variational equations.

Example 23.2*A*. *Harmonic oscillator.* As we have noticed, for the problem of small oscillations the elements of **A** are constants. In the simple special case of one degree of freedom the equations are

(23.2.20) $$\dot{\xi}_1 = \xi_2, \quad \dot{\xi}_2 = -n^2\xi_1,$$

and

(23.2.21) $$\mathbf{A} = \begin{pmatrix} 0 & 1 \\ -n^2 & 0 \end{pmatrix}.$$

Hence

(23.2.22) $$\mathbf{A}^2 = \begin{pmatrix} -n^2 & 0 \\ 0 & -n^2 \end{pmatrix}, \quad \mathbf{A}^3 = \begin{pmatrix} 0 & -n^2 \\ (-n^2)^2 & 0 \end{pmatrix}, \quad \mathbf{A}^4 = \begin{pmatrix} (-n^2)^2 & 0 \\ 0 & (-n^2)^2 \end{pmatrix},$$

and so on. Thus

(23.2.23) $$\mathbf{R}(t) = e^{t\mathbf{A}} = \begin{pmatrix} 1 - n^2t^2/2! + n^4t^4/4! - \cdots & t - n^2t^3/3! + \cdots \\ -n^2t + n^4t^3/3! - \cdots & 1 - n^2t^2/2! + \cdots \end{pmatrix}$$

$$= \begin{pmatrix} \cos nt & \dfrac{1}{n}\sin nt \\ -n\sin nt & \cos nt \end{pmatrix}.$$

The solution is therefore

(23.2.24) $$\xi_1 = \delta_1 \cos nt + \frac{\delta_2}{n}\sin nt, \quad \xi_2 = -n\delta_1 \sin nt + \delta_2 \cos nt,$$

which is the familiar solution. Of course the matter is even simpler if we reduce the matrix to diagonal form, taking the new variables $n\xi_1 \pm i\xi_2$. As we have noticed (§ 21.10) the power series (23.2.23) are those already found by another method in § 21.4.

Example 23.2*B*. *Newtonian orbit.* Here

(23.2.25) $$H = \frac{1}{2}\left(p_r^{\,2} + \frac{1}{r^2}p_\theta^{\,2}\right) - \frac{\mu}{r},$$

and the equations of motion are

(23.2.26) $$\begin{cases} \dot{r} = p_r, \quad \dot{\theta} = \dfrac{1}{r^2}p_\theta, \\ \dot{p}_r = -\dfrac{\mu}{r^2} + \dfrac{1}{r^3}p_\theta^{\,2}, \quad \dot{p}_\theta = 0. \end{cases}$$

Here $(r, \theta, p_r, p_\theta) = (x_1, x_2, x_3, x_4)$, and the matrix **A** is

(23.2.27) $$\mathbf{A} = \begin{pmatrix} 0 & 0 & 1 & 0 \\ -\dfrac{2\beta}{r^3} & 0 & 0 & \dfrac{1}{r^2} \\ \dfrac{2\mu}{r^3} - \dfrac{3\beta^2}{r^4} & 0 & 0 & \dfrac{2\beta}{r^3} \\ 0 & 0 & 0 & 0 \end{pmatrix},$$

where β is the conserved value of p_θ in the undisturbed motion, and r means the value at time t in the undisturbed motion. If the undisturbed orbit is an ellipse with period σ, the elements of **A** are known periodic functions of t with period σ.

Consider in particular the simple special case in which the undisturbed orbit is a circle of radius a traversed with angular velocity $\omega(=\sqrt{(\mu/a^3)})$. The motion in this case is a steady motion, and the elements of $\mathbf{A}$ are constants,

$$\mathbf{A} = \begin{pmatrix} 0 & 0 & 1 & 0 \\ -\dfrac{2\omega}{a} & 0 & 0 & \dfrac{1}{a^2} \\ -\omega^2 & 0 & 0 & \dfrac{2\omega}{a} \\ 0 & 0 & 0 & 0 \end{pmatrix}. \tag{23.2.28}$$

The variational equations are now

$$\dot{\xi}_1 = \xi_3, \quad \dot{\xi}_2 = -\frac{2\omega}{a}\xi_1 + \frac{1}{a^2}\xi_4, \quad \dot{\xi}_3 = -\omega^2\xi_1 + \frac{2\omega}{a}\xi_4, \quad \dot{\xi}_4 = 0, \tag{23.2.29}$$

and the solution is elementary

$$\left\{\begin{aligned} \xi_1 &= \delta_1 \cos \omega t + \frac{\delta_3}{\omega}\sin \omega t + \frac{2}{a\omega}\delta_4(1 - \cos \omega t), \\ \xi_2 &= -\frac{2}{a}\delta_1 \sin \omega t + \delta_2 - \frac{2\delta_3}{a\omega}(1 - \cos \omega t) - \frac{\delta_4}{a^2\omega}(3\omega t - 4 \sin \omega t), \\ \xi_3 &= -\omega\,\delta_1 \sin \omega t + \delta_3 \cos \omega t + \frac{2}{a}\delta_4 \sin \omega t, \\ \xi_4 &= \delta_4. \end{aligned}\right. \tag{23.2.30}$$

We notice that $|\xi_1|$, $|\xi_3|$, $|\xi_4|$ remain small for all time if $|\boldsymbol{\delta}|$ is small, but that $|\xi_2| \to \infty$ with t (unless $\delta_4 = 0$). An important special case is that in which $(\delta_1, \delta_2, \delta_3, \delta_4) = (0, 0, u, 0)$, and the solution is

$$\xi_1 = \frac{u}{\omega}\sin \omega t, \quad \xi_2 = -\frac{2u}{a\omega}(1 - \cos \omega t), \quad \xi_3 = u \cos \omega t, \quad \xi_4 = 0. \tag{23.2.31}$$

23.3 The case of constant coefficients. We consider the equations

$$\dot{\boldsymbol{\xi}} = \mathbf{A}\,\boldsymbol{\xi}, \tag{23.3.1}$$

the elements a_{rs} of $\mathbf{A}$ being constants. The solution, as we have seen, is

$$\boldsymbol{\xi} = e^{t\mathbf{A}}\,\boldsymbol{\delta}. \tag{23.3.2}$$

The result is evident by elementary reasoning if $\mathbf{A}$ is a diagonal matrix. In that case the equations are

$$\dot{\xi}_r = \lambda_r \xi_r, \qquad r = 1, 2, \ldots, m, \tag{23.3.3}$$

where $\lambda_r = a_{rr}$, and we have complete separation into m independent equations. The solution is

$$\xi_r = e^{t\lambda_r}\,\delta_r, \tag{23.3.4}$$

which is the same as (23.3.2), since $e^{t\mathbf{A}}$ is the diagonal matrix

$$\begin{pmatrix} e^{t\lambda_1} & 0 & \cdots & 0 \\ 0 & e^{t\lambda_2} & \cdots & 0 \\ . & . & \cdots & . \\ 0 & 0 & \cdots & e^{t\lambda_m} \end{pmatrix}. \tag{23.3.5}$$

Now if in (23.3.1) we make the transformation $\boldsymbol{\xi} = \mathbf{C}\boldsymbol{\eta}$, where the matrix $\mathbf{C}$ is non-singular, the equations become

(23.3.6) $$\dot{\boldsymbol{\eta}} = \mathbf{C}^{-1}\mathbf{A}\mathbf{C}\boldsymbol{\eta},$$

and we can choose $\mathbf{C}$ to give to $\mathbf{C}^{-1}\mathbf{A}\mathbf{C}$ the Jordan normal form $\mathbf{J}$, and then

(23.3.7) $$\dot{\boldsymbol{\eta}} = \mathbf{J}\boldsymbol{\eta}.$$

If the eigenvalues of $\mathbf{A}$ are distinct, or if they are not all distinct but the elementary divisors are all simple, $\mathbf{J}$ is a diagonal matrix, and in this case we can reduce the variational equations to the form (23.3.3).

In the general case

(23.3.8) $$\mathbf{A} = \mathbf{C}\mathbf{J}\mathbf{C}^{-1},$$

and

(23.3.9) $$e^{t\mathbf{A}} = \mathbf{C}e^{t\mathbf{J}}\mathbf{C}^{-1}.$$

Now

(23.3.10) $$\mathbf{J} = \begin{pmatrix} \mathbf{J}_0 & 0 & 0 & \cdots & 0 \\ 0 & \mathbf{J}_1 & 0 & \cdots & 0 \\ \cdot & \cdot & \cdot & \cdots & \cdot \\ 0 & 0 & 0 & \cdots & \mathbf{J}_k \end{pmatrix},$$

where $\mathbf{J}_0$ is a diagonal matrix with diagonal elements $\lambda_1, \lambda_2, \ldots, \lambda_q$, not necessarily all different, and

(23.3.11) $$\mathbf{J}_s = \begin{pmatrix} \lambda_{q+s} & 1 & 0 & \cdots & 0 & 0 \\ 0 & \lambda_{q+s} & 1 & \cdots & 0 & 0 \\ \cdot & \cdot & \cdot & \cdots & \cdot & \cdot \\ 0 & 0 & 0 & \cdots & \lambda_{q+s} & 1 \\ 0 & 0 & 0 & \cdots & 0 & \lambda_{q+s} \end{pmatrix}, \qquad s = 1, 2, \ldots, k.$$

The matrix $\mathbf{J}_s$ has r_s rows and columns, and

(23.3.12) $$m = q + r_1 + r_2 + \cdots + r_k.$$

Now

(23.3.13) $$e^{t\mathbf{J}} = \begin{pmatrix} e^{t\mathbf{J}_0} & 0 & 0 & \cdots & 0 \\ 0 & e^{t\mathbf{J}_1} & 0 & \cdots & 0 \\ \cdot & \cdot & \cdot & \cdots & \cdot \\ 0 & 0 & 0 & \cdots & e^{t\mathbf{J}_k} \end{pmatrix}.$$

There is no difficulty in evaluating the matrix $e^{t\mathbf{J}_0}$; it is in fact, as we have seen, the diagonal matrix whose diagonal elements are $e^{t\lambda_1}, e^{t\lambda_2}, \ldots, e^{t\lambda_q}$.

We now evaluate $e^{t\mathbf{J}_s}$. We have

(23.3.14) $$\mathbf{J}_s = \lambda_{q+s}\mathbf{I}_{r_s} + \mathbf{K}_s,$$

where

(23.3.15) $$\mathbf{K}_s = \begin{pmatrix} 0 & 1 & 0 & 0 & \cdots & 0 & 0 \\ 0 & 0 & 1 & 0 & \cdots & 0 & 0 \\ \cdot & \cdot & \cdot & \cdot & \cdots & \cdot & \cdot \\ 0 & 0 & 0 & 0 & \cdots & 0 & 1 \\ 0 & 0 & 0 & 0 & \cdots & 0 & 0 \end{pmatrix},$$

with all elements zero, except those immediately to the right of the leading diagonal. The matrix $\mathbf{K}_s^2$ has the 1's moved one place to the right, with all other elements zero, $\mathbf{K}_s^3$ has the 1's moved two places to the right, and so on. The matrix $\mathbf{K}_s^{r_s}$ is the zero matrix, and so is the matrix $\mathbf{K}_s^N$ for $N > r_s$. Thus the power series for $e^{t\mathbf{K}_s}$ is finite, and

$$e^{t\mathbf{K}_s} = \begin{bmatrix} 1 & t & \frac{t^2}{2!} & \cdots & \frac{t^{r_s-2}}{(r_s-2)!} & \frac{t^{r_s-1}}{(r_s-1)!} \\ 0 & 1 & t & \cdots & \frac{t^{r_s-3}}{(r_s-3)!} & \frac{t^{r_s-2}}{(r_s-2)!} \\ \cdot & \cdot & \cdot & \cdots & \cdot & \cdot \\ 0 & 0 & 0 & \cdots & 1 & t \\ 0 & 0 & 0 & \cdots & 0 & 1 \end{bmatrix}. \tag{23.3.16}$$

Now

$$e^{t\mathbf{J}_s} = e^{\lambda_{q+s}t}e^{t\mathbf{K}_s}, \tag{23.3.17}$$

and thus all the component matrices in (23.3.13) have been evaluated. Finally $e^{t\mathbf{A}}$ is found from (23.3.9).

As a simple illustration, let $m = 4$, and suppose that the Jordan normal form of $\mathbf{A}$ is $\mathbf{J}$, where

$$\mathbf{J} = \begin{pmatrix} \lambda_1 & 0 & 0 & 0 \\ 0 & \lambda_2 & 0 & 0 \\ 0 & 0 & \lambda_3 & 1 \\ 0 & 0 & 0 & \lambda_3 \end{pmatrix}. \tag{23.3.18}$$

Then

$$e^{t\mathbf{J}} = \begin{pmatrix} e^{t\lambda_1} & 0 & 0 & 0 \\ 0 & e^{t\lambda_2} & 0 & 0 \\ 0 & 0 & e^{t\lambda_3} & te^{t\lambda_3} \\ 0 & 0 & 0 & e^{t\lambda_3} \end{pmatrix}, \tag{23.3.19}$$

and

$$e^{t\mathbf{A}} = \mathbf{C}e^{t\mathbf{J}}\mathbf{C}^{-1}. \tag{23.3.9}$$

Thus if the matrix $\mathbf{A}$ can be reduced to diagonal form (i.e. if $\mathbf{A}$ has simple invariant factors) the solution of (23.3.1) is of the form

$$\xi_r = \sum_{s=1}^{m} A_{rs}e^{\lambda_s t}. \tag{23.3.20}$$

If therefore the λ's are all pure-imaginary numbers, the solution contains only sines and cosines of multiples of t. In this case $|\boldsymbol{\xi}|$ remains small if it is small initially, and the original motion has *first-order stability.*

In the general case the solution contains terms of the form $t^N e^{\lambda t}$. If all the λ's have negative real parts, $|\xi| \rightarrow 0$ as $t \rightarrow \infty$, and we have *first-order complete stability.* (This follows from the fact that, if N and k are positive, $t^N e^{-kt} \rightarrow 0$ as $t \rightarrow \infty$.)

If one λ has a positive real part we have *first-order instability*; the displacement defined by the linear approximation does not remain small. If one repeated λ is pure-imaginary, and the corresponding invariant factor is not simple, the solution of Jacobi's equations contains terms of the form $t^N \cos \beta t$, $t^N \sin \beta t$, and again we have first-order instability.

23.4 The case of periodic coefficients. We now return to the general case of the variational equations

$$\dot{\boldsymbol{\xi}} = \mathbf{A}\boldsymbol{\xi}, \tag{23.4.1}$$

where the coefficients a_{rs} are known functions of t.

An $m \times m$ matrix $\mathbf{F}(t)$ whose columns are m linearly independent solutions $\boldsymbol{\xi}$ of the variational equations is called a *fundamental matrix*. A fundamental matrix $\mathbf{F}(t)$ clearly satisfies the equation

$$\dot{\mathbf{F}}(t) = \mathbf{A}(t)\mathbf{F}(t). \tag{23.4.2}$$

If $\mathbf{F}(t)$ is a fundamental matrix, any other fundamental matrix can be written in the form $\mathbf{F}(t)\mathbf{C}$, where $\mathbf{C}$ is a non-singular $m \times m$ matrix whose elements c_{rs} are constants. This is true because any solution of the linear system (23.4.1) can be expressed as a linear combination, with constant coefficients, of m independent solutions. In particular $\mathbf{R}(t)$ (cf. § 23.2) is a fundamental matrix; for example its first column is the solution corresponding to the initial values $\{1, 0, 0, \ldots, 0\}$. Thus any fundamental matrix has the form $\mathbf{R}(t)\mathbf{C}$.

Consider now the situation that arises if the original characteristic from which we start corresponds to a periodic orbit with period σ. (Of course to speak of *the* period is not precise, because if σ is a period, so are $2\sigma, 3\sigma, \ldots$. We shall usually, but not always, mean by σ the smallest period.) In that case the elements a_{rs} of $\mathbf{A}$ are periodic functions of t with period σ, and

$$\mathbf{A}(t + \sigma) = \mathbf{A}(t), \tag{23.4.3}$$

for all values of t. If $\mathbf{F}(t)$ is a fundamental matrix, so is $\mathbf{F}(t + \sigma)$, and therefore there exists a non-singular matrix $\mathbf{M}$ such that

$$\mathbf{F}(t + \sigma) = \mathbf{F}(t)\mathbf{M}. \tag{23.4.4}$$

The matrix $\mathbf{M}$ is called the *monodromy matrix* of the fundamental matrix $\mathbf{F}(t)$. We notice that the monodromy matrix of the particular fundamental matrix $\mathbf{R}(t)$ is $\mathbf{R}(\sigma)$; this follows at once from the fact that $\mathbf{R}(0) = \mathbf{I}_m$.

What is the monodromy matrix $\mathbf{N}$ of another fundamental matrix $\mathbf{G}(t) = \mathbf{F}(t)\mathbf{C}$? We have

$$\begin{aligned} \mathbf{G}(t + \sigma) &= \mathbf{F}(t + \sigma)\mathbf{C} \\ &= \mathbf{F}(t)\mathbf{M}\mathbf{C} \\ &= \mathbf{G}(t)\mathbf{C}^{-1}\mathbf{M}\mathbf{C}, \end{aligned} \tag{23.4.5}$$

and therefore the monodromy matrix of the fundamental matrix $\mathbf{G}(t)$ is

$$\mathbf{N} = \mathbf{C}^{-1}\mathbf{M}\mathbf{C}. \tag{23.4.6}$$

If $\mathbf{M}$ is the monodromy matrix of a fundamental matrix, a matrix $\mathbf{N}$ is the monodromy matrix of another fundamental matrix if and only if $\mathbf{N}$ is of the form $\mathbf{C}^{-1}\mathbf{M}\mathbf{C}$. Thus, all the monodromy matrices have the same eigenvalues and the same elementary divisors, and they can all be reduced to the same Jordan normal form. The eigenvalues $\mu_1, \mu_2, \ldots, \mu_m$ are called *multipliers*. None of the multipliers vanishes, since

$$\mu_1\mu_2 \cdots \mu_m = |\mathbf{M}| \neq 0. \tag{23.4.7}$$

To find the multipliers we can use the particular monodromy matrix $\mathbf{R}(\sigma)$.

If $\mathbf{M}$ is the monodromy matrix of the fundamental matrix $\mathbf{F}(t)$, we can find a matrix $\mathbf{K}$ (not always a real matrix) such that

$$\mathbf{M} = e^{\sigma\mathbf{K}}. \tag{23.4.8}$$

If the eigenvalues of $\mathbf{K}$ are $\lambda_1, \lambda_2, \ldots, \lambda_m$, the eigenvalues of $\mathbf{M}$ are $e^{\sigma\lambda_1}, e^{\sigma\lambda_2}, \ldots, e^{\sigma\lambda_m}$,

$$\mu_r = e^{\sigma\lambda_r}. \tag{23.4.9}$$

The numbers $\lambda_1, \lambda_2, \ldots, \lambda_m$ were called by Poincaré the *characteristic exponents* for the given periodic orbit.

The most important property of the system (23.4.2), when $\mathbf{A}(t)$ is periodic with period σ, is that any fundamental matrix $\mathbf{F}(t)$ can be expressed in the form $\mathbf{P}(t)e^{t\mathbf{K}}$, where $\mathbf{P}$ is a non-singular matrix whose elements are continuous periodic functions of t with period σ, and $\mathbf{K}$ is a constant matrix. The fundamental matrix $\mathbf{F}(t)$ is thus expressed as the product of a periodic matrix and a fundamental matrix for a system of variational equations with constant coefficients.

To establish this result we observe that

$$\mathbf{F}(t + \sigma) = \mathbf{F}(t)\mathbf{M} = \mathbf{F}(t)e^{\sigma\mathbf{K}}. \tag{23.4.10}$$

Let

$$\mathbf{P}(t) = \mathbf{F}(t)e^{-t\mathbf{K}}. \tag{23.4.11}$$

Then

$$\begin{aligned} \mathbf{P}(t + \sigma) &= \mathbf{F}(t + \sigma)e^{-(t+\sigma)\mathbf{K}} \\ &= \mathbf{F}(t)e^{-t\mathbf{K}} \\ &= \mathbf{P}(t), \end{aligned} \tag{23.4.12}$$

so $\mathbf{P}(t)$ is periodic. Also $\mathbf{P}(t)$ is non-singular, since $\mathbf{F}(t)$ and $e^{t\mathbf{K}}$ are non-singular. Thus, from (23.4.11),

$$\mathbf{F}(t) = \mathbf{P}(t)e^{t\mathbf{K}}, \tag{23.4.13}$$

and this completes the proof. The characteristic exponents $\lambda_1, \lambda_2, \ldots, \lambda_m$ are uniquely defined for a given periodic matrix $\mathbf{A}$, although $\mathbf{K}$ is not uniquely determined by $\mathbf{F}(t)$.

We can find the explicit form of the solution by introducing a transformation which reduces $\mathbf{K}$ to the Jordan normal form. Let $\mathbf{L}$ be a non-singular matrix such that

$$\mathbf{L}^{-1}\mathbf{K}\mathbf{L} = \mathbf{J}, \tag{23.4.14}$$

where $\mathbf{J}$ is the normal form (23.3.10). Then

$$\mathbf{F}(t) = \mathbf{P}(t)e^{t\mathbf{K}} = \mathbf{P}(t)e^{t\mathbf{L}\mathbf{J}\mathbf{L}^{-1}} = \mathbf{P}(t)\mathbf{L}e^{t\mathbf{J}}\mathbf{L}^{-1}, \tag{23.4.15}$$

and therefore the fundamental matrix $\mathbf{F}(t)\mathbf{L}$ has the form

$$\mathbf{Q}(t)e^{t\mathbf{J}}, \tag{23.4.16}$$

where $\mathbf{Q}(t)$ is the periodic matrix $\mathbf{P}(t)\mathbf{L}$. The factor $e^{t\mathbf{J}}$ has already been evaluated in § 23.3 above.

The argument is simpler if we confine our attention to the case where the normal form of the monodromy matrix is diagonal. Then for a certain fundamental matrix $\mathbf{F}(t)$

(23.4.17)
$$\mathbf{F}(t+\sigma) = \mathbf{F}(t)\begin{pmatrix} \mu_1 & 0 & \cdots & 0 \\ 0 & \mu_2 & \cdots & 0 \\ \cdot & \cdot & \cdots & \cdot \\ 0 & 0 & \cdots & \mu_m \end{pmatrix}.$$

Thus, if we denote the first column of $\mathbf{F}(t)$ by $\boldsymbol{\xi}_1$, we have

(23.4.18)
$$\boldsymbol{\xi}_1(t+\sigma) = \mu_1\boldsymbol{\xi}_1(t) = e^{\sigma\lambda_1}\boldsymbol{\xi}_1(t),$$

whence

(23.4.19)
$$e^{-\lambda_1(t+\sigma)}\boldsymbol{\xi}_1(t+\sigma) = e^{-\lambda_1 t}\boldsymbol{\xi}_1(t),$$

and therefore $e^{-\lambda_1 t}\boldsymbol{\xi}_1(t)$ is a periodic vector function with period σ, say

(23.4.20)
$$\boldsymbol{\xi}_1(t) = e^{\lambda_1 t}\boldsymbol{\varphi}_1(t),$$

where

$$\boldsymbol{\varphi}_1(t+\sigma) = \boldsymbol{\varphi}_1(t).$$

We can now easily see, from (23.4.16), the type of solution that will appear in the various cases; the argument is reminiscent of that given in § 23.3 for the case where the elements of $\mathbf{A}$ are constants. If all the characteristic exponents λ_r have negative real parts, we have first-order complete stability in all cases. (This follows from the fact that, if N and k are positive, $t^N e^{-kt} \to 0$ as $t \to \infty$.) If all the λ's are pure-imaginary numbers, and the normal form of the monodromy matrices is diagonal, we have first-order stability. But if all the λ's are pure-imaginary numbers, and the monodromy matrices cannot be reduced to diagonal form, the solution contains terms of the form $\varphi(t)t^N \cos \beta t$, $\varphi(t)t^N \sin \beta t$ (where $\varphi(t)$ is periodic with period σ) and there is no longer first-order stability. And finally first-order stability does not occur if any λ has a positive real part.

Let us return for a moment to the case in which the elements of $\mathbf{A}$ are constants. So far the characteristic exponents have been defined only when $\mathbf{A}$ is periodic. But it is clear from § 23.3 that the eigenvalues of $\mathbf{A}$, when $\mathbf{A}$ is constant, play a very similar part in the solution of the variational equations to that played by the characteristic exponents when $\mathbf{A}$ is periodic. It is natural therefore to extend the use of the term characteristic exponents so as to include the case where the elements of $\mathbf{A}$ are constants. In a problem in which $\mathbf{A}$ is a constant matrix the characteristic exponents are its eigenvalues.

23.5 Zero exponents. In any problem of variation from a periodic orbit (but not in a problem of variation from an equilibrium position) one characteristic exponent is zero. For since the given periodic motion satisfies the equations

(23.5.1)
$$\dot{x}_r = X_r$$

we have

(23.5.2)
$$\ddot{x}_r = \sum_{s=1} \frac{\partial X_r}{\partial x_s}\dot{x}_s = \sum_{s=1}^{m} a_{rs}\dot{x}_s,$$

and the variational equations are satisfied by

(23.5.3)
$$\xi_r = \dot{x}_r, \qquad r = 1, 2, \ldots, m.$$

Thus the variational equations have a purely periodic solution with period σ, and this can only happen if one of the λ's is zero.

Next, let us suppose that the periodic orbit from which we start is a member of a one-parameter family of periodic orbits, say the member for $\alpha = 0$ of the family

(23.5.4) $$x_r = f_r\left(\frac{t}{\tau}, \alpha\right), \qquad r = 1, 2, \ldots, m,$$

where $\tau = \tau(\alpha)$, $\sigma = \tau(0)$, and

(23.5.5) $$f_r(\theta + 1, \alpha) = f_r(\theta, \alpha).$$

We can deduce a solution of the variational equations by differentiating (23.5.4) with respect to α,

(23.5.6) $$\xi_r = f_{r2}\left(\frac{t}{\sigma}, 0\right) - \frac{\tau'(0)}{\sigma^2}\, t f_{r1}\left(\frac{t}{\sigma}, 0\right), \qquad r = 1, 2, \ldots, m,$$

where f_{ri} is the derivative of f_r with respect to the ith argument. This time we have a secular solution containing not only periodic terms but also terms of the form $t\varphi(t)$, where $\varphi(t)$ is periodic. It follows (§ 23.4) that in this case *two* of the characteristic exponents have the value zero. (The argument fails if $\tau'(0) = 0$; but the conclusion stands, because in this case there are two *independent* periodic solutions, $\dot{x}_r$ and $\partial x_r/\partial\alpha$, of the variational equations.)

A familiar example of such a one-parameter family of periodic orbits is that of the circular orbits in a central field of force derived from the potential function $V(r)$. In this case (cf. *Example* 23.2*B*) we have

(23.5.7) $$H = \frac{1}{2}\left(p_r^2 + \frac{1}{r^2}p_\theta^2\right) + V(r),$$

and the equations of motion are

(23.5.8) $$\begin{cases} \dot{r} = p_r, & \dot{\theta} = \dfrac{1}{r^2}p_\theta, \\ \dot{p}_r = \dfrac{1}{r^3}p_\theta^2 - V'(r), & \dot{p}_\theta = 0. \end{cases}$$

The matrix $\mathbf{A}$ is

(23.5.9) $$\mathbf{A} = \begin{pmatrix} 0 & 0 & 1 & 0 \\ -\dfrac{2\beta}{r^3} & 0 & 0 & \dfrac{1}{r^2} \\ -\dfrac{3\beta^2}{r^4} - V''(r) & 0 & 0 & \dfrac{2\beta}{r^3} \\ 0 & 0 & 0 & 0 \end{pmatrix},$$

where β is the conserved value of p_θ, and r denotes the value at time t, in the original motion.

If the original motion is motion in a circle of radius a with angular velocity ω, then $a\omega^2 = V'(a)$ and $\beta = a^2\omega = \sqrt{\{a^3V'(a)\}}$. The elements of $\mathbf{A}$ are constants,

(23.5.10) $$\mathbf{A} = \begin{pmatrix} 0 & 0 & 1 & 0 \\ -\dfrac{2\omega}{a} & 0 & 0 & \dfrac{1}{a^2} \\ -3\dfrac{V'(a)}{a} - V''(a) & 0 & 0 & \dfrac{2\omega}{a} \\ 0 & 0 & 0 & 0 \end{pmatrix},$$

and the characteristic exponents are the roots of the equation

$$\lambda^2\left\{\lambda^2 + 3\frac{V'(a)}{a} + V''(a)\right\} = 0. \tag{23.5.11}$$

Two roots are zero.

The other two roots are zero, for an arbitrary value of a, if and only if

$$3\frac{V'(a)}{a} + V''(a) = 0, \tag{23.5.12}$$

for all values of a, and in that case

$$V'(a) = \frac{\mu}{a^3}, \tag{23.5.13}$$

and the law of attraction is that of the inverse cube.

Let us now consider more particularly an attraction μ/r^n, where n is an integer; in this case

$$V'(r) = \frac{\mu}{r^n}, \quad V''(r) = -n\frac{\mu}{r^{n+1}}, \quad \omega^2 = \frac{\mu}{a^{n+1}}, \quad -3\frac{V'(a)}{a} - V''(a) = (n-3)\omega^2, \tag{23.5.14}$$

and the equation for the characteristic exponents is

$$\lambda^2\{\lambda^2 + (3-n)\omega^2\} = 0. \tag{23.5.15}$$

Thus the characteristic exponents, for some particular cases, are:

$$\begin{aligned} n &= -1, & \lambda &= (0, 0, 2i\omega, -2i\omega),\\ n &= 2, & \lambda &= (0, 0, i\omega, -i\omega),\\ n &= 3, & \lambda &= (0, 0, 0, 0),\\ n &> 3, & \lambda &= (0, 0, \alpha, -\alpha), \end{aligned}$$

where α is real and positive, $\alpha = \omega\sqrt{(n-3)}$. The Jordan normal form for the matrix **A** is:

$n = -1$,

$$\begin{pmatrix} 0 & 0 & 0 & 0\\ 0 & 0 & 0 & 0\\ 0 & 0 & 2i\omega & 0\\ 0 & 0 & 0 & -2i\omega \end{pmatrix},$$

$n = 3$,

$$\begin{pmatrix} 0 & 1 & 0 & 0\\ 0 & 0 & 1 & 0\\ 0 & 0 & 0 & 1\\ 0 & 0 & 0 & 0 \end{pmatrix},$$

$n \neq -1$ and $n \neq 3$,

$$\begin{pmatrix} 0 & 1 & 0 & 0\\ 0 & 0 & 0 & 0\\ 0 & 0 & p & 0\\ 0 & 0 & 0 & -p \end{pmatrix},$$

where p is pure-imaginary if $n < 3$, and real if $n > 3$.

23.6 Variation from the Hamiltonian equations. If the original equations of motion are of Hamiltonian form, and there is a periodic solution, two of the characteristic exponents have the value zero. Moreover, if μ is an eigenvalue of the monodromy matrix, $1/\mu$ and $\bar{\mu}$ are also eigenvalues. Thus, if λ is a characteristic exponent which is neither real nor pure-imaginary, other characteristic exponents are $-\lambda$, $\bar{\lambda}$, and $-\bar{\lambda}$. If λ is a characteristic exponent which is real or pure-imaginary, another characteristic exponent is $-\lambda$.

In particular, for the case of two freedoms, the characteristic exponents are of the form $(0, 0, \alpha, -\alpha)$, or $(0, 0, i\alpha, -i\alpha)$, where α is real (cf. § 23.5).

We proceed to establish these important results. The original equations, which are satisfied by the given periodic motion, are

$$\dot{q}_r = \frac{\partial H}{\partial p_r}, \quad \dot{p}_r = -\frac{\partial H}{\partial q_r}, \qquad r = 1, 2, \ldots, n, \tag{23.6.1}$$

where $H = H(q_1, q_2, \ldots, q_n;\ p_1, p_2, \ldots, p_n) \in C_2$. We denote the coordinates and momenta in the varied orbit by $q_r + \xi_r$, $p_r + \eta_r$. The variational equations are

$$\begin{cases} \dot{\xi}_r = \beta_{sr}\xi_s + \gamma_{rs}\eta_s, \\ \dot{\eta}_r = -\alpha_{rs}\xi_s - \beta_{rs}\eta_s, \end{cases} \qquad r = 1, 2, \ldots, n, \tag{23.6.2}$$

the repeated suffix s on the right implying summation from 1 to n. Here

$$\alpha_{rs} = \frac{\partial^2 H}{\partial q_r\, \partial q_s} = \alpha_{sr}, \quad \beta_{rs} = \frac{\partial^2 H}{\partial q_r\, \partial p_s}, \quad \gamma_{rs} = \frac{\partial^2 H}{\partial p_r \partial p_s} = \gamma_{sr}, \tag{23.6.3}$$

where the values of the q's and p's in the original motion have been substituted after differentiation.

The equations (23.6.2) are of Hamiltonian form, with ξ for q and η for p, and the Hamiltonian function is

$$\mathscr{H} = \tfrac{1}{2}\alpha_{rs}\xi_r\xi_s + \beta_{rs}\xi_r\eta_s + \tfrac{1}{2}\gamma_{rs}\eta_r\eta_s, \tag{23.6.4}$$

where repeated suffixes imply summation. Thus, if we denote the vector $\{\xi_1, \xi_2, \ldots, \xi_n, \eta_1, \eta_2, \ldots, \eta_n\}$ by $\boldsymbol{\zeta}$, and write the Hamiltonian equations in the form (22.1.5), we have

$$\dot{\boldsymbol{\zeta}} = \mathbf{Z}\mathscr{H}_{\zeta} = \mathbf{ZS}\boldsymbol{\zeta}, \tag{23.6.5}$$

where $\mathbf{Z}$ denotes as usual the matrix

$$\mathbf{Z} = \begin{pmatrix} \mathbf{0} & \mathbf{I}_n \\ -\mathbf{I}_n & \mathbf{0} \end{pmatrix}, \tag{23.6.6}$$

and $\mathbf{S}$ is a *symmetric* periodic $2n \times 2n$ matrix.

We now prove that, if $\boldsymbol{\zeta}$, $\boldsymbol{\varkappa}$ are two independent solutions of the variational equations (23.6.5), then

$$\varphi = \boldsymbol{\zeta}'\mathbf{Z}\boldsymbol{\varkappa} \tag{23.6.7}$$

remains constant. To prove this we notice that

$$\begin{aligned} \dot{\varphi} &= \dot{\boldsymbol{\zeta}}'\mathbf{Z}\boldsymbol{\varkappa} + \boldsymbol{\zeta}'\mathbf{Z}\dot{\boldsymbol{\varkappa}} \\ &= \boldsymbol{\zeta}'\mathbf{S}'\mathbf{Z}'\mathbf{Z}\boldsymbol{\varkappa} + \boldsymbol{\zeta}'\mathbf{ZZS}\boldsymbol{\varkappa}, \end{aligned} \tag{23.6.8}$$

which vanishes, since $\mathbf{S}$ is symmetric and $\mathbf{Z}' = -\mathbf{Z}$. (The value of φ, written out *in extenso* is

$$\sum_{r=1}^{n} (\xi_r\eta_r' - \eta_r\xi_r'), \tag{23.6.9}$$

where the components of $\boldsymbol{\zeta}$ are $\xi_1, \xi_2, \ldots, \xi_n, \eta_1, \eta_2, \ldots, \eta_n$, and the components of $\boldsymbol{\varkappa}$ are $\xi_1', \xi_2', \ldots, \xi_n', \eta_1', \eta_2', \ldots, \eta_n'$.) Thus φ remains constant, and it follows that

$$\boldsymbol{\zeta}'\mathbf{Z}\boldsymbol{\varkappa} = \boldsymbol{\delta}'\mathbf{Z}\boldsymbol{\epsilon}, \tag{23.6.10}$$

where $\boldsymbol{\delta}$ is the value of $\boldsymbol{\zeta}$, and $\boldsymbol{\epsilon}$ is the value of $\boldsymbol{\varkappa}$, at $t = 0$.

Now let $\boldsymbol{\zeta}$, $\boldsymbol{\varkappa}$ refer, not to a general value of t, but to the particular value $t = \sigma$. Then

(23.6.11) $$\boldsymbol{\zeta} = \mathbf{R}(\sigma)\,\boldsymbol{\delta} = \mathbf{M}\,\boldsymbol{\delta}, \quad \boldsymbol{\varkappa} = \mathbf{R}(\sigma)\boldsymbol{\epsilon} = \mathbf{M}\boldsymbol{\epsilon},$$

where $\mathbf{M}$ now stands for $\mathbf{R}(\sigma)$, the monodromy matrix of the fundamental matrix $\mathbf{R}(t)$ (§ 23.4). Hence, from (23.6.10),

(23.6.12) $$\boldsymbol{\delta}'\mathbf{M}'\mathbf{Z}\mathbf{M}\boldsymbol{\epsilon} = \boldsymbol{\delta}'\mathbf{Z}\boldsymbol{\epsilon},$$

and since this holds for arbitrary values of $\boldsymbol{\delta}$ and $\boldsymbol{\epsilon}$, the matrix $\mathbf{M}$ must have the property

(23.6.13) $$\mathbf{M}'\mathbf{Z}\mathbf{M} = \mathbf{Z}.$$

A matrix having the property exhibited in (23.6.13) is called *symplectic*.

We recall that all monodromy matrices have the same eigenvalues. The symplectic property of $\mathbf{M}$ (which is the monodromy matrix of the fundamental matrix $\mathbf{R}(t)$) implies that if μ is an eigenvalue, so also is $1/\mu$. For if μ is an eigenvalue of $\mathbf{M}$,

(23.6.14) $$|\mathbf{M}' - \mu\mathbf{I}_{2n}| = 0.$$

Hence

(23.6.15) $$|\mathbf{M}'\mathbf{Z}\mathbf{M} - \mu\mathbf{Z}\mathbf{M}| = 0,$$

and therefore, in virtue of (23.6.13),

(23.6.16) $$|\mathbf{Z} - \mu\mathbf{Z}\mathbf{M}| = 0.$$

It follows that

(23.6.17) $$\left|\mathbf{M} - \frac{1}{\mu}\mathbf{I}_{2n}\right| = 0,$$

so $1/\mu$ is an eigenvalue of $\mathbf{M}$.

Now $\mu_r = e^{\sigma\lambda_r}$, and the theorem enunciated at the beginning of this section follows easily. We know (§ 23.5) that one λ is zero. We see now that the non-zero λ's are paired, λ_r and $-\lambda_r$, so *two* λ's must vanish, since the total number is even. Also $\mathbf{M}$ is a real matrix, so if μ is an eigenvalue of $\mathbf{M}$, so is the conjugate complex number $\bar{\mu}$. It follows that if λ is a characteristic exponent that is neither real nor pure imaginary, so is $\bar{\lambda}$; and this completes the proof.

23.7 Stability of trajectories (i). The notion of stability arises first when a system in a position of equilibrium is slightly disturbed (§ 9.1). We have also considered the extension of the notion of stability to a position of *apparent* equilibrium of a gyroscopic system (§ 9.9), and to the steady motion of a gyroscopic system (§ 9.6). And we have also defined first-order stability of motion in connexion with the variational equations (§ 23.1).

Can the notion of stability be extended in any useful way to motion in general? What should we mean by the statement that a particular *motion*, in contrast to a particular position of equilibrium, is stable?

It must be kept in mind that we are dealing here with curves in the phase-space of $2n$ dimensions, not with the q-space of n dimensions. In many cases the undisturbed characteristic from which we start is a periodic orbit.

We recall the notation introduced in § 23.1. The orbits with which we are concerned are the trajectories of the equations (23.1.1),

(23.7.1) $$\dot{x}_r = X_r(x_1, x_2, \ldots, x_m), \qquad r = 1, 2, \ldots, m,$$

or, more compactly, the equation

(23.7.2) $$\dot{\mathbf{x}} = \mathbf{X}(\mathbf{x}).$$

The solution $\mathbf{x}$ taking the value $\boldsymbol{\alpha}$ at $t = 0$ is written, as in (23.1.2),

(23.7.3) $$x_r = \varphi_r(t;\ \alpha_1, \alpha_2, \ldots, \alpha_m), \qquad r = 1, 2, \ldots, m,$$

or, compactly,

(23.7.4) $$\mathbf{x} = \boldsymbol{\varphi}(t;\ \boldsymbol{\alpha}).$$

If the initial point is changed from $\boldsymbol{\alpha}$ to a neighbouring point $\boldsymbol{\alpha} + \boldsymbol{\delta}$, and if (as in § 23.1) we denote the point reached at time t on the resulting trajectory by $\mathbf{x} + \mathbf{y}$, we have

(23.7.5) $$\mathbf{y}(t) = \boldsymbol{\varphi}(t;\ \boldsymbol{\alpha} + \boldsymbol{\delta}) - \boldsymbol{\varphi}(t;\ \boldsymbol{\alpha}).$$

The solution of the differential equations varies continuously with the initial point, and $|\mathbf{y}(t)|$ is small if $|\boldsymbol{\delta}|$ is small and t is not too large. Explicitly, if ε is a prescribed positive number, there exists a positive number κ $(= \kappa(\varepsilon))$ and a positive number t_0 $(= t_0(\varepsilon))$ such that $|\mathbf{y}(t)| < \varepsilon$ for all values of t in the range $(0, t_0)$ provided that $|\boldsymbol{\delta}| < \kappa$.

When we seek a formal definition of stability of motion our first impulse might be to say that the motion is stable if we can replace the finite interval $(0, t_0)$ by the infinite interval $(0, \infty)$. If we accept this idea we arrive at the following definition. The trajectory $\boldsymbol{\varphi}(t;\ \boldsymbol{\alpha})$ is stable if, given $\varepsilon(> 0)$, there exists a positive number κ $(= \kappa(\epsilon))$ such that $|\boldsymbol{\varphi}(t;\ \boldsymbol{\alpha} + \boldsymbol{\delta}) - \boldsymbol{\varphi}(t;\ \boldsymbol{\alpha})| < \varepsilon$ for all positive values of t, provided that $|\boldsymbol{\delta}| < \kappa$. A trajectory that satisfies this condition is said to be *stable in the sense of Liapounov.*

If the solution (23.7.4) is known, not only for a particular initial point $\boldsymbol{\alpha}$, but for all initial points in the neighbourhood of $\boldsymbol{\alpha}$, it is easy to determine whether the criterion for Liapounov stability is satisfied or not. In general, however, our position is that of § 23.1: we know the solution (23.7.4) for a particular $\boldsymbol{\alpha}$, but not for neighbouring initial points. The displacement $\mathbf{y}(t)$ is defined as the solution, taking the value $\boldsymbol{\delta}$ at $t = 0$, of (23.1.4),

(23.7.6) $$\dot{y}_r = Y_r(y_1, y_2, \ldots, y_m;\ t), \qquad r = 1, 2, \ldots, m,$$

where, as in (23.1.5),

(23.7.7) $$Y_r(y_1, y_2, \ldots, y_m;\ t) = X_r(x_1 + y_1, x_2 + y_2, \ldots, x_m + y_m) - X_r(x_1, x_2, \ldots, x_m),$$

and in the formulae on the right in (23.7.7), x_r denotes a known function of t, namely the value at time t in the undisturbed motion. The question is, does smallness of $|\boldsymbol{\delta}|$ imply smallness of $|\mathbf{y}|$ for all positive values of t?

In the theory of the sleeping top (§ 9.9) we established the stability of the position of apparent equilibrium from the existence of an integral which is a positive definite quadratic form in the variables ξ, y, z, $\dot{\xi}$, $\dot{y}$, $\dot{z}$. (We must remember that in that context we were dealing with Lagrangian equations, not Hamiltonian equations; the six variables $\xi, y, z, \dot{\xi}, \dot{y}, \dot{z}$ correspond to the six variables $y_1, y_2, y_3, y_4, y_5, y_6$ of the present theory.) Similarly in the theory of small oscillations about a position of equilibrium at which the potential function is a minimum, we derived the stability from the energy integral. This integral is not a positive definite quadratic form (unless indeed the coefficients in T are constants, and V is exactly, and not merely approximately, a positive definite quadratic form) but it has the essential properties of such a form. (Again, the $2n$ variables $q_1, q_2, \ldots, q_n, \dot{q}_1, \dot{q}_2, \ldots, \dot{q}_n$ correspond to the $m(=2n)$ variables $y_1, y_2, \ldots, y_m$ of the present theory. Smallness of $|\mathbf{y}|$ implies smallness of $|\dot{\mathbf{q}}|$ as well as smallness of $|\mathbf{q}|$.) In some cases we can use a similar method, and establish the Liapounov stability of the undisturbed characteristic by finding an integral of the equations (23.7.6) which is a positive definite quadratic form in $y_1, y_2, \ldots, y_m$, or which is a function possessing the essential properties of a positive definite quadratic form. Also we can extend the theory still further to functions which contain t as well as $y_1, y_2, \ldots, y_m$, and to functions which are not integrals of the equations (23.7.6), but which constantly decrease as the motion proceeds.

The functions we need in this context are functions whose prototype is the positive definite quadratic form. We shall say that the function $f(y_1, y_2, \ldots, y_m)$, or briefly $f(\mathbf{y})$, is a *positive definite function* if it is of class C_1 in a neighbourhood of $\mathbf{y} = \mathbf{0}$, and has the following properties:

(i) $f(\mathbf{y}) = 0$ when $r = 0$, and there is a positive number κ such that $f(\mathbf{y}) > 0$ when $0 < r \leqslant \kappa$; here, and throughout the discussion, r stands for $|\mathbf{y}| = \sqrt{(y_1^2 + y_2^2 + \cdots + y_m^2)}$;

(ii) there is a positive number k such that, if $0 < c_1 < c_2 \leqslant k$, the manifold $f(\mathbf{y}) = c_1$ lies strictly inside the manifold $f(\mathbf{y}) = c_2$; in general the manifolds $f(\mathbf{y}) = c$, for sufficiently small values of c, are closed manifolds of $(m - 1)$ dimensions.*

Certain properties of positive definite functions follow from the definition. We denote the least value of r for points on the manifold $f(\mathbf{y}) = k$ by $R\ (= R(f))$, and $0 < R \leqslant \kappa$. If $0 < a \leqslant R$, we denote by $m_a(f)$ and $M_a(f)$ the infimum and supremum of $f(\mathbf{y})$ on the sphere $r = a$. Then $0 < m_a(f) \leqslant M_a(f)$, and the functions $m_a(f)$ and $M_a(f)$, *qua* functions of a for a given f, are monotone functions which tend to zero with a. If $r \leqslant a$, $f(\mathbf{y}) \leqslant M_a(f)$, and if $r \geqslant a$, $f(\mathbf{y}) \geqslant m_a(f)$. Further, $f(\mathbf{y}) \leqslant m_a(f)$ implies $r \leqslant a$, and $f(\mathbf{y}) \geqslant M_a(f)$ implies $r \geqslant a$. If $\mathbf{y}$ varies in such a way that $f(\mathbf{y}) \to 0$, then $r \to 0$. (A general idea of the curves $f(\mathbf{y}) = c$, for the case $m = 2$, is illustrated in Fig. 23.7. The curves for $c = m_a(f)$ and for $c = M_a(f)$ are drawn with a firm line.)

As a simple concrete example, with $m = 2$, if $f(\mathbf{y}) = \alpha y_1^2 + \beta y_2^2$, where $0 < \alpha < \beta$, then $m_a(f) = \alpha a^2$ and $M_a(f) = \beta a^2$.

We extend the notion of *complete stability* or *asymptotic stability*, already defined in relation to disturbed equilibrium (§ 19.5), to disturbed motion. We say that the undisturbed trajectory $\mathbf{x}(t)$ is completely stable if there is a positive number κ such that for all values of $\boldsymbol{\delta}$ in the domain $|\boldsymbol{\delta}| < \kappa$, $r \to 0$ as $t \to \infty$: the disturbed motion tends to coincidence with the original motion as $t \to \infty$.

It is desirable to extend the notion of a positive definite function to include also functions which are functions of t as well as of $y_1, y_2, \ldots, y_m$. We shall say that

* The name "positive definite function" is sometimes given to a slightly less restricted function, the condition (ii) in the definition being replaced by the weaker condition that $f(\mathbf{y})$ small implies $\mathbf{y}$ small.

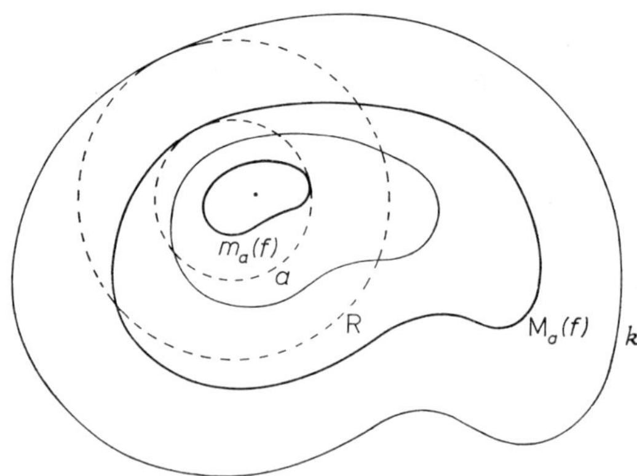

Figure 23.7

the function $g(y_1, y_2, \ldots, y_m;\ t)$, or briefly $g(\mathbf{y};\ t)$, is a positive definite function if $g(\mathbf{y};\ 0)$ is a positive definite function, and if there exists a positive definite function $h(\mathbf{y})$ such that $g(\mathbf{y};\ t) \geqslant h(\mathbf{y})$ when $r \leqslant R(h)$ and $t \geqslant 0$.

We now turn to the above-mentioned criterion for Liapounov stability. It is contained in the following theorem and its corollaries.

Liapounov's theorem. If the positive definite function $f(\mathbf{y})$ *is a space-integral of the equations* (23.7.6) *satisfied by the disturbance* $\mathbf{y}$, *the undisturbed trajectory* $\mathbf{x}(t)$ *is stable.*

We have the integral $f(\mathbf{y}) = f(\boldsymbol{\delta})$. Given $\varepsilon(> 0)$, let $c = m_\varepsilon(f)$, and let κ be the positive number defined by $c = M_\kappa(f)$. Then if $|\boldsymbol{\delta}| \leqslant \kappa$, $f(\mathbf{y}) = f(\boldsymbol{\delta}) \leqslant M_\kappa(f) = m_\varepsilon(f)$, whence $r \leqslant \varepsilon$, and the theorem is established.

Cor. 1. *If the positive definite function* $f(\mathbf{y})$ *is not an integral of the equations* (23.7.6), *but is such that the function*

$$F(\mathbf{y}; t) = -\sum_{s=1}^{m} Y_s \frac{\partial f}{\partial y_s} \tag{23.7.8}$$

is positive for sufficiently small values of r and all positive values of t, then the undisturbed trajectory $\mathbf{x}(t)$ *is stable.*

As $\mathbf{y}$ varies on the trajectory defined by (23.7.6) and originating in $\boldsymbol{\delta}$,

$$\frac{d}{dt} f(\mathbf{y}) = -F(\mathbf{y}; t) < 0, \tag{23.7.9}$$

so $f(\mathbf{y}) < f(\boldsymbol{\delta})$. This inequality, valid for all positive values of t, replaces the equation $f(\mathbf{y}) = f(\boldsymbol{\delta})$; and using the same notation as before, if $|\boldsymbol{\delta}| < \kappa$,

$$f(\mathbf{y}) < f(\boldsymbol{\delta}) \leqslant m_\varepsilon(f), \tag{23.7.10}$$

and $r \leqslant \varepsilon$ for $t > 0$.

Cor. 2. *If* $f(\mathbf{y})$ *is a positive definite function, and* $F(\mathbf{y}; t)$ *is a positive definite function (not merely* $F(\mathbf{y}; t) > 0$ *when r is small, as it was in Cor.* 1) *the undisturbed trajectory* $\mathbf{x}(t)$ *is completely stable.*

We have to prove that there exists a positive number κ such that, for all positions of the initial point $\boldsymbol{\delta}$ in the domain $|\boldsymbol{\delta}| < \kappa$, $r \to 0$ as $t \to \infty$. Now we know (*Cor.* 1) that there is a number κ such that, if $|\boldsymbol{\delta}| \leqslant \kappa$, $f(\mathbf{y})$ continually decreases as $\mathbf{y}$ moves on the trajectory defined by (23.7.6), so $f(\mathbf{y})$ tends to a limit L $(= L(\boldsymbol{\delta}))$ where $L \geqslant 0$. Let us suppose that, for a particular choice of $\boldsymbol{\delta}$, $L > 0$. Then $f(\mathbf{y}) \geqslant L$

for all positive values of t, and therefore $r \geqslant a$, where a is the positive number defined by $M_a(f) = L$. Let $h(\mathbf{y})$ be the positive definite function associated with $F(\mathbf{y}; t)$. Then $r \geqslant a$ implies $F(\mathbf{y}; t) \geqslant h(\mathbf{y}) \geqslant \lambda$, where $\lambda = m_a(h) > 0$. Thus, as $\mathbf{y}$ moves on the trajectory defined by (23.7.6),

$$f(\mathbf{y}) = f(\boldsymbol{\delta}) - \int F\,dt \leqslant f(\boldsymbol{\delta}) - \lambda t. \tag{23.7.11}$$

But this is impossible, since the second member is negative for sufficiently large values of t. Thus $L = 0$: $f(\mathbf{y}) \to 0$ as $t \to \infty$, and this implies $r \to 0$. The undisturbed trajectory $\mathbf{x}(t)$ is completely stable.

We now consider the extension of the theory to test-functions which depend upon t as well as upon $y_1, y_2, \ldots, y_m$.

Cor. 3. *If the positive definite function $g(\mathbf{y};\ t)$ is an integral of the equations* (23.7.6), *the undisturbed trajectory* $\mathbf{x}(t)$ *is stable.*

We have the integral $g(\mathbf{y};\ t) = g(\boldsymbol{\delta};\ 0)$, and there exists a positive definite function $h(\mathbf{y})$ such that

$$h(\mathbf{y}) \leqslant g(\mathbf{y};\ t) = g(\boldsymbol{\delta};\ 0). \tag{23.7.12}$$

Now $g(\mathbf{y};\ 0)$ is a positive definite function, and we can choose a positive number κ such that, if $|\boldsymbol{\delta}| \leqslant \kappa$, $g(\boldsymbol{\delta};\ 0) \leqslant m_\varepsilon(h)$. Then throughout the motion

$$h(\mathbf{y}) \leqslant m_\varepsilon(h), \tag{23.7.13}$$

and this implies $r \leqslant \varepsilon$.

Cor. 4. *If the positive definite function $g(\mathbf{y};\ t)$ is such that*

$$G(\mathbf{y};\ t) = -\left(\frac{\partial g}{\partial t} + \sum_{s=1}^{m} Y_s \frac{\partial g}{\partial y_s}\right) \tag{23.7.14}$$

is positive for all sufficiently small values of r and for all positive values of t, the undisturbed trajectory $\mathbf{x}(t)$ *is stable.*

In this case $g(\mathbf{y};\ t)$ constantly decreases as $\mathbf{y}$ moves on a trajectory of (23.7.6), and the result follows as in *Cor.* 1.

Finally, there is a simple extension of *Cor.* 2 which establishes a criterion for complete stability. This criterion demands an additional restriction on the positive definite function $g(\mathbf{y};\ t)$. Every positive definite function $f(\mathbf{y})$ has the property that, given $\varepsilon(> 0)$ however small, there exists a positive number κ $(= \kappa(\varepsilon))$ such that $r < \kappa$ implies $f(\mathbf{y}) < \varepsilon$. This is not in general true of a positive definite function $g(\mathbf{y};\ t)$*, but we now consider functions $g(\mathbf{y};\ t)$ which do possess this property for all values of t, i.e. $r < \kappa$ implies $g(\mathbf{y};\ t) < \varepsilon$ for all values of t. A positive definite function $g(\mathbf{y};\ t)$ possessing this property is said to have an infinitesimal upper bound.

Cor. 5. *If the positive definite function $g(\mathbf{y};\ t)$ has an infinitesimal upper bound, and if $G(\mathbf{y};\ t)$ is a positive definite function, then the undisturbed trajectory* $\mathbf{x}(t)$ *is completely stable.*

We denote by $h(\mathbf{y})$ the positive definite function associated with $g(\mathbf{y};\ t)$ (as in *Cor.* 3), and by $H(\mathbf{y})$ the positive definite function associated with $G(\mathbf{y};\ t)$. We choose κ, as in *Cor.* 3, such that $|\boldsymbol{\delta}| \leqslant \kappa$ implies $g(\boldsymbol{\delta};\ 0) \leqslant m_\varepsilon(h)$, and this in turn implies $r \leqslant \varepsilon$. If $|\boldsymbol{\delta}| \leqslant \kappa$, then as $\mathbf{y}$ moves on the trajectory originating in $\boldsymbol{\delta}$, $g(\mathbf{y};\ t)$ continually decreases, and tends to a limit L, where $L \geqslant 0$. Suppose that for

* A simple counter-example is given by $g(\mathbf{y};\ t) = r^2 + \sin^2(rt)$.

a particular choice of $\boldsymbol{\delta}$, $L > 0$. Then $g(\mathbf{y};\ t) \geqslant L$, and therefore (since $g(\mathbf{y};\ t)$ has an infinitesimal upper bound) there exists a positive number η such that $r \geqslant \eta$. Thus throughout the motion

(23.7.15) $$\eta \leqslant r \leqslant \varepsilon.$$

Let λ be the infimum of the positive definite function $H(\mathbf{y})$ in the closed region defined by (23.7.15). Then

(23.7.16) $$G(\mathbf{y};\ t) \geqslant H(\mathbf{y}) \geqslant \lambda > 0,$$

and

(23.7.17) $$g(\mathbf{y};\ t) = g(\boldsymbol{\delta};\ 0) - \int G\, dt < g(\boldsymbol{\delta};\ 0) - \lambda t.$$

But this is impossible, since the second member is negative for sufficiently large values of t. Hence L can only be zero, and (since $g(\mathbf{y};\ t)$ has an infinitesimal upper bound) this in turn implies $r \to 0$.

Some examples of trajectories which are stable in the sense of Liapounov follow; in the first and second we can find the general solution of the equations of motion, in the third we appeal to Liapounov's theorem.

Example 23.7*A*. *Harmonic oscillator.* With a suitable choice of the time-scale

(23.7.18) $$T = \tfrac{1}{2}\dot{q}^2, \quad V = \tfrac{1}{2}q^2, \quad H = \tfrac{1}{2}(q^2 + p^2).$$

The equations of motion are

(23.7.19) $$\dot{q} = p, \quad \dot{p} = -q,$$

and the familiar solution is

(23.7.20) $$q = \alpha \cos t + \beta \sin t, \quad p = -\alpha \sin t + \beta \cos t,$$

where $(\alpha,\ \beta)$ is the initial value of (q,p). If we now consider the trajectory originating in a neighbouring point $(\alpha',\ \beta')$ we have

(23.7.21) $$q' - q = (\alpha' - \alpha) \cos t + (\beta' - \beta) \sin t, \quad p' - p = -(\alpha' - \alpha) \sin t + (\beta' - \beta) \cos t$$

and

(23.7.22) $$r^2 = (q' - q)^2 + (p' - p)^2 = (\alpha' - \alpha)^2 + (\beta' - \beta)^2.$$

The distance between the mobiles in the undisturbed motion and in the disturbed motion remains constant; of course the result is obvious geometrically, since the mobiles move in concentric circles with the same angular velocity. The motion is stable in the sense of Liapounov, and we can take $\kappa = \varepsilon$.

More generally, if

(23.7.23) $$\begin{aligned} T &= \tfrac{1}{2}(\dot{q}_1^{\,2} + \dot{q}_2^{\,2} + \cdots + \dot{q}_n^{\,2}) = \tfrac{1}{2}(p_1^{\,2} + p_2^{\,2} + \cdots + p_n^{\,2}), \\ V &= \tfrac{1}{2}(m_1^{\,2}q_1^{\,2} + m_2^{\,2}q_2^{\,2} + \cdots + m_n^{\,2}q_n^{\,2}), \end{aligned}$$

the equations of motion are

(23.7.24) $$\dot{q}_r = p_r, \quad \dot{p}_r = -m_r^{\,2}q_r, \qquad r = 1, 2, \ldots, n.$$

We are here considering a problem in which the motion is described exactly by these equations, not merely approximately as in the theory of small oscillations. The solutions are

(23.7.25) $$q_r = \alpha_r \cos m_r t + \frac{\beta_r}{m_r} \sin m_r t, \quad p_r = -m_r\alpha_r \sin m_r t + \beta_r \cos m_r t,$$

where the initial point is $(\alpha_1, \alpha_2, \ldots, \alpha_n, \beta_1, \beta_2, \ldots, \beta_n)$. If we now take the trajectory originating in a neighbouring point $(\alpha_1', \alpha_2', \ldots, \alpha_n', \beta_1', \beta_2', \ldots, \beta_n')$ we have

$$\begin{cases} q_r' - q_r = (\alpha_r' - \alpha_r)\cos m_r t + \dfrac{\beta_r' - \beta_r}{m_r}\sin m_r t, \\ p_r' - p_r = -m_r(\alpha_r' - \alpha_r)\sin m_r t + (\beta_r' - \beta_r)\cos m_r t. \end{cases} \tag{23.7.26}$$

Hence

$$\begin{cases} (q_r' - q_r)^2 \leqslant (\alpha_r' - \alpha_r)^2 + \dfrac{1}{m_r^2}(\beta_r' - \beta_r)^2, \\ (p_r' - p_r)^2 \leqslant m_r^2(\alpha_r' - \alpha_r)^2 + (\beta_r' - \beta_r)^2, \end{cases} \tag{23.7.27}$$

and

$$r = |\mathbf{y}(t)| \leqslant K|\boldsymbol{\delta}|, \tag{23.7.28}$$

where $K/\sqrt{2}$ is the largest of the numbers m_r, $1/m_r$. The criterion for stability in the sense of Liapounov is satisfied, and we can take $\kappa = \varepsilon/K$.

Example 23.7*B*. Consider the motion defined by the equations

$$\begin{cases} \dot{x} = -x - y + a(x/r), \\ \dot{y} = x - y + a(y/r), \end{cases} \tag{23.7.29}$$

where $r = \sqrt{(x^2 + y^2)}$, and $a > 0$. In polar coordinates

$$\dot{r} = a - r, \quad \dot{\theta} = 1. \tag{23.7.30}$$

The trajectories are stable in the sense of Liapounov. Consider in particular the periodic orbit $r = a$, $\theta = t$, arising from the initial point $(a, 0)$. The neighbouring orbit through the initial point $(a + \delta_1, \delta_2)$ is

$$r = a + \delta_1 e^{-t}, \quad \theta = \delta_2 + t. \tag{23.7.31}$$

In the disturbed trajectory $r \to a$ as $t \to \infty$, and the distance between the mobiles in the spiral orbit and in the circular orbit steadily decreases, and tends to the limit $2a \sin \frac{1}{2}|\delta_2|$. The periodic orbit is stable in the sense of Liapounov, and we can take $\kappa = \varepsilon$.

Example 23.7*C*. Consider a problem in which the equations (23.7.6), defining the displacement from a certain known trajectory, have the form

$$\begin{cases} \dot{y}_1 = -(y_1 - \beta y_2)(1 - ay_1^2 - by_2^2), \\ \dot{y}_2 = -(y_2 + \alpha y_1)(1 - ay_1^2 - by_2^2), \end{cases} \tag{23.7.32}$$

where $0 < \alpha < \beta$ and $0 < a < b$. If we take the positive definite test-function

$$f = \alpha y_1^2 + \beta y_2^2, \tag{23.7.33}$$

we have

$$F = 2(\alpha y_1^2 + \beta y_2^2)(1 - ay_1^2 - by_2^2). \tag{23.7.34}$$

Now $F > 0$ provided that $r^2 < 1/b$, and F is a positive definite function inside the **circle** $r^2 = 1/(2b)$. (If we express F in polar coordinates we have

$$F = 2r^2(\alpha \cos^2\theta + \beta \sin^2\theta)\{1 - r^2(a\cos^2\theta + b\sin^2\theta)\}, \tag{23.7.35}$$

and

$$\frac{\partial F}{\partial (r^2)} = 2(\alpha\cos^2\theta + \beta\sin^2\theta)\{1 - 2r^2(a\cos^2\theta + b\sin^2\theta)\}. \tag{23.7.36}$$

Therefore $\partial F/\partial(r^2) > 0$ if

$$r^2 < \frac{1}{2(a\cos^2\theta + b\sin^2\theta)}, \tag{23.7.37}$$

which is true for all values of θ if $r^2 < 1/(2b)$). The undisturbed trajectory $\mathbf{x}(t)$ is completely stable in the sense of Liapounov (*Cor.* 2).

The Liapounov notion of stability may seem at first sight to be the natural extension to a proper characteristic of the idea of stability previously developed for an equilibrium point (which can be regarded as a degenerate characteristic). Nevertheless, this notion of stability is fruitless in the classical dynamics, because it demands too much. We have noticed a few systems for which there is stability in this sense, but in fact the criterion is not satisfied in very simple and familiar problems that we should intuitively regard as stable. Consider for example the elementary problem of a particle moving on a straight line in a field of force. According to Liapounov's definition of stability, motion in a uniform field is unstable, and so is an ordinary libration motion (apart from trivial exceptions, such as the harmonic oscillator). For a uniform field in the direction Ox, the undisturbed characteristic through the initial point (a, u), where we write y for $\dot{x}$, is

(23.7.38) $$x = a + ut + \tfrac{1}{2}ct^2, \quad y = u + ct,$$

where c (> 0) is the uniform acceleration in the field. If (x', y') is the disturbed characteristic through the neighbouring initial point $(a + \delta_1, u + \delta_2)$,

(23.7.39) $$x' - x = \delta_1 + \delta_2 t, \quad y' - y = \delta_2,$$

and $|\varphi(t;\ \boldsymbol{\alpha} + \boldsymbol{\delta}) - \varphi(t;\ \boldsymbol{\alpha})|$ tends to infinity with t unless $\delta_2 = 0$. For the libration motion we have only to observe that the period in the disturbed motion (which is also a periodic motion) is in general different from the period in the undisturbed motion, so $|x(t;\ \boldsymbol{\alpha} + \boldsymbol{\delta}) - x(t;\ \boldsymbol{\alpha})|$ cannot remain small for all time, and *a fortiori* $|\boldsymbol{\varphi}(t;\ \boldsymbol{\alpha} + \boldsymbol{\delta}) - \boldsymbol{\varphi}(t;\ \boldsymbol{\alpha})|$ cannot remain small. And similarly in less simple cases, for example in the restricted problem of three bodies (Chapter XXVIII), very few characteristics are stable in Liapounov's sense.

23.8 Stability of trajectories (ii). For the classical dynamics Liapounov's notion of stability is of no great interest, and we discard it in favour of another. In fact many different definitions of stability have been suggested. One of the simplest is this: we say that a trajectory C (in the phase space) is stable if a trajectory C', originating in a point of the phase space sufficiently near to the initial point of C, is such that each point of C' is near to *some* point of C. This is less exacting than the former definition because, although it demands that a point $\boldsymbol{\varphi}(t;\ \boldsymbol{\alpha} + \boldsymbol{\delta})$ on C' is near to some point of C, this need not be the contemporaneous point. Stability of this type is called *orbital stability.*

We can express the criterion for orbital stability in various forms.

(i) The characteristic $\boldsymbol{\varphi}(t;\ \boldsymbol{\alpha})$ is stable if, given $\varepsilon(> 0)$, there exists a positive number κ $(= \kappa(\varepsilon))$ such that, if $|\boldsymbol{\delta}| < \kappa$, then corresponding to every positive number t there is a positive number $t'(= t'(t;\ \boldsymbol{\delta}))$ such that

(23.8.1) $$|\boldsymbol{\varphi}(t;\ \boldsymbol{\alpha} + \boldsymbol{\delta}) - \boldsymbol{\varphi}(t';\ \boldsymbol{\alpha})| < \varepsilon.$$

(ii) Let $d(\mathbf{y}, C)$ be the distance of the point $\mathbf{y}$ from the positive semi-characteristic C (i.e. d is the infimum of the distance between $\mathbf{y}$ and a point $\mathbf{y}'$ of C). The characteristic C, built up of the points $\boldsymbol{\varphi}(t;\ \boldsymbol{\alpha})$ for $t \geqslant 0$, is stable if, given $\varepsilon(> 0)$, there exists a positive number κ such that $d(\boldsymbol{\varphi}(t;\ \boldsymbol{\alpha} + \boldsymbol{\delta}), C) < \varepsilon$ for all positive values of t if $|\boldsymbol{\delta}| < \kappa$.

Both motion in a uniform field and the libration motion are stable in this sense. For the uniform field we define t' (if $t > |\delta_2|/c$) by the formula

$$t' = t + \delta_2/c. \tag{23.8.2}$$

Then (cf. (23.7.38))

$$x(t;\ \boldsymbol{\alpha} + \boldsymbol{\delta}) - x(t';\ \boldsymbol{\alpha}) = \delta_1 - \frac{1}{c}\,\delta_2(u + \tfrac{1}{2}\delta_2),\quad y(t;\ \boldsymbol{\alpha} + \boldsymbol{\delta}) - y(t';\ \boldsymbol{\alpha}) = 0, \tag{23.8.3}$$

and the orbital stability is evident. For the libration motion a formal proof is not difficult, but a straightforward geometrical argument is even simpler. In the original libration motion the trajectory in the (x, y)-plane (where $y = \dot{x}$) is a simple closed oval curve symmetrical about Ox (of the type shown in Fig. 19.2*b*); the path in the disturbed motion is a simple closed oval curve nearly coincident with the former, and the orbital stability is evident.

Another example is given by the circular orbit under a Newtonian attraction; it is easy to see that the trajectory (in the phase space) is unstable in the sense of Liapounov, but stable in the sense of orbital stability.

As another simple illustration, consider the system

$$\dot{x} = -yr, \quad \dot{y} = xr, \tag{23.8.4}$$

where $r = \sqrt{(x^2 + y^2)}$. The solution through the initial point $(a \cos \beta,\ a \sin \beta)$ is

$$x = a \cos (at + \beta), \quad y = a \sin (at + \beta), \tag{23.8.5}$$

and the motion is uniform motion in a circle, a periodic orbit with period $2\pi/a$. The *equilibrium* at 0 is stable. The circular trajectories are unstable in the sense of Liapounov, but stable in the sense of orbital stability.

We can extend the notion of orbital stability to embrace the analogue of complete or asymptotic stability: The trajectory C has complete orbital stability if $d(\boldsymbol{\varphi}(t;\ \boldsymbol{\alpha} + \boldsymbol{\delta}), C) \to 0$ as $t \to \infty$ whenever $|\boldsymbol{\delta}| < \kappa$. For example, in the theory of the limit cycles (Chapter XX) we found that the orbits in the neighbourhood of a stable limit cycle were spirals approaching the limit cycle; a stable limit cycle has complete orbital stability. A concrete illustration is provided by *Example* 23.7*B*, which has complete orbital stability as well as Liapounov (but not *complete* Liapounov) stability.*

There are many other definitions of stability of motion. For example, we can frame a definition analogous to the definition of orbital stability, but concerned with the path in the q-space instead of the phase space. According to this definition the motion is stable if the orbit in the q-space that results from slightly varied initial conditions lies near the undisturbed orbit. A conspicuous example of orbital stability of this type occurs in § 17.5(i); the undisturbed motion is motion on the closed curve $x = a$, and $\varphi(a) < 0$. Even looser notions of stability have already been mentioned in § 17.5 and in § 22.7.

23.9 Stability of a periodic orbit. We have seen (§ 23.5) that, for variation from a periodic orbit, one characteristic exponent is zero. We now prove that *if all*

* The consideration of this sort of example leads us to expect that, in general, complete orbital stability is likely to imply Liapounov stability. The plausible argument in support of this conclusion is that the rate of increase of the time-lag $|t' - t|$ is roughly proportional to $|\boldsymbol{\varphi}(t;\ \boldsymbol{\alpha} + \boldsymbol{\delta}) - \boldsymbol{\varphi}(t';\ \boldsymbol{\alpha})|$, which is exponentially decreasing.

the other characteristic exponents have negative real parts, then the periodic orbit has complete orbital stability.

We take a point O on the periodic orbit as origin, and the x_m-axis in the direction of the tangent to the orbit at O. Then $X_m > 0$ at, and in the neighbourhood of, O. We consider the trajectory originating at $t = 0$ in a point P near O. The trajectory will intersect the plane $x_m = 0$, in the direction from $x_m < 0$ to $x_m > 0$, since $X_m > 0$ near O. Let this point of intersection be $(\alpha_1, \alpha_2, \ldots, \alpha_{m-1}, 0)$, and let the time of the intersection be θ (which may be positive or negative). We denote the $(m - 1)$-dimensional vector $\{\alpha_1, \alpha_2, \ldots, \alpha_{m-1}\}$ by $\boldsymbol{\alpha}$, and in the problem under discussion $|\boldsymbol{\alpha}|$ and $|\theta|$ are small. Let the characteristic cut the plane $x_m = 0$ again, in the direction from $x_m < 0$ to $x_m > 0$, in the point $\boldsymbol{\alpha}'$ at time $\sigma + \theta'$, where σ is the period of the periodic motion, and $|\boldsymbol{\alpha}'|$, $|\theta'|$ are small. The characteristic crosses the plane $x_m = 0$ many times, but the crossing at $\boldsymbol{\alpha}'$ (after a time nearly equal to σ) is defined precisely by continuity. The case $m = 2$ is illustrated in Fig. 23.9.

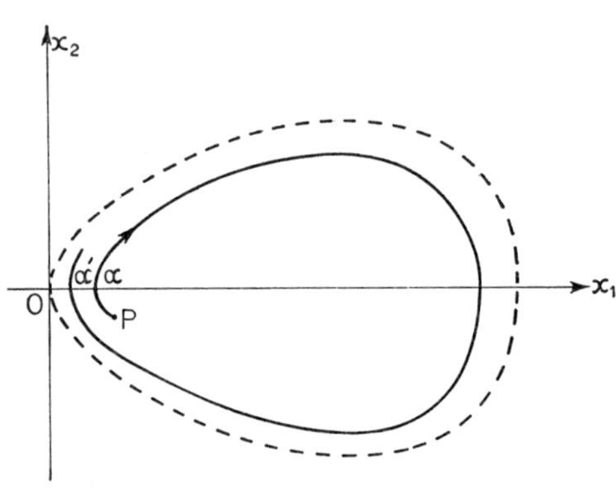

Figure 23.9

Now $\boldsymbol{\alpha}'$ is determined completely by $\boldsymbol{\alpha}$, $\boldsymbol{\alpha}' = U\boldsymbol{\alpha}$, and the operator U has $\boldsymbol{\alpha} = \mathbf{0}$ as a fixed point. The matrix $\mathbf{A}$ for the linear approximation to U (with $m - 1$ rows and $m - 1$ columns) is

$$\mathbf{A} = (\partial\alpha_r'/\partial\alpha_s)_0. \tag{23.9.1}$$

Moreover, $\theta' - \theta$ depends only on $\boldsymbol{\alpha}$,

$$\begin{aligned}\theta' &= \theta + \psi(\alpha_1, \alpha_2, \ldots, \alpha_{m-1}) \\ &= \theta + \psi(\boldsymbol{\alpha}).\end{aligned} \tag{23.9.2}$$

The function ψ vanishes when $\boldsymbol{\alpha} = \mathbf{0}$ and has continuous first derivatives, so there is a constant K such that $|\psi(\boldsymbol{\alpha})| < K|\boldsymbol{\alpha}|$ when $|\boldsymbol{\alpha}|$ is sufficiently small.

Now let the characteristic originating in P be defined by the m parameters $\alpha_1, \alpha_2, \ldots, \alpha_{m-1}, \theta$. If T is the operator defining the transformation from $(\boldsymbol{\alpha}, \theta)$ to $(\boldsymbol{\alpha}', \theta')$ the matrix for the linear approximation to T is

$$\begin{bmatrix} \dfrac{\partial\alpha_1'}{\partial\alpha_1} & \dfrac{\partial\alpha_1'}{\partial\alpha_2} & \cdots & \dfrac{\partial\alpha_1'}{\partial\alpha_{m-1}} & 0 \\ \dfrac{\partial\alpha_2'}{\partial\alpha_1} & \dfrac{\partial\alpha_2'}{\partial\alpha_2} & \cdots & \dfrac{\partial\alpha_2'}{\partial\alpha_{m-1}} & 0 \\ \cdots & \cdots & \cdots & \cdots & \cdots \\ \dfrac{\partial\alpha'_{m-1}}{\partial\alpha_1} & \dfrac{\partial\alpha'_{m-1}}{\partial\alpha_2} & \cdots & \dfrac{\partial\alpha'_{m-1}}{\partial\alpha_{m-1}} & 0 \\ \dfrac{\partial\theta'}{\partial\alpha_1} & \dfrac{\partial\theta'}{\partial\alpha_2} & \cdots & \dfrac{\partial\theta'}{\partial\alpha_{m-1}} & 1 \end{bmatrix} \tag{23.9.3}$$

and its characteristic polynomial is $(\mu - 1)P(\mu)$, where $P(\mu)$ is the characteristic polynomial (of degree $m - 1$) for $\mathbf{A}$. Let the zeros of $P(\mu)$ be $\mu_1, \mu_2, \ldots, \mu_{m-1}$. Then the characteristic exponents for the periodic orbit are $0, \lambda_1, \lambda_2, \ldots, \lambda_{m-1}$, where $e^{\lambda_r} = \mu_r$

(§ 2.15), and since the real part of each λ_r is negative, $|\mu_r| < 1$ for $r = 1, 2, \ldots, (m-1)$. Hence the transformation U is completely stable, and $|U^n\boldsymbol{\alpha}| \to 0$ as $n \to \infty$.

It follows that the periodic orbit has complete orbital stability. It is true that the argument so far is concerned only with a discrete set of points on the varied orbit, but the general result follows since the characteristic (for any finite range of values of t) varies continuously with the initial point.

Let the time of the nth crossing of $x_m = 0$ be $n\sigma + \theta^{(n)}$. We now prove that $\theta^{(n)}$ is bounded; the difference $|t' - t|$ (in the definition of orbital stability) does not increase indefinitely. We have, for positive integral values of r,

$$\theta^{(r)} = \theta^{(r-1)} + \psi(T^{r-1}\boldsymbol{\alpha}), \tag{23.9.4}$$

where $\theta^{(0)} = \theta$, and therefore

$$\theta^{(n)} = \theta + \sum_{r=0}^{n-1} \psi(T^r\boldsymbol{\alpha}). \tag{23.9.5}$$

Now

$$|\psi(T^r\alpha)| < K|T^r\boldsymbol{\alpha}|, \tag{23.9.6}$$

and

$$|T^r\boldsymbol{\alpha}| < ck^r, \qquad c > 0,\ 0 < k < 1, \tag{23.9.7}$$

for all r, provided $|\boldsymbol{\alpha}|$ is sufficiently small; the inequality (23.9.7) follows from the Corollary to the Poincaré-Liapounov theorem (§ 21.15). Thus

$$\begin{aligned} |\theta^{(n)}| &\leqslant |\theta| + Kc\sum_{r=0}^{n-1} k^r \\ &< |\theta| + Kc\sum_{r=0}^{\infty} k^r \\ &= |\theta| + Kc/(1-k), \end{aligned} \tag{23.9.8}$$

and this completes the proof that $\theta^{(n)}$ is bounded.

23.10 Forced oscillations. We have already considered (§ 9.10) the forced oscillations of the damped harmonic oscillator. In that problem the equation of motion is linear. When we leave the simple case of the linear equation, and consider the forced oscillations of a system for which the equation of motion is not linear, the difficulties are formidable, and we cannot usually make much progress without resorting to approximations that are not always easy to justify. As an example of the procedure, let us consider the motion of a simple pendulum (*Example* 5.2*A*) when there is an additional small *horizontal* force $ma\varepsilon \sin pt$, where ε is small. The equation of motion is

$$ma\ddot{\theta} = -mg \sin\theta + ma\varepsilon \sin pt \cos\theta, \tag{23.10.1}$$

giving

$$\ddot{\theta} + n^2 \sin\theta = \varepsilon \cos\theta \sin pt, \qquad n^2 = g/a. \tag{23.10.2}$$

We recall that the period of a free oscillation, when the amplitude α is small, is a little greater than $2\pi/n$; and that as the amplitude α increases from zero to π, the period σ increases steadily from $2\pi/n$ to ∞. Explicitly, $\sigma = 4K/n$, where $k = \sin\frac{1}{2}\alpha$.

We consider separately the non-resonant case, when $|n^2 - p^2|$ is not small, and the case of resonance, when p is nearly equal to n.

(i) We take first the non-resonant case. The complementary function of the differential equation (23.10.2) represents the free oscillations. But these are not of interest in this context; in practice there is always some small amount of friction, and the free oscillations are damped out. A particular integral which approximates to a periodic function of period $2\pi/p$ represents a forced oscillation. There is always a forced oscillation of small amplitude; and, if $p < n$, there are also two forced oscillations of finite amplitude.

To investigate a forced oscillation of small amplitude we use the linear approximation to (23.10.2)

(23.10.3) $$\ddot{\theta} + n^2\theta = \varepsilon \sin pt,$$

and the solution

(23.10.4) $$\theta = \frac{\varepsilon}{n^2 - p^2} \sin pt$$

gives an approximation to a forced oscillation of small amplitude.

Next, if $p < n$, there is a free oscillation of finite amplitude α with the period $2\pi/p$. (As a concrete illustration, suppose that p is such that the amplitude of the free oscillation of period $2\pi/p$ is 60°. Then $k = \sin \frac{1}{2}\alpha = \frac{1}{2}$, $K = 1{\cdot}6858$, and $\frac{p}{n} = \frac{\pi}{2K} = \frac{3{\cdot}1416}{3{\cdot}3716}$, which is roughly $\frac{27}{29}$.) The existence of the free oscillation of period $2\pi/p$ suggests the possibility of a forced oscillation of approximately the same amplitude. Let the free oscillation be expressed in the form

$$\theta = \varphi(t),$$

where $\varphi(t)$ is an odd function with period $2\pi/p$ and amplitude α; the explicit formula for $\varphi(t)$ is found from (5.2.9). Let us seek a solution of (23.10.2) of the form $\varphi(t) + y$, where y is small of order ε. Substituting in (23.10.2) we obtain the approximation, correct to the first order in ε,

(23.10.5) $$\ddot{y} + n^2 y \cos \varphi(t) = \varepsilon \cos \varphi(t) \sin pt.$$

If y satisfies this equation, $\varphi(t) + y$ and $-\varphi(t) + y$ are approximate solutions of (23.10.2).

The complementary function of (23.10.5) can be written in the form $Au(t) + Bv(t)$, where $u(= \dot{\varphi}(t))$ is an even function and v is an odd function; moreover, $u\dot{v} - v\dot{u}$ is constant, and we can choose the function v so that $u\dot{v} - v\dot{u}$ has the value 1. The complete solution of (23.10.5) is then

(23.10.6) $$y = Au(t) + Bv(t) - \varepsilon \int_0^t \{u(t)v(\xi) - v(t)u(\xi)\} \cos \varphi(\xi) \sin p\xi \, d\xi.$$

If we put $A = 0$ the second member of (23.10.6) is an odd function of t, and (since $v(\pi/p) \neq 0$) we can choose B to make y vanish at π/p (and therefore also at $-\pi/p$). Then

$$y(\pi/p) = y(-\pi/p), \quad \dot{y}(\pi/p) = \dot{y}(-\pi/p),$$

and therefore the solution is periodic with period $2\pi/p$. The solutions $\pm\varphi(t) + y$ represent two forced oscillations of amplitude α, and these are approximations (correct to order ε) to solutions of (23.10.2).

Thus if $n^2 - p^2$ is positive and not too small, there are three forced oscillations, one of small amplitude, and two with amplitude near α.

In the equation (23.10.2) there is no frictional term, though we have tacitly assumed that the free oscillation is damped out. It is important to notice that the forced oscillations with amplitude near α persist when there are small damping forces. If we include a small linear damping term, the equation (23.10.2) is replaced by

$$\ddot{\theta} + b\varepsilon\dot{\theta} + n^2 \sin\theta = \varepsilon \cos\theta \sin pt, \tag{23.10.7}$$

where the positive multiplier b is not too large. Now the function $\varphi(t - t_0)$ has period $2\pi/p$, and satisfies the equation $\ddot{\varphi} + n^2 \sin\varphi = 0$. In order that there shall be a periodic solution near $\varphi(t - t_0)$ of equation (23.10.7) we need

$$0 = [\tfrac{1}{2}\dot{\theta}^2 - n^2\cos\theta]_0^{2\pi/p} = \varepsilon\int_0^{2\pi/p}(\dot{\theta}\cos\theta\sin pt - b\dot{\theta}^2)\,dt.$$

Therefore, approximately,

$$b\int_0^{2\pi/p}\dot{\varphi}^2(t)\,dt = \int_0^{2\pi/p}\dot{\varphi}(t)\cos\varphi(t)\sin p(t + t_0)\,dt. \tag{23.10.8}$$

Provided that the integral on the right does not vanish identically, this equation gives just two values of t_0 for any value of b below a certain level; and these correspond to the two forced oscillations with amplitude near α already found.

(ii) We now turn to the case of resonance, where $n^2 - p^2$ is small. If we write the equation (23.10.2) in the form

$$\ddot{\theta} + p^2\theta = n^2(\theta - \sin\theta) - (n^2 - p^2)\,\theta + \varepsilon\cos\theta\sin pt, \tag{23.10.9}$$

we see that the non-linear perturbation $n^2(\theta - \sin\theta)$ is of the same order of magnitude as the larger of $(n^2 - p^2)\theta$ and $\varepsilon \sin pt$. Let us consider the case in which all three terms are of the same order, and then $\theta = O(\varepsilon^{1/3})$ and $n^2 - p^2 = O(\varepsilon^{2/3})$; if we write η for $\varepsilon^{2/3}$ we have $\theta = O(\eta^{1/2})$ and $n^2 - p^2 = O(\eta)$. We put $n^2 = p^2(1 + k\eta)$, and substituting $\theta = z\eta^{1/2}$ and $\varepsilon = \eta^{3/2}$ in (23.10.2), we find, retaining only terms of the first order in η,

$$\ddot{z} + p^2 z = p^2\eta\left(\tfrac{1}{6}z^3 - kz + \frac{1}{p^2}\sin pt\right). \tag{23.10.10}$$

In this equation η is small, but k is not necessarily small.

If $\eta = 0$, (23.10.10) has the solution $z = a\sin(pt - \varphi)$, where a and φ are arbitrary constants. If $\eta \neq 0$ we seek a solution of the form

$$z = a\sin(pt - \varphi) + \eta z_1 + \eta^2 z_2 + \cdots, \tag{23.10.11}$$

where a and φ are now permitted to vary. We determine these variations, first to order η, then to order η^2, and so on; and at the same time we calculate the additive terms z_1 (when working to order η), z_2 (to order η^2), and so on. The presence of the terms $\eta z_1 + \eta^2 z_2 + \cdots$ reflects the non-linearity on the left in (23.10.2), and the solution for the unperturbed equation $\ddot{\theta} + n^2\sin\theta = 0$ can be written in the same form (23.10.11) with a and φ constant. The slow variations of a and φ arise from the forcing term on the right in (23.10.2).

If we substitute the formula (23.10.11) for z in the equation (23.10.10) we find correct to the first order in η,

$$(2p\dot{a} - 2\dot{a}\dot{\varphi} - a\ddot{\varphi})C + (2pa\dot{\varphi} + \ddot{a} - a\dot{\varphi}^2)S + \eta(\ddot{z}_1 + p^2 z_1)$$
$$= p^2\eta\left\{\left(\frac{1}{p^2}\sin\varphi\right)C + \left(\tfrac{1}{8}a^3 - ka + \frac{1}{p^2}\cos\varphi\right)S - \tfrac{1}{24}a^3\sin 3(pt - \varphi)\right\}, \tag{23.10.12}$$

where C is written for $\cos(pt - \varphi)$ and S for $\sin(pt - \varphi)$. The equation is satisfied if

$$2p\dot{a} - 2\dot{a}\dot{\varphi} - a\ddot{\varphi} = \eta \sin \varphi, \tag{23.10.13}$$

$$2pa\dot{\varphi} + \ddot{a} - a\dot{\varphi}^2 = p^2\eta\left(\tfrac{1}{8}a^3 - ka + \frac{1}{p^2}\cos\varphi\right), \tag{23.10.14}$$

and

$$\ddot{z}_1 + p^2 z_1 = -\tfrac{1}{24}p^2a^3 \sin 3(pt - \varphi). \tag{23.10.15}$$

The equations (23.10.13) and (23.10.14), controlling the variation of a and of φ, are called *variational* equations. We shall find that these define slow variations of long period. The equation (23.10.15) is called a *perturbational* equation, and it determines variations of short period. For example, if a and φ were constant, (23.10.15) would have the solution

$$z_1 = \tfrac{1}{192}\, a^3 \sin 3(pt - \varphi). \tag{23.10.16}$$

Now $\dot{a}$ and $\dot{\varphi}$ are of order η, so, correct to order η, (23.10.13–14) can be replaced by the simpler equations

$$\dot{a} = \frac{\eta}{2p}\sin\varphi, \tag{23.10.17}$$

$$\dot{\varphi} = \frac{p\eta}{2a}\left(\tfrac{1}{8}a^3 - ka + \frac{1}{p^2}\cos\varphi\right). \tag{23.10.18}$$

These are the equations defining the slow variation of a and φ.

The equations (23.10.17–18) are of the familiar form (19.3.1), and it is convenient to picture the variation of a and φ in terms of the motion of a mobile in an auxiliary diagram, (a, φ) being the polar coordinates of the mobile at time t. The singular points in the field are given by $\varphi = 0$ and

$$\tfrac{1}{8}a^3 - ka + \frac{1}{p^2} = 0, \tag{23.10.19}$$

and there are one or three singular points according as the cubic equation (23.10.19) has one or three real roots. (The equations

$$\varphi = \pi, \quad \tfrac{1}{8}a^3 - ka - \frac{1}{p^2} = 0,$$

merely define the same points again.) The singular points correspond to solutions of (23.10.16–17) in which a and φ are constants. These are the so-called *stationary oscillations* in which the leading term in (23.10.11) is a purely sinusoidal oscillation $z = a\sin(pt - \varphi)$, with a and φ constant, a being a real root of (23.10.19).

The value of a as a function of k is shown in Fig. 23.10a. If we neglect the a^3 term in (23.10.19) we get $a = 1/(kp^2)$, which is equivalent to the elementary small-amplitude solution (23.10.4). There is a critical value k_0 of k, and the equation (23.10.19) has one or three real roots according as $k < k_0$ or $k > k_0$. There is one stationary oscillation if $k < k_0$, and there are three stationary oscillations if $k > k_0$ The explicit value of k_0 is $3/(2^{5/3}p^{4/3})$.

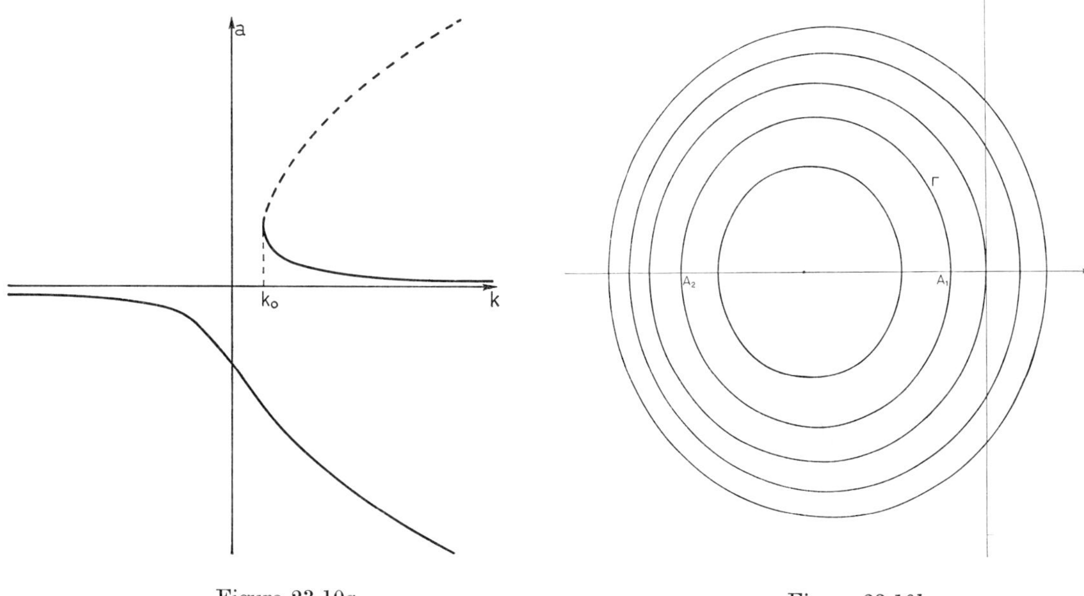

Figure 23.10a Figure 23.10b

Let us now turn from the stationary oscillations to the general case in which the amplitude a and the phase φ vary slowly in accordance with the equations (23.10.17-18). These equations have the first integral

$$\frac{1}{32}a^4 - \frac{1}{2}ka^2 + \frac{a}{p^2}\cos\varphi = c, \tag{23.10.20}$$

and the curves represented by (23.10.20) are the paths of the mobile in the auxiliary diagram. These curves are shown in Fig. 23.10b and Fig. 23.10c; the first of these refers to the case in which (23.10.19) has one real root, and the second to the case in which it has three real roots. The rate of travel of the mobile on the particular trajectory is defined by the equations (23.10.17–18).

The singular points in these figures represent the stationary oscillations; the curves in the neighbourhood of a singular point exhibit the variation of the parameters that results when a stationary oscillation is slightly disturbed. We can therefore appeal to the theory of Chapter XIX to determine the stability or instability (in the sense of § 23.8) of the stationary oscillations. In Fig. 23.10b there is one singular point, and it is a centre, so the corresponding stationary oscillation is stable. In Fig. 23.10c there are three singular points. Two of these are centres, and the corresponding stationary oscillations are stable; one is a saddle point, and the corresponding stationary oscillation is unstable. In Fig. 23.10a, exhibiting the amplitudes of the stationary oscillations, the part of the curve drawn with a firm line indicates that the corresponding stationary oscillations are stable; and the part of the curve drawn with a broken line indicates that the corresponding stationary oscillations are unstable.

Let us consider the variation of a and φ in the neighbourhood of a stable stationary oscillation, say, to fix the ideas, the variation defined by the curve Γ in Fig. 23.10b. The curve is a closed curve, and the variation is periodic. These long-period periodic

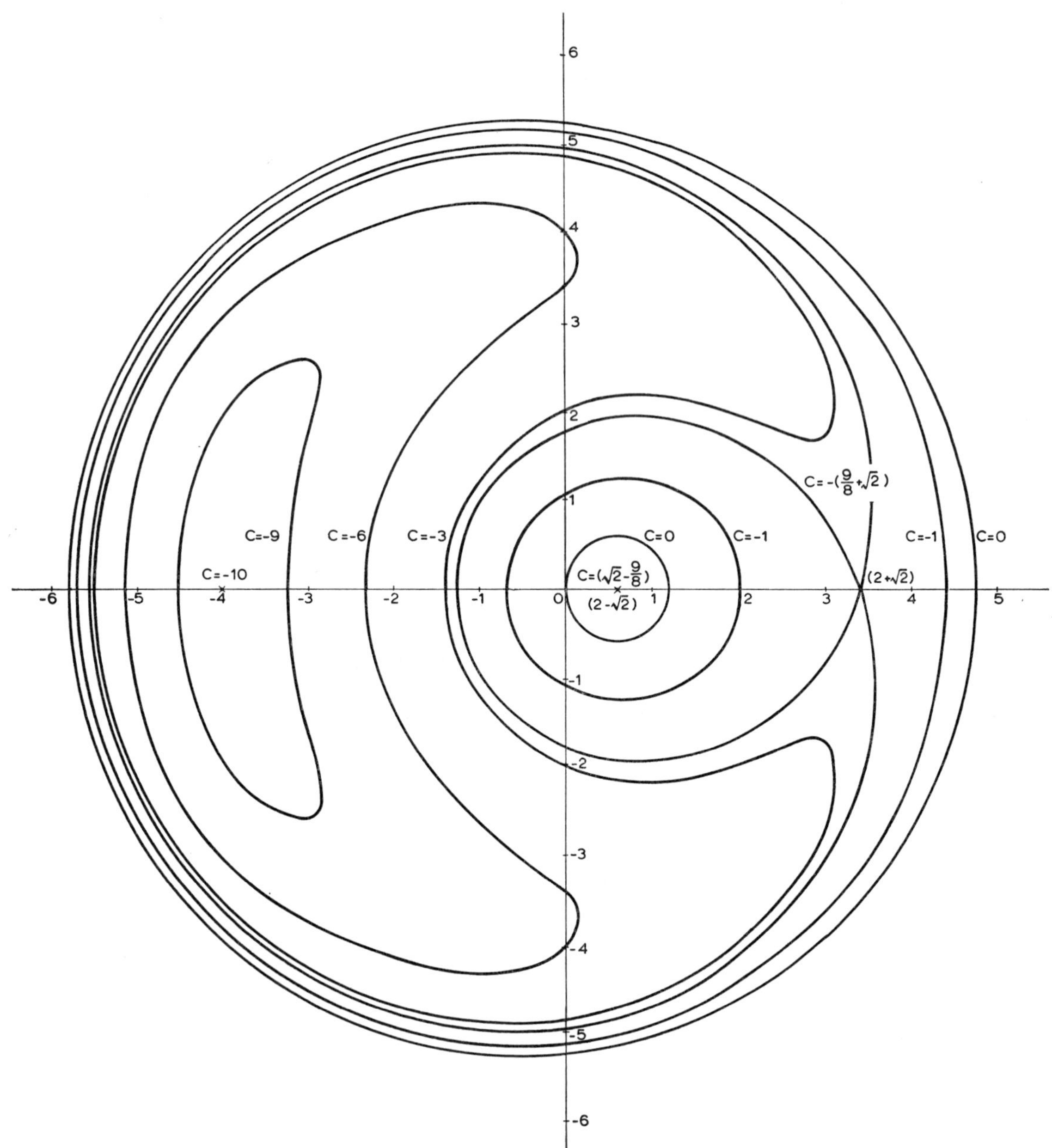

Figure 23.10*c*

variations in the parameters a and φ are called *beats*. Thus, working to the first order in η, the pendulum motion is a periodic motion $z = a \sin (pt - \varphi)$ of period $2\pi/p$, with amplitude a and phase φ slowly varying with a long period $\sum$, and an additive term approximately periodic with short period $2\pi/3p$.

To find the period $\sum$ we have, substituting for φ from (23.10.20) in (23.10.17),

$$\dot{s} = \frac{\eta}{p} f(s) \tag{23.10.21}$$

where s is written for a^2, and

$$[f(s)]^2 = s - p^4(c + \tfrac{1}{2}ks - \tfrac{1}{32}s^2)^2. \tag{23.10.22}$$

The period Σ is therefore given by the elliptic integral

$$\Sigma = \frac{2p}{\eta}\int_{a_1^2}^{a_2^2} \frac{ds}{f(s)}, \tag{23.10.23}$$

where a_1 and a_2 are the minimum and maximum values of a (attained respectively at A_1 and A_2).

If now (by a suitable choice of the time-scale) we give to p the value 1, the roots of the equation (23.10.19), giving the values of x at the singular points, can be written in the form

$$-2\alpha, \quad \alpha - \beta, \quad \alpha + \beta,$$

where $\beta = \sqrt{\left(\alpha^2 - \frac{4}{\alpha}\right)}$; the corresponding value of k is $\frac{1}{2}\left(\alpha^2 - \frac{1}{\alpha}\right)$. Fig. 23.10*b* is drawn for the case $\alpha = \frac{1}{2}$; the value of k is $-7/8$, and there is one singular point, $(-1, 0)$. Fig. 23.10*c* is drawn for the case $\alpha = 2$; the value of k is $7/4$, and there are three singular points, $(-4, 0)$, $(2 - \sqrt{2}, 0)$, $(2 + \sqrt{2}, 0)$.

In these calculations no account has been taken of friction; the introduction of damping may result in replacing a centre by a stable or an unstable focus.

The analysis can be continued to include terms of order $\eta^2, \eta^3, \ldots$, but, for the higher powers, the calculations become rather laborious.

Chapter XXIV

Contact transformations

24.1 Contact transformations. The motion of a dynamical system defines a continuous group of transformations in the phase space (§ 21.3). The transformations carry the point

$$q_{10}, q_{20}, \ldots, q_{n0}, p_{10}, p_{20}, \ldots, p_{n0},$$

occupied by the representative point at $t = 0$ into the point

$$q_1, q_2, \ldots, q_n, p_1, p_2, \ldots, p_n,$$

occupied by the representative point at time t. The equations defining the transformation are the solutions of Hamilton's equations, and they are of the form

$$q_r = \varphi_r(q_{10}, q_{20}, \ldots, q_{n0}; p_{10}, p_{20}, \ldots, p_{n0}; t), \qquad r = 1, 2, \ldots, n, \tag{24.1.1}$$

$$p_r = \varphi_{n+r}(q_{10}, q_{20}, \ldots, q_{n0}; p_{10}, p_{20}, \ldots, p_{n0}; t), \qquad r = 1, 2, \ldots, n, \tag{24.1.2}$$

and we shall assume that the functions φ are of class C_2 when $(q_{10}, q_{20}, \ldots, q_{n0}, p_{10}, p_{20}, \ldots, p_{n0})$ lies in a certain domain D, and t lies in an interval I (which in many cases is the infinite interval $-\infty < t < \infty$). We shall often write, for the sake of brevity,

$$q_r = \varphi_r(q_0; p_0; t), \quad p_r = \varphi_{n+r}(q_0; p_0; t).$$

We must bear in mind throughout that we are dealing with a $2n$-fold of a special kind, involving n associated pairs of variables $(q_1, p_1), (q_2, p_2), \ldots, (q_n, p_n)$. We recall that the transformations are measure-preserving,

$$\frac{\partial(q_r; p_r)}{\partial(q_{r0}; p_{r0})} = 1. \tag{24.1.3}$$

Also, since the first member of (24.1.3) does not vanish, we can solve the equations (24.1.1–2) for the q_{r0}'s and p_{r0}'s, giving the inverse transformation

$$q_{r0} = \psi_r(q; p; t), \qquad r = 1, 2, \ldots, n, \tag{24.1.4}$$

$$p_{r0} = \psi_{n+r}(q; p; t), \qquad r = 1, 2, \ldots, n. \tag{24.1.5}$$

The equations (24.1.1–2) define an operator T_t (§ 21.3), and the equations (24.1.4–5) define the inverse operator $(T_t)^{-1}$. In the autonomous case (when H does not contain t) the inverse operator is T_{-t}, and

$$\psi_s(q; p; t) = \varphi_s(q; p; -t), \qquad s = 1, 2, \ldots, 2n. \tag{24.1.6}$$

The relations can be expressed in other forms that we shall sometimes need. For example, we can in general solve the equations (24.1.4) for the p's in terms of q's q_0's and t,

$$p_r = \chi_r(q; q_0; t), \qquad r = 1, 2, \ldots, n. \tag{24.1.7}$$

The condition for this to be possible is that the Jacobian

$$\frac{\partial(\psi_1, \psi_2, \ldots, \psi_n)}{\partial(p_1, p_2, \ldots, p_n)}$$

should not vanish identically. That the solution is possible in general is evident from the fact that in general the motion is determined by the terminal points in the q-space and the time (§ 15.6). We should obtain the same relations (24.1.4) and (24.1.7) by elimination of the p_0's from (24.1.1–2).

In a similar way, from the equations (24.1.5), we can in general express the p's in terms of q's, p_0's, and t.

We recall another fundamental property of the transformation (24.1.1–2). If S $(= S(q;\ q_0;\ t))$ is the principal function (§ 15.5) we have

$$p_r\, dq_r = p_{r0}\, dq_{r0} + H\, dt + dS, \tag{24.1.8}$$

where the repeated suffix r implies summation from 1 to n. In the present context it is natural to think of H (in the second member of (24.1.8)) as expressed in terms of $(q;\ q_0;\ t)$ by means of (24.1.7). The equation (24.1.8) shows that the transformation (24.1.1–2) has the property that, for a fixed value of t,

$$p_r\, dq_r - p_{r0}\, dq_{r0} \tag{24.1.9}$$

is a perfect differential of a uniform (single-valued) function of $(q;\ q_0;\ t)$; this property is characteristic of the transformation defined by Hamilton's equations. We shall call any transformation having this property a *contact transformation*. In the particular case where the form (24.1.9) vanishes identically, we speak of a *homogeneous contact transformation*. (Such a transformation has already appeared in § 15.8.) It is clear that contact transformations form a group, and that Poincaré's line-integral $\oint p_r\, dq_r$ is invariant for the group.

Thus, the motion of a dynamical system in the phase space defines a contact transformation; and this is the way in which the idea of a contact transformation first arises.

From (24.1.8) we readily deduce explicit formulae for the particular contact transformation defined by the motion of the given dynamical system. Comparing coefficients we find

$$\begin{cases} p_r = \dfrac{\partial S}{\partial q_r}, \\[2ex] p_{r0} = -\dfrac{\partial S}{\partial q_{r0}}, \\[2ex] H = -\dfrac{\partial S}{\partial t}. \end{cases} \tag{24.1.10}$$

We have met these formulae before, in § 15.8 and in § 16.1. In that context they provided the solution of the Hamiltonian problem; here they define the contact transformation. As we have seen, these are two aspects of the same thing.

The deduction of (24.1.10) from (24.1.8) is only valid if there exists no identical relation connecting q's and q_0's and t. That no such relation exists is clearly true, because if such a relation existed it would imply an identical relation connecting q_0's and p_0's and t, and this is impossible since these are independent variables. But we must be alive to the possibility that such identical relations may exist in other cases; examples of this phenomenon will appear shortly.

Conversely, if we start from an arbitrary function S $(= S(q;\ q_0;\ t))$ of class C_3, the equations

(24.1.11) $$p_r = \frac{\partial S}{\partial q_r}, \quad p_{r0} = -\frac{\partial S}{\partial q_{r0}},$$

in general define a contact transformation. (A condition that must be satisfied by S will be determined in the next section.)

We have already (in § 15.8) had occasion to introduce new parameters $(\alpha_1, \alpha_2, \ldots, \alpha_n;\ \beta_1, \beta_2, \ldots, \beta_n)$ which are functions of the q_0's and p_0's, and which are related to them by a homogeneous contact transformation, so that

(24.1.12) $$\beta_r\, d\alpha_r = p_{r0}\, dq_{r0}.$$

The numerical values of the α's and β's identify an orbit in the phase space as effectively as the values of the q_0's and p_0's. The transformation from $(\alpha;\ \beta)$ to $(q;\ p)$ is the product of two contact transformations, and is itself a contact transformation; indeed we have

(24.1.13) $$p_r\, dq_r = \beta_r\, d\alpha_r + H'\, dt + dS',$$

where, in the second member, the accent denotes expression in terms of q's and α's and t. Some comments on the two formulae $\partial S/\partial q_r$ and $\partial S'/\partial q_r$, each representing p_r, have already been made in § 15.8(iv).

24.2 Explicit formulae for a contact transformation. We consider the transformation from the variables

$$q_1, q_2, \ldots, q_n, p_1, p_2, \ldots, p_n,$$

to the variables

$$Q_1, Q_2, \ldots, Q_n, P_1, P_2, \ldots, P_n,$$

defined by the equations

(24.2.1) $$Q_r = \varphi_r(q_1, q_2, \ldots, q_n;\ p_1, p_2, \ldots, p_n;\ t), \qquad r = 1, 2, \ldots, n,$$

(24.2.2) $$P_r = \varphi_{n+r}(q_1, q_2, \ldots, q_n;\ p_1, p_2, \ldots, p_n;\ t), \qquad r = 1, 2, \ldots, n.$$

We shall frequently write these formulae in the compact form

$$Q_r = \varphi_r(q;\ p;\ t), \quad P_r = \varphi_{n+r}(q;\ p;\ t).$$

The functions φ are of class C_2 when $(q;\ p)$ lies in a domain D, and t lies in an interval I. For each t in I the equations represent a topological mapping of D onto a domain E_t of $(Q;\ P)$, and the transformation is reversible,

(24.2.3) $$q_r = \psi_r(Q;\ P;\ t),$$

(24.2.4) $$p_r = \psi_{n+r}(Q;\ P;\ t),$$

when $(Q;\ P)$ lies in E_t and t belongs to I. In the particular case considered in § 24.1 the functions φ, ψ were defined by the motion of a particular dynamical system, but no such restriction of these functions is presupposed here. Indeed in many cases of practical importance the functions φ and ψ occurring in (24.2.1–2) and (24.2.3–4) do not involve t. A simple example of a contact transformation of this type is given by the formulae (24.1.1–2) if the symbol t is replaced by a constant; and many other transformations of this type (i.e. transformations in which the equations of transformation do not involve t) will appear in the discussion of the problem of three bodies (Chapter XXIX).

Let us suppose now that the transformation defined by (24.2.1–2) is a contact transformation. If we take the Pfaffian form $P_r\,dQ_r$ and express it in terms of $(q;\ p;\ t)$ by means of the formulae (24.2.1–2) we have

$$P_r\,dQ_r = p_r\,dq_r + R\,dt - dW, \tag{24.2.5}$$

where R and W are functions of $(q;\ p;\ t)$. Now two cases arise:

(i) If the Jacobian

$$\frac{\partial(\varphi_1, \varphi_2, \ldots, \varphi_n)}{\partial(p_1, p_2, \ldots, p_n)} \tag{24.2.6}$$

does not vanish identically, we can solve the equations (24.2.1) for $p_1, p_2, \ldots, p_n$ in terms of $(q;\ Q;\ t)$, and we can then express R and W in terms of $(q;\ Q;\ t)$. There exists no identical relation connecting q's and Q's and t, and the contact transformation is defined by the equations

$$p_r = \frac{\partial W}{\partial q_r}, \qquad r = 1, 2, \ldots, n, \tag{24.2.7}$$

$$P_r = -\frac{\partial W}{\partial Q_r}, \qquad r = 1, 2, \ldots, n, \tag{24.2.8}$$

$$R = \frac{\partial W}{\partial t}, \tag{24.2.9}$$

where the symbols R and W now denote functions of $(q;\ Q;\ t)$, and $W \in C_3$ in the relevant domain of $(q;\ Q;\ t)$. The formulae (24.2.7–8) exhibit the contact transformation in terms of the *generating function* $W(q;\ Q;\ t)$.

Conversely, if we start from an arbitrary function $W(q;\ Q;\ t)$, the equations (24.2.7–8) define a contact transformation provided that the matrix

$$\left(\frac{\partial^2 W}{\partial q_r\,\partial Q_s}\right) \tag{24.2.10}$$

is non-singular. For in that case we can solve the equations (24.2.7) for the Q's in terms of $(q;\ p;\ t)$ to obtain equations of the form (24.2.1), and, since (24.2.7) is satisfied identically when we substitute these formulae for the Q's, we have

$$\frac{\partial^2 W}{\partial Q_s\,\partial q_r}\frac{\partial \varphi_s}{\partial p_m} = \delta_r^{\ m}. \tag{24.2.11}$$

Thus the matrix inverse to the non-singular matrix (24.2.10) is $(\partial\varphi_r/\partial p_s)$, and this matrix is itself non-singular. The Jacobian (24.2.6) does not vanish, and this ensures that the equations (24.2.7–8) define a contact transformation.

(ii) If the Jacobian (24.2.6) is identically zero, there exists at least one identical relation connecting q's and Q's and t. Let us suppose, in the first instance, that the matrix $(\partial\varphi_r/\partial p_s)$ has rank $(n - 1)$. Then there is one, and only one, identical relation connecting the q's and Q's and t, say

$$\Omega(q_1, q_2, \ldots, q_n;\ Q_1, Q_2, \ldots, Q_n;\ t) = 0. \tag{24.2.12}$$

In this case the expressions for R and W in terms of $(q;\ Q;\ t)$ are not unique, and, further, the equations (24.2.7–9) are no longer valid. They must be replaced by the equations

$$p_r = \frac{\partial W}{\partial q_r} + \lambda \frac{\partial \Omega}{\partial q_r}, \qquad r = 1, 2, \ldots, n, \tag{24.2.13}$$

$$P_r = -\frac{\partial W}{\partial Q_r} - \lambda \frac{\partial \Omega}{\partial Q_r}, \qquad r = 1, 2, \ldots, n, \tag{24.2.14}$$

$$R = \frac{\partial W}{\partial t} + \lambda \frac{\partial \Omega}{\partial t}, \tag{24.2.15}$$

where λ is an undetermined multiplier. Similarly if the matrix $(\partial\varphi_r/\partial p_s)$ has rank $(n - l)$, there are l identical relations connecting the q's and Q's and t, and then we need formulae involving l multipliers $\lambda_1, \lambda_2, \ldots, \lambda_l$.

24.3 Other formulae. In practice it is possible to avoid the slight awkwardness of the multipliers by a simple change in the attack. Consider again the case in which the Jacobian (24.2.6) is identically zero, so that there is at least one identical relation connecting the q's and Q's and t. But suppose that the Jacobian

$$\frac{\partial(\varphi_1, \varphi_2, \ldots, \varphi_n)}{\partial(q_1, q_2, \ldots, q_n)} \tag{24.3.1}$$

is not identically zero. In that case we can solve the equations (24.2.1) for the q's in terms of $(p;\ Q;\ t)$, and there is no identical relation connecting p's and Q's and t. If now we write (24.2.5) in the form

$$P_r\, dQ_r = -q_r\, dp_r + R\, dt - dU, \tag{24.3.2}$$

where $U = W - q_r p_r$, and if we express R and U in terms of $(p;\ Q;\ t)$, we have

$$q_r = -\frac{\partial U}{\partial p_r}, \qquad r = 1, 2, \ldots, n, \tag{24.3.3}$$

$$P_r = -\frac{\partial U}{\partial Q_r}, \qquad r = 1, 2, \ldots, n, \tag{24.3.4}$$

$$R = \frac{\partial U}{\partial t}. \tag{24.3.5}$$

The contact transformation is thus defined in terms of the generating function $U(p;\ Q;\ t)$.

We have thus found two ways of defining a contact transformation in terms of a generating function, and it is easy to obtain two more of similar type. Let us consider a contact transformation in which there is no identical relation between the small letters $x_1, x_2, \ldots, x_n$ and the large letters $X_1, X_2, \ldots, X_n$, where the x's are all q's or all p's, and the X's are all Q's or all P's, and let us, in the fundamental relation (24.2.1), take the x's and X's as the independent variables. Then it is easily verified that the two forms already found (24.2.7–8 and 24.3.3–4), and also the two not yet explicitly stated, are all comprehended in the formulae

(24.3.6) $$\pm y_r = \frac{\partial U}{\partial x_r}, \qquad r = 1, 2, \ldots, n,$$

(24.3.7) $$\pm Y_r = -\frac{\partial U}{\partial X_r}, \qquad r = 1, 2, \ldots, n,$$

(24.3.8) $$R = \frac{\partial U}{\partial t},$$

where U $(= U(x;\ X;\ t)) \in C_3$, the y's and Y's represent the sets of variables not occurring in U, and the ambiguous sign is fixed in each case by the mnemonic "plus precedes p (or P)." The formulae (24.3.6–7) define a contact transformation when U is a function of class C_3, arbitrary save for the restriction that the matrix $(\partial^2 U/\partial x_r \partial X_s)$ is non-singular (cf. § 24.2).

The cases that we use most frequently in practice are those in which the x's and X's are (i) p's and Q's, or (ii) q's and P's. For (i) the formulae defining the transformation are (24.3.3–4), which we can also write in the form

(24.3.9) $$q_r = \frac{\partial W}{\partial p_r}, \quad P_r = \frac{\partial W}{\partial Q_r},$$

with $R = -\partial W/\partial t$. (The only advantage of the form (24.3.3–4), with the minus signs on the right, is that it preserves the relation $R = +\partial U/\partial t$; and this of course is irrelevant if the transformation does not involve t.) For (ii) the formulae defining the transformation are

(24.3.10) $$p_r = \frac{\partial U}{\partial q_r}, \quad Q_r = \frac{\partial U}{\partial P_r},$$

and $R = \partial U/\partial t$.

For the development of the abstract theory it is usually immaterial which of the various formulae of transformation we use; and in fact the various forms are closely related to one another. For example, suppose we first make the contact transformation from $(q;\ p)$ to $(Q;\ P)$ derived from the generating function $U(q;\ Q;\ t)$ and defined by the formulae

(24.3.11) $$p_r = \frac{\partial U}{\partial q_r}, \quad P_r = -\frac{\partial U}{\partial Q_r}, \quad R = \frac{\partial U}{\partial t};$$

and suppose that we then make the contact transformation from $(Q;\ P)$ to $(Q';\ P')$ defined by the formulae

(24.3.12) $$Q_r = P_r', \quad P_r = -Q_r'.$$

Then the transformation from $(q;\ p)$ to $(Q';\ P')$ is defined in terms of the generating function $U(q;\ P';\ t)$ by the formulae

(24.3.13) $$p_r = \frac{\partial U}{\partial q_r}, \quad Q_r' = \frac{\partial U}{\partial P_r'}, \quad R = \frac{\partial U}{\partial t}.$$

This shows the simple relation that connects the first set of formulae established (24.2.7–9) (where the generating function contains q's and Q's) and the last set mentioned (24.3.10) (where the generating function contains q's and P's).

Another point that may be mentioned here concerns the Hamilton-Jacobi theorem. We saw (§ 16.2) that if $S(q; \alpha; t)$ is a complete integral of Hamilton's partial differential equation, then the solution of the Lagrange problem can be deduced from the n equations

$$\frac{\partial S}{\partial \alpha_r} = \text{constant}. \tag{24.3.14}$$

In (16.2.4) we wrote $-\beta_r$ for the constant on the right in (24.3.14). This implies that the transformation from $(q_0; p_0)$ to $(\alpha; \beta)$ is a contact transformation; and it is natural to think of α_r as a Lagrangian coordinate and β_r as a momentum component. If on the contrary we write $+\beta_r$ for the constant on the right in (24.3.14) the transformation from $(q_0; p_0)$ to $(\beta; \alpha)$ is a contact transformation, so that β_r is thought of as a Lagrangian coordinate and α_r as a momentum component. This suggests that we should call the constant $+\beta_r$ if the significance of this constant is a coordinate rather than a momentum component. For example in planetary theory the constants on the right in (24.3.14) usually represent angles, so it is natural to regard the β's as coordinates rather than as momenta, and to write

$$\frac{\partial S}{\partial \alpha_r} = +\beta_r. \tag{24.3.15}$$

But we must remember that, when we use a contact transformation, the distinction between coordinates and momenta is no longer absolute; we see this very clearly, for example, in (24.3.12), where the "coordinate" Q_r and the "momentum component" P_r' both represent the same physical quantity.

In this book we shall take as the standard formula in the Hamilton-Jacobi theorem

$$\frac{\partial S}{\partial \alpha_r} = -\beta_r \tag{24.3.16}$$

as in (16.2.4).

24.4 Extended point transformations and other homogeneous contact transformations. Let us consider a point transformation

$$q_r = F_r(Q_1, Q_2, \ldots, Q_n), \qquad r = 1, 2, \ldots, n, \tag{24.4.1}$$

representing the change from one set of Lagrangian coordinates to another; the F's are n independent functions of $(Q_1, Q_2, \ldots, Q_n)$, each of class C_2. Let us consider a natural system, and denote the momenta in the two notations as usual by p's and P's. Then the transformation from $(q;\ p)$ to $(Q;\ P)$,which we speak of as an *extended point transformation*, is a homogeneous contact transformation. This follows from the fact that the inner product $p_r\dot{q}_r$, where $\dot{\mathbf{q}}$ is *any* velocity, not necessarily the velocity corresponding to the momentum $\mathbf{p}$, is invariant. (Strictly speaking, to conform to the usage of tensor theory, we ought to write $\dot{q}^r$ rather than $\dot{q}_r$, since the vector $\dot{\mathbf{q}}$ is covariant.) Thus $P_r\dot{Q}_r = p_r\dot{q}_r$, and

$$P_r\, dQ_r = p_r\, dq_r, \tag{24.4.2}$$

so the transformation is a homogeneous contact transformation.

We easily complete the explicit formulae for the transformation. If

$$2T = a_{rs}\dot{q}_r\dot{q}_s = A_{rs}\dot{Q}_r\dot{Q}_s, \tag{24.4.3}$$

we have

$$P_r = A_{rs}\dot{Q}_s = a_{ij}\frac{\partial F_i}{\partial Q_r}\frac{\partial F_j}{\partial Q_s}\dot{Q}_s = a_{ij}\frac{\partial F_i}{\partial Q_r}\dot{q}_j = p_i\frac{\partial F_i}{\partial Q_r}. \tag{24.4.4}$$

The relations (24.4.1) and (24.4.4) define the contact transformation. As we expect on physical grounds, the P's are homogeneous linear functions of the p's. The equations of transformation do not involve the time.

It is of course easy to reconcile the formulae just found with the more analytic approach of § 24.3. We have here a problem in which the q's and Q's are not independent, in fact there are precisely n independent relations connecting them, namely the relations (24.4.1). The rank of the matrix (24.2.6) is zero. But there is no identical relation connecting p's and Q's and t, for such a relation would imply a relation connecting the independent variables $(q_1, q_2, \ldots, q_n;\ p_1, p_2, \ldots, p_n;\ t)$. Thus we can express the transformation in the form (24.3.3–4); in fact if

(24.4.5) $$U = -p_r F_r$$

the formulae (24.3.3–4) become

(24.4.6) $$q_r = F_r, \quad P_r = p_i \frac{\partial F_i}{\partial Q_r},$$

agreeing with (24.4.1) and (24.4.4).

If instead we use q's and Q's in the generating function (which is clearly not a convenient usage here, though it may be of interest as an illustration) we have for an arbitrary fixed value of t,

(24.4.7) $$P_r\, dQ_r = p_r\, dq_r - \lambda_r(dq_r - dF_r),$$

whence

(24.4.8) $$\lambda_r = p_r, \quad P_r = \lambda_i \frac{\partial F_i}{\partial Q_r},$$

and the multipliers λ_r are identified with the momenta p_r.

The application of the theory to the case of extended point transformations which involve t, so that the functions F_r in (24.4.1) contain t, is immediate. We can still use the generating function (24.4.5) and the formulae (24.4.6) are unaltered in form, though they do now involve t.

The theory is easily adapted to the case in which the Q's are given explicitly as functions of the q's (and possibly also of t). The equations (24.4.1) are replaced by

(24.4.9) $$Q_r = f_r(q_1, q_2, \ldots, q_n;\ t),$$

and we need the generating function

(24.4.10) $$U = P_r f_r.$$

The equations of transformation (24.3.10) take the form

(24.4.11) $$p_r = P_i \frac{\partial f_i}{\partial q_r}, \quad Q_r = f_r.$$

In an extended point transformation not involving t, which is a special case of a homogeneous contact transformation, there are n identical relations connecting q's and Q's. In fact in any homogeneous contact transformation not involving t there is at least one identical relation connecting q's and Q's. To prove this we have only to observe that the equation

(24.4.12) $$P_r\, dQ_r = p_r\, dq_r$$

implies the n equations

(24.4.13) $$P_r \frac{\partial Q_r}{\partial p_s} = 0, \qquad s = 1, 2, \ldots, n.$$

It follows that the determinant

$$\left\| \frac{\partial Q_r}{\partial p_s} \right\| \tag{24.4.14}$$

vanishes identically, and this implies (§ 24.2) a relation connecting q's and Q's.

24.5 A special form of the equations of transformation, infinitesimal contact transformations. Let us consider a contact transformation in which there is no identical relation connecting q's and P's (and possibly t). In the general formulae of transformation (24.3.6–8) let us take

$$U = q_r P_r + M, \tag{24.5.1}$$

where $M = M(q;\ P;\ t)$, and we have

$$Q_r - q_r = \frac{\partial M}{\partial P_r}, \tag{24.5.2}$$

$$P_r - p_r = -\frac{\partial M}{\partial q_r}, \tag{24.5.3}$$

$$R = \frac{\partial M}{\partial t}. \tag{24.5.4}$$

(There is also a similar form in which the variables in the generating function are p's and Q's and t.)

The particular interest of the formulae (24.5.2–3) lies in their resemblance to the Hamiltonian equations of motion. The contact transformation that we first considered was that defined by the motion of a dynamical system. We now see that the general contact transformation can be defined by equations of somewhat similar form.

The similarity is even closer if the terms on the right in (24.5.2–4) are small, say $M = \mu\varphi$, where μ is a small constant. If we are content with an approximation in which μ^2 is neglected, we need not distinguish between small and large letters in terms multiplied by μ, and the equations become

$$Q_r - q_r = \mu\frac{\partial \varphi}{\partial p_r}, \tag{24.5.5}$$

$$P_r - p_r = -\mu\frac{\partial \varphi}{\partial q_r}, \tag{24.5.6}$$

$$R = \mu\frac{\partial \varphi}{\partial t}, \tag{24.5.7}$$

where $\varphi = \varphi(q;\ p;\ t)$. The transformation defined by the equations (24.5.5–7) is called an *infinitesimal contact transformation*. It can be interpreted as the change in position in the phase space that takes place in the small time-interval from t to $t + \mu$ for a dynamical system whose Hamiltonian function is φ.

24.6 The extension of Liouville's theorem. The measure-preserving property of the transformation defined by Hamilton's equations (which, as we have seen, define a contact transformation) holds also for the general contact transformation. We have to prove that the Jacobian

$$\frac{\partial(Q_1, Q_2, \ldots, Q_n, P_1, P_2, \ldots, P_n)}{\partial(q_1, q_2, \ldots, q_n, p_1, p_2, \ldots, p_n)} \tag{24.6.1}$$

has the value $+1$. Let us take for definiteness the case in which there exists no identical relation connecting q's and Q's. The transformation is defined by the equations (24.2.7–8), in which the independent variables are the q's and Q's. Writing $\dfrac{\partial(Q;\ P)}{\partial(q;\ p)}$ for the Jacobian (24.6.1) we have

$$\frac{\partial(Q;\ P)}{\partial(q;\ p)} = \frac{\partial(Q;\ P)}{\partial(q;\ Q)}\bigg/\frac{\partial(q;\ p)}{\partial(q;\ Q)} = (-)^n \frac{\partial(P)}{\partial(q)}\bigg/\frac{\partial(p)}{\partial(Q)} \tag{24.6.2}$$

$$= \frac{\partial\left(\dfrac{\partial W}{\partial Q}\right)}{\partial(q)}\Bigg/\frac{\partial\left(\dfrac{\partial W}{\partial q}\right)}{\partial(Q)} = 1,$$

where $\dfrac{\partial(P)}{\partial(q)}$, for example, means $\dfrac{\partial(P_1, P_2, \ldots, P_n)}{\partial(q_1, q_2, \ldots, q_n)}$, and the theorem is proved. A similar proof establishes the result in the other cases.

24.7 The conditions for a contact transformation expressed in terms of Lagrange brackets. If each of the variables $q_1, q_2, \ldots, q_n, p_1, p_2, \ldots, p_n$ is a function, of class C_2, of N arguments $u, v, w, \ldots$, the sum of the n Jacobians

$$\frac{\partial(q_r, p_r)}{\partial(u, v)} \tag{24.7.1}$$

is of importance; it is called a *Lagrange bracket*, and is denoted by $[u, v]$. In the case in which we are interested at the moment, $N = 2n + 1$, and the arguments $u, v, w, \ldots$ are $Q_1, Q_2, \ldots, Q_n, P_1, P_2, \ldots, P_n, t$. *We can express the necessary and sufficient conditions for a contact transformation in the form*

$$[Q_r, Q_s] = 0, \quad [P_r, P_s] = 0, \quad [Q_r, P_s] = \delta_r^s, \tag{24.7.2}$$

for all pairs of integers r, s in the range $1, 2, \ldots, n$, and for any fixed value of t.

The proof is immediate. Referring to the defining property (24.2.5), and taking the Q's and P's as independent variables, we see that the necessary and sufficient condition for a contact transformation is that

$$\left(p_i \frac{\partial q_i}{\partial Q_r} - P_r\right) dQ_r + \left(p_i \frac{\partial q_i}{\partial P_r}\right) dP_r \tag{24.7.3}$$

should be a perfect differential for any fixed value of t. Now (24.7.3) is a perfect differential if and only if

$$\left\{\begin{aligned} \frac{\partial}{\partial Q_s}\left(p_i \frac{\partial q_i}{\partial Q_r} - P_r\right) &= \frac{\partial}{\partial Q_r}\left(p_i \frac{\partial q_i}{\partial Q_s} - P_s\right), \\ \frac{\partial}{\partial P_s}\left(p_i \frac{\partial q_i}{\partial P_r}\right) &= \frac{\partial}{\partial P_r}\left(p_i \frac{\partial q_i}{\partial P_s}\right), \\ \frac{\partial}{\partial P_s}\left(p_i \frac{\partial q_i}{\partial Q_r} - P_r\right) &= \frac{\partial}{\partial Q_r}\left(p_i \frac{\partial q_i}{\partial P_s}\right), \end{aligned}\right. \tag{24.7.4}$$

and these conditions are equivalent to (24.7.2).

24.8 Relations between the two sets of derivatives. If the domain D of $(q;\ p)$ is mapped on the domain E of $(Q;\ P)$ by a contact transformation (for a given fixed value of t) there exist very simple relations between the derivatives of the Q's and P's, *qua* functions of $(q;\ p)$, at a point of D, and the derivatives of the q's and p's, *qua* functions of $(Q;\ P)$, at the corresponding point of E. These relations are:

$$\frac{\partial Q_r}{\partial q_s} = \frac{\partial p_s}{\partial P_r}, \quad \frac{\partial Q_r}{\partial p_s} = -\frac{\partial q_s}{\partial P_r}, \tag{24.8.1}$$

$$\frac{\partial P_r}{\partial q_s} = -\frac{\partial p_s}{\partial Q_r}, \quad \frac{\partial P_r}{\partial p_s} = \frac{\partial q_s}{\partial Q_r}. \tag{24.8.2}$$

These results follow very simply from the Lagrange bracket conditions established in the proceding paragraph. We denote by r any one of the integers $1, 2, \ldots, n$, and we consider the Pfaffian form

(24.8.3)

$$\begin{aligned}\frac{\partial p_i}{\partial P_r} dq_i - \frac{\partial q_i}{\partial P_r} dp_i &= \frac{\partial p_i}{\partial P_r}\left(\frac{\partial q_i}{\partial Q_s} dQ_s + \frac{\partial q_i}{\partial P_s} dP_s\right) - \frac{\partial q_i}{\partial P_r}\left(\frac{\partial p_i}{\partial Q_s} dQ_s + \frac{\partial p_i}{\partial P_s} dP_s\right)\\ &= [Q_s, P_r]\, dQ_s + [P_s, P_r]\, dP_s\\ &= dQ_r.\end{aligned}$$

The results (24.8.1) follow: and the results (24.8.2) follow similarly from

$$\frac{\partial p_i}{\partial Q_r} dq_i - \frac{\partial q_i}{\partial Q_r} dp_i = -dP_r. \tag{24.8.4}$$

A simple and elegant way of proving the results (24.8.1–2) is provided by the *bilinear covariant*. We consider two arbitrary variations $d\mathbf{x}$ and $\delta\mathbf{x}$ from the point $\mathbf{x}_0(=(q_{10}, q_{20}, \ldots, q_{n0}, p_{10}, p_{20}, \ldots, p_{n0}))$ in the phase space. We denote by $d\mathbf{X}$ and $\delta\mathbf{X}$ the corresponding variations from the related point $\mathbf{X}_0$ $(=(Q_{10}, Q_{20}, \ldots, Q_{n0}, P_{10}, P_{20}, \ldots, P_{n0}))$. *Then*

$$dQ_r\delta P_r - dP_r\delta Q_r = dq_r\delta p_r - dp_r\delta q_r, \tag{24.8.5}$$

where the repeated suffix r implies summation from 1 *to* n. The expression appearing in either member of (24.8.5) is the bilinear covariant.

We can establish (24.8.5) directly from the definition of a contact transformation. To do so, it is expedient to extend the significance of the symbols d and δ. We consider a two-dimensional manifold M through $\mathbf{x}_0$ containing $d\mathbf{x}$ and $\delta\mathbf{x}$. We introduce coordinates ξ, η to define position on M; the coordinates $q_1, q_n, \ldots, q_n\ p_1, p_2, \ldots, p_n$ of the point $\mathbf{x}$ on M are functions of (ξ, η) of class C_2, the curve $\eta =$ constant through $\mathbf{x}_0$ is in the direction $d\mathbf{x}$, the curve $\xi =$ constant through $\mathbf{x}_0$ is in the direction $\delta\mathbf{x}$. Thus, the displacement $d\mathbf{x}$ from $\mathbf{x}_0$ is given by $dx_s = \left(\frac{\partial x_s}{\partial \xi}\right)_0 d\xi$, for $s = 1, 2, \ldots, n$, and the displacement $\delta\mathbf{x}$ is given similarly by $\delta x_s = \left(\frac{\partial x_s}{\partial \eta}\right)_0 \delta\eta$. We now extend the use of the symbols d and δ to define displacements from other points $\mathbf{x}$ on M in the neighbourhood of $\mathbf{x}_0$, so that, in general, $dx_s = \left(\frac{\partial x_s}{\partial \xi}\right) d\xi$ and $\delta x_s = \left(\frac{\partial x_s}{\partial \eta}\right) \delta\eta$. The variations $d\xi$, $\delta\eta$ are fixed once for all, so that $\delta d\xi = d\delta\eta = 0$. It follows that $\delta dx_r = d\delta x_r$, and, more generally, if f is any function of $(q_1, q_2, \ldots\ q_n, p_1, p_2, \ldots, p_n)$ of class c

$$\delta df = d\delta f. \tag{24.8.6}$$

The desired result now follows easily. Using the fundamental defining property (24.2.5). of a contact transformation we have

(24.8.7) $$\delta(P_r\, dQ_r) - d(P_r\, \delta Q_r) = \delta(p_r\, dq_r - dw) - d(p_r\, \delta q_r - \delta w),$$

and (24.8.5) follows from (24.8.7) in virtue of (24.8.6).

To derive the relations (24.8.1–2) from the bilinear covariant, let d denote a variation in which none of the q's and p's change save q_s, and let δ denote a variation in which none of the Q's and P's change save Q_r. Then in (24.8.5) only one term survives on each side

(24.8.8) $$-dP_r\, \delta Q_r = dq_s\, \delta p_s \qquad \text{(not summed)}$$

whence

(24.8.9) $$-\frac{\partial P_r}{\partial q_s}\, dq_s\, \delta Q_r = dq_s \frac{\partial p_s}{\partial Q_r}\, \delta Q_r, \qquad \text{(not summed)}$$

giving

(24.8.10) $$\frac{\partial P_r}{\partial q_s} = -\frac{\partial p_s}{\partial Q_r}.$$

The other relations (24.8.1–2) are established in the same way.

The conditions for a contact transformation expressed in terms of Lagrange brackets (§ 24.7) can also be derived from the bilinear covariant. If we expand the second member of (24.8.5) in terms of dQ's and dP's and δQ's and δP's, we obtain

(24.8.11)
$$\left(\frac{\partial q_i}{\partial Q_r}\, dQ_r + \frac{\partial q_i}{\partial P_r}\, dP_r\right)\left(\frac{\partial p_i}{\partial Q_s}\, \delta Q_s + \frac{\partial p_i}{\partial P_s}\, \delta P_s\right) - \left(\frac{\partial p_i}{\partial Q_r}\, dQ_r + \frac{\partial p_i}{\partial P_r}\, dP_r\right)\left(\frac{\partial q_i}{\partial Q_s}\, \delta Q_s + \frac{\partial q_i}{\partial P_s}\, \delta P_s\right).$$

The coefficient of $dQ_r\, \delta P_s - dP_s\, \delta Q_r$ is $[Q_r, P_s]$, the coefficient of $dQ_r\, \delta Q_s$ is $[Q_r\, Q_s]$, and the coefficient of $dP_r\, \delta P_s$ is $[P_r, P_s]$. Comparing the two sides of the equation we recover the conditions (24.7.2).

24.9 The conditions for a contact transformation expressed in terms of Poisson brackets. The relations between the two sets of derivatives established in § 24.8 allow us to express the conditions for a contact transformation in terms of Poisson brackets (§ 22.2). Thus

(24.9.1)
$$\begin{aligned}[Q_r, Q_s] &= \frac{\partial q_i}{\partial Q_r}\frac{\partial p_i}{\partial Q_s} - \frac{\partial p_i}{\partial Q_r}\frac{\partial q_i}{\partial Q_s}\\ &= -\frac{\partial P_r}{\partial p_i}\frac{\partial P_s}{\partial q_i} + \frac{\partial P_r}{\partial q_i}\frac{\partial P_s}{\partial p_i}\\ &= (P_r, P_s).\end{aligned}$$

Similarly

(24.9.2) $$[Q_r, P_s] = (Q_s, P_r), \quad [P_r, P_s] = (Q_r, Q_s).$$

Hence, if the transformation from $(q;\ p)$ to $(Q;\ P)$ is a contact transformation.

(24.9.3) $$(Q_r, Q_s) = 0, \quad (P_r, P_s) = 0, \quad (Q_r, P_s) = \delta_r^s.$$

We shall see that these conditions are not only necessary, but also sufficient, to ensure that the transformation from $(q;\ p)$ to $(Q;\ P)$ is a contact transformation.

24.10 Relations between Lagrange brackets and Poisson brackets. Let us suppose that $q_1, q_2, \ldots, q_n, p_1, p_2, \ldots, p_n$ are $2n$ independent functions, of class C_2 in a domain D of the phase space, of the $2n$ arguments $u_1, u_2, \ldots, u_{2n}$; the transformation is such that it gives a topological mapping of the domain D of the phase space on a domain E of the u-space. (We are not supposing for the moment that the transformation is necessarily a contact transformation.) *The fundamental relation between Lagrange brackets and Poisson brackets is*

$$\sum_{r=1}^{2n} [u_r, u_s]\,(u_r, u_k) = \delta_s^{\,k}. \tag{24.10.1}$$

The proof is immediate; the first member of (24.10.1) is

$$\left(\frac{\partial q_i}{\partial u_r}\frac{\partial p_i}{\partial u_s} - \frac{\partial p_i}{\partial u_r}\frac{\partial q_i}{\partial u_s}\right)\left(\frac{\partial u_r}{\partial q_j}\frac{\partial u_k}{\partial p_j} - \frac{\partial u_k}{\partial q_j}\frac{\partial u_r}{\partial p_j}\right) = \left(\frac{\partial q_i}{\partial u_r}\frac{\partial u_r}{\partial q_j}\right)\frac{\partial p_i}{\partial u_s}\frac{\partial u_k}{\partial p_j} \tag{24.10.2}$$

$$- \left(\frac{\partial q_i}{\partial u_r}\frac{\partial u_r}{\partial p_j}\right)\frac{\partial p_i}{\partial u_s}\frac{\partial u_k}{\partial q_j} - \left(\frac{\partial p_i}{\partial u_r}\frac{\partial u_r}{\partial q_j}\right)\frac{\partial q_i}{\partial u_s}\frac{\partial u_k}{\partial p_j} + \left(\frac{\partial p_i}{\partial u_r}\frac{\partial u_r}{\partial p_i}\right)\frac{\partial q_i}{\partial u_s}\frac{\partial u_k}{\partial q_j},$$

where the suffix r is summed from 1 to $2n$, and i, j are summed from 1 to n. Of the four expressions, the second and third clearly vanish, and the first and fourth yield

$$\frac{\partial u_k}{\partial p_i}\frac{\partial p_i}{\partial u_s} + \frac{\partial u_k}{\partial q_i}\frac{\partial q_i}{\partial u_s} = \delta_s^{\,k}, \tag{24.10.3}$$

and this completes the proof.

If we write λ_{rs} for the Lagrange bracket $[u_r, u_s]$ and ϖ_{rs} for the Poisson bracket (u_r, u_s) the result (24.10.1) is very simply expressed in terms of the $2n \times 2n$ matrices $\boldsymbol{\lambda}$ and ϖ whose typical elements are λ_{rs} and ϖ_{rs}. The result (24.10.1) can be expressed in the form

$$\boldsymbol{\lambda}'\varpi = \mathbf{I}_{2n}. \tag{24.10.4}$$

24.11 Application to a contact transformation. Let us now consider the special case where the functions $u_1, u_2, \ldots, u_{2n}$ are the functions $Q_1, Q_2, \ldots, Q_n, P_1, P_2, \ldots P_n$ that appear in a contact transformation. In virtue of the Lagrange bracket conditions (24.7.2) the matrix λ is

$$\boldsymbol{\lambda} = \mathbf{Z} = \begin{pmatrix} \mathbf{0} & \mathbf{I}_n \\ -\mathbf{I}_n & \mathbf{0} \end{pmatrix}, \tag{24.11.1}$$

and hence

$$\varpi = (\boldsymbol{\lambda}')^{-1} = \mathbf{Z}. \tag{24.11.2}$$

Thus the Poisson bracket conditions (24.9.3) are precisely equivalent to the Lagrange bracket conditions. The Poisson bracket conditions, like the Lagrange bracket conditions, are both necessary and sufficient for a contact transformation.

24.12 Invariance of a Poisson bracket. *The Poisson bracket of two functions is invariant under a contact transformation.* Explicitly, if the transformation from $(q;\ p)$ to $(Q;\ P)$ is a contact transformation, and if

$$u(q;\ p) = U(Q;\ P), \quad v(q;\ p) = V(Q;\ P), \tag{24.12.1}$$

then

$$(u, v) = (U, V), \tag{24.12.2}$$

where (U, V) denotes the Poisson bracket formed with the large letters as independent variables, namely $\sum_{r=1}^{n} \frac{\partial(U, V)}{\partial(Q_r, P_r)}$. If t enters into the equations of transformation, (24.12.2) holds for every fixed value of t.

The result follows easily from the Poisson bracket conditions (24.9.3). We have

$$(u, v) = \frac{\partial u}{\partial q_r}\frac{\partial v}{\partial p_r} - \frac{\partial v}{\partial q_r}\frac{\partial u}{\partial p_r}$$

$$= \left(\frac{\partial U}{\partial Q_i}\frac{\partial Q_i}{\partial q_r} + \frac{\partial U}{\partial P_i}\frac{\partial P_i}{\partial q_r}\right)\left(\frac{\partial V}{\partial Q_j}\frac{\partial Q_j}{\partial p_r} + \frac{\partial V}{\partial P_j}\frac{\partial P_j}{\partial p_r}\right)$$

$$- \left(\frac{\partial U}{\partial Q_i}\frac{\partial Q_i}{\partial p_r} + \frac{\partial U}{\partial P_i}\frac{\partial P_i}{\partial p_r}\right)\left(\frac{\partial V}{\partial Q_j}\frac{\partial Q_j}{\partial q_r} + \frac{\partial V}{\partial P_j}\frac{\partial P_j}{\partial q_r}\right)$$

$$= \frac{\partial U}{\partial Q_i}\frac{\partial V}{\partial Q_j}(Q_i, Q_j) + \frac{\partial U}{\partial Q_i}\frac{\partial V}{\partial P_j}(Q_i, P_j) + \frac{\partial U}{\partial P_i}\frac{\partial V}{\partial Q_j}(P_i, Q_j) + \frac{\partial U}{\partial P_i}\frac{\partial V}{\partial P_j}(P_i, P_j)$$

$$= (U, V).$$

24.13 Another form of the conditions for a contact transformation. Let us for a moment replace the symbols

$$q_1, q_2, \ldots, q_n, p_1, p_2, \ldots, p_n,$$

by

$$x_1, x_2, \ldots, x_n, x_{n+1}, x_{n+2}, \ldots, x_{2n},$$

as in § 22.1. Let us also replace the symbols

$$Q_1, Q_2, \ldots, Q_n, P_1, P_2, \ldots, P_n,$$

by

$$X_1, X_2, \ldots, X_n, X_{n+1}, X_{n+2}, \ldots, X_{2n}.$$

Consider the $2n \times 2n$ square matrix $\mathbf{M}$ whose typical element is $\partial X_r/\partial x_s$. Thus

(24.13.1) $$\mathbf{M} = \begin{pmatrix} \mathbf{A} & \mathbf{B} \\ \mathbf{C} & \mathbf{D} \end{pmatrix},$$

where $\mathbf{A}$, $\mathbf{B}$, $\mathbf{C}$, $\mathbf{D}$ are the $n \times n$ square matrices whose typical elements are

(24.13.2) $$a_{rs} = \frac{\partial Q_r}{\partial q_s}, \quad b_{rs} = \frac{\partial Q_r}{\partial p_s}, \quad c_{rs} = \frac{\partial P_r}{\partial q_s}, \quad d_{rs} = \frac{\partial P_r}{\partial p_s}.$$

Then

(24.13.3) $$\mathbf{MZM}' = \begin{pmatrix} \mathbf{AB}' - \mathbf{BA}' & \mathbf{AD}' - \mathbf{BC}' \\ \mathbf{CB}' - \mathbf{DA}' & \mathbf{CD}' - \mathbf{DC}' \end{pmatrix} = \begin{pmatrix} ((Q_r, Q_s)) & ((Q_r, P_s)) \\ ((P_r, Q_s)) & ((P_r, P_s)) \end{pmatrix} = \mathbf{Z}.$$

Thus we can express the necessary and sufficient conditions for a contact transformation in the form

(24.13.4) $$\mathbf{MZM}' = \mathbf{Z}.$$

The condition (24.13.4) satisfied by $\mathbf{M}$ is also satisfied by the inverse matrix $\mathbf{m}$ whose typical element is $\partial x_r/\partial X_s$. This follows by multiplying both sides of (24.13.4) on the left by $\mathbf{m}$ and on the right by $\mathbf{m}'$; of course the result is evident also from the fact that the transformation from (Q, P) to (q, p) is itself a contact transformation. Thus

(24.13.5) $$\mathbf{mZm}' = \mathbf{Z}.$$

If now we take the inverse of each member of (24.13.5) we find

(24.13.6) $$\mathbf{M}'\mathbf{ZM} = \mathbf{Z},$$

so the condition satisfied by $\mathbf{M}$ is also satisfied by its transpose. The same is true of the matrix $\mathbf{m}'$, the transpose of the inverse,

$$\mathbf{m}'\mathbf{Z}\mathbf{m} = \mathbf{Z}, \tag{24.13.7}$$

and in fact the four conditions (24.13.4–7) are all equivalent, each implies the other three. A matrix $\mathbf{M}$ of this kind is called *symplectic* (cf. § 23.6). If $\mathbf{M}$ is symplectic, the same is true of its inverse and of its transpose.

In particular, if we consider a linear transformation

$$\mathbf{x} = \mathbf{C}\mathbf{X}, \tag{24.13.8}$$

where $\mathbf{C}$ is a non-singular matrix whose elements are constants, we have $\mathbf{m} = \mathbf{C}$, and the transformation is a contact transformation if and only if

$$\mathbf{C}'\mathbf{Z}\mathbf{C} = \mathbf{Z}. \tag{24.13.9}$$

24.14 Functions in involution. We have seen that, if the transformation from $(q;\ p)$ to $(Q;\ P)$ is a contact transformation, the n components $Q_1, Q_2, \ldots, Q_n$, *qua* functions of $(q;\ p;\ t)$, satisfy the condition $(Q_r, Q_s) = 0$. Such a set of functions, i.e. a set of functions for which the Poisson bracket of every pair is identically zero, is said to be *in involution.*

It is clear that n *arbitrary* functions of $(q;\ p;\ t)$ cannot be the first n components $Q_1, Q_2, \ldots, Q_n$ in a contact transformation, for in a contact transformation these functions must be in involution. The question that naturally suggests itself is this: *if we take n functions $Q_1, Q_2, \ldots, Q_n$ that are in involution, can we find a further n functions $P_1, P_2, \ldots, P_n$ such that the transformation from $(q;\ p)$ to $(Q;\ P)$ is a contact transformation?*

The answer to this question is certainly affirmative in the simplest case, that of an extended point transformation (§ 24.4); it is also affirmative in the other cases, as we now proceed to prove.

We start with n functions $\varphi_1, \varphi_2, \ldots, \varphi_n$ in involution, and we write the proof for the case in which the Jacobian J,

$$J = \frac{\partial(\varphi_1, \varphi_2, \ldots, \varphi_n)}{\partial(p_1, p_2, \ldots, p_n)} \tag{24.14.1}$$

is not identically zero. There is no identical relation connecting q's and Q's and t, and we can solve the n equations

$$Q_r = \varphi_r(q;\ p;\ t) \tag{24.14.2}$$

for $p_1, p_2, \ldots, p_n$ in the form

$$p_r = \psi_r(q;\ Q;\ t), \qquad r = 1, 2, \ldots, n. \tag{24.14.3}$$

We shall prove that

$$\frac{\partial \psi_r}{\partial q_s} = \frac{\partial \psi_s}{\partial q_r} \tag{24.14.4}$$

for all pairs of values of r and s.

If we substitute ψ_r for p_r in (24.14.2) we obtain an identity in the variables $(q; Q; t)$,

$$\varphi_i(q;\ \psi;\ t) - Q_i = 0, \qquad i = 1, 2, \ldots, n. \tag{24.14.5}$$

Hence, differentiating partially with respect to q_s,

$$\frac{\partial\varphi_i}{\partial q_s} + \frac{\partial\varphi_i}{\partial p_r}\frac{\partial\psi_r}{\partial q_s} = 0, \qquad i = 1, 2, \ldots, n, \tag{24.14.6}$$

whence, multiplying by $\dfrac{\partial\varphi_j}{\partial p_s}$, and summing from $s = 1$ to $s = n$, we find

$$\frac{\partial\varphi_i}{\partial q_s}\frac{\partial\varphi_j}{\partial p_s} + \frac{\partial\varphi_i}{\partial p_r}\frac{\partial\varphi_j}{\partial p_s}\frac{\partial\psi_r}{\partial q_s} = 0. \tag{24.14.7}$$

We write the corresponding equation found by interchanging i and j, and subtract, and using $(\varphi_i, \varphi_j) = 0$ we have

$$\frac{\partial\varphi_i}{\partial p_r}\frac{\partial\varphi_j}{\partial p_s}\frac{\partial\psi_r}{\partial q_s} - \frac{\partial\varphi_j}{\partial p_r}\frac{\partial\varphi_i}{\partial p_s}\frac{\partial\psi_r}{\partial q_s} = 0, \tag{24.14.8}$$

which (interchanging the dummy suffixes r and s in the last term) we can write in the form

$$\frac{\partial\varphi_i}{\partial p_r}\frac{\partial\varphi_j}{\partial p_s}\left(\frac{\partial\psi_r}{\partial q_s} - \frac{\partial\psi_s}{\partial q_r}\right) = 0. \tag{24.14.9}$$

There are n^2 such equations, corresponding to the pairs of values of i and j, and they are homogeneous linear equations to determine the n^2 unknown quantities

$$\left(\frac{\partial\psi_r}{\partial q_s} - \frac{\partial\psi_s}{\partial q_r}\right).$$

The determinant of the coefficients is J^{2n}, and does not vanish, and therefore

$$\frac{\partial\psi_r}{\partial q_s} = \frac{\partial\psi_s}{\partial q_r} \tag{24.14.10}$$

for all pairs of values of r and s.

It follows that there exists a function W $(= W(q;\ Q;\ t))$ such that

$$p_r = \psi_r(q;\ Q;\ t) = \frac{\partial W}{\partial q_r}, \qquad r = 1, 2, \ldots, n, \tag{24.14.11}$$

and the matrix $\left(\dfrac{\partial^2 W}{\partial q_r\,\partial Q_s}\right)$ is non-singular (because, if it were, there would be an identical relation connecting q's and p's and t). If therefore we take

$$P_r = -\frac{\partial W}{\partial Q_r}, \qquad r = 1, 2, \ldots, n, \tag{24.14.12}$$

the equations (24.14.11–12) define a contact transformation (as in (24.2.7–8)), and this completes the proof.

24.15 Some concrete examples. To begin with, let us consider a system with only one freedom. In that case the matter is simple; the only condition we need for a contact transformation is the measure-preserving property

$$\frac{\partial(Q, P)}{\partial(q, p)} = 1. \tag{24.15.1}$$

This is the Poisson bracket condition (§ 24.9); alternatively, we may notice that $\oint p\,dq$ taken round a simple closed curve in the phase space (i.e. the (q, p)-plane) is minus the area enclosed, and the conservation of area implies that $PdQ - pdq$ is a perfect differential.

The *linear* transformation

$$Q = aq + bp + c, \quad P = a'q + b'p + c', \tag{24.15.2}$$

where the coefficients a, b, c, a', b', c', are functions of t, is a contact transformation if and only if

$$ab' - ba' = 1. \tag{24.15.3}$$

A simple way in which to construct a contact transformation is to consider the motion of a dynamical system; (q, p) is the initial point, and (Q, P) is the point reached at time t. These transformations, arising from actual motions, reduce to the identity when $t = 0$; they reduce to contact transformations not involving the time if we replace t by a non-zero constant. Two familiar examples, derived from elementary problems of rectilinear motion, are

$$Q = q + pt + \tfrac{1}{2}gt^2, \quad P = p + gt; \tag{24.15.4}$$

$$Q = q\cos nt + (p/n)\sin nt, \quad P = -nq\sin nt + p\cos nt. \tag{24.15.5}$$

Other simple special cases of the linear contact transformation are:

$$Q = q - q_0, \quad P = p - p_0, \tag{24.15.6}$$

$$Q = \alpha q, \quad P = p/\alpha, \tag{24.15.7}$$

$$Q = \alpha p, \quad P = -q/\alpha, \tag{24.15.8}$$

$$\sqrt{2}Q = \alpha q + \beta p, \quad \sqrt{2}P = -(1/\beta)q + (1/\alpha)p. \tag{24.15.9}$$

Other transformations are obtained by using two of these successively. Two noteworthy special cases of (24.15.8) are those given by $\alpha = \pm 1$ namely

$$Q = p, \quad P = -q, \tag{24.15.10}$$

$$Q = -p, \quad P = q. \tag{24.15.11}$$

The transformation

$$Q = f(q)\cos p, \quad P = f(q)\sin p, \tag{24.15.12}$$

is a contact transformation if $ff' = 1$, $f^2 = 2(q + a)$, and this gives the formulae

$$Q = \sqrt{\{2(q + a)\}}\cos p, \quad P = \sqrt{\{2(q + a)\}}\sin p. \tag{24.15.13}$$

We can also write this in the inverse form

$$2(q + a) = Q^2 + P^2, \quad p = \tan^{-1}(P/Q). \tag{24.15.14}$$

We easily verify the fundamental property, that $PdQ - pdq$ is a perfect differential,

$$PdQ - pdq = d\{(\cos p\sin p - p)(q + a)\}. \tag{24.15.15}$$

Or again we can derive (24.15.13) from the generating function $U(p, Q)$ as in (24.3.3–4); in fact

$$U = -\tfrac{1}{2}Q^2\tan p + ap. \tag{24.15.16}$$

If we combine (24.15.13) and (24.15.10) we obtain the contact transformation

$$Q = \sqrt{\{2(p + a)\}}\cos q, \quad P = -\sqrt{\{2(p + a)\}}\sin q. \tag{24.15.17}$$

The transformation

$$Q = e^{kp}f(q), \quad P = e^{-kp}g(q), \tag{24.15.18}$$

is a contact transformation if

(24.15.19) $$-k(fg' + gf') = 1, \quad -kfg = q + a.$$

For example the formulae

(24.15.20) $$Q = e^{kp}\sqrt{(q + a)}, \quad P = -(1/k)e^{-kp}\sqrt{(q + a)}$$

define a contact transformation.

In the first instance we are concerned with real variables, but we shall need to extend the idea of a contact transformation to the complex field, where the variables $(q; p)$ and $(Q; P)$ can take complex values. In the concrete applications the final results will be expressed in a real form. As an elementary illustration, take $\alpha = 1$, $\beta = -i/n$, with n real and positive, in (24.15.9), giving

(24.15.21) $$\sqrt{2Q} = -(i/n)(p + inq), \quad \sqrt{2P} = p - inq.$$

If in (24.15.20) we put $k = i$ we obtain the contact transformation

(24.15.22) $$Q = e^{ip}\sqrt{(q + a)}, \quad P = ie^{-ip}\sqrt{(q + a)},$$

a result which can also be found by combining (24.15.9), with $\alpha = 1$ and $\beta = i$, and (24.15.13).

The examples considered so far refer to a system with one freedom; let us now consider the general case of n freedoms. A simple special case is that of an extended point transformation (§ 24.4). As a concrete illustration, consider the transformation from Cartesian to polar coordinates for a particle moving in a plane; here

(24.15.23) $$q_1 = x, \quad q_2 = y; \quad Q_1 = r, \quad Q_2 = \theta,$$

and the formulae (24.4.6) are

(24.15.24) $$\begin{cases} x = r\cos\theta, & y = r\sin\theta; \\ p_r = p_x\cos\theta + p_y\sin\theta, & p_\theta = r(-p_x\sin\theta + p_y\cos\theta). \end{cases}$$

There are many other ways in which contact transformations arise. The motion of a dynamical system defines a contact transformation from $(q_0; p_0)$ to $(q; p)$. Moreover, if we use new parameters $(\alpha; \beta)$ to distinguish a particular orbit in the phase space, where $\beta_r\, d\alpha_r = p_{r0}\, dq_{r0}$, then the transformation from $(\alpha; \beta)$, to $(q; p)$ is a contact transformation (§ 24.1). In fact such a contact transformation is defined whenever we solve a particular dynamical problem by means of the Hamilton-Jacobi theorem; some comments on this fact will appear later (§ 25.2). Finally, we can define a contact transformation in terms of a generating function (§ 24.3); many examples will appear later in connexion with the problem of three bodies (Chapter XXIX).

Chapter XXV

Transformation theory

25.1 The equations of motion after a contact transformation. We now consider the equations of motion that are obtained when a dynamical system is described in terms of new variables which are related to the original coordinates and momenta by a contact transformation. We deal with a dynamical system whose Hamiltonian function is $H(q_1, q_2, \ldots, q_n; p_1, p_2, \ldots, p_n; t)$, and for which the equations of motion are

$$\dot{q}_r = \frac{\partial H}{\partial p_r}, \quad \dot{p}_r = -\frac{\partial H}{\partial q_r}, \qquad r = 1, 2, \ldots, n. \tag{25.1.1}$$

We then transform to new variables $Q_1, Q_2, \ldots, Q_n, P_1, P_2, \ldots, P_n$, which are related to the original variables by a contact transformation such that

$$P_r\, dQ_r = p_r\, dq_r + R\, dt - dW. \tag{25.1.2}$$

The famous theorem of Jacobi asserts that *the equations of motion in the new variables are of Hamiltonian form.*

A simple way of proving Jacobi's theorem is given by combining the equivalence theorem (§ 16.3) with the defining property (25.1.2) of a contact transformation. Suppose that the solutions of the equations (25.1.1) are expressed in terms of $2n$ independent parameters $\gamma_1, \gamma_2, \ldots, \gamma_{2n}$ (as in § 16.3). Then

$$p_r\, dq_r - H\, dt = d\psi + \omega, \tag{25.1.3}$$

where ω is a Pfaffian form $\sum_{s=1}^{2n} K_s\, d\gamma_s$, and the K's are functions of the γ's. Moreover (25.1.3) implies that the q's and p's satisfy (25.1.1).

With the new variables the motion is defined by expressing the Q's and P's, through the q's and p's, as functions of the γ's and t. Now from (25.1.3) and (25.1.2) we have

$$P_r\, dQ_r - (H + R)\, dt = d(\psi - W) + \omega. \tag{25.1.4}$$

Jacobi's theorem now follows from the second part of the equivalence theorem. *The new equations of motion are*

$$\dot{Q}_r = \frac{\partial H^*}{\partial P_r}, \quad \dot{P}_r = -\frac{\partial H^*}{\partial Q_r}, \qquad r = 1, 2, \ldots, n, \tag{25.1.5}$$

where H^* is $H + R$ expressed in terms of Q's *and* P's *and* t. This is Jacobi's theorem.

If the contact transformation is defined by a generating function U, as in (24.3.6–7), the new Hamiltonian function H^* is $H + \dfrac{\partial U}{\partial t}$ expressed in terms of Q's and P's and t. In particular, if the equations defining the transformation do not contain t, the new Hamiltonian equations in the variables $(Q;\ P)$ are derived from the Hamiltonian function H^* which is simply *the original Hamiltonian function H expressed in terms of the new variables.*

We consider some simple special cases.

If we use the transformation

(25.1.6) $$q_r = P_r, \quad p_r = -Q_r, \qquad r = 1, 2, \ldots, n,$$

already noticed in § 24.3 and in § 24.15, the new Hamiltonian function is $H(P; -Q; t)$. In the context of transformation theory the distinction between coordinates and momenta is not immutable; in particular, a Lagrangian coordinate can assume the role of a momentum component.

Here is another important special case. Let $(a_1, a_2, \ldots, a_n; b_1, b_2, \ldots, b_n)$ be a stationary point for the autonomous system whose Hamiltonian function is H, so that $q_r = a_r$, $p_r = b_r$ is an equilibrium solution of the Hamiltonian equations. The contact transformation derived from the generating function

(25.1.7) $$U = \sum_{r=1}^{n} (q_r - a_r)(P_r + b_r)$$

is

(25.1.8) $$q_r = a_r + Q_r, \quad p_r = b_r + P_r,$$

so $(Q; P)$ measures the deviation from the equilibrium solution. The new Hamiltonian function H^* is $H(a + Q; b + P)$. If H is analytic, and we expand as a multiple power series in the variables Q_r and P_r, there are no linear terms in H^*. Further, we obtain the linear approximation to the equations of motion by retaining in H^* only the terms of the second degree.

More generally, let $q_r = u_r(t)$, $p_r = v_r(t)$ be a known solution of the Hamiltonian equations for an autonomous system. The contact transformation derived from the generating function

(25.1.9) $$U = \sum_{r=1}^{n} (q_r - u_r)(P_r + v_r)$$

is

(25.1.10) $$q_r = u_r + Q_r, \quad p_r = v_r + P_r,$$

so $(Q; P)$ represents the deviation from the known solution. The new Hamiltonian function is

(25.1.11) $$H(u + Q; v + P) + \sum_{r=1}^{n} Q_r \dot{v}_r - \sum_{r=1}^{n} P_r \dot{u}_r,$$

and the new equations of motion can be written in the form

(25.1.12)
$$\dot{Q}_r = H_{p_r}(u + Q; v + P) - H_{p_r}(u, v), \quad \dot{P}_r = -H_{q_r}(u + Q; v + P) + H_{q_r}(u, v),$$

where H_{q_r} stands for $\partial H/\partial q_r$ and H_{p_r} stands for $\partial H/\partial p_r$ (as in § 16.2). We obtain the linear approximation to the deviation from the given solution (i.e. the variational equations) by expanding $H(u + Q; v + P)$ in powers of Q's and P's, and keeping as the Hamiltonian function only the terms of the second degree. Of course the linear approximation can be found quite simply without the theory of contact transformations, as in (23.1.4).

The transformations (25.1.8) and (25.1.10) are extended point transformations, but extended point transformations of a very special type. Not only are the q's functions of $(Q_1, Q_2, \ldots, Q_n)$ but the p's are functions of $(P_1, P_2, \ldots, P_n)$; further, each q_r is a function of the corresponding Q_r and t, and each p_r is a function of the corresponding P_r and t.

Here is another simple example of a contact transformation for which the equations of transformation involve t. A particle of unit mass moves in a plane under a central attraction to O, so that, using fixed rectangular axes,

$$L = \tfrac{1}{2}(\dot{x}^2 + \dot{y}^2) - V, \quad H = \tfrac{1}{2}(p_x{}^2 + p_y{}^2) + V, \quad V = V(r), \quad r = \sqrt{(x^2 + y^2)}. \tag{25.1.13}$$

We use the contact transformation derived from the generating function

$$U = P_X(x \cos \omega t + y \sin \omega t) + P_Y(y \cos \omega t - x \sin \omega t), \tag{25.1.14}$$

where ω is constant. The equations of transformation are

$$\begin{cases} X = x \cos \omega t + y \sin \omega t, & Y = y \cos \omega t - x \sin \omega t, \\ p_x = P_X \cos \omega t - P_Y \sin \omega t, & p_y = P_X \sin \omega t + P_Y \cos \omega t. \end{cases} \tag{25.1.15}$$

The new Hamiltonian function H^* is found by expressing $H + \dfrac{\partial U}{\partial t}$ in terms of $(X, Y;\ P_X, P_Y)$, and

$$H^* = \tfrac{1}{2}(P_X{}^2 + P_Y{}^2) - \omega(XP_Y - YP_X) + V \tag{25.1.16}$$

Of course the geometric meaning is evident: (X, Y) are the coordinates of the particle referred to axes rotating steadily with angular velocity ω. If we start with these axes we have

$$T = \tfrac{1}{2}\{(\dot{X} - Y\omega)^2 + (\dot{Y} + X\omega)^2\}, \tag{25.1.17}$$

$$P_X = \dot{X} - Y\omega, \quad P_Y = \dot{Y} + X\omega, \tag{25.1.18}$$

and H^* is $T_2 + V - T_0$ expressed in terms of (P_X, P_Y) instead of $(\dot{X}, \dot{Y})$, i.e.

$$\begin{aligned} H^* &= \tfrac{1}{2}\{(P_X + Y\omega)^2 + (P_Y - X\omega)^2\} + V - \tfrac{1}{2}\omega^2(X^2 + Y^2) \\ &= \tfrac{1}{2}(P_X{}^2 + P_Y{}^2) - \omega(XP_Y - YP_X) + V, \end{aligned} \tag{25.1.19}$$

and we recover the formula (25.1.16).

25.2 The variation of the elements. Suppose we have found, by the method of the Hamilton-Jacobi theorem, the solutions of the Hamiltonian equations of motion for a system whose Hamiltonian function is H. We then consider a new problem for which the Hamiltonian function is $H + K$. Then the solution of the new problem can be effected by the integration of the equations of motion for a Hamiltonian system of a strikingly simple type.

Let $S = S(q_1, q_2, \ldots, q_n;\ \alpha_1, \alpha_2, \ldots, \alpha_n;\ t)$ be the known complete integral of Hamilton's partial differential equation for the original system. Let us consider the transformation from $(q;\ p)$ to new variables $(\alpha;\ \beta)$ defined by the equations

$$\begin{cases} p_r = \dfrac{\partial S}{\partial q_r}, \\ \beta_r = -\dfrac{\partial S}{\partial \alpha_r}, \end{cases} \qquad r = 1, 2, \ldots, n. \tag{25.2.1}$$

Then the transformation is a contact transformation, for

$$\begin{aligned}\beta_r\,d\alpha_r &= -\frac{\partial S}{\partial \alpha_r}\,d\alpha_r \\ &= -dS + \frac{\partial S}{\partial q_r}\,dq_r + \frac{\partial S}{\partial t}\,dt \\ &= p_r\,dq_r - H\,dt - dS.\end{aligned} \tag{25.2.2}$$

Let us now consider the new problem with Hamiltonian function $H + K$, and let us find the equations of motion in terms of the new variables $(\alpha;\ \beta)$. In virtue of Jacobi's theorem (§ 25.1) *the new equations of motion are*

$$\begin{cases}\dot{\alpha}_r = \dfrac{\partial K^*}{\partial \beta_r}, \\ \dot{\beta}_r = -\dfrac{\partial K^*}{\partial \alpha_r}, \end{cases} \qquad r = 1, 2, \ldots, n, \tag{25.2.3}$$

where K^* is K expressed in terms of α's and β's and t. This is the required result.

We append some comments on the theorem just proved.

(i) If $K = 0$, we see from (25.2.3) that the α's and β's are constants, and this is precisely the Hamilton-Jacobi theorem.

(ii) If $K \neq 0$, the form in which the solution of the new problem is obtained is of particular interest. For the original problem, the motion was described by expressing the q's and p's in terms of t and of certain $2n$ constants $(\alpha;\ \beta)$. The solution of the new problem is given by the same formulae, provided only that we replace the *constants* $(\alpha;\ \beta)$ by the general solution of the equations (25.2.3). This general solution will involve $2n$ new constants.

We are thus led to regard the new problem in a special way. We think of the motion at any instant as motion in one of the old orbits whose *elements* are $(\alpha;\ \beta)$, but these elements are not constants (as they were in the original problem) but are now varying with t. Instead of regarding the modification of the Hamiltonian function, from H to $H + K$, as constituting a new and independent problem, we think of the added term K as continually modifying the original motion. We may speak of K as the *perturbation function.* (But in celestial mechanics the *disturbing function* R is usually an addition to the *gravitational* potential, and $K = -R$.)

(iii) The theorem as stated above is exact. But its usefulness is most marked when the perturbation is small, i.e. when K contains a small factor μ, and only an approximation to the exact solution for small values of μ is required. It is in this case, when the perturbation is small, that the idea of the gradual modification of the original notion is most important.

Example 25.2*A*. It will perhaps serve to make the theorem more objective if we verify it in a simple concrete case.

Let the original system be the isotropic oscillator, for which

$$H = \tfrac{1}{2}(n^2q^2 + p^2), \tag{25.2.4}$$

and let us consider the motion that ensues when a uniform field g,

$$K = -gq, \tag{25.2.5}$$

is superposed. Of course the effect of the superposed field is evident by elementary considerations, but it may be of interest to recover the result by means of the theorem just proved.

The solution of the original problem by the Hamilton-Jacobi theorem is (§ 16.7)

$$\begin{cases} q = \alpha \sin\left(nt - \dfrac{\beta}{n\alpha}\right), \\ p = n\alpha \cos\left(nt - \dfrac{\beta}{n\alpha}\right). \end{cases} \tag{25.2.6}$$

Our theorem asserts that the new problem is solved by these same formulae, provided that we substitute for α and β the general solution of the equations

$$\dot{\alpha} = \frac{\partial K^*}{\partial \beta}, \quad \dot{\beta} = -\frac{\partial K^*}{\partial \alpha}, \tag{25.2.7}$$

where

$$K^* = -g\alpha \sin\left(nt - \frac{\beta}{n\alpha}\right). \tag{25.2.8}$$

This is a new Hamiltonian problem. The Hamilton-Jacobi theorem is not well suited for its solution, and we tackle the equations of motion directly; they are

$$\begin{cases} \dot{\alpha} = \dfrac{g}{n} \cos\left(nt - \dfrac{\beta}{n\alpha}\right), \\ \dot{\beta} = g \sin\left(nt - \dfrac{\beta}{n\alpha}\right) + \dfrac{g\beta}{n\alpha} \cos\left(nt - \dfrac{\beta}{n\alpha}\right). \end{cases} \tag{25.2.9}$$

If we write θ for $\left(nt - \dfrac{\beta}{n\alpha}\right)$ we have

$$\begin{aligned} \dot{\theta} &= n + \frac{\beta}{n\alpha^2}\dot{\alpha} - \frac{1}{n\alpha}\dot{\beta} \\ &= n + \frac{\beta}{n\alpha^2}\left(\frac{g}{n}\cos\theta\right) - \frac{1}{n\alpha}\left(g\sin\theta + \frac{g\beta}{n\alpha}\cos\theta\right) \\ &= n - \frac{g}{n\alpha}\sin\theta. \end{aligned} \tag{25.2.10}$$

To integrate (25.2.9) we write

$$\lambda = \alpha \sin\theta, \quad \mu = n\alpha\cos\theta, \tag{25.2.11}$$

and we have

$$\begin{aligned} \dot{\lambda} &= \dot{\alpha}\sin\theta + \alpha\dot{\theta}\cos\theta \\ &= \frac{g}{n}\cos\theta\sin\theta + \alpha\cos\theta\left(n - \frac{g}{n\alpha}\sin\theta\right) \\ &= n\alpha\cos\theta = \mu, \end{aligned} \tag{25.2.12}$$

and

$$\begin{aligned} \dot{\mu} &= n\dot{\alpha}\cos\theta - n\alpha\dot{\theta}\sin\theta \\ &= n\cos\theta\left(\frac{g}{n}\cos\theta\right) - n\sin\alpha\theta\left(n - \frac{g}{n\alpha}\sin\theta\right) \\ &= g - n^2\alpha\sin\theta = g - n^2\lambda. \end{aligned} \tag{25.2.13}$$

Hence

$$\lambda = \frac{g}{n^2} + A\sin n(t - t_0), \quad \mu = nA\cos n(t - t_0), \tag{25.2.14}$$

and the solution for the new problem is $q = \lambda, p = \mu$; this is of course the familiar elementary solution of the problem.

Example 25.2*B*. *The simple pendulum, second approximation.* As in *Example* 5.2*A*, measuring θ from the downward vertical,

(25.2.15) $$T = \tfrac{1}{2}ma^2\dot{\theta}^2, \quad V = mga(1 - \cos\theta),$$

or, say

(25.2.16) $$T = \tfrac{1}{2}\dot{\theta}^2, \quad V = n^2(1 - \cos\theta),$$

where $n^2 = g/a$. Then $p = \dot{\theta}$, and the Hamiltonian function is

(25.2.17) $$\tfrac{1}{2}p^2 + n^2(1 - \cos\theta).$$

If the amplitude is small, we can write, as a first approximation,

(25.2.18) $$H = \tfrac{1}{2}p^2 + \tfrac{1}{2}n^2\theta^2,$$

and we can take as a second approximation the problem with Hamiltonian function $H + K$ where

(25.2.19) $$K = -\tfrac{1}{24}n^2\theta^4.$$

If we solve the original problem (which is, of course, simply the problem of the harmonic oscillator) by means of the Hamilton-Jacobi theorem, the solution of the new problem is given by the same formulae, provided we interpret α and β, not as constants, but as solutions of (25.2.3)

For the first approximation Hamilton's partial differential equation is

(25.2.20) $$\frac{\partial S}{\partial t} + \frac{1}{2}\left(\frac{\partial S}{\partial \theta}\right)^2 + \tfrac{1}{2}n^2\theta^2 = 0,$$

and a complete integral (rather more convenient for our present purpose than (16.7.7)) is

(25.2.21) $$S = -n\alpha t + \int_0^\theta \sqrt{(2n\alpha - n^2\varphi^2)}\, d\varphi.$$

The solution of the problem is given by $p = \dfrac{\partial S}{\partial \theta}$, $\beta = -\dfrac{\partial S}{\partial \alpha}$, and the solution can be written in the form

(25.2.22) $$\begin{cases} \theta = \sqrt{\left(\dfrac{2\alpha}{n}\right)} \sin(nt - \beta), \\ p = \sqrt{(2n\alpha)} \cos(nt - \beta). \end{cases}$$

For the second approximation the formulae (25.2.22) still hold if the symbols α and β now denote the solutions of (25.2.3), with

(25.2.23) $$K^* = -\tfrac{1}{6}\alpha^2 \sin^4(nt - \beta) = -\tfrac{1}{48}\alpha^2\{3 - 4\cos 2(nt - \beta) + \cos 4(nt - \beta)\}.$$

Thus

(25.2.24) $$\begin{cases} \dot{\alpha} = \tfrac{1}{12}\alpha^2\{2\sin 2(nt - \beta) - \sin 4(nt - \beta)\}, \\ \dot{\beta} = \tfrac{1}{24}\alpha\{3 - 4\cos 2(nt - \beta) + \cos 4(nt - \beta)\}. \end{cases}$$

If the amplitude of the motion is small, α remains small, and $\dot{\alpha}$ is equal to α^2 multiplied by an oscillatory term, so α is nearly constant; and, using this approximation, the leading terms in β are $\beta' + \tfrac{1}{8}\alpha t$, where β' is a constant. Therefore a closer approximation than (25.2.22) is given by

(25.2.25) $$\theta = \sqrt{\left(\frac{2\alpha}{n}\right)} \sin\{(n - \tfrac{1}{8}\alpha)t - \beta'\},$$

which we can write in terms of the amplitude A in the form

(25.2.26) $$\theta = A \sin\left\{n\left(1 - \frac{A^2}{16}\right)t + \beta'\right\}.$$

The period is approximately

(25.2.27) $$\frac{2\pi}{n}\left(1 + \frac{A^2}{16}\right).$$

(Of course, we have already found better approximations in § 5.2; for example, the approximation a_1 for μ gives for the period

$$\frac{2\pi}{n}\sec^2\frac{A}{4} = \frac{2\pi}{n}\left(1 + \tan^2\frac{A}{4}\right), \tag{25.2.28}$$

which is approximately equal to (25.2.27).)

Before leaving the problem it may be of interest to look at it from another point of view. Let us start from the Hamiltonian function (25.2.23) and use the contact transformation, from (α, β) to (α', β'), derived from the generating function $U(\alpha, \beta')$,

$$U = \alpha\beta' + \frac{\alpha^2}{48n}\{3nt - 2\sin 2(nt - \beta') + \tfrac{1}{4}\sin 4(nt - \beta')\}. \tag{25.2.29}$$

Thus

$$\begin{cases} \beta = \dfrac{\partial U}{\partial \alpha} = \beta' + \dfrac{\alpha}{24n}\{3nt - 2\sin 2(nt - \beta') + \tfrac{1}{4}\sin 4(nt - \beta')\}, \\ \alpha' = \dfrac{\partial U}{\partial \beta'} = \alpha + \dfrac{\alpha^2}{48n}\{4\cos 2(nt - \beta') - \cos 4(nt - \beta')\}, \end{cases} \tag{25.2.30}$$

and

$$\frac{\partial U}{\partial t} = \frac{\alpha^2}{48}\{3 - 4\cos 2(nt - \beta') + \cos 4(nt - \beta')\}. \tag{25.2.31}$$

The Hamiltonian function for the new variables is $K^* + \dfrac{\partial U}{\partial t}$ expressed in terms of α' and β' and t. Now

$$K^* + \frac{\partial U}{\partial t} = \tfrac{1}{48}\alpha^2\{4[\cos 2(nt - \beta) - \cos 2(nt - \beta')] - [\cos 4(nt - \beta) - \cos 4(nt - \beta')]\}, \tag{25.2.32}$$

and we need to express the second member of (25.2.32) in terms of (α', β', t). But α is nearly equal to α', and β to β', so the new Hamiltonian function is nearly zero, and α' and β' are nearly constant; we recover the same approximation $\beta = \beta' + \frac{1}{8}\alpha t$ as before.

25.3 The variation of the elliptic elements. A special case of the theory developed in § 25.2 arises when the original problem is that of two particles, sun and planet, moving under their mutual gravitation. If there is a small disturbance, how do the elliptic elements a, e, i, t_0, u_0, φ_0 (§18.13) change as time goes on?

We have already found the relations connecting the elliptic elements with the α's and β's of the solution by the Hamilton-Jacobi theorem. We have, as in (18.13.16),

$$\begin{cases} \alpha_1 = -\mu/(2a), & \beta_1 = t_0, \\ \alpha_2 = \sqrt{\{\mu a(1 - e^2)\}}, & \beta_2 = -u_0, \\ \alpha_3 = \sqrt{\{\mu a(1 - e^2)\}}\cos i, & \beta_3 = -\varphi_0. \end{cases} \tag{25.3.1}$$

If we solve these equations for the elliptic elements we have

$$\begin{cases} a = -\dfrac{\mu}{2\alpha_1}, & t_0 = \beta_1, \\ e^2 = 1 + \dfrac{2\alpha_1\alpha_2{}^2}{\mu^2}, & u_0 = -\beta_2, \\ \cos i = \dfrac{\alpha_3}{\alpha_2}, & \varphi_0 = -\beta_3. \end{cases} \tag{25.3.2}$$

Suppose now that we have a perturbation function $K^*(\alpha;\ \beta;\ t)$, and that we express it in terms of $a, e, i, t_0, u_0, \varphi_0$ and t to obtain the *disturbing function* R, where

(25.3.3) $$K^*(\alpha;\ \beta;\ t) = -R(a, e, i, t_0, u_0\ \varphi_0;\ t).$$

We now establish the equations governing the variation of $a, e, i, t_0, u_0, \varphi_0$ with t. This requires the expression of (25.2.3) in terms of the elliptic elements. We proceed systematically in two steps; first we find $\dot{a}, \ldots$ in terms of $\dot{\alpha}, \ldots$, and hence in terms of $\dfrac{\partial K^*}{\partial \alpha_1}, \cdots$; then we express $\dfrac{\partial K^*}{\partial \alpha_1}, \cdots$ in terms of $\dfrac{\partial R}{\partial a}, \cdots$.

For the first step,

(25.3.4)
$$\begin{cases} \dot{a} = \dfrac{\mu}{2\alpha_1{}^2}\dot{\alpha}_1 = \dfrac{2a^2}{\mu}\dfrac{\partial K^*}{\partial \beta_1}, \\[2ex] e\dot{e} = \dfrac{\alpha_2{}^2}{\mu^2}\dot{\alpha}_1 + \dfrac{2\alpha_1\alpha_2}{\mu^2}\dot{\alpha}_2 = \dfrac{a}{\mu}(1-e^2)\dfrac{\partial K^*}{\partial \beta_1} - \sqrt{\left(\dfrac{1-e^2}{\mu a}\right)}\dfrac{\partial K^*}{\partial \beta_2}, \\[2ex] -\sin i\dfrac{di}{dt} = -\dfrac{\alpha_3}{\alpha_2{}^2}\dot{\alpha}_2 + \dfrac{1}{\alpha_2}\dot{\alpha}_3 = -\dfrac{\cos i}{\sqrt{\{\mu a(1-e^2)\}}}\dfrac{\partial K^*}{\partial \beta_2} + \dfrac{1}{\sqrt{\{\mu a(1-e^2)\}}}\dfrac{\partial K^*}{\partial \beta_3}, \\[2ex] \dot{t}_0 = \dot{\beta}_1 = -\dfrac{\partial K^*}{\partial \alpha_1}, \\[2ex] \dot{u}_0 = -\dot{\beta}_2 = \dfrac{\partial K^*}{\partial \alpha_2}, \\[2ex] \dot{\varphi}_0 = -\dot{\beta}_3 = \dfrac{\partial K^*}{\partial \alpha_3}. \end{cases}$$

Then for the second step,

(25.3.5)
$$\begin{cases} \dfrac{\partial K^*}{\partial \alpha_1} = -\dfrac{\partial R}{\partial a}\dfrac{\partial a}{\partial \alpha_1} - \dfrac{\partial R}{\partial e}\dfrac{\partial e}{\partial \alpha_1} = -\dfrac{\mu}{2\alpha_1{}^2}\dfrac{\partial R}{\partial a} - \dfrac{\alpha_2{}^2}{\mu^2 e}\dfrac{\partial R}{\partial e} = -\dfrac{2a^2}{\mu}\dfrac{\partial R}{\partial a} - \dfrac{a(1-e^2)}{\mu e}\dfrac{\partial R}{\partial e}, \\[2ex] \dfrac{\partial K^*}{\partial \alpha_2} = -\dfrac{\partial R}{\partial e}\dfrac{\partial e}{\partial \alpha_2} - \dfrac{\partial R}{\partial i}\dfrac{\partial i}{\partial \alpha_2} = -\dfrac{2\alpha_1\alpha_2}{\mu^2 e}\dfrac{\partial R}{\partial e} - \dfrac{\alpha_3}{\alpha_2{}^2\sin i}\dfrac{\partial R}{\partial i} \\[2ex] \qquad = \dfrac{1}{e}\sqrt{\left(\dfrac{1-e^2}{\mu a}\right)}\dfrac{\partial R}{\partial e} - \dfrac{\cot i}{\sqrt{\{\mu a(1-e^2)\}}}\dfrac{\partial R}{\partial i}, \\[2ex] \dfrac{\partial K^*}{\partial \alpha_3} = -\dfrac{\partial R}{\partial i}\dfrac{\partial i}{\partial \alpha_3} = \dfrac{1}{\alpha_2 \sin i}\dfrac{\partial R}{\partial i} = \dfrac{1}{\sin i\sqrt{\{\mu a(1-e^2)\}}}\dfrac{\partial R}{\partial i}, \\[2ex] \dfrac{\partial K^*}{\partial \beta_1} = -\dfrac{\partial R}{\partial t_0}, \\[2ex] \dfrac{\partial K^*}{\partial \beta_2} = \dfrac{\partial R}{\partial u_0}, \\[2ex] \dfrac{\partial K^*}{\partial \beta_3} = \dfrac{\partial R}{\partial \varphi_0}. \end{cases}$$

Thus finally, combining the two sets of formulae, we have

$$(25.3.6)\quad \begin{cases} \dot{a} = -\dfrac{2a^2}{\mu}\dfrac{\partial R}{\partial t_0}, \\[2ex] \dot{e} = -\dfrac{a(1-e^2)}{\mu e}\dfrac{\partial R}{\partial t_0} - \dfrac{1}{e}\sqrt{\left(\dfrac{1-e^2}{\mu a}\right)}\dfrac{\partial R}{\partial u_0}, \\[2ex] \dfrac{di}{dt} = \dfrac{\cot i}{\sqrt{\{\mu a(1-e^2)\}}}\dfrac{\partial R}{\partial u_0} - \dfrac{1}{\sin i\sqrt{\{\mu a(1-e^2)\}}}\dfrac{\partial R}{\partial \varphi_0}, \\[2ex] t_0 = \dfrac{2a^2}{\mu}\dfrac{\partial R}{\partial a} + \dfrac{a(1-e^2)}{\mu e}\dfrac{\partial R}{\partial e}, \\[2ex] \dot{u}_0 = \dfrac{1}{e}\sqrt{\left(\dfrac{1-e^2}{\mu a}\right)}\dfrac{\partial R}{\partial e} - \dfrac{\cot i}{\sqrt{\{\mu a(1-e^2)\}}}\dfrac{\partial R}{\partial i}, \\[2ex] \dot{\varphi}_0 = \dfrac{1}{\sin i\sqrt{\{\mu a(1-e^2)\}}}\dfrac{\partial R}{\partial i}. \end{cases}$$

*These are the equations determining the variation of the elliptic elements with the time.**

The first problem that presents itself is the effect on the motion of a planet arising from the presence of a second planet; the disturbing function R, expressed in terms of the positions of the two planets relative to the sun, has been found in § 18.17, and to use (25.3.6) we must express R in terms of the elliptic elements of the two planets. The complete problem involves twelve equations, since the elements a', e', i', t_0', u_0', φ_0' of the second planet are also slowly changing. The discussion of this system of twelve equations is one of the first objects of planetary theory, and anything approaching a complete discussion would be out of place here; but a few introductory remarks may be of interest.

We recall that the masses m_1, m_2 of the planets are small in comparison with the mass M of the sun. We can attack the problem by seeking solutions of the twelve equations in the form

$$(25.3.7)\qquad a = a_0 + a_1 + a_2 + \ldots, \qquad a' = a_0' + a_1' + a_2' + \ldots,$$

and similarly for the other elements, where a_0 is the initial value of a, a_1 is of order 1 in m_1/M and m_2/M, a_2 is of order 2, and so on. We may speak of a_1 and a_2 as perturbations of the first and second orders, and similarly for the other elements. If we need only the first-order perturbation the matter is comparatively simple, because, since R itself is of order 1, we can give to the elements of both planets in the second members of (25.3.6) their (constant) initial values. To this order of approximation, therefore, the second members of (25.3.6) are known functions of t, and we can find the solutions by mechanical quadratures.

The classical technique for attacking the general problem is to expand R in the form $\Sigma\, C \cos D$, where

$$(25.3.8)\qquad D = \nu_1 l + \nu_1' l' + \nu_2 u_0 + \nu_2' u_0' + \nu_3 \varphi_0 + \nu_3' \varphi_0',$$

* But the equations as exhibited here are not quite in the form that is most useful to the astronomer—see the note on p. 633.

where the ν's and ν''s are integers, positive, negative, or zero, and the coefficients C depend on the six parameters a, a', e, e', i, i'. The method is feasible because in many concrete applications a few terms suffice to give a sufficiently good approximation. But some theoretical questions as to the convergence of the series remain unsolved.

More generally, in some problems of planetary theory, K^* has the form

$$K^* = m \sum_s C_s(\alpha) \cos D_s, \tag{25.3.9}$$

where m is a small constant, the coefficients C are functions of the α's (as indicated), and

$$D_s = \sum_i \nu_{si}\beta_i + n_s t, \tag{25.3.10}$$

where the ν's are integers, positive, negative, or zero. We suppose in the first instance that no n_s is zero. The variation of the α's and β's is determined by the equations (25.2.3).

An important method of attacking the problem employs the contact transformation, from $(\alpha;\ \beta)$ to $(\alpha';\ \beta')$, derived from the generating function $U(\alpha';\ \beta)$,

$$U = -\sum_i \alpha'_i\beta_i - m \sum_s \frac{1}{n_s} C_s(\alpha') \sin D_s. \tag{25.3.11}$$

The equations corresponding to (24.3.3–4) are

$$\alpha_r = -\frac{\partial U}{\partial \beta_r}, \quad \beta_r' = -\frac{\partial U}{\partial \alpha_r'}, \tag{25.3.12}$$

giving

$$\begin{cases} \alpha_r = \alpha_r' + m \sum_s \dfrac{\nu_{sr}}{n_s} C_s(\alpha') \cos D_s, \\ \beta_r' = \beta_r + m \sum_s \dfrac{1}{n_s} \dfrac{\partial C_s(\alpha')}{\partial \alpha_r'} \sin D_s. \end{cases} \tag{25.3.13}$$

Also

$$\frac{\partial U}{\partial t} = -m \sum_s C_s(\alpha') \cos D_s. \tag{25.3.14}$$

The new Hamiltonian function is

$$m \sum_s \{C_s(\alpha) - C_s(\alpha')\} \cos D_s. \tag{25.3.15}$$

expressed in terms of α''s and β''s and t. Now α_r' differs from α_r, and β_r' differs from β_r, by a term of order m; it follows that *the new Hamiltonian function is of order* m^2.

If there are terms in K^* with $n_s = 0$, the corresponding terms must be omitted from (25.3.11). It may be convenient to omit also the long-period terms, i.e. terms with small, but non-zero, values of n_s. The important point is that the short-period terms of order m are all removed from the Hamiltonian function in the one operation.

25.4 Other proofs of Jacobi's theorem. A proof of Jacobi's theorem on the form of the equations of motion after a contact transformation to new variables was given in § 25.1. This proof depends on the equivalence theorem, and this is probably the simplest line of attack. But it may be of value, in view of the importance of the theorem, to exhibit two other proofs; each of these proofs has some features of interest. The second proof sets out from the definition of a contact transformation in terms of a generating function (§ 24.2 and § 24.3), and it brings in some ideas that are important in the subsequent theory. The third proof depends on the fact that the matrix **M** is symplectic (§ 24.13); this proof brings out the fact that a contact transformation is not the most general type of transformation in which the Hamiltonian form of the equations of motion is preserved.

Second proof of Jacobi's theorem. We define the contact transformation by means of a generating function. We take for definiteness the case where the transformation is one in which there is no identical relation connecting q's and Q's and t, the transformation being defined by the equations (24.2.7–9),

(25.4.1) $$p_r = \frac{\partial W}{\partial q_r}, \quad P_r = -\frac{\partial W}{\partial Q_r}, \quad R = \frac{\partial W}{\partial t}.$$

We first prove two lemmas, and then deduce Jacobi's theorem.

Lemma 1. *If*

(25.4.2) $$\begin{cases} q_r = \varphi_r(\gamma_1, \gamma_2, \ldots, \gamma_{2n};\ t), \\ p_r = \varphi_{n+r}(\gamma_1, \gamma_2, \ldots, \gamma_{2n};\ t), \end{cases} \qquad r = 1, 2, \ldots, n,$$

is the general solution of the Hamiltonian equations, the functions φ *being of class* C_2 *in a domain* D *of* $(\gamma_1, \gamma_2, \ldots, \gamma_{2n};\ t)$, *and if*

(25.4.3) $$H(q;\ p;\ t) = G(\gamma_1, \gamma_2, \ldots, \gamma_{2n};\ t),$$

then $G \in C_2$, *and*

(25.4.4) $$\frac{\partial G}{\partial \gamma_i} = [t, \gamma_i], \qquad i = 1, 2, \ldots, 2n.$$

The proof is immediate, for

(25.4.5) $$\frac{\partial G}{\partial \gamma_i} = \frac{\partial H}{\partial q_r}\frac{\partial q_r}{\partial \gamma_i} + \frac{\partial H}{\partial p_r}\frac{\partial p_r}{\partial \gamma_i} = \frac{\partial q_r}{\partial t}\frac{\partial p_r}{\partial \gamma_i} - \frac{\partial p_r}{\partial t}\frac{\partial q_r}{\partial \gamma_i},$$

where the repeated suffix r implies summation from 1 to n, and the proof is complete.

Lemma 2. *Conversely, if* $q_1, q_2, \ldots, q_n;\ p_1, p_2, \ldots, p_n$ *are* $2n$ *independent functions, of class* C_2, *of* $\gamma_1, \gamma_2, \ldots, \gamma_{2n};\ t$; *and if there exists a function* $G(\gamma_1, \gamma_2, \ldots, \gamma_{2n};\ t)$ *such that*

(25.4.4) $$\frac{\partial G}{\partial \gamma_i} = [t, \gamma_i], \qquad i = 1, 2, \ldots, 2n,$$

then the q's *and* p's *satisfy Hamilton's equations*

(25.4.6) $$\frac{\partial q_r}{\partial t} = \frac{\partial H}{\partial p_r}, \quad \frac{\partial p_r}{\partial t} = -\frac{\partial H}{\partial q_r}, \qquad r = 1, 2, \ldots, n,$$

where H *is constructed by expressing* G *in terms of* q's *and* p's *and* t,

(25.4.7) $$G(\gamma;\ t) = H(q;\ p;\ t).$$

We are to think of the equations (25.4.2) as solved for the γ's (as functions of q's and p's and t); we then construct H as in (25.4.7), and we have

(25.4.8) $$\frac{\partial G}{\partial \gamma_i} = \frac{\partial H}{\partial q_r}\frac{\partial q_r}{\partial \gamma_i} + \frac{\partial H}{\partial p_r}\frac{\partial p_r}{\partial \gamma_i}.$$

But from (25.4.4)

(25.4.9) $$\frac{\partial G}{\partial \gamma_i} = \frac{\partial q_r}{\partial t}\frac{\partial p_r}{\partial \gamma_i} - \frac{\partial p_r}{\partial t}\frac{\partial q_r}{\partial \gamma_i}.$$

Comparing (25.4.8) and (25.4.9) we have

(25.4.10) $$\frac{\partial p_r}{\partial \gamma_i}\left(\frac{\partial q_r}{\partial t} - \frac{\partial H}{\partial p_r}\right) - \frac{\partial q_r}{\partial \gamma_i}\left(\frac{\partial p_r}{\partial t} + \frac{\partial H}{\partial q_r}\right) = 0.$$

There are $2n$ such equations, one for each value of i from 1 to $2n$, and the determinant of the coefficients does not vanish in D; the lemma follows.

The reader will not have failed to notice the similarity between the two lemmas and the two parts of the equivalence theorem. The ideas underlying the present proof of Jacobi's theorem do not differ essentially from those underlying the proof given in § 25.1, but the technical details are different.

We now turn to the proof of Jacobi's theorem. The variables $q_1, q_2, \ldots, q_n, p_1, p_2, \ldots, p_n$ defined by (25.4.2) satisfy Hamilton's equations (25.4.6), and we transform to new variables $Q_1, Q_2, \ldots, Q_n, P_1, P_2, \ldots, P_n$, where the transformation is the contact transformation defined by (25.4.1). Let us express W in terms of the γ's and t,

$$W(q;\ Q;\ t) = F(\gamma;\ t). \tag{25.4.11}$$

Then, if i has any of the values $1, 2, \ldots, 2n$,

$$\frac{\partial F}{\partial \gamma_i} = \frac{\partial W}{\partial q_r}\frac{\partial q_r}{\partial \gamma_i} + \frac{\partial W}{\partial Q_r}\frac{\partial Q_r}{\partial \gamma_i} = p_r\frac{\partial q_r}{\partial \gamma_i} - P_r\frac{\partial Q_r}{\partial \gamma_i}, \tag{25.4.12}$$

and

$$\frac{\partial F}{\partial t} = \frac{\partial W}{\partial q_r}\frac{\partial q_r}{\partial t} + \frac{\partial W}{\partial Q_r}\frac{\partial Q_r}{\partial t} + \frac{\partial W}{\partial t} = p_r\frac{\partial q_r}{\partial t} - P_r\frac{\partial Q_r}{\partial t} + \frac{\partial W}{\partial t}. \tag{25.4.13}$$

Now $F \in C_2$, so

$$\frac{\partial^2 F}{\partial t\, \partial \gamma_i} = \frac{\partial^2 F}{\partial \gamma_i\, \partial t}, \tag{25.4.14}$$

and therefore, from (25.4.12) and (25.4.13),

$$\frac{\partial}{\partial t}\left(p_r\frac{\partial q_r}{\partial \gamma_i} - P_r\frac{\partial Q_r}{\partial \gamma_i}\right) = \frac{\partial}{\partial \gamma_i}\left(p_r\frac{\partial q_r}{\partial t} - P_r\frac{\partial Q_r}{\partial t} + \frac{\partial W}{\partial t}\right). \tag{25.4.15}$$

Hence

$$\begin{aligned} \frac{\partial Q_r}{\partial t}\frac{\partial P_r}{\partial \gamma_i} - \frac{\partial P_r}{\partial t}\frac{\partial Q_r}{\partial \gamma_i} &= \frac{\partial q_r}{\partial t}\frac{\partial p_r}{\partial \gamma_i} - \frac{\partial p_r}{\partial t}\frac{\partial q_r}{\partial \gamma_i} + \frac{\partial^2 W}{\partial \gamma_i\, \partial t} \\ &= \frac{\partial H}{\partial p_r}\frac{\partial p_r}{\partial \gamma_i} + \frac{\partial H}{\partial q_r}\frac{\partial q_r}{\partial \gamma_i} + \frac{\partial^2 W}{\partial \gamma_i\, dt} \\ &= \frac{\partial}{\partial \gamma_i}\left(H + \frac{\partial W}{\partial t}\right) \\ &= \frac{\partial G}{\partial \gamma_i}, \end{aligned} \tag{25.4.16}$$

where G is $H + \dfrac{\partial W}{\partial t}$ expressed in terms of the γ's and t. Thus, if $[[t, \gamma_i]]$ denotes the Lagrange bracket for the large letters $(Q;\ P)$, we have

$$\frac{\partial G}{\partial \gamma_i} = [[t, \gamma_i]]. \tag{25.4.17}$$

Therefore, by Lemma 2, the variables $Q_1, Q_2, \ldots, Q_n, P_1, P_2, \ldots, P_n$ satisfy Hamilton's equations

$$\frac{\partial Q_r}{\partial t} = \frac{\partial H^*}{\partial P_r}, \quad \frac{\partial P_r}{\partial t} = -\frac{\partial H^*}{\partial Q_r}, \qquad r = 1, 2, \ldots, n, \tag{25.4.18}$$

where H^* is $H + \dfrac{\partial W}{\partial t}$ expressed in terms of Q's and P's and t; and this is Jacobi's theorem.

The proof follows the same lines in other cases. Suppose, for example, that there is no identical relation connecting q's and P's and t, and we define the transformation in terms of a generating function $U(q;\ P;\ t)$ by the equations (24.3.9). If $U(q;\ P;\ t) = F(\gamma;\ t)$, the equation $\dfrac{\partial^2 F}{\partial t\,\partial \gamma_i} = \dfrac{\partial^2 F}{\partial \gamma_i\,\partial t}$ leads to (25.4.17), and the result follows as before.

Third proof of Jacobi's theorem. We have seen (§ 22.1) that the Hamiltonian equations of motion can be written in the form

$$\dot{\mathbf{x}} = \mathbf{Z}\mathbf{H}_x, \tag{25.4.19}$$

where $\dot{\mathbf{x}}$ is the column matrix whose rth component is $\dot{x}_r$, and $\mathbf{H}_x$ is the column matrix whose rth component is $\partial H/\partial x_r$. We consider a transformation to new variables $X_1, X_2, \ldots, X_{2n}$,

$$X_r = \varphi_r(x_1, x_2, \ldots, x_{2n};\ t), \qquad r = 1, 2, \ldots, 2n, \tag{25.4.20}$$

and we assume the transformation to be reversible in a certain domain of $(\mathbf{x};\ t)$. Then

$$\dot{\mathbf{x}} = \frac{\partial \mathbf{x}}{\partial t} + \mathbf{m}\dot{\mathbf{X}}, \quad \mathbf{H}_x = \mathbf{M}'\mathbf{K}_X, \tag{25.4.21}$$

where K denotes the Hamiltonian function expressed in terms of $X_1, X_2, \ldots, X_{2n}, t$,

$$H(x_1, x_2, \ldots, x_{2n};\ t) = K(X_1, X_2, \ldots, X_{2n};\ t), \tag{25.4.22}$$

and $\mathbf{m}$ is the matrix $(\partial x_r/\partial X_s)$, $\mathbf{M}$ is the matrix $(\partial X_r/\partial x_s)$, as in § 24.13. Thus

$$\dot{\mathbf{x}} - \mathbf{Z}\mathbf{H}_x = \frac{\partial \mathbf{x}}{\partial t} + \mathbf{m}\dot{\mathbf{X}} - \mathbf{Z}\mathbf{M}'\mathbf{K}_X, \tag{25.4.23}$$

whence

$$\mathbf{M}(\dot{\mathbf{x}} - \mathbf{Z}\mathbf{H}_x) = \mathbf{M}\frac{\partial \mathbf{x}}{\partial t} + \dot{\mathbf{X}} - \mathbf{M}\mathbf{Z}\mathbf{M}'\mathbf{K}_X. \tag{25.4.24}$$

The equations of motion in the new variables are

$$\dot{\mathbf{X}} = \mathbf{M}\mathbf{Z}\mathbf{M}'\mathbf{K}_X - \mathbf{M}\frac{\partial \mathbf{x}}{\partial t}, \tag{25.4.25}$$

and we can write this in the form

$$\dot{\mathbf{X}} = \mathbf{M}\mathbf{Z}\mathbf{M}'\left(\mathbf{K}_X + \mathbf{m}'\mathbf{Z}\frac{\partial \mathbf{x}}{\partial t}\right). \tag{25.4.26}$$

So far we have made no assumptions as to the character of the transformation; let us now assume that it is a contact transformation. Then

$$\mathbf{M}\mathbf{Z}\mathbf{M}' = \mathbf{Z}, \tag{25.4.27}$$

and the new equations of motion have the Hamiltonian form

$$\dot{\mathbf{X}} = \mathbf{Z}\mathbf{H}^*_X, \tag{25.4.28}$$

provided that the column matrix $\mathbf{m}'\mathbf{Z}\dfrac{\partial \mathbf{x}}{\partial t}$ has the form $\mathbf{L}_X$. We easily verify that this is so. If for the moment we write $\mathbf{u}$ for $\mathbf{Z}\dfrac{\partial \mathbf{x}}{\partial t}$, the condition is that, for all values of r and s,

$$\frac{\partial}{\partial X_s}\left(u_i\frac{\partial x_i}{\partial X_r}\right) = \frac{\partial}{\partial X_r}\left(u_i\frac{\partial x_i}{\partial X_s}\right), \tag{25.4.29}$$

which is equivalent to

(25.4.30) $$\frac{\partial u_i}{\partial X_s}\frac{\partial x_i}{\partial X_r} = \frac{\partial u_i}{\partial X_r}\frac{\partial x_i}{\partial X_s},$$

Now (25.4.30) is true if the matrix $\mathbf{m}'\mathbf{Z}\mathbf{m}_t$ (where $\mathbf{m}_t$ is obtained from $\mathbf{m}$ by differentiating each element partially with respect to t) is symmetric,

(25.4.31) $$\mathbf{m}'\mathbf{Z}\mathbf{m}_t = \mathbf{m}_t'\mathbf{Z}'\mathbf{m},$$

and this is equivalent (since $\mathbf{Z}' = -\mathbf{Z}$) to

(25.4.32) $$\mathbf{m}'\mathbf{Z}\mathbf{m}_t + \mathbf{m}_t'\mathbf{Z}\mathbf{m} = 0.$$

The condition required is that $\mathbf{m}'\mathbf{Z}\mathbf{m}$ should be independent of t, which is certainly true in virtue of (24.13.7), and this completes the proof of Jacobi's theorem.

If we consider a transformation satisfying, not $\mathbf{MZM}' = \mathbf{Z}$, but the more general condition

(25.4.33) $$\mathbf{MZM}' = \lambda\mathbf{Z},$$

where λ is a scalar non-zero constant, then

(25.4.34) $$\mathbf{mZm}' = \frac{1}{\lambda}\mathbf{Z},$$

and the new equations of motion are still of the Hamiltonian form (25.4.28). The condition (25.4.33) represents a generalization of (25.4.27), and it would be reasonable to extend the term *contact transformation* to include the wider class of transformations satisfying (25.4.33). We shall however confine the term to the particular case already discussed, in which λ has the value $+1$.

Conversely, if we take a general transformation (25.4.20), and ask in what circumstances the new equations of motion (25.4.26) have the Hamiltonian form, we find that the transformation must satisfy (25.4.33). For the second member of (25.4.26) must have the form ZH^*_X for all Hamiltonian functions H, and this implies that each term must separately have this form; and this in turn implies (25.4.33).

25.5 The constancy of Lagrange brackets. *If the general solution of the Hamiltonian equations for a given dynamical system is*

(25.5.1) $$\begin{cases} q_r = \varphi_r(\gamma_1, \gamma_2, \ldots, \gamma_{2n};\ t), \\ p_r = \varphi_{n+r}(\gamma_1, \gamma_2, \ldots, \gamma_{2n};\ t), \end{cases}$$

then $[\gamma_i, \gamma_j]$ *remains constant throughout the motion.*

We know that the theorem is true if the γ's are the initial values of the q's and p's; for the transformation from $(q_0;\ p_0)$ to $(q;\ p)$ is a contact transformation, and

(25.5.2) $$[q_{i0}, q_{j0}] = [p_{i0}, p_{j0}] = 0, \quad [q_{i0}, p_{j0}] = \delta_i^{\,j}.$$

We can deduce the result for a general choice of γ's from this special case. Alternatively, the theorem can be proved very simply by means of thc bilinear covariant (§ 24.8). We know that

(25.5.3) $$dq_r\,\delta p_r - dp_r\,\delta q_r$$

is invariant for any contact transformation; in particular, it remains constant during the motion of a dynamical system. Let d denote a variation to a neighbouring orbit in the phase space in which only γ_i varies, and let δ denote a variation to a neighbouring orbit in which only γ_j varies. Then

$$(25.5.4)\qquad dq_r\,\delta p_r - dp_r\,\delta q_r = \frac{\partial q_r}{\partial \gamma_i}\,d\gamma_i\,\frac{\partial p_r}{\partial \gamma_j}\,\delta\gamma_j - \frac{\partial p_r}{\partial \gamma_i}\,d\gamma_i\,\frac{\partial q_r}{\delta \gamma_j}\,\delta\gamma_j$$

$$= [\gamma_i, \gamma_j]\,d\gamma_i\,\delta\gamma_j, \qquad \text{(not summed)}$$

and the result follows.

Alternatively, we can deduce the constancy of the Lagrange brackets from the ideas underlying the second proof of Jacobi's theorem in § 25.4. Let

$$(25.5.5)\qquad H(q;\ p;\ t) = G(\gamma;\ t)$$

as in (25.4.3), so that $G \in C_2$, and

$$(25.5.6)\qquad \frac{\partial G}{\partial \gamma_i} = [t, \gamma_i],$$

as in (25.4.4). Now we easily verify that

$$(25.5.7)\qquad \frac{\partial}{\partial t}[\gamma_i, \gamma_j] + \frac{\partial}{\partial \gamma_j}[t, \gamma_i] + \frac{\partial}{\partial \gamma_i}[\gamma_j, t] = 0,$$

a result reminiscent of Poisson's identity (§ 22.2). Thus

$$\frac{\partial}{\partial t}[\gamma_i, \gamma_j] = \frac{\partial}{\partial \gamma_i}[t, \gamma_j] - \frac{\partial}{\partial \gamma_j}[t, \gamma_i]$$

$$= \frac{\partial}{\partial \gamma_i}\frac{\partial G}{\partial \gamma_j} - \frac{\partial}{\partial \gamma_j}\frac{\partial G}{\partial \gamma_i} = 0,$$

and the theorem is established.

25.6 Infinitesimal contact transformation. The equations

$$(25.6.1)\qquad \begin{cases} Q_r - q_r = \mu\dfrac{\partial \varphi}{\partial p_r}, \\[2ex] P_r - p_r = -\mu\dfrac{\partial \varphi}{\partial q_r}, \end{cases}$$

where μ is a small constant, and $\varphi \in C_2$, define a contact transformation if we neglect terms of order μ^2 (§ 24.5). The displacement from $(q;\ p)$ to $(Q;\ P)$ in the phase space is small of order μ. We agree to neglect terms of order μ^2 throughout, so that we need not distinguish between small and large letters in terms multiplied by μ, and this remark greatly simplifies the calculations connected with the transformation.

Suppose, for example, that $f(q_1, q_2, \ldots, q_n;\ p_1, p_2, \ldots, p_n;\ t)$ (or, say, $f(q;\ p;\ t)$) is a given function of the q's and p's and t, of class C_2. There is a simple formula for the increment in f when we move from $(q;\ p)$ to $(Q;\ P)$, t being unchanged. We have, correct to order μ,

$$(25.6.2)\qquad f(Q;\ P;\ t) - f(q;\ p;\ t) = (Q_r - q_r)\frac{\partial f}{\partial q_r} + (P_r - p_r)\frac{\partial f}{\partial p_r}$$

$$= \mu\frac{\partial f}{\partial q_r}\frac{\partial \varphi}{\partial p_r} - \mu\frac{\partial \varphi}{\partial q_r}\frac{\partial f}{\partial p_r}$$

$$= \mu(f, \varphi),$$

and we need not distinguish between small and large letters in $\mu(f, \varphi)$ because we have agreed to neglect terms of order μ^2.

Suppose then that we have a system with Hamiltonian function $H(q;\ p;\ t)$, and we apply the infinitesimal contact transformation (25.6.1). The Hamiltonian function for the transformed system is H^*, which is

$$H(q;\ p;\ t) + \mu \frac{\partial \varphi}{\partial t} \tag{25.6.3}$$

expressed in terms of $(Q;\ P;\ t)$ (§ 25.1). Thus, in virtue of (25.6.2),

$$\begin{aligned} H^*(Q;\ P;\ t) &= H(Q;\ P;\ t) - \mu(H, \varphi) + \mu \frac{\partial \varphi}{\partial t} \\ &= H(Q;\ P;\ t) + \mu \left\{ \frac{\partial \varphi}{\partial t} + (\varphi, H) \right\}. \end{aligned} \tag{25.6.4}$$

In the term multiplied by μ in the second member we can write Q_r, P_r in place of q_r, p_r, so we have found the required Hamiltonian function H^* for the new variables Q_r, P_r.

A case of particular interest is this. Suppose that $\varphi(q;\ p;\ t)$ is an integral of the original Hamiltonian system. Then, as in (22.2.5),

$$\frac{\partial \varphi}{\partial t} + (\varphi, H) \tag{25.6.5}$$

is identically zero, and the new Hamiltonian function is the same as the old, with merely the large letters written in place of the corresponding small letters. In this case, therefore, the family of orbits in the (Q, P)-space is identical with the family of orbits in the (q, p)-space. The transformation transforms any orbit of the system into an adjacent orbit. In these circumstances the system is said to *admit* the transformation.

We can deduce an alternative, and very elegant, proof of Poisson's theorem (§ 22.3). We take for φ a known integral of the original Hamiltonian system, so that the family of orbits in the phase space transforms into itself, i.e. each orbit is transformed into a neighbouring orbit of the system. If $\psi(q;\ p;\ t)$ is a second integral of the Hamiltonian equations, the increment of ψ under the transformation (i.e. $\psi(Q;P;t) - \psi(q;\ p;\ t)$) is $\mu(\psi, \varphi)$, and this remains constant, since the transformed orbit is also an orbit for the original system. Thus (ψ, φ) is a function of $(q;\ p;\ t)$ that remains constant on an orbit of the Hamiltonian system; if φ and ψ are known integrals, (ψ, φ) is also an integral, and this is Poisson's theorem.

25.7 Integrals in involution. We found (§ 24.14) that if we take n functions $\varphi_r(q;\ p;\ t)$ in involution (i.e. n functions such that the Poisson bracket of every pair is identically zero), if each φ is of class C_2, and if the Jacobian

$$\frac{\partial(\varphi_1, \varphi_2, \ldots, \varphi_n)}{\partial(p_1, p_2, \ldots, p_n)}$$

does not vanish identically in the relevant domain of $(q;\ p;\ t)$, then we can find a contact transformation from $(q;\ p)$ to $(Q;\ P)$ in which

$$Q_r = \varphi_r(q;\ p;\ t), \qquad r = 1, 2, \ldots, n. \tag{25.7.1}$$

Explicitly, we found that if we solve the equations (25.7.1) for the p's in the form

$$p_r = \psi_r(q;\ Q;\ t), \tag{25.7.2}$$

then

$$\frac{\partial \psi_r}{\partial q_s} = \frac{\partial \psi_s}{\partial q_r}, \tag{25.7.3}$$

and there is a function $W(q;\ Q;\ t)$ such that

$$\psi_r = \frac{\partial W}{\partial q_r}. \tag{25.7.4}$$

The required contact transformation is defined by the equations

$$p_r = \frac{\partial W}{\partial q_r}, \quad P_r = -\frac{\partial W}{\partial Q_r}, \qquad r = 1, 2, \ldots, n. \tag{25.7.5}$$

We now consider what happens when the n functions φ are integrals for a dynamical system with Hamiltonian function H. We know that the equations of motion in the new variables $(Q;\ P)$ are the Hamiltonian equations derived from the Hamiltonian function H^*, where H^* is $H + \dfrac{\partial W}{\partial t}$ expressed in terms of Q's and P's and t. But the Q's remain constant during the motion (because they are integrals) so H^* cannot contain any of the P's. But this is not the whole truth; in fact we can choose the transformation in such a way that H^* vanishes identically, so *the P's as well as the Q's remain constant during the motion*. The upshot is that, if we know n integrals in involution, then n further single-valued integrals exist. The $2n$ integrals together enable us to complete the solution of the problem.

We first prove that, if we form the function $G(q;\ Q;\ t)$ by substituting ψ_r for p_r in $H(q;\ p;\ t)$, then

$$\frac{\partial \psi_r}{\partial t} + \frac{\partial G}{\partial q_r} = 0, \qquad r = 1, 2, \ldots, n. \tag{25.7.6}$$

If we substitute φ_r for Q_r in the second member of (25.7.2) we obtain an identity in $(q;\ p;\ t)$, so, differentiating in turn with respect to q_s, p_s, t we have

$$\frac{\partial \psi_r}{\partial q_s} + \frac{\partial \psi_r}{\partial Q_i}\frac{\partial \varphi_i}{\partial q_s} = 0, \tag{25.7.7}$$

$$\frac{\partial \psi_r}{\partial Q_i}\frac{\partial \varphi_i}{\partial p_s} = \delta_r^{\,s}, \tag{25.7.8}$$

$$\frac{\partial \psi_r}{\partial t} + \frac{\partial \psi_r}{\partial Q_i}\frac{\partial \varphi_i}{\partial t} = 0. \tag{25.7.9}$$

But, since φ_i is an integral,

$$\frac{\partial \varphi_i}{\partial t} + (\varphi_i, H) = 0, \tag{25.7.10}$$

and using this relation (25.7.9) becomes

$$\frac{\partial \psi_r}{\partial t} = \frac{\partial \psi_r}{\partial Q_i}\left(\frac{\partial \varphi_i}{\partial q_s}\frac{\partial H}{\partial p_s} - \frac{\partial H}{\partial q_s}\frac{\partial \varphi_i}{\partial p_s}\right), \tag{25.7.11}$$

and this in turn, using (25.7.7) and (25.7.8), yields

$$\frac{\partial \psi_r}{\partial t} = -\frac{\partial H}{\partial p_s}\frac{\partial \psi_r}{\partial q_s} - \frac{\partial H}{\partial q_r}. \tag{25.7.12}$$

But

$$\frac{\partial G}{\partial q_r} = \frac{\partial H}{\partial q_r} + \frac{\partial H}{\partial p_s}\frac{\partial \psi_s}{\partial q_r}, \tag{25.7.13}$$

and the functions on the right in (25.7.12) and (25.7.13) are equal and opposite in virtue of (25.7.3); and (25.7.6) follows.

The theorem now follows easily. From (25.7.3) and (25.7.6) we see that there exists a function $W(q;\ Q;\ t)$ such that

$$\psi_r = \frac{\partial W}{\partial q_r}, \quad G = -\frac{\partial W}{\partial t}. \tag{25.7.14}$$

If we employ the contact transformation derived from the generating function W by the equations (25.7.5), the new Hamilton function H^* is $G + \dfrac{\partial W}{\partial t}$ expressed in terms of $(Q;\ P;\ t)$. But H^* vanishes identically, in virtue of (25.7.14), and this is the result stated. The P's are functions of $(q;\ p;\ t)$ which are n new integrals of the original Hamiltonian equations, and they are in fact n integrals in involution (in virtue of the Poisson bracket conditions for a contact transformation, § 24.9).

We can now state the theorem in a somewhat different form, as follows. We solve the equations

$$\varphi_r(q;\ p;\ t) = \alpha_r, \qquad r = 1, 2, \ldots, n, \tag{25.7.15}$$

for the p's, obtaining

$$p_r = \psi_r(q;\ \alpha;\ t), \qquad r = 1, 2, \ldots, n. \tag{25.7.16}$$

Next, we form the function

$$G = G(q;\ \alpha;\ t) \tag{25.7.17}$$

by substituting ψ_r for p_r in $H(q;\ p;\ t)$. Then

$$\psi_r\, dq_r - G\, dt \tag{25.7.18}$$

is a complete differential dW, where $W = W(q;\ \alpha;\ t)$, and n further integrals of the Hamiltonian system are given by

$$-\beta_r = \frac{\partial W}{\partial \alpha_r}, \qquad r = 1, 2, \ldots, n. \tag{25.7.19}$$

The close relationship of the theorem just proved to the Hamilton-Jacobi theorem is now evident. From the n known integrals in involution we construct the function W derived from (25.7.18), and since

$$\frac{\partial W}{\partial t} + H\left(q;\ \frac{\partial W}{\partial q};\ t\right) = 0, \tag{25.7.20}$$

W is in fact a complete integral of Hamilton's partial differential equation.

The theorem takes an even simpler form when H does not contain t, and when the φ's also do not contain t. We have n integrals in involution

(25.7.21) $$\varphi_r(q;\ p) = \alpha_r, \qquad r = 1, 2, \ldots, n,$$

where

(25.7.22) $$\varphi_1 \equiv H(q;\ p),$$

and α_1 is the energy constant. (The integrals $\varphi_2, \varphi_3, \ldots, \varphi_n$ are necessarily in involution with $\varphi_1 (\equiv H)$, and in this case they are also in involution with one another.) If we solve the equations (25.7.21) for the p's we find

(25.7.23) $$p_r = \psi_r(q;\ \alpha),$$

and the functions ψ_r have the property

(25.7.24) $$\psi_r = \partial K/\partial q_r,$$

where $K = K(q;\ \alpha)$. The function W is $-\alpha_1 t + K$, and the n further integrals are

(25.7.25) $$\begin{cases} \dfrac{\partial K}{\partial \alpha_1} - t = -t_0, & \\ \dfrac{\partial K}{\partial \alpha_r} = -\beta_r, & r = 2, 3, \ldots, n. \end{cases}$$

The solution thus appears in a form similar to that provided by the modified Hamilton-Jacobi theorem, equations (16.5.5–7). The special case $n = 2$ has already been established (from the theorem of the last multiplier) in § 22.13.

25.8 Lie's theorem on involution-systems. In the preceding section we were concerned with a set of functions $u_1, u_2, \ldots, u_N$, each of class C_2 in a certain domain D of $(q_1, q_2, \ldots, q_n;\ p_1, p_2, \ldots, p_n;\ t)$, with the property that the Poisson bracket (u_r, u_s) of any pair is identically zero. Such a set of functions is called an *involution-system*.

We now prove the following theorem. *If*

(25.8.1) $$v = v(u_1, u_2, \ldots, u_N), \quad w = w(u_1, u_2, \ldots, u_N),$$

are functions of $(u_1, u_2, \ldots, u_N)$ *of class* C_2 *in the range of values of the* u*'s corresponding to the domain* D *of* $(q;\ p;\ t)$, *then*

(25.8.2) $$(v, w) = 0.$$

The theorem is easily established by deliberate differentiation; but it will be more illuminating for our present purpose to derive it from the theory of infinitesimal contact transformations. We recall that the infinitesimal contact transformation (25.6.1) transforms the function f into itself if $(\varphi, f) = 0$. Consider first an infinitesimal contact transformation with $\varphi = u_1$. Each of the functions u_r is transformed into itself by the transformation, and so therefore is v. Therefore $(u_1, v) = 0$, and by a similar argument

$$(u_r, v) = 0, \qquad r = 1, 2, \ldots, N.$$

Now consider an infinitesimal contact transformation with $\varphi = v$. Each of the functions $u_1, u_2, \ldots, u_N$ is transformed into itself, and therefore so is w. Therefore $(v, w) = 0$, and this completes the proof of the theorem.

The theorem can be expressed in a modified form which is often useful: if the equations $v = 0$, $w = 0$ are consequences of the equations $u_1 = 0, u_2 = 0, \ldots, u_N = 0$, then $(v, w) = 0$. We shall speak of this form of the theorem as Lie's theorem.

As a first application of Lie's theorem we prove very simply a result already needed in § 24.14 and again in § 25.7. If $\varphi_1, \varphi_2, \ldots, \varphi_n$ are n functions in involution, and if we solve the equations

(25.8.3) $$Q_r - \varphi_r(q;\ p;\ t) = 0$$

for the p's in the form

(25.8.4) $$p_r - \psi_r(q;\ Q;\ t) = 0,$$

then

(25.8.5) $$\frac{\partial \psi_r}{\partial q_s} = \frac{\partial \psi_s}{\partial q_r}.$$

We proved (25.8.5) by a pedestrian method in § 24.14; we now see that it is an immediate consequence of Lie's theorem. For, treating the Q's as constants, the equations (25.8.4) are consequences of the equations (25.8.3), and since the first members in (25.8.3) form an involution-system, so also do the first members in (25.8.4); therefore

(25.8.6) $$\begin{aligned} 0 &= \frac{\partial(p_r - \psi_r)}{\partial q_i}\frac{\partial(p_s - \psi_s)}{\partial p_i} - \frac{\partial(p_s - \psi_s)}{\partial q_i}\frac{\partial(p_r - \psi_r)}{\partial p_i} \\ &= -\frac{\partial \psi_r}{\partial q_i}\delta_i^s + \frac{\partial \psi_s}{\partial q_i}\delta_i^r \\ &= -\frac{\partial \psi_r}{\partial q_s} + \frac{\partial \psi_s}{\partial q_r}, \end{aligned}$$

and (25.8.5) is proved.

Another result of the same type arises in connexion with the Hamilton-Jacobi theorem. Suppose that, for a given dynamical system whose Hamiltonian function is H, we know a complete integral $S(q;\ \alpha;\ t)$ of Hamilton's partial differential equation. Let us solve the equations

(25.8.7) $$p_r - \frac{\partial S}{\partial q_r} = 0 \qquad r = 1, 2, \ldots, n,$$

for the α's in the form

(25.8.8) $$\alpha_r = \psi_r(q;\ p;\ t), \qquad r = 1, 2, \ldots, n.$$

Then the ψ's are integrals of Hamilton's equations of motion, *and they are integrals in involution*. For we easily verify that the first members of (25.8.7) are in involution, and the result follows from Lie's theorem.

25.9 Integrals linear in the momenta. If the dynamical system is described by Lagrangian coordinates for which one coordinate q_n is ignorable, the corresponding momentum p_n remains constant during the motion. We shall prove that, conversely, *any autonomous system possessing a space-integral which is linear in the momenta can be described, by an appropriate choice of Lagrangian coordinates, as a system with an ignorable coordinate.*

Let the known integral be

(25.9.1) $$\psi_1 p_1 + \psi_2 p_2 + \cdots + \psi_n p_n,$$

where the ψ's are known functions of the q's. The proof depends on constructing an extended point transformation, from $(q;\ p)$ to $(Q;\ P)$, in which

$$P_n = \psi_1 p_1 + \psi_2 p_2 + \cdots + \psi_n p_n, \tag{25.9.2}$$

and this depends in turn on the theory of the linear partial differential equation of the first order.

Let us consider the equations

$$\frac{dq_1}{\psi_1} = \frac{dq_2}{\psi_2} = \cdots = \frac{dq_n}{\psi_n}, \tag{25.9.3}$$

which define a family of curves in the q-space. The solutions are defined as the intersections of $(n-1)$ independent integrals of the partial differential equation

$$\psi_1 \frac{\partial z}{\partial q_1} + \psi_2 \frac{\partial z}{\partial q_2} + \cdots + \psi_n \frac{\partial z}{\partial q_n} = 0. \tag{25.9.4}$$

We call these integrals

$$\varphi_r(q_1, q_2, \ldots, q_n) = \text{constant}, \qquad r = 1, 2, \ldots, (n-1), \tag{25.9.5}$$

and we consider a point transformation

$$Q_r = \varphi_r, \qquad r = 1, 2, \ldots, n, \tag{25.9.6}$$

where the first $(n-1)$ of the φ's are the functions appearing in (25.9.5).

It remains to determine φ_n; we choose $Q_n = \varphi_n$ such that, for a displacement on one of the curves defined by (25.9.3),

$$\frac{dq_1}{\psi_1} = \frac{dq_2}{\psi_2} = \cdots = \frac{dq_n}{\psi_n} = dQ_n. \tag{25.9.7}$$

We can find Q_n, for example, by integration of

$$dQ_n = \frac{dq_1}{\Psi_1}, \tag{25.9.8}$$

where Ψ_1 is ψ_1 expressed in terms of $q_1, Q_1, Q_2, \ldots, Q_{n-1}$. We notice that φ_n is an integral of the partial differential equation

$$\psi_1 \frac{\partial z}{\partial q_1} + \psi_2 \frac{\partial z}{\partial q_2} + \cdots + \psi_n \frac{\partial z}{\partial q_n} = 1. \tag{25.9.9}$$

Let us now assume that the transformation (25.9.6) is reversible, so that the q's can be expressed as functions of the Q's in the appropriate domain of the Q-space,

$$q_r = F_r(Q_1, Q_2, \ldots, Q_n), \qquad r = 1, 2, \ldots, n, \tag{25.9.10}$$

and then

$$\frac{\partial F_r}{\partial Q_n} = \psi_r, \qquad r = 1, 2, \ldots, n. \tag{25.9.11}$$

This follows from the fact that $Q_1, Q_2, \ldots, Q_{n-1}$ satisfy (25.9.4) and that Q_n satisfies (25.9.9); or geometrically, from (25.9.7), by considering a displacement on one of the curves defined by (25.9.3), since in such a displacement $Q_1, Q_2, \ldots, Q_{n-1}$ remain constant.

The theorem now follows easily. We consider the extended point transformation (24.4.6)

(25.9.12) $$q_r = F_r, \quad P_r = p_i \frac{\partial F_i}{\partial Q_r}.$$

In the new variables

(25.9.13) $$P_n = p_i \frac{\partial F_i}{\partial Q_n} = p_i \varphi_i,$$

so P_n remains constant during the motion. The coordinate Q_n is ignorable, and the proof is complete.

25.10 The case of a Hamiltonian function which is a homogeneous quadratic form. In the theory of small oscillations, if we use normal coordinates, the Hamiltonian function has the simple form

(25.10.1) $$H = \tfrac{1}{2} \sum_{r=1}^{n} (p_r^2 + n_r^2 q_r^2).$$

If we apply the contact transformation

(25.10.2) $$\sqrt{2}Q_r = -(i/n_r)(p_r + in_r q_r), \quad \sqrt{2}P_r = p_r - in_r q_r, \quad r = 1, 2, \ldots, n,$$

the new equations of motion are derived from the Hamiltonian function

(25.10.3) $$H^* = \sum_{r=1}^{n} in_r Q_r P_r,$$

and the equations of motion take the simple form

(25.10.4) $$\dot{Q}_r = in_r Q_r, \quad \dot{P}_r = -in_r P_r, \qquad r = 1, 2, \ldots, n.$$

The Hamiltonian function (25.10.1) is the sum of two independent homogeneous quadratic forms, one containing q's only and one containing p's only. Our present purpose is to show that a reduction similar to (25.10.3) can be achieved whenever *H is a homogeneous quadratic form in the $2n$ variables* $(q_1, q_2, \ldots, q_n, p_1, p_2, \ldots, p_n)$. A Hamiltonian function of this type appears, for example, in the theory of the variational equations (equation (23.6.4)).

We use the notation of § 24.13, replacing the symbols

$$q_1, q_2, \ldots, q_n, p_1, p_2, \ldots, p_n,$$

by

$$x_1, x_2, \ldots, x_n, x_{n+1}, x_{n+2}, \ldots, x_m,$$

where $m = 2n$, and we can express the homogeneous quadratic form H as

(25.10.5) $$H = \tfrac{1}{2}\mathbf{x}'\mathbf{S}\mathbf{x}$$

where $\mathbf{x}$ is the column vector whose rth member is x_r, and $\mathbf{S}$ is a real symmetric $m \times m$ matrix. We shall prove that we can find a matrix $\mathbf{K}$, whose elements are constants, which is such that the linear transformation

(25.10.6) $$\mathbf{x} = \mathbf{K}\mathbf{y}$$

is a contact transformation, and moreover a contact transformation that reduces H to the form

(25.10.7) $$H^* = \sum_{r=1}^{n} \lambda_r y_r y_{n+r} = \lambda_1 Q_1 P_1 + \lambda_2 Q_2 P_2 + \cdots + \lambda_n Q_n P_n.$$

35

If the problem is expressed in this form the solution is simple. The equations of motion are

(25.10.8) $$\dot{Q}_r = \lambda_r Q_r, \qquad \dot{P}_r = -\lambda_r P_r,$$

and the solution is

(25.10.9) $$Q_r = A_r e^{\lambda_r t}, \qquad P_r = B_r e^{-\lambda_r t},$$

where A_r is the value of Q_r, and B_r is the value of P_r, at $t = 0$. If one λ_r, say λ_1, is pure-imaginary, we can have a periodic motion in which $Q_2, Q_3, \ldots, Q_n, P_2, P_3, \ldots, P_n$ are all zero.

We now turn to the problem of finding a contact transformation such that the new Hamiltonian function has the form (25.10.7). This is equivalent to finding an $m \times m$ matrix $\mathbf{K}$ (where $m = 2n$) such that

(25.10.10) $$\mathbf{K'ZK} = \mathbf{Z},$$

and

(25.10.11) $$\mathbf{K'SK} = \begin{pmatrix} \mathbf{0} & \mathbf{L} \\ \mathbf{L} & \mathbf{0} \end{pmatrix},$$

where $\mathbf{L}$ is the diagonal $n \times n$ matrix

(25.10.12) $$\begin{pmatrix} \lambda_1 & & & & \\ & \lambda_2 & & & \\ & & \cdot & & \\ & & & \cdot & \\ & & & & \cdot \\ & & & & & \lambda_n \end{pmatrix}.$$

Let us consider the eigenvalues of the matrix $\mathbf{A}$ $(= \mathbf{ZS})$, i.e. the roots $\lambda_1, \lambda_2, \ldots, \lambda_m$ of the equation $f(\lambda) = 0$, where

(25.10.13) $$f(\lambda) = |\mathbf{A} - \lambda \mathbf{I}_m| = |\mathbf{ZS} - \lambda \mathbf{I}_m| .$$

Now

(25.10.14) $$\mathbf{Z}(\mathbf{S} + \lambda \mathbf{Z}) = \mathbf{ZS} - \lambda \mathbf{I}_m,$$

and therefore, since $|\mathbf{Z}| = 1$,

(25.10.15) $$f(\lambda) = |\mathbf{S} + \lambda \mathbf{Z}| .$$

None of the roots $\lambda_1, \lambda_2, \ldots, \lambda_m$ is zero, since $\mathbf{S}$ is non-singular, and we shall consider only the case in which the roots are all distinct.

The polynomial $f(\lambda)$ contains only even powers of λ; this follows from the facts, pertinent throughout the discussion, that $\mathbf{S}$ is symmetric and $\mathbf{Z}$ is skew-symmetric. Thus

(25.10.16) $$(\mathbf{S} + \lambda \mathbf{Z})' = \mathbf{S} - \lambda \mathbf{Z},$$

so $f(\lambda)$ is an even function,

(25.10.17) $$f(\lambda) = f(-\lambda).$$

The roots occur in equal and opposite pairs, say $\pm\lambda_r$ for $r = 1, 2, \ldots, n$. Let us range them in the order

$$\lambda_1, \lambda_2, \ldots, \lambda_n, -\lambda_1, -\lambda_2, \ldots, -\lambda_n,$$

so that, for $r \leqslant n$, $\lambda_{n+r} = -\lambda_r$. None of $\lambda_1, \lambda_2, \ldots, \lambda_n$ is zero, no two are equal, and no two are equal and opposite.

There exist $2n$ linearly independent eigenvectors $\mathbf{c}_r$, $\mathbf{c}_{n+r}$ $(r = 1, 2, \ldots, n)$ such that

(25.10.18) $$\mathbf{Sc}_r = -\lambda_r \mathbf{Zc}_r, \qquad \mathbf{Sc}_{n+r} = \lambda_r \mathbf{Zc}_{n+r},$$

(and also

(25.10.19) $$\mathbf{Ac}_r = \mathbf{ZSc}_r = \lambda_r \mathbf{c}_r, \qquad \mathbf{Ac}_{n+r} = \mathbf{ZSc}_{n+r} = -\lambda_r \mathbf{c}_{n+r}).$$

Let $\mathbf{B}$ be the $m \times m$ matrix whose typical element b_{ij} is given by

(25.10.20) $$b_{ij} = \mathbf{c}_i'\mathbf{Sc}_j.$$

Then, if $r \leqslant n$ and $s \leqslant n$,

(25.10.21) $$b_{rs} = \mathbf{c}_r'\mathbf{Sc}_s = -\lambda_s \mathbf{c}_r'\mathbf{Zc}_s.$$

But also

(25.10.22) $$b_{rs} = \mathbf{c}_s'\mathbf{Sc}_r = -\lambda_r \mathbf{c}_s'\mathbf{Zc}_r = \lambda_r \mathbf{c}_r'\mathbf{Zc}_s,$$

and therefore, since $\lambda_r \neq -\lambda_s$, $b_{rs} = 0$. And similarly $b_{n+r,n+s} = 0$.

Next we consider

(25.10.23) $$\begin{aligned} b_{r,n+s} &= \mathbf{c}_r'\mathbf{Sc}_{n+s} = \lambda_s \mathbf{c}_r'\mathbf{Zc}_{n+s} \\ &= \mathbf{c}_{n+s}'\mathbf{Sc}_r = -\lambda_r \mathbf{c}_{n+s}'\mathbf{Zc}_r = \lambda_r \mathbf{c}_r'\mathbf{Zc}_{n+s}, \end{aligned}$$

so $b_{r,n+s} = 0$ unless $r = s$. Similarly $b_{n+r,s} = 0$ unless $r = s$, and further, since $\mathbf{Z}$ is skew-symmetric.

(25.10.24) $$b_{n+r,s} = -b_{s,n+r}$$

Let $\mathbf{K}$ be the matrix $(\mathbf{c}_1, \mathbf{c}_2, \ldots, \mathbf{c}_m)$, and let $\mathbf{C}$ be the matrix $\mathbf{K}'\mathbf{ZK}$. The typical element c_{ij} of $\mathbf{C}$ is

(25.10.25) $$c_{ij} = \mathbf{c}_i'\mathbf{Zc}_j,$$

so $\mathbf{C}$ is skew-symmetric, and indeed

(25.10.26) $$\mathbf{C} = \begin{pmatrix} \mathbf{0} & \mathbf{D} \\ -\mathbf{D} & \mathbf{0} \end{pmatrix},$$

where $\mathbf{D}$ is the diagonal $n \times n$ matrix

(25.10.27) $$\begin{pmatrix} d_1 & & & & \\ & d_2 & & & \\ & & \cdot & & \\ & & & \cdot & \\ & & & & \cdot \\ & & & & & d_n \end{pmatrix},$$

and

(25.10.28) $$d_r = \mathbf{c}_r'\mathbf{Zc}_{n+r}.$$

We now multiply $\mathbf{c}_r$ (or $\mathbf{c}_{n+r}$, or each of them) by a suitable (complex) scalar factor to make $d_r = 1$. If we do this for each value of r in the range $1, 2, \ldots, n$, then $\mathbf{C} = \mathbf{Z}$, and $\mathbf{K}$ satisfies the symplectic condition (25.10.10). Further,

(25.10.29) $$\mathbf{K}'\mathbf{SK} = \mathbf{E},$$

where

(25.10.30) $$e_{ij} = \mathbf{c}_i'\mathbf{Sc}_j = -\lambda_j \mathbf{c}_i'\mathbf{Zc}_j,$$

so $\mathbf{E}$ is the symmetric matrix

(25.10.31) $$\begin{pmatrix} \mathbf{0} & \mathbf{L} \\ \mathbf{L} & \mathbf{0} \end{pmatrix}.$$

Thus the matrix **K** has the required properties (25.10.10) and (25.10.11); the transformation $\mathbf{x} = \mathbf{K}\mathbf{y}$ is a contact transformation, and the new Hamiltonian function

(25.10.32) $$H^* = \mathbf{y}'\mathbf{K}'\mathbf{S}\mathbf{K}\mathbf{y}$$

has the required form (25.10.7).

We return to the equation $f(\lambda) = 0$. Since the polynomial $f(\lambda)$ has real coefficients, the roots occur in conjugate pairs. If λ_k (where $k \leqslant n$) is an eigenvalue which is neither real nor pure-imaginary, there is an eigenvalue λ_l (where $l = l(k) \leqslant n$) such that $\lambda_l = \bar{\lambda}_k$. Now

(25.10.33) $$(\mathbf{A} - \lambda_k \mathbf{I}_m)\mathbf{c}_k = \mathbf{0},$$

whence

(25.10.34) $$(\mathbf{A} - \bar{\lambda}_k \mathbf{I}_m)\bar{\mathbf{c}}_k = (\mathbf{A} - \lambda_l \mathbf{I}_m)\bar{\mathbf{c}}_k = \mathbf{0},$$

and therefore, since $(\mathbf{A} - \lambda_l \mathbf{I}_m)$ has rank $(m - 1)$, $\mathbf{c}_l$ is a scalar multiple of $\bar{\mathbf{c}}_k$,

(25.10.35) $$\mathbf{c}_l = \rho_k \bar{\mathbf{c}}_k.$$

Similarly

(25.10.36) $$\mathbf{c}_k = \rho_l \bar{\mathbf{c}}_l,$$

and $\rho_l \bar{\rho}_k = 1$. We can, if we wish, choose forms for the eigenvectors, by multiplying one or other by a suitable scalar factor, to make $|\rho_k| = |\rho_l| = 1$, but it is not always convenient to do so.

Now the solution for **y** is given by the formulae

(25.10.37) $$y_r = A_r e^{\lambda_r t}, \qquad r = 1, 2, \ldots, m,$$

and therefore

(25.10.38) $$\mathbf{x} = \mathbf{K}\mathbf{y} = \sum_{r=1}^{m} y_r \mathbf{c}_r = \sum_{r=1}^{m} A_r e^{\lambda_r t} \mathbf{c}_r.$$

The terms

(25.10.39) $$A_k e^{\lambda_k t} \mathbf{c}_k + A_l e^{\lambda_l t} \mathbf{c}_l$$

in the formula for **x** in (25.10.38) will give a result in real form if

(25.10.40) $$\bar{A}_k = \rho_k A_l.$$

If one eigenvalue λ_k (where $k \leqslant n$) is a pure-imaginary number $i\mu$, where μ is real, then $\lambda_{n+k} = -i\mu$, and $\mathbf{c}_{n+k}$ is a scalar multiple of $\bar{\mathbf{c}}_k$. In this case, if we choose $\mathbf{c}_{n+k}$ *equal* to $\bar{\mathbf{c}}_k$, $\mathbf{c}_k'\mathbf{Z}\mathbf{c}_{n+k}$ is pure-imaginary. If one eigenvalue λ_k (where $k \leqslant n$) is real, λ_{n+k} is also real, and we can choose the corresponding eigenvalues to be real; with this choice, the corresponding contributions to the formula for **x** in (25.10.38) give a real form if the coefficients A_k and A_{n+k} are real.

Example 25.10. As a concrete illustration of the theory, let us consider the problem, with $n = 3$, in which **S** is the matrix

$$\begin{bmatrix} 1 & 0 & 0 & 1 & 0 & 0 \\ 0 & -1 & 0 & 0 & 0 & 0 \\ 0 & 0 & 1 & 0 & 0 & 0 \\ 1 & 0 & 0 & 2 & 0 & 0 \\ 0 & 0 & 0 & 0 & 0 & 1 \\ 0 & 0 & 0 & 0 & 1 & 0 \end{bmatrix}.$$

The equation for the eigenvalues is

$$(\lambda^2 + 1)(\lambda^4 + 1) = 0,$$

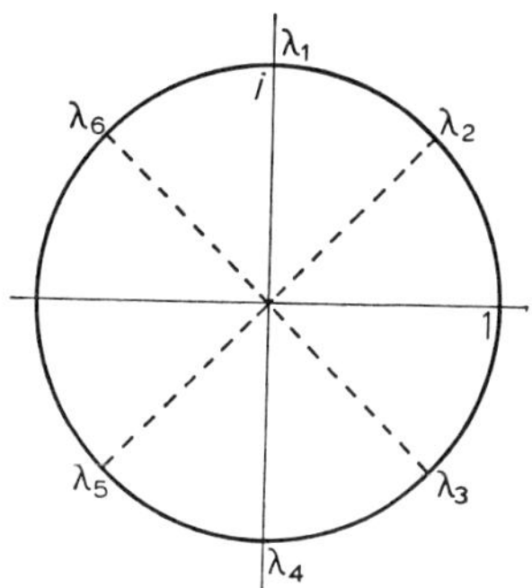

Figure 25.10

so the eigenvalues lie on the unit circle in the complex λ-plane, as shown in Fig. 25.10. The matrix $(\mathbf{c}_1, \mathbf{c}_2, \ldots, \mathbf{c}_6)$, with the eigenvectors not yet normalized, is

$$\begin{bmatrix} (1+i) & 0 & 0 & (1-i) & 0 & 0 \\ 0 & (1+i) & (1-i) & 0 & -(1+i) & -(1-i) \\ 0 & (1-i) & (1+i) & 0 & -(1-i) & -(1+i) \\ -1 & 0 & 0 & -1 & 0 & 0 \\ 0 & \sqrt{2} & \sqrt{2} & 0 & \sqrt{2} & \sqrt{2} \\ 0 & i\sqrt{2} & -i\sqrt{2} & 0 & i\sqrt{2} & -i\sqrt{2} \end{bmatrix}.$$

With these vectors

$$d_1 = \mathbf{c}_1'\mathbf{Z}\mathbf{c}_4 = -2i,\ d_2 = \mathbf{c}_2'\mathbf{Z}\mathbf{c}_5 = 4\sqrt{2}(1+i),\ d_3 = \mathbf{c}_3'\mathbf{Z}\mathbf{c}_6 = 4\sqrt{2}(1-i).$$

If we multiply by suitable scalar factors to obtain $d_1 = d_2 = d_3 = 1$, we find, as one form of the matrix $\mathbf{K}$,

$$\mathbf{K} = \begin{bmatrix} (1-i) & 0 & 0 & -(1-i)/2 & 0 & 0 \\ 0 & \sqrt{2} & \sqrt{2} & 0 & -(1+i)/8 & -(1-i)/8 \\ 0 & -i\sqrt{2} & i\sqrt{2} & 0 & -(1-i)/8 & -(1+i)/8 \\ i & 0 & 0 & 1/2 & 0 & 0 \\ 0 & (1-i) & (1+i) & 0 & \sqrt{2}/8 & \sqrt{2}/8 \\ 0 & (1+i) & (1-i) & 0 & i\sqrt{2}/8 & -i\sqrt{2}/8 \end{bmatrix}.$$

Chapter XXVI

Variation principles

26.1 Hamilton's principle. The simplest of the variation principles of dynamics, Hamilton's principle, has already been established in § 3.7. We can express the principle in terms of any chosen coordinates, and in § 6.3 we expressed it in terms of Lagrangian coordinates, and deduced Lagrange's equations of motion.

We recall the statement of Hamilton's principle. Let us describe the configuration of the system by Lagrangian coordinates $q_1, q_2, \ldots, q_n$, where we take the smallest possible choice for n. Thus, if the system is holonomic, $n = k$, where k denotes as usual the number of degrees of freedom; if the system is not holonomic, $n = k + l$, where l is the number of independent non-integrable constraints. The principle asserts that

(26.1.1) $$\int_{t_0}^{t_1} \delta L \, dt = 0,$$

where the symbol δ refers to a displacement from the point $(q_1, q_2, \ldots, q_n)$ on the actual orbit in the q-space to a contemporaneous point $(q_1 + \delta q_1, q_2 + \delta q_2, \ldots, q_n + \delta q_n)$ on the varied path. The essential point to keep in mind is that $\delta \mathbf{q}$ is a virtual displacement at time t. The variations δq_r, *qua* functions of t, are of class C_2, and vanish at t_0 and at t_1. Thus the terminal points P_0 and P_1 in the q-space are fixed, and so are the instant t_0 of departure from P_0, and the instant t_1 of arrival at P_1. We recall that if the system is not holonomic the varied path is not in general a geometrically possible path, i.e. the varied path does not in general conform to the equations of constraint (§ 3.8, § 5.11).

The theory is simple if the system is holonomic. In that case we can replace (26.1.1) by the equation

(26.1.2) $$\delta \int_{t_0}^{t_1} L \, dt = 0.$$

We compare the value of the integral $\int L \, dt$ along the orbit in the q-space with a neighbouring path joining the same terminal points and occupying the same interval of time. If we change the point of view a little, and think in terms of the $(n + 1)$-fold space $(t, q_1, q_2, \ldots, q_n)$ we have a standard problem (of the *ordinary*, not the *parametric*, type) in the calculus of variations, with fixed end-points. We consider the family of curves

(26.1.3) $$q_1(t), q_2(t), \ldots, q_n(t),$$

joining the point R_0,

(26.1.4) $$t_0, q_{10}, q_{20}, \ldots, q_{n0},$$

to the point R_1,

(26.1.5) $$t_1, q_{11}, q_{21}, \ldots, q_{n1},$$

where $q_r(t) \in C_2$. The curve in the $(n+1)$-fold defining the actual motion is distinguished by the fact that it renders stationary the integral $\int L\,dt$. In many cases, but not universally, the integral is a minimum for the actual motion.

If the system is not holonomic, however, the forms (26.1.1) and (26.1.2) are no longer equivalent, and we must adhere to the original form (26.1.1). Indeed for a non-holonomic system the statement (26.1.2), if interpreted in the natural way, as implying comparison with neighbouring *geometrically possible* paths, is false.

To prove this statement, it will suffice to consider a simple concrete example. Suppose a particle moves in space, with the single (non-integrable) constraint

(26.1.6) $$z\,dx - dy = 0.$$

The system is non-holonomic ($k = 2, l = 1, n = 3$). We will suppose, for the sake of simplicity, that there are no given forces, so the only force on the particle is that provided by the smooth constraint. We know of course that though the system has only two degrees of freedom, a threefold infinity of points is accessible from a given point by a geometrically possible path; indeed any point of space is accessible from any other point (§ 1.8). On the other hand, only a two-fold infinity of points is accessible from a given point by dynamically possible paths.

Let us suppose, to fix the ideas, that the particle is projected from the origin at $t = 0$ with velocity $(u, 0, w)$. The equations of motion are

(26.1.7) $$\ddot{x} = \lambda z, \quad \ddot{y} = -\lambda, \quad \ddot{z} = 0,$$

and we have also the equation of constraint

(26.1.8) $$z\dot{x} - \dot{y} = 0.$$

The integration is simple, and yields the solution (for $w \neq 0$)

(26.1.9) $$x = \frac{u}{w}\,\theta, \quad y = \frac{u}{w}\,(\cosh\theta - 1), \quad z = \sinh\theta,$$

where the variable θ, replacing the time, is defined by the equation

(26.1.10) $$\sinh\theta = wt.$$

In this case P_0 is the origin O, and P_1 must be some point on the ruled surface Γ defined by (26.1.9); the two parameters defining a point on the surface are u/w and θ. As we foresaw, only a two-fold infinity of points is accessible by projection from O. Any point on Γ can be reached in a prescribed time by projection from O with a suitable velocity.

Suppose now that we prescribe P_0 (at O) and P_1, and the instant t_0 of leaving O, and also the instant t_1 of reaching P_1. If P_1 is not a point of Γ there is no hope of finding a solution of the dynamical problem; though there are, as we know, geometrically possible paths joining O to P_1. If P_1 *is* a point of Γ, there is a dynamically possible motion in which the particle leaves O at t_0 and reaches P_1 at t_1; but *this motion does not make* $\int_{t_0}^{t_1} L\,dt$ *stationary in the class of geometrically possible paths.*

To prove this, we appeal to a well-known theorem in the calculus of variations. A geometrically possible path satisfying the prescribed end-conditions, and making $\int_{t_0}^{t_1} L\,dt$ stationary in comparison with neighbouring geometrically possible paths, must satisfy the *multiplier rule.* This requires that the motion satisfies the Lagrangian equations of motion derived from the Lagrangian function

(26.1.11) $$\tfrac{1}{2}(\dot{x}^2 + \dot{y}^2 + \dot{z}^2) - \mu(z\dot{x} - \dot{y}),$$

where μ is a function of t to be determined. The equations of motion derived from (26.1.11) are

$$\frac{d}{dt}(\dot{x} - \mu z) = 0, \quad \frac{d}{dt}(\dot{y} + \mu) = 0, \quad \ddot{z} + \mu\dot{x} = 0, \tag{26.1.12}$$

and to these we must adjoin the equation of constraint (26.1.8). Now the motion given by (26.1.9) does not satisfy (26.1.12) for any choice of μ, and this proves that the motion of the system does not satisfy (26.1.2). It does of course satisfy (26.1.1).

It may be of interest to notice a direct proof, not depending on the multiplier rule, of the fact that the integral $\int_0^{t_1} L\,dt$ is not stationary for the actual path in comparison with neighbouring geometrically possible paths. Consider the neighbouring geometrically possible path

$$x = k\theta + \alpha(\theta), \quad y = k(\cosh\theta - 1) + \beta(\theta), \quad z = \frac{y'}{x'} = \frac{k\sinh\theta + \beta'(\theta)}{k + \alpha'(\theta)}, \tag{26.1.13}$$

where k stands for u/w, the parameter θ is defined as before by (26.1.10), and accents denote differentiation with respect to θ. The functions $\alpha(\theta)$ and $\beta(\theta)$ are of class C_3, and α, β, α', β' all vanish at $\theta = 0$ and at $\theta = \theta_1$, where $\sinh\theta_1 = wt_1$. In the case in which we are primarily interested, α and β and their derivatives are small. Let δI denote the change in the integral $\int_0^{\theta_1} L\,dt$ when we change from the undisturbed path (26.1.9) to the varied path (26.1.13). Now

$$\int_0^{t_1} L\,dt = \tfrac{1}{2}mw\int_0^{\theta_1} \frac{1}{\cosh\theta}(x'^2 + y'^2 + z'^2)\,d\theta, \tag{26.1.14}$$

and if the integral were stationary for the undisturbed path, the linear terms in δI would vanish. But in fact these terms are

$$\begin{aligned} mu\int_0^{\theta_1}(\alpha'\operatorname{sech}\theta + \beta'\tanh\theta)\,d\theta + m\frac{w^2}{u}\int_0^{\theta_1}(-\alpha'\cosh\theta - \alpha''\sinh\theta + \beta'')\,d\theta \\ = mu\int_0^{\theta_1}(\alpha'\operatorname{sech}\theta + \beta'\tanh\theta)\,d\theta, \end{aligned} \tag{26.1.15}$$

and this clearly does not vanish in general.

Thus the result stated is established. *For holonomic systems the two forms of Hamilton's principle given by* (26.1.1) *and* (26.1.2) *are both valid. For non-holonomic systems, only the first form* (26.1.1) *is valid.*

26.2 Livens's theorem. In this section we are concerned only with holonomic systems. In § 6.3 we derived Lagrange's equations from Hamilton's principle. It is natural to ask if we can also derive Hamilton's equations, and this leads to a result of great interest. But this problem demands some care, because of the difficulty that we cannot in the first instance make independent variations in q's and ω's; for when the variation $\delta\mathbf{q}$ has been prescribed at each instant the variation of $\boldsymbol{\omega}$ is determined by the equations

$$\delta\omega_r = \frac{d}{dt}\delta q_r, \qquad r = 1, 2, \ldots, n. \tag{26.2.1}$$

To cope with this difficulty we appeal again to the multiplier rule.

Let us represent the motion of the system by the motion of a representative point in the $2n$-fold space of $(q_1, q_2, \ldots, q_n, \omega_1, \omega_2, \ldots, \omega_n)$. The equation (26.1.2) tells us that $\int L(\mathbf{q};\ \boldsymbol{\omega};\ t)\,dt$ is stationary in the family of arcs satisfying the n differential equations

$$\dot{q}_r = \omega_r, \qquad r = 1, 2, \ldots, n. \tag{26.2.2}$$

The q's and the times are fixed at the end-points, but not the ω's. Since our attention is confined to arcs satisfying (26.2.2), and the variations are contemporaneous, the condition (26.2.1) is surely satisfied.

The theorem of the multiplier rule asserts that

$$\int_{t_0}^{t_1} \{L(\mathbf{q};\ \boldsymbol{\omega};\ t) + \sum \lambda_r(\dot{q}_r - \omega_r)\}\, dt \tag{26.2.3}$$

(where $\sum$ denotes summation from 1 to n) is stationary for arbitrary variations of q's and ω's, the λ's being certain functions of t to be determined. The conditions for a stationary value are given by the $2n$ equations

$$\frac{d}{dt}\lambda_r = \frac{\partial L}{\partial q_r}, \quad 0 = \frac{\partial L}{\partial \omega_r} - \lambda_r, \tag{26.2.4}$$

and we must append the n equations (26.2.2). Of course we could derive immediately Lagrange's equations from (26.2.4) and (26.2.2). But this is not the important point. The important point is that

$$\int_{t_0}^{t_1} \{L(\mathbf{q};\ \boldsymbol{\omega};\ t) + \sum \frac{\partial L}{\partial \omega_r}(\dot{q}_r - \omega_r)\}\, dt \tag{26.2.5}$$

is stationary for arbitrary variations of the path in the $(q,\ \omega)$-space. Now arbitrary variation of q's and ω's is equivalent to arbitrary variation of q's and p's, and if we interpret the result in terms of the phase space we get *the theorem that*

$$\int_{t_0}^{t_1} (-H + \sum p_r\dot{q}_r)\, dt \tag{26.2.6}$$

is stationary for arbitrary variation of q's and p's. This is Livens's theorem. The symbol H in the integrand stands for

$$\sum \omega_r \frac{\partial L}{\partial \omega_r} - L \tag{26.2.7}$$

expressed in terms of q's and p's; to achieve this, we must solve the equations

$$p_r = \frac{\partial L}{\partial \omega_r} \tag{26.2.8}$$

for the ω's (as in § 10.13). The time and the q's are fixed at the end-points, but not the p's. We have thus a variable end-point problem in the space of $t,\ q_1,\ q_2,\ \ldots,\ q_n,$ $p_1\ p_2\ \ldots,\ p_n$ to deal with; but the end-conditions give no information since the integrand does not contain any $\dot{p}_r$.

The Euler-Lagrange equations expressing necessary conditions for (26.2.6) to be stationary are Hamilton's equations

$$\dot{q}_r = \frac{\partial H}{\partial p_r}, \quad \dot{p}_r = -\frac{\partial H}{\partial q_r}, \qquad r = 1, 2, \ldots, n. \tag{26.2.9}$$

26.3 Minima and saddle points. We consider a holonomic system with n degrees of freedom. The system moves in such a way that the path $\mathbf{q} = \mathbf{q}(t)$ in the space of $t,\ q_1,\ q_2,\ \ldots,\ q_n$ gives a stationary value to the integral $\int L\, dt$ in comparison with neighbouring curves $\mathbf{q} = \mathbf{q}(t) + \delta\mathbf{q}(t)$ joining the same end-points. If we consider instead the motion in the phase space, the path $\mathbf{q} = \mathbf{q}(t),\ \mathbf{p} = \mathbf{p}(t)$ in the space of $t,\ q_1, q_2,\ \ldots,\ q_n,\ p_1, p_2,\ \ldots,\ p_n$ gives a stationary value to the integral $\int (-H + \Sigma\, p_r\dot{q}_r)\, dt$ in comparison with neighbouring curves $\mathbf{q} = \mathbf{q}(t) + \delta\mathbf{q}(t)$, $\mathbf{p} = \mathbf{p}(t) + \delta\mathbf{p}(t)$, the values of t and of the q's being prescribed at the end-points, but not the values of the p's. The two integrals have of course the same value for the actual motion in any particular case. It was noticed by Hilbert, however, that the former integral may be a genuine minimum, whereas the latter, for the same problem, may be neither a maximum nor a minimum.

To illustrate this situation, it will suffice to consider a very simple problem, that of a particle of unit mass moving on a straight line in a uniform field g. The displacement at time t is

(26.3.1) $$x = ut + \tfrac{1}{2}gt^2,$$

and we take the end-points to be $t = 0$, $x = 0$ and $t = \theta$, $x = n\theta + \tfrac{1}{2}g\theta^2$. That the integral $\int_0^\theta L\, dt$, where $L = \tfrac{1}{2}\dot{x}^2 + gx$, is a minimum for the actual motion follows very simply from the fundamental sufficiency theorem of the calculus of variations; but it is easy also to construct an *ad hoc* proof. Let us compare the actual motion, given by (26.3.1), with a neighbouring motion in which

(26.3.2) $$x = ut + \tfrac{1}{2}gt^2 + \alpha(t),$$

where $\alpha(t) \in C_2$, and $\alpha(0) = \alpha(\theta) = 0$. For this varied motion

(26.3.3) $$\begin{aligned} I + \delta I &= \int_0^\theta (\tfrac{1}{2}\dot{x}^2 + gx)\, dt \\ &= \int_0^\theta \{\tfrac{1}{2}(u + gt + \dot{\alpha})^2 + g(ut + \tfrac{1}{2}gt^2 + \alpha)\}\, dt. \end{aligned}$$

Hence

(26.3.4) $$\begin{aligned} \delta I &= \int_0^\theta \{\tfrac{1}{2}\dot{\alpha}^2 + (u + gt)\dot{\alpha} + g\alpha\}\, dt \\ &= \int_0^\theta \tfrac{1}{2}\dot{\alpha}^2\, dt + (u + gt)\alpha \Big|_0^\theta \\ &= \int_0^\theta \tfrac{1}{2}\dot{\alpha}^2\, dt, \end{aligned}$$

since $\alpha(0) = \alpha(\theta) = 0$. Thus $\delta I > 0$ unless $\alpha(t)$ vanishes identically. The integral $\int_0^\theta L\, dt$ is a genuine minimum for (26.3.1) in comparison with other motions having the same terminal points in the q-space and the same times of departure and arrival.

Let us now consider the integral $\int_0^\theta (-H + \sum p_r\dot{q}_r)\, dt$ taken along a curve in the space of t, $\mathbf{q}$, $\mathbf{p}$. In the simple problem under discussion $H = \tfrac{1}{2}p^2 - gx$, and the integral to be considered is

(26.3.5) $$J = \int_0^\theta (-\tfrac{1}{2}p^2 + gx + p\dot{x})\, dt$$

taken along a curve in the space of t, x, p. We can write the integral in the form

(26.3.6) $$J = \int_0^\theta \{-\tfrac{1}{2}(p - \dot{x})^2 + \tfrac{1}{2}\dot{x}^2 + gx\}\, dt.$$

In the actual motion

(26.3.7) $$x = ut + \tfrac{1}{2}gt^2, \quad p = u + gt,$$

and if we consider a varied motion in which

(26.3.8) $$x = ut + \tfrac{1}{2}gt^2 + \alpha(t), \quad p = u + gt + \beta(t),$$

where $\alpha(t)$ vanishes at $t = 0$ and at $t = \theta$, but $\beta(t)$ does not necessarily vanish at these limits, we have

(26.3.9) $$\delta J = \int_0^\theta \tfrac{1}{2}\{-(\beta - \dot{\alpha})^2 + \dot{\alpha}^2\}\, dt.$$

Thus $\delta J < 0$ if $\beta \neq 0$ and $\alpha = 0$, whereas $\delta J > 0$ if $\beta = \dot{\alpha}$ and $\alpha \neq 0$. The integral J has a stationary value for (26.3.7), but it is neither a maximum nor a minimum.

26.4 Non-contemporaneous variations, Hölder's principle. In Hamilton's principle the operator δ represents a contemporaneous variation: the point P (in the q-space), occupied at time t on the actual path, is correlated with a point P' occupied *at the same time* t on the varied path. This is possible because, in Hamilton's principle, not only the end-points, but also the times of departure and arrival, are prescribed; the original and the varied motion both occupy the same interval of time. We now consider the situation that arises when a point $\mathbf{q}$, occupied at time t on the original path, is correlated with a point $\mathbf{q} + \delta\mathbf{q}$, occupied at time $t + \delta t$ on the varied path. We shall assume that $\delta q_1, \delta q_2, \ldots, \delta q_n, \delta t$ are functions of t of class C_2.

In the theory involving non-contemporaneous variations we shall assume that the relations connecting x's and q's (6.1.1) do not involve the time, so that a particular configuration of the system is represented by the same point in the q-space for all values of t.

Let us evaluate $\int_{t_0}^{t_1} \delta L\, dt$, remembering now that the lower terminus $\mathbf{q}^{(0)}$ occupied at time t_0 shifts to $\mathbf{q}^{(0)} + \delta\mathbf{q}^{(0)}$ occupied at time $t_0 + \delta t_0$, and that the upper terminus $\mathbf{q}^{(1)}$ occupied at time t_1 shifts to $\mathbf{q}^{(1)} + \delta\mathbf{q}^{(1)}$ occupied at time $t_1 + \delta t_1$. The system is not necessarily holonomic. We have

(26.4.1) $$\int_{t_0}^{t_1} \delta L\, dt = \int_{t_0}^{t_1} \left(\frac{\partial L}{\partial t}\,\delta t + \sum \frac{\partial L}{\partial q_r}\,\delta q_r + \sum \frac{\partial L}{\partial \dot{q}_r}\,\delta \dot{q}_r\right) dt,$$

where $\sum$ denotes summation from 1 to n. Now

(26.4.2) $$\delta \dot{q}_r = \frac{d}{dt}\,\delta q_r - \dot{q}_r \frac{d}{dt}\,\delta t,$$

so, substituting for $\delta\dot{q}_r$ in (26.4.1) and integrating, we have

(26.4.3) $$\int_{t_0}^{t_1} \delta L\, dt = \sum \frac{\partial L}{\partial \dot{q}_r}\,\delta q_r \Bigg|_{t_0}^{t_1} + \int_{t_0}^{t_1} \left\{\frac{\partial L}{\partial t}\,\delta t - \left(\sum \dot{q}_r \frac{\partial L}{\partial \dot{q}_r}\right) \frac{d}{dt}\,\delta t\right\} dt - \int_{t_0}^{t_1} \left[\sum \left\{\frac{d}{dt}\left(\frac{\partial L}{\partial \dot{q}_r}\right) - \frac{\partial L}{\partial q_r}\right\} \delta q_r\right] dt.$$

Consider now the last integral in the second member of (26.4.3). In virtue of the fourth form of the fundamental equation (6.1.11) the integrand vanishes at each instant *if* $\delta\mathbf{q}$ *is a virtual displacement* at time t. In that case

(26.4.4) $$\int_{t_0}^{t_1} \left\{\delta L + \left(\sum \dot{q}_r \frac{\partial L}{\partial \dot{q}_r}\right) \frac{d}{dt}\,\delta t - \frac{\partial L}{\partial t}\,\delta t\right\} dt = \sum \frac{\partial L}{\partial \dot{q}_r}\,\delta q_r \Bigg|_{t_0}^{t_1}$$

Suppose now that we choose the virtual displacement $\delta\mathbf{q}$ to vanish at t_0 and at t_1; the configuration of the system at t_0 and at t_1 is prescribed. *Then we have the theorem*

(26.4.5) $$\int_{t_0}^{t_1} \left\{\delta L + \left(\sum \dot{q}_r \frac{\partial L}{\partial \dot{q}_r}\right) \frac{d}{dt}\,\delta t - \frac{\partial L}{\partial t}\,\delta t\right\} dt = 0.$$

This is Hölder's principle.

The conditions under which Hölder's principle holds should be carefully noticed. We choose at each instant a virtual displacement $\delta\mathbf{q}$ from the actual motion; each component $\delta\mathbf{q}_r$, *qua* function of t, is of class C_2, and vanishes at t_0 and at t_1. We then choose a function δt of t, also of class C_2, and the varied motion is that in which the point $\mathbf{q} + \delta\mathbf{q}$ is occupied at $t + \delta t$; δt does not necessarily vanish at t_0 and at t_1. Of course if the system is not holonomic this varied path will not in general satisfy the equations of constraint. If the function δt is identically zero, we recover Hamilton's principle.

26.5 Voss's principle. In Hölder's principle the variation $\delta\mathbf{q}$ is a *virtual* displacement at time t, but the corresponding point $\mathbf{q} + \delta\mathbf{q}$ is occupied at time $t + \delta t$. The somewhat artificial nature of this situation suggests the search for a variation principle in which the displacement $\delta\mathbf{q}$ is a *possible* displacement in the time-interval δt. It is such a principle that we now establish.

To begin with, we notice that if $(\delta q_1, \delta q_2, \ldots, \delta q_n)$ is a *possible* displacement in the interval from t to $t + \delta t$, and $(\dot{q}_1, \dot{q}_2, \ldots, \dot{q}_n)$ is a possible velocity at time t, then

(26.5.1) $$(\delta q_1 - \dot{q}_1\,\delta t, \delta q_2 - \dot{q}_2\,\delta t, \ldots, \delta q_n - \dot{q}_n\,\delta t)$$

is a *virtual* displacement. The proof is immediate: for by (5.12.2)

$$\left.\begin{aligned} \sum_{s=1}^{n} B_{rs}\,\delta q_s + B_r\,\delta t &= 0, \\ \sum_{S=1}^{n} B_{rs}\,\dot{q}_s + B_r &= 0, \end{aligned}\right\} \qquad r = 1, 2, \ldots, l,$$

whence

$$\sum_{s=1}^{n} B_{rs}(\delta q_s - \dot{q}_s\,\delta t) = 0, \qquad r = 1, 2 \ldots, l,$$

so (26.5.1) satisfies the conditions (5.12.5) for a virtual displacement.

Consider now an orbit of the system in the q-space, and a varied path, the point $\mathbf{q}$ occupied at time t on the original orbit being correlated with the point $\mathbf{q} + \delta\mathbf{q}$ occupied at time $t + \delta t$ on the varied path. We calculate the corresponding change in $\int_{t_0}^{t_1} L\,dt$. We have

(26.5.2)

$$\begin{aligned}
\delta\int_{t_0}^{t_1} L\,dt &= \int_{t_0}^{t_1}\left(\delta L + L\frac{d}{dt}\,\delta t\right)dt \\
&= \int_{t_0}^{t_1}\left(\frac{\partial L}{\partial t}\,\delta t + \sum\frac{\partial L}{\partial q_r}\,\delta q_r + \sum\frac{\partial L}{\partial \dot{q}_r}\,\delta\dot{q}_r + L\frac{d}{dt}\,\delta t\right)dt \\
&= \int_{t_0}^{t_1}\left\{\frac{\partial L}{\partial t}\,\delta t + \sum\frac{\partial L}{\partial q_r}\,\delta q_r + \sum\frac{\partial L}{\partial \dot{q}_r}\frac{d}{dt}\,\delta q_r - \left(\sum\dot{q}_r\frac{\partial L}{\partial \dot{q}_r} - L\right)\frac{d}{dt}\,\delta t\right\}dt \\
&= \int_{t_0}^{t_1}\left[\frac{d}{dt}\left\{\sum\frac{\partial L}{\partial \dot{q}_r}\,\delta q_r - \left(\sum\dot{q}_r\frac{\partial L}{\partial \dot{q}_r} - L\right)\delta t\right\} - \sum\left\{\frac{d}{dt}\left(\frac{\partial L}{\partial \dot{q}_r}\right) - \frac{\partial L}{\partial q_r}\right\}\delta q_r\right. \\
&\qquad\left. + \left\{\frac{d}{dt}\left(\sum\dot{q}_r\frac{\partial L}{\partial \dot{q}_r} - L\right) + \frac{\partial L}{\partial t}\right\}\delta t\right]dt
\end{aligned}$$

The coefficient of δt in the integrand is

$$\frac{d}{dt}\left(\sum \dot{q}_r \frac{\partial L}{\partial \dot{q}_r} - L\right) + \frac{\partial L}{\partial t} = \sum \left\{\frac{d}{dt}\left(\frac{\partial L}{\partial \dot{q}_r}\right) - \frac{\partial L}{\partial q_r}\right\} \dot{q}_r, \tag{26.5.3}$$

and using this result we find

$$\delta\int_{t_0}^{t_1} L\, dt = \left(\sum \frac{\partial L}{\partial \dot{q}_r}\, \delta q_r - E\,\delta t\right)\Bigg|_{t_0}^{t_1} - \int_{t_0}^{t_1}\left[\sum\left\{\frac{d}{dt}\left(\frac{\partial L}{\partial \dot{q}_r}\right) - \frac{\partial L}{\partial q_r}\right\}(\delta q_r - \dot{q}_r\,\delta t)\right] dt, \tag{26.5.4}$$

where E stands for $\left(\sum \dot{q}_r \dfrac{\partial L}{\partial \dot{q}_r} - L\right)$. If now $\delta\mathbf{q}$ is a *possible* displacement in time δt, the formulae $\delta q_r - \dot{q}_r\,\delta t$ represent components of a *virtual* displacement, and the integrand in the last integral on the right vanishes at each instant. In these circumstances, therefore,

$$\delta\int_{t_0}^{t_1} L\, dt = \left(\sum \frac{\partial L}{\partial \dot{q}_r}\, \delta q_r - E\,\delta t\right)\Bigg|_{t_0}^{t_1}. \tag{26.5.5}$$

If we choose the variations so that $\delta q_1, \delta q_2, \ldots, \delta q_n, \delta t$ all vanish at t_0 and at t_1, then

$$\delta\int_{t}^{t_1} L\, dt = 0, \tag{26.5.6}$$

and this is Voss's principle. If the system is holonomic, the result is equivalent to the second form of Hamilton's principle (26.1.2).

We cannot fail to notice the striking resemblance between (26.5.5) and the classical formula (15.5.11) for the variation of the principal function. In § 15.5, where we studied the theory of the principal function, we were concerned with a variation to a neighbouring natural orbit; here no such restriction is imposed on the variation. It is now clear that (15.5.11) is in fact a special case of the general result (26.5.5).

26.6 The generalization of Hamilton's Principle. In the theorem just proved we require not only fixed termini, but also fixed times of departure and arrival. The requirement of fixed terminal points is unimportant, but the requirement of fixed terminal times is a serious embarrassment. If however we impose a suitable restriction, we can find a variation principle in which the terminal times may be varied at will.

Let us assume that the system satisfies the following conditions: the system is catastatic, the relations connecting x's and q's do not involve t, and L does not contain t explicitly. In this case the class of virtual displacements is the same as the class of possible displacements, and there is an integral $E = h$. If therefore we fix the terminal points, but not the terminal times, we have, from (26.5.5),

$$\delta\int_{t_0}^{t_1} (L + h)\, dt = (h - E)\,\delta t\Big|_{t_0}^{t_1}, \tag{26.6.1}$$

and *we thus arrive at the theorem*

$$\delta\int_{t_0}^{t_1} (L + h)\, dt = 0. \tag{26.6.2}$$

The important point is that the terminal times are not fixed. It is of interest to observe (bearing in mind the restrictions now imposed on the system) that the theorem (26.6.2) can also be deduced from Hölder's principle; both routes lead to the same goal when we restrict the system in the way described.

26.7 Change of the independent variable. An important and valuable property of the variation principles is they can be expressed readily in terms of any chosen coordinates. We have noticed this already in § 6.3, where we deduced Lagrange's equations of motion from Hamilton's principle. The generalization of Hamilton's principle (26.6.2) allows us to go further and introduce a change of the *independent* variable. Let us adopt a new independent variable θ in place of t, where the relation between θ and t is defined by

(26.7.1) $$dt = u\,d\theta,$$

where u is a given positive function of the q's of class C_1. We may think of θ as an artificial time measured on a clock carried by the representative point in the q-space, the rate of the clock being a given function of position in the space; we have already met this notion of an artificial time in § 17.3 and in § 18.1 and in § 18.3. The generalization of Hamilton's principle (26.6.2) allows us to assert that

(26.7.2) $$\delta\int_{\theta_0}^{\theta_1} u(L + h)\,d\theta = 0,$$

the termini in the q-space being fixed, but not the terminal values of θ. If therefore we express L in terms of q's and q''s, where $q_r' = dq_r/d\theta$, we can derive equations of motion with θ as independent variable. The equations are the Euler-Lagrange equations for the variational problem (26.7.2). They are the Lagrangian equations for the Lagrange function

(26.7.3) $$\Lambda = u(L' + h),$$

where L' represents L expressed in terms of q''s instead of $\dot{q}$'s. We must remember however that not all the solutions of these equations represent possible motions of the system, but only those with $E = h$. The equations define the orbit in the q-space, but not immediately the relation between position in the orbit and the time.

We easily find the explicit form for Λ. We write as usual

$$T = T_2 + T_1 + T_0,$$

where

$$T_2 = \tfrac{1}{2}\sum\sum a_{rs}\dot{q}_r\dot{q}_s$$

as in (6.1.6), and

$$T = \sum a_r\dot{q}_r$$

as in (6.1.7). We write T_2' and T_1' for the similar forms in $q_1', q_2', \ldots, q_n'$,

(26.7.4) $$T_2' = \tfrac{1}{2}\sum\sum a_{rs}q_r'q_s', \quad T_1' = \sum a_rq_r'.$$

Then

(26.7.5) $$T_2 = \dot{\theta}^2T_2' = T_2'/u^2, \quad T_1 = \dot{\theta}T_1' = T_1'/u,$$

and

(26.7.6) $$\Lambda = u(T_2 + T_1 + T_0 - V + h),$$

so finally

(26.7.7) $$\Lambda = \frac{T_2'}{u} + T_1' + u(T_0 - V + h).$$

We must remember that only the motions satisfying

$$\frac{T_2{}'}{u^2} + V - T_0 = h \tag{26.7.8}$$

are relevant to the dynamical problem. If the system is not holonomic the equations of motion will involve l multipliers λ as in (6.6.4). The simplest case, and the one that occurs most commonly, is that of a natural system; there are no λ's, and $T_1{}'$ and T_0 are absent from (26.7.7) and from (26.7.8), so that in this case

$$\Lambda = \frac{T_2{}'}{u} + u(h - V), \tag{26.7.9}$$

and the restriction (26.7.8) becomes

$$\frac{T_2{}'}{u^2} + V = h. \tag{26.7.10}$$

It is interesting to verify by direct transformation that the equations of motion derived from (26.7.7) are in fact satisfied by the motions of the system with energy h. Now

$$\frac{\partial T_2{}'}{\partial q_r{}'} = u\frac{\partial T_2}{\partial \dot{q}_r}, \qquad \frac{\partial T_2{}'}{\partial q_r} = u^2\frac{\partial T_2}{\partial q_r}, \tag{26.7.11}$$

$$\frac{\partial T_1{}'}{\partial q_r{}'} = \frac{\partial T_1}{\partial \dot{q}_r}, \qquad \frac{\partial T_1{}'}{\partial q_r} = u\frac{\partial T_1}{\partial q_r}. \tag{26.7.12}$$

Thus

$$\frac{\partial \Lambda}{\partial q_r{}'} = \frac{1}{u}\left(u\frac{\partial T_2}{\partial \dot{q}_r}\right) + \frac{\partial T_1}{\partial \dot{q}_r} = \frac{\partial (T_2 + T_1)}{\partial \dot{q}_r}, \tag{26.7.13}$$

$$\begin{aligned}\frac{\partial \Lambda}{\partial q_r} &= \frac{1}{u}\left(u^2\frac{\partial T_2}{\partial q_r}\right) + u\frac{\partial T_1}{\partial q_r} + u\frac{\partial (T_0 - V)}{\partial q_r} + \frac{\partial u}{\partial q_r}\left(-\frac{T_2{}'}{u^2} + T_0 - V + h\right)\\ &= u\frac{\partial}{\partial q_r}(T_2 + T_1 + T_0 - V),\end{aligned} \tag{26.7.14}$$

since the coefficient of $\dfrac{\partial u}{\partial q_r}$ is zero in virtue of (26.7.8). We have finally

$$\frac{d}{d\theta}\left(\frac{\partial \Lambda}{\partial q_r{}'}\right) - \frac{\partial \Lambda}{\partial q_r} = u\frac{d}{dt}\left\{\frac{\partial (T_2 + T_1)}{\partial \dot{q}_r}\right\} - u\frac{\partial}{\partial q_r}(T_2 + T_1 + T_0 - V), \tag{26.7.15}$$

and the second member vanishes since the motion satisfies Lagrange's equations.

26.8 Normal form for a system with two degrees of freedom. We consider a holonomic system with two freedoms for which

$$T_2 = \tfrac{1}{2}(a_{11}\dot{q}_1{}^2 + 2a_{12}\dot{q}_1\dot{q}_2 + a_{22}\dot{q}_2{}^2), \quad T_1 = a_1\dot{q}_1 + a_2\dot{q}_2. \tag{26.8.1}$$

By a suitable transformation, to so-called *isothermal* or *isometric* coordinates, we can express T_2 in the form

$$\tfrac{1}{2}U(\dot{Q}_1{}^2 + \dot{Q}_2{}^2), \tag{26.8.2}$$

where $U = U(Q_1, Q_2) > 0$. It will be convenient however to call the new coordinates q_1 and q_2, and to write

$$T_2 = \tfrac{1}{2}u(\dot{q}_1{}^2 + \dot{q}_2{}^2), \quad T_1 = \alpha\dot{q}_1 + \beta\dot{q}_2. \tag{26.8.3}$$

We now apply the theorem of § 26.7, taking a new independent variable θ, where $dt = u\,d\theta$. We have, from (26.7.7),

$$\Lambda = \tfrac{1}{2}(q_1'^2 + q_2'^2) + \alpha q_1' + \beta q_2' - \gamma, \tag{26.8.4}$$

where

$$\gamma = u(V - T_0 - h), \tag{26.8.5}$$

and V and T_0 are expressed in terms of the new coordinates. The equations of motion are now

$$\begin{cases} q_1'' = -\zeta q_2' - \dfrac{\partial \gamma}{\partial q_1}, \\ q_2'' = \zeta q_1' - \dfrac{\partial \gamma}{\partial q_2}, \end{cases} \tag{26.8.6}$$

where

$$\zeta = -\left(\frac{\partial \beta}{\partial q_1} - \frac{\partial \alpha}{\partial q_2}\right). \tag{26.8.7}$$

The orbits with energy h are the integrals of (26.8.6) satisfying

$$\tfrac{1}{2}(q_1'^2 + q_2'^2) + \gamma = 0. \tag{26.8.8}$$

This is sometimes called the *normal form* for a system with two freedoms. The equations are those for the motion of a particle in a plane under the action of a conservative field derived from the potential function γ, and a gyroscopic force of magnitude ζv at right angles to the velocity $\mathbf{v}$. The gyroscopic force is of a more general type than those appearing in § 8.8 and § 9.8, since here the multiplier ζ is not constant, but is a function of q_1 and q_2. If the original system is a natural system, $\zeta = 0$, and the general problem is reduced to one of motion of a particle in a plane under the action of a conservative field of force.

26.9 Liouville's system. The theorem of § 26.7 is particularly well suited to the study of Liouville's system, already considered in § 18.1. The system is a natural system with n freedoms. The simplest case is that in which

$$T = T_2 = \tfrac{1}{2}us, \quad V = \frac{w}{u}, \tag{26.9.1}$$

where

$$s = \dot{q}_1^2 + \dot{q}_2^2 + \cdots + \dot{q}_n^2, \quad u = X_1 + X_2 + \cdots + X_n, \tag{26.9.2}$$
$$w = \xi_1 + \xi_2 + \cdots + \xi_n,$$

and X_r, ξ_r are functions of q_r; the symbols u and w denote sums of separate functions of the individual coordinates. Introducing a new independent variable θ, as in § 26.7, where $dt = u\,d\theta$, we have

$$\Lambda = \tfrac{1}{2}(q_1'^2 + q_2'^2 + \cdots + q_n'^2) + hu - w, \tag{26.9.3}$$

and the energy integral (26.7.8) is

$$\tfrac{1}{2}(q_1'^2 + q_2'^2 + \cdots + q_n'^2) = hu - w. \tag{26.9.4}$$

The Lagrangian function (26.9.3) exhibits a striking phenomenon, the complete separation of the Lagrangian function into n independent Lagrangian functions. The typical member is

$$\tfrac{1}{2}q_r'^2 + hX_r - \xi_r. \tag{26.9.5}$$

The corresponding equation of motion is

$$q_r'' = \frac{d}{dq_r}(hX_r - \xi_r), \tag{26.9.6}$$

and the corresponding energy integral is

$$\tfrac{1}{2}q_r'^2 = hX_r - \xi_r + c_r, \tag{26.9.7}$$

where, in virtue of (26.9.4), $\Sigma\, c_r = 0$. The orbits in the q-space for motions with energy h can be found by expressing each q_r in terms of θ from the equation

$$\frac{dq_r}{\sqrt{\{2(hX_r - \xi_r + c_r)\}}} = d\theta. \tag{26.9.8}$$

The theory can be extended very simply to deal with the more general system

$$T = \tfrac{1}{2}uS, \quad V = \frac{w}{u}, \tag{26.9.9}$$

where

$$S = \sum \dot{q}_r^2/P_r, \tag{26.9.10}$$

where P_r is a function of q_r. (In fact this is not essentially distinct from the preceding; if we introduce new coordinates Q_r such that

$$dQ_r = dq_r/\sqrt{P_r}, \tag{26.9.11}$$

S becomes $\Sigma\, \dot{Q}_r^2$, and u and w are still of the requisite form, sums of separate functions of the individual coordinates.) For the system (26.9.9), taking the new independent variable θ as before, with $dt = u\, d\theta$, we have

$$\Lambda = \frac{1}{2}\sum \frac{q_r'^2}{P_r} + hu - w. \tag{26.9.12}$$

We notice as before the separation into n distinct systems: the typical Lagrangian function is

$$\frac{1}{2}\frac{q_r'^2}{P_r} + hX_r - \xi_r. \tag{26.9.13}$$

The energy integral (26.7.8) is

$$\frac{1}{2}\sum \frac{q_r'^2}{P_r} = hu - w, \tag{26.9.14}$$

and the energy integrals for the separate systems are

$$\tfrac{1}{2}q_r'^2 = P_r(hX_r - \xi_r + c_r), \tag{26.9.15}$$

where $\Sigma\, c_r = 0$. We can express each q_r in terms of θ by integration of the equation

$$\frac{dq_r}{\sqrt{\{2P_r(hX_r - \xi_r + c_r)\}}} = d\theta. \tag{26.9.16}$$

a result which we have found already in (18.1.10).

In the two systems just considered it appears at first sight that we have complete separation into n independent systems, as we have when we use normal coordinates in the theory of small oscillations. But the appearance is to some extent illusory. The relation between a particular q_r and θ can be isolated from the other q_r's, as in (26.9.8) and (26.9.16), but no such statement is true of the relation between a particular q_r and the time. We must bear in mind that θ is not the actual time-variable, and indeed that the relation between θ and t involves all the q's, since $d\theta = dt/u$.

26.10 Conformal transformation. Let us consider the system with Lagrangian function

(26.10.1) $$L = \tfrac{1}{2}(\dot{x}^2 + \dot{y}^2) - V(x, y).$$

It is natural to think of it as a particle moving in a plane in a conservative field of force, x and y being ordinary Cartesian coordinates. But it might also be a more complicated system, in which x and y are Lagrangian coordinates.

If we change to new variables (ξ, η) given by the conformal transformation

(26.10.2) $$x + iy = z = f(\zeta) = f(\xi + i\eta),$$

where f is a regular function in a suitable domain of ζ, we have

(26.10.3) $$|dz| = M|d\zeta|, \quad \text{where } M = |f'(\zeta)|,$$

and

(26.10.4) $$L = \tfrac{1}{2}M^2(\dot{\xi}^2 + \dot{\eta}^2) - W(\xi, \eta),$$

where

(26.10.5) $$W(\xi, \eta) = V(x, y).$$

Let us apply the theorem of § 26.7 to the system (26.10.4), taking $u = M^2$. The new Lagrangian function (26.7.7) for the motions with energy h is

(26.10.6) $$\Lambda = \tfrac{1}{2}(\xi'^2 + \eta'^2) + M^2(h - W),$$

and the energy integral (26.7.8) is

(26.10.7) $$\tfrac{1}{2}(\xi'^2 + \eta'^2) = M^2(h - W).$$

Consider, as a concrete example, the transformation

(26.10.8) $$z = \zeta^2,$$

where the right-hand half of the ζ plane is mapped on the z-plane, with a cut along the negative real axis. In this case

(26.10.9) $$M^2 = 4|\zeta|^2 = 4|z| = 4r,$$

where as usual

(26.10.10) $$r^2 = x^2 + y^2.$$

The Lagrangian function is

(26.10.11) $$\Lambda = \tfrac{1}{2}(\xi'^2 + \eta'^2) + 4r(h - W),$$

and the energy integral is

$$\tfrac{1}{2}(\xi'^2 + \eta'^2) = 4r(h - W). \tag{26.10.12}$$

The curves $\xi =$ constant, $\eta =$ constant in the ζ-plane are mapped into two families of confocal parabolas intersecting orthogonally (Fig. 26.10). These families of parabolas have already been used in § 17.9.

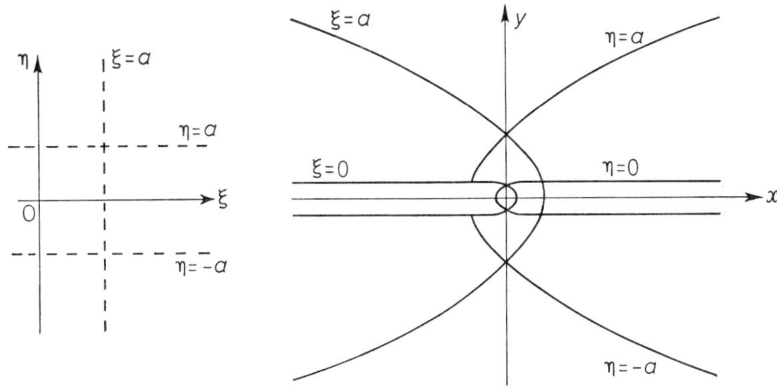

Figure 26.10

The transformation (26.10.8) is peculiarly well adapted to the Newtonian problem, with $V = -\mu/r$,

$$\begin{aligned}\Lambda &= \tfrac{1}{2}(\xi'^2 + \eta'^2) + 4hr + 4\mu \\ &= \tfrac{1}{2}(\xi'^2 + \eta'^2) + 4h(\xi^2 + \eta^2) + 4\mu,\end{aligned} \tag{26.10.13}$$

and we have again the phenomenon of separation into two systems. The equations of motion are

$$\xi'' = 8h\xi, \quad \eta'' = 8h\eta, \tag{26.10.14}$$

and the energy integral is

$$\xi'^2 + \eta'^2 - 8h(\xi^2 + \eta^2) = 8\mu. \tag{26.10.15}$$

It is evident that the solution depends markedly on the sign of h, as indeed we know well already. Let us consider more particularly the case in which $h < 0$, say $8h = -p^2$, where p is real and positive. It is not difficult to find the general solution, but we can simplify the formulae a little by projecting from an apse, $\xi' = \eta = 0$ when $\theta = 0$, and then

$$\xi = \alpha \cos p\theta, \quad \eta = \beta \sin p\theta, \tag{26.10.16}$$

with the condition

$$\alpha^2 + \beta^2 = -\mu/h = 2a, \tag{26.10.17}$$

say; the choice of notation is not quite ingenuous, for we know that the energy in the elliptic orbit is $-\mu/2a$, where $2a$ is the major axis of the ellipse. Let us write

$$\alpha^2 = a(1 - e), \quad \beta^2 = a(1 + e), \quad |e| < 1. \tag{26.10.18}$$

(We shall find that if the apse from which we project is the perihelion, then $e > 0$.)

Then

$$\begin{cases} x = \xi^2 - \eta^2 = a(1 - e)\cos^2 p\theta - a(1 + e)\sin^2 p\theta = a(\cos v - e), \\ y = 2\xi\eta = a\sqrt{(1 - e^2)}\sin v, \\ r = \xi^2 + \eta^2 = a(1 - e)\cos^2 p\theta + a(1 + e)\sin^2 p\theta = a(1 - e\cos v), \end{cases} \tag{26.10.19}$$

where $v = 2p\theta$.

We now consider the relation between position in the orbit and the time. We have

$$dt = 4r\,d\theta = 4a(1 - e\cos v)\,dv/2p, \tag{26.10.20}$$

$$t - t_0 = \frac{2a}{p}(v - e\sin v), \tag{26.10.21}$$

and since $p^2 = 4\mu/a$,

$$v - e\sin v = n(t - t_0), \tag{26.10.22}$$

where $n^2 = \mu/a^3$. It is now clear that v is the eccentric anomaly, and (26.10.22) is Kepler's equation.

Finally, to find the polar equation of the orbit (using now φ to denote the polar angle measured from Ox) we have

$$1 + e\cos\varphi = \frac{r + ex}{r} = \frac{a(1 - e^2)}{r}, \tag{26.10.23}$$

which represents an ellipse; the positive x-axis, $\varphi = 0$, is towards the perihelion if $e > 0$. In the first instance we are concerned with the part of the curve (26.10.16) in the right-hand half of the ζ-plane, and then the orbit in the z-plane does not cross the cut; but we may now discard this restriction.

Chapter XXVII

The principle of least action

27.1 The variation of the action. We now turn to a variation principle of a type different from those discussed in the preceding Chapter, the famous principle of Least Action. We shall assume throughout that the conditions of § 26.6 are satisfied; the system is catastatic, the relations connecting x's and q's do not involve t, and L does not contain t explicitly. In these circumstances there is no distinction between possible and virtual displacements, and there is an integral of energy $E = h$, where

$$E = \sum \dot{q}_r \frac{\partial L}{\partial \dot{q}_r} - L, \tag{27.1.1}$$

and Σ denotes summation from $r = 1$ to $r = n$.

The distinguishing feature of the theory is that *the varied motion is subject throughout to the restriction that on it E remains constant.* The varied motion is built up by making at time t a virtual displacement $\delta\mathbf{q}$ from the actual motion, the varied point $\mathbf{q} + \delta\mathbf{q}$ being occupied at time $t + \delta t$. The varied motion does not in general take the same time as the original motion. It is not in general a natural motion of the system (i.e. it is not a dynamically possible motion), and if the system is not holonomic it is not even a geometrically possible motion. But the varied motion is restricted by the requirement of having constant energy. We assume as before that the δq's and δt, *qua* function of t, are of class C_2.

We define the action $\mathscr{K}$ by the integral, taken along the orbit in the q-space,

$$\mathscr{K} = \int_{t_0}^{t_1} \left(\sum \dot{q}_r \frac{\partial L}{\partial \dot{q}_r}\right) dt. \tag{27.1.2}$$

This is equivalent to

$$\mathscr{K} = \int_{t_0}^{t_1} (2T_2 + T_1)\, dt, \tag{27.1.3}$$

or, for a natural system, to

$$\mathscr{K} = \int_{t_0}^{t_1} 2T\, dt. \tag{27.1.4}$$

The fundamental theorem is that, *if we make a variation of the prescribed type from the actual motion, we have*

$$\delta\mathscr{K} = \sum \frac{\partial L}{\partial \dot{q}_r}\delta q_r \Big|_{t_0}^{t_1} + (t_1 - t_0)\delta h, \tag{27.1.5}$$

where $h + \delta h$ is the (constant) value of E on the varied path. We give two proofs of this result.

(i) We start from the equation (26.4.4),

$$\int_{t_0}^{t_1} \left\{ \delta L + \left(\sum \dot{q}_r \frac{\partial L}{\partial \dot{q}_r} \right) \frac{d}{dt} \delta t \right\} dt = \sum \frac{\partial L}{\partial \dot{q}_r} \delta q_r \Big|_{t_0}^{t_1}. \tag{27.1.6}$$

Now

$$\delta E = \delta \left(\sum \dot{q}_r \frac{\partial L}{\partial \dot{q}_r} \right) - \delta L = \delta h, \tag{27.1.7}$$

so (27.1.6) becomes

$$\int_{t_0}^{t_1} \left\{ \delta \left(\sum \dot{q}_r \frac{\partial L}{\partial \dot{q}_r} \right) + \left(\sum \dot{q}_r \frac{\partial L}{\partial \dot{q}_r} \right) \frac{d}{dt} \delta t \right\} dt - (t_1 - t_0)\, \delta h = \sum \frac{\partial L}{\partial \dot{q}_r} \delta q_r \Big|_{t_0}^{t_1}, \tag{27.1.8}$$

which is equivalent to

$$\delta \int_{t_0}^{t_1} \left(\sum \dot{q}_r \frac{\partial L}{\partial \dot{q}_r} \right) dt = \sum \frac{\partial L}{\partial \dot{q}_r} \delta q_r \Big|_{t_0}^{t_1} + (t_1 - t_0)\, \delta h, \tag{27.1.9}$$

and this establishes the result.

(ii) We start from the equation (26.5.5), which yields

$$\delta \int_{t_0}^{t_1} L\, dt = \sum \frac{\partial L}{\partial \dot{q}_r} \delta q_r \Big|_{t_0}^{t_1} - h(\delta t_1 - \delta t_0). \tag{27.1.10}$$

Now

$$\sum \dot{q}_r \frac{\partial L}{\partial \dot{q}_r} - L = h$$

on the original path, and a similar result holds on the varied path if we replace h by $h + \delta h$. So (27.1.10) becomes

$$\delta \int_{t_0}^{t_1} \left(\sum \dot{q}_r \frac{\partial L}{\partial \dot{q}_r} \right) dt - \delta \{ h(t_1 - t_0) \} = \sum \frac{\partial L}{\partial \dot{q}_r} \delta q_r \Big|_{t_0}^{t_1} - h(\delta t_1 - \delta t_0), \tag{27.1.11}$$

which is equivalent to (27.1.5).

27.2 The principle of Least Action. Our first deduction from the fundamental result (27.1.5) is that *if we fix the end-points and choose* $\delta h = 0$ *then*

$$\delta \mathscr{K} = 0. \tag{27.2.1}$$

This is the principle of Least Action. The action is stationary for the actual path in comparison with neighbouring paths having the same end-points (in the q-space) and the same energy.

The interpretation of the principle is simplest if the system is holonomic; in that case the complication that the varied path may violate the constraints does not arise. We consider a family κ of paths by which the system moves from one prescribed configuration to another, the motion on each path being such that E is constant, and indeed has the prescribed value h. For the actual path the action is stationary in the family κ.

The principle of Least Action is usually attributed to Maupertius, whose *Essai de Cosmologie* appeared in 1751. But in fact the theory of Maupertuis, which was based partly on metaphysical grounds, was vague and unscientific, and it was Euler who first put the theory into a satisfactory form.

The principle of Least Action, like Hamilton's principle (§ 3.7), is sufficient as well as necessary for the motion. We can therefore deduce from it the equations of motion. This is a much more difficult exercise than the deduction from Hamilton's principle, because of the restriction $E = h$ on the varied path. We have a *Lagrange problem* in the calculus of variations. To illustrate the technique it will suffice to consider a natural system. The principle asserts that the actual motion gives to $\int_{t_1}^{t_2} 2T\,dt$ a stationary value *in the class of curves*

$$q_1(t),\quad q_2(t), \ldots, q_n(t)$$

satisfying the differential equation

$$T + V - h = 0. \tag{27.2.2}$$

We consider curves in the $(n + 1)$-fold $(t, q_1, q_2, \ldots, q_n)$ and the end-conditions are that the lower terminus R_0 is fixed, i.e. $t_0, q_1(t_0), q_2(t_0), \ldots, q_n(t_0)$ are all fixed, and that at the upper terminus R_1 the time t_1 is *not* fixed, but $q_1(t_1), q_2(t_1), \ldots, q_n(t_1)$ are fixed.

We need for the Lagrange problem the theorem of the *multiplier rule*, already referred to in § 26.1 and § 26.2. We need the conditions for a stationary value of $\int_{t_0}^{t_1} F\,dt$, where

$$F = 2T + \lambda(T + V - h), \tag{27.2.3}$$

and λ is a function of t to be determined. The end-condition at the upper terminus is

$$F - \sum \dot{q}_r \frac{\partial F}{\partial \dot{q}_r} = 0 \tag{27.2.4}$$

at $t = t_1$.

The Euler equations, expressing necessary conditions for a stationary value of $\int_{t_0}^{t_1} F\,dt$, are

$$\frac{d}{dt}\left\{(2 + \lambda)\frac{\partial T}{\partial \dot{q}_r}\right\} = (2 + \lambda)\frac{\partial T}{\partial q_r} + \lambda\frac{\partial V}{\partial q_r}, \qquad r = 1, 2, \ldots, n. \tag{27.2.5}$$

We can write these equations in the form

$$(2 + \lambda)\left\{\frac{d}{dt}\left(\frac{\partial T}{\partial \dot{q}_r}\right) - \frac{\partial(T - V)}{\partial q_r}\right\} = 2(1 + \lambda)\frac{\partial V}{\partial q_r} - \frac{d\lambda}{dt}\frac{\partial T}{\partial \dot{q}_r}, \qquad r = 1, 2, \ldots, n. \tag{27.2.6}$$

If we multiply the rth equation by $\dot{q}_r$, and sum from $r = 1$ to $r = n$, we get

$$(2 + \lambda)\left\{\sum \dot{q}_r \frac{d}{dt}\left(\frac{\partial T}{\partial \dot{q}_r}\right) - \sum \dot{q}_r \frac{\partial T}{\partial q_r} + \sum \dot{q}_r \frac{\partial V}{\partial q_r}\right\} = 2(1 + \lambda)\sum \dot{q}_r \frac{\partial V}{\partial q_r} - \frac{\partial \lambda}{dt}\left(\sum \dot{q}_r \frac{\partial T}{\partial \dot{q}_r}\right). \tag{27.2.7}$$

Hence

$$(2 + \lambda)\left\{\frac{d}{dt}\left(\sum \dot{q}_r \frac{\partial T}{\partial \dot{q}_r}\right) - \frac{dT}{dt} + \frac{dV}{dt}\right\} = 2(1 + \lambda)\frac{dV}{dt} - 2T\frac{d\lambda}{dt}, \tag{27.2.8}$$

where $\dfrac{dV}{dt}$ means $\sum \dfrac{\partial V}{\partial q_r}\dot{q}_r$, and $\dfrac{dT}{dt}$ means $\sum\left(\dfrac{\partial T}{\partial q_r}\dot{q}_r + \dfrac{\partial T}{\partial \dot{q}_r}\ddot{q}_r\right)$. Thus

$$(2 + \lambda)\frac{d}{dt}(T + V) = 2(1 + \lambda)\frac{dV}{dt} - 2T\frac{d\lambda}{dt}. \tag{27.2.9}$$

The first member of (27.2.9) is identically zero, and the second is equal to

$$-2(1 + \lambda)\frac{dT}{dt} - 2T\frac{d\lambda}{dt} = -2\frac{d}{dt}(T + \lambda T). \tag{27.2.10}$$

Hence $(1 + \lambda)T$ is constant on the curve, and the end-condition (27.2.4) shows that this constant value is zero. Hence $\lambda = -1$ for all values of t. The equations (27.2.6) are therefore equivalent to Lagrange's equations of motion.

27.3 Jacobi's form of the principle of Least Action. The difficulty arising from the restriction imposed on the variations in the principle of Least Action, which is very evident in the proof just given, makes it natural to seek for a modified form of the principle in which this restriction can be discarded. Such a form is very easy to find.

We consider now a holonomic system with n degrees of freedom, and to begin with we confine our attention to the case of a natural system. We have, both in the original and in the varied motion,

$$T = h - V = \sqrt{\{T(h - V)\}}, \tag{27.3.1}$$

and the principle of Least Action implies that

$$\int^{t_1} 2\sqrt{\{T(h - V)\}}\, dt \tag{27.3.2}$$

is stationary in the class of motions with conserved energy h. But the restriction (that all the motions considered have constant energy h) is now irrelevant. The integrand in (27.3.2) is homogeneous of the first degree in the velocities, and the value of the integral depends only on the path (in the q-space), not on the speed at which it is traversed. We thus arrive at the following theorem: *the integral*

$$\int_{t_0}^{t_1} 2\sqrt{\{T(h - V)\}}\, dt$$

is stationary for the actual path as compared with neighbouring paths joining the same two end-points in the q-space. This is Jacobi's form of the principle of Least Action. The problem of determining the path of the representative point in the q-space has been reduced to a straightforward problem, with fixed end-points, in the calculus of variations.

For the problem of a particle moving in space under the action of a conservative field derived from the potential V, the equation (27.3.2) takes the form

$$\delta\int \sqrt{\{2(h - V)\}}\, ds = 0, \tag{27.3.3}$$

where s represents the length of the arc. We are reminded of Fermat's principle in optics. Fermat's principle asserts that the path of light from a point A to a point B is a path for which the time has a minimum (or at least a stationary) value. This is valid even for a path with abrupt changes of direction, where the ray meets a mirror, or where it meets the surface of a lens at which the refractive index changes abruptly. However the case most similar to the one with which we are concerned in dynamics is that of light travelling in a medium whose refractive index μ varies continuously. The speed of light is proportional to $1/\mu$, and the path of least time is that for which

$$\int \mu\, ds$$

is a minimum. The problem of finding the paths in the dynamical problem is the same as the problem of finding the paths in the optical problem if the field and the energy constant in the first problem are related to the refractive index in the second problem by the equation

$$\mu = C\sqrt{(h - V)}.$$

If the system is not natural (27.3.2) must be replaced by

$$\int_{t_0}^{t_1} \{2\sqrt{[T_2(h - V + T_0)]} + T_1\}\, dt. \tag{27.3.4}$$

Consider, as a simple illustration, the problem of a particle moving in a plane in a uniform field. The orbits are the curves that make stationary the integral $\int \sqrt{\{2(h - V)\}}\, ds$. For a uniform field g (per unit mass) in the direction Oy we have $V = -gy$, and the integral becomes $\int \sqrt{\{2(h + gy)\}}\, ds$. If now we choose the axis Ox as the energy level for the problem we have $h = 0$, and the problem becomes that of finding the extremals for the integral

$$\int \sqrt{y}\, ds = \int \sqrt{\{y(1 + y'^2)\}}\, dx. \tag{27.3.5}$$

The integrand f does not contain x, so we have the well-known first integral

$$f - y'\frac{\partial f}{\partial y'} = \text{constant}, \tag{27.3.6}$$

giving

$$y = b(1 + y'^2) = b \sec^2 \psi, \qquad (b > 0), \tag{27.3.7}$$

where $\tan \psi$ is the slope of the curve, $\tan \psi = y'$. To complete the integration* we have

$$dx = \cot \psi\, dy = 2b \sec^2 \psi\, d\psi, \tag{27.3.8}$$

whence

$$x - a = 2b \tan \psi. \tag{27.3.9}$$

The orbits, found by eliminating ψ between (27.3.7) and (27.3.9), are the curves

$$(x - a)^2 = 4b(y - b). \tag{27.3.10}$$

They are the parabolas in the upper half-plane having the axis Ox (the energy level) as directrix.

An immediate deduction from Jacobi's form of the principle of Least Action (still confining attention to natural systems) is that the function

$$L' = 2\sqrt{\{T(h - V)\}} \tag{27.3.11}$$

may be used as a Lagrangian function from which we can derive equations of motion which are satisfied by the motions with energy h. It is not difficult to verify this fact by direct calculation. It must be observed, however, that the n differential equations obtained from the Langrangian function (27.3.11) are not independent, a fact very familiar in the *parametric problem* in the calculus of variations. The equations determine only the paths in the q-space for the motions with energy h. To determine the actual speed of the representative point on its path, we must bring in the fact that the total energy $T + V$ has the value h.

To prove that the equations derived from (27.3.11) are not independent we have only to observe that, if we multiply the rth equation by $\dot{q}_r$, and sum, from 1 to n, we have (as in § 6.7)

$$\sum \dot{q}_r \left\{\frac{d}{dt}\left(\frac{\partial L'}{\partial \dot{q}_r}\right) - \frac{\partial L'}{\partial q_r}\right\} = \frac{d}{dt}\left(\sum \dot{q}_r \frac{\partial L'}{\partial \dot{q}_r} - L'\right), \tag{27.3.12}$$

* Alternatively we can integrate the equation $by'^2 = y - b$ by using the substitution $y - b = z^2$.

and the second member vanishes identically, since L' is homogeneous of degree 1 in the $\dot{q}$'s.

As a simple example of the use of the Lagrangian function (27.3.11) we may take again the example of a particle moving in a plane in a uniform field g in the direction Oy. Here

$$L' = \sqrt{\{2(h + gy)(\dot{x}^2 + \dot{y}^2)\}}, \tag{27.3.13}$$

and the coordinate x is ignorable. Thus the x-equation of motion leads to

$$\sqrt{\{2(h + gy)\}}\,\frac{\dot{x}}{\sqrt{(\dot{x}^2 + \dot{y}^2)}} = \text{constant}, \tag{27.3.14}$$

which is equivalent to (27.3.7). As we have noticed, the y-equation is not an independent result, and the one equation suffices to determine the orbit.

The observation that (27.3.2) depends only on the path of the representative point in the q-space, not on the speed at which the curve is traversed, implies that we can discard the time as independent variable in favour of a new variable ξ. The new variable ξ might be, for example, one of the q's. We introduce the function T', a homogeneous quadratic form in $q_1', q_2', \ldots, q_n'$, where $q_r' = dq_r/d\xi$. Explicitly, if

$$T = \tfrac{1}{2} \sum\sum a_{rs}\dot{q}_r\dot{q}_s, \tag{27.3.15}$$

$$T' = \tfrac{1}{2} \sum\sum a_{rs}q_r'q_s'. \tag{27.3.16}$$

For a time-interval in which ξ varies monotonically with t,

$$\int_{t_0}^{t_1} 2\sqrt{\{T(h - V)\}}\,dt = \int_{\xi_0}^{\xi_1} 2\sqrt{\{T'(h - V)\}}\,d\xi, \tag{27.3.17}$$

and we can, in virtue of Jacobi's form of the principle of Least Action, use

$$\Lambda = 2\sqrt{\{T'(h - V)\}} \tag{27.3.18}$$

as a new Lagrangian function, with the independent variable ξ replacing the time. The equations of motion derived in this way again only determine the orbit, not the rate at which it is traversed.

As a simple illustration, consider the problem of a particle moving in a plane under a central attraction derived from the potential function $V = V(r)$. Using polar coordinates

$$T = \tfrac{1}{2}(\dot{r}^2 + r^2\dot{\theta}^2). \tag{27.3.19}$$

If we take $\xi = r$ we have

$$\Lambda = \sqrt{\{2(1 + r^2\theta'^2)(h - V)\}}. \tag{27.3.20}$$

For the Lagrangian function Λ the coordinate θ is ignorable, and the first integral

$$\frac{\partial \Lambda}{\partial \theta'} = \alpha \tag{27.3.21}$$

leads to the equation

$$\theta'^2 = \frac{\alpha^2/r^4}{2(h - V) - (\alpha^2/r^2)}, \tag{27.3.22}$$

which is the familiar differential equation of the orbit (5.2.42).

27.4 Whittaker's theorem. It is interesting to construct an elementary proof of Jacobi's form of the principle of Least Action for the simple case of a particle moving in a plane in a conservative field. We consider an arc C in the plane; we denote the arc-length, measured from the end A to a point P of the arc, by s, and the inclination to Ox of the outward normal at P by θ. The arc C is assumed to be of a simple type in which θ always increases with s, and in which θ is a differentiable function of s. In particular, if the curve is a closed curve, it is convex.

Let us calculate the variation in

$$I = \int \sqrt{\{2(h - V)\}}\, ds \tag{27.4.1}$$

when we change from C to an arc C' which is obtained from C by displacement through a distance δp along the outward normal. The displacement δp is to vary continuously with s. The consequent increment in I is

$$\delta I = \int \frac{-\delta V}{\sqrt{\{2(h - V)\}}}\, ds + \int \sqrt{\{2(h - V)\}}\, \delta ds. \tag{27.4.2}$$

Now

$$-\delta V = N \delta p, \tag{27.4.3}$$

where N is the component of the field of force along the outward normal, and

$$\delta ds = \delta p\, d\theta = \delta p\, ds/\rho, \tag{27.4.4}$$

where ρ is the radius of curvature at P. Thus

$$\delta I = \int \frac{1}{\sqrt{\{2(h - V)\}}} \left\{N + \frac{2(h - V)}{\rho}\right\} \delta p\, ds. \tag{27.4.5}$$

As a first application of (27.4.5) we recover Jacobi's form of the principle of Least Action for this special problem. Suppose that the arc C, from A to B, is part of an orbit, and let us choose δp $(= \delta p(s))$ to vanish at A and at B. Now if v is the velocity of the particle at a point of the orbit

$$N = -\frac{mv^2}{\rho} = -\frac{2(h - V)}{\rho}, \tag{27.4.6}$$

and the integrand in (27.4.5) vanishes at each point of C. Thus $\delta I = 0$, which is Jacobi's result.

As a second application of (27.4.5) we establish a theorem, due to Whittaker, concerning the existence of simple periodic orbits. We consider a fixed value of h, such that $h > V$ throughout the domain considered. Let C be a simple closed convex curve of the type mentioned above, and let us consider the value of the test function

$$\mathscr{W} \equiv N + \frac{2(h - V)}{\rho} \tag{27.4.7}$$

at points of C; the function $\mathscr{W}$ is well-defined at each point of the curve. Now if $\mathscr{W} < 0$ and $\delta p > 0$ at all points of C, then (27.4.5) $\delta I < 0$. The value of I decreases if we change from C to a neighbouring simple closed curve enclosing C.

Suppose now that there exists another simple closed convex curve D surrounding C, and that $\mathscr{W} > 0$ at all points of D. Then if $\delta p < 0$ at all points of D, $\delta I < 0$, so the value of I decreases if we change from D to a neighbouring simple closed curve lying inside D.

Consider then the value of I for members of the class κ of simple closed curves Γ lying in the annulus between C and D. The annulus is assumed to contain no singularity of V. We have seen that I decreases when Γ moves outwards from C or inwards from D. If therefore we assume that I is bounded below in the class κ, and that the infimum value m is attained, then there exists at least one curve Γ_0 for which $I(\Gamma_0) = m$. For this curve I has a minimum value. The curve Γ_0 clearly cannot be C or D, nor indeed can it coincide with C or D for any part of its length. Thus *there is at least one periodic orbit lying in the annulus if* $\mathscr{W} < 0$ on C *and* $\mathscr{W} > 0$ *on* D.

Consider in particular the case where the curves C and D are themselves periodic orbits, the energy for C being h_1, and the energy for D being h_2, where $h_1 > h_2$. Let h be any number lying between h_1 and h_2,

$$h_1 > h > h_2.$$

Then $\mathscr{W} < 0$ on C and $\mathscr{W} > 0$ on D, and therefore, in virtue of the theorem just proved, there is a periodic orbit with energy h lying in the annulus between C and D. We have a one-parameter family of periodic orbits, such as that considered in § 15.8(vi).

27.5 The ignoration of coordinates. The theory of the ignoration of coordinates, established in § 10.1, can be derived from a variation principle of somewhat similar type to the principle of Least Action, i.e. we exhibit a functional which is stationary, not in the whole class of varied paths joining the prescribed end-points, but in a class of paths restricted in a particular way. We shall merely recover the result established in § 10.1, and no new result will be found, but the delicate argument required is worthy of record. We deal with a holonomic system with n freedoms in which the first m coordinates $q_1, q_2, \ldots, q_m$ are ignorable.

Consider the integral

$$I = \int_{t_0}^{t_1} \left\{ L - \frac{d}{dt}\left(\sum_{r=1}^{m} q_r \frac{\partial L}{\partial \dot{q}_r} \right) \right\} dt. \tag{27.5.1}$$

For a variation to a neighbouring path in the q-space we have, from (26.5.5),

$$\begin{aligned} \delta I &= \left(\sum_{r=1}^{n} \frac{\partial L}{\partial \dot{q}_r} \delta q_r - E\,\delta t \right) \Bigg|_{t_0}^{t_1} - \sum_{r=1}^{m} \left\{ \frac{\partial L}{\partial \dot{q}_r} \delta q_r + q_r\, \delta\left(\frac{\partial L}{\partial \dot{q}_r} \right) \right\} \Bigg|_{t_0}^{t_1} \\ &= \left\{ \sum_{r=m+1}^{n} \frac{\partial L}{\partial \dot{q}_r} \delta q_r - E\,\delta t - \sum_{r=1}^{m} q_r\, \delta\left(\frac{\partial L}{\partial \dot{q}_r} \right) \right\} \Bigg|_{t_0}^{t_1}. \end{aligned} \tag{27.5.2}$$

Now throughout the motion

$$\frac{\partial L}{\partial \dot{q}_r} = \beta_r, \qquad r = 1, 2, \ldots, m, \tag{27.5.3}$$

and we now restrict the varied motion to be such that these equations (27.5.3) remain satisfied; the first m momentum components are kept constant, and indeed with the same constant values as in the original motion. If the variations are restricted in this way

$$\delta \int_{t_0}^{t_1} \left(L - \sum_{r=1}^{m} \dot{q}_r \frac{\partial L}{\partial \dot{q}_r} \right) dt = \left(\sum_{r=m+1}^{n} \frac{\partial L}{\partial \dot{q}_r} \delta q_r - E\,\delta t \right) \Bigg|_{t_0}^{t_1}. \tag{27.5.4}$$

The desired result follows readily from (27.5.4.) We express the integrand in the first member of (27.5.4) in terms of $\beta_1, \beta_2, \ldots, \beta_m, \dot{q}_{m+1}, \dot{q}_{m+2}, \ldots, \dot{q}_n$, suppressing the first m velocities in favour of the corresponding momenta by means of (27.5.3), as in § 10.1. The integrand is now the Routhian function R, a function of the palpable coordinates q_{m+1},

$q_{m+2}, \ldots, q_n$ and their derivatives $\dot{q}_{m+1}, \dot{q}_{m+2}, \ldots, \dot{q}_n$; of course R also contains the β's. If now we fix the palpable coordinates at the ends of the range (not the ignorable coordinates), and fix the times of departure and arrival, we have

$$\delta \int_{t_0}^{t_1} R\,dt = 0, \tag{27.5.5}$$

and Routh's equations (10.1.9) follow from (27.5.5) just as Lagrange's equations follow from Hamilton's principle. This theory is due to Larmor.

27.6 The characteristic function. We return to the fundamental result (27.1.5) We confine our attention in what follows to a natural system with n degrees of freedom; thus

$$L = T - V, \tag{27.6.1}$$

where

$$T = \tfrac{1}{2} \sum\sum a_{rs}\dot{q}_r\dot{q}_s. \tag{27.6.2}$$

We recall that the variation contemplated is to a varied path traversed with constant energy $h + \delta h$. It should be observed that there is nothing particularly recondite about this restriction; when the varied path in the q-space has been defined we merely adjust the speed of the representative point on it to satisfy the condition $T + V = h + \delta h$. The time of duration of the journey on the varied path is not restricted.

Now, in the fundamental result (27.1.5) we are concerned with a variation from a dynamically possible path (i.e. one satisfying the equations of motion) to a neighbouring path. The varied path is not, in the first instance, a dynamically possible path. We now turn our attention to the particular case in which the varied path is also a dynamically possible path. The varied motion is the motion of the system when the initial position and velocity are slightly changed.

We define the characteristic function of Hamilton. It is the value of the action integral $\mathscr{K}$ taken along the actual path, and expressed as a function of the initial and final coordinates and the energy constant h. We denote the characteristic function by $K(q_{10}, q_{20}, \ldots, q_{n0}; q_{11}, q_{21}, \ldots, q_{n1}; h)$. The fundamental equation (27.1.5) gives us a formula for the variation of K consequent on arbitrary variations in its $(2n + 1)$ arguments. The formula is analogous to the classical formula for the variation of the principal function (15.5.11). Explicitly (writing now p_r for $\partial L/\partial \dot{q}_r$)

$$dK = \sum p_{r1}\,dq_{r1} - \sum p_{r0}\,dq_{r0} + (t_1 - t_0)\,dh. \tag{27.6.3}$$

The formula

$$p_{r1} = \frac{\partial K}{\partial q_{r1}}, \tag{27.6.4}$$

reminiscent of (16.5.7), gives the value of the momentum component at the upper limit of the path in terms of q_{r1}'s, q_{r0}'s and h. The characteristic function bears to the modified Hamilton-Jacobi theorem (16.5.5–7) a relation similar to the relation that the principal function bears to the Hamilton-Jacobi theorem itself.

Of the two functions, principal function S and characteristic function K, S is the simpler. A familiar example will explain this. Consider a particle moving in the (x, y)-plane in a uniform field. If we prescribe the starting point (x_0, y_0), the final point (x_1, y_1) and the times t_0, t_1 of departure and arrival, the motion is uniquely determined. It follows that S is a *uniform* (single-valued) function of the five arguments, $(x_0, y_0, x_1, y_1, t_1 - t_0)$, and it is defined for all values of the arguments; in fact this function has been calculated already, in § 15.9. But if we prescribe the points (x_0, y_0) and (x_1, y_1) *and the energy constant* h there may be two orbits from (x_0, y_0) to (x_1, y_1), or one only, or none. Thus K is a *many-valued* function of its five arguments (x_0, y_0, x_1, y_1, h), and it is defined only for some values of the arguments. We shall determine the actual form of K for this problem later (§ 27.10).

27.7 The configuration space. As we have seen in § 27.3, Jacobi's form of the principle of Least Action reduces the problem of finding the path of a particle, moving in a field of force in space, to a simple variational problem. The path minimizes, or at least makes stationary, the integral

(27.7.1) $$\int \sqrt{\{2(h - V)\}}\, ds.$$

We now achieve a similar reduction of the problem for a system of more general type.

We consider a natural system for which

(27.7.2) $$T = \tfrac{1}{2} \sum\sum a_{rs}\dot{q}_r\dot{q}_s,$$

where the coefficients a_{rs} are functions, of class C_1, of $(q_1, q_2, \ldots, q_n)$. We introduce a Riemannian metric into the q-space, the element of length between two neighbouring points $\mathbf{q}$ and $\mathbf{q} + d\mathbf{q}$ being defined by the equation

(27.7.3) $$ds^2 = \sum\sum a_{rs}\, dq_r\, dq_s.$$

The q-space with a metrical structure defined by (27.7.3) is called the *configuration space.* If we go back to the ν particles of which the system is composed,

(27.7.4) $$ds^2 = \sum_{r=1}^{N} m_r\, dx_r^{\,2}.$$

When we have defined infinitesimal distances in the configuration space by (27.7.3) we go on to define finite distances in the natural way. We define the length of a rectifiable curve in the space by integration along the curve, and we then define the distance between any two configurations as the infimum (greatest lower bound) of the lengths of rectifiable curves joining the two configurations. We denote the distance so defined between two configurations P_1 and P_2 by $|P_1P_2|$. We now have a natural way of defining neighbourhoods. Let P_0 be any configuration, and ε a positive number. We define the set of configurations P such that

(27.7.5) $$|P_0P| < \varepsilon$$

as a spherical neighbourhood of P_0. Any set of configurations P which contains a spherical neighbourhood of P_0 is called a neighbourhood of P_0. Thus, having introduced the notion of neighbourhood in the configuration space, we can discuss its topological properties.

The kinetic energy of the system is

(27.7.6) $$T = \tfrac{1}{2}\dot{s}^2,$$

as though the representative point were itself a particle of unit mass moving in the space. But this is by no means the complete picture. The analogy of the general dynamical system to a particle moving in the configuration space applies also to the equations of motion. The rth Lagrangian equation of motion for the system has the form

$$\sum a_{rs}\ddot{q}_s + \sum\sum [uv, r]\dot{q}_u\dot{q}_v = -\frac{\partial V}{\partial q_r}, \tag{27.7.7}$$

as in (6.4.5), where $[uv, r]$ denotes as usual the first Christoffel symbol; of course, to conform to the usage of tensor theory, we ought to write $\dot{q}^r$ instead of $\dot{q}_r$. Now the first member of (27.7.7) is simply the covariant component of acceleration in the configuration space. The Lagrangian equation of motion for the system is precisely the equation expressing Newton's law of motion when a particle of unit mass moves in the configuration space under the action of the field whose potential function is V.

Further, Jacobi's form of the principle of Least Action (27.3.2) for the general dynamical system takes the form

$$\delta\int \sqrt{\{2(h - V)\}}\, ds = 0, \tag{27.7.8}$$

just as it does for the elementary problem of a particle moving in ordinary space; the integration is now along a curve in the configuration space, and s denotes the arc-length of the curve.

27.8 System with two degrees of freedom. In some simple cases, with two degrees of freedom, we can find a surface (in ordinary Euclidean space) which is homeomorphic with the

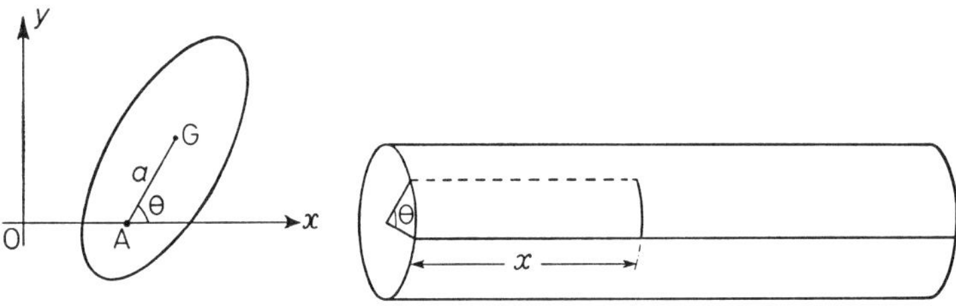

Figure 27.8

configuration space; i.e. there exists a continuous $1 - 1$ mapping of the configuration space onto the surface. We consider two elementary examples.

(i) A rigid lamina moves in a plane, being so constrained that a point A of the lamina moves on a fixed straight line Ox. We describe the configuration at time t by means of two Lagrangian coordinates x and θ, where x is the displacement OA, and θ defines the orientation; θ may be taken as the inclination of AG to Ox, where G is the centre of mass of the lamina (Fig. 27.8). The configuration space is homeomorphic with the surface of a circular cylinder, with x, θ as cylindrical coordinates, x being measured along the axis of the cylinder, and θ from a fixed plane through the axis.

If A is free to move on the whole length of the x-axis, the cylinder must be of infinite length. But there may be restrictions defined by inequalities such as

$$x_1 \leqslant x \leqslant x_2, \tag{27.8.1}$$

or

$$x_1 < x < x_2, \tag{27.8.2}$$

and in these cases only a finite length of the cylinder, bounded by planes normal to the axis, is relevant. The barriers in (27.8.1) are sometimes spoken of as *inelastic stops*, and those in (27.8.2) as *elastic stops*.

It may be of interest to notice that in this case, by making a different choice of Lagrangian coordinates, we can obtain actual equality of the line-elements in the configuration space and on the topologically equivalent cylinder. We have

(27.8.3) $$T = \tfrac{1}{2}M\{\dot{x}^2 - 2a\dot{x}\dot{\theta}\sin\theta + (a^2 + p^2)\dot{\theta}^2\},$$

where a denotes the length AG, and Mp^2 is the moment of inertia of the lamina about G. Thus, in the configuration space, now taking $M = 1$, we have

(27.8.4) $$ds^2 = dx^2 - 2a\sin\theta\, dx\, d\theta + (a^2 + p^2)\, d\theta^2.$$

If now we take new Lagrangian coordinates ξ, φ, defined by the equations

(27.8.5) $$\xi = x + a\cos\theta, \quad \varphi = \frac{\pi}{2E}\int_0^\theta \sqrt{(1 - k^2\sin^2\psi)}\, d\psi, \quad k^2 = \frac{a^2}{a^2 + p^2},$$

so that ξ is the x-coordinate of G, and φ is a monotone increasing function of θ with $\varphi = 2\pi$ when $\theta = 2\pi$, then (2.8.4) becomes

(27.8.6) $$ds^2 = d\xi^2 + b^2\, d\varphi^2,$$

where

(27.8.7) $$b = \frac{2E}{\pi}\sqrt{(a^2 + p^2)}.$$

The element of length in the configuration space of ξ, φ is equal to the element of length on a cylinder of radius b, with b, φ, ξ as cylindrical coordinates. If there are no given forces (so that $V = 0$ in (27.7.8)) the orbits in the configuration space correspond to the geodesics on the cylinder, and these are the straight lines if the cylinder is developed into a plane.

(ii) Consider a double pendulum, consisting of two rods AB, BC jointed together at B, and freely attached to a fixed support at A. The system is free to move in a vertical plane through A. Or instead of the two rods we might have a light string ABC tied to a fixed support at A, with massive particles attached at B and C. We take as Lagrangian coordinates the inclinations θ, φ of AB, BC to the downward vertical. The configuration space is homeomorphic with a torus, with θ as the azimuthal angle, and φ as the angular displacement in the circular section from the central plane.

27.9 Kelvin's theorem. We return to the discussion of a system with n degrees of freedom, the metrical structure of the configuration space being defined by (27.7.3). There is a very simple interpretation of the momentum $(p_1, p_2, \ldots, p_n)$. For

(27.9.1) $$p_r = \sum_{s=1}^{n} a_{rs}\dot{q}_s,$$

so the momentum vector is simply the covariant vector corresponding to the velocity $(\dot{q}_1, \dot{q}_2, \ldots, \dot{q}_n)$, which is contravariant. The condition that a displacement $d\mathbf{q}$ should be orthogonal to a velocity $\dot{\mathbf{q}}$ is

(27.9.2) $$\sum\sum a_{rs}\dot{q}_s\, dq_r = 0,$$

which we can write compactly in the form

(27.9.3) $$\sum p_r\, dq_r = 0.$$

Let us now consider a family of orbits in the configuration space all having the same energy h. In this case the formula (27.6.3) for the variation of the characteristic function becomes

(27.9.4) $$dK = \sum p_{r1}\, dq_{r1} - \sum p_{r0}\, dq_{r0}.$$

Suppose therefore that we take the orbits with energy h originating in a given point P_0 $(q_{10}, q_{20}, \ldots, q_{n0})$ of the configuration space. The velocity of projection is the same for all the orbits, since

(27.9.5) $$\tfrac{1}{2}\dot{s}^2 = T = h - V,$$

but the directions of setting out from P_0 vary. Then

(27.9.6) $$dK = \sum p_{r1}\, dq_{r1},$$

and, if $(dq_1, dq_2, \ldots, dq_n)$ represents a displacement on the surface K = constant = k, we have

(27.9.7) $$\sum p_{r1}\, dq_{r1} = 0,$$

so the orbit cuts the surface orthogonally. The surface $K = k$ is constructed by moving along each orbit from P_0 to a point P_1 at which the action integral $\int 2T\, dt$ along the orbit has attained the value k. The surfaces $K = k$ are called the *surfaces of equal action* for P_0. We have found that *the family of orbits starting with given energy from a given point intersect the surfaces of equal action for that point orthogonally.* This is the first part of *Kelvin's theorem.*

Next consider the points $(q_{10}, q_{20}, \ldots, q_{n0})$ lying on a "surface" Γ_0,

(27.9.8) $$\varphi(q_{10}, q_{20}, \ldots, q_{n0}) = 0,$$

where $\varphi \in C_1$. Consider the orbits in the configuration space obtained by projection normally from this surface (all to the same side) with the prescribed energy h. If $d\mathbf{q}_0$ represents a displacement in the surface Γ_0 we have, since we project normally,

(27.9.9) $$\sum p_{r0}\, dq_{r0} = 0,$$

so that the equation $dK = 0$ again implies

(27.9.10) $$\sum p_{r1}\, dq_{r1} = 0.$$

The surfaces $K = k$ are cut orthogonally by the orbits. *The orbits obtained by normal projection, with prescribed energy, from a given surface* Γ_0 *are cut orthogonally by a family of surfaces* Γ_k, and the increment of action from one of these surfaces to another is the same for all the orbits. This is the second part of *Kelvin's theorem.*

The surface Γ_k is also *the envelope of the surfaces of equal action* $K = k$ *for points on* Γ_0. The surface of equal action $K = k$ for P_0 is

(27.9.11) $$K(q_{10}, q_{20}, \ldots, q_{n0}, q_{11}, q_{21}, \ldots, q_{n1}) = k,$$

where $(q_{11}, q_{21}, \ldots, q_{n1})$ are current coordinates. For a point on the envelope

(27.9.12) $$\sum \frac{\partial K}{\partial q_{r0}}\, dq_{r0} = 0,$$

subject to

$$\Sigma \frac{\partial \varphi}{\partial q_{r0}} dq_{r0} = 0, \tag{27.9.13}$$

so

$$\frac{\partial K}{dq_{r0}} \Big/ \frac{\partial \varphi}{\partial q_{r0}} = \text{constant}, \tag{27.9.14}$$

and therefore the (covariant) vector $\partial K/\partial q_{r0}$ is in the direction of the normal to Γ_0. The point of contact of (27.9.11) with its envelope lies on the orbit leaving Γ_0 normally.

We cannot fail to observe the close analogy of this theory with Huygen's principle in optics. The orbits correspond to the light-rays, the surfaces of equal action to the wave-fronts. The wave-front is the envelope of the partial wave-fronts arising from the points of a former wave-front. But in the dynamical theory we are concerned with increments of action, not increments of time.

The determination of surfaces of equal action in any but the simplest cases is a formidable task. We give two examples in which the calculations are easy.

(i) A particle moves in ordinary space under no forces. The orbits are straight lines traversed with velocity $v = \sqrt{(2h)}$. The action integral is

$$\int 2T\, dt = v^2 t = vr = r\sqrt{(2h)},$$

where r is the length of the path from P_0 to P_1. The surfaces of equal action for P_0 are the spheres with P_0 as centre; the surface $K = k$ is the sphere of radius $k/\sqrt{(2h)}$. If we start from an arbitrary surface Γ_0 the surface Γ_k, representing prescribed increments of action, are the *parallel surfaces* obtained from Γ_0 by moving along the normal through a distance $k/\sqrt{(2h)}$.

(ii) A particle moves on a smooth surface under no forces save the smooth constraint. The orbits through a point P_0 of the surface are the geodesics through P_0. The surfaces of equal action for P_0 are the *geodesic circles* with P_0 as centre.

27.10 Uniform field. We now turn to the task mentioned at the end of § 27.6. We calculate the characteristic function, and hence the equation of the surfaces of equal action, for the problem of a particle of unit mass moving in a plane under the action of a uniform field. In this case the configuration space is simply the Euclidian plane in which the particle moves. We take the field in the direction Oy, and the energy level as the axis Ox, so $V = -gy$ and $h = 0$. If the velocity of projection from $P_0(x_0, y_0)$ is (u, v) we have

$$x - x_0 = ut, \quad y - y_0 = vt + \tfrac{1}{2}gt^2, \tag{27.10.1}$$

and therefore

$$K = \int_0^\theta 2T\, dt = \int_0^\theta (u^2 + v^2 + 2vgt + g^2t^2)\, dt, \tag{27.10.2}$$

$$K = (u^2 + v^2)\theta + vg\theta^2 + \tfrac{1}{3}g^2\theta^3, \tag{27.10.3}$$

where we have taken $t_0 = 0$, $t_1 = \theta$. Now

$$u^2 + v^2 = 2gy_0, \tag{27.10.4}$$

so, suppressing u and v in the second member of (27.10.3), we have K expressed in terms of θ,

$$K = 2gy_0\theta + g\theta(y_1 - y_0 - \tfrac{1}{2}g\theta^2) + \tfrac{1}{3}g^2\theta^3 \tag{27.10.5}$$
$$= g\theta(y_1 + y_0) - \tfrac{1}{6}g^2\theta^3$$
$$= g\theta s - \tfrac{1}{6}g^2\theta^3,$$

where we write s for $y_1 + y_0$.

It now only remains to find θ in terms of (x_0, y_0, x_1, y_1). The equation for θ is

$$2gy_0\theta^2 = (u^2 + v^2)\theta^2 \tag{27.10.6}$$
$$= (x_1 - x_0)^2 + (y_1 - y_0 - \tfrac{1}{2}g\theta^2)^2$$
$$= (x_1 - x_0)^2 + (y_1 - y_0)^2 - g\theta^2(y_1 - y_0) + \tfrac{1}{4}g^2\theta^4,$$

which we can write in the form

$$g^2\theta^4 - 4gs\theta^2 + 4r^2 = 0, \tag{27.10.7}$$

where

$$r^2 = (x_1 - x_0)^2 + (y_1 - y_0)^2. \tag{27.10.8}$$

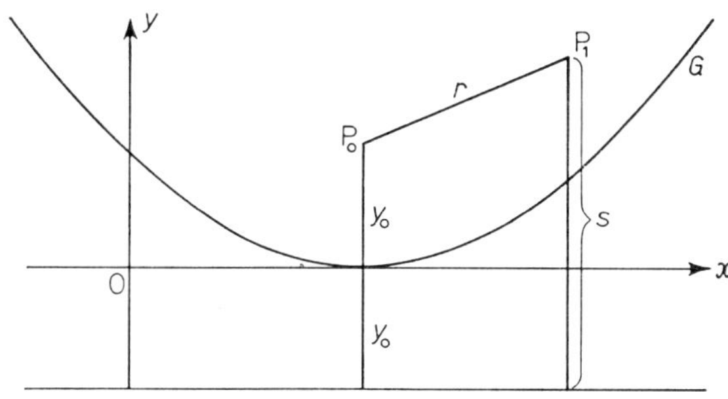

Figure 27.10a

The parabola $s = r$ is the enveloping parabola G, and for real positive values of θ we need $s \geqslant r$ (Fig. 27.10a). In fact, solving (27.10.7) for θ, we have

$$g\theta^2 = 2s \pm 2\sqrt{(s^2 - r^2)} = \{\sqrt{(s + r)} \pm \sqrt{(s - r)}\}^2, \tag{27.10.9}$$

giving (as we expect) *two* values for θ if $s > r$,

$$\begin{cases} \sqrt{g}\theta_1 = \sqrt{(s + r)} + \sqrt{(s - r)}, \\ \sqrt{g}\theta_2 = \sqrt{(s + r)} - \sqrt{(s - r)}, \end{cases} \tag{27.10.10}$$

and $g\theta_1\theta_2 = 2r$. Thus

$$K = g\theta s - \tfrac{1}{6}g^2\theta^3 = g\theta s - \frac{1}{6\theta}(4gs\theta^2 - 4r^2) = \tfrac{1}{3}gs\theta + \frac{2r^2}{3\theta}, \tag{27.10.11}$$

whence

$$\frac{3K}{\sqrt{g}} = s(\sqrt{g}\theta) + r\left(\frac{2r}{\sqrt{g}\theta}\right) \tag{27.10.12}$$
$$= s\{\sqrt{(s + r)} \pm \sqrt{(s - r)}\} + r\{\sqrt{(s + r)} \mp \sqrt{(s - r)}\}$$
$$= (s + r)^{3/2} \pm (s - r)^{3/2}.$$

The two-valued answer is not unexpected (§ 27.6). For example, if we put $(x_1, y_1) = (x_0, y_0)$, so that $s = 2y_0$, $r = 0$, one value of K vanishes, the other is $[\frac{4}{3}\sqrt{(2g)}]y_0^{3/2}$; the former corresponds to the instant of departure, the latter to the instant of return, in the rectilinear motion when the particle is projected in a direction opposite to that of the field.

The surfaces of equal action for P_0 are the curves

$$(s + r)^{3/2} \pm (s - r)^{3/2} = \text{constant}, \tag{27.10.13}$$

and these, in virtue of the first part of Kelvin's theorem, are the orthogonal trajectories of the orbits (Fig. 27.10*b*). The lower sign relates to the intersection with a point of the orbit from P_0 before it reaches the envelope, the upper sign relates to the intersection after reaching the envelope. The curves have cusps on the enveloping parabola.

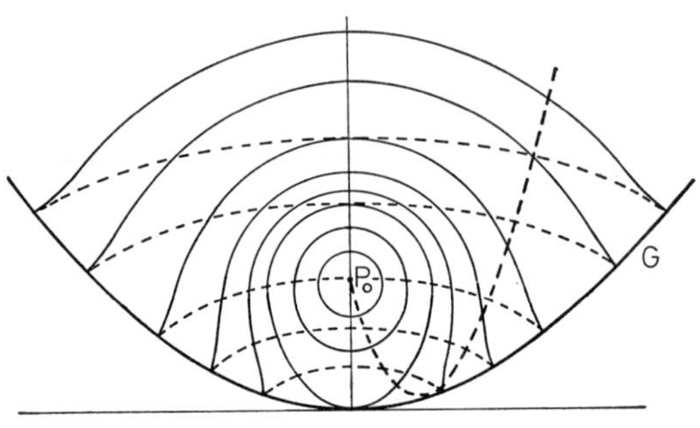

Figure 27.10*b*

27.11 Tait's problem, direct solution. We now consider an example of the second part of Kelvin's theorem (§ 27.9), namely the surfaces of equal action generated by normal projection from a given initial surface. (Actually we deal with a two-dimensional problem, so we are now concerned with curves instead of surfaces.) We take again the problem of the motion of a particle in a uniform field, and the particular problem proposed is that in which the initial curve is *a straight line parallel to the field*.

We choose the axes with Oy in the direction of the field, $y = 0$ being the energy level, and $x = 0$ the line from which the particle is projected. Thus the orbits are got by projection from points (O, y_0) with velocity $(u, 0)$, where $u^2 = 2gy_0$. The calculation is very similar to that in the previous section. We have

$$x = ut, \quad y = y_0 + \tfrac{1}{2}gt^2, \tag{27.11.1}$$

and

$$K = \int_0^\theta (u^2 + g^2t^2)\, dt = u^2\theta + \tfrac{1}{3}g^2\theta^3 = \frac{x_1^2}{\theta} + \tfrac{1}{3}g^2\theta^3, \tag{27.11.2}$$

taking $t_0 = 0$, $t_1 = \theta$ as before. The equation for θ is

$$x_1^2 = 2gy_0\theta^2 = 2g\theta^2(y_1 - \tfrac{1}{2}g\theta^2), \tag{27.11.3}$$

giving

$$g^2\theta^4 - 2gy_1\theta^2 + x_1^2 = 0, \tag{27.11.4}$$

whence

$$g\theta^2 = y_1 \pm \sqrt{(y_1^2 - x_1^2)} = \tfrac{1}{2}\{\sqrt{(y_1 + x_1)} \pm \sqrt{(y_1 - x_1)}\}^2. \tag{27.11.5}$$

The two values for θ are therefore given by

(27.11.6)
$$\begin{cases} \sqrt{(2g)}\theta = \xi \pm \eta, \\ \dfrac{1}{\sqrt{(2g)}\theta} = \dfrac{\xi \mp \eta}{2x_1}, \end{cases}$$

where we write, for the sake of brevity, ξ for $\sqrt{(y_1 + x_1)}$ and η for $\sqrt{(y_1 - x_1)}$.

We now easily find the explicit form of K,

(27.11.7)
$$\begin{aligned} K &= \frac{x_1^2}{\theta} + \frac{1}{3\theta}(2gy_1\theta^2 - x_1^2) = \frac{2}{3\theta}x_1^2 + \frac{2}{3}gy_1\theta \\ &= \tfrac{1}{3}\sqrt{(2g)}\{x_1(\xi \mp \eta) + y_1(\xi \pm \eta)\} \\ &= \tfrac{1}{3}\sqrt{(2g)}\{\tfrac{1}{2}(\xi^2 - \eta^2)(\xi \mp \eta) \\ &\quad + \tfrac{1}{2}(\xi^2 + \eta^2)(\xi \pm \eta)\} \\ &= \tfrac{1}{3}\sqrt{(2g)}(\xi^3 \pm \eta^3). \end{aligned}$$

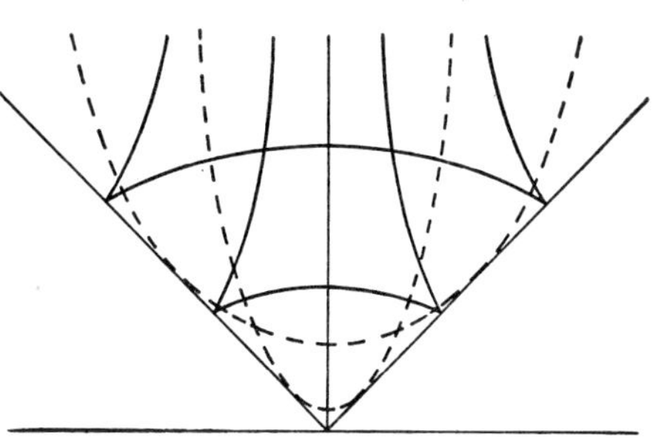

Figure 27.11

The surfaces of equal action (Fig. 27.11) are the curves

(27.11.8)
$$(y_1 + x_1)^{3/2} \pm (y_1 - x_1)^{3/2} = \text{constant}.$$

The orbits are the parabolas

(27.11.9)
$$x_1^2 = 4y_0(y_1 - y_0),$$

and this equation can also be written in the form

(27.11.10)
$$\xi \pm \eta = 2\sqrt{y_0}.$$

The parabolas (27.11.9) all touch the lines $y_1 = \pm x_1$, and the surfaces of equal action (27.11.8) have cusps on these lines.

27.12 Tait's problem, envelope theory. It is an interesting exercise to derive the solution of Tait's problem from the envelope theory; the surface of equal action Γ_k arising from a surface Γ_0 is the envelope of the surfaces of equal action for the individual points of Γ_0 (§ 27.9). The problem involves a rather delicate point. Since the projection from $(0, y_0)$ is horizontal, only the shorter of the two possible times to (x_1, y_1) is involved, and we can write, as in § 27.10,

(27.12.1)
$$\sqrt{g}\theta = \sqrt{(s + r)} - \sqrt{(s - r)},$$

(27.12.2)
$$\frac{3K}{\sqrt{g}} = (s + r)^{3/2} - (s - r)^{3/2},$$

where now

(27.12.3)
$$s = y_1 + y_0, \quad r^2 = x_1^2 + (y_1 - y_0)^2,$$

and k is the increment of action along the orbit from $(0, y_0)$ to (x_1, y_1).

In order to find the envelope we have to suppress y_0 in (27.12.2) by means of the equation

(27.12.4)
$$\frac{\partial}{\partial y_0}\{(s + r)^{3/2} - (s - r)^{3/2}\} = 0.$$

But this last equation (27.12.4) is equivalent to the equation of the orbit (as we can verify directly) so we may replace it by the simpler equation

(27.12.5)
$$x_1^2 = 4y_0(y_1 - y_0).$$

The envelope of these parabolas is, as we have noticed already, the line-pair $y_1^2 = x_1^2$, and the point of contact is at $y_1 = 2y_0$. For (i) the arc AB in Fig. 27.12, $y_0 < y_1 < 2y_0$, and (ii) for the arc BC, $2y_0 < y_1$.

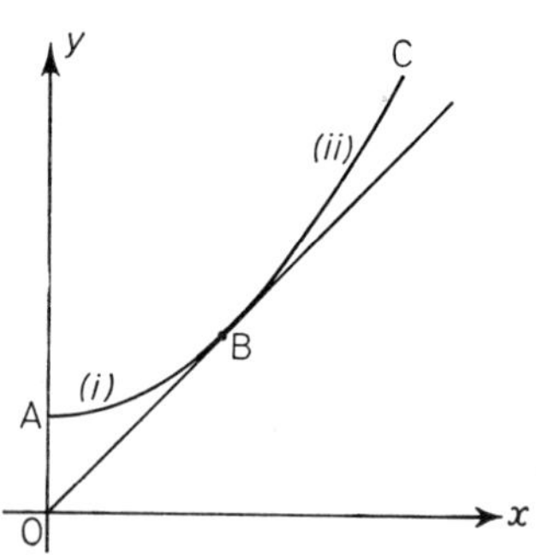

Figure 27.12

Our problem is now simply the elimination of y_0 from (27.12.2) and (27.12.5). We have

(27.12.6) $$s^2 - r^2 = 4y_0y_1 - x_1^2,$$

whence, in virtue of (27.12.5),

(27.12.7) $$\sqrt{(s^2 - r^2)} = 2y_0.$$

Thus

(27.12.8) $$y_1 - y_0 = s - 2y_0 = s - \sqrt{(s^2 - r^2)}$$
$$= \tfrac{1}{2}\{\sqrt{(s + r)} - \sqrt{(s - r)}\}^2 = \tfrac{1}{2}(\lambda - \mu)^2,$$

where for the moment we write λ for $\sqrt{(s + r)}$ and μ for $\sqrt{(s - r)}$. Further

(27.12.9) $$y_1^2 - x_1^2 = y_1^2 - 4y_0(y_1 - y_0) = (y_1 - 2y_0)^2,$$

giving

(27.12.10) $$\sqrt{(y_1^2 - x_1^2)} = 2y_0 - y_1, \quad \text{on } AB,$$

(27.12.11) $$\sqrt{(y_1^2 - x_1^2)} = y_1 - 2y_0, \quad \text{on } BC.$$

Hence, on AB,

(27.12.12) $$2(y_1 - y_0) = y_1 - \sqrt{(y_1^2 - x_1^2)} = \tfrac{1}{2}\{\sqrt{(y_1 + x_1)} - \sqrt{(y_1 - x_1)}\}^2 = \tfrac{1}{2}(\xi - \eta)^2,$$

and on BC,

(27.12.13) $$2(y_1 - y_0) = y_1 + \sqrt{(y_1^2 - x_1^2)} = \tfrac{1}{2}\{\sqrt{(y_1 + x_1)} + \sqrt{(y_1 - x_1)}\}^2 = \tfrac{1}{2}(\xi + \eta)^2.$$

We now easily derive the equation of the envelope. We must take the two cases separately. For AB,

(27.12.14) $$\begin{cases} y_1 - y_0 = \tfrac{1}{2}(\lambda - \mu)^2 = \tfrac{1}{4}(\xi - \eta)^2, \\ \lambda^2 + \lambda\mu + \mu^2 = 2s + \sqrt{(s^2 - r^2)} = 2y_1 + 4y_0, \\ \xi^2 + \xi\eta + \eta^2 = 2y_1 + \sqrt{(y_1^2 - x_1^2)} = y_1 + 2y_0, \end{cases}$$

and therefore

(27.12.15) $$\lambda^3 - \mu^3 = (\lambda - \mu)(\lambda^2 + \lambda\mu + \mu^2) = \frac{1}{\sqrt{2}}(\xi - \eta)\, 2(\xi^2 + \xi\eta + \eta^2) = \sqrt{2}(\xi^3 - \eta^3),$$

and finally

(27.12.16) $$\frac{3k}{\sqrt{g}} = \sqrt{2}(\xi^3 - \eta^3).$$

Similarly for BC,

(27.12.17) $$\begin{cases} y_1 - y_0 = \tfrac{1}{2}(\lambda - \mu)^2 = \tfrac{1}{4}(\xi + \eta)^2, \\ \lambda^2 + \lambda\mu + \mu^2 = 2y_1 + 4y_0, \quad \text{as before}, \\ \xi^2 - \xi\eta + \eta^2 = 2y_1 - \sqrt{(y_1^2 - x_1^2)} = y_1 + 2y_0, \end{cases}$$

giving

$$\lambda^3 - \mu^3 = (\lambda - \mu)(\lambda^2 + \lambda\mu + \mu^2) = \frac{1}{\sqrt{2}}(\xi + \eta)2(\xi^2 - \xi\eta + \eta^2) = \sqrt{2}(\xi^3 + \eta^3), \tag{27.12.18}$$

and finally

$$\frac{3k}{\sqrt{g}} = \sqrt{2}(\xi^3 + \eta^3). \tag{27.12.19}$$

The formulae (27.12.16) and (27.12.19) are the equations (27.11.7) for $K = k$, and the reconciliation between the direct calculation of the surfaces of equal action and the envelope theory is complete.

Chapter XXVIII

The restricted problem of three bodies

28.1 The problem of three bodies. One of the most famous problems of classical dynamics is the problem of three bodies. Three particles move in space under their mutual gravitational attraction. The problem is to find the position of the particles at any subsequent time when their positions and velocities at $t = 0$ are prescribed. The study of this problem has had a profound effect on the development of dynamics. Indeed, many of the most important advances in the subject have been inspired by researches connected, more or less closely, with the problem of three bodies.

The problem of two bodies, which we have already discussed briefly in §§ 5.4 *et seqq*, was one of the greatest triumphs of Newton's theory. We can regard this problem as completely solved in the sense indicated above: that is to say, we can find the positions of the particles at any subsequent time when their positions and velocities at $t = 0$ are prescribed. The problem of three bodies cannot be regarded as solved in this sense. On the other hand, for many particular cases of the problem that occur in astronomy, an approximate solution can be found which is correct to a very high degree of accuracy. The heavenly bodies are approximately spherical with a spherically symmetrical distribution of mass, and the attraction between two such bodies is the same as that between two particles at their centres. If the three bodies are the sun and two planets, the main factor of simplification is the fact that the masses m_1, m_2 of the planets are small in comparison with the mass M of the sun, and terms of the third order in m_1/M and m_2/M are usually negligible. (For example the mass of the earth is less than 1/300,000 of the mass of the sun.) If the three bodies are the sun (M) and a planet (m) and a satellite (μ) the numbers m/M and μ/M are small, and in addition μ/m is small, though not of the same order of smallness as m/M. (For example the mass of the moon is about 1/80 of the mass of the earth.) Another factor of practical help in seeking an accurate approximation is the fact that the eccentricities of the nearly-elliptic orbits of the planets are small. (The eccentricity of the earth's orbit is about 1/60.)

Two approaches towards the problem of three bodies have been made in earlier Chapters. In § 17.10 we considered the motion of a planet under the attraction of two fixed suns. As we saw, if we confine our attention to motion in a plane through the suns, the complete classification of the orbits can be carried out. Moreover we can go further, and find explicit formulae for the orbits in terms of elliptic functions. The difficulty of even this comparatively simple problem serves as a warning of the complexity of the general three-body problem. In § 25.3 we studied the variation of the elliptic elements. In that context we consider first the motion of a single planet relative to the sun; we then consider how the planet moves in the presence of the sun and a second planet. The outlook here is that we do not regard the second problem as a new and independent problem, but instead we regard the new motion as the gradual modification of the original elliptic motion. The method is feasible because, as we have noticed, the masses of the planets are small in comparison with the mass of the sun.

28.2 The restricted problem, the equations of motion. The *restricted problem* of three bodies is this: a particle A of mass α and a particle B of mass β move under their mutual attraction. The centre of mass G of the two particles moves uniformly in a straight line, and without loss of generality we may suppose G to be at rest. The initial conditions are such that the orbit of B relative to A is a circle: therefore the orbit of each particle relative to G is a circle. A massless particle P, the *planetoid*, moves in the plane of motion of A and B. By saying that P is massless we mean that it is subject to the attraction of A and B, but that its mass m is so small that it does not sensibly influence their motion. The problem is to determine the motion of P.

We take rotating axes with G as origin and GB as axis of x (Fig. 28.2). We denote the length AB by l, and the angular velocity by ω, so

(28.2.1) $$\omega^2 = \frac{\gamma(\alpha + \beta)}{l^3}.$$

Thus A is permanently at rest (relative to the rotating axes) at the point $(-a, 0)$, and B is permanently at rest at the point $(b, 0)$, where

(28.2.2) $$a = \frac{\beta}{\alpha + \beta}\, l, \quad b = \frac{\alpha}{\alpha + \beta}\, l.$$

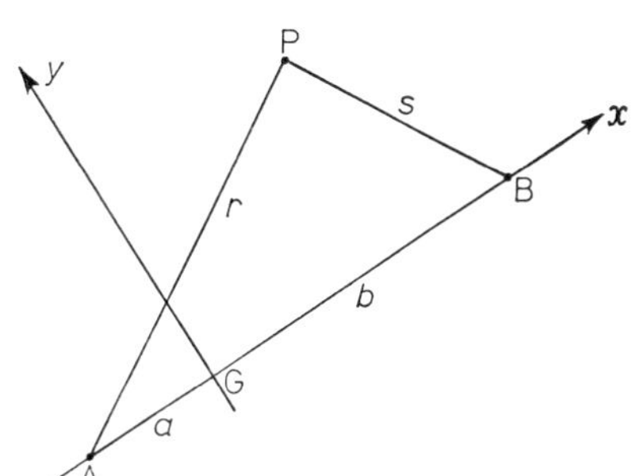

Figure 28.2

We may suppose, without loss of generality, that $\alpha > \beta > 0$. The motion of $P(x, y)$ is the same as it would be if A and B were constrained to move as they do move, so

(28.2.3) $$T = \tfrac{1}{2}m\{(\dot{x} - y\omega)^2 + (\dot{y} + x\omega)^2\}, \quad V = -\frac{\gamma m\alpha}{r} - \frac{\gamma m\beta}{s},$$

where r is the distance AP and s is the distance BP,

(28.2.4) $$r^2 = (x + a)^2 + y^2, \quad s^2 = (x - b)^2 + y^2.$$

Thus, omitting the positive coefficient m,

(28.2.5) $$L = \tfrac{1}{2}(\dot{x}^2 + \dot{y}^2) + \omega(x\dot{y} - y\dot{x}) + \tfrac{1}{2}\omega^2(x^2 + y^2) + \frac{\gamma\alpha}{r} + \frac{\gamma\beta}{s},$$

and L is of the form $T_2 + T_1 + T_0 - V$. If the terms T_1 and T_0 were absent we should have the problem of motion under the attraction of two fixed suns; this problem has been discussed already in §§ 17.10 *et seqq.* We notice that L does not contain t explicitly, and Jacobi's integral (6.8.3) is

(28.2.6) $$T_2 + V - T_0 = \tfrac{1}{2}(\dot{x}^2 + \dot{y}^2) - \tfrac{1}{2}\omega^2(x^2 + y^2) - \frac{\gamma\alpha}{r} - \frac{\gamma\beta}{s} = h.$$

We write

(28.2.7) $$T_0 - V = \gamma U,$$

where

(28.2.8) $$U = U(x, y) = \frac{1}{2}\frac{\alpha + \beta}{l^3}(x^2 + y^2) + \frac{\alpha}{r} + \frac{\beta}{s},$$

and the equations of motion are

$$\text{(28.2.9)} \qquad \begin{cases} \ddot{x} - 2\omega\dot{y} = \gamma \dfrac{\partial U}{\partial x}, \\ \ddot{y} + 2\omega\dot{x} = \gamma \dfrac{\partial U}{\partial y}. \end{cases}$$

The equations (28.2.9) exhibit the motion as that of a particle of unit mass in a conservative field of force derived from the potential function $-\gamma U$, with a gyroscopic force superposed. Jacobi's integral (28.2.6) shows that, throughout the motion, $\gamma U + h > 0$, so motion can only take place in the region

$$\text{(28.2.10)} \qquad U > U_0,$$

where $U_0 = -h/\gamma$.

Since

$$\text{(28.2.11)} \qquad br^2 + as^2 = l(x^2 + y^2) + ab(a + b),$$

we can readily express U in terms of two variables r and s,

$$\text{(28.2.12)} \qquad U = \frac{1}{2l^3}(\alpha r^2 + \beta s^2) + \frac{\alpha}{r} + \frac{\beta}{s} - \frac{1}{2}\frac{\alpha\beta}{\alpha + \beta}\frac{1}{l}.$$

If we put $r = \rho l$, $s = \sigma l$, we find

$$\text{(28.2.13)} \qquad lU = \alpha\left(\frac{1}{2}\rho^2 + \frac{1}{\rho}\right) + \beta\left(\frac{1}{2}\sigma^2 + \frac{1}{\sigma}\right) - \frac{1}{2}\frac{\alpha\beta}{\alpha + \beta},$$

which is a convenient formula to use in constructing the curves $U =$ constant. In the regions $y > 0$ and $y < 0$, ρ and σ are independent variables; but on $y = 0$, ρ and σ are not independent. If we divide the axis $y = 0$ into three regions $\mathscr{R}_1(-\infty < x < -a)$, $\mathscr{R}_2(-a < x < b)$, and $\mathscr{R}_3(b < x < \infty)$, we have

$$\text{(28.2.14)} \qquad \sigma - \rho = 1 \text{ in } \mathscr{R}_1, \quad \sigma + \rho = 1 \text{ in } \mathscr{R}_2, \quad \rho - \sigma = 1 \text{ in } \mathscr{R}_3.$$

28.3 Positions of equilibrium. The planetoid can rest in equilibrium, relative to the rotating axes, at the points at which U has a stationary value. If we think of the surface defined by the equation

$$\text{(28.3.1)} \qquad z = U,$$

the points of equilibrium are the points at which the tangent plane is parallel to $z = 0$. The surface (28.3.1) tends to infinity at A and B, and it approximates to the paraboloid

$$\text{(28.3.2)} \qquad z = \frac{1}{2}\frac{\alpha + \beta}{l^3}(x^2 + y^2)$$

as $x^2 + y^2 \to \infty$. Now

$$\text{(28.3.3)} \qquad \frac{\partial U}{\partial x} = \frac{\alpha + \beta}{l^3}x - \frac{\alpha(x + a)}{r^3} - \frac{\beta(x - b)}{s^3}.$$

$$\text{(28.3.4)} \qquad \frac{\partial U}{\partial y} = \left(\frac{\alpha + \beta}{l^3} - \frac{\alpha}{r^3} - \frac{\beta}{s^3}\right)y,$$

and we can write these formulae in the alternative forms

$$\frac{\partial U}{\partial x} = \lambda x - \frac{\alpha\beta l}{\alpha + \beta}\left(\frac{1}{r^3} - \frac{1}{s^3}\right), \tag{28.3.5}$$

$$\frac{\partial U}{\partial y} = \lambda y, \tag{28.3.6}$$

where we write for the moment, as a convenient shorthand,

$$\lambda = \frac{\alpha + \beta}{l^3} - \frac{\alpha}{r^3} - \frac{\beta}{s^3}. \tag{28.3.7}$$

For the second derivatives (which we shall need later) we have

$$\frac{\partial^2 U}{\partial x^2} = \lambda + \frac{3\alpha(x + a)^2}{r^5} + \frac{3\beta(x - b)^2}{s^5}, \tag{28.3.8}$$

$$\frac{\partial^2 U}{\partial x\, \partial y} = \frac{\partial^2 U}{\partial y\, \partial x} = \frac{3\alpha(x + a)y}{r^5} + \frac{3\beta(x - b)y}{s^5}, \tag{28.3.9}$$

$$\frac{\partial^2 U}{\partial y^2} = \lambda + \frac{3\alpha y^2}{r^5} + \frac{3\beta y^2}{s^5}. \tag{28.3.10}$$

At a point of equilibrium $\dfrac{\partial U}{\partial x} = \dfrac{\partial U}{\partial y} = 0$, so, by (28.3.6), at a point of equilibrium either $y = 0$ or $\lambda = 0$. We consider these two cases in turn.

28.4 Equilibrium points on AB. On $y = 0$ we have $r = |x + a|$, $s = |x - b|$, and therefore (except at the anomalous points A and B)

$$\frac{\partial^2 U}{\partial x^2} = \frac{\alpha + \beta}{l^3} + \frac{2\alpha}{r^3} + \frac{2\beta}{s^3}, \tag{28.4.1}$$

so $\partial^2 U/\partial x^2 > 0$ on $y = 0$. Let us consider how $U(x, 0)$ varies as x increases from $-\infty$ to $+\infty$. Now $U(x, 0)$ has infinities at $x = -a$ and at $x = b$, and it tends to infinity with $|x|$. Moreover $\partial U/\partial x$ increases steadily from $-\infty$ to $+\infty$ in each of the three regions $\mathscr{R}_1(-\infty < x < -a)$, $\mathscr{R}_2(-a < x < b)$, and $\mathscr{R}_3(b < x < \infty)$. Thus $\partial U/\partial x$ passes just once through the value zero in each of the three regions, and there are three equilibrium points on AB, U having minima at the points $N_1(x = n_1)$, $N_2(x = n_2)$, and $N_3(x = n_3)$, one in each of the three regions. Of course the existence of three equilibrium points on AB is evident on physical grounds if we interpret U as a potential function.

The equilibrium point N_1 is at a distance less than l from A, and the equilibrium point N_3 is at a distance less than l from B. To prove these statements we notice that

$$\frac{r}{x + a} = (-1, +1, +1), \quad \frac{s}{x - b} = (-1, -1, +1), \tag{28.4.2}$$

in the three regions, so that in $\mathscr{R}_1$ for example

$$\frac{\partial U}{\partial x} = \frac{\alpha + \beta}{l^3}x + \frac{\alpha}{r^2} + \frac{\beta}{s^2}. \tag{28.4.3}$$

Hence at the point of $\mathscr{R}_1$ at which

$$x = -a - l = -\frac{\alpha + 2\beta}{\alpha + \beta}\, l, \quad r = l, \quad s = 2l, \tag{28.4.4}$$

we have

$$\frac{\partial U}{\partial x} = -\frac{\alpha + 2\beta}{l^2} + \frac{\alpha}{l^2} + \frac{\beta}{4l^2} < 0, \tag{28.4.5}$$

and it follows that N_1 lies between $x = -a - l$ and $x = -a$. Similarly N_3 lies between $x = b$ and $x = b + l$. The equilibrium point N_2 lies between G and B, for at G

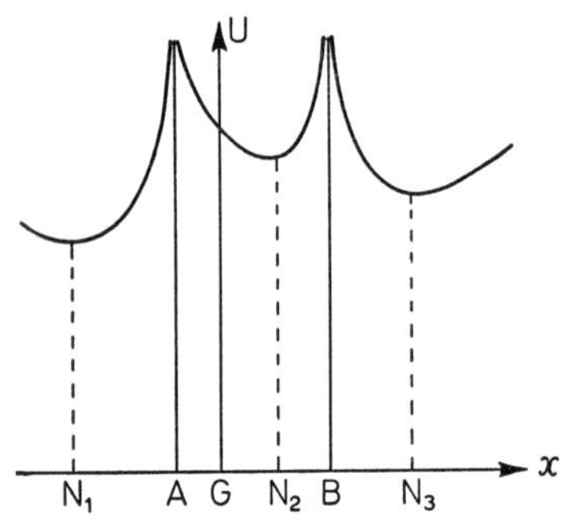

Figure 28.4

$$\frac{\partial U}{\partial x} = -\frac{\alpha}{r^2} + \frac{\beta}{s^2} = -\frac{\alpha}{a^2} + \frac{\beta}{b^2} \tag{28.4.6}$$

$$= -(\alpha^3 - \beta^3)\left(\frac{\alpha + \beta}{\alpha\beta l}\right)^2 < 0.$$

The graph of $U(x, 0)$ is therefore of the form shown in Fig. 28.4.

We notice also (for future reference) that at each of the points N_1, N_2, N_3,

$$\frac{\partial^2 U}{\partial x^2} > 0, \quad \frac{\partial^2 U}{\partial x\, \partial y} = 0, \quad \frac{\partial^2 U}{\partial y^2} < 0. \tag{28.4.7}$$

The first of these statements has been proved already in (28.4.1), and the second follows from (28.3.9). To prove the third we have at N_1, by (28.3.10), $\dfrac{\partial^2 U}{\partial y^2} = \lambda$: and since at N_1, $\dfrac{\partial U}{\partial x} = 0$, we have, from (28.3.5),

$$\frac{\partial^2 U}{\partial y^2} = \lambda = \frac{\alpha\beta l}{\alpha + \beta}\left(\frac{1}{r^3} - \frac{1}{s^3}\right)\frac{1}{x}, \tag{28.4.8}$$

which is negative, since (at N_1) $x < 0$ and $r < s$. The proof is similar for N_3. At N_2

$$\frac{\partial^2 U}{\partial y^2} = \lambda = \frac{\alpha + \beta}{l^3} - \frac{\alpha}{r^3} - \frac{\beta}{s^3}, \tag{28.4.9}$$

which is negative, because in $\mathscr{R}_2$ both r and s are less than l.

We return to the graph of $U(x, 0)$. There are minima at N_1 and N_2 and N_3 (Fig. 28.4), and we wish to determine at which of these three points U has the greatest value, and at which it has the least value. Actually (supposing still that $\alpha > \beta > 0$)

$$U(n_2) > U(n_3), \quad U(n_3) > U(n_1). \tag{28.4.10}$$

To establish these results, let $Q_3(x = q_3)$ be the point of $\mathscr{R}_3$ whose distance from B is equal to the distance of N_2 from B, say $N_2B = BQ_3 = h$. Then

(28.4.11)

$$U(n_2) - U(q_3) = \left\{\frac{\alpha + \beta}{2l^3}(b - h)^2 + \frac{\alpha}{l - h} + \frac{\beta}{h}\right\} - \left\{\frac{\alpha + \beta}{2l^3}(b + h)^2 + \frac{\alpha}{l + h} + \frac{\beta}{h}\right\}$$

$$= -\frac{\alpha + \beta}{2l^3}\, 4bh + \frac{2\alpha h}{l^2 - h^2} = 2\alpha h\left(\frac{1}{l^2 - h^2} - \frac{1}{l^2}\right) > 0.$$

Hence $U(n_2) > U(q_3)$. But $U(q_3) \geqslant U(n_3)$, since U has a smaller value at N_3 than at any other point of $\mathscr{R}_3$, and the first result follows.

Let $Q_1(x = q_1)$ be the point of $\mathscr{R}_1$ whose distance from G is equal to the distance of N_3 from G, say $Q_1G = GN_3 = k$. Then

$$U(n_3) - U(q_1) = \left(\frac{\alpha}{k+a} + \frac{\beta}{k-b}\right) - \left(\frac{\alpha}{k-a} + \frac{\beta}{k+b}\right) \tag{28.4.12}$$

$$= -\frac{2\alpha a}{k^2 - a^2} + \frac{2\beta b}{k^2 - b^2}$$

$$= \frac{2\alpha\beta l}{\alpha+\beta}\left(-\frac{1}{k^2-a^2} + \frac{1}{k^2-b^2}\right)$$

$$= \frac{2\alpha\beta l(b^2 - a^2)}{(\alpha+\beta)(k^2-a^2)(k^2-b^2)} > 0.$$

Hence $U(n_3) > U(q_1)$. But $U(q_1) \geqslant U(n_1)$, since U has a smaller value at N_1 than at any other point of $\mathscr{R}_1$, and the second result follows.

28.5 Equilibrium points not on AB. We now turn to the second alternative mentioned at the end of § 28.3, namely $\lambda = 0$. This ensures $\partial U/\partial y = 0$, and since at each equilibrium point $\partial U/\partial x = 0$ also, the formula (28.3.5) implies $r = s$. It now follows from (28.3.7) that $r = s = l$. Thus there are two more equilibrium points N_4 and N_5 which are the vertices of the equilateral triangles having AB as base. The coordinates of N_4 are $\left(\frac{\alpha-\beta}{\alpha+\beta}\frac{l}{2}, \sqrt{3}\frac{l}{2}\right)$, and the coordinates of N_5 are $\left(\frac{\alpha-\beta}{\alpha+\beta}\frac{l}{2}, -\sqrt{3}\frac{l}{2}\right)$.

The values of the second derivatives of U at N_4 and at N_5 are given by the formulae (28.3.8–10). At each of these points

$$\lambda = 0, \quad x + a = b - x = \tfrac{1}{2}l, \quad r = s = l, \tag{28.5.1}$$

giving

$$\frac{\partial^2 U}{\partial x^2} = \frac{3}{4}\frac{\alpha+\beta}{l^3}, \quad \frac{\partial^2 U}{\partial x\,\partial y} = \pm\frac{3\sqrt{3}}{4}\frac{\alpha-\beta}{l^3}, \quad \frac{\partial^2 U}{\partial y^2} = \frac{9}{4}\frac{\alpha+\beta}{l^3}, \tag{28.5.2}$$

the upper sign referring to N_4 and the lower to N_5.

It is interesting to verify the existence of the equilibrium points N_4 and N_5 by elementary reasoning. If for example the planetoid is at N_4, the component of the resultant force in the direction perpendicular to GN_4 is zero, since (with the notation indicated in Fig. 28.5)

$$\frac{\gamma\alpha}{l^2}\sin\theta_1 = \frac{\gamma\beta}{l^2}\sin\theta_2. \tag{28.5.3}$$

This follows because

$$\frac{\sin\theta_1}{\sin\theta_2} = \frac{AG}{GB} = \frac{\beta}{\alpha}. \tag{28.5.4}$$

Now take the point K on N_4B such that GK is parallel to AN_4, so that

$$N_4K = AG = \frac{\beta}{\alpha+\beta}l, \quad KG = GB = \frac{\alpha}{\alpha+\beta}l. \tag{28.5.5}$$

The component of force (per unit mass) on the planetoid in the direction N_4G is

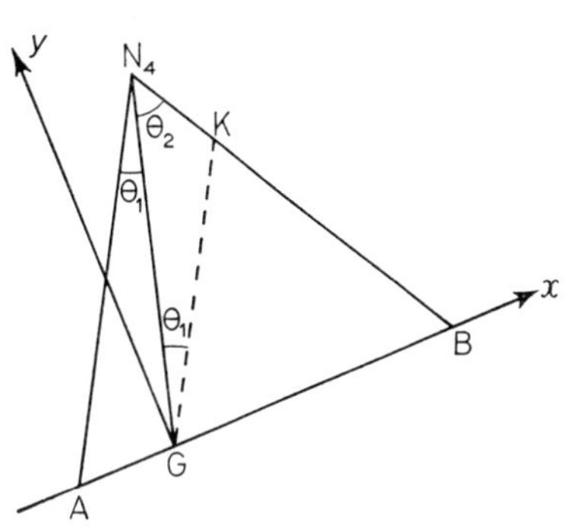

Figure 28.5

$$\frac{\gamma\alpha}{l^2}\cos\theta_1 + \frac{\gamma\beta}{l^2}\cos\theta_2 \tag{28.5.6}$$

$$= \frac{\gamma(\alpha+\beta)}{l^3}(N_4K\cos\theta_2 + KG\cos\theta_1)$$

$$= \frac{\gamma(\alpha+\beta)}{l^3}GN_4 = GN_4\,.\,\omega^2,$$

and this completes the proof.

28.6 The surface $z = U$. The tangent plane to the surface is parallel to $z = 0$ at each of the five points N_i. At each of the equilibrium points on AB

$$\frac{\partial^2 U}{\partial x^2}\frac{\partial^2 U}{\partial y^2} - \left(\frac{\partial^2 U}{\partial x\,\partial y}\right)^2 < 0, \tag{28.6.1}$$

in virtue of (28.4.7), and these are saddle points, not minima. At N_4 and at N_5

$$\frac{\partial^2 U}{\partial x^2} > 0, \qquad \frac{\partial^2 U}{\partial x^2}\frac{\partial^2 U}{\partial y^2} - \left(\frac{\partial^2 U}{\partial x\,\partial y}\right)^2 = \frac{27\alpha\beta}{4l^6} > 0, \tag{28.6.2}$$

by (28.5.2), and these are genuine minima. It is now clear that

$$U_2 > U_3 > U_1 > U_4 = U_5, \tag{28.6.3}$$

where U_i is the value of U at N_i, and we now have a good idea of the form of the surface $z = U(x, y)$.

We saw, in (28.2.16), that, for a prescribed value of the energy constant h, motion can only take place in the region $U > U_0$, where $U_0 = -h/\gamma$. Let us consider the form of the boundaries of this region for different values of U_0.

(i) If $U_0 > U_2$, the boundaries are closed ovals about A and B, and a large oval (Fig. 28.6*a*). If V_0 is very large the ovals approximate to circles. The permitted regions are those inside the small ovals and outside the large oval. If the planetoid moves inside one of the small ovals it is a satellite of A or of B; the gravitational attraction of A or of B is the paramount factor in determining the motion.

(ii) If $U_2 > U_0 > U_3$ there are only two boundary curves (Fig. 28.6*b*). The most interesting case is that in which the planetoid moves in the inner region, and the calculations of § 17.11 suggest that there will be lemniscate-like orbits in which the planetoid is shared as a satellite between A and B.

(iii) If $U_3 > U_0 > U_1$, there is only one boundary curve (Fig. 28.6*c*).

(iv) If $U_1 > U_0 > U_4$ there are two closed boundary curves (Fig. 28.6*d*); the region in which motion is possible is the region *outside* these two curves.

(v) If $U_4 > U_0$ there are no boundaries. The region $U > U_0$ in which motion is possible is the whole plane.

In general the cases (i) and (ii), in which $U_0 > U_3$, are those of the greatest interest.

The figures are drawn for the case $\alpha = 2\beta$, and for the values $\lambda = 2{\cdot}2,\ 2{\cdot}0,\ 1{\cdot}8$, and $1{\cdot}6$, where (cf. (28.2.13))

$$\lambda = 2\left(\tfrac{1}{2}\rho^2 + \frac{1}{\rho}\right) + \left(\tfrac{1}{2}\sigma^2 + \frac{1}{\sigma}\right). \tag{28.6.4}$$

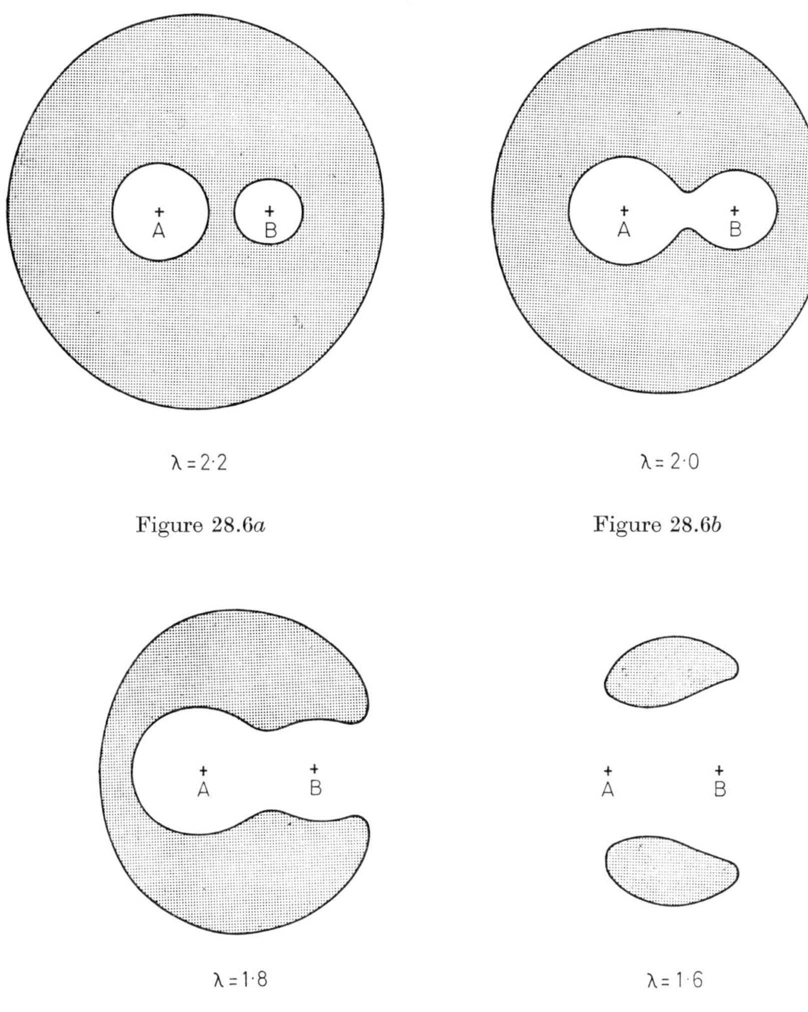

Figure 28.6*a*

Figure 28.6*b*

Figure 28.6*c*

Figure 28.6*d*

28.7 Motion near a point of equilibrium. Are the positions of equilibrium stable? Are there motions of the planetoid in which it remains permanently near to one of the points N_i?

To discuss this question, let (x_0, y_0) be one of the points N_i; and let us write in the equations of motion

$$x = x_0 + \xi, \quad y = y_0 + \eta. \tag{28.7.1}$$

If we expand the second members in powers of ξ and η, and retain only terms of the first order, we obtain the linear approximation

$$\begin{cases} \ddot{\xi} - 2\omega\dot{\eta} = \gamma(A\xi + B\eta), \\ \ddot{\eta} + 2\omega\dot{\xi} = \gamma(B\xi + C\eta), \end{cases} \tag{28.7.2}$$

where the constants A, B and C are the values of $\dfrac{\partial^2 U}{\partial x^2}$, $\dfrac{\partial^2 U}{\partial x\, \partial y}$ and $\dfrac{\partial^2 U}{\partial y^2}$ at (x_0, y_0). The equations (28.7.2) are the variational equations of § 23.1, though here we are concerned with the special case of displacements from a position of equilibrium, not with displacements from a known orbit.

The equations (28.7.2) are linear differential equations with constant coefficients, and the solutions contain terms which are multiples of e^{st}, where s is a root of the quadratic equation

$$\begin{vmatrix} s^2 - \gamma A & -2\omega s - \gamma B \\ 2\omega s - \gamma B & s^2 - \gamma C \end{vmatrix} = 0, \tag{28.7.3}$$

which we can write in the form

$$s^4 - \{\gamma(A + C) - 4\omega^2\}s^2 + \gamma^2(AC - B^2) = 0. \tag{28.7.4}$$

This is a quadratic equation for s^2, and for first-order stability its roots must be real and negative

It is clear at once that the equilibrium at each of N_1, N_2, and N_3 is unstable. For, in virtue of (28.6.1), $AC - B^2 < 0$, and one value of s^2 is positive and one negative. The values of s are of the form $\pm p$, $\pm ip'$ where p and p' are real and positive.

Let us now consider one of the points N_4, N_5. For these points the equation (28.7.4) becomes

$$s^4 + (\alpha + \beta)\frac{\gamma}{l^3}s^2 + \frac{27}{4}\alpha\beta\frac{\gamma^2}{l^6} = 0, \tag{28.7.5}$$

where we have used the values of A, B, C found already in (28.5.2). The roots for s^2 are real and negative if

$$\alpha^2 - 25\alpha\beta + \beta^2 > 0, \tag{28.7.6}$$

and this is true if α/β is greater than the larger root of

$$x^2 - 25x + 1 = 0, \tag{28.7.7}$$

which is a little less than 25, about 24·96 · · · . Thus there is first-order stability at N_4 and N_5 if the mass of A is greater than about 25 times the mass of B. The condition would be amply fulfilled if, for example, A were the sun and B were one of the planets.

Two comments on this result are called for. The first is that first-order stability does not necessarily ensure that there is stability when we turn from the linear approximation to the complete equations (Chapter XIX); and in this case we cannot infer stability from the energy equation, as we did in the theory of small oscillations (Chapter IX). The second is that if there is stability for the complete equations, as well as for the linear approximation, it must be due to the linear terms T_1 in L. These terms give rise to the gyroscopic terms in the equations of motion. If the terms T_1 were absent from L the problem would be one of motion in a conservative field of force, and for this field the potential function has a *maximum* at N_4 and at N_5, which would be points of unstable equilibrium.

The equations of motion in the linear approximation (28.7.2) are the Lagrangian equations of motion derived from the Lagrangian function

$$L = \tfrac{1}{2}(\dot\xi^2 + \dot\eta^2) + \omega(\xi\dot\eta - \eta\dot\xi) + \tfrac{1}{2}\gamma(A\xi^2 + 2B\xi\eta + C\eta^2). \tag{28.7.8}$$

The corresponding Hamiltonian function is

$$H = \tfrac{1}{2}(\{\theta + \omega\eta)^2 + (\varphi - \omega\xi)^2\} - \tfrac{1}{2}\gamma(A\xi^2 + 2B\xi\eta + C\eta^2), \tag{28.7.9}$$

where θ, φ denote the momentum components p_ξ, p_η. The Hamiltonian equations of motion are

$$(28.7.10)\qquad \begin{cases} \dot{\xi} = \theta + \omega\eta, & \dot{\theta} = \omega(\varphi - \omega\xi) + \gamma(A\xi + B\eta), \\ \dot{\eta} = \varphi - \omega\xi, & \dot{\varphi} = -\omega(\theta + \omega\eta) + \gamma(B\xi + C\eta). \end{cases}$$

28.8 Lunar theory. We now consider more particularly the case in which the planetoid is a satellite of B, so that s/l remains small throughout the motion. We take new coordinates (ξ, η) with origin at B,

$$(28.8.1)\qquad x = b + \xi, \quad y = \eta,$$

and the Lagrangian function (28.2.5) becomes

$$(28.8.2)\qquad L = \tfrac{1}{2}(\dot{\xi}^2 + \dot{\eta}^2) + \omega(\xi\dot{\eta} - \eta\dot{\xi}) + \omega^2 b\xi + \tfrac{1}{2}\omega^2(\xi^2 + \eta^2) + \frac{\gamma\alpha}{r} + \frac{\gamma\beta}{s},$$

where now

$$(28.8.3)\qquad r^2 = l^2 + 2l\xi + \xi^2 + \eta^2, \quad s^2 = \xi^2 + \eta^2.$$

In the formula (28.8.2) we have omitted a constant term, and also a term $\omega b\dot{\eta}$ which, as we know from § 6.8, has no effect on the motion.

The form (28.8.2) is exact. We now introduce certain approximations which are appropriate to a problem in which s/l remains small throughout the motion, and in which also β/α is small. (As we have noticed, if A were the Sun and B the Earth, β/α would be of the order of 1/300,000. For the present theory to be applicable, we must suppose that the orbit of the Earth relative to the Sun is, to a sufficiently close approximation, circular.) Let us consider the terms

$$(28.8.4)\qquad \Theta = \omega^2 b\xi + \tfrac{1}{2}\omega^2(\xi^2 + \eta^2) + \frac{\gamma\alpha}{r}.$$

If we expand $1/r$ in powers of ξ/l and η/l, and neglect terms of order $(s/l)^3$, we have

$$(28.8.5)\qquad \begin{aligned} \Theta &= \frac{\gamma\alpha}{l^2}\xi + \frac{1}{2}\frac{\gamma(\alpha+\beta)}{l^3}(\xi^2 + \eta^2) + \frac{\gamma\alpha}{l}\left(1 - \frac{\xi}{l} - \frac{\xi^2 + \eta^2}{2l^2} + \frac{3}{2}\frac{\xi^2}{l^2}\right) \\ &= \frac{\gamma\alpha}{l} + \frac{\gamma\beta}{2l^3}(\xi^2 + \eta^2) + \frac{3\gamma\alpha}{2l^3}\xi^2. \end{aligned}$$

We make two further changes in this formula. First, we neglect the term containing βs^2 in comparison with the term containing $\alpha\xi^2$, since β/α is small and s/l remains small throughout. Second, the surviving term

$$(28.8.6)\qquad \frac{3\gamma\alpha}{2l^3}\xi^2 = \frac{3}{2}\frac{\alpha}{\alpha+\beta}\omega^2\xi^2,$$

and to a sufficient approximation we can replace the coefficient $\dfrac{\alpha}{\alpha+\beta}$ by 1. So finally Θ can be replaced by $\tfrac{3}{2}\omega^2\xi^2$, and the required approximation for L is

$$(28.8.7)\qquad L = \tfrac{1}{2}(\dot{\xi}^2 + \dot{\eta}^2) + \omega(\xi\dot{\eta} - \eta\dot{\xi}) + \tfrac{3}{2}\omega^2\xi^2 + \frac{\gamma\beta}{s}.$$

The problem differs from the Newtonian problem with fixed axes by the presence in L of the linear terms $\omega(\xi\dot{\eta} - \eta\dot{\xi})$ and the term $\frac{3}{2}\omega^2\xi^2$. The equations of motion derived from (28.8.7) are

$$\left\{\begin{aligned} &\ddot{\xi} - 2\omega\dot{\eta} - 3\omega^2\xi = -\gamma\beta\xi/s^3, \\ &\ddot{\eta} + 2\omega\dot{\xi} \qquad\quad\;\; = -\gamma\beta\eta/s^3. \end{aligned}\right. \tag{28.8.8}$$

Jacobi's integral is

$$\tfrac{1}{2}(\dot{\xi}^2 + \dot{\eta}^2) = \frac{\gamma\beta}{s} + \tfrac{3}{2}\omega^2\xi^2 + h. \tag{28.8.9}$$

This time there are only two equilibrium points, N_1 and N_3. They lie on AB $(\eta = 0)$ at the points

$$\xi = \pm\left(\frac{\gamma\beta}{3\omega^2}\right)^{1/3}. \tag{28.8.10}$$

Now $\dfrac{\gamma\beta}{3\omega^2} = \dfrac{\beta}{3(\alpha+\beta)}\,l^3$, or, to a sufficient approximation, $\dfrac{\beta}{3\alpha}\,l^3$, so (28.8.10) becomes

$$\frac{\xi}{l} = \pm\left(\frac{\beta}{3\alpha}\right)^{1/3}. \tag{28.8.11}$$

We can readily deduce alternative equations of motion which are free of the singularity at $s = 0$. If we multiply the equations (28.8.8) by η, ξ respectively, and subtract, we find

$$\xi\ddot{\eta} - \eta\ddot{\xi} + 2\omega(\xi\dot{\xi} + \eta\dot{\eta}) + 3\omega^2\xi\eta = 0. \tag{28.8.12}$$

If we multiply the equations by ξ, η respectively and add, and then substitute for $\gamma\beta/s$ from (28.8.9), we have

$$\xi\ddot{\xi} + \eta\ddot{\eta} - 2\omega(\xi\dot{\eta} - \eta\dot{\xi}) + \tfrac{1}{2}(\dot{\xi}^2 + \dot{\eta}^2) - \tfrac{9}{2}\omega^2\xi^2 = h. \tag{28.8.13}$$

The most important application is that in which A is the Sun, B is the Earth, and the planetoid is the Moon. The application assumes that, to a sufficient approximation, the orbit of the Earth relative to the Sun is circular, and that the mass of the Moon is negligible. The equations (28.8.8) are Hill's equations, which are of fundamental importance in the study of the motion of the Moon. A detailed study of the solutions would be out of place here. It may be mentioned, however, that in general the first object of the astronomer is the determination of the periodic motions. We can start the search for a periodic motion, of period σ, by assuming expansions of the form

$$\xi = \sum_{n=0}^{\infty} a_n \cos(2n+1)\tau, \quad \eta = \sum_{n=0}^{\infty} b_n \sin(2n+1)\tau,$$

where τ is a new time-variable, $\tau = 2\pi t/\sigma$; we can then endeavour to determine the coefficients a_n, b_n (which depend of course upon σ) by substitution in the equations (28.8.8) or (28.8.12–13).

Chapter XXIX

The problem of three bodies

29.1 The classical integrals. Three particles A_1, A_2, A_3, whose masses are m_1, m_2, m_3, respectively, move in space under the action of their mutual gravitational attraction. The positions and velocities of the particles at $t = 0$ are prescribed. The problem is to determine their positions at any subsequent time.

We take fixed rectangular axes (i.e. axes fixed in a Newtonian base) and denote the coordinates of A_r at time t by x_r, y_r, z_r. The coordinates of the centre of mass G of the three particles are denoted by X, Y, Z, so that

$$MX = \sum_{r=1}^{3} m_r x_r, \quad MY = \sum_{r=1}^{3} m_r y_r, \quad MZ = \sum_{r=1}^{3} m_r z_r, \tag{29.1.1}$$

where M denotes the mass of the whole system

$$M = m_1 + m_2 + m_3. \tag{29.1.2}$$

We write

$$x_r = X + \alpha_r, \quad y_r = Y + \beta_r, \quad z_r = Z + \gamma_r, \tag{29.1.3}$$

so that α_r, β_r, γ_r are the coordinates of A_r relative to axes in the chosen fixed directions with origin at G.

The kinetic energy function T for the system can be expressed in various forms as follows:

$$T = \tfrac{1}{2} \sum_{r=1}^{3} m_r\,(\dot{x}_r^{\,2} + \dot{y}_r^{\,2} + \dot{z}_r^{\,2}), \tag{29.1.4}$$

$$T = \tfrac{1}{2} M(\dot{X}^2 + \dot{Y}^2 + \dot{Z}^2) + \tfrac{1}{2} \sum_{r=1}^{3} m_r\,(\dot{\alpha}_r^{\,2} + \dot{\beta}_r^{\,2} + \dot{\gamma}_r^{\,2}), \tag{29.1.5}$$

$$T = \tfrac{1}{2} M(\dot{X}^2 + \dot{Y}^2 + \dot{Z}^2) + \frac{1}{2} \sum_{r<s} \frac{m_r\, m_s}{M} v_{rs}^{\,2}, \tag{29.1.6}$$

where v_{rs} denotes the speed of A_s relative to A_r,

$$\begin{aligned} v_{rs}^{\,2} &= (\dot{x}_s - \dot{x}_r)^2 + (\dot{y}_s - \dot{y}_r)^2 + (\dot{z}_s - \dot{z}_r)^2 \\ &= (\dot{\alpha}_s - \dot{\alpha}_r)^2 + (\dot{\beta}_s - \dot{\beta}_r)^2 + (\dot{\gamma}_s - \dot{\gamma}_r)^2. \end{aligned} \tag{29.1.7}$$

To establish (29.1.6) we need the elementary algebraic identity

$$\begin{aligned} (m_1 + m_2 + m_3)(m_1\dot{x}_1^{\,2} + m_2\dot{x}_2^{\,2} + m_3\dot{x}_3^{\,2}) &= (m_1\dot{x}_1 + m_2\dot{x}_2 + m_3\dot{x}_3)^2 \\ &+ m_2m_3(\dot{x}_3 - \dot{x}_2)^2 + m_3m_1(\dot{x}_1 - \dot{x}_3)^2 + m_1m_2(\dot{x}_2 - \dot{x}_1)^2. \end{aligned} \tag{29.1.8}$$

The potential energy function for the system is $-U$, where

$$U = \gamma\left(\frac{m_2m_3}{r_1} + \frac{m_3m_1}{r_2} + \frac{m_1m_2}{r_3}\right), \tag{29.1.9}$$

where r_1 (for example) is the distance A_2A_3,

$$r_1^2 = (x_3 - x_2)^2 + (y_3 - y_2)^2 + (z_3 - z_2)^2 \tag{29.1.10}$$
$$= (\alpha_3 - \alpha_2)^2 + (\beta_3 - \beta_2)^2 + (\gamma_3 - \gamma_2)^2.$$

The system is a holonomic system with nine degrees of freedom, so we need nine Lagrangian, or eighteen Hamiltonian equations of motion. The equations are, in Lagrangian form,

$$m_r\ddot{x}_r = \frac{\partial U}{\partial x_r}, \quad m_r\ddot{y}_r = \frac{\partial U}{\partial y_r}, \quad m_r\ddot{z}_r = \frac{\partial U}{\partial z_r}, \qquad r = 1, 2, 3, \tag{29.1.11}$$

or in Hamiltonian form,

$$\begin{cases} m_r\dot{x}_r = \xi_r, \quad m_r\dot{y}_r = \eta_r, \quad m_r\dot{z}_r = \zeta_r, \\ \dot{\xi}_r = \dfrac{\partial U}{\partial x_r}, \quad \dot{\eta}_r = \dfrac{\partial U}{\partial y_r}, \quad \dot{\zeta}_r = \dfrac{\partial U}{\partial z_r}, \end{cases} \qquad r = 1, 2, 3, \tag{29.1.12}$$

where we denote the momentum components, for the moment, by $\xi_1, \eta_1, \zeta_1, \xi_2, \eta_2, \zeta_2, \xi_3, \eta_3, \zeta_3$.

There are ten classical integrals of the Lagrangian equations, and correspondingly ten integrals of the Hamiltonian equations. Six express the fact that G moves uniformly in a straight line,

$$\dot{X} = U_0, \quad \dot{Y} = V_0, \quad \dot{Z} = W_0, \tag{29.1.13}$$

$$X = U_0t + X_0, \quad Y = V_0t + Y_0, \quad Z = W_0t + Z_0, \tag{29.1.14}$$

and three express the constancy of the components of angular momentum about the origin

$$\begin{cases} \sum_{r=1}^{3} m_r(y_r\dot{z}_r - z_r\dot{y}_r) = a, \\ \sum_{r=1}^{3} m_r(z_r\dot{x}_r - x_r\dot{z}_r) = b, \\ \sum_{r=1}^{3} m_r(x_r\dot{y}_r - y_r\dot{x}_r) = c. \end{cases} \tag{29.1.15}$$

The equations (29.1.15) can also be written in the form

$$\begin{cases} M(Y\dot{Z} - Z\dot{Y}) + \sum_{r=1}^{3} m_r(\beta_r\dot{\gamma}_r - \gamma_r\dot{\beta}_r) = a, \\ M(Z\dot{X} - X\dot{Z}) + \sum_{r=1}^{3} m_r(\gamma_r\dot{\alpha}_r - \alpha_r\dot{\gamma}_r) = b, \\ M(X\dot{Y} - Y\dot{X}) + \sum_{r=1}^{3} m_r(\alpha_r\dot{\beta}_r - \beta_r\dot{\alpha}_r) = c. \end{cases} \tag{29.1.16}$$

The tenth classical integral is the integral of energy

$$T - U = h. \tag{29.1.17}$$

We have written the ten integrals in the Lagrangian form, involving coordinates and velocities. If we express them in Hamiltonian form, involving coordinates and momenta, we have

$$(29.1.18)\quad \begin{cases} \xi_1 + \xi_2 + \xi_3 = MU_0, \quad \eta_1 + \eta_2 + \eta_3 = MV_0, \quad \zeta_1 + \zeta_2 + \zeta_3 = MW_0, \\ m_1x_1 + m_2x_2 + m_3x_3 = M(U_0t + X_0), \\ m_1y_1 + m_2y_2 + m_3y_3 = M(V_0t + Y_0), \\ m_1z_1 + m_2z_2 + m_3z_3 = M(W_0t + Z_0), \\ \sum_{r=1}^{3} (y_r\zeta_r - z_r\eta_r) = a, \quad \sum_{r=1}^{3} (z_r\xi_r - x_r\zeta_r) = b, \quad \sum_{r=1}^{3} (x_r\eta_r - y_r\xi_r) = c, \\ \frac{1}{2}\sum_{r=1}^{3} \frac{1}{m_r}(\xi_r^2 + \eta_r^2 + \zeta_r^2) - U = h. \end{cases}$$

The ten integrals (29.1.18) of the Hamiltonian equations of motion are independent integrals, and they are all *algebraic* functions of coordinates and momenta and time. The question arises, are there any new algebraic integrals independent of the ten already found? The answer to this question is given by a remarkable theorem proved by Bruns in 1887. There are no further algebraic integrals independent of those already found; any algebraic integral of the Hamiltonian equations for the problem of three bodies is merely a combination of the ten classical integrals.

Since G moves uniformly in a straight line we can refer to a Newtonian base with axes in fixed directions through G as origin. This is equivalent to saying that, without loss of generality, we may suppose G to be at rest. In fact we shall usually make this assumption, and we shall usually take the fixed point G as origin of coordinates. Then, if we wish, we can choose the orientation of the axes so that the axis Gz is in the direction of the angular momentum vector; if we choose the axes in this way, the first two components of angular momentum vanish.

29.2 The case of vanishing angular momentum. It may happen that each of the constants a, b, c in (29.1.15) is zero, but this can only happen in very special circumstances. Explicitly, for the angular momentum about the origin to vanish, the motion must take place in a plane through G (G is assumed to be at rest) and in addition the motion in this plane at $t = 0$ must be such that the moment of momentum about O is zero.

To prove that, if $a^2 + b^2 + c^2 = 0$, the motion must take place in a plane, let us take G as origin, and the plane occupied by the particles at $t = 0$ as the plane $z = 0$. Now if the angular momentum vector about some point vanishes the angular momentum vector about all points vanishes (G being at rest) and the three components on the left in (29.1.15) vanish whatever the orientation of the axes. The vanishing of the first two components gives, since (at $t = 0$) $z_1 = z_2 = z_3 = 0$,

$$(29.2.1)\quad \begin{cases} m_1y_1\dot{z}_1 + m_2y_2\dot{z}_2 + m_3y_3\dot{z}_3 = 0, \\ m_1x_1\dot{z}_1 + m_2x_2\dot{z}_2 + m_3x_3\dot{z}_3 = 0, \end{cases}$$

so the velocity-components $\dot{z}_1$, $\dot{z}_2$, $\dot{z}_3$ at $t = 0$ satisfy

$$(29.2.2)\quad \frac{m_1\dot{z}_1}{x_2y_3 - x_3y_2} = \frac{m_2\dot{z}_2}{x_3y_1 - x_1y_3} = \frac{m_3\dot{z}_3}{x_1y_2 - x_2y_1},$$

which is equivalent to

$$\frac{m_1\dot{z}_1}{\Delta GP_2P_3} = \frac{m_2\dot{z}_2}{\Delta GP_3P_1} = \frac{m_3\dot{z}_3}{\Delta GP_1P_2}, \tag{29.2.3}$$

where the symbol ΔGP_2P_3, for example, denotes the area of the triangle GP_2P_3. But (29.2.3) implies $\dot{z}_1 = \dot{z}_2 = \dot{z}_3$, say

$$\dot{z}_1 = \dot{z}_2 = \dot{z}_3 = u, \tag{29.2.4}$$

and it follows that the centre of mass of the three particles has a velocity whose component in the direction Gz is u. But the centre of mass is at rest, so $u = 0$. The velocities of the particles at $t = 0$ all lie in the plane $z = 0$, and therefore the motion takes place in this plane for all time. (Conversely, if the motion takes place in the plane $z = 0$, the first two components of angular momentum vanish; this is a sufficient, but by no means a necessary, condition for the first two components to vanish.)

The vanishing of the third component of angular momentum requires

$$m_1(x_1\dot{y}_1 - y_1\dot{x}_1) + m_2(x_2\dot{y}_2 - y_2\dot{x}_2) + m_3(x_3\dot{y}_3 - y_3\dot{x}_3) = 0, \tag{29.2.5}$$

and this is only satisfied in exceptional circumstances; if the positions of all the particles in the plane are known, and the velocities of the first two are known, then (29.2.5) is satisfied if and only if the velocity of the third is such that the moment $m_3(x_3\dot{y}_3 - y_3\dot{x}_3)$ has the value defined by (29.2.5). We shall usually exclude this anomalous case and assume that $a^2 + b^2 + c^2 > 0$.

29.3 Lagrange's three particles. Lagrange observed that there are a number of cases where exact solutions of the equations of motion can be found; in particular there are two problems in which the lengths r_1, r_2, r_3 remain constant throughout the motion. In the first problem the particles are at the vertices of a triangle of invariable size and shape; in the second they are collinear.

Let us first ask if it is possible for the system to move so that the triangle $A_1A_2A_3$ rotates in a plane about G (assumed at rest) with constant angular velocity ω. The resultant force on A_3 at any instant must be $m_3GA_3\omega^2$ in the direction A_3G, so the conditions that must be satisfied are

$$\frac{m_2}{r_1^{\,2}}\sin\theta_1 = \frac{m_1}{r_2^{\,2}}\sin\theta_2, \tag{29.3.1}$$

and

$$GA_3\,.\,\omega^2 = \gamma\left(\frac{m_2}{r_1^{\,2}}\cos\theta_1 + \frac{m_1}{r_2^{\,2}}\cos\theta_2\right), \tag{29.3.2}$$

where H is the centre of mass of A_1 and A_2, and θ_1, θ_2 are the angles HA_3A_2, A_1A_3H (Fig. 29.3). Now

$$\frac{r_1\sin\theta_1}{r_2\sin\theta_2} = \frac{HA_2}{A_1H} = \frac{m_1}{m_2}, \tag{29.3.3}$$

and (29.3.1) and (29.3.3) together imply $r_1 = r_2$. Similarly, by considering the motion of A_2, we

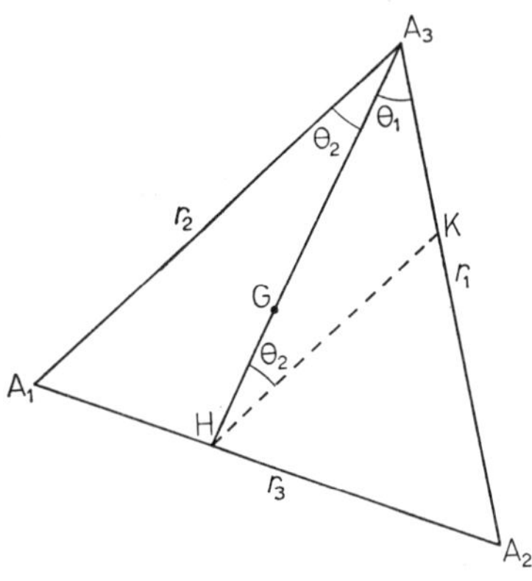

Figure 29.3

find $r_1 = r_3$, so if a motion of this type is possible the triangle must be equilateral. Let us denote the length of each side by l.

Now consider the second condition (29.3.2). If HK is drawn parallel to A_1A_3, as in the diagram,

$$HK = HA_2 = \frac{m_1}{m_1 + m_2}\, l, \quad KA_3 = A_1H = \frac{m_2}{m_1 + m_2}\, l, \tag{29.3.4}$$

and therefore

$$HA_3 = HK \cos\theta_2 + KA_3 \cos\theta_1 = (m_1 \cos\theta_2 + m_2 \cos\theta_1)\, l/(m_1 + m_2). \tag{29.3.5}$$

Thus (29.3.2) requires

$$GA_3 \,.\, \omega^2 = \frac{\gamma}{l^2}(m_1 + m_2)\frac{HA_3}{l}, \tag{29.3.6}$$

which is equivalent to

$$\omega^2 = \gamma M/l^3. \tag{29.3.7}$$

It is clear that the conditions for the other particles are satisfied, and that a motion is possible in which the particles are at the vertices of an equilateral triangle of side l which rotates with angular velocity $\sqrt{(\gamma M/l^3)}$. The length l can have any value, and the angular velocity is proportional to $l^{-3/2}$ (as is evident also from the theory of dimensions).

We next prove that a motion is possible in which the particles lie always on a line through G which rotates uniformly in a plane. Let us denote the distances from G, measured in the same sense, by x_1, x_2, x_3. We may suppose, without loss of generality, that $x_1 < x_2 < x_3$, so $x_1 < 0$ and $x_3 > 0$. If the angular velocity is ω we need

$$\omega^2 x_1 = -\frac{\gamma m_2}{(x_2 - x_1)^2} - \frac{\gamma m_3}{(x_3 - x_1)^2}, \tag{29.3.8}$$

$$\omega^2 x_2 = -\frac{\gamma m_3}{(x_3 - x_2)^2} + \frac{\gamma m_1}{(x_2 - x_1)^2}, \tag{29.3.9}$$

$$\omega^2 x_3 = \frac{\gamma m_1}{(x_3 - x_1)^2} + \frac{\gamma m_2}{(x_3 - x_2)^2}. \tag{29.3.10}$$

It should be noticed that (29.3.9) is valid whether x_2 is positive or negative. We verify at once that

$$m_1 x_1 + m_2 x_2 + m_3 x_3 = 0. \tag{29.3.11}$$

It is easy to see that definite values of the ratios $r_1 : r_2 : r_3$ are determined by (29.3.8–10). If we write $r_1/r_3 = k$, so that

$$\frac{r_1}{k} = \frac{r_2}{k+1} = \frac{r_3}{1}, \tag{29.3.12}$$

we have

$$k = \frac{x_3 - x_2}{x_2 - x_1} = \frac{\dfrac{m_1}{(k+1)^2} + \dfrac{m_2 + m_3}{k^2} - m_1}{-\dfrac{m_3}{k^2} + (m_1 + m_2) + \dfrac{m_3}{(k+1)^2}} \tag{29.3.13}$$

$$= \frac{(m_2 + m_3)(k+1)^2 - m_1 k^2(k^2 + 2k)}{(m_1 + m_2)k^2(k+1)^2 - m_3(2k+1)},$$

giving for k the quintic equation

$$(m_1 + m_2)k^5 + (3m_1 + 2m_2)k^4 + (3m_1 + m_2)k^3 - (m_2 + 3m_3)k^2 - (2m_2 + 3m_3)k - (m_2 + m_3) = 0. \tag{29.3.14}$$

The equation has one real root, and it is positive, so there is a unique value k for the ratio r_1/r_3. The actual distance r_3 can have any value, and $\omega^2 \propto r_3^{-3}$. If r_3 is prescribed, the values of x_1, x_2, x_3 are easily found. For

$$kx_1 - (k + 1)x_2 + x_3 = 0, \tag{29.3.15}$$

and from (29.3.11) and (29.3.15) we have

$$\frac{Mx_1}{-\{m_2 + (k + 1)m_3\}} = \frac{Mx_2}{m_1 - km_3} = \frac{Mx_3}{(k + 1)m_1 + km_2} = \frac{r_1}{k} = \frac{r_2}{k + 1} = \frac{r_3}{1}. \tag{29.3.16}$$

Then from (29.3.8) and (29.3.10) we have

$$\omega^2 = \frac{\gamma}{r_3^3}\left\{\frac{1}{(k + 1)^3}m_1 + \frac{k^2 + 1}{k^2(k + 1)}m_2 + \frac{1}{(k + 1)^3}m_3\right\}. \tag{29.3.17}$$

The formula for ω^2 can be written, of course, in many other forms.

We have supposed in the preceding discussion that A_2 lies between A_1 and A_3. There are two other straight-line solutions, with A_1 and A_3 in the intermediate position.

29.4 Fixed-shape solutions. In the equilateral-triangle solution of Lagrange the triangle is invariant in size as well as in shape. Lagrange also considered the question: "Are there solutions in which the three particles move so that the shape of the triangle is invariant, but its size varies?" Let us refer to fixed rectangular axes, and ask if solutions exist in which

$$w_r = x_r + iy_r = c_r w, \qquad r = 1, 2, 3, \tag{29.4.1}$$

where the c's are complex constants, and w is a complex-valued function of t. The equations of motion can be written in the form

$$\ddot{w}_1 = \gamma\left\{m_2\frac{(w_2 - w_1)}{|w_2 - w_1|^3} + m_3\frac{(w_3 - w_1)}{|w_3 - w_1|^3}\right\}, \tag{29.4.2}$$

with two similar equations. To obtain a solution of the form (29.4.1) we need

$$c_1\ddot{w} = \gamma\left\{m_2\frac{(c_2 - c_1)}{|c_2 - c_1|^3} + m_3\frac{(c_3 - c_1)}{|c_3 - c_1|^3}\right\}\frac{w}{|w|^3}, \tag{29.4.3}$$

with two similar equations. Thus if c_1, c_2, c_3 exist such that

$$-\mu c_r = \gamma\sum_{s\neq r} m_s\frac{c_s - c_r}{|c_s - c_r|^3}, \qquad r = 1, 2, 3, \tag{29.4.4}$$

where μ is real and positive, the equations of motion (29.4.2) are satisfied by any solution of

$$\ddot{w} = -\mu \frac{w}{|w|^3}. \tag{29.4.5}$$

Now we know already some solutions of the equations (29.4.2), for example $w_r = c_r e^{i\omega t}$, where c_1, c_2, c_3 represent the positions of Lagrange's three particles at $t = 0$, the origin being at G. In the first case the points c_1, c_2, c_3 are the vertices of an equilateral triangle, and $\omega^2 = \gamma M/l^3$. Therefore these values of c_1, c_2, c_3 satisfy (29.4.4) with $\mu = \gamma M/l^3$.

The equation (29.4.5) represents the familiar problem of a particle attracted to a fixed Newtonian centre, and for this problem the solutions are well known. Thus we have solutions of the three body problem in which each particle describes a conic with the centre of mass (which is fixed in space) in one focus. The triangle formed by the three particles is equilateral throughout the motion, and the conics described by the three particles all have the same eccentricity. If the conics are ellipses the motion is periodic.

A case of great interest is that in which the period in the elliptic motion is $2\pi/\omega$, the same as the period of rotation in the Lagrange equilateral-triangle solution. Then the motion relative to axes rotating with angular velocity ω is also periodic with this same period. Let us consider more particularly the case in which the particles are originally moving in circles in the Lagrange configuration, and the elliptic motion is set up by an appropriate small impulse on each particle at a given instant. Then the eccentricity e of each ellipse is small; and the disturbance is to be such that the period in the elliptic motion is the same as the period in the original circular motion. Then each particle remains (relative to the rotating axes) near to its undisturbed position. To study the motion relative to the rotating axes, let us take axes Ox, Oy, with Ox inclined at an angle ωt to the major axis of the ellipse in which the particle moves. Then the coordinates of the particle, relative to the rotating axes, are

$$\begin{cases} x = a(\cos\varphi - e)\cos\omega t + b\sin\varphi\sin\omega t, \\ y = -a(\cos\varphi - e)\sin\omega t + b\sin\varphi\cos\omega t, \end{cases} \tag{29.4.6}$$

where a, b are the semi-axes of the ellipse, and φ is the eccentric angle. But in the elliptic motion, taking $t = 0$ at perihelion, we have (§ 5.5)

$$\omega t = \varphi - e\sin\varphi, \tag{29.4.7}$$

and the formulae (29.4.6) become

$$\begin{cases} x = a(\cos\varphi - e)\cos(\varphi - e\sin\varphi) + b\sin\varphi\sin(\varphi - e\sin\varphi), \\ y = -a(\cos\varphi - e)\sin(\varphi - e\sin\varphi) + b\sin\varphi\cos(\varphi - e\sin\varphi). \end{cases} \tag{29.4.8}$$

These formulae are exact, whether e is small or not. But the case in which we are interested at the moment is that in which e is small. If we expand the formulae on the right in (29.4.8) in powers of e, and retain only terms of the first degree, we find

$$x = a(1 - e\cos\varphi), \quad y = 2ae\sin\varphi. \tag{29.4.9}$$

The orbit relative to the rotating axes is approximately an ellipse, with its centre at $(a, 0)$, in which the length of the major axis is twice the length of the minor axis.

Similarly there are solutions, derived from the second (rectilinear) case of Lagrange's three particles, in which the particles are collinear throughout the motion. In these motions k ($= r_1/r_3$) has the value given by (29.3.14), and μ ($= \omega^2$) is given by (29.3.17).

There is also a solution in which the particles move permanently on a straight line. The ratio r_1/r_3 has the same constant value k as before. This solution was known to Euler, who also found the quintic equation (29.3.14) for k.

The extension of the theory to the problem of n bodies moving in a plane is immediate. If we can find a solution in which G is at rest, and the bodies lie at the vertices of a polygon of fixed size and shape rotating uniformly, we can deduce solutions (and in particular periodic solutions) in which the bodies lie at the vertices of a polygon of fixed shape but variable size. The simplest case is that in which the n bodies all have the same mass m. It is evident that there is a solution in which the particles lie at the vertices of a regular polygon rotating uniformly. If the circumradius of the polygon is a, the angular velocity is given by

(29.4.10) $$\omega^2 = \frac{\gamma k m}{a^3},$$

where

(29.4.11) $$k = \frac{1}{4}\sum_{s=1}^{n-1} \frac{1}{\sin(s\pi/n)}.$$

The extension of the theory given above for $n = 3$ shows that there are solutions in which the particles lie at the vertices of a regular polygon of varying size.

29.5 Motion in a plane. Let us consider more generally the case in which the three particles move in a plane. Let us refer to axes rotating about a fixed origin O with constant angular velocity ω. If the coordinates of the three particles with respect to the moving axes are now written (x_1, y_1), (x_2, y_2), (x_3, y_3), the kinetic energy function is

(29.5.1) $$T = \tfrac{1}{2}\sum_{r=1}^{3} m_r\{(\dot{x}_r - \omega y_r)^2 + (\dot{y}_r + \omega x_r)^2\},$$

and the potential energy function is $-U$, where

(29.5.2) $$U = \gamma\left(\frac{m_2 m_3}{r_1} + \frac{m_3 m_1}{r_2} + \frac{m_1 m_2}{r_3}\right),$$

and

(29.5.3) $$r_1^2 = (x_3 - x_2)^2 + (y_3 - y_2)^2, \quad r_2^2 = (x_1 - x_3)^2 + (y_1 - y_3)^2,$$
$$r_3^2 = (x_2 - x_1)^2 + (y_2 - y_1)^2.$$

To find the Hamiltonian function we have (as in § 10.14) to express

(29.5.4) $$T_2 - U - T_0 = \tfrac{1}{2}\sum_{r=1}^{3} m_r(\dot{x}_r^2 + \dot{y}_r^2) - \tfrac{1}{2}\omega^2 \sum_{r=1}^{3} m_r(x_r^2 + y_r^2) - U$$

in terms of momenta instead of velocities. Let us denote the momenta by ξ_r ($= p_{x_r}$) and η_r ($= p_{y_r}$), so that

(29.5.5) $$\xi_r = m_r(\dot{x}_r - \omega y_r), \quad \eta_r = m_r(\dot{y}_r + \omega x_r),$$

and then we have

(29.5.6) $$H = \frac{1}{2m_1}(\xi_1^2 + \eta_1^2) + \frac{1}{2m_2}(\xi_2^2 + \eta_2^2) + \frac{1}{2m_3}(\xi_3^2 + \eta_3^2)$$
$$- \omega(x_1\eta_1 - y_1\xi_1 + x_2\eta_2 - y_2\xi_2 + x_3\eta_3 - y_3\xi_3) - U.$$

The equations of motion are

$$\begin{cases} \dot{x}_r = \dfrac{1}{m_r}\xi_r + \omega y_r, & \dot{y}_r = \dfrac{1}{m_r}\eta_r - \omega x_r, \\ \dot{\xi}_r = \omega\eta_r + \dfrac{\partial U}{\partial x_r}, & \dot{\eta}_r = -\omega\xi_r + \dfrac{\partial U}{\partial y_r}, \end{cases} \tag{29.5.7}$$

for $r = 1, 2, 3$.

The coefficient of $-\omega$ in the formula (29.5.6) for H, namely

$$\sum_{r=1}^{3} (x_r\eta_r - y_r\xi_r) \tag{29.5.8}$$

represents the angular momentum of the system about O. It remains constant for all time, as is easily verified from the equations of motion (29.5.7).

Is there a solution in which the particles remain at rest relative to the rotating axes? We may call such a solution an *equilibrium solution*. If such a solution exists, the second members of the equations (29.5.7) all vanish, from which it follows that

$$\frac{\partial U}{\partial x_r} + m_r\omega^2 x_r = 0, \quad \frac{\partial U}{\partial y_r} + m_r\omega^2 y_r = 0. \tag{29.5.9}$$

Conversely, if there exist values of $x_1, y_1, x_2, y_2, x_3, y_3$ satisfying (29.5.9), there is an equilibrium solution in which the value of ξ_r is $-m_r\omega y_r$ and the value of η_r is $m_r\omega x_r$. Thus the equilibrium solutions are given by the points in the $(x_1, y_1, x_2, y_2, x_3, y_3)$-space at which the function

$$U + \tfrac{1}{2}\,\omega^2 \sum_{r=1}^{3} m_r(x_r^2 + y_r^2) \tag{29.5.10}$$

has a stationary value.

It is clear that in an equilibrium solution the centre of mass of the three particles must be at rest at O. It is easy to verify this from the equations (29.5.9); for, when written out at length, these equations are

$$\begin{cases} \omega^2 x_1 = \gamma\left\{\dfrac{m_3}{r_2^3}(x_1 - x_3) + \dfrac{m_2}{r_3^3}(x_1 - x_2)\right\}, \\ \omega^2 y_1 = \gamma\left\{\dfrac{m_3}{r_2^3}(y_1 - y_3) + \dfrac{m_2}{r_3^3}(y_1 - y_2)\right\}, \end{cases} \tag{29.5.11}$$

with two similar pairs. We see at once that

$$m_1x_1 + m_2x_2 + m_3x_3 = 0, \tag{29.5.12}$$

$$m_1y_1 + m_2y_2 + m_3y_3 = 0, \tag{29.5.13}$$

showing again that the centre of mass of the three particles is at rest at O.

Let us now take the positive x-axis through the particle A_3 (as we can do without loss of generality) so that $x_3 > 0$ and $y_3 = 0$. Then the last y-equation in (29.5.11) leads to

$$\frac{m_1y_1}{r_2^3} + \frac{m_2y_2}{r_1^3} = 0, \tag{29.5.14}$$

and, since

$$m_1y_1 + m_2y_2 = 0, \tag{29.5.15}$$

we have

(29.5.16) $$m_1 y_1 \left(\frac{1}{r_2{}^3} - \frac{1}{r_1{}^3}\right) = 0.$$

Thus $r_1 = r_2$ or $y_1 = 0$.

If $r_1 = r_2 = l$, the last x-equation in (29.5.11), with (29.5.12), leads to $\omega^2 = \gamma M/l^3$, as in (29.3.7), and then the first y-equation, with (29.5.15), gives $r_3 = l$.

If $y_1 = 0$, then also $y_2 = 0$, and the three particles lie on a straight line. If we suppose A_2 to lie between A_1 and A_3, and A_3 to be on the positive x-axis, we have

(29.5.17) $$x_1 < 0, \quad x_3 > 0, \quad r_1 = x_3 - x_2, \quad r_2 = x_3 - x_1, \quad r_3 = x_2 - x_1,$$

and then the x-equations in (29.5.11) are identical with the equations (29.3.8–10).

Thus *the only equilibrium solutions are those already found*, in which the particles lie either at the vertices of an equilateral triangle or on a straight line.

29.6 Coordinates relative to A_3. We return to the general theory of motion in a plane, using the same notation as in § 29.5. In particular, the Hamiltonian function is (29.5.6).

We now introduce the coordinates of A_1 and A_2 relative to A_3, as follows

(29.6.1) $$\begin{cases} q_1 = x_1 - x_3, & q_2 = y_1 - y_3, \\ q_3 = x_2 - x_3, & q_4 = y_2 - y_3, \\ q_5 = x_3, & q_6 = y_3. \end{cases}$$

The coordinates of A_1 relative to A_3 are (q_1, q_2), and the coordinates of A_2 relative to A_3 are (q_3, q_4). The contact transformation which is the extended point transformation arising from (29.6.1) is defined by the generating function

(29.6.2) $$W = p_1(x_1 - x_3) + p_2(y_1 - y_3) + p_3(x_2 - x_3) + p_4(y_2 - y_3) + p_5 x_3 + p_6 y_3.$$

The equations defining the transformation are

(29.6.3) $$q_r = \frac{\partial W}{\partial p_r}; \quad \xi_s = \frac{\partial W}{\partial x_s}, \quad \eta_s = \frac{\partial W}{\partial y_s}; \qquad r = 1, 2, \ldots, 6; \; s = 1, 2, 3,$$

giving (29.6.1) and

(29.6.4) $$\xi_1 = p_1, \quad \eta_1 = p_2, \quad \xi_2 = p_3, \quad \eta_2 = p_4,$$
$$\xi_3 = -p_1 - p_3 + p_5, \quad \eta_3 = -p_2 - p_4 + p_6.$$

Thus (since W does not contain t) the new Hamiltonian function is

(29.6.5) $$H = \tfrac{1}{2}\mu_1(p_1{}^2 + p_2{}^2) + \tfrac{1}{2}\mu_2(p_3{}^2 + p_4{}^2) + \tfrac{1}{2}\mu_3\{(p_1 + p_3 - p_5)^2 + (p_2 + p_4 - p_6)^2\} - \omega(q_1p_2 - q_2p_1 + q_3p_4 - q_4p_3 + q_5p_6 - q_6p_5) - U,$$

where $\mu_r = 1/m_r$, and

(29.6.6) $$U = \gamma\left(\frac{m_2m_3}{r_1} + \frac{m_3m_1}{r_2} + \frac{m_1m_2}{r_3}\right),$$

with

(29.6.7) $$r_1{}^2 = q_3{}^2 + q_4{}^2, \quad r_2{}^2 = q_1{}^2 + q_2{}^2, \quad r_3{}^2 = (q_1 - q_3)^2 + (q_2 - q_4)^2.$$

29.7 Motion near the equilibrium solution. We now use the Hamiltonian function (29.6.5) to study the question of stability (in the sense of first-order stability) of

Lagrange's three particles. We start from an equilibrium solution in the rotating axes: let us take for definiteness the equilateral-triangle solution. We assume provisionally that there exists a solution of the equations of motion in which the deviation from the equilibrium solution remains small. We denote the equilibrium solution by $(q_r{}^0, p_r{}^0)$, and we write

$$q_r = q_r{}^0 + u_r, \quad p_r = p_r{}^0 + v_r, \qquad r = 1, 2, \ldots, 6. \tag{29.7.1}$$

Now the transformation (29.7.1) is a contact transformation, and the new Hamiltonian function, in terms of the coordinates u_r and the momenta v_r, contains no linear terms. Since the u's and v's remain small we obtain an approximation to the motion by retaining only the linear terms in the equations of motion, and this is equivalent to retaining only the quadratic terms H_2 in the Hamiltonian function. The desired linear approximation is given by the equations

$$\dot{u}_r = \frac{\partial H_2}{\partial v_r}, \quad \dot{v}_r = -\frac{\partial H_2}{\partial u_r}, \qquad r = 1, 2, \ldots, 6. \tag{29.7.2}$$

We choose the orientation of the axes so that

$$q_1{}^0 = -q_3{}^0 = \tfrac{1}{2}l, \quad q_2{}^0 = q_4{}^0 = \frac{\sqrt{3}}{2}\,l. \tag{29.7.3}$$

Now in finding H_2 the quadratic terms in (29.6.5) give no difficulty; we have only to replace (q_r, p_r) by (u_r, v_r). (Notice that we do not need to calculate the undisturbed values $p_r{}^0$ for the p's.) For the terms in H_2 arising from U we notice that

$$r_1{}^2 = (-\tfrac{1}{2}l + u_3)^2 + \left(\frac{\sqrt{3}}{2}\,l + u_4\right)^2, \tag{29.7.4}$$

$$\frac{1}{r_1} = \{l^2 + l(-u_3 + \sqrt{3}u_4) + (u_3{}^2 + u_4{}^2)\}^{-\frac{1}{2}}, \tag{29.7.5}$$

and the second-order terms in the expansion of $1/r_1$ are

$$\frac{1}{8l^3}(-u_3{}^2 - 6\sqrt{3}u_3u_4 + 5u_4{}^2). \tag{29.7.6}$$

Dealing in the same way with r_2 and r_3 we find, for the second-order terms in U,

$$\tfrac{1}{8}\theta\{\mu_1(-u_3{}^2 - 6\sqrt{3}u_3u_4 + 5u_4{}^2) + \mu_2(-u_1{}^2 + 6\sqrt{3}u_1u_2 + 5u_2{}^2) + 4\mu_3[2(u_1 - u_3)^2 - (u_2 - u_4)^2]\}, \tag{29.7.7}$$

where

$$\theta = \gamma\frac{m_1m_2m_3}{l^3} = \frac{m_1m_2m_3}{M}\,\omega^2. \tag{29.7.8}$$

Thus we derive the linear approximation from the Hamiltonian function

$$H_2 = \tfrac{1}{2}\mu_1(v_1{}^2 + v_2{}^2) + \tfrac{1}{2}\mu_2(v_3{}^2 + v_4{}^2) + \tfrac{1}{2}\mu_3\{(v_1 + v_3 - v_5)^2 + (v_2 + v_4 - v_6)^2\} - \omega(u_1v_2 - u_2v_1 + u_3v_4 - u_4v_3 + u_5v_6 - u_6v_5) - U_2. \tag{29.7.9}$$

We can now write down the second members of the equations (29.7.2), and the equations have the form

$$\dot{\mathbf{w}} = \mathbf{A}\mathbf{w}, \tag{29.7.10}$$

where $\mathbf{w}$ is the vector $\{u_1, u_2, \ldots, u_6, v_1, v_2, \ldots, v_6\}$. To discuss the first-order stability we need the eigenvalues of $\mathbf{A}$. Now

$$|-\lambda\mathbf{I}_{12} + \mathbf{A}| = (\lambda^2 + \omega^2)^2 \begin{vmatrix} -\mathbf{C} & \mathbf{D} \\ -\mathbf{B} & -\mathbf{C} \end{vmatrix}, \tag{29.7.11}$$

where $\mathbf{B}$, $\mathbf{C}$, $\mathbf{D}$ are the 4×4 matrices

$$\mathbf{B} = \frac{\theta}{4}\begin{pmatrix} \mu_2 - 8\mu_3 & -3\sqrt{3}\mu_2 & 8\mu_3 & 0 \\ -3\sqrt{3}\mu_2 & 4\mu_3 - 5\mu_2 & 0 & -4\mu_3 \\ 8\mu_3 & 0 & \mu_1 - 8\mu_3 & 3\sqrt{3}\mu_1 \\ 0 & -4\mu_3 & 3\sqrt{3}\mu_1 & 4\mu_3 - 5\mu_1 \end{pmatrix}, \tag{29.7.12}$$

$$\mathbf{C} = \begin{pmatrix} \lambda & -\omega & 0 & 0 \\ \omega & \lambda & 0 & 0 \\ 0 & 0 & \lambda & -\omega \\ 0 & 0 & \omega & \lambda \end{pmatrix}, \tag{29.7.13}$$

$$\mathbf{D} = \begin{pmatrix} \mu_1 + \mu_3 & 0 & \mu_3 & 0 \\ 0 & \mu_1 + \mu_3 & 0 & \mu_3 \\ \mu_3 & 0 & \mu_2 + \mu_3 & 0 \\ 0 & \mu_3 & 0 & \mu_2 + \mu_3 \end{pmatrix}. \tag{29.7.14}$$

The evaluation of the 8×8 determinant in (29.7.11) is a formidable task, but the work can be simplified by the following device. We have

$$\begin{pmatrix} -\mathbf{C} & \mathbf{D} \\ -\mathbf{B} & -\mathbf{C} \end{pmatrix}\begin{pmatrix} \mathbf{I}_4 & \mathbf{0} \\ \mathbf{D}^{-1}\mathbf{C} & \mathbf{I}_4 \end{pmatrix} = \begin{pmatrix} \mathbf{0} & \mathbf{D} \\ -\mathbf{B} - \mathbf{C}\mathbf{D}^{-1}\mathbf{C} & -\mathbf{C} \end{pmatrix}, \tag{29.7.15}$$

so in virtue of (29.7.11) the equation

$$|-\lambda\mathbf{I}_{12} + \mathbf{A}| = 0 \tag{29.7.16}$$

is equivalent to

$$(\lambda^2 + \omega^2)^2\, |\mathbf{DB} + \mathbf{DCD}^{-1}\mathbf{C}| = 0, \tag{29.7.17}$$

and

$$\mathbf{D}^{-1} = \frac{1}{\sigma}\begin{pmatrix} \mu_2 + \mu_3 & 0 & -\mu_3 & 0 \\ 0 & \mu_2 + \mu_3 & 0 & -\mu_3 \\ -\mu_3 & 0 & \mu_1 + \mu_3 & 0 \\ 0 & -\mu_3 & 0 & \mu_1 + \mu_3 \end{pmatrix}, \tag{29.7.18}$$

where

$$\sigma = \mu_2\mu_3 + \mu_3\mu_1 + \mu_1\mu_2 = M/(m_1 m_2 m_3). \tag{29.7.19}$$

Hence

$$\mathbf{DCD}^{-1}\mathbf{C} = \begin{pmatrix} \lambda^2 - \omega^2 & -2\lambda\omega & 0 & 0 \\ 2\lambda\omega & \lambda^2 - \omega^2 & 0 & 0 \\ 0 & 0 & \lambda^2 - \omega^2 & -2\lambda\omega \\ 0 & 0 & 2\lambda\omega & \lambda^2 - \omega^2 \end{pmatrix}. \tag{29.7.20}$$

The evaluation of the 4×4 determinant $|\mathbf{DB} + \mathbf{DCD}^{-1}\mathbf{C}|$ is now a straightforward, and not uninteresting exercise, and we obtain finally, as the equation for the eigenvalues of $\mathbf{A}$,

$$\lambda^2(\lambda^2 + \omega^2)^3(\lambda^4 + \omega^2\lambda^2 + k\omega^4) = 0, \tag{29.7.21}$$

where

$$k = \frac{27}{4}\frac{m_2m_3 + m_3m_1 + m_1m_2}{(m_1 + m_2 + m_3)^2}. \tag{29.7.22}$$

Now if the equation (29.7.21) had only simple pure imaginary roots we could deduce that the equilibrium solution from which we set out has at least first-order stability. We cannot make this deduction at this stage, because of the factor λ^2, and the repetition of the factor $(\lambda^2 + \omega^2)$, in the first member of (29.7.21). In the next section we shall show how to reduce the order of the system from 12 to 6. The equation for the eigenvalues for the reduced system is of degree 6, and the equation is in fact

$$(\lambda^2 + \omega^2)(\lambda^4 + \omega^2\lambda^2 + k\omega^4) = 0, \tag{29.7.23}$$

in which the disagreeable factors do not appear.

29.8 Reduction to the sixth order. We return to the Hamiltonian function (29.6.5), and we first notice that U does not contain q_5 or q_6 (as is, of course, evident geometrically). The last two Hamiltonian equations are

$$\dot{p}_5 - \omega p_6 = 0, \quad \dot{p}_6 + \omega p_5 = 0. \tag{29.8.1}$$

Now the components of linear momentum are

$$\xi_1 + \xi_2 + \xi_3 = p_5, \quad \eta_1 + \eta_2 + \eta_3 = p_6, \tag{29.8.2}$$

so (29.8.1) expresses the conservation of linear momentum. If the centre of mass G of the system is at rest,

$$p_5 = p_6 = 0 \tag{29.8.3}$$

for all time. If then the initial conditions are such that G is at rest, and if we place the origin O of coordinates at G, the remaining coordinates q_5, q_6 are determined, when q_1, q_2, q_3, q_4 have been found, from the equations

$$Mq_5 = -m_1q_1 - m_2q_3, \quad Mq_6 = -m_1q_2 - m_2q_4, \tag{29.8.4}$$

which follow immediately from (29.6.1) and (29.5.12–13).

We have thus, assuming the centre of mass to be at rest, and taking O at this point, effectively reduced the system from the 12th to the 8th order. The equations to determine the eight variables $q_1, q_2, q_3, q_4, p_1, p_2, p_3, p_4$ are the Hamiltonian equations derived from the Hamiltonian function

$$\begin{aligned} H = \tfrac{1}{2}\mu_1(p_1^2 + p_2^2) + \tfrac{1}{2}\mu_2(p_3^2 + p_4^2) + \tfrac{1}{2}\mu_3\{(p_1 + p_3)^2 + (p_2 + p_4)^2\} \\ - \omega(q_1p_2 - q_2p_1 + q_3p_4 - q_4p_3) - U. \end{aligned} \tag{29.8.5}$$

We now show how to reduce the order still further, from eight to six, by a procedure due to Jacobi, and called *the elimination of the nodes.** The coefficient of $-\omega$ in (29.8.5) represents the angular momentum about O; we know that this has a constant

* The nomenclature is more apposite to the general problem when the motion is not confined to one plane; cf. § 29.12 below.

value, a fact that is easily verified from the equations of motion. The central idea of Jacobi's method is to apply a contact transformation in which the expression for the angular momentum

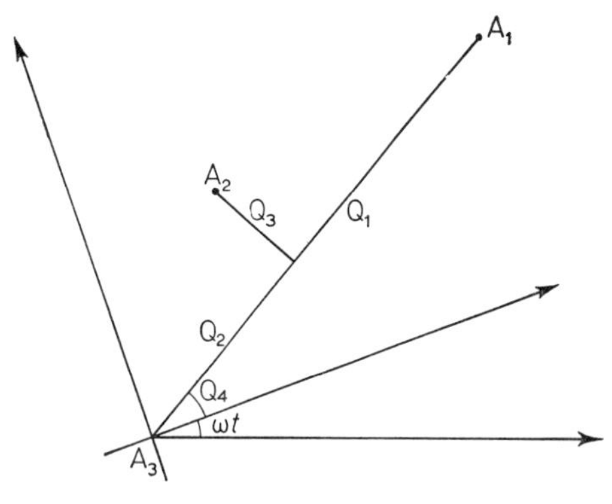

Figure 29.8

(29.8.6) $$q_1p_2 - q_2p_1 + q_3p_4 - q_4p_3$$

is one of the new variables.

To achieve this end, we start from the point transformation

(29.8.7)
$$q_1 = CQ_1, \quad q_2 = SQ_1,$$
$$q_3 = CQ_2 - SQ_3,$$
$$q_4 = SQ_2 + CQ_3,$$

where

(29.8.8) $$C = \cos Q_4, \quad S = \sin Q_4.$$

The geometrical meaning is evident: for (Q_1, Q_4) are polar coordinates of (q_1, q_2) in the moving axes, and (Q_2, Q_3) are the components of the vector (q_3, q_4) along and perpendicular to the vector (q_1, q_2), as shown in Fig. 29.8. To find the contact transformation which is the extended point transformation arising from (29.8.7–8) we need the generating function

(29.8.9) $$W = p_1CQ_1 + p_2SQ_1 + p_3(CQ_2 - SQ_3) + p_4(SQ_2 + CQ_3).$$

The equations defining the transformation are

(29.8.10) $$q_r = \frac{\partial W}{\partial p_r}, \quad P_r = \frac{\partial W}{\partial Q_r}, \qquad r = 1, 2, 3, 4,$$

from which it follows that the explicit expression of the transformation is given by the equations (29.8.7–8) and the equations

(29.8.11) $$p_1 = CP_1 - SK, \quad p_2 = SP_1 + CK, \quad p_3 = CP_2 - SP_3, \quad p_4 = SP_2 + CP_3,$$

where K is written for the expression $(P_4 - Q_2P_3 + Q_3P_2)/Q_1$. We notice that

(29.8.12) $$P_4 = q_1p_2 - q_2p_1 + q_3p_4 - q_4p_3,$$

the conserved angular momentum, and this is the characteristic property of the transformation. The new Hamiltonian function is

(29.8.13) $$H = \tfrac{1}{2}\mu_1(P_1{}^2 + K^2) + \tfrac{1}{2}\mu_2(P_2{}^2 + P_3{}^2) + \tfrac{1}{2}\mu_3\{(P_1 + P_2)^2 + (P_3 + K)^2\} - \omega P_4 - U.$$

Now H does not contain Q_4, and it follows that P_4 remains constant throughout the motion,

(29.8.14) $$P_4 = \Gamma,$$

as we know already. The system is thus reduced effectively to a system with only six variables,

(29.8.15) $$H = \tfrac{1}{2}\mu_1(P_1{}^2 + K^2) + \tfrac{1}{2}\mu_2(P_2{}^2 + P_3{}^2) + \tfrac{1}{2}\mu_3\{(P_1 + P_2)^2 + (P_3 + K)^2\} - U,$$

where K now stands for $(\Gamma - Q_2P_3 + Q_3P_2)/Q_1$. If the sixth-order system has been integrated the remaining variable Q_4 can be found by a quadrature from the equation

$$\dot{Q}_4 = \{\mu_1 K + \mu_3(P_3 + K)\}/Q_1 - \omega. \tag{29.8.16}$$

29.9 Stability of Lagrange's three particles. We return to the problem considered in § 29.7. We considered the equilibrium solution with the particles at rest (in the rotating axes) at the vertices of an equilateral triangle, and we ask if the motion is stable. The first point is that we cannot hope for stability if the disturbance is such that the centre of gravity does not stay at rest; for otherwise the system will gradually drift farther and farther from its original position. We must therefore confine our attention to disturbances in which G remains at rest. For such disturbances we can reduce to the sixth order, as in § 29.8, and the sixth equation for the eigenvalues in the linear approximation for the disturbed motion is

$$(\lambda^2 + \omega^2)(\lambda^4 + \omega^2\lambda^2 + k\omega^4) = 0, \tag{29.9.1}$$

where, as in (29.7.22),

$$k = \frac{27}{4}\,\frac{m_2m_3 + m_3m_1 + m_1m_2}{(m_1 + m_2 + m_3)^2}. \tag{29.9.2}$$

Thus we have first-order stability if the roots of

$$x^2 + \omega^2 x + k\omega^4 = 0 \tag{29.9.3}$$

are real and negative, and this is true if

$$k < \tfrac{1}{4}, \tag{29.9.4}$$

i.e. if

$$27(m_2m_3 + m_3m_1 + m_1m_2) < (m_1 + m_2 + m_3)^2. \tag{29.9.5}$$

The significance of (29.9.5) becomes clearer if we use a geometrical illustration. We take (m_1, m_2, m_3) as rectangular Cartesian coordinates in a subsidiary diagram. The condition (29.9.5) can be written

$$m_1 + m_2 + m_3 < \frac{3\sqrt{3}}{5}\,a, \tag{29.9.6}$$

where

$$m_1^2 + m_2^2 + m_3^2 = a^2. \tag{29.9.7}$$

Now (29.9.7) is the equation of a sphere of radius a with its centre at the origin O, and the equation

$$m_1 + m_2 + m_3 = \frac{3\sqrt{3}}{5}\,a \tag{29.9.8}$$

represents a plane ϖ, whose perpendicular distance from O is three-fifths of the distance to the parallel tangent plane. The condition (29.9.6) implies that the point (m_1, m_2, m_3) lies on the region of the sphere in the positive octant bounded by the coordinate planes and the plane ϖ. This region consists of three detached parts, each bounded by two great circles and a small circle, near the points $(a, 0, 0)$, $(0, a, 0)$, $(0, 0, a)$ respectively, so one mass must be a good deal larger than the others. If m_1 is the greatest of the three masses, a sufficient condition is

$$m_1 > 26(m_2 + m_3). \tag{29.9.9}$$

If the condition (29.9.5) is satisfied by the numbers m_1, m_2, m_2, the Lagrange equilateral-triangle solution has first-order stability. But, as we have seen, this does not necessarily ensure that there is stability when we replace the linear approximation by the exact equations of motion.

29.10 Reduced form of the equations of motion. We now leave the discussion of motion in a plane, and return to the general problem. For the moment we relinquish the assumption that G is at rest. We denote the vector A_1A_2 by $\mathbf{u}$ and the vector HA_3 (where H is the centre of mass of A_1 and A_2) by $\mathbf{v}$ (Fig. 29.10). The vector A_2A_3 is $-\alpha_1\mathbf{u} + \mathbf{v}$, and the vector A_1A_3 is $\alpha_2\mathbf{u} + \mathbf{v}$, where

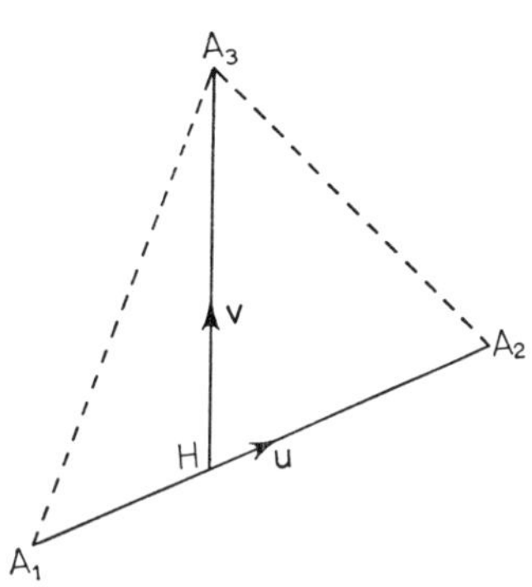

Figure 29.10

$$(29.10.1) \qquad \alpha_1 = \frac{m_1}{m_1 + m_2}, \quad \alpha_2 = \frac{m_2}{m_1 + m_2}.$$

We now denote the components of $\mathbf{u}$ by x, y, z, and the components of $\mathbf{v}$ by ξ, η, ζ, and we express T in terms of these coordinates by means of (29.1.6). Omitting for the moment the term arising from the motion of G, the x-terms arising from the motion relative to G give

$$(29.10.2) \qquad \frac{1}{2M}\{m_2m_3(-\alpha_1\dot{x} + \dot{\xi})^2 + m_3m_1(\alpha_2\dot{x} + \dot{\xi})^2 + m_1m_2\dot{x}^2\}$$

$$= \frac{1}{2M}\left\{\left[\frac{m_2m_3m_1^2 + m_3m_1m_2^2}{(m_1 + m_2)^2} + m_1m_2\right]\dot{x}^2 + (m_1 + m_2)m_3\dot{\xi}^2\right\}$$

$$= \frac{1}{2M}\left\{\frac{m_1m_2M}{m_1 + m_2}\dot{x}^2 + (m_1 + m_2)m_3\dot{\xi}^2\right\}$$

$$= \tfrac{1}{2}m\dot{x}^2 + \tfrac{1}{2}\mu\dot{\xi}^2,$$

where

$$(29.10.3) \qquad m = \frac{m_1m_2}{m_1 + m_2}, \quad \mu = \frac{(m_1 + m_2)m_3}{m_1 + m_2 + m_3}.$$

Thus, writing the corresponding formulae for y and x, we have the neat and compact formula

$$(29.10.4) \quad T = \tfrac{1}{2}M(\dot{X}^2 + \dot{Y}^2 + \dot{Z}^2) + \tfrac{1}{2}m(\dot{x}^2 + \dot{y}^2 + \dot{z}^2) + \tfrac{1}{2}\mu(\dot{\xi}^2 + \dot{\eta}^2 + \dot{\zeta}^2).$$

Next, we have

$$(29.10.5) \qquad U = \gamma\left(\frac{m_2m_3}{r_1} + \frac{m_3m_1}{r_2} + \frac{m_1m_2}{r_3}\right),$$

where

$$(29.10.6) \qquad \begin{cases} r_1^2 = |-\alpha_1\mathbf{u} + \mathbf{v}|^2 = (-\alpha_1x + \xi)^2 + (-\alpha_1y + \eta)^2 + (-\alpha_1z + \zeta)^2, \\ r_2^2 = |\alpha_2\mathbf{u} + \mathbf{v}|^2 = (\alpha_2x + \xi)^2 + (\alpha_2y + \eta)^2 + (\alpha_2z + \zeta)^2, \\ r_3^2 = |\mathbf{u}|^2 = x^2 + y^2 + z^2. \end{cases}$$

The Lagrangian equations of motion are

$$(29.10.7) \qquad M\ddot{X} = \frac{\partial U}{\partial X}, \quad m\ddot{x} = \frac{\partial U}{\partial x}, \quad \mu\ddot{\xi} = \frac{\partial U}{\partial \xi},$$

with the corresponding equations for y and x.

The first point to notice is that U does not contain X, Y, Z, and the first of the equations (29.10.7) gives $\ddot{X} = 0$. Similarly

$$(29.10.8) \qquad \ddot{X} = \ddot{Y} = \ddot{Z} = 0,$$

and this implies the familiar fact, already noticed, that G moves uniformly in a straight line. The vectors **u** and **v** defining the relative positions of the particles then satisfy the equations derived from

$$(29.10.9) \qquad T = \tfrac{1}{2}m(\dot{x}^2 + \dot{y}^2 + \dot{z}^2) + \tfrac{1}{2}\mu(\dot{\xi}^2 + \dot{\eta}^2 + \dot{\zeta}^2),$$

with U defined by (29.10.5–6), and we have reduced the problem to one with only six degrees of freedom instead of nine. Actually, as we have already noticed, we may suppose, without any serious loss of generality, that G remains at rest. The second and third of the equations (29.10.7) now give

$$(29.10.10) \qquad m\ddot{x} = -Ax + B\xi, \quad \mu\ddot{\xi} = Bx - C\xi,$$

where

$$(29.10.11) \qquad \begin{cases} A = \gamma \dfrac{m_1m_2m_3}{(m_1+m_2)^2}\left(\dfrac{m_1}{r_1^{\,3}} + \dfrac{m_2}{r_2^{\,3}}\right) + \gamma\dfrac{m_1m_2}{r_3^{\,3}}, \\[2ex] B = \gamma \dfrac{m_1m_2m_3}{m_1+m_2}\left(\dfrac{1}{r_1^{\,3}} - \dfrac{1}{r_2^{\,3}}\right), \\[2ex] C = \gamma m_3\left(\dfrac{m_2}{r_1^{\,3}} + \dfrac{m_1}{r_2^{\,3}}\right). \end{cases}$$

If we bring in the corresponding equations for y, z, η, ζ, we have

$$(29.10.12) \qquad m\ddot{\mathbf{u}} = -A\mathbf{u} + B\mathbf{v}, \quad \mu\ddot{\mathbf{v}} = B\mathbf{u} - C\mathbf{v}.$$

If **u** and **v** have been determined, the positions of the three particles relative to G are given by the vectors

$$(29.10.13) \qquad -\alpha_2 u - \theta v, \quad \alpha_1 u - \theta v, \quad \varphi v,$$

where

$$(29.10.14) \qquad \theta = \frac{m_3}{M}, \quad \varphi = \frac{m_1 + m_2}{M}.$$

It is important to notice the elegant form taken by the integrals of angular momentum (29.1.15) when they are expressed in terms of the vectors **u** and **v**. The angular momentum about Ox is

$$\begin{aligned} (29.10.15) \quad & m_1(y_1\dot{z}_1 - z_1\dot{y}_1) + m_2(y_2\dot{z}_2 - z_2\dot{y}_2) + m_3(y_3\dot{z}_3 - z_3\dot{y}_3) \\ &= m_1\{(Y - \alpha_2 y - \theta\eta)(\dot{Z} - \alpha_2\dot{z} - \theta\dot{\zeta}) - (Z - \alpha_2 z - \theta\zeta)(\dot{Y} - \alpha_2\dot{y} - \varphi\dot{\eta})\} \\ &\quad + m_2\{(Y + \alpha_1 y - \theta\eta)(\dot{Z} + \alpha_1\dot{z} - \theta\dot{\zeta}) - (Z + \alpha_1 z - \theta\zeta)(\dot{Y} + \alpha_1\dot{y} - \theta\dot{\eta})\} \\ &\quad + m_3\{(Y + \varphi\eta)(\dot{Z} + \varphi\dot{\zeta}) - (Z + \varphi\zeta)(\dot{Y} + \varphi\dot{\eta})\} \\ &= M(Y\dot{Z} - Z\dot{Y}) + (m_1\alpha_2^{\,2} + m_2\alpha_1^{\,2})(y\dot{z} - z\dot{y}) + (m_1\theta^2 + m_2\theta^2 + m_3\varphi^2)(\eta\dot{\zeta} - \zeta\dot{\eta}) \\ &= M(Y\dot{Z} - Z\dot{Y}) + m(y\dot{z} - z\dot{y}) + \mu(\eta\dot{\zeta} - \zeta\dot{\eta}). \end{aligned}$$

The integrals of angular momentum (29.1.15) therefore take the form

$$(29.10.16)\qquad \begin{cases} M(Y\dot{Z} - Z\dot{Y}) + m(y\dot{z} - z\dot{y}) + \mu(\eta\dot{\zeta} - \zeta\dot{\eta}) = a, \\ M(Z\dot{X} - X\dot{Z}) + m(z\dot{x} - x\dot{z}) + \mu(\zeta\dot{\xi} - \xi\dot{\zeta}) = b, \\ M(X\dot{Y} - Y\dot{X}) + m(x\dot{y} - y\dot{x}) + \mu(\xi\dot{\eta} - \eta\dot{\xi}) = c. \end{cases}$$

Actually, of course, since G moves uniformly in a straight line, the terms $M(Y\dot{Z} - Z\dot{Y})$ and $[m(y\dot{z} - z\dot{y}) + \mu(\eta\dot{\zeta} - \zeta\dot{\eta})]$ are separately constant. This is easily verified independently, since

$$(29.10.17)\qquad \frac{d}{dt}[m(y\dot{z} - z\dot{y}) + \mu(\eta\dot{\zeta} - \zeta\dot{\eta})] = m(y\ddot{z} - z\ddot{y}) + \mu(\eta\ddot{\zeta} - \zeta\ddot{\eta})$$

$$= \left(y\frac{\partial}{\partial z} - z\frac{\partial}{\partial y} + \eta\frac{\partial}{\partial \zeta} - \zeta\frac{\partial}{\partial \eta}\right)U,$$

which vanishes, since r_1, r_2, and r_3 are all annihilated by the operator

$$\left(y\frac{\partial}{\partial z} - z\frac{\partial}{\partial y} + \eta\frac{\partial}{\partial \zeta} - \zeta\frac{\partial}{\partial \eta}\right).$$

The reduction we have described is a valuable simplification of the problem of three bodies. It allows us to consider the problem as a system of *two* particles, a particle of mass m at (x, y, z) and a particle of mass μ at (ξ, η, ζ). The forces are derived from the potential function $-U$, where U is defined by (29.10.5–6). The forces are not in the line joining the particles, but nevertheless they are such that their moment about the origin, namely

$$(29.10.18)\qquad \mathbf{u} \times (-A\mathbf{u} + B\mathbf{v}) + \mathbf{v} \times (B\mathbf{u} - C\mathbf{v}),$$

is zero; the angular momentum about the origin remains constant.

29.11 Lagrange's three particles reconsidered. As a first application of the equations (29.10.12) let us consider again a problem in which r_1, r_2, r_3 remain constant. In that case $\mathbf{u.u}$, $\mathbf{u.v}$, $\mathbf{v.v}$ are all constants, and the coefficients A, B, C in (29.10.12) are constants; A and C are positive, and

$$(29.11.1)\qquad AC - B^2 = \gamma^2 m_1 m_2 m_3\left(\frac{m_1}{r_2{}^3 r_3{}^3} + \frac{m_2}{r_3{}^3 r_1{}^3} + \frac{m_3}{r_1{}^3 r_2{}^3}\right) > 0.$$

Since $\mathbf{u.u}$ is constant,

$$(29.11.2)\qquad \mathbf{u} \cdot \dot{\mathbf{u}} = 0, \quad \dot{\mathbf{u}} \cdot \dot{\mathbf{u}} + \mathbf{u} \cdot \ddot{\mathbf{u}} = 0,$$

and therefore

$$(29.11.3)\qquad m\dot{\mathbf{u}} \cdot \dot{\mathbf{u}} + \mathbf{u} \cdot (-A\mathbf{u} + B\mathbf{v}) = 0.$$

Hence, since $\mathbf{u.u}$ and $\mathbf{u.v}$ are constant, $\dot{\mathbf{u}} \cdot \dot{\mathbf{u}}$ is constant, whence

$$(29.11.4)\qquad \dot{\mathbf{u}} \cdot \ddot{\mathbf{u}} = 0.$$

Therefore

$$(29.11.5)\qquad \dot{\mathbf{u}} \cdot (-A\mathbf{u} + B\mathbf{v}) = 0,$$

giving

$$(29.11.6)\qquad B\dot{\mathbf{u}} \cdot \mathbf{v} = 0.$$

Thus, either $B = 0$, or, throughout the motion, $\dot{\mathbf{u}} \cdot \mathbf{v} = 0$.

(i) If $B = 0$, $r_1 = r_2$ $(= l$, say) and the vectors $\mathbf{u}$ and $\mathbf{v}$ satisfy equations of the form

$$(29.11.7)\qquad \ddot{\mathbf{u}} + n^2\mathbf{u} = 0, \quad \ddot{\mathbf{v}} + p^2\mathbf{v} = 0,$$

where n and p are positive. Each of these equations is the equation for an isotropic oscillator. Since $|\mathbf{u}|$ is constant the solution is

$$\mathbf{u} = \mathbf{u}_0 \cos nt + \mathbf{u}_1 \sin nt, \tag{29.11.8}$$

where the vectors $\mathbf{u}_0$ and $\mathbf{u}_1$ are at right angles to one another and of equal magnitude. If we denote the vector $\mathbf{u}$ in a subsidiary diagram by OP, the point P moves on a circle in the plane of $\mathbf{u}_0$ and $\mathbf{u}_1$, and the angular velocity has the constant value n. Similarly

$$\mathbf{v} = \mathbf{v}_0 \cos pt + \mathbf{v}_1 \sin pt, \tag{29.11.9}$$

where $\mathbf{v}_0$, $\mathbf{v}_1$ are at right angles and of equal magnitude. The constancy of $\mathbf{u}.\mathbf{v}$ requires that $\mathbf{u}_0$, $\mathbf{u}_1$, $\mathbf{v}_0$, $\mathbf{v}_1$ should be coplanar, and that $p = n$ (the twist from $\mathbf{v}_0$ to $\mathbf{v}_1$ being taken in the same sense as the twist from $\mathbf{u}_0$ to $\mathbf{u}_1$). The equation $n^2 = p^2$ is

$$\gamma\left(\frac{m_1 + m_2}{r_3{}^3} + \frac{m_3}{l^3}\right) = \gamma\,\frac{m_1 + m_2 + m_3}{l^3}, \tag{29.11.10}$$

so $r_3 = l$, and the triangle is equilateral. It rotates with angular velocity n, where $n^2 = \gamma M/l^3$, as in (29.3.7).

(ii) If $B \neq 0$, $\dot{\mathbf{u}}.\mathbf{v} = \mathbf{u}.\dot{\mathbf{v}} = 0$, and this implies that $\mathbf{u}$ and $\mathbf{v}$ are parallel, and the particles are collinear. For suppose on the contrary that $\mathbf{u}$ and $\mathbf{v}$ are not parallel. Then, since $\dot{\mathbf{u}}.\mathbf{v} = \dot{\mathbf{u}}.\mathbf{u} = 0$, $\dot{\mathbf{u}}$ is perpendicular to the plane of $\mathbf{u}$ and $\mathbf{v}$; similarly $\dot{\mathbf{v}}$ is perpendicular to this plane, and therefore, since $|\dot{\mathbf{u}}|$ and $|\dot{\mathbf{v}}|$ are both constant,

$$\dot{\mathbf{v}} = p\dot{\mathbf{u}}, \tag{29.11.11}$$

where p is a scalar constant. Hence $\ddot{\mathbf{v}} = p\ddot{\mathbf{u}}$, giving

$$m(B\mathbf{u} - C\mathbf{v}) = p\mu(-A\mathbf{u} + B\mathbf{v}); \tag{29.11.12}$$

but this is impossible, since it implies $AC - B^2 = 0$, in contradiction of (29.11.1). Thus $\mathbf{v}$ is parallel to $\mathbf{u}$, the particles are collinear, and $\mathbf{v} = p\mathbf{u}$. We see from (29.11.12) that p satisfies the quadratic equation

$$\mu B p^2 - (\mu A - mC)p - mB = 0. \tag{29.11.13}$$

We can deduce the quintic equation (29.3.14) satisfied by k ($= r_1/r_3$), though in fact the direct attack of § 29.3 is simpler. Assuming $p > \alpha_1$ (which involves no serious loss of generality, since it merely prescribes the order of the particles on the line) we have (since $|\mathbf{u}| = r_3$, $|\mathbf{v}| = r_1 + \alpha_1 r_3$)

$$\alpha_1 r_3 + r_1 = p r_3, \tag{29.11.14}$$

whence

$$p = k + \alpha_1, \tag{29.11.15}$$

and

$$r_2 = r_1 + r_3 = (k + 1)r_3. \tag{29.11.16}$$

For the coefficients in (29.11.13) we now have the formulae

$$\left\{\begin{aligned}
\frac{A}{m} &= \frac{\gamma}{r_3{}^3}\left\{\frac{\alpha_1 m_3}{k^3} + \frac{\alpha_2 m_3}{(k+1)^3} + m_1 + m_2\right\},\\
\frac{B}{m} &= \frac{\gamma}{r_3{}^3}\, m_3\left(\frac{1}{k^3} - \frac{1}{(k+1)^3}\right),\\
\frac{B}{\mu} &= \frac{\gamma}{r_3{}^3}\, M\alpha_1\alpha_2\left(\frac{1}{k^3} - \frac{1}{(k+1)^3}\right),\\
\frac{C}{\mu} &= \frac{\gamma}{r_3{}^3}\, M\left(\frac{\alpha_2}{k^3} + \frac{\alpha_1}{(k+1)^3}\right),
\end{aligned}\right. \tag{29.11.17}$$

and, substituting these values in the equation

$$\frac{B}{m}(k + \alpha_1)^2 - \left(\frac{A}{m} - \frac{C}{\mu}\right)(k + \alpha_1) - \frac{B}{\mu} = 0, \tag{29.11.18}$$

we obtain an equation of the seventh degree

$$\begin{aligned} k(k+1)\{(m_1 + m_2)k^5 + (3m_1 + 2m_2)k^4 + (3m_1 + m_2)k^3 \\ - (m_2 + 3m_3)k^2 - (2m_2 + 3m_3)k - (m_2 + m_3)\} = 0. \end{aligned} \tag{29.11.19}$$

Rejecting the roots $k = 0, -1$, which correspond to two particles coincident, we recover the quintic equation (29.3.14).

29.12 Reduction to the eighth order. We return to the theory given in § 29.10. We found that the problem of three bodies can be reduced in effect to a problem of only two bodies, a particle of mass m at (x, y, z) and a particle of mass μ at (ξ, η, ζ) moving under forces derived from a potential function $-U$. The motion of the two particles is defined by a system of twelve Hamiltonian equations of motion. We now apply the theory of contact transformations to reduce the system of twelve equations to a system of only eight equations.

It will be convenient at this point to introduce a change of notation, writing (q_1, q_2, q_3) in place of (x, y, z), and (q_4, q_5, q_6) in place of (ξ, η, ζ). The Hamiltonian function for the system is then

$$H = \frac{1}{2m}(p_1^2 + p_2^2 + p_3^2) + \frac{1}{2\mu}(p_4^2 + p_5^2 + p_6^2) - U, \tag{29.12.1}$$

where

$$U = \gamma\left(\frac{m_2m_3}{r_1} + \frac{m_3m_1}{r_2} + \frac{m_1m_2}{r_3}\right), \tag{29.12.2}$$

and r_1, r_2, r_3 are given by the equations (29.10.6)

$$\begin{cases} r_1^2 = (-\alpha_1 q_1 + q_4)^2 + (-\alpha_1 q_2 + q_5)^2 + (-\alpha_1 q_3 + q_6)^2, \\ r_2^2 = (\alpha_2 q_1 + q_4)^2 + (\alpha_2 q_2 + q_5)^2 + (\alpha_2 q_3 + q_6)^2, \\ r_3^2 = q_1^2 + q_2^2 + q_3^2. \end{cases} \tag{29.12.3}$$

We recall that

$$\begin{cases} p_1 = m\dot{q}_1, \quad p_2 = m\dot{q}_2, \quad p_3 = m\dot{q}_3, \\ p_4 = \mu\dot{q}_4, \quad p_5 = \mu\dot{q}_5, \quad p_6 = \mu\dot{q}_6. \end{cases} \tag{29.12.4}$$

We accomplish the desired reduction in two stages. First, we transform from $(q; p)$ to new coordinates $(Q; P)$ using the contact transformation defined by the equations

$$q_r = \frac{\partial W}{\partial p_r}, \quad P_r = \frac{\partial W}{\partial Q_r}, \qquad r = 1, 2, \ldots, 6, \tag{29.12.5}$$

where

$$\begin{aligned} W = W(p; Q) = (p_1 \cos Q_3 + p_2 \sin Q_3)Q_1 \cos Q_2 + \rho Q_1 \sin Q_2, \\ + (p_4 \cos Q_6 + p_5 \sin Q_6)Q_4 \cos Q_5 + \sigma Q_4 \sin Q_5, \end{aligned} \tag{29.12.6}$$

and

$$\begin{cases} \rho^2 = (-p_1 \sin Q_3 + p_2 \cos Q_3)^2 + p_3^2, \\ \sigma^2 = (-p_4 \sin Q_6 + p_5 \cos Q_6)^2 + p_6^2. \end{cases} \tag{29.12.7}$$

It will be noticed that W is the sum of two expressions, the second of which is obtained from the first by the replacing the suffixes 1, 2, 3 by the suffixes 4, 5, 6. Explicitly

$$(29.12.8)\quad \begin{cases} q_1 = Q_1\left\{\cos Q_2 \cos Q_3 - \dfrac{(-p_1 \sin Q_3 + p_2 \cos Q_3)}{\rho} \sin Q_2 \sin Q_3\right\}, \\ q_2 = Q_1\left\{\cos Q_2 \sin Q_3 + \dfrac{(-p_1 \sin Q_3 + p_2 \cos Q_3)}{\rho} \sin Q_2 \cos Q_3\right\}, \\ q_3 = \qquad Q_1 \dfrac{p_3}{\rho} \sin Q_2, \end{cases}$$

$$(29.12.9)\quad \begin{cases} P_1 = (p_1 \cos Q_3 + p_2 \sin Q_3) \cos Q_2 + \rho \sin Q_2, \\ P_2 = Q_1\{-(p_1 \cos Q_3 + p_2 \sin Q_3) \sin Q_2 + \rho \cos Q_2\}, \\ P_3 = \dfrac{(-p_1 \sin Q_3 + p_2 \cos Q_3)}{\rho} P_2, \end{cases}$$

and there are similar formulae for the suffixes 4, 5, 6.

The physical significance of the new coordinates can now be identified. We notice first that

$$(29.12.10)\qquad Q_1{}^2 = q_1{}^2 + q_2{}^2 + q_3{}^2,$$

so Q_1 is the distance of m from O in the equivalent two-body problem, i.e. the distance r_3 in the original three-body problem. Next let us consider the motion of m in the equivalent two-body problem. Let the radius Om cut the unit sphere in M, and let the plane ϖ containing O and the instantaneous line of motion of m cut the great circle $z = 0$ on the unit sphere at A. *Then Q_3 is the longitude of the node A, and $AM = Q_2$* (Fig. 29.12). To verify these statements, we shall show that if, in Fig. 29.12, we denote the angle xA by Q_3 and the angle AM by Q_2, then the formulae of transformation are identical with (29.12.8). Let the point on $z = 0$ with longitude $\frac{1}{2}\pi + Q_3$ be B, and let the plane ϖ cut the great circle zB in N. The linear momentum of m has components p_1, p_2, p_3 along Ox, Oy, Oz; therefore its component in the direction OB is $(-p_1 \sin Q_3 + p_2 \cos Q_3)$, and since the momentum vector lies in the plane ϖ,

$$(29.12.11)\qquad \cos\theta = (-p_1 \sin Q_3 + p_2 \cos Q_3)/\rho, \qquad \sin\theta = p_3/\rho,$$

where θ is the angle BN. A unit vector in OM is equivalent to $\cos Q_2$ in OA, $\sin Q_2 \cos\theta$ in OB, and $\sin Q_2 \sin\theta$ in Oz. Therefore the components of a unit vector in OM along Ox, Oy, Oz are

$$\cos Q_2 \cos Q_3 - \sin Q_2 \cos\theta \sin Q_3,$$

$$\cos Q_2 \sin Q_3 + \sin Q_2 \cos\theta \cos Q_3,$$

$$\sin Q_2 \sin\theta,$$

and equating these to q_1/Q_1, q_2/Q_1, q_3/Q_1 we recover the formulae (29.12.8).

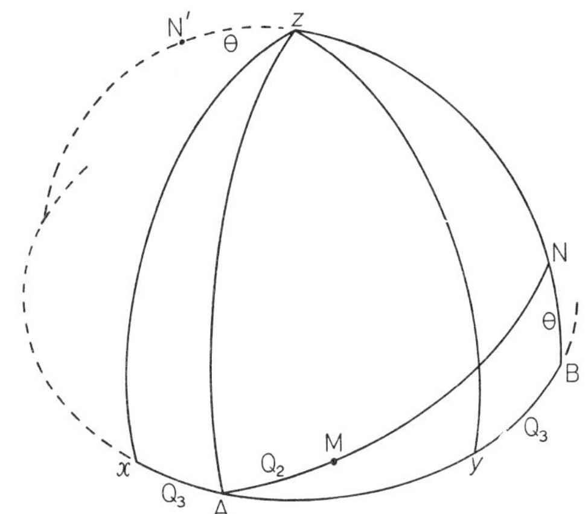

Figure 29.12

The physical significance of the P's can be seen from the formulae (29.12.9). The linear momentum of m is the vector sum of $(p_1 \cos Q_3 + p_2 \sin Q_3)$ in OA and ρ in ON. Thus, P_1 is the component of linear momentum in the direction OM, $P_1 = m\dot{Q}_1$. Next, P_2 is the *magnitude* of the angular momentum about O (the direction of the angular momentum vector is ON', where N' is the pole of the plane ϖ). And finally P_3 $(= P_2 \cos\theta)$ is the component of angular momentum (for the motion of m) about Oz.

From the transformation formulae (29.12.8–9), and the corresponding formulae with the suffixes 4, 5, 6, we have

$$(29.12.12) \qquad p_1^2 + p_2^2 + p_3^2 = P_1^2 + \frac{P_2^2}{Q_1^2}, \quad p_4^2 + p_5^2 + p_6^2 = P_4^2 + \frac{P_5^2}{Q_4^2},$$

and

$$(29.12.13) \qquad (q_1q_4 + q_2q_5 + q_3q_6)/Q_1Q_4 = c_2c_5C + c_2s_5 S \cos\varphi - s_2c_5 S \cos\theta \\ + s_2s_5 C \cos\theta \cos\varphi + s_2s_5 \sin\theta \sin\varphi,$$

where $c_r = \cos Q_r$, $s_r = \sin Q_r$, $C = \cos(Q_3 - Q_6)$, $S = \sin(Q_3 - Q_6)$, and φ is defined for the suffixes 4, 5, 6 as θ is defined for 1, 2, 3. Also, since

$$(29.12.14) \qquad \cos\theta = \frac{P_3}{P_2}, \quad \cos\varphi = \frac{P_6}{P_5},$$

we can express the q's in terms of Q's and P's, so we are now in a position to express the formula (29.12.1) for H in terms of Q's and P's.

To express the components of angular momentum in terms of the new variables we have, from (29.12.8–9),

$$(29.12.15) \qquad \begin{cases} q_2p_3 - q_3p_2 = P_2 \sin\theta \sin Q_3, \\ q_3p_1 - q_1p_3 = -P_2 \sin\theta \cos Q_3, \\ q_1p_2 - q_2p_1 = P_3. \end{cases}$$

The last of these has already been noticed, and the other two can also be verified from the figure. The integrals of angular momentum are

$$(29.12.16) \qquad \begin{cases} P_2 \sin\theta \sin Q_3 + P_5 \sin\varphi \sin Q_6 = a, \\ -P_2 \sin\theta \cos Q_3 - P_5 \sin\varphi \cos Q_6 = b, \\ P_3 + P_6 = c. \end{cases}$$

This completes the first stage in the reduction. It should be observed that the transformation used is *not* an extended point transformation: the variables Q_1, Q_2, Q_3 cannot be expressed as function of (q_1, q_2, q_3) only.

We now turn to the second stage. We wish to make use of the integrals of angular momentum. To do this we first choose Oz in the direction of the (constant) angular momentum vector, so that $a = b = 0$, and we use a contact transformation in which the third component $P_3 + P_6$ becomes a single momentum variable.

The vanishing of the first two components in (29.12.16) implies $\sin(Q_3 - Q_6) = 0$, and we may take $Q_3 = Q_6$ without loss of generality, and then

$$(29.12.17) \qquad P_2 \sin\theta = -P_5 \sin\varphi,$$

as is also evident geometrically.

We must now disturb the division into two independent sets of formulae, one for (1, 2, 3) and one for (4, 5, 6). We use the transformation from $(Q; P)$ to $(q'; p')$ defined by the equations

$$Q_r = \frac{\partial W}{\partial P_r}, \quad p_r' = \frac{\partial W}{\partial q_r'}, \tag{29.12.18}$$

where

$$W = W(P; q') = q_1'P_1 + q_2'P_4 + q_3'P_2 + q_4'P_5 + q_5'(P_3 - P_6) + q_6'(P_3 + P_6). \tag{29.12.19}$$

Thus

$$\begin{cases} Q_1 = q_1',\ Q_2 = q_3',\ Q_3 = q_5' + q_6',\ Q_4 = q_2',\ Q_5 = q_4',\ Q_6 = -q_5' + q_6', \\ p_1' = P_1, p_2' = P_4, p_3' = P_2, p_4' = P_5, p_5' = P_3 - P_6, p_6' = P_3 + P_6. \end{cases} \tag{29.12.20}$$

Now both the transformations we have used are independent of t, so to get the new equations of motion we have only to express H, defined by (29.12.1), in terms of q''s and p''s.

The first point is that q_6' is ignorable, as we can foresee from the fact that p_6' remains constant throughout the motion; we write $p_6' = \beta$. Next, $q_5' = 0$ throughout, and (29.12.17) and (29.12.14) together imply that, for all t,

$$P_2^2 - P_3^2 = P_5^2 - P_6^2, \tag{29.12.21}$$

so that

$$p_3'^2 - p_4'^2 = P_2^2 - P_5^2 = (P_3 + P_6)(P_3 - P_6) = \beta p_5'. \tag{29.12.22}$$

Now we can substitute this value for p_5' in H *before* forming the equations of motion. For if the function so formed is $H'(q_1', q_2', q_3', q_4', q_5', p_1', p_2', p_3', p_4', p_6')$ we have (denoting for the moment any of the variables $q_1', q_2', q_3', q_4', p_1', p_2', p_3', p_4'$ by ψ)

$$\frac{\partial H'}{\partial \psi} = \frac{\partial H}{\partial \psi} + \frac{\partial H}{\partial p_5'}\frac{\partial p_5'}{\partial \psi}, \tag{29.12.23}$$

and $\dfrac{\partial H}{\partial p_5'} = \dot{q}_5'$ is zero for all time. The upshot is that in forming the Hamiltonian function (which does not contain q_6' anyway) we can put $q_5' = 0$, $p_6' = \beta$, and

$$p_5' = (p_3'^2 - p_4'^2)/\beta. \tag{29.12.24}$$

We thus have a Hamiltonian function with only the eight variables $(q_1', q_2', q_3', q_4', p_1', p_2', p_3', p_4')$: *the problem has been reduced to a system of order eight.* Incidentally we may notice that, if this system has been integrated, the ignorable coordinate q_6' can be found by a quadrature from the equation

$$\dot{q}_6' = \frac{\partial H}{\partial \beta}. \tag{29.12.25}$$

For the explicit formula for H, the only terms that give any trouble are those arising from the expression $\cos\theta\cos\varphi + \sin\theta\sin\varphi$ in (29.12.13). Now, by (29.12.17),

$$\begin{aligned}\cos\theta\cos\varphi + \sin\theta\sin\varphi &= \cos\theta\cos\varphi - \frac{P_2}{P_5}\sin^2\theta \\ &= \frac{P_3P_6}{P_2P_5} - \frac{P_2}{P_5}\left(1 - \frac{P_3{}^2}{P_2{}^2}\right) \\ &= \frac{1}{P_2P_5}(P_3P_6 - P_2{}^2 + P_3{}^2) \\ &= \frac{1}{2p_3'p_4'}(\beta^2 - p_3'^2 - p_4'^2).\end{aligned} \tag{29.12.26}$$

Finally, therefore, now suppressing the accents, the equations of motion are those derived from the Hamiltonian function, with only eight variables $q_1, q_2, q_3, q_4, p_1, p_2, p_3, p_4$, defined by the formula

$$H = \frac{1}{2m}\left(p_1{}^2 + \frac{p_3{}^2}{q_1{}^2}\right) + \frac{1}{2\mu}\left(p_2{}^2 + \frac{p_4{}^2}{q_2{}^2}\right) - \frac{\gamma m_2m_3}{r_1} - \frac{\gamma m_3m_1}{r_2} - \frac{\gamma m_1m_2}{q_1}, \tag{29.12.27}$$

where

(29.12.28)

$$\begin{cases} r_1{}^2 = \alpha_1{}^2q_1{}^2 - 2\alpha_1q_1q_2\left(\cos q_3\cos q_4 + \dfrac{\beta^2 - p_3{}^2 - p_4{}^2}{2p_3p_4}\sin q_3\sin q_4\right) + q_2{}^2, \\ r_2{}^2 = \alpha_2{}^2q_1{}^2 + 2\alpha_2q_1q_2\left(\cos q_3\cos q_4 + \dfrac{\beta^2 - p_3{}^2 - p_4{}^2}{2p_3p_4}\sin q_3\sin q_4\right) + q_2{}^2. \end{cases}$$

Theoretically we can use the integral of energy, as in § 22.4, to reduce the order of the system still further, from eight to six, but the procedure is hardly practicable in this case.

29.13 Impossibility of a triple collision. We consider the problem of three bodies, supposing as before that G is at rest, and we introduce the function R defined by the equation

$$MR^2 = m_2m_3r_1{}^2 + m_3m_1r_2{}^2 + m_1m_2r_3{}^2. \tag{29.13.1}$$

The function R is a non-negative function of t, symmetrical with respect to the three bodies. If we use the notation of § 29.10 (in which we reduced the problem to one involving only two particles) the formulae (29.10.6) show that

$$R^2 = mr^2 + \mu\rho^2, \tag{29.13.2}$$

where

$$r^2 = |\mathbf{u}|^2 = x^2 + y^2 + z^2, \quad \rho^2 = |\mathbf{v}|^2 = \xi^2 + \eta^2 + \zeta^2. \tag{29.13.3}$$

We recall that the kinetic energy is given by the formula

$$T = \tfrac{1}{2}m(\dot{x}^2 + \dot{y}^2 + \dot{z}^2) + \tfrac{1}{2}\mu(\dot{\xi}^2 + \dot{\eta}^2 + \dot{\zeta}^2), \tag{29.13.4}$$

that the integral of energy is

$$T = h + U, \tag{29.13.5}$$

and that the integrals of angular momentum are

$$m(y\dot{z} - z\dot{y}) + \mu(\eta\dot{\zeta} - \zeta\dot{\eta}) = a, \tag{29.13.6}$$

$$m(z\dot{x} - x\dot{z}) + \mu(\zeta\dot{\xi} - \xi\dot{\zeta}) = b, \tag{29.13.7}$$

$$m(x\dot{y} - y\dot{x}) + \mu(\xi\dot{\eta} - \eta\dot{\xi}) = c. \tag{29.13.8}$$

Now

$$\frac{d^2}{dt^2} R^2 = 2m(x\ddot{x} + y\ddot{y} + z\ddot{z} + \dot{x}^2 + \dot{y}^2 + \dot{z}^2) + 2\mu(\xi\ddot{\xi} + \eta\ddot{\eta} + \zeta\ddot{\zeta} + \dot{\xi}^2 + \dot{\eta}^2 + \dot{\zeta}^2). \tag{29.13.9}$$

But, in virtue of (29.10.7),

$$m(x\ddot{x} + y\ddot{y} + z\ddot{z}) + \mu(\xi\ddot{\xi} + \eta\ddot{\eta} + \zeta\ddot{\zeta}) = \left(x\frac{\partial}{\partial x} + y\frac{\partial}{\partial y} + z\frac{\partial}{\partial z} + \xi\frac{\partial}{\partial \xi} + \eta\frac{\partial}{\partial \eta} + \zeta\frac{\partial}{\partial \zeta}\right)U = -U, \tag{29.13.10}$$

since U is homogeneous of dimensions -1 in x, y, z, ξ, η, ζ, and using this result and (29.13.5) we have Lagrange's result

$$\frac{d^2}{dt^2} R^2 = 2U + 4h. \tag{29.13.11}$$

Again

$$R\dot{R} = mr\dot{r} + \mu\rho\dot{\rho}, \tag{29.13.12}$$

so

$$R^2\dot{R}^2 = (mr^2 + \mu\rho^2)(m\dot{r}^2 + \mu\dot{\rho}^2) - m\mu(r\dot{\rho} - \rho\dot{r})^2, \tag{29.13.13}$$

whence

$$\dot{R}^2 = m\dot{r}^2 + \mu\dot{\rho}^2 - \frac{m\mu}{R^2}(r\dot{\rho} - \rho\dot{r})^2. \tag{29.13.14}$$

Moreover

$$(x^2 + y^2 + z^2)(\dot{x}^2 + \dot{y}^2 + \dot{z}^2) = (x\dot{x} + y\dot{y} + z\dot{z})^2 + \{(y\dot{z} - z\dot{y})^2 + (z\dot{x} - x\dot{z})^2 + (x\dot{y} - y\dot{x})^2\}, \tag{29.13.15}$$

whence

$$\dot{r}^2 = \dot{x}^2 + \dot{y}^2 + \dot{z}^2 - \frac{1}{r^2}\{(y\dot{z} - z\dot{y})^2 + (z\dot{x} - x\dot{z})^2 + (x\dot{y} - y\dot{x})^2\}. \tag{29.13.16}$$

substituting this formula for $\dot{r}^2$, and the corresponding formula for $\dot{\rho}^2$, in the second member of (29.13.14), and using (29.13.5), we obtain Sundman's result

$$\dot{R}^2 = 2h + 2U - S, \tag{29.13.17}$$

where

$$S = \frac{m}{r^2}\{(y\dot{z} - z\dot{y})^2 + (z\dot{x} - x\dot{z})^2 + (x\dot{y} - y\dot{x})^2\} + \frac{\mu}{\rho^2}\{(\eta\dot{\zeta} - \zeta\dot{\eta})^2 + (\zeta\dot{\xi} - \xi\dot{\zeta})^2 + (\xi\dot{\eta} - \eta\dot{\xi})^2\} + \frac{m\mu}{R^2}(r\dot{\rho} - \rho\dot{r})^2. \tag{29.13.18}$$

If we eliminate U between (29.13.17) and (29.13.11) we find

$$2R\ddot{R} + \dot{R}^2 - 2h = S. \tag{29.13.19}$$

Let us now consider S as a function of the seven variables $(y\dot{z} - z\dot{y})$, $(z\dot{x} - x\dot{z})$, ..., $(\xi\dot{\eta} - \eta\dot{\xi})$, $(r\dot{\rho} - \rho\dot{r})$, subject to the relations (29.13.6–8). The least value that

$$\frac{m}{r^2}(y\dot{z} - z\dot{y})^2 + \frac{\mu}{\rho^2}(\eta\dot{\zeta} - \zeta\dot{\eta})^2 \tag{29.13.20}$$

can have, subject to (29.13.6), is a^2/R^2. This is evident from the elementary identity

$$(mr^2 + \mu\rho^2)\left(\frac{m}{r^2}\theta^2 + \frac{\mu}{\rho^2}\varphi^2\right) = m\mu r^2\rho^2\left(\frac{\theta}{r^2} - \frac{\varphi}{\rho^2}\right)^2 + (m\theta + \mu\varphi)^2. \tag{29.13.21}$$

From this and the analogous results we have the inequality

$$S \geqslant \delta^2/R^2, \tag{29.13.22}$$

where

$$\delta^2 = a^2 + b^2 + c^2, \tag{29.13.23}$$

and $\delta > 0$, since we exclude the case where a, b, c all vanish (§ 29.2). From (29.13.19) and (29.13.22) we have

$$2R\ddot{R} + \dot{R}^2 - 2h \geqslant \delta^2/R^2. \tag{29.13.24}$$

If now we write

$$F = R\dot{R}^2 - 2hR + \frac{\delta^2}{R}, \tag{29.13.25}$$

we have

$$\dot{F} = \dot{R}\left(2R\ddot{R} + \dot{R}^2 - 2h - \frac{\delta^2}{R^2}\right), \tag{29.13.26}$$

and therefore, in virtue of (29.13.24), F increases (or at any rate does not decrease) as R increases, and F decreases (or at any rate does not increase) as R decreases.

We can now see that a triple collision cannot occur if $\delta > 0$. For suppose on the contrary that $R \to 0$ as $t \to t_0$ (from below). Then $F \to \infty$ as $t \to t_0$. Further, by (29.13.11), $d^2(R^2)/dt^2 \to \infty$ as $t \to t_0$, and therefore $d^2(R^2)/dt^2 > 0$ when t is sufficiently near to t_0, say when t lies in the interval I defined by $t_1 \leqslant t < t_0$. In I, $d(R^2)/dt$ increases with t, and it follows that $d(R^2)/dt \leqslant 0$ in I; for if $d(R^2)/dt > 0$ at a point t_2 of I, $d(R^2)/dt > 0$ for $t_2 \leqslant t < t_0$, which is impossible since $R \to 0$ as $t \to t_0$. Thus $\dot{R} < 0$ in I, and therefore $\dot{F} \leqslant 0$ in I; and this leads to a contradiction, since $F \to \infty$ as $t \to t_0$.

A triple collision *can* occur if $\delta = 0$; as a trivial example, there will be a triple collision if the particles are all of the same mass, and start from rest at the vertices of an equilateral triangle.

A double collision *can* occur with $\delta > 0$. If it does, we suppose the motion to continue after the collision as in § 5.6. (In a short interval of time containing the instant of collision, the effect of the third particle is negligible in comparison with the attraction of the colliding particles, and during this interval the problem is effectively a problem of two bodies only.) Thus the singularities in the formulae corresponding to a collision of two of the bodies are not of an essential kind; they can be removed by a suitable choice of a new independent variable. This result appeared in Sundman's famous paper of 1912. Sundman showed further that the coordinates of the three particles and the time can be represented as functions of a complex variable τ which are regular inside the unit circle $|\tau| = 1$. The coordinates can be represented by power-series in τ convergent for all values of the time. The only case not covered by the theory is the excluded case of a triple collision.

29.14 Motion in a plane, another method of reduction to the sixth order. We have already, in § 29.8, shown that the equations of motion for the problem of three bodies, for the case where the bodies are moving in a plane, can be reduced to the sixth order. There is an alternative attack on the same problem for which the starting point is the reduced form of the equations of motion described in § 29.10.

We assume the motion to be such that the centre of mass of the system is at rest, and we take the plane of motion to be $z = 0$. With the notation of § 29.10

(29.14.1) $$T = \tfrac{1}{2}m(\dot{x}^2 + \dot{y}^2) + \tfrac{1}{2}\mu(\dot{\xi}^2 + \dot{\eta}^2),$$

(29.14.2) $$U = \gamma\left(\frac{m_2m_3}{r_1} + \frac{m_3m_1}{r_2} + \frac{m_1m_2}{r_3}\right),$$

where

(29.14.3) $$\begin{cases} r_1^2 = (-\alpha_1 x + \xi)^2 + (-\alpha_1 y + \eta)^2, \\ r_2^2 = (\alpha_2 x + \xi)^2 + (\alpha_2 y + \eta)^2, \\ r_3^2 = x^2 + y^2. \end{cases}$$

Let us now refer to axes rotating with constant angular velocity ω about Oz. If, when measured relative to the moving axes, $\mathbf{u} = (q_1, q_2)$, $\mathbf{v} = (q_3, q_4)$, we have

(29.14.4) $$T = \tfrac{1}{2}m\{(\dot{q}_1 - \omega q_2)^2 + (\dot{q}_2 + \omega q_1)^2\} + \tfrac{1}{2}\mu\{(\dot{q}_3 - \omega q_4)^2 + (\dot{q}_4 + \omega q_3)^2\},$$

and the formulae for r_1, r_2, r_3 are unchanged in form (as is evident geometrically, and easily verified directly), *viz*

(29.14.5) $$\begin{cases} r_1^2 = (-\alpha_1 q_1 + q_3)^2 + (-\alpha_1 q_2 + q_4)^2, \\ r_2^2 = (\alpha_2 q_1 + q_3)^2 + (\alpha_2 q_2 + q_4)^2, \\ r_3^2 = q_1^2 + q_2^2. \end{cases}$$

To find the Hamiltonian function we must express

(29.14.6) $$\tfrac{1}{2}m(\dot{q}_1^2 + \dot{q}_2^2) + \tfrac{1}{2}\mu(\dot{q}_3^2 + \dot{q}_4^2) - \tfrac{1}{2}m\omega^2(q_1^2 + q_2^2) - \tfrac{1}{2}\mu\omega^2(q_3^2 + q_4^2) - U$$

in terms of p's instead of $\dot{q}$'s, where

(29.14.7) $$\begin{cases} p_1 = m(\dot{q}_1 - \omega q_2), & p_2 = m(\dot{q}_2 + \omega q_1), \\ p_3 = \mu(\dot{q}_3 - \omega q_4), & p_4 = \mu(\dot{q}_4 + \omega q_3), \end{cases}$$

giving as the Hamiltonian function

(29.14.8)
$$H = \frac{1}{2m}(p_1^2 + p_2^2) + \frac{1}{2\mu}(p_3^2 + p_4^2) - \omega(q_1p_2 - q_2p_1 + q_3p_4 - q_4p_3) - U.$$

Now the coefficient of $-\omega$ in this formula,

(29.14.9) $$q_1p_2 - q_2p_1 + q_3p_4 - q_4p_3,$$

is a measure of the angular momentum about G as given by (29.10.15), and we easily verify from the Hamiltonian equations that the expression (29.14.9) does in fact retain a constant value throughout the motion. We make use of this property to effect the reduction to a system of the sixth order. A similar technique has been used already, in § 29.8.

The components of the vector **u** relative to the rotating axes are (q_1, q_2), and we introduce polar coordinates (Q_1, Q_4) so that

(29.14.10) $$q_1 = CQ_1, \quad q_2 = SQ_1,$$

where

(29.14.11) $$C = \cos Q_4, \quad S = \sin Q_4.$$

We denote the components of **v** along and perpendicular to **u** by Q_2, Q_3,

(29.14.12) $$q_3 = CQ_2 - SQ_3, \quad q_4 = SQ_2 + CQ_3,$$

as is evident from the figure (Fig. 29.14). The contact transformation we need is

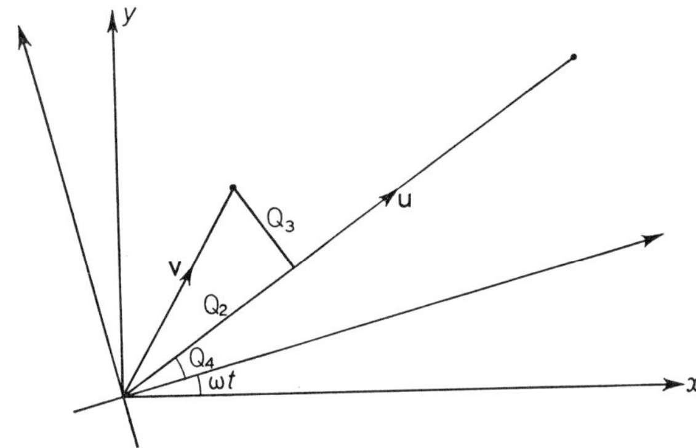

Figure 29.14

therefore the extended point transformation defined by

(29.14.13) $$q_r = \frac{\partial W}{\partial p_r}, \quad P_r = \frac{\partial W}{\partial Q_r}, \qquad r = 1, 2, 3, 4,$$

where the generating function W is

(29.14.14) $$W = p_1CQ_1 + p_2SQ_1 + p_3(CQ_2 - SQ_3) + p_4(SQ_2 + CQ_3).$$

Explicitly the equations defining the transformation are (29.14.10–12) and

(29.14.15) $$\begin{cases} p_1 = CP_1 - SK, & p_2 = SP_1 + CK, \\ p_3 = CP_2 - SP_3, & p_4 = SP_2 + CP_3, \end{cases}$$

where K is written for $(P_4 - Q_2P_3 + Q_3P_2)/Q_1$. We notice that

(29.14.16) $$P_4 = \frac{\partial W}{\partial Q_4} = -p_1SQ_1 + p_2CQ_1 + p_3(-SQ_2 - CQ_3) + p_4(CQ_2 - SQ_3)$$
$$= q_1p_2 - q_2p_1 + q_3p_4 - q_4p_3,$$

and P_4 represents the angular momentum about G. Since the contact transformation does not contain t, the new Hamiltonian function is obtained by expressing the old one in terms of the new variables, so

(29.14.17) $$H = \frac{1}{2m}(P_1^2 + K^2) + \frac{1}{2\mu}(P_2^2 + P_3^2) - \omega P_4 - U.$$

The formula is somewhat simpler than the corresponding formula (29.8.13) found by the earlier method.

Now

(29.14.18)

$$\begin{cases} r_1^2 = (-\alpha_1 q_1 + q_3)^2 + (-\alpha_1 q_2 + q_4)^2 \\ \quad = (-\alpha_1 CQ_1 + CQ_2 - SQ_3)^2 + (-\alpha_1 SQ_1 + SQ_2 + CQ_3)^2 = (-\alpha_1 Q_1 + Q_2)^2 + Q_3^2, \\ r_2^2 = (\alpha_2 q_1 + q_3)^2 + (\alpha_2 q_4 + q_4)^2 \\ \quad = (\alpha_2 CQ_1 + CQ_2 - SQ_3)^2 + (\alpha_2 SQ_1 + SQ_2 + CQ_3)^2 = (\alpha_2 Q_1 + Q_2)^2 + Q_3^2, \\ r_3^2 = q_1^2 + q_2^2 = Q_1^2, \end{cases}$$

so H does not contain Q_4, and $\dot{P}_4 = 0$. Thus P_4 is constant throughout, as we know already, say

(29.14.19) $$P_4 = \Gamma.$$

We have thus effectively a system of the sixth order only, with the six variables $Q_1, Q_2, Q_3, P_1, P_2, P_3$, and

(29.14.20) $$H = \frac{1}{2m}(P_1^2 + K^2) + \frac{1}{2\mu}(P_2^2 + P_3^2) - U,$$

where now K means $(\Gamma - Q_2 P_3 + Q_3 P_2)/Q_1$, and we have achieved the reduction proposed.

We notice that if the sixth-order system has been integrated we can determine the remaining variable, the angle Q_4, by a quadrature from the equation

(29.14.21) $$\dot{Q}_4 = \frac{1}{mQ_1^2}\Big(\Gamma - Q_2 P_3 + Q_3 P_2\Big) - \omega.$$

29.15 Equilibrium solutions. As a simple application of the theory developed in the preceding section we consider again the question of the existence of equilibrium solutions, i.e. solutions in which the particles are at rest relative to the moving axes. We first notice, from (29.14.21), that if there is such a solution, then in it

(29.15.1) $$\omega = K/(mQ_1).$$

The equations of motion for the sixth order system (29.14.20) are

(29.15.2)

$$\begin{cases} \dot{Q}_1 = \frac{1}{m} P_1, \\ \dot{Q}_2 = \frac{1}{\mu} P_2 + \frac{1}{m}\frac{KQ_3}{Q_1}, \\ \dot{Q}_3 = \frac{1}{\mu} P_3 - \frac{1}{m}\frac{KQ_2}{Q_1}, \\ \dot{P}_1 = \frac{1}{m}\frac{K^2}{Q_1} + \frac{\partial U}{\partial Q_1}, \\ \dot{P}_2 = \frac{1}{m}\frac{KP_3}{Q_1} + \frac{\partial U}{\partial Q_2}, \\ \dot{P}_3 = -\frac{1}{m}\frac{KP_2}{Q_1} + \frac{\partial U}{\partial Q_3}. \end{cases}$$

For an equilibrium solution the second members of these equations all vanish, so, in virtue of (29.15.1),

$$\left\{\begin{aligned} &P_1 = 0, \quad P_2 = -\mu\omega Q_3, \quad P_3 = \mu\omega Q_2, \\ &mQ_1\omega^2 + \frac{\partial U}{\partial Q_1} = 0, \quad P_3\omega + \frac{\partial U}{\partial Q_2} = 0, \quad P_2\omega - \frac{\partial U}{\partial Q_3} = 0, \end{aligned}\right. \tag{29.15.3}$$

whence

$$mQ_1\omega^2 + \frac{\partial U}{\partial Q_1} = 0, \quad \mu Q_2\omega^2 + \frac{\partial U}{\partial Q_2} = 0, \quad \mu Q_3\omega^2 + \frac{\partial U}{\partial Q_3} = 0. \tag{29.15.4}$$

The equilibrium solutions are the points in the (Q_1, Q_2, Q_3)-space at which the function

$$U + \tfrac{1}{2}(mQ_1^2 + \mu Q_2^2 + \mu Q_3^2)\omega^2 \tag{29.15.5}$$

has a stationary value.

The equations (29.15.4), exhibited *in extenso*, are

$$mQ_1\omega^2 - \gamma\left\{\frac{m_2m_3}{r_1^3}\alpha_1(\alpha_1Q_1 - Q_2) + \frac{m_3m_1}{r_2^3}\alpha_2(\alpha_2Q_1 + Q_2) + \frac{m_1m_2}{r_3^3}Q_1\right\} = 0, \tag{29.15.6}$$

$$\mu Q_2\omega^2 - \gamma\left\{-\frac{m_2m_3}{r_1^3}(\alpha_1Q_1 - Q_2) + \frac{m_3m_1}{r_2^3}(\alpha_2Q_1 + Q_2)\right\} = 0, \tag{29.15.7}$$

$$\mu Q_3\omega^2 = \gamma m_3Q_3\left(\frac{m_2}{r_1^3} + \frac{m_1}{r_2^3}\right). \tag{29.15.8}$$

From (29.15.8) we see that either

$$\mu\omega^2 = \gamma m_3\left(\frac{m_2}{r_1^3} + \frac{m_1}{r_2^3}\right), \tag{29.15.9}$$

or

$$Q_3 = 0. \tag{29.15.10}$$

Suppose first that (29.15.9) holds. Then, substituting for $\mu\omega^2$ from (29.15.9) in the first member of (29.15.7), we obtain

$$Q_1\left(\frac{1}{r_1^3} - \frac{1}{r_2^3}\right) = 0, \tag{29.15.11}$$

whence, since $Q_1 = r_3 \neq 0$, $r_1 = r_2$, say

$$r_1 = r_2 = l, \tag{29.15.12}$$

and then, from (29.15.9),

$$\omega^2 = \frac{\gamma M}{l^3}. \tag{29.15.13}$$

If we substitute this value for ω^2 in the first member of (29.15.6) we find

$$\frac{M}{l^3} = \frac{m_3}{l^3} + \frac{m_1 + m_2}{r_3^3}. \tag{29.15.14}$$

Thus

$$r_3 = l, \tag{29.15.15}$$

and we have the Lagrange equilateral-triangle solution.

Next, suppose instead that (29.15.10) holds. Then the three particles are in line, and (taking as before the case where A_2 lies between A_1 and A_3),

$$Q_1 = r_3,\ Q_2 = r_1 + \alpha_1 r_3,\ Q_3 = 0,\ r_2 = r_1 + r_3, \tag{29.15.16}$$

and, using the notation of (29.3.12),

$$\frac{r_1}{k} = \frac{r_2}{k+1} = \frac{r_3}{1}. \tag{29.15.17}$$

The equation (29.15.8) is satisfied, since $Q_3 = 0$, and the equations (29.15.6-7) give

$$r_3\omega^2 = \gamma\left(-\frac{m_3}{r_1^{\,2}} + \frac{m_3}{r_2^{\,2}} + \frac{m_1 + m_2}{r_3^{\,2}}\right), \tag{29.15.18}$$

and

$$(r_1 + \alpha_1 r_3)\omega^2 = \gamma\,\frac{m_3}{\mu}\left(\frac{m_2}{r_1^{\,2}} + \frac{m_1}{r_2^{\,2}}\right). \tag{29.15.19}$$

If we divide the second of these equations by the first, and use (29.15.17), we have

$$k + \alpha_1 = \frac{m_3}{\mu}\,\frac{m_2(k+1)^2 + m_1k^2}{(m_1 + m_2)k^2(k+1)^2 - m_3(k+1)^2 + m_3k^2}, \tag{29.15.20}$$

which is equivalent to the quintic equation (29.3.14). We thus recover the result already found, that the only equilibrium solutions are the equilateral-triangle case and the rectilinear case of Lagrange's three particles.

Chapter XXX

Periodic orbits

30.1 Periodic orbits. The complete integration of the equations of motion for a dynamical system, with initial conditions arbitrarily prescribed, is usually impracticable. This is true, in particular, of the problem of three bodies. Even the classification of the possible types of orbit may be very laborious, as we have seen (§ 17.10). We may however be able to find, or at least to prove the existence of, periodic orbits. Poincaré, in his classical work on the problem of three bodies, regarded the study of the periodic orbits as a matter of prime importance, a starting point for the attack on the general problems of classification and integration.* The orbits may be periodic in an absolute sense (of motion relative to fixed axes, i.e. relative to axes fixed in a Newtonian base) or in a relative sense (of motion relative to axes moving in a particular way). For example, in the restricted problem of three bodies we speak of orbits as periodic orbits when it is motion relative to a system of rotating axes that is periodic.

30.2 Periodic motion near a singular point. In Chapter XIX we discussed the motion of an autonomous dynamical system with one degree of freedom near a point of equilibrium, or singular point. We considered first the linear approximation, i.e. the approximation derived from the equations of motion

(30.2.1) $$\dot{x}_r = X_r, \qquad r = 1, 2,$$

when only terms of the first order are retained in the second members of the equations; the origin is a singular point, and there is no constant term in the expansion of X_r. For the linear approximation the equations of motion take the form

(30.2.2) $$\dot{\mathbf{x}} = \mathbf{A}\mathbf{x},$$

where $\mathbf{A}$ is a 2×2 matrix whose elements are real constants. Our main concern was with the question how far the conclusions about stability based on the linear approximation (30.2.2) hold for the actual motion defined by the complete equations (30.2.1).

A case of particular interest is that of a vortex point; for such a point the eigenvalues of $\mathbf{A}$ are pure imaginary numbers. In this case (for a system with one degree of freedom) the position of equilibrium is stable for the motion defined by the linear approximation. But, as we saw, this property does not always persist when we replace the linear approximation by the exact equations of motion.

When we turn from the case of one degree of freedom to the general case of n degrees of freedom, the equations of motion are

(30.2.3) $$\dot{x}_r = X_r, \qquad r = 1, 2, \ldots, m,$$

* "Ce qui nous rend ces solutions périodiques si précieuses, c'est qu'elles sont, pour ainsi dire, la seule brèche par où nous puissions essayer de pénétrer dans une place jusqu'ici réputée inabordable."

where $m = 2n$. If the origin is a position of equilibrium, the functions X_r all vanish when $x_1 = x_2 = \cdots = x_m = 0$. The linear approximation is (as in § 21.11)

$$\dot{\mathbf{x}} = \mathbf{A}\mathbf{x}, \tag{30.2.4}$$

where $\mathbf{A}$ is now an $m \times m$ matrix. If the eigenvalues of $\mathbf{A}$ are all pure imaginary numbers and all different, the origin is, for the motion defined by the linear approximation, a point of stable equilibrium. But it is clear from the special case $m = 2$ that this property does not necessarily persist when we replace the linear approximation by the exact equations of motion.

Nevertheless one property associated with the notion of stable equilibrium does persist in general if the system is Hamiltonian, and if one pair of eigenvalues are conjugate pure imaginary numbers $\pm i\mu_0$. It is this: *there exists in the neighbourhood of the point of equilibrium a family of periodic motions.* The members of this family depend analytically on a real parameter ρ; they exist for sufficiently small values of ρ, and tend to the equilibrium solution (in which the mobile stays at rest at the origin) as $\rho \to 0$. The period $\sigma(\rho)$ tends to the value $2\pi/\mu_0$ as ρ tends to zero.

To begin with we consider, not specifically a Hamiltonian system, but the general system (30.2.3). The second members X_r all vanish when $\mathbf{x} = \mathbf{0}$, and we assume that each X_r can be expressed, for sufficiently small values of $|\mathbf{x}|$, as a multiple power-series in $(x_1, x_2, \ldots, x_m)$, with real coefficients and with no constant term. The linear approximation is (30.2.4), and we assume that the matrix $\mathbf{A}$ has the following properties. No two of the eigenvalues $\lambda_1, \lambda_2, \ldots, \lambda_m$ are equal: two of the eigenvalues, say λ_1 and λ_2, are equal and opposite pure imaginary numbers, $\lambda_1 = -\lambda_2 = i\mu_0$: none of the ratios $\lambda_3/\lambda_1, \lambda_4/\lambda_1, \ldots, \lambda_m/\lambda_1$ is an integer.

Let us first consider the linear approximation (30.2.4). If we apply the non-singular linear transformation

$$\mathbf{x} = \mathbf{C}\mathbf{y} \tag{30.2.5}$$

we get

$$\dot{\mathbf{y}} = \mathbf{C}^{-1}\mathbf{A}\mathbf{C}\mathbf{y}. \tag{30.2.6}$$

We choose the matrix $\mathbf{C}$ so that $\mathbf{C}^{-1}\mathbf{A}\mathbf{C}$ is the diagonal matrix $\mathbf{L}$,

$$\mathbf{L} = \begin{pmatrix} \lambda_1 & & & & \\ & \lambda_2 & & & \\ & & \cdot & & \\ & & & \cdot & \\ & & & & \cdot \\ & & & & & \lambda_m \end{pmatrix}. \tag{30.2.7}$$

The equations of motion are now

$$\dot{y}_k = \lambda_k y_k, \tag{30.2.8}$$

and a motion in which

$$y_1 = \alpha e^{i\mu_0 t}, \quad y_2 = \beta e^{-i\mu_0 t}, \quad y_3 = y_4 = \cdots = y_m = 0, \tag{30.2.9}$$

is a periodic motion with period $2\pi/\mu_0$. The complex coefficients α, β must be so chosen that the x's are real.

If now we apply the same linear transformation to the exact equations (30.2.3) we obtain

$$\dot{y}_k = \lambda_k y_k + g_k, \qquad k = 1, 2, \ldots, m, \tag{30.2.10}$$

where g_k is a power-series in $(y_1, y_2, \ldots, y_m)$ beginning with terms of the second degree. We wish to establish the existence of periodic solutions analogous to (30.2.9), and to do this we adopt a device suggested by the idea of variation of parameters. We assume tentatively that a solution exists in which each y_k is represented as a function of two variables ξ, η, the functions being defined by multiple power-series as follows,

$$y_1 = \xi + z_1 = \xi + \sum a_{rs}{}^1 \xi^r \eta^s, \tag{30.2.11}$$

$$y_2 = \eta + z_2 = \eta + \sum a_{rs}{}^2 \xi^r \eta^s, \tag{30.2.12}$$

$$y_k = \quad z_k = \quad \sum a_{rs}{}^k \xi^r \eta^s, \qquad k > 2, \tag{30.2.13}$$

where the series $z_1, z_2, \ldots, z_m$ begin with terms of the second degree. We make the following assumptions about the series for z_1 and z_2. We assume that $a_{rs}{}^1 = 0$ when $r = s + 1$, so the series for z_1 contains no term of the form $\xi(\xi\eta)^s$, and therefore the series for $\partial z_1/\partial\xi$ contains no term of the form $(\xi\eta)^s$. Similarly we assume that $a_{rs}{}^2 = 0$ when $s = r + 1$, so the series for z_2 contains no term of the form $(\xi\eta)^r\eta$, and therefore the series for $\partial z_2/\partial\eta$ contains no term of the form $(\xi\eta)^r$. The reason for these restrictions will appear in a moment.

Next, we assume that the subsidiary variables ξ and η are functions of t satisfying the differential equations

$$\dot{\xi} = u\xi, \quad \dot{\eta} = v\eta, \tag{30.2.14}$$

where u is a function of the product $\xi\eta$, expressible as a power-series in $\xi\eta$, with λ_1 as its constant term,

$$u = \lambda_1 + u_1\xi\eta + u_2\xi^2\eta^2 + \cdots, \tag{30.2.15}$$

and v is a function of $\xi\eta$, expressible as a power-series in $\xi\eta$, with λ_2 as its constant term,

$$v = \lambda_2 + v_1\xi\eta + v_2\xi^2\eta^2 + \cdots. \tag{30.2.16}$$

Assuming for the moment the convergence of the series for sufficiently small values of ξ and η, the equations of motion (30.2.10) now take the form

$$u\xi\frac{\partial y_k}{\partial\xi} + v\eta\frac{\partial y_k}{\partial\eta} = \lambda_k y_k + g_k, \qquad k = 1, 2, \ldots, m. \tag{30.2.17}$$

We shall show that, if we substitute the appropriate series for y_k, u, v in these equations, and compare coefficients of like terms $\xi^r\eta^s$, all the coefficients $a_{rs}{}^k$, u_r, v_r can be found.

The equation (30.2.17) for $k = 1$ is

$$u\xi + u\xi\frac{\partial z_1}{\partial\xi} + v\eta\frac{\partial z_1}{\partial\eta} - \lambda_1(\xi + z_1) = g_1,$$

or, written *in extenso*,

(30.2.18)

$$\xi(u_1\xi\eta + u_2\xi^2\eta^2 + \cdots) + (\sum r a_{rs}{}^1\xi^r\eta^s)(\lambda_1 + u_1\xi\eta + \cdots)$$
$$+ (\sum s a_{rs}{}^1\xi^r\eta^s)(\lambda_2 + v_1\xi\eta + \cdots) - \lambda_1\sum a_{rs}{}^1\xi^r\eta^s = g_1.$$

Similarly the second equation leads to

(30.2.19)

$$\eta(v_1\xi\eta + v_2\xi^2\eta^2 + \cdots) + (\sum r a_{rs}{}^2\xi^r\eta^s)(\lambda_1 + u_1\xi\eta + \cdots) + (\sum s a_{rs}{}^2\xi^r\eta^s)(\lambda_2 + v_1\xi\eta + \cdots) - \lambda_2\sum a_{rs}{}^2\xi^r\eta^s = g_2,$$

and the others to

(30.2.20)

$$(\sum r a_{rs}{}^k\xi^r\eta^s)(\lambda_1 + u_1\xi\eta + \cdots) + (\sum s a_{rs}{}^k\xi^r\eta^s)(\lambda_2 + v_1\xi\eta + \cdots) - \lambda_k\sum a_{rs}{}^k\xi^r\eta^s = g_k.$$

In the functions g_k on the right the appropriate series are to be substituted for $y_1, y_2, \ldots, y_m$.

We recall that in the first member of (30.2.18) there are no terms of the form $\xi^{s+1}\eta^s$ except in the expression ξu, and in the first member of (30.2.19) there are no terms of the form $\xi^r\eta^{r+1}$ except in the expression ηv. We now find the coefficients step by step by equating coefficients. If all the coefficients $a_{rs}{}^k$ $(k = 1, 2, \ldots, m)$ have been found for $r + s < N$, and the coefficients u_r, v_r for $2r < N - 1$, the coefficients $a_{rs}{}^k$ for $r + s = N$ can be found by comparing coefficients of $\xi^r\eta^r$. Setting aside the cases $r - s = 1$ when $k = 1$, and $r - s = -1$ when $k = 2$, we find

(30.2.21)
$$[(r - s)\lambda_1 - \lambda_k]a_{rs}{}^k = p,$$

where p is a polynomial in the coefficients already found. The coefficient of $a_{rs}{}^k$ in the first member of (30.2.21) is never zero. For if $k = 1$, $r - s \neq 1$, and if $k = 2$, $r - s \neq -1$; and if $k > 2$ the coefficient $[(r - s)\lambda_1 - \lambda_k]$ cannot vanish, because none of the ratios λ_k/λ_1 is an integer. Finally the coefficients u_r are found by equating the coefficients of terms $\xi^{r+1}\eta^r$ in (30.2.18), which expresses u_r in terms of coefficients already known; and similarly the coefficients v_r are found from (30.2.19). Thus, setting aside for the moment the question of convergence, the existence of the series for the $(m + 2)$ variables y_k, u, v is established.

30.3 Reality conditions. We can write the equations (30.2.1) in the form

(30.3.1)
$$\dot{\mathbf{x}} = \mathbf{f}(\mathbf{x}),$$

where $\mathbf{f}(\mathbf{x})$ is the vector $\{X_1, X_2, \ldots, X_m\}$, and $\mathbf{f}(\mathbf{x})$ is real when $x_1, x_2, \ldots, x_m$ are real. Under the transformation $\mathbf{x} = \mathbf{C}\mathbf{y}$ the equation (30.3.1) becomes

(30.3.2)
$$\dot{\mathbf{y}} = \mathbf{C}^{-1}\mathbf{f}(\mathbf{C}\mathbf{y}),$$

and (30.2.17) takes the form

(30.3.3)
$$u\xi\frac{\partial\mathbf{y}}{\partial\xi} + v\eta\frac{\partial\mathbf{y}}{\partial\eta} = \mathbf{C}^{-1}\mathbf{f}(\mathbf{C}\mathbf{y}).$$

We denote by $\bar{y}_k$, $\bar{u}$, $\bar{v}$ the series obtained from the series for y_k, u, v when each coefficient is replaced by its complex conjugate. It follows from (30.3.3) that

(30.3.4)
$$\bar{u}\xi\frac{\partial\bar{\mathbf{y}}}{\partial\xi} + \bar{v}\eta\frac{\partial\bar{\mathbf{y}}}{\partial\eta} = \bar{\mathbf{C}}^{-1}\mathbf{f}(\bar{\mathbf{C}}\bar{\mathbf{y}}),$$

since $\mathbf{f}(\mathbf{x})$ is real when $\mathbf{x}$ is real.

We introduce the matrix $\mathbf{T}$ defined by

(30.3.5)
$$\bar{\mathbf{C}} = \mathbf{C}\mathbf{T}, \quad \mathbf{T} = \mathbf{C}^{-1}\bar{\mathbf{C}}.$$

The second member of (30.3.4) is

$$\mathbf{T}^{-1}\mathbf{C}^{-1}\mathbf{f}(\mathbf{C}\mathbf{T}\bar{\mathbf{y}}), \tag{30.3.6}$$

and therefore (30.3.3) still holds if we replace $\mathbf{y}$ by $\mathbf{T}\bar{\mathbf{y}}$, u by $\bar{u}$, and v by $\bar{v}$.

Let us consider the transformation $\mathbf{w} = \mathbf{T}\bar{\mathbf{y}}$. It is equivalent to $\mathbf{C}\mathbf{w} = \bar{\mathbf{C}}\bar{\mathbf{y}}$, which implies

$$w_k = \bar{\rho}_k \bar{y}_l, \tag{30.3.7}$$

where the notation is that of § 25.10. In particular

$$w_1 = \bar{\rho}_1 \bar{y}_2, \quad w_2 = \bar{\rho}_2 \bar{y}_1, \tag{30.3.8}$$

and $\bar{\rho}_1 \rho_2 = 1$. The first two components of $\mathbf{T}\bar{\mathbf{y}}$ are

$$\bar{\rho}_1 \bar{y}_2 = \bar{\rho}_1 \eta + \cdots, \tag{30.3.9}$$

and

$$\bar{\rho}_2 \bar{y}_1 = \bar{\rho}_2 \xi + \cdots, \tag{30.3.10}$$

and the other components begin with quadratic terms in ξ, η.

The equation (30.3.3) is satisfied if we replace

$$\mathbf{y}(\xi, \eta), \quad u(\xi, \eta), \quad v(\xi, \eta), \tag{30.3.11}$$

by

$$\mathbf{T}\bar{\mathbf{y}}(\rho_1\eta, \rho_2\xi), \quad \bar{v}(\rho_1\eta, \rho_2\xi), \quad \bar{u}(\rho_1\eta, \rho_2\xi), \tag{30.3.12}$$

and therefore, since the solution subject to the prescribed conditions is unique,

$$\mathbf{C}\mathbf{y}(\xi, \eta) = \bar{\mathbf{C}}\bar{\mathbf{y}}(\rho_1\eta, \rho_2\xi), \quad u(\xi, \eta) = \bar{v}(\rho_1\eta, \rho_2\xi). \tag{30.3.13}$$

Now

$$\mathbf{x}(\xi, \eta) = \mathbf{C}\mathbf{y}(\xi, \eta), \tag{30.3.14}$$

and therefore, in virtue of (30.3.13), the formulae give $\mathbf{x}$ in real form provided that

$$\bar{\xi} = \rho_1\eta, \bar{\eta} = \rho_2\xi. \tag{30.3.15}$$

In the important special case in which the eigenvalues are all pure imaginary numbers $\lambda_1, \lambda_2, \ldots, \lambda_n, -\lambda_1, -\lambda_2, \ldots, -\lambda_n$, and where the eigenvectors forming the columns of $\mathbf{C}$ are normalized, so that the multipliers ρ_r are all unity, the $(n + r)$th column of $\mathbf{C}$ (for $r = 1, 2, \ldots, n$) is precisely the conjugate of the rth column. In this case $T\bar{y}$ is the vector $\{\bar{y}_{n+1}, \bar{y}_{n+2}, \ldots, \bar{y}_{2n}, \bar{y}_1, \bar{y}_2, \ldots, \bar{y}_n\}$, and $\mathbf{T}$ is the matrix

$$\begin{pmatrix} \mathbf{0} & \mathbf{I}_n \\ \mathbf{I}_n & \mathbf{0} \end{pmatrix}.$$

30.4 Hamiltonian equations. The case in which we are primarily interested is that in which the equations (30.2.1) are of Hamiltonian form, and in which two eigenvalues are equal and opposite pure imaginary numbers. To begin with, we use a linear transformation, as in § 25.10, to reduce the terms of lowest order (i.e. the quadratic terms) in H to the form

$$H_2 = \lambda_1 q_1 p_1 + \lambda_2 q_2 p_2 + \cdots + \lambda_n q_n p_n. \tag{30.4.1}$$

The eigenvalues are $\lambda_1, \lambda_2, \ldots, \lambda_n, \; -\lambda_1, -\lambda_2, \ldots, -\lambda_n$, and the fundamental eigenvalues are now λ_1, λ_{n+1} (where $\lambda_1 = -\lambda_{n+1} = i\mu_0$) instead of λ_1, λ_2, which were the fundamental eigenvalues in the preceding sections. When the leading terms H_2 in H have the form (30.4.1) the equations of motion have the required form (30.2.10).

Let us denote by K the result of substituting for the q's and p's in H their values as functions of (ξ, η),

(30.4.2) $$H\,(q;\; p) = K(\xi, \eta).$$

The equation of energy requires

(30.4.3) $$\frac{dH}{dt} = u\xi\,\frac{\partial K}{\partial \xi} + v\eta\,\frac{\partial K}{\partial \eta} = 0,$$

and we recall that u and v are functions of $\omega\;(= \xi\eta)$. It is easy to see that K also must be a function of ω. If we express K as a multiple power-series in ξ and η, the only term of order 2 in K is $\lambda_1\xi\eta$, and if K is represented by the series

(30.4.4) $$\lambda_1\xi\eta + \sum k_{rs}\xi^r\eta^s,$$

where $r + s > 2$, the equation (30.4.3) leads to

(30.4.5) $$(\lambda_1 + \textstyle\sum u_r\xi^r\eta^r)(\lambda_1\xi\eta + \sum rk_{rs}\xi^r\eta^s) + (-\lambda_1 + \sum v_r\xi^r\eta^r)(\lambda_1\xi\eta + \sum sk_{rs}\xi^r\eta^s) = 0,$$

and, determining the coefficients step by step, we see that $k_{rs} = 0$ if $r \neq s$. Thus K is a function of ω, say $\varphi(\omega)$, and (30.4.3) becomes

(30.4.6) $$(u + v)\,\omega\,\frac{d\varphi}{d\omega} = 0,$$

whence

(30.4.7) $$u + v = 0,$$

a result which is also evident from (30.4.5).

Now

(30.4.8) $$\frac{d\omega}{dt} = \frac{d}{dt}\,(\xi\eta) = (u + v)\xi\eta = 0,$$

so ω is constant throughout the motion, and u and $v\;(= -u)$, which are functions of ω, are also constants. Hence

(30.4.9) $$\xi = \xi_0 e^{ut}, \quad \eta = \eta_0 e^{vt}.$$

If we choose ξ_0, η_0 such that $\bar{\xi}_0 = \rho_1\eta_0$, then, as in § 30.3, $u\;(= u(\xi, \eta) = u(\xi_0, \eta_0))$ and $v\;(= v(\xi, \eta) = v(\xi_0, \eta_0))$ are conjugate complex numbers, and therefore, since $u + v = 0$,

(30.4.10) $$u = i\mu, \quad v = -i\mu.$$

The equations

(30.4.11) $$\xi = \xi_0 e^{i\mu t}, \quad \eta = \eta_0 e^{-i\mu t},$$

represent, for sufficiently small values of $|\xi|$, a family of periodic solutions of the Hamiltonian equations. We can write $\xi_0 e^{i\mu t}$ in the form $\rho e^{i\mu(t-t_0)}$, where ρ is real and positive, and by changing the zero of the time-scale we can write

(30.4.12) $$\xi = \rho e^{i\mu t}, \quad \eta = \rho\bar{\rho}_2 e^{-i\mu t}.$$

(We can take the matrix **C** in a form that makes $\rho_2 = 1$.) The period is $2\pi/\mu$, and, since

$$u = i\mu = i\mu_0 + \xi_0 \eta_0 (u_1 + \cdots), \tag{30.4.13}$$

the period $2\pi/\mu$ tends to $2\pi/\mu_0$ as $\rho \to 0$. The periodic motion tends to the equilibrium solution as $\rho \to 0$. The coordinates x_r can be expressed as Fourier series of the form

$$\tfrac{1}{2}a_0 + \sum (a_\nu \cos \nu\mu t + b_\nu \sin \nu\mu t).$$

Many examples of such families of periodic orbits in the neighbourhood of a singularity have already been noticed in the case $n = 1$, when the singularity is a vortex point; see *Example* 19.10*A*(i) (Fig. 19.10*a*), *Example* 19.10*C* (Fig. 19.10*b*), *Example* 19.11*A* (Fig. 19.11*b*). In *Example* 19.10*A*(i) the period of each of the periodic motions is exactly, not merely approximately, equal to $2\pi/\mu_0$. In *Example* 19.10*C* the period is approximately $2\pi(1 + \frac{1}{6}a^2)$, which tends to 2π $(= 2\pi/\mu_0)$ as $a \to 0$.

The theorem refers specifically to a system which is, or which can be transformed into, a Hamiltonian system, and these families of periodic orbits do not necessarily exist in other cases; for example, no such orbits exist in *Example* 19.10*A*(ii), *Example* 19.10*A*(iii), or in *Example* 19.10*B*.

Example 30.4. A simple illustration, with $n = 2$, is provided by the Hamiltonian function (21.16.11),

$$H = \tfrac{1}{2}n(q_1^2 + p_1^2) - n(q_2^2 + p_2^2) + \tfrac{1}{2}\alpha(q_1^2 q_2 - q_2 p_1^2 - 2q_1 p_1 p_2), \tag{30.4.14}$$

where $n > 0$ and $\alpha > 0$. The equations of motion are

$$\begin{cases} \dot{q}_1 = np_1 - \alpha(q_2 p_1 + q_1 p_2), & \dot{p}_1 = -nq_1 - \alpha(q_1 q_2 - p_1 p_2), \\ \dot{q}_2 = -2np_2 - \alpha q_1 p_1, & \dot{p}_2 = 2nq_2 - \tfrac{1}{2}\alpha(q_1^2 - p_1^2). \end{cases} \tag{30.4.15}$$

The origin is a vortex point, and, as we saw, it is a point of unstable equilibrium. The eigenvalues are

$$\lambda_1 = 2in,\ \lambda_2 = in,\ -\lambda_1,\ -\lambda_2, \tag{30.4.16}$$

and the requisite conditions are satisfied, since λ_2/λ_1 $(= 1/2)$ is not an integer. There exists a family of periodic orbits near the origin, with periods approximating to π/n.

It is easy to verify directly that such a family does exist, for the equations of motion (30.4.15) are clearly satisfied if q_1 and p_1 are permanently zero, and if

$$\dot{q}_2 = -2np_2, \quad \dot{p}_2 = 2nq_2. \tag{30.4.17}$$

Thus we have a family of periodic orbits in which

$$\begin{cases} q_1 = 0, \quad p_1 = 0, \\ q_2 = a_2 \cos 2nt - b_2 \sin 2nt, \quad p_2 = b_2 \cos 2nt + a_2 \sin 2nt. \end{cases} \tag{30.4.18}$$

In this simple case the period of each of the motions is exactly, not merely approximately, equal to π/n; and, further, the orbits exist for large values of q_2 and p_2, not merely in the neighbourhood of O.

But if we take λ_2 instead of λ_1 as the fundamental eigenvalue, everything is changed. The theory is no longer applicable, since $\lambda_1/\lambda_2 = 2$, and we have no reason to expect periodic solutions with period approximating to $2\pi/n$. In fact it is easy to see that no such periodic solutions exist; no solution is periodic unless initially $q_1 = p_1 = 0$ (and then $q_1 = p_1 = 0$ for all time). If we write $\theta = q_1^2 + p_1^2$, $\varphi = q_2^2 + p_2^2$, we have

(30.4.19) $$\ddot{\theta} = \alpha^2(4\theta\varphi + \theta^2),$$

a relation that is easily verified on substituting for $\dot{q}_1, \dot{p}_1, \dot{q}_2, \dot{p}_2$ from the differential equations (30.4.15). Now $\theta > 0$ throughout, since if θ is zero at any time it remains zero for all time. Thus $\ddot{\theta} > 0$, and the motion cannot be periodic.

30.5 Convergence. We now establish the convergence of the series in ξ, η for $y_k (k = 1, 2, \ldots, m)$, u, v, for sufficiently small values of $|\xi|$ and $|\eta|$. We confine our attention to the Hamiltonian case, in which $u + v = 0$. We revert to the notation of § 30.2 (in which $\lambda_1 = -\lambda_2$), and we denote by $d_{rs}{}^k$ the coefficient of $\xi^r\eta^s$ in the series obtained from g_k when we substitute for $y_1, y_2, \ldots, y_n$ the appropriate series in ξ, η. The equations obtained by comparing coefficients of $\xi^r\eta^s$ in (30.2.18–20) are of the form

(30.5.1) $$[(r - s)\lambda_1 - \lambda_k]a_{rs}{}^k + (r - s) \sum u_\nu a^k_{r-\nu s-\nu} = d_{rs}{}^k, \qquad k = 1, 2, \ldots, m,$$

the summation for ν running from $\nu = 1$ to $\nu = \min(r, s)$. The cases $k = 1$, $r - s = 1$, and $k = 2$, $s - r = 1$, are anomalous; in the first of these the first term on the left in (30.5.1) is replaced by u_s, and in the second it is replaced by v_r $(= -u_r)$; from (30.2.18), comparing coefficients of $\xi^{r+1}\eta^r$, and from (30.2.19), comparing coefficients of $\xi^r\eta^{r+1}$, we find

(30.5.2) $$u_r = d^1_{r+1,r} = -d^2_{r,r+1}.$$

Apart from the two anomalous cases, the coefficient of $a_{rs}{}^k$ in (30.5.1) is never zero, and there is a positive constant c_1, independent of k, r, s, such that

(30.5.3) $$\left| \frac{1}{(r - s)\lambda_1 - \lambda_k} \right| < c_1, \quad \left| \frac{r - s}{(r - s)\lambda_1 - \lambda_k} \right| < c_1,$$

and therefore, from (30.5.1),

(30.5.4) $$|a_{rs}{}^k| \leqslant c_1 \, |d_{rs}{}^k| + c_1 \sum |u_\nu a^k_{r-\nu,s-\nu}|.$$

Further,

(30.5.5) $$|u_r| = |d^1_{r+1,r}| = |d^2_{r,r+1}|.$$

Let us denote the series

$$\sum |a_{rs}{}^k| \, \xi^r\eta^s$$

by Z_k. The convergence of this series would imply the convergence of the series for y_k. Similarly we denote the series

$$\sum |u_r| \, \xi^r\eta^r$$

by U, and the series

$$\sum |d_{rs}{}^k| \, \xi^r\eta^s$$

by G_k. The series Z_k, U, G_k are obtained from z_k, $u - \lambda_1$, g_k by replacing each coefficient in the power series by its modulus. Finally Y_k denotes the series obtained from the series for y_k by replacing each coefficient by its modulus. If we multiply (30.5.4–5) by $\xi^r\eta^s$, and sum over k, r, s, we obtain the relation, fundamental for what follows,

(30.5.6) $$(\xi + \eta)U + Z \prec c_1(G + UZ),$$

where

(30.5.7) $$G = G_1 + G_2 + \cdots + G_m, \quad Z = Z_1 + Z_2 + \cdots + Z_m,$$

and the meaning of the symbol $\prec$ is that the series on the right is a majorant for the series on the left. The majorant symbol relates only to the coefficients in the formal development in multiple power series, and its use does not require that the series are convergent.

We now determine a majorant for G. The m functions $X_r(x_1, x_2, \ldots, x_m)$ are assumed to be regular in a neighbourhood of $\mathbf{x} = \mathbf{0}$, and therefore the m functions $g_k(y_1, y_2, \ldots, y_m)$ are also regular in a neighbourhood of $\mathbf{y} = \mathbf{0}$. The same is therefore true of the functions $G_k^*(y_1, y_2, \ldots, y_m)$ obtained from $g_k(y_1, y_2, \ldots, y_m)$ by replacing each coefficient in the multiple power series in $y_1, y_2, \ldots, y_m$ by its modulus. Further, the series for each G_k^* begins with quadratic terms, so there exists a positive constant a such that

(30.5.8) $$\sum_{k=1}^{m} G_h^*(Y_1, Y_2, \ldots, Y_m) \prec \sum_{n=2}^{\infty} (aW)^n = \frac{a^2W^2}{1 - aW},$$

where

(30.5.9) $$W = Y_1 + Y_2 + \cdots + Y_m = \xi + \eta + Z,$$

and the last expression in (30.5.8) is to be regarded initially as an abbreviation for the geometric series without any presumption of convergence. (If the series Z proves to be convergent in a neighbourhood of $(\xi, \eta) = (0, 0)$, the geometric series will in fact be convergent in some (possibly smaller) neighbourhood.) The symbol $\prec$ in (30.5.8) relates (exceptionally) to multiple power series in $Y_1, Y_2, \ldots, Y_m$; but, since all coefficients are positive, the relation holds in the usual sense when both sides are expressed as power series in ξ, η. Moreover it follows from the definition of d_{rs}^k that, in terms of power series in ξ, η,

(30.5.10) $$G_k \prec G_k^*(Y_1, Y_2, \ldots, Y_m).$$

Combining (30.5.6–10), we obtain

(30.5.11) $$(\xi + \eta)U + Z \prec c_1\left(\frac{a^2(\xi + \eta + Z)^2}{1 - a(\xi + \eta + Z)} + UZ\right).$$

It will suffice to establish the convergence of U and of Z in a neighbourhood of $(\xi, \eta) = (0, 0)$, and further, since all the coefficients involved are non-negative, it will suffice to prove the convergence for the special case $\xi = \eta$. If we put $\xi = \eta$, the first member of (30.5.11) becomes $2\xi U + Z$, and we write

(30.5.12) $$2\xi U + Z = \xi P,$$

so that P is a power series in ξ without a constant term. Then (putting $\xi = \eta$ throughout in U and Z)

(30.5.13) $$2\xi + Z \prec 2\xi(1 + P),$$

and

(30.5.14) $$UZ \prec \tfrac{1}{4}\xi P^2 \prec 4\xi P^2,$$

and therefore (30.5.11) leads to

(30.5.15) $$P \prec 4c_1\left(\frac{a^2\xi(1 + P)^2}{1 - 2a\xi(1 + P)} + P^2\right).$$

We now write

(30.5.16) $$\xi + P + \xi P = Q,$$

and we have the majorant relations

(30.5.17) $$\xi + \xi P \prec Q, \quad \xi P \prec Q^2, \quad \xi(1 + P)^2 \prec \xi + Q^2.$$

Then

$$
\begin{aligned}
Q &= \xi + P + \xi P \\
&\prec \xi + P + Q^2 \\
&\prec \xi + Q^2 + 4c_1\left(\frac{a^2(\xi + Q^2)}{1 - 2aQ} + Q^2\right) \\
&\prec \xi + Q^2 + 4c_1\left(\frac{a^2(\xi + Q^2)}{1 - 2aQ} + \xi + Q^2\right) \\
&\prec c_2\frac{\xi + Q^2}{4 - c_3Q} \\
&\prec c_2\frac{2\xi + Q^2}{4 - c_3Q} \\
&\prec \alpha\frac{2\xi + Q^2}{4 - \alpha Q},
\end{aligned}
\tag{30.5.18}
$$

where α is the larger of the positive constants c_2 and c_3. It will suffice for our purpose to establish the convergence of the series Q for sufficiently small positive values of ξ.

Consider the equation

$$R = \alpha\frac{2\xi + R^2}{4 - \alpha R}, \tag{30.5.19}$$

where R is a power series in ξ. We write

$$Q = \sum_{r=1}^{\infty} \alpha_r \xi^r, \qquad R = \sum_{r=1}^{\infty} \beta_r \xi^r. \tag{30.5.20}$$

The coefficients β_r are readily determined, step by step, by comparing coefficients of powers of ξ in the relation $2R = \alpha\xi + \alpha R^2$; in fact

$$\beta_1 = \tfrac{1}{2}\alpha, \quad \beta_2 = \tfrac{1}{8}\alpha^3, \quad \beta_3 = \tfrac{1}{16}\alpha^5, \ldots \tag{30.5.21}$$

Moreover, we can prove step by step that $\alpha_r \leqslant \beta_r$, so that R is a majorant for Q, and the convergence of R will establish also the convergence of Q. The convergence of Q implies the convergence of P, and this in turn implies the convergence of Z and of U.

We can write (30.5.19) in the form

$$(1 - \alpha R)^2 = 1 - \alpha^2\xi, \tag{30.5.22}$$

whence

$$2\alpha R \prec (1 - \alpha R)^{-2} - 1 = \frac{\alpha^2\xi}{1 - \alpha^2\xi}, \tag{30.5.23}$$

and hence R is convergent for $|\xi| < 1/\alpha^2$. This completes the proof.

30.6 Lagrange's three particles. The theorem of § 30.2 is applicable to the equilibrium solution in which the three particles are at rest, relative to the rotating axes, at the vertices of an equilateral triangle. We take the reduced form of the equations of motion found in § 29.8, and the equation for the eigenvalues in the linear approximation to the disturbed motion is

$$(\lambda^2 + \omega^2)(\lambda^4 + \omega^2\lambda^2 + k\omega^4) = 0, \tag{30.6.1}$$

where

$$k = \frac{27}{4}\,\frac{m_2m_3 + m_3m_1 + m_1m_2}{(m_1 + m_2 + m_3)^2}. \tag{30.6.2}$$

The eigenvalues are

(30.6.3) $$\lambda_1 = i\omega,\ \lambda_2,\ \lambda_3,\ -\lambda_1,\ -\lambda_2,\ -\lambda_3.$$

Neither of the ratios λ_2/λ_1, λ_3/λ_1 is an integer. For, in the unstable case ($k > \frac{1}{4}$), λ_2 and λ_3 are not pure imaginary numbers; and in the stable case ($k < \frac{1}{4}$), when λ_2 and λ_3 are pure imaginary numbers in_2 and in_3, we have

(30.6.4) $$0 < {n_2}^2 < \tfrac{1}{2}\omega^2 < {n_3}^2 < \omega^2,$$

and λ_2/λ_1 and λ_3/λ_1 both lie between 0 and 1. Hence the conditions for the theorem of § 30.2 are satisfied, and there exists a family of periodic motions (relative to the rotating axes) in the neighbourhood of the equilibrium solution, with periods approximating to $2\pi/\omega$.

Actually these motions are already known to us; they have been considered already in § 29.4. They are fixed-shape solutions in which the motion of each particle in space is a nearly-circular ellipse, with period $2\pi/\omega$, and its motion relative to the rotating axes is approximately an ellipse in the neighbourhood of the equilibrium position. In this case the periods are exactly, not merely approximately, equal to $2\pi/\omega$.

If the stability condition $k < \frac{1}{4}$ is satisfied, there is another set of periodic motions in the neighbourhood of the equilibrium solution, with periods approximating to $2\pi/n_3$. Neither of the numbers $\dfrac{\omega}{n_3}$, $\dfrac{n_2}{n_3}$ is an integer, since

(30.6.5) $$1 < \frac{\omega^2}{{n_3}^2} < 2, \quad 0 < \frac{{n_2}^2}{{n_3}^2} < 1,$$

so the requisite conditions are fulfilled. The existence of these periodic solutions is a new result, not deducible from § 29.4.

Finally, if $k < \frac{1}{4}$, there is a third set of periodic solutions near the equilibrium solution, with periods approximating to $2\pi/n_2$, if neither $\dfrac{\omega}{n_2}$ nor $\dfrac{n_3}{n_2}$ is an integer. Now $\dfrac{\omega}{n_2}$ is an integer ν (> 1) if

(30.6.6) $$\frac{1}{\frac{1}{2} - \sqrt{(\frac{1}{4} - k)}} = \nu^2,$$

giving

(30.6.7) $$k = \frac{\nu^2 - 1}{\nu^4};$$

and $\dfrac{n_3}{n_2}$ is an integer ν (> 1) if

(30.6.8) $$\frac{\frac{1}{2} + \sqrt{(\frac{1}{4} - k)}}{\frac{1}{2} - \sqrt{(\frac{1}{4} - k)}} = \nu^2,$$

giving

(30.6.9) $$k = \left(\frac{\nu}{\nu^2 + 1}\right)^2.$$

Thus the third set of periodic motions exists in the neighbourhood of the equilibrium solution, provided that k is not a rational number of the form (30.6.7) or of the form (30.6.9).

30.7 Systems involving a parameter. We now consider systems in which the functions X_r in the equations of motion contain a parameter μ. The equations take the form

$$\dot{x}_r = X_r(x_1, x_2, \ldots, x_m; \mu) = X_r(\mathbf{x}; \mu), \tag{30.7.1}$$

and we now assume the functions X_r to be regular functions of the (complex) variables $x_1, x_2, \ldots, x_m, \mu$ in a suitable domain. Poincaré proposed the following question: "If a periodic motion is known to exist when the parameter μ has a particular value μ_0, do periodic motions exist for values of μ sufficiently near to μ_0?" We can take μ_0, without loss of generality, to be zero, and then the question is: "If a periodic motion exists for $\mu = 0$, do periodic motions exist for all sufficiently small values of μ?"

As a concrete illustration, consider again the restricted problem of three bodies (Chapter XXVIII). We now suppose the ratio β/α to be capable of adjustment, but with $\alpha + \beta$ and l fixed, so the angular velocity ω has the fixed value $\gamma(\alpha + \beta)/l^3$, as in (28.2.1). We take $\mu = \beta/(\alpha + \beta)$. The value $\mu = 0$ corresponds to $\beta = 0$, so if $\mu = 0$ the problem of the motion of the planetoid is simply the problem of motion under the attraction of a fixed Newtonian centre. In this case there certainly exist periodic motions (relative to the rotating axes). For example, there are the elliptic orbits (relative to fixed axes) with period $2\pi/\omega$; and, what is more germane to our present purpose, there are the uniform motions in a circle about A (which is coincident with G when $\mu = 0$) as centre. Is it true that periodic motions still exist for sufficiently small positive values of μ?

Let the general solution of the equations (cf. (21.1.4)) be denoted by

$$x_r = \varphi_r(x_1{}^0, x_2{}^0, \ldots, x_m{}^0; \mu; t) = \varphi(\mathbf{x}^0; \mu; t), \tag{30.7.2}$$

where $\mathbf{x}^0$ is the starting point, the value of $\mathbf{x}$ at $t = 0$. We use a notation similar to that used in § 21.5, denoting the partial derivative $\partial\varphi_r/\partial x_s{}^0$ by φ_{rs}. We start from a known periodic solution (for $\mu = 0$) which is not an equilibrium solution: if $\mu = 0$ the solution starting from the point A, $\mathbf{x}^0 = \boldsymbol{\alpha}$, is periodic with period σ. Then we have

$$\mathbf{X}(\boldsymbol{\alpha}; 0) \neq \mathbf{0}, \tag{30.7.3}$$

$$\varphi_r(\boldsymbol{\alpha}; 0; 0) = \alpha_r, \qquad r = 1, 2, \ldots, m, \tag{30.7.4}$$

$$\varphi_r(\boldsymbol{\alpha}; 0; t + \sigma) = \varphi_r(\boldsymbol{\alpha}; 0; t), \qquad r = 1, 2, \ldots, m, \tag{30.7.5}$$

for all values of t.

But the last statement can be simplified: to say that (30.7.5) holds for all values of t is equivalent to saying that it holds for a particular value of t. This follows from the uniqueness of the solution. Thus we can safely replace (30.7.5) by the simpler equation

$$\varphi_r(\boldsymbol{\alpha}; 0; \sigma) = \alpha_r, \qquad r = 1, 2, \ldots, m. \tag{30.7.6}$$

Poincaré first asked the question: "If we replace the zero value of μ in the equations of motion by a small non-zero value, are there still periodic orbits with the same period σ?" Now such orbits will exist if, given $\mu \neq 0$, we can find $\beta_1, \beta_2, \ldots, \beta_m$ to satisfy the m equations

$$\varphi_r(\boldsymbol{\beta};\ \mu;\ \sigma) = \beta_r, \qquad r = 1, 2, \ldots, m. \tag{30.7.7}$$

We know that these equations have the solutions $\beta_r = \alpha_r$, if $\mu = 0$, and we can find solutions for sufficiently small values of μ if the determinant of the matrix

$$(\varphi_{rs}(\boldsymbol{\beta};\ \mu;\ t) - \delta_{rs}) \tag{30.7.8}$$

is not zero for $\boldsymbol{\beta} = \boldsymbol{\alpha}$, $\mu = 0$, $t = \sigma$. We call this matrix $\mathbf{F}$,

$$f_{rs} = \varphi_{rs}(\boldsymbol{\alpha};\ 0;\ \sigma) - \delta_{rs}, \tag{30.7.9}$$

and if

$$|\mathbf{F}| \neq 0 \tag{30.7.10}$$

we can solve the equations (30.7.7) for $\beta_1, \beta_2, \ldots, \beta_m$. The variables $\beta_r - \alpha_r$ are functions of μ, vanishing when $\mu = 0$, and each is expressible as a power series in μ without a constant term.

But this is fruitless, because in fact $|\mathbf{F}| = 0$ always. If we put $t = \sigma$ in (21.5.7) we have

$$\mathbf{F}\mathbf{X}(\boldsymbol{\alpha};\ 0) = \mathbf{0}, \tag{30.7.11}$$

in which the second member is the zero column matrix or vector. Since $\mathbf{X}(\boldsymbol{\alpha};\ 0)$ is not zero, it follows that

$$|\mathbf{F}| = 0. \tag{30.7.12}$$

We cannot deduce by this method that periodic solutions with period σ exist for values of μ near $\mu = 0$.

Now the reason why $|\mathbf{F}|$ is zero is apparent from § 21.5; it is due in essence to the fact that we can change the point A in which the orbit originates from $\boldsymbol{\alpha}$ to any other point on the orbit. This suggests that we may be able to avoid the embarrassment arising from the vanishing of $|\mathbf{F}|$ by restricting the displacement of A to a plane through $\boldsymbol{\alpha}$ normal to the given orbit, or indeed to any surface not tangent to the orbit at $\boldsymbol{\alpha}$. We know, from (30.7.3), that not all the components $X_r(\boldsymbol{\alpha};\ 0)$ vanish, and we may suppose, without loss of generality, that

$$X_m(\boldsymbol{\alpha};\ 0) \neq 0. \tag{30.7.13}$$

(If we wished we could go even further. We could choose locally rectangular coordinates with the tangent to the orbit at $\boldsymbol{\alpha}$, i.e. the direction of the vector $\mathbf{X}$ at $\boldsymbol{\alpha}$, as the direction of x_m increasing, and then all the components of $\mathbf{X}$ except X_m would vanish. But this seems hardly worth while in practice.) Let us then ask if a periodic orbit exists, for $\mu \neq 0$, with its initial point at $\boldsymbol{\beta}$, where $\beta_m = \alpha_m$ but $\beta_r \neq \alpha_r$ for all values of r less than m. We still have to satisfy m conditions, so we must now allow the period to vary, say from σ to τ, and the m conditions are

$$\varphi_r(\boldsymbol{\beta};\ \mu;\ \tau) = \boldsymbol{\beta}_r, \tag{30.7.14}$$

with the restriction $\beta_m = \alpha_m$. The m unknowns are now $\beta_1, \beta_2, \ldots, \beta_{m-1}, \tau$, and we know that the solution $\alpha_1, \alpha_2, \ldots, \alpha_{m-1}, \sigma$ exists if $\mu = 0$. We can find solutions (with $\beta_1 - \alpha_1, \beta_2 - \alpha_2, \ldots, \beta_{m-1} - \alpha_{m-1}, \tau - \sigma$ all vanishing at $\mu = 0$) if the determinant $|\mathbf{G}| \neq 0$, where the first $(m - 1)$ columns of the matrix $\mathbf{G}$ are the same as those of $\mathbf{F}$, and the last column is the vector $\mathbf{X}(\boldsymbol{\alpha};\ 0)$.

Now examples can be constructed in which the condition $|\mathbf{G}| \neq 0$ is fulfilled, and in these cases there are periodic solutions for $\mu \neq 0$ with period nearly equal to σ when μ is small. But in the cases of practical interest $|\mathbf{G}| = 0$, and again the method fails to prove that periodic orbits exist when μ is not zero.

The vanishing of $|\mathbf{G}|$ follows from the existence of Jacobi's integral, or indeed of any uniform space-integral. Suppose that $f(x_1, x_2, \ldots, x_m;\ \mu)$ is such an integral, and let us for the moment denote the derivative $\partial f/\partial x_r$ by f_r. We will assume that $f(\mathbf{x};\ 0)$ is not stationary at $\mathbf{x} = \boldsymbol{\alpha}$, so not all of the numbers $f_r(\boldsymbol{\alpha};\ 0)$ vanish. Then the first $(m - 1)$ of these numbers $f_r(\boldsymbol{\alpha};\ 0)$ cannot all vanish (in virtue of (21.1.9) and (30.7.13)) and we may suppose the variables so ordered that

(30.7.15) $$f_{m-1}(\boldsymbol{\alpha};\ 0) \neq 0.$$

Now f is constant along an orbit, so

(30.7.16) $$f\{\boldsymbol{\varphi}(\boldsymbol{\beta};\ \mu;\ t),\ \mu\} = f(\boldsymbol{\beta};\ \mu)$$

for all values of $\boldsymbol{\beta}$, μ, t. Hence, differentiating with respect to β_s,

(30.7.17) $$\sum_{r=1}^{m} f_r(\mathbf{x};\ \mu)\varphi_{rs}(\boldsymbol{\beta};\ \mu;\ t) = f_s(\boldsymbol{\beta};\ \mu), \qquad s = 1, 2, \ldots, m.$$

Putting $\boldsymbol{\beta} = \boldsymbol{\alpha}$, $\mu = 0$, $t = \sigma$, we can write (30.7.17) in the form

(30.7.18) $$\sum_{r=1}^{m} f_r(\boldsymbol{\alpha};\ 0)\{\varphi_{rs}(\boldsymbol{\alpha};\ 0;\ \sigma) - \delta_{rs}\} = 0,$$

or again in the form

(30.7.19) $$\mathbf{DF} = \mathbf{0},$$

where $\mathbf{D}$ is the row-matrix whose rth component is $f_r(\boldsymbol{\alpha};\ 0)$. Now we have also, from (21.1.9),

(30.7.20) $$\mathbf{DX}(\boldsymbol{\alpha};\ 0) = \mathbf{0},$$

and it follows from (30.7.19) and (30.7.20) that

(30.7.21) $$\mathbf{DG} = 0.$$

Since $\mathbf{D} \neq \mathbf{0}$ we see that $|\mathbf{G}| = 0$, which is the result stated above.

So far we have failed to prove the existence of periodic orbits when $\mu \neq 0$, but a slight modification of the attack will lead to success. Let us first consider the existence of periodic orbits with period σ. We put $\beta_m = \alpha_m$ as before, and begin by solving the $(m - 1)$ equations (30.7.7), for $r \neq m - 1$, for the $(m - 1)$ variables $\beta_1, \beta_2, \ldots, \beta_{m-1}$ as functions of μ. As usual the functions $\beta_1 - \alpha_1, \beta_2 - \alpha_2, \ldots, \beta_{m-1} - \alpha_{m-1}$ will be defined as power-series in μ without constant terms. The condition we need for the solution to be possible is $|\mathbf{H}| \neq 0$, where the matrix $\mathbf{H}$ is formed from $\mathbf{F}$ by omitting the $(m - 1)$th row and the mth column. Now if all but one of the equations (30.7.7) are satisfied, the remaining one must also be satisfied, because of Jacobi's integral. This is evident geometrically. To construct a formal proof, let us write $\bar{\beta}_r$ for $\varphi_r(\boldsymbol{\beta};\ \mu;\ \sigma)$, so that $\bar{\beta}_r = \beta_r$ except for $r = m - 1$. Since $f(\mathbf{x};\ \mu)$ is an integral

$$0 = f(\bar{\boldsymbol{\beta}};\ \mu) - f(\boldsymbol{\beta};\ \mu) = (\bar{\beta}_{m-1} - \beta_{m-1}) f_{m-1}(\bar{\bar{\boldsymbol{\beta}}};\ \mu), \tag{30.7.22}$$

where $\bar{\bar{\beta}}_r = \bar{\beta}_r = \beta_r$ unless $r = m - 1$, and $\bar{\bar{\beta}}_{m-1}$ lies between $\bar{\beta}_{m-1}$ and β_{m-1}. But $f_{m-1}(\boldsymbol{\alpha};\ 0) \neq 0$, so $f_{m-1}(\bar{\bar{\beta}};\ \mu) \neq 0$ if μ is sufficiently small, and therefore $\bar{\beta}_{m-1} = \beta_{m-1}$, and the remaining equation of (30.7.7) is also satisfied. Thus, provided $|\mathbf{H}| \neq 0$, there exist periodic orbits with period σ when $\mu \neq 0$.

Finally, if $\mu \neq 0$, there exist periodic orbits with prescribed period τ, where $\tau - \sigma$ is small enough, but not zero, and for which the constant value of the integral $f(\mathbf{x};\ \mu)$ is the same as it is for the original periodic orbit. This time we have to add to the $(m - 1)$ equations (30.7.14), for $r \neq m - 1$, the equation

$$f(\boldsymbol{\beta};\ \mu) = f(\boldsymbol{\alpha};\ 0). \tag{30.7.23}$$

We solve for the m variables $\beta_1, \beta_2, \ldots, \beta_{m-1}, \tau$, and we recognize again that $\beta_1 - \alpha_1, \beta_2 - \alpha_2, \ldots, \beta_{m-1} - \alpha_{m-1}, \tau - \sigma$ will appear as power series in μ without constant terms. The condition for the solution to be possible is $|\mathbf{K}| \neq 0$, where $\mathbf{K}$ is the matrix obtained from

$$\mathbf{L} = \begin{pmatrix} \mathbf{F} & \mathbf{X}(\boldsymbol{\alpha};\ 0) \\ \mathbf{D} & \mathbf{0} \end{pmatrix} \tag{30.7.24}$$

by omitting the $(m - 1)$th row and the mth column. Now the $(m - 1)$th row is linearly dependent on the other rows, from (30.7.19) and (30.7.20); and the mth column is linearly dependent on the other columns, from (30.7.11) and (30.7.20). Thus the condition we need is that the matrix (30.7.24) has rank m. If this is true, then there are periodic orbits with period τ ($\neq \sigma$) when $\mu \neq 0$.

It may appear at first sight that the analysis is of little value, since to construct the matrix $\mathbf{F}$ we need to know the solution (30.7.2) of the equations of motion. But this is not the case. We only need the values of φ_{rs} for $\boldsymbol{\beta} = \boldsymbol{\alpha}$, $\mu = 0$, $t = \sigma$, and for this purpose it suffices to know the solution of the linear approximation given by the variational equations, for the case $\mu = 0$, and this can always be found (Chapter XXIII). Thus the theory of Poincaré gives us a practicable method of proving the existence of periodic orbits.

30.8 Application to the restricted problem of three bodies. We suppose $\alpha + \beta$ and l fixed, so $\omega = \gamma(\alpha + \beta)/l^3$ is fixed throughout, and we take $\mu = \beta/(\alpha + \beta)$. The case $\mu = 0$ is the problem of motion under the attraction of a single fixed Newtonian centre. In this case, using the notation of § 28.2, the equations of motion are

$$\begin{cases} \ddot{x} - 2\omega\dot{y} = \partial W/\partial x, \\ \ddot{y} + 2\omega\dot{x} = \partial W/\partial y, \end{cases} \tag{30.8.1}$$

where

$$W = \tfrac{1}{2}\omega^2(x^2 + y^2) + \omega^2 \frac{l^3}{r}. \tag{30.8.2}$$

If we write u for $\dot{x}$ and v for $\dot{y}$ we obtain the system

$$(30.8.3)\qquad \begin{cases} \dot{x} = u, \\ \dot{y} = v, \\ \dot{u} = 2\omega v + \omega^2 x - \omega^2 l^3 \dfrac{x}{r^3}, \\ \dot{v} = -2\omega u + \omega^2 y - \omega^2 l^3 \dfrac{y}{r^3}. \end{cases}$$

The uniform motion in a circle of radius k given by

$$(30.8.4)\qquad x = ks, \quad y = -kc, \quad u = pkc, \quad v = pks,$$

where

$$(30.8.5)\qquad c = \cos pt, \quad s = \sin pt,$$

is a possible motion if

$$(30.8.6)\qquad k^3(p + \omega)^2 = l^3\omega^2.$$

This is evident by elementary reasoning, or by substitution in the equations of motion. The period σ of the motion relative to the rotating axes is $2\pi/|p|$. We must exclude the equilibrium solution $p = 0$. We must also exclude the cases $p = -\omega$ and $p = -2\omega$. The first of these would require an infinite value of k; the second must be excluded because it implies $k = l$, and if $\mu \neq 0$, the point $B((1 - \mu)l, 0)$ is a singular point, and this tends to a point on the circle $r = l$ as $\mu \to 0$.

Let us now, to come into line with the general theory, write x_1, x_2, x_3, x_4 for x, y, u, v, and let us establish the variational equations, writing

$$(30.8.7)\qquad x_1 = ks + y_1, \quad x_2 = -kc + y_2, \quad x_3 = pkc + y_3, \quad x_4 = pks + y_4.$$

Since

$$(30.8.8)\qquad r^2 = k^2 + 2k(y_1 s - y_2 c) + (y_1{}^2 + y_2{}^2),$$

$$(30.8.9)\qquad \frac{1}{r^3} = \frac{1}{k^3}\left(1 - 3\,\frac{y_1 s - y_2 c}{k} + \cdots\right),$$

and we readily find the variational equations

$$(30.8.10)\qquad \begin{cases} \dot{y}_1 = y_3, \\ \dot{y}_2 = y_4, \\ \dot{y}_3 = -(p^2 + 2p\omega)y_1 + 2\omega y_4 + 3(p + \omega)^2 s(y_1 s - y_2 c), \\ \dot{y}_4 = -(p^2 + 2p\omega)y_2 - 2\omega y_3 - 3(p + \omega)^2 c(y_1 s - y_2 c). \end{cases}$$

If we transform to the new variables z, where

$$(30.8.11)\qquad z_1 = y_1 s - y_2 c, \quad z_2 = y_1 c + y_2 s, \quad z_3 = y_3 s - y_4 c, \quad z_4 = y_3 c + y_4 s,$$

the equations for the z's are linear equations with constant coefficients,

$$(30.8.12)\qquad \begin{cases} \dot{z}_1 = pz_2 + z_3, \\ \dot{z}_2 = -pz_1 + z_4, \\ \dot{z}_3 = (2p^2 + 4p\omega + 3\omega^2)z_1 + (p + 2\omega)z_4, \\ \dot{z}_4 = -(p + 2\omega)(pz_2 + z_3). \end{cases}$$

The solution is

$$(30.8.13)\qquad \begin{cases} z_1 = -2A - (\theta C + \varphi S), \\ z_2 = B + 3(p + \omega)At - 2(\varphi C - \theta S), \\ z_3 = -p\{B + 3(p + \omega)At\} + (p - \omega)(\varphi C - \theta S), \\ z_4 = (p + 3\omega)A + (p + 2\omega)(\theta C + \varphi S), \end{cases}$$

where

$$(30.8.14)\qquad C = \cos(p + \omega)t, \quad S = \sin(p + \omega)t,$$

and A, B, θ, φ are the constants defined by

$$(30.8.15)\qquad \begin{cases} (p + \omega)A = (p + 2\omega)\gamma_2 - \gamma_3, \\ (p + \omega)B = -(p - \omega)\gamma_1 + 2\gamma_4, \\ (p + \omega)\theta = -(p + 3\omega)\gamma_2 + 2\gamma_3, \\ (p + \omega)\varphi = -p\gamma_1 + \gamma_4, \end{cases}$$

where γ_r is the initial value of y_r. Hence, $(p + \omega)\mathbf{L}$ is the matrix

(30.8.16)

$$\begin{bmatrix} -2p(1-C) & 3(p+\omega)(p+2\omega)\sigma - 2(p+3\omega)S & -3(p+\omega)\sigma + 4S & 2(1-C) & pk(p+\omega) \\ -pS & (p+3\omega)(1-C) & -2(1-C) & S & 0 \\ -p(p+2\omega)S & (p+2\omega)(p+3\omega)(1-C) & -2(p+2\omega)(1-C) & (p+2\omega)S & 0 \\ -p(p-\omega)(1-C) & 3p(p+\omega)(p+2\omega)\sigma - (p-\omega)(p+3\omega)S & -3p(p+\omega)\sigma + 2(p-\omega)S & (p-\omega)(1-C) & p^2k(p+\omega) \\ 0 & -pk(p+\omega)(p+2\omega) & pk(p+\omega) & 0 & 0 \end{bmatrix}$$

where now

$$(30.8.17)\qquad C = \cos(p + \omega)\sigma = \cos 2\pi\frac{\omega}{p}, \quad S = \sin(p + \omega)\sigma = \sin 2\pi\frac{\omega}{p}.$$

The predictions of the theory are easily verified. The matrix $\mathbf{F}$ is obtained from $\mathbf{L}$ by omitting the fifth row and the fifth column. It is evident, as we expect, that the third row of $\mathbf{F}$ is not independent of the other rows, and that the fourth column of $\mathbf{F}$ is not independent of the other columns. The determinant of the 3×3 matrix $\mathbf{H}$ obtained by omitting this row and column is

$$(30.8.18)\qquad -24\pi\sin^2\frac{\omega\pi}{p},$$

and there are periodic solutions with period σ for sufficiently small values of μ if

$$(30.8.19)\qquad p \neq \pm\frac{\omega}{\nu},$$

where ν is a positive integer. The value $p = -\omega$ has already been excluded, and, as we have seen, we must also reject the values $p = 0$ and $p = -2\omega$.

Next, the matrix $\mathbf{G}$ obtained from $\mathbf{L}$ by omitting the fifth row and the fourth column, is clearly singular, as we expect from the theory. The matrix $\mathbf{K}$ is obtained from $\mathbf{L}$ by omitting the third row and the fourth column, and

$$(30.8.20)\qquad |\mathbf{K}| = -4p^3k^2\sin^2\frac{\omega\pi}{p}.$$

The prohibited values of p are the same as before, and therefore, provided p has not one of these values, there are periodic motions with period $\tau \neq \sigma$ if μ is sufficiently small.

In each case the periodic motion is periodic relative to the rotating axes.

30.9 Fixed-point theory. The method of § 30.8 establishes the existence of periodic orbits, under certain circumstances, for small values of the parameter μ. But it does not, in the first instance, prove the existence of these orbits for larger values of μ. Poincaré attacked this problem through the theory of transformations having a fixed point.

It is easy to see how such theorems are associated with the existence of periodic orbits. Consider the usual equations

$$\dot{x}_r = X_r(\mathbf{x}), \qquad r = 1, 2, \ldots, m, \tag{30.9.1}$$

where the functions on the right are of class C_1 in a domain D of $(x_1, x_2, \ldots, x_m)$. Consider a plane parallel to $x_m = 0$, say the plane ϖ defined by $x_m = \alpha_m$. Let A be the set of points of ϖ at which $X_m > 0$, and let β be a domain of A with the property that the orbits originating in points of β all lie in D. Let P be a point of β, and let us consider a mobile, whose motion is defined by (30.9.1), starting from P.

The mobile moves into the region $x_m > 0$ (since $X_m > 0$ at P). It may happen that later it crosses from the region $x_m > 0$ to the region $x_m < 0$ (crossing ϖ at a point not belonging to A) and that later still it crosses again from the region $x_m < 0$ to the region $x_m > 0$, this time crossing ϖ in a point P' of A. (The figure illustrates the case $m = 2$.) The transformation from P to P', say $P' = TP$, is a topological mapping of β onto a region β' of A.

Now if the mapping $P' = TP$ has a fixed point P_0, so that

$$TP_0 = P_0, \tag{30.9.2}$$

the orbit through P_0 is periodic. More generally, if there is a point P_0 such that for some positive integer n

$$T^n P_0 = P_0, \tag{30.9.3}$$

then again the orbit through P_0 is periodic.

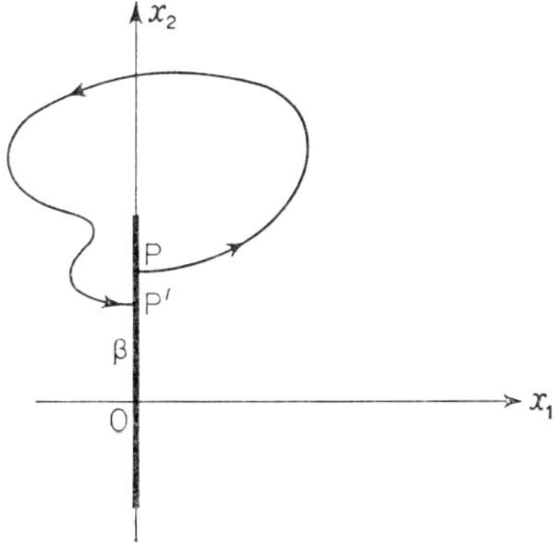

Figure 30.9

If div $\mathbf{X} = 0$, a condition which is, as we know, always satisfied by the Hamiltonian equations, the integral

$$\int X_m \, dx_1, dx_2 \cdots dx_{m-1}, \tag{30.9.4}$$

taken over a region of β, is invariant under the transformation T. The proof has already been given effectively in § 22.17 (cf. equation (22.17.1)).

30.10 Poincaré's ring theorem. There is one particular fixed-point theorem with which the name of Poincaré is most closely associated; it is sometimes spoken of as *Poincaré's last theorem*, or as *Poincaré's ring theorem*. In his exhaustive study of the restricted problem of three bodies, Poincaré was led to believe that the existence of an infinity of periodic orbits (in the motion relative to the rotating axes), for all values of μ $(= \beta/(\alpha + \beta))$, not merely for small values of μ, would follow from the truth of the theorem. He failed to produce a satisfactory proof of the theorem, though he was convinced of its truth; the theorem was proved after Poincaré's death by G. D. Birkhoff. The theorem is as follows.

We consider the annular region bounded by the circles $r = a$ and $r = b$, where $0 < a < b$. There is a topological mapping of the closed region $a \leqslant r \leqslant b$ onto itself, defined by the equations

$$(30.10.1) \qquad r' = \varphi(r, \theta), \quad \theta' = \psi(r, \theta).$$

The mapping has the following properties:

(i) it is measure-preserving,

(ii) it is such that each of the bounding circles is mapped onto itself, i.e. $\varphi(a, \theta) = a$ and $\varphi(b, \theta) = b$,

(iii) it is such that the points on $r = a$ move anti-clockwise in the mapping, and points on $r = b$ move clockwise, i.e. $\psi(a, \theta) > \theta$ and $\psi(b, \theta) < \theta$.

The theorem asserts that, when these conditions are fulfilled, the mapping has two fixed points.

There is the difficulty that $\psi(r, \theta)$ is in the first instance only defined to mod 2π; however the difficulty is not serious, because the fixing of $\psi(r, \theta)$ at one point of the ring defines it throughout by continuity. The theorem is still valid if we replace the measure-preserving property of the transformation by the weaker condition that there exists an invariant integral with positive integrand. It is still valid if we replace the measure-preserving property by the still weaker condition that no region is transformed into part of itself.

The ingenious, but largely intuitive, argument by which Poincaré connected the existence of periodic orbits with the truth of the ring theorem is open to criticism at various points, and is not entirely convincing; nevertheless it may be worth recording on account of its intrinsic interest and because of its importance in the history of the subject. A brief account is given in the next section.

30.11 Periodic orbits and the ring theorem. Let us consider a dynamical system with two degrees of freedom. We describe the configuration of the system by Lagrangian coordinates x, y, and we picture the motion of the system as the motion of the mobile (x, y) in the plane $z = 0$. The system is such that it possesses an integral of the type

$$(30.11.1) \qquad \tfrac{1}{2}(\dot{x}^2 + \dot{y}^2) + W = h,$$

where W is a given function of (x, y). Then the motion takes place in the region β defined by $W < h$, and we consider a value of h for which the region β is the interior of a simple closed oval curve α.

The problem in which we are primarily interested is the restricted problem of three bodies, when we consider the motion of the planetoid relative to the rotating axes (§ 28.2). An integral of the requisite type exists, namely (28.2.6), with $W = -\gamma U$; and if $-h > \gamma U_3$ the region $W < h$ consists in part of one or two interior regions bounded externally by closed oval curves, and in part by an exterior region bounded internally by a closed oval curve (Figs. 28.6a, b). In each case an interior region is the region β with which we are concerned here.

At each point of β the velocity is determined as to magnitude by (30.11.1), but its direction is arbitrary. Let this direction be inclined at an angle ψ to Ox, where

$0 \leqslant \psi < 2\pi$. Thus to each point of β there corresponds an infinity of *elements*, the term element comprising both speed and direction. At each point of the bounding curve α the velocity is zero, so effectively only one element corresponds to a point of α. This remark suggests the geometrical representation which follows.

First we make a topological mapping of the region β onto a region β' which is the interior of a circle, and α is mapped onto the circumference α' of the circle. We now consider the motion in the region β' into which the original motion is transformed (cf. § 21.2). Let M be a point of β', M' the inverse of M with respect to the circle α', and let us construct the circle Γ which has MM' as diameter, and which lies in a plane perpendicular to the plane of β'. To each element through M we correlate one point of Γ, the direction of the trajectory at M determining the particular point of Γ; for example we can take $\psi' = 0$ to correspond to M', $\psi' = \pi$ to M, and $0 < \psi' < \pi$ to points $z > 0$. (Here $z = 0$ is the plane of β', ψ' the inclination of the element in the transformed motion to Ox.) If $M \in \beta'$ there are an infinity of related points, one for each element; if $M \in \alpha'$ there is only one related point. Thus to each element there corresponds one point of space, and conversely.

The trajectories are thus represented by the members C of a family κ of twisted curves in space, and one and only one curve C passes through each point of space. We notice that the representation of the trajectory changes if the direction of motion is reversed. The closed curves C represent the periodic orbits.

Suppose now that there is a periodic orbit G_0 which has first-order stability (§ 23.1); it will be convenient to choose the unit of time so that the period is 2π. Let C_0 be the closed curve of the family κ that corresponds to G_0, and let A be an area bounded by C_0 and lying on a curved surface S. We assume that A is simply-connected, and that it is *without contact*, i.e. none of the curves C is tangent to S at a point of A. (Compare the notion of a segment without contact in § 20.3.)

Let P be a point of A. Through P there passes just one curve C, and we follow this curve until it meets A again in P'; we call P' the *consequent* of P. The transformation T which transforms P into P' is a topological mapping of A onto itself.

It might appear possible for the transformation to be discontinuous, say when P is at Q, but in fact this is impossible. For example, if P, P', P'', P''', ... are successive points of intersection of C with A, it might at first sight seem to be possible that, as P moves from Q, P' and P'' first coalesce, and then become imaginary, so that the consequent of P becomes P'''. But this is prohibited by the condition that A is without contact. The appearance of two new intersections between P and P' (so that the consequent of P becomes a point P_1 instead of P') is impossible for the same reason. Again, as P moves from a position Q, P' cannot cross C_0, since no curve C can pass through a point of C_0 except C_0 itself.

The transformation T admits a positive invariant integral; the proof is similar to that given in § 22.17. If P coincides with P', or with any of the later consequents P'', P''', ..., the curve C is closed, and the trajectory that it represents is periodic.

Now let us consider the nature of the transformation T when P is a point of A very near to the bounding curve C_0. Let C_1 be the curve through P of the class K, so that C_1 represents a trajectory G_1 which is very near to G_0. To find an approximation to the equations defining C_1 we appeal to the theory of § 23.4. We choose a particular system of coordinates u, v, w such that (1) the coordinates of a point of a trajectory depend only on u and v, while the direction of the element depends also on w, and (2) the equations of C_0 are $v = w = 0$, while u varies from 0 to 2π as we make a circuit of the closed curve C_0. Now in the motion on C_0

$$t = u + \varphi(u), \tag{30.11.2}$$

where $\varphi(u)$ is periodic with period 2π. If the characteristic exponents for the stable periodic orbit G_0 are $(0, 0, i\alpha, -i\alpha)$, as in § 23.5, we can write the equations of C_1 in the form

$$\frac{v}{a} = \rho \sin(\tau + \eta), \quad \frac{w}{a} = \rho_1 \sin(\tau + \eta) + \rho_2 \cos(\tau + \eta), \tag{30.11.3}$$

where a and η are constants of integration, a being small, and τ is written for αt, so that

$$\tau = \alpha u + \alpha\varphi(u), \tag{30.11.4}$$

and τ increases always with u.

We obtain the points of intersection of G_1 with G_0 by putting $v = 0$, giving

$$\tau + \eta = N\pi, \tag{30.11.5}$$

where N is an integer. If M_1 is one point of intersection, and M_2 is the next following intersection, M_2 is called the *kinetic focus* of M_1. If τ_1 and τ_2 are the values of τ at M_1 and M_2 on C_1, we have

$$\tau_2 - \tau_1 = \pi. \tag{30.11.6}$$

If the equation of the surface S containing A is

$$F(u, v, w) = 0, \tag{30.11.7}$$

and if we expand F in powers of v and w, there is no term of degree zero, since F contains the curve C_0 defined by $v = w = 0$. The linear approximation is therefore of the form

$$g_1 v + g_2 w = 0, \tag{30.11.8}$$

where g_1 and g_2 are periodic functions of u. To find the intersections of C_1 with A we substitute for v and w from (30.11.3) in (30.11.8), giving

$$p_1 \sin(\tau + \eta) + p_2 \cos(\tau + \eta) = 0, \tag{30.11.9}$$

where p_1 and p_2 are periodic functions of u. We can write (30.11.9) in the form

$$R \sin(\tau + \lambda + \eta) = 0, \tag{30.11.10}$$

where $\tan\lambda = p_2/p_1$. Thus λ is a function of u whose derivative is periodic, so λ has the form $mu + \psi(u)$, where m is an integer and $\psi(u)$ is periodic. The points in which C_1 meets A are given by (30.11.10), so $\tau + \lambda + \eta$ must be a multiple of π; but since the area A is bounded by C_0, and does not extend beyond C_0, only even multiples of π appear, and

$$\tau + \lambda + \eta = 2k\pi, \tag{30.11.11}$$

where k is an integer. If P_1 and P_2 are two consecutive points of intersection, we have

$$(\tau_2 + \lambda_2) - (\tau_1 + \lambda_1) = 2\pi, \tag{30.11.12}$$

where τ_2, λ_2 refer to P_2 and τ_1, λ_1 to P_1.

The function $\tau + \lambda$ is a monotonic function of u. We prove this as follows. If we denote the first member of (30.11.10) by $f(u, v, w)$, there is a point on C_1 at which it touches A if there is a value of u at which $f = f' = 0$, i.e. at which

$$\begin{cases} R \sin(\tau + \lambda + \eta) = 0, \\ R' \sin(\tau + \lambda + \eta) + R(\tau' + \lambda') \cos(\tau + \lambda + \eta) = 0. \end{cases} \tag{30.11.13}$$

If $\tau' + \lambda'$ vanishes for some value u_0 of u, we can choose for η the value of $-(\tau + \lambda)$ at u_0, and then both the equations (30.11.13) are satisfied. But this is impossible, since A is without contact. Thus $\tau' + \lambda'$ never vanishes; therefore it always has the same sign, and without loss of generality we may suppose that $\tau' + \lambda'$ is always positive.

We introduce, in place of u, the new variable

$$\mu = \frac{\tau + \lambda}{\alpha + m} \tag{30.11.14}$$

which increases steadily with u; when we make a complete circuit of C_0, μ increases by 2π. We can use μ instead of u to define the position of a point on C_0. If P_1 is very near to C_0, and P_2 is its consequent, we have

$$\mu_2 - \mu_1 = \frac{2\pi}{\alpha + m}, \tag{30.11.15}$$

where μ_1 is the value of μ at P_1 and μ_2 is the value of μ at P_2.

Now consider a topological mapping of the area A onto the interior of a circle, so that, using polar coordinates, C_0 becomes the circle $r = b$, and such that, on this circle, $\theta = \mu$. The transformation T is such that the circle $r = b$ is mapped onto itself, and such that in this transformation, each point on the circle is moved through the angle $2\pi/(\alpha + m)$. Now such a mapping has an odd number of fixed points, and to each of these points there corresponds a periodic orbit. One at least of these has first-order stability; let P_0 be the corresponding point. We now make a further topological mapping of the interior of the circle onto itself, the mapping being such that P_0 becomes the centre, and such that the effect of T at points of the circumference is as before. Thus we have a transformation T which leaves the centre of the circle unchanged, and maps the circumference onto itself in such a way that all points of the circumference move anti-clockwise through the same angle.

Our next objective must be to determine the effect of the transformation at points very near to the centre of the circle.

Let C_0' be the periodic orbit through P_0, and let us choose a system of coordinates u', v', w'. These coordinates differ from those formerly introduced for C_0, because this time we suppose the equation of the surface S containing A to be $u' = 0$. With this choice of coordinates it is no longer possible to arrange that u' and v' alone determine a point of the trajectory, and that a change in the value of w' only changes the direction of the element; but this is not important. The equations of a curve C very near to C_0' are

$$\frac{v'}{a'} = \rho' \sin(\tau' + \eta'), \quad \frac{w'}{a'} = \rho_1' \sin(\tau' + \eta') + \rho_2' \cos(\tau' + \eta'), \tag{30.11.16}$$

where a' is small,

$$\tau' = \beta u' + \psi(u'), \tag{30.11.17}$$

where ψ is periodic, and the characteristic exponents for the stable periodic orbit C_0' are $(0, 0, i\beta, -i\beta)$. When u' changes by 2π, τ' changes by $2\pi\beta$. We can choose the polar coordinates so that, for points near P_0 (i.e. for small values of r),

$$\frac{v'}{r} = \rho' \sin\theta, \quad \frac{w'}{r} = \rho_1' \sin\theta + \rho_2' \cos\theta, \tag{30.11.18}$$

approximately, where ρ', ρ_1', ρ_2' have the values for $u' = 0$.

If P is a point near the centre P_0. when we pass from P to its consequent P', u' increases by 2π, and θ increases by $2\pi\beta$; or, since θ is only determined to mod 2π, θ increases by $2\pi(\beta + n)$, where n is an integer. The value of n is fixed throughout by continuity when its value at one point has been prescribed.

Consider now the transformation T^p, where p is a positive integer, which maps the interior of the circle onto itself, and the circumference onto itself. The transformation admits a positive invariant integral. If $T(r, \theta) = (r', \theta')$ we know that on $r = b$,

$$\theta' - \theta = 2\pi\frac{p}{\alpha + m}, \tag{30.11.19}$$

and near $r = 0$,

$$\theta' - \theta = 2\pi p(\beta + \eta). \tag{30.11.20}$$

We do not alter the transformation if we replace θ' by θ'', where $\theta'' = \theta' - 2q\pi$, where q is an integer, and then, on $r = b$,

$$\theta'' - \theta = 2\pi\left(\frac{p}{\alpha + m} - q\right) \tag{30.11.21}$$

and near $r = 0$,

$$\theta'' - \theta = 2\pi\{p(\beta + n) - q\}. \tag{30.11.22}$$

We choose n so that $(\alpha + m)(\beta + n) \neq 1$, and then we can choose an infinity of pairs of values of p and q such that either

$$\frac{1}{\alpha + m} > \frac{q}{p} > \beta + n, \tag{30.11.23}$$

or

$$\frac{1}{\alpha + m} < \frac{q}{p} < \beta + n, \tag{30.11.24}$$

and the conditions of Poincaré's ring theorem (for the case when the inner radius tends to zero) are fulfilled. Hence, if the theorem is true, and if one stable periodic orbit G_0 exists, an infinity of periodic orbits exists.

30.12 Proof of Poincaré's ring theorem. We now turn to the proof of the theorem enunciated in § 30.10. We plot the ring $a \leqslant r \leqslant b$ onto the strip $0 \leqslant y \leqslant 1$ in the (x, y)-plane by means of the transformation

$$x = \frac{\theta}{2\pi}, \quad y = \frac{r^2 - a^2}{b^2 - a^2}. \tag{30.12.1}$$

The measure-preserving property (i) of the transformation T persists in the new coordinates. We write

$$T(x, y) = (x', y'), \tag{30.12.2}$$

and we notice that, on $y = 0$,

$$x' > x, \quad y' = 0, \tag{30.12.3}$$

and on $y = 1$,

$$x' < x, \quad y' = 1. \tag{30.12.4}$$

If we divide the strip into squares by drawing the lines $x = n$, where n is an integer, we have a periodic structure, since congruent points in the various squares all represent the same point of the ring.

We prove first that the transformation has one fixed point.

In the proof we shall use all three of the conditions enumerated in § 30.10, and the theorem may fail if we drop one of them. Consider for example a transformation in which first each concentric circle is rotated, positively for $r > \frac{1}{2}(a + b)$ and negatively for $r < \frac{1}{2}(a + b)$, and then the points of the circles are moved radially outwards. As a concrete example, suppose that

$$\theta' = \theta + k\{r - \tfrac{1}{2}(a + b)\}, \quad r' = r + \frac{1}{2(b - a)}\{(b - r)(r - a)\}, \tag{30.12.5}$$

where $k > 0$. This transformation has no fixed point, since $\theta' \neq \theta$ unless $r = \frac{1}{2}(a + b)$, and if $r = \frac{1}{2}(a + b)$, $r' > r$.

If we denote the point (x, y) by p, and the point (x', y') by p', we can write (30.12.2) in the form $Tp = p'$. The attack starts from the supposition that no fixed point exists; we shall find that this supposition is untenable, since it leads to a contradiction. We denote the vector directed from p to p' by $\mathbf{V}p$, its magnitude by $R(p)$, and its inclination to Ox by $\psi(p)$. Since the transformation has no fixed point, $R(p)$ has a positive lower bound H. The angle $\psi(p)$ is defined to mod 2π; on the lower boundary L_0, $y = 0$, ψ has the value $2m\pi$, and on the upper boundary L_1, $y = 1$, ψ has the values $(2n + 1)\pi$, where m and n are integers. We can take $m = 0$ at all points of L_0 without loss of generality. Then $\psi(p)$ is defined, by continuity, as a one valued and continuous function of p in the strip $0 \leqslant y \leqslant 1$. In particular, the integer n has the same value at all points of L_1. Consider two paths A_0A_1, B_0B_1, and joining a point of L_0 to a point of L_1; each of the paths cuts any line $y = y_0$ in only one point. Let us consider a continuous deformation of one curve into the other, the points moving horizontally. The increment in $\psi(p)$ as p moves along the curve from L_0 to L_1 varies continuously, and thus the value of $\psi(p)$ on L_1 cannot jump, during the deformation, from one odd multiple of π to another.

Actually $n = 0$; the value of ψ at all points of L_1 is π. This is the crucial point of the argument.

To prove that $n = 0$, we introduce a new transformation U, which is the transformation T follows by a vertical displacement ε, where $0 < \varepsilon < H$,

$$U(x, y) = (x', y' + \varepsilon). \tag{30.12.6}$$

The transformation U is area-preserving, and has no fixed point, and it plots the strip $0 \leqslant y \leqslant 1$ onto the strip $\varepsilon \leqslant y \leqslant 1 + \varepsilon$.

The transformation U transforms L_0 into the line K_1, $y = \varepsilon$; it transforms K_1 into a curve K_2, nowhere intersecting K_1, and so on (Fig. 30.13). The strip S_0 between L_0 and K_1 is mapped onto the strip S_1 between K_1 and K_2, and so on. The curves $K_1, K_2, K_3, \ldots$, are repeated periodically in each unit interval, and the area of the strip S_r between $x = 0$ and $x = 1$ is ε. The area (in $0 < x < 1$) beneath K_r is $r\varepsilon$, so for large integers r, K_r must have points above L_1. Let n be the least such integer. Then we can find a point p_0 on L_0 such that $U^n p_0$ lies on or above L_1.

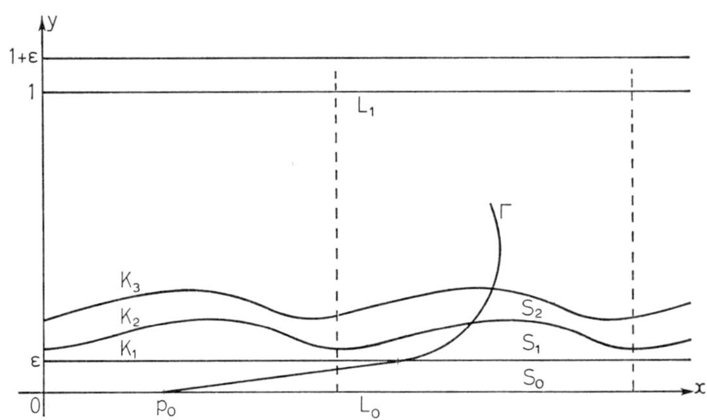

Figure 30.13

Consider now the straight line joining p_0 (on L_0) to Up_0 (on K_1). The transformation U transforms the points of this segment into the points of an arc lying in S_1, joining a point of K_1 to a point of K_2. The transformation U transforms the points of this arc into the points of an arc lying in S_2, and so on. We thus construct a simple curve Γ joining p_0 (on L_0) to $U^n p_0$ (on or above L_1).

Let us now consider how $\psi(p)$ varies as p moves along Γ from p_0 to $U^{n-1}p_0$. If ε is small, $\psi(p)$ is small and positive when p is at p_0, and $\psi(p)$ is near $(2n + 1)\pi$ when p is at $U^{n-1}p_0$. We wish to trace the change in the inclination of the chord joining p to Up as p moves on Γ; at each stage the lower end of the chord lies say in S_r and the upper end in S_{r+1}, or the lower end lies on K_r and the upper on K_{r+1}.

Now the change in the inclination of the chord is the same as the change produced in two stages as follows. In the first stage the lower end of the chord is fixed at p_0 and the upper end q moves from Up_0 to $U^n p_0$. In the second stage the upper end of the chord is fixed at $U^n p_0$, and the lower end q moves from p_0 to $U^{n-1}p_0$. But in each of these stages the increment in the inclination of the chord is less than π; the total change is less than 2π, so n can only be zero. Thus $\psi(p) = \pi$ when p lies on L_1, and this is the result we set out to prove.

By the same argument, if we consider the inverse transformation T^{-1}, the change in the inclination of the chord joining p to $T^{-1}p$, as p moves from L_0 to L_1, must be $-\pi$. But in fact the variation in the inclination of the chord joining p to Tp is identically the same as the variation in the inclination of the chord joining Tp to p.

We thus reach a contradiction, and the hypothesis that no invariant point exists cannot hold.

To prove that there are two invariant points, we have only to observe that the variation in $\psi(p)$ as p moves round the perimeter of the unit square is zero. But the change in $\psi(p)$ when p moves round a simple closed contour enclosing only one invariant point is $\pm 2\pi$ (cf. § 20.1). Therefore there must be at least two invariant points inside the unit square.

Notes

§ 1.2 The terms Libration motion and Limitation motion, and an account of the theory from a somewhat different point of view, will be found in C. L. Charlier, Die Mechanik des Himmels, (Leipzig, 1902) erster Band, pp. 85–97.

§ 1.8 Heinrich Hertz was a man of extraordinary genius, who, in his short life (he died before reaching the end of his thirty-sixth year) made two contributions of the first importance in science—the detection of wireless waves, and the book on the principles of mechanics (**6**). In this book Hertz emphasized and considered at length the distinction between holonomic and non-holonomic systems. The term holonomic comes from *ὅλος* (whole) and *νόμος* (laws).

§ 3.1 A result equivalent to the first form of the fundamental equation is given by Lagrange, Mécanique Analytique, (1811 Edition) Tome I, p. 251.

§ 3.7 Hamilton's principle appears, rather incidentally, in the first of his great papers of 1834 (**16**).

§ 3.8 The simple example given here (to show that the varied path is not in general a possible path if the system is not holonomic) seems to be the most natural illustration to use. It has probably been discovered independently many times, perhaps by nearly every worker in this field. It occurs, for example, in Hölder's famous paper on the variation principles of dynamics (*Göttinger Nachrichten*, 1896, p. 122). Other examples will be found in § 5.11.

§ 4.3 For the original account of Gauss's principle of Least Constraint, see the paper, Über ein neues allgemeines Grundgesetz der Mechanik, *Crelle's Journal*, iv (1829), p. 232.

§ 5.1 Lagrangian coordinates are introduced in the Mécanique Analytique, p. 305 of Tome I in the edition of 1811. Lagrange wrote $\xi, \psi, \varphi, \ldots$ where we write $q_1, q_2, q_3, \ldots$

§ 5.2 The method of approximation to the period of the simple pendulum, using the sequences of arithmetic and geometric means, is due to Mr. A. E. Ingham.

§§ 5.4, 5.5, 5.6 This very summary account of the elliptic motion could be magnified enormously, and even though the discussion is carried a little further later (§ 18.12) it is still inadequate for the purposes of the professional astronomer. An account of the various expansions connected with the elliptic motion will be found in treatises on Astronomy, for example in Wintner (**29**), Chapter IV.

§ 7.5 Corresponding to the theory of screws there is a theory relating to a system of forces acting on a rigid body. If we choose an arbitrary origin O the system of forces can be reduced to a force $\mathbf{F}$ through O and a couple $\mathbf{N}$. It is possible to choose the position of O so that $\mathbf{N}$ is parallel to $\mathbf{F}$, i.e. the plane of the couple is at right angles to the direction of the force. The system reduced in this way is called a *wrench.*

There is an elaborate theory of screws and wrenches; see for example R. S. Ball, A Treatise on the Theory of Screws (Cambridge, 1900).

§ 9.2 Both Lagrange (in the first edition of the Mécanique Analytique, 1788, and again in the second edition, 1811, published three years before his death) and Laplace (in the Mécanique Céleste, Première Partie, Livre II, Art. 57) made the mistake of supposing that equality among the eigenvalues necessarily implies terms in the solution of the form $t \cos pt$ or $te^{\lambda t}$, and that therefore for stability the eigenvalues must be all different. That such terms do sometimes occur when two eigenvalues are equal will be proved in § 23.3; but they do not occur in the case here considered, that of small oscillations about a position of minimum potential energy. This is evident, without more detailed analysis, from the equation of energy (§ 9.1). The error was noticed by Weierstrass in 1858 and by Routh in 1877. There is a well-known comment by Thomson and Tait (Treatise on National Philosophy, 1912 edition, Part I, Art. 343*m*): "It would be curious if such an error had remained for twenty-three years in Lagrange's mind. It could scarcely have existed even during the writing and printing of the article for his last edition if he had been in the habit of considering particular applications of his splendid analytical work: if he had he would have seen that a proposition which asserted that the equilibrium of a particle in the bottom of a frictionless bowl is unstable if the bowl be a figure of revolution with its axis vertical, cannot be true."

§ 10.1 A more detailed account of gyroscopic systems is given by Thomson and Tait, Treatise on Natural Philosophy (**22**) 1912 edition, Part I, Art. 345. The Routhian function was introduced by Routh, The stability of motion, London, 1877.

§ 10.9 A closer approximation to the motion of Foucault's pendulum is given by T. J. I'A. Bromwich, *Proc. L. M. S.*, 2, Vol. 13, pp. 224–235.

§ 10.15 Some further developments of the ideas of this section will be found in J. le Roux, Principes mathématiques de la théorie de la Gravitation, Gauthier-Villars, Paris, 1931.

§ 12.5 The history of the Gibbs-Appell equations is remarkable. The equations were discovered by Willard Gibbs in 1879 (On the fundamental formulae of Dynamics, *American Journal of Mathematics*, II, 1879, pp. 49–64; collected papers, Vol. II, 1928). Gibbs established the equations for a holonomic system, but seems to have realized that they are also valid for a non-holonomic system. The importance and generality of the method was not appreciated at the time, and the discovery seems to have aroused little interest. In 1896 Appell published the first edition of his Mécanique Rationelle (**21**). This edition contains a serious error. The Lagrangian function for a non-holonomic system is expressed in terms of k velocity-components $\dot{q}_r$, and Lagrange's equations are derived from the Lagrangian function so obtained. (This fallacy has appeared many times in the history of Dynamics. See for example A. B. Basset, Motion of one solid on another, *Quarterly Journal of Pure and Applied Mathematics*, XLVIII, 1920, pp. 310–320.) After the appearance of the first edition Appell discovered the mistake, and he then set about the task of finding a form of the equations of motion that should be applicable immediately to holonomic and non-holonomic systems alike. The Gibbs-Appell equations were published in the *Comptes*

Rendus for 1899, and in the second edition of the Mécanique Rationelle, published in 1904.

§ 13.10 It is hardly necessary to remind the reader that Euler's equations, here found as a deduction from the Gibbs-Appell equations, are easily established otherwise by elementary methods. The equations were discovered by Euler, probably in 1758, and they appear in his book of 1765 (**3**). The date of the discovery is noteworthy. It is remarkable that Euler should have found the equations so long before the use of moving axes had become commonplace in mathematics; it is perhaps still more remarkable that he immediately recognized the value of his discovery.

§ 14.7 The name Bertrand's theorem is well-established, but it is not now easy to discover when it was first enunicated: it is given by Sturm, *Comptes Rendus* XIII (1841) p. 1046. Sturn recognized that Carnot's theorem and Bertrand's theorem are essentially the same (cf. § 14.7(iv)). Kelvin's theorem is in *Proc. Royal Society of Edinburgh* (1863) p. 113, and in Thomson and Tait, Natural Philosophy, 1912 edition, p. 286. The theorem that the gain in energy in Kelvin's theorem is greater than the loss of energy in Bertrand's theorem is given by G. I. Taylor, *Proc. London Math. Soc.*, Series 2, Vol. 21, p. 413.

§ 15.5 The Principal Function appears in the second of Hamilton's two great papers of 1834 (**16**).

§ 16.2 Hamilton's partial differential equation, and the special case of the Hamilton-Jacobi theorem in which the α's and β's are the initial values of the q's and p's, appear in the paper of 1834 quoted above. The complete theorem, for a more general choice of the α's and β's, was established by Jacobi in 1837(*Crelle's Journal*, XXVII, p. 97). See also Jacobi's lectures (**17**) p. 157.

§ 17.10 Other accounts of the problem of two fixed Newtonian centres will be found in Jacobi's lectures (**17**) pp. 221–231 and in C. L. Charlier, Die Mechanik des Himmels, Leipzig, 1902, erster Band, pp. 117–163.

§ 18.1 Liouville's system appears in *Journal de Math*, XIV (1849) p. 257. The integration can be achieved directly from Lagrange's equations without appeal to the Hamilton-Jacobi theorem; see for example Whittaker (**27**), 4th edition, p. 67. A different elementary treatment is given later in this book (§ 26.9).

§ 18.2 See P. Stäckel, Ueber die Integration der Hamilton-Jacobi'schen Differentialgleichung mittels Separation der Variabeln, *Habilitationsschrift*, Halle, 1891. Further papers by Stäckel on the theorem are in *Comptes Rendus*, 1893, pp. 485–487 and pp. 1284–1286; also in *Comptes Rendus*, 1895, pp. 489–492. Stäckel's theorem can be established immediately from Lagrange's equations without appeal to the Hamilton-Jacobi theorem; see, for example, An elementary proof of Stäckel's theorem, *American Mathematical Monthly*, Vol. LVI, No. 6, pp. 394–396.

§ 19.1 Proofs of the results quoted in this section will be found in Coddington and Levinson (**40**). The general theory of non-linear systems is very extensive; see, for example, nos. **42–46** of the bibliography. See also S. Lefschetz, Lectures on Differential Equations (Princeton, 1948) and an anthology edited by S. Lefschetz, Contributions to the theory of non-linear oscillations (Princeton, 1950).

§ 19.7 The example (19.7.12) is due to Mr. H. P. F. Swinnerton-Dyer.

§ 21.6 Integral-invariants were introduced by Poincaré, *Acta Mathematica* XIII (1890) and they are used extensively in Vol. III of the Méthodes nouvelles (**18**). See also E. Cartan, Leçons sur les Invariants Intégraux, Paris, 1922.

§ 21.7 The theory of the multipliers is given in Jacobi's lectures (**17**), pp. 71–143.

§ 22.9 The first proof of the Ergodic Theorem was given by G. D. Birkhoff, Proc. Nat. Academy of Sciences, Vol. 17 (1931) p. 656. A slightly weaker result had been established a little earlier by J. von Neumann. The proof given in the text is due in essence to A. N. Kolmogorov. There is a very attractive account of the theorem, for the case where the average is taken for discrete values of t, by F. Riesz, *Comment. Math. Helv.*, Vol. 17 (1945) p. 221.

§ 23.10 Problems of forced oscillations are important in astronomy and in engineering. The particular problem considered here is discussed by E. W. Brown (Rice Institute Pamphlets, 1932; Elements of the Theory of Resonance, Cambridge, 1932; Planetary Theory, by E. W. Brown and C. A. Shook, Cambridge, 1933), by H. Jeffreys (*Quarterly Journal of Mechanics and Applied Mathematics*, XII (1959), p. 124), and by R. A. Struble (*Quarterly Journal of Mechanics and Applied Mathematics*, XV (1962), p. 245).

§ 25.1 Jacobi's proof that a contact transformation conserves the Hamiltonian form of the equations of motion appears in Comptes Rendus, 1837, p. 61.

§ 25.3 The equations (25.3.6) for the variation of the elliptic elements with time are not, in fact, in the form which is most convenient for planetary theory. If we expand R in the form (25.3.8) we have, since n depends upon a,

$$\frac{\partial R}{\partial a} = \sum \frac{\partial C}{\partial a} \cos D - t \frac{\partial n}{\partial a} \sum \nu_1 C \sin D,$$

and the fact that t appears explicitly as a factor in some of the terms on the right is a source of embarrassment. For the technical details of the method by which the astronomer meets this difficulty see for example Tisserand, Traité de Mécanique Céleste, Tome I, Ch. XI.

§ 25.10 This method of reduction is due to Dr. A. J. Ward.

§ 26.2 For the original account of the theorem see G. H. Livens, On Hamilton's Principle and the Modified Function in Analytical Dynamics, *Proc. Royal Soc. Edinburgh*, XXXIX (1919) p. 113.

§ 26.4 and § 26.5 Hölder's famous paper on the Variation Principles is in *Göttinger Nachrichten.*, 1896, p. 122, and Voss's principle is in *Göttinger Nachrichten.* 1900, p. 322.

§ 27.2 Maupertuis was President of the Berlin Academy under Frederick the Great. The Essai de Cosmologie contains the germ of the principle of Least Action, but the real founder of the theory was Euler. See P. E. B. Jourdain, The principle of Least Action, The Open Court Publishing Co., Chicago, 1913; he says "Maupertuis did dishonestly, pretentiously, and unskilfully what Euler did honestly, humbly, and skilfully." There was no lack of critics of Maupertuis in his own day, and one of them was König, Professor at the Hague. The quarrel between Maupertuis and

König was taken up by Frederick the Great and Voltaire (much as the gods in the Iliad take up the quarrels of the mortals!). Frederick sided with Maupertuis, Voltaire with König, and the result was the still more famous quarrel between Frederick and Voltaire which led to their final rupture and separation. Maupertuis, with his conceit and his eccentricities, was the perfect target for Voltaire's satire, and the brilliant and incisive *Histoire du docteur Akakia et du natif de Saint Malo* is a devastating and vastly entertaining attack on Maupertuis. It is an accident, and an unfortunate one for the development of Dynamics, that the somewhat recondite principle of Least Action should have been discovered long before the much simpler principle of Hamilton. There is an echo of this in Hamilton's two great papers of 1834. The Characteristic Function, which is naturally associated with the principle of Least Action, appears in the first paper; the Principal Function, which is naturally related to Hamilton's Principle, appears only in the second.

§ 27.4 See E. T. Whittaker, Monthly Notices R. A. S., LXII (1902), p. 186.

§ 29.1 See H. Bruns, Ueber die Integrale des Vielkörper-Problems, *Berichte der Königlich Sächsischen Gesellschaft der Wissenschaften zu Leipzig*, 1887, pp. 1–39.

§ 30.11 The argument of this section is substantially that of the paper that Poincaré published in 1912 shortly before his death, Sur un théorème de géométrie, *Rend. Circ. mat. Palermo*, 33 (1912) pp. 375–407. The paper is a remarkable one. Poincaré was convinced of the truth of the ring theorem, and gave a long account of various special cases, but failed to give a proof of the general result, and suggested the problem for the consideration of other mathematicians

§ 30.12 See G. D. Birkhoff, Proof of Poincaré's geometric theorem, *Trans. Amer. Math. Soc.*, 14 (1913) pp. 14–22.

Bibliography

I *Foundations*

1. Newton, I., "Philosophiae naturalis principia mathematica" (1st Edition, London, 1687). There are many reprints and translations; see especially "Sir Isaac Newton's Mathematical Principles of Natural Philosophy" edited by F. Cajori, based on Andrew Motte's translation of 1729 (Cambridge, 1934).

2. d'Alembert, J. le R., "Traité de dynamique" (Paris, 1743).

3. Euler, L., "Mechanica, sive motus scientia analytice exposita" (St. Petersburg, 1736), and "Theoria motus corporum solidorum seu rigidorum" (Greifswald, 1765).

4. Lagrange, J. L., "Mécanique Analytique" (Paris, 1788). Many later editions.

II *Critical-Historical Survey*

5. Mach, E., "The Science of Mechanics" (Chicago, 1902); English translation of "Die Mechanik in ihrer Entwicklung historisch-kritisch dargestellt" (Leipzig, 1883).

6. Hertz, H., "The Principles of Mechanics" (London, 1899); English translation of "Die Principien der Mechanik in neuem Zusammenhange dargestellt" (Leipzig, 1894).

7. Dugas, R., "A History of Mechanics" (London, 1957); English translation of "Histoire de Mécanique" (Neuchatel, 1950).

III *For References to original sources*

8. Cayley, A., "Report on the Recent Progress of Theoretical Dynamics," 1857, and the later "Report on Special Problems," 1862, (*Collected Papers*, Cambridge, 1890, Vol. III, pp. 156–204 and Vol. IV, pp. 513–593).

9. Royal Society Index (to the Catalogue of Scientific Papers, 1800–1900), Vol. II, Mechanics.

10. International Catalogue of Scientific Literature, B (Mechanics). Covers the period 1900–1913.

11. Jahrbüch über die Fortschritte der Mathematik, 1862–1942.

12. Revue semestrielle des publications mathematiques, 1893–1932.

13. Mathematical Reviews, 1940– .

For the literature devoted specifically to the Problem of Three Bodies:

14. Whittaker, E. T., "Report on the progress of the solution of the problem of Three Bodies" (*British Association Report*, 1899).

15. Lovett, E. O., "Generalizations of the problem of several bodies" (Quarterly Journal of Mathematics, XLII, 1911, pp. 252–315). This gives references to papers published between 1898 and 1908.

IV *Later sources*

16. Hamilton, W. R., "On a general method in Dynamics", and "Second Essay on a general method in Dynamics", 1834 (*Collected Papers*, Vol. II, Cambridge, 1940, pp. 103–211).

17. Jacobi, C. G. J., "Vorlesungen über Dynamik" (Berlin, 1884).

18. Poincaré, H., "Les méthodes nouvelles de la Mécanique Celeste" (3 volumes, Paris, 1892–1899).

19. Gibbs, J. Willard., *Collected Works*, Vol. II (New York, 1928).

20. Routh, E. J., "Elementary Rigid Dynamics" and "Advanced Rigid Dynamics" (1st Edition, London, 1860). Many later editions.

21. Appell, P., "Traité de Mécanique Rationelle, Tome II" (Paris, 1896; 3rd edition, 1911).

V *Further references*

(*a*) 22. Thomson, W. (Lord Kelvin) and Tait, P. G., "Treatise on Natural Philosophy" (Cambridge, Vol. I, 1879, Vol. II, 1883; new impression, edited by Darwin. G. and Lamb. H., 1912).

23. Encyklopädie der Mathematischen Wissenschaften, IV.1 and IV.2 (Leipzig, 1901–1908).

24. Handbuch der Physik, V, "Grundlagen der Mechanik, Mechanik der Punkte und starren Körper" (Berlin, 1927).

25. Lord Rayleigh, "Theory of Sound" (London, Vol. I, 1878, Vol. II, 1879; second edition, 1894–1896).

26. Jeffreys, H. and Jeffreys, B. S., "Methods of Mathematical Physics" (Cambridge, 1946; 3rd edition, 1956).

(*b*) 27. Whittaker, E. T., "A treatise on the analytical dynamics of particles and rigid bodies, with an introduction to the problem of three bodies" (Cambridge, 1904; 4th edition, 1937).

28. Levi-Civita, T., and Amaldi, U., "Lezioni di Meccanica Razionale" (Bologna, 1922).

29. Wintner, A., "The Analytical Foundations of Celestial Mechanics" (Princeton, 1941).

30. Siegal, C. L., "Vorlesungen über Himmelsmechanik" (Berlin, 1956).

31. Moulton, F. R., "Periodic Orbits" (Washington, 1920).

(*c*) 32. Routh, E. J., "A treatise on Dynamics of a Particle" (Cambridge, 1898).

33. Klein, F. and Sommerfeld, A., "Uber die Theorie des Kreisels" (4 Vols., Leipzig, 1897–1910).

34. Lamb, H., "Higher Mechanics" (Cambridge, 1920; 2nd edition, 1929).

35. Birkhoff, G. D., "Dynamical Systems" (New York, 1927).

36. Goldstein, H., "Classical Mechanics" (Cambridge, Mass., 1951).

37. Sommerfeld, A., "Mechanics" (New York, 1952); English translation of "Vorlesungen uber Theoretische Physik, Band I, Mechanik" (Leipzig, 1942; 4th edition, 1949).

38. Pérès, J., "Mécanique Générale" (Paris, 1953).

39. Lanczos, C., "The Variational Principles of Mechanics" (Toronto, 1949).

(*d*) 40. Coddington, E. A. and Levinson, N., "Theory of ordinary differential equations" (New York, 1955).

41. Liapounoff, A., "Problème général de la Stabilité du Mouvement" (Princeton, 1947); French translation of the original paper in Russian published at Kharkow in 1892.

42. Stoker, J. J., "Nonlinear Vibrations" (New York, 1950).

43. Minorsky, N., "Nonlinear Oscillations" (Princeton, 1962).

44. Kryloff, N. and Bogoliuboff, N., "Introduction to non-linear mechanics" (Princeton, 1943); condensed English version, by S. Lefschetz, of papers published in Russian in 1934 and 1937.

45. La Salle, J. and Lefschetz, S. "Stability by Liapounov's Direct Method" (New York, 1961).

46. Cesari, L., "Asymptotic behavior and stability problems in ordinary differential equations" (Berlin, 1959).

(*e*) 47. Hopf, E., "Ergodentheorie" (Berlin, 1937).

48. Halmos, P. R., "Lectures on Ergodic Theory" (New York, 1956).

49. Dunford, N. and Schwartz, J. T., "Linear Operators, Part I" (New York, 1958); ergodic theory occupies pp. 657–726.

50. Jacobs, K., "Neuere Methoden und Ergebnisse der Ergodentheorie" (Berlin, 1961).

Index